BIOTECHNOLOGY

BIOTECHNOLOGY
The Science and the Business

Vivian Moses

Queen Mary and Westfield College, University of London,
Archæus Technology Group Ltd, London, UK

and

Ronald E. Cape

Cetus Corporation, Emeryville, California, USA
Queen Mary and Westfield College, University of London, UK

harwood academic publishers

chur london paris new york melbourne

Harwood Academic Publishers

Post Office Box 197
London WC2E 9PX
United Kingdom

58, rue Lhomond
75005 Paris
France

Post Office Box 786
Cooper Station
New York, New York 10276
United States of America

Private Bag 8
Camberwell, Victoria 3124
Australia

Library of Congress Cataloging-in-Publication Data

Biotechnology, the science and the business/edited by Vivian Moses
and Ronald E. Cape.
p. cm.
Includes index.
ISBN 3-7186-5094-0. – ISBN 3-7186-5111-4 (pbk.)
1. Biotechnology. 2. Biotechnology industries. I. Moses,
Vivian., 1928 II. Cape, Ronald E., 1932–
TP248.2.B576 1991
660′.6–dc20 90-26538
CIP

 Printed in the United States of America by Braun Brumfield Inc.

CONTENTS

Contents

Section II Underlying Technologies and Economics

Section III Biotechnology and Industry

PREFACE

Any book is a major undertaking and one with forty contributors can at times be a nightmare. It all started from one of those dangerous conversations with publishers. "This," says the publisher taking another cookie with his coffee, "is our list in your subject area. I wonder what you think of it and whether you have any suggestions of what else could be done?" Put in the right way, the gullible scientist cannot resist. "Well," he answers, "what you really need is...". And then follows with great enthusiasm, and at corresponding length, an outline of his pet scheme, the subject of his dreams for the past several years. From that moment on the scientist is hooked and the whole beastly business begins.

So it was, more or less, with us. There are undoubtedly plenty of good books dealing with the scientific and technical sides of biotechnology. But any references to selling the products and evaluating the markets into which they might be sold are usually confined to an odd paragraph here or a line there in the middle of a technical exposition. We find such an almost total emphasis on the technology less than satisfactory for practising scientists (including research students) who may be deeply involved with biotechnology at the bench but have no more than the haziest idea of what happens in the real world.

It is for those readers that we have worked so hard to get this book into print as well as for undergraduate and postgraduate students taking courses in the subject, who, we hope, will find its balanced view particularly useful. Biotechnology is an activity in which success depends on coupling an understanding of the scientific and technical base to an appreciation of the commercial realities of developing, manufacturing and marketing products. All too often this balance is missing from more formal programmes of instruction. In this volume a broad view has been taken of biotechnology, by no means concentrating, for example, on health care applications or the benefits of genetic engineering. Biotechnology is understood to refer essentially to all commercialisation of the biological sciences; we have accordingly sought to encompass the whole range of applications from the traditional activities of brewing and sewage disposal (themselves, of course, continually undergoing improvement and change) to the most advanced prospects for new technologies and their uses in industry. The book thus provides students with a unique opportunity to appreciate the complete process of bringing biotechnological processes and products to market.

Those who come to biotechnology with another view, from business, government, the law or public administration, will also find much to interest them. Making the correct commercial or policy decisions surely depends on a perception of what the technology has to offer, what its problems are and what the consequences may be for other activities in society now, in the near term and in the more distant future. Technology is always difficult for the uninitiated to understand in detail. But in truth much of this book will readily be understood by nonscientists, and we think it will be useful for those readers to appreciate the scope and scale of the technology and to learn more about what it actually amounts to.

In producing a multiauthored textbook the editors' job is threefold: to decide on the range of topic coverage, to find the authors to write the chapters and later to edit the manuscripts. It was easy to draft a first outline of the topics that ought to be included. We knew from the beginning the sort of book we wanted and we knew equally certainly that neither of us was actually going to do most of the writing: the range of specialities if far too broad and our own in-depth knowledge too limited. But over the five-year period that the book has been under development, new chapters have been added as the opportunity arose to interest an additional author. Now that it is all finished we are gratified to find that we really can understand all that has been written and are convinced more than ever that we could not have done most of it ourselves.

It may be trite to say that the quality of any publication depends in the first instance on its authors, but nevertheless it must be true. Our first acknowledgements are therefore to the authors including, by the way, those five who never actually delivered. They have generously contributed their time and knowledge to this broad view of biotechnology as it manifests itself in industry, in the laboratory and in the world of business and commerce. It is always a great pleasure to deal with people who know their own field, and without exception that has been the case in this endeavour. Our brief to the contributors was fairly clear but not, we hoped, constraining. We wanted them to stress the commercial view of biotechnology and to that they all responded. Naturally, the book is even now unlikely to be comprehensive but one has to stop somewhere.

Contributors, and particularly the scientists among them, were asked as far as they could to relate their technical descriptions to market opportunities. There must be a host of potentially good scientific ideas which will never see the light of day as products or services because markets for them, at the prices at which they would have to be sold, are simply not going to exist. So most of the technical chapters contain market assessments which will help the reader to form his own view about the commercial viability of many of the biotechnological propositions discussed in these pages.

Editing the manuscripts themselves was a pleasure. It is sometimes not until you go through a script looking at absolutely everything, and not allowing the eye to jump a word here and there, that you actually understand what it is all about. The wealth of information and the lucidity of the writing are all we might have wished. True, not everybody has the same idea about where and how often to use commas, and views about split infinitives clearly differ, but the subject matter itself has been splendidly handled and we wish to express our gratitude to all our collaborators for their magnificent contributions.

Our sincere thanks must go equally to the publishers without whom nothing would have happened. They offered us unswerving interest and support through those dark days when only two authors delivered their manuscripts before the agreed deadline and the others sent nothing at all. The editorial staff helped us early on with developing and shaping the book as an integrated concept, guided us through contracts and suggested one or two of the authors in essential areas of the subject with which we were then not familiar. Later, when all the manuscripts had finally arrived, they were joined by their production colleagues and the discussions extended to type fonts, page layouts and the uses of colour and cover designs. Finally the marketing group became involved and we talked about how to prepare the public for the feast that was about to be offered to them.

Spouses and secretaries sometimes have a thin time when a book is on the stocks, particularly, as in our case, when the editors are normally thousands of miles apart. We hope we did not burden them unduly and that if they have not read the text while it was in preparation, they might like to do so now!

We must not conclude without acknowledging, and indeed thanking, a host of unknowns. All those people, for instance, who wanted to see us or talk over the phone and who were unable to do so because we were busy with the book. And the myriad organisations who probably know next to nothing of biotechnology and care even less: the airlines which enabled us safely to see one another from time to time; the post offices, courier services and telecom companies who delivered our packages and messages; and last but not least, the people who provide those marvels of the modern age without which we are quite sure these words would never have been composed – the manufacturers of word processors.

So now, gentle reader, over to you.

Vivian Moses
Ronald E. Cape

LIST OF CONTRIBUTORS

Brian Ager:
Consultant on biotechnology regulations to the Concertation Unit for Biotechnology in Europe and to the OECD, SDM 2/66, European Commission, 200 Rue de la Loi, B-1049 Bruxelles, Belgium. Present appointment: Director — Senior Advisory Group Biotechnology, c/o Conseil Européen des Fédération de l'Industrie Chimique, Avenue Louise 250, bte 71, B-1050 Bruxelles, Belgium.

Carl Batt:
Professor of Biotechnology, Institute of Food Science, Department of Food Science, New York State College of Agriculture and Life Sciences, Cornell University, 107 Stocking Hall, Ithaca, NY 14853, U.S.A.

Richard J.F. Bewley:
Scientific and Technical Manager, Biotreatment Ltd., 5 Chiltern Close, Llanishen, Cardiff CF4 5DL, U.K.

David Brown:
Senior Research Scientist, ICI Films, P.O. Box 6, Shire Park, Bessemer Road, Welwyn Garden City, Herts AL7 1HD, U.K.

Melanie J. Brown:
Research Director, Archæus Technology Group Ltd., Queens Building, Kidderpore Avenue, London NW3 7ST, U.K.

Ronald E. Cape:
Chairman, Cetus Corporation, 1400–53rd Street, Emeryville, CA 94608, U.S.A. and Visiting Professor in Biotechnology, School of Biological Sciences, Queen Mary and Westfield College (University of London), London E1 4NS, U.K.

Peter Cheetham:
Research Manager, Unilever Research, Colworth Laboratory, Colworth House, Sharnbrook, Bedford MK44 1LQ, U.K.

Yusuf Chisti:
Supervisor, Biological Production Department, Chembiomed Ltd., P.O. Box 8050, Station F, Edmonton, Alberta T6H 4N9, Canada.

Donald A. Cowan:
Lecturer in Biochemistry, Department of Biochemistry, University College (University of London), London WC1E 6BT, U.K.

Anita Crafts-Lighty:
Managing Director, BioCommerce Data Ltd., 95 High Street, Slough, Berks., SL1 1DH, U.K.

Ellen Daniell;
Director, PCR Commercial Development, Cetus Corporation, 1400–53rd Street, Emeryville, CA 94608, U.S.A.

Allen J. Dines:
Director, Business Development, Agracetus, 8520 University Green, Middleton, WI 53562, U.S.A.

Thomas Egli:
Senior Scientist, Institut für Gewässerschutz und Wassertechnologie, ETH-Zürich, Überlandstraße 133, CH-8600 Dübendorff, Switzerland.

Usher Fleising:
Professor of Anthropology, Department of Anthropology, University of Calgary, 2500 University Drive N.W., Calgary, Alberta T2N 1N4, Canada.

James L. Garraway:
Senior Lecturer in Agricultural Chemistry, Department of Biochemistry, Physiology and Soil Science, Wye College (University of London), Ashford, Kent TN25 5AH, U.K.

List of Contributors

D. Miles Gaythwaite:
Partner, Bird & Bird, 2 Gray's Inn Square, London WC1R 5AF, U.K.

Thomas J. Graddis:
Research Associate, Smith, Kline-Beachem Pharmaceutical Company, King of Prussia, PA 19406, U.S.A.

Lorance L. Greenlee:
President, Greenlee and Associates, P.C., 5370 Manhattan Circle, Suite 201, Boulder, CO 80303, U.S.A.

Michael Gronow:
Managing Director, Cambridge Research Laboratories, 181A Huntingdon Road, Cambridge CB3 0DJ, U.K.

Geoffrey Hamer:
Professor of Environmental Biotechnology, Institut für Gewässerschutz und Wassertechnologie, ETH-Zürich, Überlandstraße 133, CH-8600 Dübendorff, Switzerland.

Nicholas J. Haritatos:
Engineering Consultant, Chevron Research and Technology Company, 100 Chevron Way, Richmond, CA 94802-0627, U.S.A.

Roger Jeffcoat:
Director of Natural Polymer Research and Biotechnology, Unilever Research, Colworth Laboratory, Colworth House, Sharnbrook, Bedford MK44, 1LQ, U.K.

Robert F. Johnson:
President, Johnston Associates Inc., 181 Cherry Valley Road, Princeton, NJ 08540, U.S.A.

Shane Maloney:
Student, School of Biological Sciences, Queen Mary and Westfield College (University of London), London E1 4NS, U.K.

Douglas K. McCormick:
Editor, Bio/Technology, Managing Editor, Nature Publishing Co., 65 Bleecker Street, New York, NY 10012, U.S.A.

Murray Moo-Young:
Professor of Chemical Engineering, Director, Industrial Biotechnology Centre, Department of Chemical Engineering, University of Waterloo, Waterloo, Ontario N2L 3G1, Canada.

Vivian Moses:
Professor of Microbiology, School of Biological Sciences, Queen Mary and Westfield College (University of London), London E1 4NS, U.K. and Scientific Director, Archæus Technology Group Ltd., Queen's Building, Kidderpore Avenue, London NW3 7ST, U.K.

Saul Neidleman:
Distinguished Research Fellow, Associate Director, Chemistry Department, Cetus Corporation, 1400-53rd Street, Emeryville, CA 94608, U.S.A. Present appointment: Senior Director, Project Acquisition and Planning, Biosource Genetics Corporation, 3333 Vaca Valley Parkway, Vacaville, CA 95688, U.S.A.

Robert B. Nicholas:
Partner, McDermott, Will and Emery, 1850 K Street NW, Washington DC 20006-2296, U.S.A.

Michael O. Ostrach:
Senior Vice President, Law and Administration and General Counsel, Cetus Corporation, 1400-53rd Street, Emeryville, CA 94608, U.S.A.

Dale L. Oxender:
Professor of Biological Chemistry, Director, Center for Molecular Genetics, Department of Biological Chemistry, Medical Science Building I M5319/0606, University of Michigan Medical School, 1301 Catherine Road, Ann Arbor, MI 48109-0606, U.S.A.

George B. Rathmann:
Chief Executive Officer, Amgen, 1900 Oak Terrace Lane, Thousand Oaks, CA 91320, U.S.A.

John F. Rees:
Director and General Manager, Biotreatment Ltd., 5 Chiltern Close, Llanishen, Cardiff CF4 5DL, U.K.

List of Contributors

Katherine A. Russell:
Vice President, Public Affairs, Cetus Corporation, 1400-53rd Street, Emeryville, CA 94608, U.S.A.

Robert Sleat: Scientific and Technical Manager, Biotreatment Ltd., 5 Chiltern Close, Llanishen, Cardiff CF4 5DL, U.K.

Derek G. Springham:
Lecturer in Microbiology, School of Biological Sciences, Queen Mary and Westfield College (University of London), London E1 4NS, U.K.

Jennifer Van Brunt:
Managing Editor, Bio/Technology, 65 Bleecker Street, New York, NY 10012, U.S.A.

Chapter 1

The Science and the Business: An Introduction

Vivian Moses and Ronald Cape

RESEARCH AND THE MARKET PLACE

There are so many definitions of biotechnology that we do not feel inclined to add to them. Often they are rather noble in character, expressing lofty aspirations like *biology in the service of mankind* or *providing products and services for industry*. Not that such descriptions are wrong but they do not (in our view) convey very realistically the idea that biotechnology is not some academic activity, a consequence of innovative laboratory experimentation or a kind of social crusade, but is itself an intensely industrial and commercial matter. So we have tried to assemble in this book a series of contributions offering a realistic balance between the scientific and the technical contributions on the one hand and the objectives of business and the public on the other. Perhaps, if pushed, we might describe biotechnology as *making money with biology* because without the discipline of the market place there might indeed be elegant science but there would be no technology.

Although the activity is almost as old as the hills, the word *biotechnology* is rather new. The Oxford Shorter English Dictionary in its 1955 edition does not list it at all; it gets as far as *biotaxy* and then skips to *biotic*. By 1979 the word had certainly appeared but not always, perhaps, in the form we might expect. One well-known dictionary published in that year (and which will here remain unidentified) is quite clear what it means: *biotechnology: the U.S. name for ergonomics*. This volume is not about ergonomics!

Most people seem to think of biotechnology as a relatively recent concept although they admit that any discontinuity between making money with biology the old way and doing so with the aid of biotechnology is a very fuzzy one. Through the ages people have used biology in agriculture, to breed better plants and animals and to promote productivity and control pests. The introduction of crop rotation by "Turnip" Townsend at the turn of the 18th century was every bit as much a part of biotechnology as the contemporary production of bacterial soil inoculants but it took more than two centuries for the new word to come into use. Through those same ages people have been fermenting sugars and starches to make beers and wines, allowing the natural bacterial souring of milk to produce cheese and yoghurt and used respiring yeast for generating bubbles of carbon dioxide in leavening dough to give that lightness of texture we so much enjoy in good bread. All of this was accomplished by trial and error without a hint of the underlying mechanisms until (at least for these authors) our own grandfathers' generation; all of it is within the brief of this book.

Our own century has witnessed some truly remarkable events in the onward march of what we now choose to call biotechnology. Not only did an understanding of biochemical and genetic mechanisms make astounding advances but industrial microbiology dedicated to the manufacture of specific products came of age. It was only in 1917 that Chaim Weizmann first used a pure culture in an industrial process, the fermentation of corn starch by *Clostridium acetobutylicum* to produce the acetone Britain so badly needed in the first World War for the manufacture of explosives. The really spectacular flowering of the fermentation industry took place after 1945 with the increasing importance of antibiotics in human and veterinary medicine. Fermentation skills developed apace, ready for the most recent phase of biotechnology that came with genetic engineering. Even the youngest of our readers will no doubt be familiar with the events of the mid- and late 1970s: the enhanced understanding of protein structure, a growing knowledge of metabolic regulation, the discovery of DNA restriction (followed by the realisation of what that might mean for recombinant DNA technology in ways unimaginable a few short years earlier) and the invention of monoclonal antibodies. The impact on biological thinking and experimentation was immediate and profound. Its effects were felt far beyond the laboratory: in the executive suites of industry and investment banks (where tycoons and bankers quickly had the new opportunities pointed out to them), in lawyers' offices, legislatures, parliaments, civil services and government agencies (faced with new and hitherto inconceivable problems of regulation and intellectual property protection) and in the managements of large corporations who in time realised not only that they could do it too but that if they did not some of their market share would surely begin to slip away.

Biotechnology is in some ways unusual in the business world since much of it, but by no means all, seeks to commercialise technologies which depend on very recent frontier discoveries in the underlying sciences. Many of its markets are being created in step with its own technical development, reminiscent of the parallel growth of computing. In fact, the biotech. revolution, if that is what it was, shared many characteristics with computing: significant technical advances were made; the major establishment corporations did not act on them rapidly; thus, opportunities arose for new companies to fill the novel market niche; but ultimately the niche closed and activity had to be justified by the normal standards of commercial operation.

The very fact of operating at the scientific frontier has encouraged within biotechnology establishments an air of intellectual excitement more commonly encountered in top-flight research laboratories in the universities and public sector institutes than in the average industrial laboratory. Just as in academic departments, first rate research opportunities attract the most imaginative and capable researchers; like their academic colleagues, many biotechnologists in the commercial sector were initially very unfamiliar with the disciplines of working for the market place. It takes a good deal of practice for a scientist unused to commercial life to realise that a good experiment does not necessarily yield a saleable product: there also has to be a receptive market either already in existence or created to receive the new product or service. Conflicts inevitably develop between *technology push* and *market pull*, the tendency of scientists to push for funds for the development of good ideas before the markets are properly explored and identified versus the experience of the sales executives that, however good the science, if there is no market there will be no sales. None of this is exclusive to biotechnology; it merely emphasises that any successful commercial activity needs both a good product and a market in which to sell it.

Because biotechnology is about selling it is not enough to comprehend only its technical aspects. The whole range of business concepts is relevant for an understanding not only of what can technically be accomplished but how it can be given physical and commercial reality. Running a biotechnology business is basically like running any other but as with any industry there are many special factors. Put briefly, successful biotechnology in the private sector depends on generating products and services for sale into the relevant market at prices which cover not only all the costs of development, production and marketing but also generate acceptable profits for the investors. Without the prospects of profits, investors will not invest; and without investment there will be no laboratories, no equipment and no supplies for scientists to make their discoveries nor, indeed, will there be any salaries to keep them employed.

Things may appear to be different in the public sector but really they are not. One can envisage situations in which a potential biotechnological development (say, a drug to treat an uncommon but gravely serious disease) might be socially desirable. But if there is no more than a small number of sufferers, potentially comprising no more than a limited market coupled, perhaps, with high development costs, private corporations would probably be unwilling to invest because of the unlikelihood of an adequate return. Governments both in the industrialised societies and in developing countries might take a different view; recognising social needs, they may decide that the expenditure of public funds is justified to stimulate developments which would not otherwise be undertaken under *ordinary* market conditions. Examples of their concerns might include malaria vaccines and treatments, the exploitation of carbohydrate energy sources in petroleum-poor countries or drugs for rare diseases such as human growth hormone to treat pituitary dwarfism. Such initiatives already exist and the U.S. so-called *orphan drug* regulations are a case in point: they create incentives, including market exclusivity, deliberately to encourage the development of drugs for rare diseases. But governments, too, will expect the best value for their contributions which, while often described as *grants*, are just as much investments as comparable initiatives in the private sector. The rewards, however, may come in the form of social benefits rather than money profits. Similar considerations may hold on an international scale. Biotechnology is expensive but many of the acute needs for its products lie in underdeveloped, poor countries able to muster neither the resources nor the skills to harness the new techniques to solve their problems. Biotechnologists in the developed countries may fail to perceive the market which is a prerequisite for *their* involvement. There is clearly a rôle then for national governments and international agencies and indeed many have shouldered the responsibility for such initiatives. But once more, all resources are limited and every granting agency wants to make sure that its funds are well spent; it will weigh the costs and benefits of investment in one activity against what might be achieved by investment in another.

THE "NEW" BIOTECHNOLOGY: LIFE AFTER 1975

Cohen wrote his paper, *The Manipulation of Genes*, in 1975[1]; perhaps more than anything else, that paper, and the intellectual environment in which it was published, stimulated developments in applied biology which we have since learned to call "biotechnology". It led directly to the formation of new companies dedicated specifically to exploiting the opportunities many perceived would flow from genetic manipulation; not far behind came other groups of people who, while impressed with the change of attitude implied by a mutation of applied biology into biotechnology, realised that recombinant DNA was not necessarily the only route to success.

Why new companies? Were they necessary? Could not the existing pharmaceutical and chemical corporations be the vehicles for capitalising on the new discoveries? Did not the universities and research institutes have a part to play? In practice, the fact that the pharmaceutical and chemical companies did not immediately respond to the new technologies left opportunities open for others to do so. Because the universities do not see it as their primary function to pursue business interests nor, indeed, do they normally have the experience or personnel to do so, a window opened for a new type of commercial activity, one we have come to recognise as a *biotechnology company*. But why companies? Why are companies formed? There is only one answer: to make money. It is, of course, not necessary to have a company structure in which to make scientific advances; that can be accomplished at least as well in the universities if the resources are available. But a commercial structure *is* necessary to make money. In the early days there was indeed a measure of embarrassment over the commercialisation of the new science and many pious statements were made about public good and the advancement of the subject. Do not be misled: biotechnology companies were perceived as being socially, politically and academically appropriate but their objective was always to make money for their investors. Nevertheless, once they began to take shape, many scientists saw in them an opportunity to secure better resources for the pursuit of that frontier science with which they themselves had been involved in the universities and research institutes.

Promoting the advance of science in a commercial environment has its limitations; as time passed they became increasingly clear. At the beginning the new technology was more promise than reality; nobody doubted that further basic research was necessary before development and commercialisation could become possible. But in the long term that is not a viable way of conducting a company's strategy because companies that do not make money do not survive; money making and financial viability soon become paramount. In only a very few cases is research likely to provide ongoing financial stability; in time the common pattern will be a move from an activity which is all research and exploration (the *research boutique*) more and more towards manufacturing or its equivalent in the provision of services. That change in some instances might pose personnel problems because the scientists originally recruited for their imagination and research abilities may not take kindly to finding themselves in a so-called *vertically integrated company*; however, the problem so far seems to be less severe than some people expected. It is interesting to note that despite the take-over of Genentech by Hoffmann-LaRoche, Genentech will remain a separate entity with its own management and traded stock in order to preserve the ethic and culture of exploration.

Having formed a company to exploit the technology, the management team soon faces the complexity of running it. They need money: money for salaries, for buildings, equipment and supplies; they also need working capital. Managements without experience tend to be naïve and unless they rapidly learn about product selection, market evaluation, financing, manufacturing, marketing and selling, the company will fail. All these activities are an integral part of initiating and sustaining advances in biotechnology and that is why this book devotes a third of its length to these critical matters.

Since the late 1970s the scene has changed markedly. From the few runners of those days, companies like Biogen, Cetus and Genentech, several hundreds of other companies have been formed all over the world although still predominantly in the U.S. At the beginning of their lives they mostly recruited enthusiasts for biotechnology: entrepreneurial businessmen and entrepreneurial scientists. For those early recruits, a start-up company could be very attractive. There seemed to be nowhere to go but up. The science was exciting and technology marvels beckoned. There was more than a hint of considerable wealth in the not too distant future. But before very long this supply of talent tended to be insufficient for their developing needs and, as the companies found themselves moving towards manufacturing, their personnel requirements changed. Now they needed professional managers, accountants and lawyers so that quite soon what had been start-up companies began to develop along traditional corporate lines. They tended to become more conservative, less adventurous. And in time, of course, the competition began to stiffen: the major pharmaceutical and chemicals manufacturers appreciated the relevance of biotechnology for their own product lines and they, too, began to constitute a major presence in the field. The whole biotechnological industry approached maturity.

There have been some signals that maturity may produce culture-clash difficulties of its own. The problems became ones of being easier to say "no" to innovation than to say "yes"; is it not worse, five or ten years out, to have been responsible for a failure rather than to have failed to authorise what might (who knows?) have been a success? The new companies began to acquire a need for champions, people who would argue for the resources to develop a new idea through to success; this book contains more than one example.

ABOUT THIS BOOK

Assuming, wisely or not, that our readers will be familiar with the underlying sciences of biochemistry, genetics and microbiology, we have not attempted to review even the most rudimentary aspects of those fields. Instead, the emphasis is on the biotechnology itself.

A multi-author text inevitably yields manuscripts written in many different styles. Editors are faced with the choice of rewriting the whole book to achieve uniformity or allowing the differences to stand. We chose the latter course, and not entirely for reasons of laziness. Biotechnology is an industry comprising many different sorts of people. Their approaches to their own contributions vary widely: in many ways they often do look at things differently from one another and we found it quite acceptable and indeed desirable that their range of attitudes should not be concealed. The reader will not fail to observe that business people frequently write differently from laboratory scientists and that both are usually distinguishable from lawyers. The editors had also to address the problem of potential overlap and repetition. These were, of course, minimised in drawing up the draft synopsis and many were eliminated in specific discussions with authors but some matters are genuinely relevant to more than one topic and they may well be treated in very different ways when considered from diverse viewpoints. So some overlap does exist and we hope that what remains will be accepted as legitimate in the contexts in which it occurs.

All the chapters are written by people who have an expert view of their subject matter and who have mostly spent many years in their fields. Nearly a third of them are concerned directly with the problems of running commercial operations in general, and of biotechnology businesses in particular. Here, too, we have not gone back to absolute basics but, in the expectation that more readers than not will already have scientific rather than commercial backgrounds, a fairly comprehensive account is presented of the most important business aspects of biotechnology. There follows a short section of six chapters addressing a number of significant underlying technical and economic issues. At that point we felt it appropriate also to offer a limited discussion of the special biology of biotechnology in order to bring out the novelty of some of the new techniques and hence to clarify the technical basis of the new industry. Finally, the longest part of the book, sixteen chapters in all, is directed to a view of those industries which already have been, or are likely in the comparatively near future, to be impacted by the new technologies.

We would particularly like to bring a number of points in the business section to the attention of our scientific readers. The chapter on *Managing a Biotechnology Business* draws extensively on general business experience because managing a biotechnology business shares much in common with managing any sort of enterprise. Do note that the process of decision-making in biotechnology is relatively new and it is sometimes easier to think of the problems of choices in terms of more familiar products and services. The general questions and principles are the same; it is only the details that are different.

Every business, of course, needs capital — funds with which to carry on its daily activities. Even a mature and successful profit-making company, regularly distributing some of the profits to shareholders as dividends and keeping the rest to increase its own liquidity or to build or buy new plants or other fixed facilities, may from time to time need to raise money in the investment world ("Wall Street"/"The City") in order to undertake a major expansion or acquire other companies; this is called *financial management*. However, a new company with no track record, no products and no near-term likelihood of a positive cash flow may have very special problems of financial management. This is worth remembering when reading about the *Financing of Biotechnology* and the venture capitalist's postscript. New biotechnology ventures, as we have already hinted, often need considerable up-front investment before there is any prospect of profit, hardly an attractive prospect to the usual sort of investor who looks for security as well as profit. Biotechnology investments, especially in start-up companies, are risky and only certain kinds of investor are willing to take that sort of risk.

It is not only the investor who takes a risk. Recruiting a chief executive officer with the right personality or experience may itself be difficult to achieve. Without him (or her: no discrimination is intended, only the traditions of English language usage!) a company will have nobody at the tiller yet the CEO will also be embarking on a risky voyage because the new business could well fail and he might find himself unemployed. What sort of people are willing to start new companies? Why are they seemingly unfazed by the risks and indifferent to surrendering the secure and often well-paid positions they have held before? The editors believe that these questions are best answered by following the matters that concern the manager of a start-up. Are they exactly the same as those on the minds of the venture capitalists?

There follow two chapters on intellectual property. They are very different in style and approach, deliberately so. One is a formal presentation, the other almost a free-form essay, but then lawyers have strong and differing views about the problems with which they deal. The message that comes over very clearly: is that the patent world is convoluted on both sides of the Atlantic!

And so to public perception. In every country in modern times, and particularly in those with democratic traditions (the location, incidentally, of most of the world's biotechnology: there must be a message there), a new technology is soon brought to the attention of the populace. Lobbies develop, protagonists and antagonists of the new developments. Their motives are often pure and moral and their arguments may develop into major topics of public debate. Who are the real beneficiaries of biotechnology? There are many who feel they are only the biotechnologists themselves! It is ironic that two very disparate groups who often take this view are the bankers and the activists. But this is surely too simple a conclusion: any activity potentially so profound will eventually have enormous and widespread consequences throughout society. In time (hopefully) everybody benefits. It is not surprising that contributing to this study is an anthropologist who has made a special study of people's reactions to the new field of biotechnology. Is it perceived as a force for good or for evil? Are there really risks to mankind and, if so, what are they? What happens if the utopias of the protagonists are realised? What happens if the nightmares of the activists come true? Those questions lead directly to matters of regulation. For the good of society, governments regulate the activities of the citizenry, biotechnologists included. With such a new field, which some members of the public welcome unhesitatingly while others view with concern and foreboding, governments have a clear rôle (so they tell us) in establishing ground rules for practice. Advocates of biotechnology have attracted much attention as they seek to convince investors, customers and governments of the profound impact these new capabilities will have. Small wonder, then, that many observers, mindful of past misuses and the failed promises of earlier technologies, insist on closely monitoring plans and calling for regulations to govern the applications of biotechnology. Scientific data are facts. Perceptions are facts, too. Politicians and regulators try to deal with them all; the results are often confusing and unpredictable.

The business section closes with a chapter on *Communication*. Any technology, and particularly one as fast moving as this, depends critically on the ability of all involved to communicate readily and accurately among themselves. Scientists need, as always, to keep abreast of their colleagues' experimentation; managers need to know what the competition is doing; legislators must take account of the public impact of biotechnological advances and lawyers have to keep up with the legislators; sales executives want to maintain close contact with their present and future clients while financiers require an up-to-the minute sense of trends in the markets. It all adds up to a major effort in information transfer which includes formal publication in the form of research papers, reviews and books (such as this one!) as well as conferences, press releases, news sheets and data bases.

Then to the technology, first the general considerations and later the individual applications and industries. This is the point where it is time to take stock of *The New Biology* to remind ourselves just what all the fuss is about; why have the academic and industrial sectors and, indeed, governments, all identified it as a major concern and opportunity for the next generation? Although the term "biotechnology" has been defined in dozens of ways, some of which include processes as old as civilisation, today's excitement clearly reflects the dramatic scientific breakthroughs which occurred in the 1970s and 1980s. The next several chapters discuss the underlying technologies.

The first is important not only for the technology itself but because it conveys a powerful sense of the excitement and enthusiasm attendant on the development of a good new idea. As with so many successful innovations, once the ideas behind *Polymerase Chain Reaction (PCR)* had grown into a reliable working system and the details published, the whole concept became widely understood, accepted and, in a sense, incorporated into the "molecular biological scene". What is particularly interesting, especially in the context of this textbook, is how PCR grew from an idea into reality. Such sequences of events are among the most difficult for someone to appreciate unless he has himself been a participant. With time and repeated telling, the details become blurred, the mythology grows, the story is embedded in history and valuable lessons are lost. So, while the events leading to PCR are still fresh in the minds of the people involved, this is the time to recount the tale for the benefit both of those who were not there and those who will come later. We make no apology for this narrative historical record, recalling the facts as they happened and emphasizing how the decisions and contributions of individual people were critical to the whole development.

Now we move into techniques and technicalities. Biotechnology has the fantastic promise of protein design and manipulation on which to build. It also has to make most of its products in fermenters and use other well developed items of equipment to extract, concentrate and purify them. Manufacture depends on feedstocks, and input costs may very significantly influence the final price of products and services. The whole problem of how to make things, how to cost them and how to maximise production efficiency are the subjects of the next three chapters.

In coming to deal with *The Established Industries* we need to remember that while the elegance and precision available to industrial microbiologists has grown substantially in recent years, the harnessing and improving of microbiological processes provides the heritage on which today's biotechnology builds. The underlying explanations in terms of biochemistry, genetics and physiology have yielded their secrets only in the past few decades while empiricism has served us since before recorded human history began. Some have said that until the secrets of DNA were revealed, humans practised industrial genetics with their eyes closed; now we do it, or could do it, better and more precisely because we can see what we are doing down to the molecular level. In any event, no understanding of today's accomplishments and tomorrow's possibilities is complete without an examination of the "traditional" industrial microbiology. *Industrial Chemicals* and *Industrial Enzymes* are part of that same tradition. So varied are the reactions that can be catalysed by enzymes that some microbiologists have said, not without a measure of truth, that "anything a chemist can do a microorganism or enzyme can do better". They sometimes add: "...and cleaner, quicker and cheaper, too". In any event, the challenge of exploring the limits of this assertion lead in some interesting directions, as the following chapters show. The very next one deals with *New Materials*, a subject frequently forgotten in discussions of biotechnology, but its promise compares favourably with many better-known examples.

Electronics and biotechnology are often discussed as two separate "high tech" phenomena with many economic and commercial parallels but few actual connections. One reads articles about "biochips", expecting to discover that silicon has been replaced by DNA and that computers of the future will use nature's system of storing and manipulating information. Not really or, at least, not yet. Important advances are being made which do create an interface between biology and electronics, as the chapter on *Biosensors* describes. But, returning to the notion of replacing silicon with biological molecules, we include a chapter on *Bioelectronics* in which imagination runs free about possible future directions. It is reminiscent of essays written just before recombinant DNA was announced, with authors speculating about all the wonderful things that could be done if only a way were found to "programme" bacteria with DNA from others sources so that they would do what "we" wanted instead of just what they had evolved to do for themselves.

So, at last, we come to *Healthcare*, to the applications of biotechnology which are of the most immediate interest and indeed familiarity to most laymen. They represent its clearest visible benefit, its most dramatic results and the first profitable application of recombinant DNA and monoclonal antibodies. Without question, these health-related developments get the most publicity: the scientific journals and the popular media follow them from initial discovery through all the ups and downs of trials and regulation until marketing begins sometimes as much as ten or more years later. Hopes and disappointments are exaggerated by everyone concerned and the net effect is that, to many untutored observers, this chapter's subject matter is all there is to biotechnology. At the time of writing it is certainly the busiest area of scientific and commercial activity, a situation likely to continue until, perhaps twenty or more years from now, agricultural applications fulfil the predictions of enthusiasts who point out that more money has been and always will be spent on food than on medicines. (Or until the bugs actually do get more oil out of the ground, as we will find out later on.) But to the present generation, at least, healthcare seems to be much of what biotechnology is all about.

However, since biotechnology's major impact on the quality of life may well be in the area of food production, a discussion of agriculture in the round is followed by chapters on *Pesticides*, *Foods* and *Flavours and Fragrances* which address this promise from different, somewhat overlapping points of view. Short-term impediments may include "not in my back yard" (NIMBY) objections to testing new ideas in the field. Longer term problems not to be ignored involve cultural issues whose importance cannot be overemphasised. "We are what we eat" means different things to different people.

Towards the end of the book, we concern ourselves with different types of industrial processes, procedures which require biological systems to function in environments very difficult to control and optimise and which have to be accepted more or less as they are. An unsung hero of today's industrial microbiology is its widespread use in waste management. Here is an application where the feedstock is itself the problem to be dealt with. It is an ongoing challenge, one which will get worse and worse as people over much of the world become richer and discard more garbage and one which encourages much speculation about the applicability of the newest developments in biotechnology. The release of genetically engineered organisms into the environment (usually in an agricultural context) has been complicated by regulatory delays. Similar concerns may also delay the widespread use of recombinant organisms for waste treatment and pollution control. These big outdoor industries also make use of processes and materials involving matters of scale far beyond anything yet addressed (except for agricultural systems which are not really comparable for obvious reasons). Some (like biomass conversion) have some history and some accomplishment, albeit with sketchy economic success. Others, such as microbial enhanced oil recovery (MEOR) and coal desulphurisation, challenge the imagination because of their very scale: people in pharmaceutics and the fermentation industry talk about the problems of scale-up but these pale into insignificance by comparison with the really monstrous scale-up implied in MEOR and the challenge to oilfield operators to commit major industrial installations to new technology. Paradoxically, and notwithstanding the issue of large-scale operation, wild-type organisms have for centuries been employed in mineral recovery.

So here it is, the pattern of today's biotechnology. In such a rapidly changing activity much of the technology will appear very different next year, next month, even tomorrow — but the organisational structures and the problems with which they have to deal are going to remain much as they are now. Hopefully this book will not be solely of historical interest five years hence.

REFERENCE

1. Cohen, S.N. (1975) The manipulation of genes. *Scientific American*, **233**, 24–33.

Section I

Matters of Business

Chapter 2

Managing a Biotechnology Business

Katherine A. Russell

INTRODUCTION

The scientific world in the latter part of the twentieth century is extremely complex and characterized by a high degree of differentiation. Yet physicists and biologists share certain basic ways of doing things, starting with the scientific method. The world of business is no different. The corner grocery and the conglomerate, the bakery and the biotechnology company need, in the end, to achieve the same objective. These organizations must meet some need for society, or some segment thereof. In a capitalist economy, the people who supply the wherewithal (ideas, cash, etc.) which the organization requires to meet the societal need are the owners. Owners who supply only capital are called "investors". They expect to receive something in return for their contribution; thus, the organization must make a profit.

Fulfilling societal need generally involves adding value to something (making a product) or someone (providing a service). The baker adds value to flour and yeast by mixing them in a pleasing way, applying energy and timing the delivery of this appetizing finished product so that we can buy it fresh, perhaps still warm from the oven, at a convenient location just down the street. The biotechnologist adds value by . . ., ah, but that is what this volume is all about, so let's not get ahead of ourselves! In free market countries, unless the organization is state-owned or in a special category such as utilities, it will have to pursue its objectives in a competitive environment. In short, to be successful or at least survive it must more often than not create better value than other organizations producing the same product or service. In addition, the organization must operate within certain constraints. Some are as straightforward as the scarcity of resources. Others are quite complex, involving regulations imposed by governments to achieve a social objective such as equality or comprising import barriers brought about by trade deficits.

We have now defined, albeit in a very simplistic way, the role of business in society, including a biotechnology business. Is a business always an organization? No, it is possible for a single individual to engage in value creation; however, in our advanced economy the creation, production and delivery of goods and services is increasingly accomplished by organizations of many people with a wide array of specialized talents utilizing a vast number of complicated and costly inputs. And the growth in complexity of the business organization created the need for a special kind of individual — the manager.

We think of the manager as a person who manages people and/or things. But this focuses too narrowly on his supervisory and planning functions. We also know that computers can manage resources and perform feats of scheduling and analysis in the twinkling of an eye. What gives the manager the right to direct the activities of a scientist who knows more about a specific technical issue than he does? Or a lawyer? Or an accountant? What really makes a manager necessary? It is his ability (and his willingness) to make decisions — complex, real time, high risk decisions — and put them into action.

The description of business set forth above is so far theoretical. If business X adds value to certain resources, it can sell them to customer Y for a profit. But businesses operate in the real world. Precisely what resources? Where are they obtained? What quantities of each? Exactly who is customer Y and what can he afford? Where is he located? How much profit? In what time frame?

It is the manager's job to make these decisions. And since he will make them in the real world, only one thing is certain: he will make them with less than the optimum amount of information. He will make them anyway; he has to because his competitor will. He will make decisions based on a variety of inputs from disciplines (scientific, legal, financial) in which he is not expert. He will use judgement . . . and intuition. He will make mistakes and he will learn from them: he will change his decisions. In short, he will take risks.

A word about risk. Risk has acquired various meanings both in the scientific world and the world of the layman. However, it has a rather special meaning in the world of management which contrasts with its connotations elsewhere. (Actually, it has several business meanings depending on whether you are an insurance company actuary, an investment portfolio manager, an arbitrageur, etc., but in the present context the definition is the one used by the general manager.)

To the manager, risk is directly related to reward. The higher the risk, the higher the expected potential returns. Thus, risk is inherently natural and necessary, even desireable, if you are to make a profit. But notice the "potential" returns. The successful manager takes "calculated" risks and then does everything he can to "manage" them.

This, then, a rough job description for a manager. Regardless of his basic training, be he an accountant or a scientist, a salesman or a production supervisor, once he becomes a manager his job is to make decisions. Lest all this decision making begins to sound too exciting, take note that many of the judgements he will be called upon to make in the course of a normal business day are remarkably petty. Yes, there are those days when he will have to make the big decisions, the strategic choices, the major project commitments. He may even make profound decisions, such as going forward with the first field test of a genetically engineered organism or the first gene therapy product. But he also will have to cope with the employees angry about the potholes in the car park and the shareholder who thinks the company should invest in research focused on the lower back problems of Great Danes. Managers must have a capacity for the sublime and a tolerance for the ridiculous.

It has been said that scientists can best relate to the manager's world through the analogy of the experiment. Business decision making is simply a large, complex and lengthy experiment, something any scientist can readily visualize. Close your eyes and picture this big experiment. Now, do one more thing. Move yourself from the position of experimentalist and observer to that of one of the laboratory rats. You are now "in" the experiment. You are now a manager.

HOW TO PORTRAY MANAGEMENT?

This chapter is about the biotechnology manager. It is an attempt to provide you with a sense of the different types of decisions he makes, the variety of issues they represent, their relative importance and their interrelatedness. It is not an exhaustive study. Although it attempts to touch upon all the major aspects — manufacturing, marketing, finance, etc. — that are part of a business, it would be impossible to truly do justice to these topics in one chapter, even though when limiting the story to a single industry. And what an exciting industry it is! It is entrepreneurial and leading edge. It is new and changing all the time. It is fascinating and frustrating. It is risky and deeply rewarding. It is periodically profound and frequently funny. It is never dull (well, almost never!) This chapter cannot properly convey this excitement to the reader. For that, you must become, like me, part of the experiment.

The style of this chapter may seem a little strange to a scientist but a student of business will have met it before. Scientists expect to find their science described and expounded in sober terms: jokes, witticisms and dramatizations are not common in scientific textbooks. Teachers of business and management often use a very different technique, that of the fictional case history. Dramatization is normal and is indeed a very good way of encapsulating in a few short sentences a range of complicated situations so characteristic of human behavior. It can be a much more powerful way than a catalog of somber facts for getting the ideas across. The writers of management texts and professors in business schools often choose whimsical names for the characters and organizations in their presentations: it is less boring than calling people "Ann Jones" or "Bob Smith" and helps to stop the reader trying to identify them with real people and companies. So do not be put off when this chapter does the same: get behind the whimsy and try to perceive the reality.

The discussion that follows is conducted from the point of view of a manager in a small entrepreneurial publicly traded biotechnology firm based in the United States. Biotechnology companies come in all shapes and sizes, from startups to conglomerates. The startup, of course, faces special hurdles and is not sufficiently integrated to provide us with an opportunity to discuss the full range of decisions facing the typical biotechnology manager. Other chapters in this book have been designed to bring alive the world of the startup company and the venture capitalist. In the large established firm, many important decisions have in a sense already been made for the manager. For instance, a large company can internally finance many activities and the need to make decisions about raising capital does not arise. Biotechnology is such a powerful technology that it is being pursued commercially in almost every industrialized country. However, its emergence as an industry occurred in the United States and the largest concentration of biotechnology companies is still found there today. Thus, if there is such a thing as a typical biotechnology manager, he would be found in a small public U.S. company.

Meet Daniel N. Anthony, President and Chief Executive Officer of a seven year old biotechnology company. Like all biotechnology managers, Mr. Anthony is a something of an optimist; he named his company Cloneglobe, Inc.

New Ideas, New Developments — And New Products?

All businesses have to keep ahead of the competition and the life blood of every developing company is new ideas: there can surely be no business activity more dependent on innovation than biotechnology.

Where do new ideas come from? How readily do they grow into products? What does it cost to develop a new product line and what returns can be expected from it, and when? A few diagrams will help to provide some answers.

Sources of new ideas

Ideas can come from anywhere, from the imagination of people. People inside the company generate new concepts directly from their own work but also as a result of all their conversations around the coffee pot or over the lunch table. Scientists are forever talking about their work and one thought leads to another. Sooner or later someone will say: "How about ....?" or "Why don't we ....?" and an idea may be born. Whether it will go much further depends on a whole lot of other factors.

The management team can be an equally prolific source of new initiatives but theirs may perhaps come more often from a perception of a market niche, an opportunity to satisfy an unfilled need, even one which will have to be created from scratch, than from the exuberance of progressing the technology *per se*. All those employees of the company who are in some way in contact with their markets will have a contribution to make.

Ideas come from everywhere, from outside the company just as much as from within. Everybody is continually in touch with the world outside through constant reading, talking, looking and listening. Other people's ideas taken in via public channels or through private conversation often provoke the spark which sets a group of potential innovators thinking. Those ideas from outside might have come from a totally unrelated context; oftentimes they originate from government agencies indicating new areas of interest, from the business world at large, from competitors' publicity as they go about their own marketing and public relations activities and, of course, from the world's universities and research institutes. Figure 1 portrays a selection of these sources.

Naturally, most new ideas do not lead directly to new products or services even though they are part of that ferment of discussion which produces more novel thoughts than most communities can digest and from which the really valuable notions arise. Filters are needed for refining, improving and generally making the new propositions more realistic, closer to being turned into something valuable for the company. Techniques for dealing with novelty are in no way confined to commercial companies: in various guises they permeate all activities which depend on innovation and creative thought. The simple diagram reproduced in Figure 2 stresses the point about recycling and refining while Figure 3 points up the reality that most ideas for new products and services fall by the wayside: they cannot actually be turned into something real, they don't work well enough, the market does not materialize or they get beaten by a competitor. The rate of attrition might appear to some people to be very gloomy indeed but really it is not that depressing: "ideas industries" like biotechnology typically generate much more innovation than they can cope with. The more difficult problem comes in deciding which ones, all things considered, are most *worth* developing.

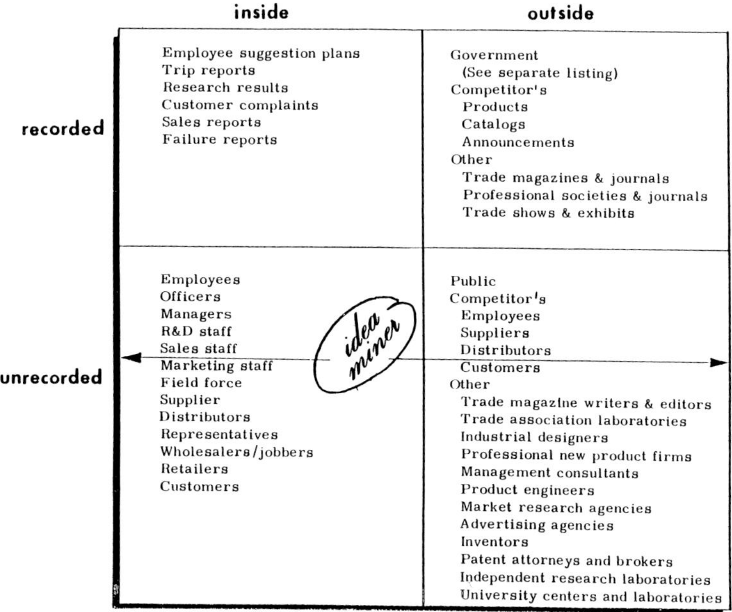

Figure 1. Sources of new product ideas.
(Reproduced by permission of the Forum Corporation.)

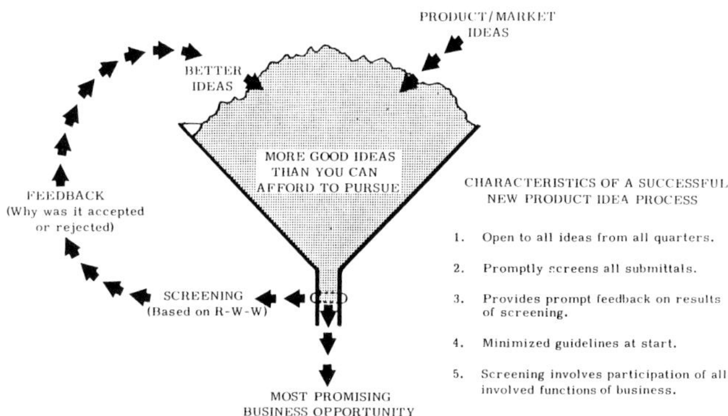

Figure 2. New product ideas and their selection.
(Reproduced by permission of the Forum Corporation.)

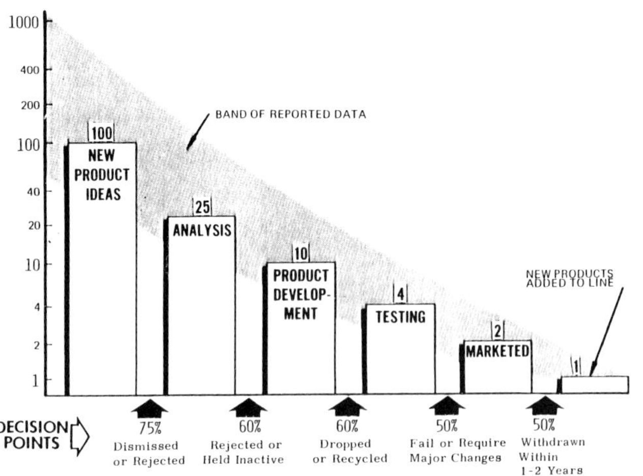

Figure 3. New product stages.
(Reproduced by permission of the Forum Corporation.)

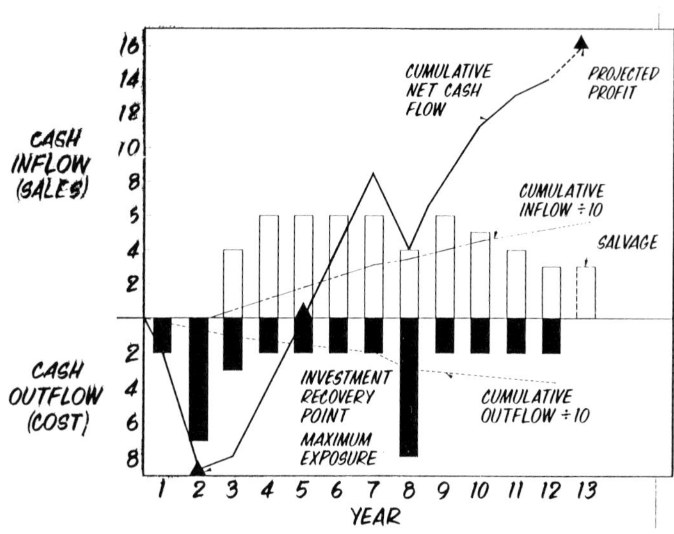

Figure 4. Cash flow for a new product.
(Reproduced by permission of the Forum Corporation.)

Costs of development

An appreciation of development costs becomes essential. Going anywhere with a new idea starts off costing money: in the beginning there are expenses for development but, for the moment at least and for some time to come, no sales revenue. The trick is to generate sales revenue as soon as possible, staunch the outflow of resources, turn the initial negative cash flow positive and, if possible, keep it there for ever after, as Figure 4 shows. As it happens, much of biotechnology has taken longer to turn positive than many early investors expected and that has sometimes produced problems for individual companies. It is not uncommon for the breakeven point of a biotech company, and even of individual products if they require regulatory approval, to be as much as eight or ten years after startup. That is a very long time for an investor to wait for a return, so much so that for some of them biotechnology has lost part of its early appeal.

Rewards of success

When a new product is really successful, success can last a long time. As product volume rises, development costs are amortized and production costs tend to fall but sales price does not necessarily fall in step (Figure 5) so that a successful

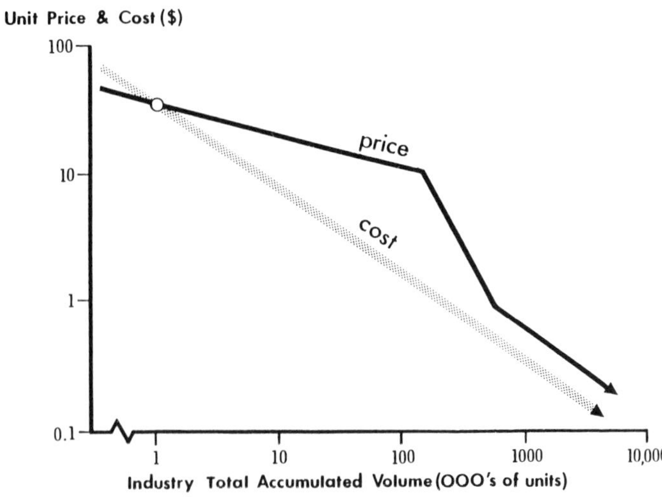

Figure 5. Product price/cost/volume.
(Reproduced by permission of the Forum Corporation.)

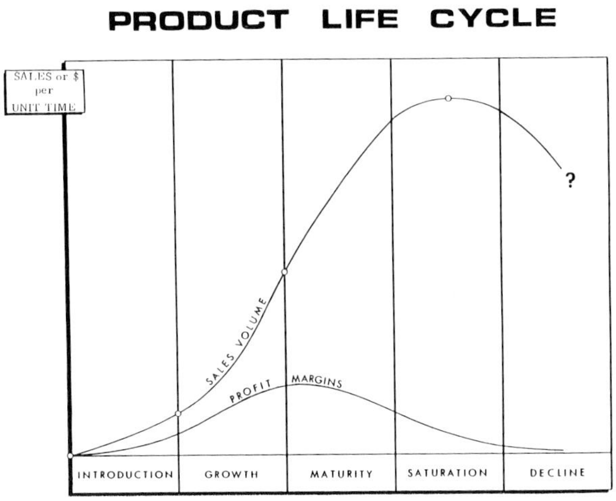

Figure 6. Product life cycle.
(Reproduced by permission of the Forum Corporation.)

mature product often becomes more and more profitable with passing time. That is what a biotechnology company, like any other, aims for. Typically, a new product, if it is to be successful, generates sales right from the beginning: it starts off in a small way either in a market which is itself developing or as a novelty clawing its way to market share in an existing market which may, of course, be thereby expanded in size. As the product matures its sales volume may grow ever greater but eventually the market becomes saturated and while *growth* may cease, the product can nevertheless continue to generate substantial revenues for its owners. That state of affairs may last a long time but one day a better competitor might show up and do exactly to our product what we did to the market when our product was new. Unless we can improve the efficacy of our product, reduce its price, enlarge its market or promote its sales in some other way, we risk it going into decline and completing its life cycle. Figure 6 tells the story. All products are presumably going to do that sooner or later: we want ours to be one of the later ones!

TECHNOLOGY DECISION MAKING

In the general discussion of businesses above, it was implied that businesses come into existence to fulfill a need. The need, then, exists before the business. While it is true in most cases, this pattern does not provide an accurate model of a technology business such as biotechnology. The tools of biotechnology, the ability, for example, to move genetic information from one cell to another, even one species to another, were created and immediately recognized as having great commercial value before anyone articulated a specific market need. So it would appear that this is a clear case of the chicken coming before the egg. Technological breakthroughs, however, are more akin to the chicken suddenly becoming a peacock. The means of production change in a radical way, opening up an array of new opportunities to fulfill, not one, but a cornucopia of needs. Some needs may have been previously unmet, others may have been partially or fully met by older technologies. However, the availability of the new technology creates opportunities to overcome barriers to entry in various businesses.

To make matters even more interesting, our technological peacock does not arrive on the scene as a mature bird. She develops over time. Keeping up with her development is a key challenge for the biotechnology manager. And, of course, one hen does not a successful egg business make. Our manager will have to acquire, feed and care for a bevy of birds, and make sure they get along with each other, to assure a continuous flow of eggs.

Daniel Anthony waited impatiently for the elevator at 8:55 a.m. He had called a 9:00 meeting of Cloneglobe's senior managers to discuss several important technical issues. While Cloneglobe was a recognized leader in recombinant DNA technology, the company had no internal expertise in monoclonal antibody technology. The company's marketing manager, responsible for developing a therapeutics business, felt that antibody-based products would play a significant role in Cloneglobe's chosen market and wanted to add Mab products to Cloneglobe's product line. Cloneglobe's vice president of research and development was anxious to build an internal capability for generating and screening monoclonals. This would require a 20% increase in R & D staff. The Chief Financial Officer is horrified at such a proposal. There is no way, he believes, that, given the current state of Cloneglobe's balance sheet, the company can internally fund such an increase or acquire the additional laboratory space to house the additional people. As Daniel exited the elevator and entered the meeting room he felt a bit like that other Daniel entering the lion's den.

Everyone has arrived, including Dr. Fred Brilliant of Excaliber University, a consultant to the company. Anthony retained Brilliant several years previously as a means of staying current with the rapidly evolving field of monoclonal antibody technology. Cloneglobe had relationships with twelve such consultants with expertise in different bioscience fields in various universities in the United States and Europe. These connections had produced, among other things, several technology transfer agreements, an important process technology license and a significant research collaboration on a protein analog to potentially treat colon cancer.

Anthony started the meeting. The first to speak was Dr. Bruce Team, head of R & D. He pointed out that the lack of a monoclonal antibody research group not only meant that Cloneglobe could not produce Mab products, but that the full capabilities of his recombinant DNA group were not being realized. He gave as an example the work of Steinmetz, one of Cloneglobe's most productive scientists. In some of his earlier work, Sam Steinmetz had cloned certain bacterial toxins and produced them recombinantly. If Cloneglobe had monoclonal antibody capability, these recombinant toxins could be linked to Mabs selected to bind to cancer cells and tested as anticancer therapeutics.

"This is the kind of research synergy that would be possible with a broadly capable R & D team," concluded Bruce.

Ted Papadopolous, the marketing director, said: "Several competitors already have advanced such products into late clinical testing. Any Cloneglobe products would have to fill a niche or represent a significant advance to allow us to carve a position in the market since our entry would be so late."

The head of development, Juan Martinez, glanced nervously at his boss, Dr. Team, before saying: "The R & D department's estimate of ten production personnel and 3,000 square feet of additional production space for a Mab scaleup facility is simply too low. I will never be able to meet normal clinical delivery schedules for multiple products with such limited resources. And producing conjugate products such as immunotoxins is simply out of the question!"

Al Haupmann, the financial officer, was white as a sheet and could hold back no longer. "The equity markets are extremely unfavorable to offerings at this time and we are having a difficult enough time as it is staying within budget on our current programs. Our balance sheet is adequate but not exactly robust, and Peter Brischle (Cloneglobe's lawyer) told me yesterday that we have been sued for infringement of a competitor's patent; the cost of the legal defense is likely to eat significantly into our capital. Just where is the extra capital, which I estimate to be $25 million over the next three years, going to come from?" Haupmann asked.

"Perhaps we could kill some of our less promising programs, such as the B-cell proliferation factor project," Martinez suggested.

Team, the original champion of BPFs before he was promoted to head of department, said the company would be crazy to do that just when a technical breakthrough was expected. Haupmann rolled his eyes to the ceiling at this remark.

Hoping to avoid fisticuffs, Anthony asked Brilliant, who had been silent up to this point, for his views.

Brilliant said, "To get into traditional antibody technology at this point would be a waste of time. However, there are a number of university groups working on leading edge stuff with great promise. What you need to do is to leapfrog current technology and get into something like octromas."

Brilliant suggested several people with whom the firm could develop a collaboration. One was Dr. Joe Valente at Redoubtable Research Institute.

Team said that he had been very intrigued by several of Valente's recent papers. Martinez reminded the group that Sam Steinmetz had done postgraduate work with Valente when they both were at Western State University.

Brischle the lawyer, who had entered the meeting late because of the law suit, said: "The original patent applications on octroma technology were filed by Dr. Bjorn Nelson of the Southern Polytechnic Institute and, although they have not issued as yet, they are expected to be broad. If we were to decide to enter this field, we would probably have to obtain a license under these patent applications."

Team, looking at no one in particular, wondered out loud whether octromas will be highly immunogenic. He speculated that immunogenicity would greatly reduce Ted's market opportunity and probably make it difficult to get the products through the federal regulatory review process. He bemoaned the fact that Vicky Ching, Cloneglobe's head of medical affairs, was absent from the meeting due to a visit with a key clinical collaborator because she could have shed some light on these questions.

Martinez murmured that producing octromas would undoubtedly require four times as many people as producing conjugates.

Team, unperturbed, erupted. "Just think how many diagnostic products we can make with this technology!"

This outburst was followed by a squeal from Ted: "But we don't have a diagnostics sales force you dolt! We're in the therapeutics business!"

Anthony restored order with some difficulty.

"We are a technology-driven business and it is very important for us to stay at the leading edge of bioscience", he said. "However, there is no way at this point for Cloneglobe to develop a leadership position in traditional Mab technology. The competition would eat us alive. I'm sorry Bruce, but we are not going to create an internal Mab research organization. Ted, if you want to market monoclonals along with our recombinant protein products, get your marketing guys to license some existing products from some of these small research boutiques".

"We simply can't acquire every technology around," Anthony continued. "We have finite resources. But we do have sufficient capital — Al, stop grimacing — to contemplate getting into technical areas directed at focuses important to us such as therapeutics and *where we have a chance of establishing a leadership position. Now, this octroma area sounds promising, but we need some answers before committing".*

"Bruce, get some of your scientific gurus to assess this technology. How useful is it likely to be? How feasible is octroma product development, particularly as it relates to therapeutics? Why don't you send Sam out to see Valente for a preliminary discussion, and follow up on those other researchers too. Are there technologies which compete with octromas? How does this technology fit with our current capabilities?"

"And, Peter, we'll need to look more thoroughly at the patent and licensing situation. Can we gain access to this technology? Will we have sufficient freedom to operate in this area or not?"

"We need to get a better feel for implementing a program in this area, and I don't mean adding forty people next

quarter! Bruce, come up with a realistic proposal after you have completed your technical assessment".

"And group, don't bother Vicky about immunogenicity and regulatory issues at this point. You're getting ahead of yourselves. This technology is too new and nobody has the answers to that yet, so don't waste your time speculating".

"We'll plan to meet again in about three weeks," Anthony decided.

As he left the room, Anthony looked at his watch. It was 11:00 and he was late for his next meeting. When he arrived in his office three minutes later, Claude Roget, Cloneglobe's director of personnel, was already waiting for him.

RESOURCE DECISION MAKING

Human Resources

Of course, there is no such thing as a biotechnologist. Biotechnology is the result of the coordination of various skills and talents, from molecular biology to protein chemistry and cell biology to chromatography. And for a biotechnology business to function effectively, individuals with a variety of non-scientific skills are also necessary: marketing specialists, manufacturing experts, lawyers, public relations people, computer specialists and accountants. The primary resource of any technology enterprise is its people. Attracting, motivating and retaining these highly trained individuals is a key concern of the manager. As with all other resources required by his business, people are a finite commodity which must be sought in an atmosphere of fierce competition. The manager must ensure that his company offers attractions that are at least as good, if not better than those of competitive entities — other companies, large and small, and other organizations where an individual might perform the same or similar work, such as universities or government agencies.

In today's job market, individuals who have acquired a high degree of special expertise through extensive education and/or experience have come to be known as "knowledge" workers, people who make their contribution not through the sweat of their brow, but through the quality of the ideas generated inside it! What job opportunities or attributes attract a knowledge worker? The chance to perform challenging work and the opportunity to learn, grow and advance in one's chosen career are extremely important. An attractive salary and benefits such as paid life insurance, a pension plan, medical and dental coverage and so forth also are recruiting attractions. Many companies, especially entrepreneurial firms, offer a stake in the business through special stock ownership plans, including stock option grants. These plans are based on the premise that as the individual contributes to the company's achievement through his own work, the stock appreciates and the individual shares directly in the firm's success by owning a piece of the business. The firm's environment, its very culture, also plays an important role in attracting talent. The chance to work closely with top-ranked scientists in an atmosphere where junior members of the team are allowed to voice their opinions can be very compelling. A company that actively promotes rather than discourages publishing by its scientific personnel is likely to be much more attractive to a talented young scientist. A less structured environment where employees are not expected to conform to rigid work schedules can tip the balance.

If the manager is successful in attracting the desired talent, he has, however, won only half the battle. The other half involves arranging these valuable people resources into an effective organization. This organization must be configured to elicit the most productivity out of these expensive assets and the productivity must be directed at the objectives of the firm. The manager maximizes the flow of tasks and information by assigning the appropriate levels of responsibility and authority up and down the organization. If he does an effective job, the tasks are delegated to the optimum level within the structure, authority is delegated to assure the function of adequate directions, controls and constraints to keep things moving toward the right target in a timely fashion and information flows back up to the manager so that he knows whether things are proceeding as intended.

The organization also is configured so that interdependent work is aligned closely in the structure and access to support groups is facilitated. Research and development, and marketing and sales organizations, cannot function in today's competitive world without the support of computer and information services groups. Line organizations also generate needs for other kinds of staff, including legal, public relations, and strategical planning departments. Portions of the company's organizational chart must be mimicked in the physical layout of the operation, in addition to being tied through the firm's reporting structure, for certain activities must be located in proximity to each other in order to function efficiently.

If he wins the second half of the battle, the manager still has not won the war. In a company that is growing and changing, no organization can remain static. A biotechnology company with an objective of growing from a research firm into a fully-integrated business manufacturing and marketing its own products will require a very different structure as it approaches that objective. The manager will add to and alter his existing organization as he requires new activities. The timing of these changes is critical. He cannot wait to hire a sales department until the day his product is ready to sell. On the other hand, he cannot afford to have hundred of sales people waiting around while the product works its way through various stages of research and development. Misjudgments in organization planning can have untoward financial and motivational consequences.

"Hi, Claude," said Dan as he sank into his desk chair. "What's the problem?"

"We have a very angry young scientist on our hands," said Claude. "I met with George and he is about at the end of his rope. He feels that he has to get his supervisor's permission for every little thing. He says he has to spend entirely too much time getting approvals to move ahead with the project he is responsible for instead of doing the science. His frustration level is very high and I think he is contacting head hunters about job opportunities elsewhere."

"This is unacceptable, Claude. George Swann is one of our brightest talents. What's your assessment of the situation?" Dan asked.

"I think the problem lies with George's supervisor, Anita Takagawa. In my opinion, Anita is not demonstrating good management skills. She is not delegating the necessary authority to the project members who report to her. Anita hasn't been in a management position for very long, and she is having trouble staying out of the scientific work and focusing on her new managerial tasks. The project managers feel like they have all the responsibility but no authority since she makes them come to her for every decision. Several of her people have asked for transfers," Claude offered, ominously.

"The projects are undoubtedly suffering as a result of this situation," said Daniel. "Look, I'll have a word with Anita. I'll reemphasize the importance of her management role and get her to rethink the way she is relating to her subordinates. She has a lot of potential and it's not unusual for people new to management to make these kinds of mistakes".

"What is happening with the offer we made to Jack Frederick for the new pharmacology position?" Dan inquired.

"Good news, he has accepted!" answered Claude. "The stock options we offered him were the deciding factor. They helped offset the loss of equity he faced from walking away from his employer's pension plan. He'll start in three weeks."

"Great! Let's hope he can adjust to Cloneglobe's culture. It's a different environment from that of the big company situation he's used to," Dan observed.

As Claude collected his papers and departed, Daniel turned to the pile of phone messages his secretary had arranged on his desk blotter. He had twenty minutes before his luncheon appointment and he started to return the calls.

Financial Resources

Biotechnology is a very capital intensive business. The development of a single biopharmaceutical, for example, requires in excess of $100 million. It follows that a major challenge for the biotechnology manager is the timely acquisition of adequate funding. This activity requires careful assessment of the firm's ongoing capital needs. It also requires a familiarity with the various options for accessing capital, from the familiar equity and debt approaches to less traditional vehicles such as research and development limited partnerships. Each method has its own advantages and disadvantages; analyzing the merits of each as well as the relative cost of capital to the firm is an important management challenge. In addition, the capital markets are not always favorable and the manager must stay far enough ahead of his operating capital needs, for the opportunity to raise additional cash may not be there when he requires funding.

He also must manage his cash flow situation carefully. Good planning and budgeting practices create internal control and discipline. However, no planning system ever accounts for every eventuality and decisions to change plans and programs must be made along the way to take advantage of opportunities or correct mistaken assumptions.

Entrepreneurial biotechnology companies generally operate in a deficit mode for an extended period because they are developing their first products and have no established business to generate profits while these products are in development. Thus, the biotech firm has a "burn rate" as it spends down the capital on its balance sheet. The manager must reach the market and generate revenue through product sales before his capital is exhausted. His ability to manage this "transition" is crucial. Balancing spending needs against maintaining a protective cushion of cash while trying to accurately predict the timing of product-driven revenues is a task which can be likened to juggling knives while blindfolded.

Many biotechnology companies are publicly traded companies. This means that at some time in their past they elected to raise capital by selling equity — shares in their company to investors at large (as opposed to private funding from selected institutions and wealthy individuals). They did this because public offerings are a means of raising large amounts of capital at reasonable cost. A very important point is that shares in a public company are traded through stockbrokers on the stock market, usually daily. Any good or bad news, or rumors, can affect the price at which the stock is traded. However, the decision to become a public company involves special obligations. Since the company now has a new group of owners (including the general public), the investors mentioned at the beginning of this chapter, the firm takes on the government enforced obligation of reporting to them on a regular basis the status of the operation and its prospects. The public company's board of directors has enlarged responsibilities for overseeing managerial decision making on behalf of the shareholders between the annual meetings when the shareholders themselves vote on important company business in person or by proxy.

The price of a publicly traded stock multiplied by the number of share outstanding is the "value" of the firm. This value is the market's current assessment of the company's assets plus its potential to generate profits. Since analyzing potential involves judgements about future events, investors' perceptions about future events affect valuation. Large, established companies with earnings track records in stable business sectors are easier for investors to assess than growth companies. Biotechnology companies are, in a sense all "potential" and no track record. It is much more difficult for investors to weigh their prospects. Changes in investor perception regarding a company's performance, competitive situation, proprietary position, research expertise and a host of other factors can cause volatility in its stock. Valuation also is affected by the market's perception of the management — the skills, experience and capabilities of the company's leadership. Managers of public companies have both an obligation and a need to communicate frequently and effectively with shareholders in order to insure that these owners have an accurate perception of the prospects of the company. This also involves communicating with others who influence shareholders, including investment counselors, stockbrokers, securities analysts and journalists.

Daniel dialed a number in Ames, Iowa. He had called this number many times in the past. It was the number of Russell Lyon, a retired stockbroker who owned a large block of Cloneglobe stock. Mr. Lyon read Cloneglobe's quarterly reports cover to cover. Since he was retired, he had the time to follow his investments closely. He was a bit of a curmudgeon. But he was a curmudgeon who could vote 100,000 shares of stock.

"Hello, Mr. Lyon, this is Daniel Anthony returning your call.

"What the hell do you people think you are doing!" Mr. Lyon fumed. "The stock price is ten dollars below my purchase price."

"Mr. Lyon, the biotechnology stocks have been underperforming the market lately. I believe that certain recently announced patent litigations among companies in the field have caused investors to overreact to the implications of these uncertainties and their attitudes have affected the performance of the entire group. Cloneglobe's stock has gone down with the rest," Dan intoned patiently.

"That may be so, but I think the market is disappointed with your financial results. I know I am!" Lyon shouted into the phone. "At the last stockholder's meeting you said you expected your new product, ANTIONKIN, to be on the market by now. What's the holdup? Don't your people know how to deal with the regulatory agencies?"

"We had hoped that the regulators would move our product along a little faster, Mr. Lyon," Dan responded. "We have supplied them with all the necessary information, but we can't control the timeliness with which they review it."

Daniel talked with Mr. Lyon for several more minutes about the company's performance, and by the time he concluded the conversation, Mr. Lyon was mollified, for the time being.

His next call was to a stock analyst in New York.

"Hello, Elizabeth, this is Dan Anthony returning your call," he opened.

"Thanks for getting back to me, Dan," Elizabeth said. "I need to check out a rumor with you. There's a rumor that your competitor, Recombicorp, is getting results in the clinic with their product that are far superior to those of your lung cancer product. If that's true, I'm going to have to change my projections. I currently show Cloneglobe with 60% of the market in 1994. If I lower that to 20%, it really changes my numbers on your company."

Dan explained that Cloneglobe's product was approximately two years ahead of Recombicorp's in the clinic, and that even if his competitor was getting good results, which was, as Elizabeth had said, only a rumor, Cloneglobe would still be on the market with its product long before Recombicorp.

As he put the receiver back in its cradle, Dan felt relatively confident that he had dissuaded Elizabeth from lowering her recommendation on Cloneglobe.

Dan rushed from his office to the luncheon meeting down the hall. The meeting was the monthly review of Cloneglobe's financial performance with the company's finance and accounting group.

As he entered the conference room, Charles Jones, the company's chief accountant, was circulating the financial statements. Dan took his seat and, Charles began his review of the numbers.

"We are unfavorable to budget in revenues primarily due to the delay in the approval and launch of ANTIONKIN," Jones said. "We also are unfavorable to budget in costs and expenses primarily due to over spending on research and development and on the clinical testing programs. This was partially offset by lower than expected spending on staffing. Specifically, we have not hired additional sales people to support the launch of the new product. Fortunately, interest income on our cash was slightly higher than expected but this may change going forward because interest rates are expected to fall."

"Well, we can't control interest rates," said Al Haupmann, "but we can control expenses. We need to reduce expenses now on some of our programs or our year end results are going to be far worse."

Dan said: "Let's look more closely at what is really causing the over spending."

Charles directed everyone to turn to page three in handout which contained the breakdown of expenses by department and program and reviewed these numbers for the group.

"It looks like the major problems are in development and clinical testing," Dan concluded. "I'm going to talk with Vicky about these clinical numbers. We simply have to stop following up every single lead with a new clinical trial. We have to be more selective. I'll meet with Martinez too. I don't know the answer to why our development expenses are running unfavorable to budget."

Al commented that Martinez' group has experienced unexpected problems in scaling up the BPF product. Multiple product lots had been discarded and nearly three times as much staff time had been booked against the program than originally proposed.

"Well, that may be it, but I'll look into it further," said Dan. "We have to go now Al, if we're to be on time for the meeting with that construction firm."

Facilities and equipment resources

The location of a company and the commitment to the purchase, lease and construction of facilities, the "bricks and mortar" of an operation, are long term obligations which require careful decision making by the manager. In addition to involving major capital allocations, these decisions have other important implications. Many biotechnology companies were founded close to major universities because close working relationships with academic scientists necessitated a physical proximity to campuses. Certain geographic areas offer a venture capital infrastructure which is of major importance to startup firms. Moreover, some areas, through government and/or combined government/university action, boast incubator facilities where young companies can locate their operations in the early years at very attractive rates. Since biotechnology firms employ a high percentage of extremely well educated people, considerations such as the proximity of cultural amenities, attractive housing and good schools for the children of employees may also play a role. It would be unwise to chose a rural location for a research complex because of cheap land and attractive leasing rates only to find that attracting top scientific personnel was made extremely difficult because no one wanted to live one hundred miles from the nearest opera. On the other hand, locating a large, highly automated manufacturing plant on expensive urban real estate in close proximity to an exclusive residential area is neither a wise financial decision nor a good public relations move. Access to airports and other transportation facilities also is a factor.

Decisions regarding the relative merits of leasing or owning property are critical both in terms of capital requirements and timing. Committing to the construction of a manufacturing facility too early in the company's growth cycle can burden it will financial obligations too far in advance of commercial production needs and resulting revenues. Conversely, production capability must be in place and functioning in advance of market demand. Locating a wide selection of leasable space for office facilities in most urban industrial areas is easy. However, the options for space already configured or at least suitable for laboratory facilities may be more limited. Lease obligations and the acquisition of hard assets such as buildings and the equipment they contain are commitments that are long term and relatively fixed. Once acquired they cannot be quickly or easily disposed of should the firm's prospects change. They cannot be killed or postponed like a project, or asked to work part time like a person.

In Al's office Dan and Al greeted Adam Welsh, president of Earthworks Construction, and his team of engineers. Along the walls Adam had already set up the blueprints of the proposed commercial scale addition to Cloneglobe's production facility. Together, they looked at the detailed plans of pharmaceutical production suites for the manufacturing of recombinant protein products. Earthworks Construction had extensive experience in the design and construction of these specialized types of facilities with their stringent specifications for clean rooms and other sophisticated features.

After some discussion with Al and Hans Doetsch, Cloneglobe's manufacturing manager, Dan approved the plans. He directed Hans and Al to prepare a presentation for the company's next meeting of the board of directors so that management could inform the board of the magnitude and costs associated with this project.

"There's one problem which has emerged which is going to require your personal attention, Dan." Adam said. "The town council has refused to issue us the necessary building permits."

"What's the problem?" inquired Dan.

"As you know, you are the only biotechnology company within the borders of Berkland," Adam reminded him. "Neighboring Santa Katarina has three genetic engineering companies and its council has more knowledge of these types of facilities, but the recently elected Berkland city fathers are looking at a proposal for a commercial manufacturing plant of this type for the first time. They need to be educated about the technology. I think a few of them deep down inside believe that you guys are capable of producing monsters. They need to be reassured about the safety of this technology."

"All right, what do you need from me?" Dan sighed.

"Could you perhaps invite the council members over for a tour of your present facilities and a presentation about genetic engineering? Once they gain a better understanding of the process, I'll schedule another planning meeting with them. They will be in a much better position to review these blueprints then," Adam suggested.

"Fine, I'll get it scheduled," said Dan. "I'd better move quickly, because if you don't get permit approval in the next three months our construction schedule will slip and our product production planning will go out the window."

Strategic Decision Making

What is it that the firm does with the resources that it has — technical, human, physical and fiscal? It tries to maximize the value it can produce with these resources through the right strategy. Strategic decision making puts all of these assets in motion toward a single objective or set of objectives. Strategy encompasses the most fundamental decisions about the business, including what kind of a business it is or what business it wishes to engage in — its mission. Important in any business, this kind of positioning is particularly critical in biotechnology because biotechnology itself is not a business but a collection of technical tools. A "biotechnology" company must decide whether it wishes to use these tools in the pharmaceutical business, the diagnostics business, the agricultural business, the animal healthcare business or the consumer products business. It must decide what kind of a company it wishes to be in yet another sense. Does the firm want to be a research company, working for other companies under contract, or does it want to become a fully integrated firm, manufacturing and marketing products directly? With each answer additional questions arise. If the firm chooses to be a pharmaceutical company, what pharmaceutical markets should it pursue — cancer products, cardiovascular products, anti-inflammatories? What geographical markets should it target? Strategic decision making involves both short term and long term objective setting as well. A manager might establish a short term goal of becoming a contract research house and a longer term goal of becoming a fully integrated company.

Once established, the strategic goals of the firm should not change appreciably for extended periods, unless of course, the basic assumptions underlying the strategy are altered or proven unfounded. The manager revisits the strategy periodically to reassess its viability and adjusts his course to accommodate new information. Occasionally, the new information is of such a radical nature that the firm must fundamentally alter its strategic goals. This can occur when a company's technology or products are made obsolete by major innovations or the market for the company's products is profoundly changed by new laws or new forms of competition. By and large, however, the manager spends his time making the decisions that flow from the strategy, acquiring the resources the strategy necessitates and making the tactical decisions required to deploy those resources in a manner that will achieve the established objective. These decisions which address the "how" of the strategy can be relatively straightforward, such as deciding how many sales people will be required to achieve an effective launch of a new product, or more complex, such as choosing between an acquisition or a joint venture as the best means for entering a new market.

Dan returned to his office to find the draft of a press release written by Brad Evans, the public relations manager. It announced the divestment by Cloneglobe of a small veterinary products business. While Cloneglobe was primarily focused on the development of pharmaceutical products for human use, the company had seen an opportunity to leverage the knowledge and effort required for this endeavor to develop related products for use in treating animals. The strategy had proven successful scientifically. The company had developed four promising veterinary products and advanced them into the late stages of testing. This progress had been achieved at only incremental costs to the business' human product programs. As the veterinary products neared the market, however, Cloneglobe's management had to decide how they were to be commercialized. Originally, it had been assumed that Cloneglobe's pharmaceutical business would be well established by the time the veterinary products were viable. Dan had expected to use revenue generated by the pharmaceutical sales to fund the creation of a separate veterinary business. The timing had not worked out as expected. Regulatory delays and development glitches had slowed the growth of the company's drug business. The business was growing, but Cloneglobe was in no position to undertake the development of a new business on its own. Management discussed various alternatives and decided to spin off and sell the veterinary business.

Dan proofread the release which disclosed the sale of the assets, including the proprietary technology, of Cloneglobe's veterinary operation to Agrivet, a Maryland-based conglomerate with an established presence in the veterinary market but no expertise in biotechnology. Dan sat back in his chair and reflected on the negotiations with a smile. Because this acquisition was such a good fit for Agrivet, Cloneglobe had been able to get $20 million from the deal. It had taken three months of meetings to reach the contract signing stage, but it had been worth it. That cash would come in handy given what he had seen in the budget meeting earlier. He would have to remember to recognize Al Haupmann, who had spearheaded the negotiating team, in some special way. Peter Brischle, who had worked late into the night on the complex contracts involved, also should be rewarded. He approved the wording in the press release and placed it in his out box. As he left his office, he started to formulate his statements to the stock analysts who would be calling in the morning when the news became public. They should view the deal positively both because of the proceeds and because Cloneglobe could now focus more fully on developing its main business, but he would have to sell the deal to those analysts and investors who felt that Cloneglobe was closing the door on opportunities in the veterinary market.

PRODUCT MARKETING DECISIONS

The ultimate test of corporate strategy occurs in the marketplace. The ultimate judge of the company's success in adding value is the customer. This customer does not evaluate the company's product or service in a vacuum but in a real world situation where he has various alternatives provided by the company's competitors. The company must be not only technologically successful but also must be an adept marketer of its products. As we have discussed, the product itself must embody added value to the customer. Moreover, its benefits must be clearly and aggressively articulated or promoted so that the customer is aware of these attributes and has enough information to make a buying decision. Promotional strategies involving advertising, direct selling, customer education programs and market research; all may be required in the marketing mix. The product also must be "located" where the customer can obtain it. For the baker, this means leasing a store at a busy street corner. With sophisticated medical products this means a complex delivery system involving multiple warehouses, distributors, hospital and retail pharmacies, co-marketing relationships and other arrangements. And, of course, the price of the product must be appropriate in relation to competitive alternatives as well as providing the company with an attractive return on its sizable investment.

Deciding Which Products

In effect, consciously or not, making decisions about products involves asking a series of questions and choosing between alternative answers. The details are specific to those doing the asking but the categories of questions are rather similar no matter the business. A sequence of charts sets the scene and will help to systematize the process.

Figure 7 asks: "Is it (i.e. the product) real?" and goes on to clarify what that means in terms of market demands ("Is the market real?") and the product itself ("Is the product real?"). These points are then explored in Figures 8 and 9 through further sets of queries intended to provoke in-depth analyses of technical and market factors. Each company will frame the questions in a form specific to its own problems so as to provide the answers most relevant to itself.

Figures 10–12 narrow the inquiry towards us as a particular company and our own product as a particular product,

IS IT REAL? DECISION FACTORS

Figure 7. IS IT REAL? Decision factors.
(Reproduced by permission of the Forum Corporation.)

DECISION CONSIDERATIONS I

IS THE MARKET REAL?

IS THERE A NEED/WANT?	CAN THE CUSTOMER BUY?	WILL THE CUSTOMER BUY?
KIND OF NEED/WANT	STRUCTURE OF MARKET	PRIORITY OF NEED/WANT
TIMING OF NEED/WANT	MARKET SIZE AND POTENTIAL	PRODUCT AWARENESS
COMPETING WAYS TO SATISFY NEED/WANT	AVAILABILITY OF FUNDS	PERCEIVED BENEFITS OR RISKS
		FUTURE EXPECTATIONS
		PRICE VS DESIGN/PERFORMANCE FEATURES

Figure 8. Decision considerations I: Is the market real?
(Reproduced by permission of the Forum Corporation.)

DECISION CONSIDERATIONS II

IS THE PRODUCT REAL?

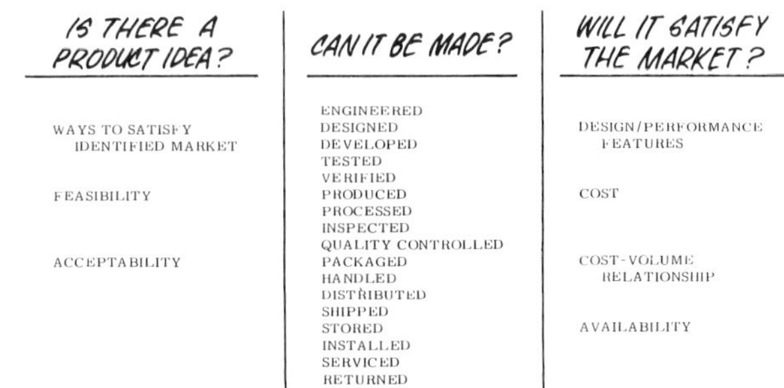

IS THERE A PRODUCT IDEA?	CAN IT BE MADE?	WILL IT SATISFY THE MARKET?
WAYS TO SATISFY IDENTIFIED MARKET	ENGINEERED DESIGNED DEVELOPED TESTED VERIFIED	DESIGN/PERFORMANCE FEATURES
FEASIBILITY	PRODUCED PROCESSED INSPECTED QUALITY CONTROLLED	COST
ACCEPTABILITY	PACKAGED HANDLED DISTRIBUTED SHIPPED	COST-VOLUME RELATIONSHIP
	STORED INSTALLED SERVICED RETURNED	AVAILABILITY

Figure 9. Decision considerations II: Is the product real?
(Reproduced by permission of the Forum Corporation.)

CAN WE WIN? DECISION FACTORS

Figure 10. CAN WE WIN? Decision factors.
(Reproduced by permission of the Forum Corporation.)

DECISION CONSIDERATIONS III

CAN OUR PRODUCT BE COMPETITIVE?

ON DESIGN/PERFORMANCE FEATURES?	ON PROMOTION?	IS THE PRICE RIGHT?	IS THE TIMING RIGHT?
QUALITY UTILITY	CONSUMER ADVERTISING	COST	INTRODUCTION
CONVENIENCE	TRADE ADVERTISING	PRICING POLICIES	DESIGN/PERFORMANCE CHANGES
VERSATILITY RELIABILITY	PACKAGING	TERMS AND CONDITIONS	SALES PROMOTION CAMPAIGNS
DURABILITY	TECHNICAL SERVICES	COMPETITION	PRICE CHANGES
SERVICEABILITY SENSORY FEATURES	OTHER SALES PROMOTION CONSIDERATIONS	OTHER PRICING CONSIDERATIONS	OTHER COMPETITIVE TIMING CONSIDERATIONS
SAFETY UNIQUENESS OTHER AREAS OF PRODUCT DIFFERENTIATION			

Figure 11. Decision considerations III: Can our product be competitive?
(Reproduced by permission of the Forum Corporation.)

DECISION CONSIDERATIONS IV

CAN OUR COMPANY BE COMPETITIVE?

ON ENGINEERING/ PRODUCTION?	ON SALES/ DISTRIBUTION?	ON MANAGEMENT?	ON OTHER COMPETITIVE CONSIDERATIONS?
APPLICABLE ENGINEERING/ PRODUCTION EXPERIENCE	APPLICABLE SALES/ DISTRIBUTION EXPERIENCE	APPLICABLE MANAGEMENT EXPERIENCE	PAST PERFORMANCE
ENGINEERING CAPABILITIES	SALES CAPABILITIES	MANAGEMENT CAPABILITIES AND RESOURCES	GENERAL REPUTATION
PRODUCTION CAPABILITIES	DISTRIBUTION CHANNELS	OTHER MANAGEMENT ASPECTS	PRESENT MARKET POSITION
OTHER ENGINEERING/ PRODUCTION ASPECTS	OTHER SALES/ DISTRIBUTION ASPECTS		GEOPOLITICAL

Figure 12. Decision considerations IV: Can our company be competitive?
(Reproduced by permission of the Forum Corporation.)

IS IT WORTH IT? DECISION FACTORS

IS IT WORTH IT?
WILL IT BE PROFITABLE?
CAN WE AFFORD IT?
IS THE RETURN ADEQUATE?
IS THE RISK ACCEPTABLE?
DOES IT SATISFY OTHER COMPANY NEEDS?
DOES IT SUPPORT CO. OBJECTIVES?
EXTERNAL RELATIONS?
IS THERE AN OVERRIDING FACTOR?

Figure 13. IS IT WORTH IT? Decision factors.
(Reproduced by permission of the Forum Corporation.)

while Figures 13–15 ask whether it should be us (rather than somebody else) who produces and markets this product. It might in principle be a good product but, keeping in mind what our company is and what it is already trying to do, is this proposal right *for us*?

With these thoughts in mind, let us return to Cloneglobe to see how Dan Anthony and Ted Papadopoulous addressed their own particular problems.

DECISION CONSIDERATIONS V

WILL IT BE PROFITABLE?

CAN WE AFFORD IT?	IS THE RETURN ADEQUATE?	IS THE RISK ACCEPTABLE?
CASH OUTFLOW WITH TIME	ABSOLUTE PROFIT	WHAT CAN GO WRONG?
CASH INFLOW WITH TIME	RELATIVE RETURN	HOW LIKELY IS IT?
NET CASH FLOW	COMPARED TO OTHER INVESTMENTS	HOW SERIOUS IF IT HAPPENS?
		WHAT CAN BE DONE ABOUT IT?
		UNKNOWN-UNKNOWNS

Figure 14. Decision considerations V: Will it be profitable?
(Reproduced by permission of the Forum Corporation.)

DECISION CONSIDERATIONS VI

DOES IT SATISFY OTHER COMPANY NEEDS?

DOES IT SUPPORT COMPANY OBJECTIVES AND GOALS?	ARE EXTERNAL RELATIONSHIPS IMPROVED?	ARE THERE OVERRIDING FACTORS?
FUTURE BUSINESS IMPLICATIONS	REPRESENTATIVES	LABOR
RELATION TO PRESENT PRODUCT LINES	DISTRIBUTORS	LEGAL
RELATION TO PRESENT MARKETS	JOBBERS	POLITICAL
UTILIZATION OF AVAILABLE RESOURCES	DEALERS	SHAREHOLDERS/ OWNERS OPINION
OTHER COMPANY DESIRES	CUSTOMERS	COMPANY IMAGE
	COMMUNITY	EXECUTIVE JUDGEMENT
	GENERAL PUBLIC	
	GOVERNMENT	

Figure 15. Decision considerations VI: Does it satisfy other company needs?
(Reproduced by permission of the Forum Corporation.)

Dan arrived late for the marketing meeting. The marketing group was considering its promotional and pricing strategies for ANTIONKIN which Cloneglobe expected to begin marketing next quarter. Ted Papadopoulous was reviewing the merits of the product as measured against competitive products already on the market or expected to enter the market shortly.

"As you know," said Ted, "our product is entering a market where there are already two products approved to treat the same form of lung cancer. While our product has an improved efficacy profile, the existing products have been around for a long time, are well understood and are relatively easy to use. It will not be easy to get physicians to try out product because they are comfortable with what they know. What we have here are two different advertising approaches. One focuses almost exclusively on the efficacy differential. The other is a

two-pronged approach, featuring efficacy, but subtly positioning our product as the wave of things to come. We are trying to show the oncologists that they are going to be seeing more and more genetically engineered products and that it is in their interests to learn how to use these new proteins."

Kathy Enzel of Wells, Lewis & Berman, Cloneglobe's advertizing agency, presented mockups of the two campaigns. She explained that the first campaign had broad appeal but that the second was aimed at thought leaders in the oncology community. She also presented market research data showing that anti-cancer drugs were adopted first by thought leaders and then by the broader oncology market. She concluded her presentation with a recommendation to accept the second campaign.

"Ted, how much of an efficacy differential do we have?" asked Dan.

"Our drug is useful in treating approximately 45% of patients," said Ted. "Of these, approximately 20% of patients have a complete response. All their tumor mass is absent on X-ray after a course of treatment. The other two drugs have roughly a 20% response rate with about 12% showing complete response. Recurrences are about equal in both complete response groups but much greater among the partial responders for our competitors' products.

"That's quite a difference," said Dan. "Why would any physician resist switching to a drug that offers this much of an improvement in performance?" he mused.

"Both the other drugs can be given orally," said Ted. "Our product must be injected. This can mean patient management and compliance problems, even though the drug only has to be administered twice a week. Many patients simply cannot be taught to give themselves injections and they will have to come to the physician's office for their medication."

"Sounds like we are creating some extra work for the nursing staff," said Ted. "What are we doing to communicate with them?"

Kathy distributed copies of the advertising placement schedule. It showed a high frequency of placements in two respected oncology nursing journals.

The general discussion that followed focused on ways to overcome medical community resistance to adopting an injectable medication.

Dan directed Ted and Kathy to conduct research on other injectables frequently used by oncology practitioners to see how much of an issue this was.

"I think you've identified the problem correctly, but I don't think your solution is on target," said Dan. "Telling the physician he should try this drug because he is going to be seeing a lot of genetically engineered injectables, while an accurate reflection of the direction of research, isn't the right message. We have to develop a more practical approach. Back to the drawing board, people!"

Dan headed for the elevator because his next meeting was across the street at Cloneglobe's manufacturing facility.

Production operations in the biotechnology industry are sophisticated, capital intensive and highly regulated. While they require specialized knowledge of front-end processes which are relatively unique to biotechnology, they also necessitate a thorough understanding of finishing processes, quality assurance procedures, documentation protocols and other capabilities utilized in various industries within which biotechnology is practiced. The pharmaceutical, chemical and agricultural industries, for example, have well established bodies of standards, practices and regulations. In addition to a full understanding of these aspects of production, the manager also must be an expert at planning and scheduling to assure efficient use of his capital intensive facilities and the production capacity they afford.

Dan met Juan Martinez as he entered the plant and the two men walked together to the second floor conference room. Hans Doetsch, Cloneglobe's manufacturing manager, was congratulating his production staff on a recent regulatory agency inspection.

"The inspectors had very positive comments about our production operations," said Hans. "We only had one negative comment. The inspectors thought that we could improve the documentation of the second phase of our purification process and have asked to see a rewritten procedure incorporating their suggested enhancements. Well done, group!"

After general congratulations all around, Hans steered the meeting to the main topic of discussion, the initiation of commercial scale manufacturing on a new product coming out of development. It had been scheduled to reach this stage six months previously but the development group had experienced a very difficult time with scaleup. The problems in development had necessitated several reschedulings in manufacturing, including layoffs on the swing shift. The manufacturing managers, who bore the brunt of worker dissatisfaction, were not on the best of terms with the development team.

"Development tells us they are ready to transfer the CG-320 protein to us at last," said Hans, casting a skeptical glance at Juan.

"This one was a bear," replied Juan in defense of his organization. "Since we have been the ones to work out all the kinks in the process, you guys should be able to make up for lost time once the product is transferred."

"We'll be the judges of how well you have solved the problems once we get CG-320 over here," retorted Hans.

Dan interrupted, "Let's stop posturing and get on with it. Things don't always go the way we want them to and schedules have to be changed. We can't undo the past. Let's focus on getting this product into production as efficiently as we can."

The managers reviewed the production specifications and directed numerous, and for the most part constructive, questions at Juan. Then the discussion turned to scheduling. Hans pointed out that fitting CG-320 into the quarterly schedule was going to be difficult because manufacturing operations was busy building inventory for the ANTIONKIN product in preparation for its introduction to the market.

"The inventory buildup must continue to take first priority," said Dan. "We have to be in a position to supply our sales force with everything they need. After all, ANTIONKIN will be producing revenues while CG-320 is still in testing."

Further discussions resulted in the conclusion that manufacturing would be able to supply only about 70% of the originally projected quantity of CG-320 by the following quarter.

"Well, try to beat that projection, people," said Dan, "but I will advise Vicky that she will have to cut back on her plans to add additional testing centers until the third quarter."

Dan excused himself and left the meeting. He reflected that he had accomplished his primary goal in attending, in that he had diffused the tension between development and manufacturing and refocused his managers on the production challenges at hand.

THE EXTERNAL ENVIRONMENT

Although not entirely predictable, the internal environment of the firm is within the direct control of the manager. Management decides what the company's strategy will be, how it will utilize its resources and deploy its personnel. When events do not unfold according to plan, management has the flexibility to alter those plans. The external environment, however, is not controlled by the manager. It may not even be possible for management to influence events outside the company and yet these events may have a profound impact on the firm and its business.

The external environment is made up of a broad range of entities which have the power to affect the company's ability to achieve its objectives. We have already discussed the importance of the capital markets and investor perception. We also have touched briefly on competition which may be local, national or global and may be product specific or technological in nature. Regulatory agencies also have been shown to control the way a firm operates. In fact, local, state and federal government can affect a firm's environment through executive, legislative and judicial actions. Changes in import or export laws, patent laws, statutes regulating the treatment of employees, antitrust legislation, tax policy, accounting and other corporate reporting rules, securities regulation, environmental legislation and laws governing commercial "speech" or advertising can each have a major impact on the corporation.

Investors, competitors and governments are major external influences but the list does not stop here. Suppliers, consultants, the families of employees, potential new employees, and the people who live in the community immediately surrounding a company facility all can affect the way the company does business. The good opinion of these influencers has become sufficiently recognized that they are often referred to as "stakeholders" in the firm. Customers, interestingly, are also a kind of stakeholder, with a strong interest in the continued viability and integrity of the company. The relative importance of each group (the stakeholders, stockholders and government — "the nation") often varies from one situation to another and especially between different countries.

Moreover, special interest groups who focus on a single issue or a collection of issues may be allies or adversaries. Community groups, trade associations and even activists fall into this category.

The first challenge of management with regard to the external environment is awareness. Recognizing and understanding the intimate interrelationships of the firm with the myriad of influencers and stakeholders is very important. This may require special information gathering and outreach activities from competitive intelligence to issues management. Understanding these interrelationships must occur within the firm at various levels. Obviously, personnel who deal directly with these audiences must both understand the relationship and recognize their role as primary information resources with regard to that audience. Managers at more senior levels must understand the company's connectedness with all its audiences. Companies who do not have a sufficient grasp of their external relationships, and even some that do, often miss changes in external factors or perceptions. These changes gain momentum and ultimately destabilize the company, necessitating radical and painful reactive measures; this is called "crisis management".

Beyond knowledge and recognition, the manager must be able to communicate effectively with external groups. He must be able to persuasively articulate the company's role in serving society and to explain how the company is fulfilling that role both in terms of products and corporate "citizenship".

Most of a corporation's interaction with the external environment is reactive. If a competitor introduces a better product, the company will have to change its own product in order to compete successfully. If regulations are changed, the company will have to alter its operations to comply. Occasionally, however, the company can influence or even alter its external environment. Lobbying for new legislation favorable to industry, or working with a community alliance to achieve a major airport expansion, are examples of taking positive action to improve the business environment. Given the profound effect the external environment can have on the freedom of operation of the average business, it should not be surprising that chief executive officers estimate that approximately 50% of their time is spent on external issues and audiences. Some companies designate someone else as "chief operating officer" with special responsibility for hands-on day-to-day management of the company's operations.

Dan returned to his office to collect his notes for a speech he was giving that evening. He has been invited to make a presentation at the monthly meeting of the local medical society about new developments in the biotechnology industry.

The society's members included some of Cloneglobe's potential customers and also several professors from local universities where Cloneglobe focused much of its recruiting efforts. The president of the society also sat on the local planning commission. Dan made a mental note to look for Dr. Fowler at the meeting. Fowler was recently named to a seat on a national advisory committee charged with making recommendations about conflict-of-interest guidelines for university/industry relationships. Dan had some specific views of this subject he wanted to share with Fowler.

While Dan dialed his home number, he sifted through the pile of messages on his desk. One message was from a journalist who wants to interview Dan about his position on a bill before the legislature. The bill called for an increase in basic research funding in the biological sciences.

"Hello, dear'" Dan said, looking at his watch which said 6:15. "Yes, I just wanted to remind you that I won't be home until about ten. No, I won't forget. No, it was a normal day, nothing unusual. See you later."

Dan wrote a note to his secretary to schedule the interview with the journalist for Thursday after the management committee meeting and before his flight to London. He also wrote himself a note to call his congressman about the basic research bill, a vital piece of legislation with important consequences for the future of the biotechnology industry. Since it was so late, he could only return two of the other phone calls. One was to a research associate in Japan, the other to an investor in Hawaii.

Dan left the building by the back way in order to avoid the crowd of people protesting the use of animals in research who were gathered at the front of the building.

EPILOGUE

Actions, even fictional ones, have consequences:
Cloneglobe was able to fulfill its near term needs for monoclonal antibody based products by licensing two Mabs in late development at a small biotechnology firm based in Scotland. MacMabWorld Ltd. was planning to become a fully integrated company in the European Community but lacked the resources to reach the U.S. market. Cloneglobe paid MacMabWorld a 7% royalty to license the products for the U.S. market and for access to the clinical data for use in designing clinical trials and filing for registration in the United States. MacMabWorld also contracted to manufacture the products for Cloneglobe since the latter did not have the facilities or additional production personnel for these products. Thus, for an incremental cost and very little risk, Cloneglobe was able to compete in the growing Mab market.

The company's longer term interests in this area of the technology were resolved in a different way. When Sam Steinmetz visited his old friend Joe Valente at Redoubtable Research Institute, his timing was perfect. Joe's progress with octromas was much more advanced than anyone had realized. Octromas were no longer simply basic research ideas; Joe had made the breakthroughs necessary to advance into applied research and begin the exciting challenge of commercializing these new entities. And Joe had also reached an important personal decision. He wanted to follow through on his discovery and be a part of the effort to turn octromas into real products. He had been quietly exploring ways to set up his own company but had been frustrated by his limited knowledge in writing a business plan and his lack of contacts for seeking funding. Sam was quick to provide him with the right contacts at Cloneglobe and a series of discussions ensued with Sam and with technology transfer experts at Redoubtable. While these negotiations were ongoing, Peter Brischle was able to obtain a non-exclusive license under the Nelson patents to the basic octroma technology from Southern Polytechnic, giving Cloneglobe freedom to operate in this field.

What resulted was a startup company located in low cost, leased laboratory space in Redoubtable's new research park. The rights to the octroma work performed by Joe while at the university were licensed exclusive to the new company in return for a future royalty. Cloneglobe committee $2 million in startup funding in return for 20% of the venture and a first option on all resulting products. This commercial interest permitted Joe to raise the remaining capital he needed for salaries and equipment from venture capitalists introduced to him by Dan Anthonoy. The venture was very productive, creating five viable products in the first six years. Cloneglobe was able to monitor this progress and plan accordingly. After the first three years, it began to create a manufacturing infrastructure for antibody products. The company gained expertise by transferring U.S. production of first one and then both of the MacMabWorld products to its own facilities. It exercised its option of three of the venture's five octromas. By the time these products were advanced to the final testing phases, Cloneglobe was in a position to produce them on site.

In 1999, the venture, now named Octagon Enterprises, went public. The resulting valuation of this exciting new company meant that Cloneglobe's initial startup investment was worth $20 million. Anita Takagawa, having learned from her experiences as a research manager and been promoted several times, left Cloneglobe to become Octagon's vice president of research and development. Cloneglobe's sales of the products licensed from MacMabWorld were $50 million in 1999 and analysts projected that the company's share of the U.S. Mab market in the oncology sector would rise to $250 million by the year 2005. This was indeed fortunate for Cloneglobe because in 1995, a competitor, Recombicorp, devised a way to make an oral form of a protein positioned against ANTIONKIN, introduced it to the market in 1998 and Cloneglobe's dominant position in this sector evaporated within the year. The BPF project was abandoned in 1994 due to unacceptable side effects in humans, but CG-320 became a viable product for the treatment of breast cancer and was *approved for marketing under the tradename ANTICARSIN in late 1997. Thanks to close cooperation between the development and manufacturing groups, Cloneglobe developed a novel production process which gave it competitive advantage in what had become by then a highly competitive segment. Through the efforts of Dan Anthony and a large number of allies in industry and academia, the bill to increase funding for basic research was passed into law.*

Hopefully you have enjoyed the story of Cloneglobe and found it instructive and helpful. Dan Anthony is not, of course, the perfect manager. For one thing, he seems to be trying to do too much himself and appears rather reluctant to delegate. Delegation is a very important skill: properly used it enables the manager to direct his attention and resources to the matters best resolved by his intervention and avoid getting bogged down in decision-making which colleagues might do with advantage. But the manager does, of course, need to be in touch with all the important developments within his company as well as with those outside which might affect it. There is a delicate and shifting balance of responses he needs to display.

Case studies are frequently employed in the teaching of management. Although many subjects valuable to managers can be taught by more formal methods, such as finance and accounting, statistics, production operations and market research, general management itself defies formal instruction. It is a discipline learned through experience, through making real decisions and living with their consequences. Cloneglobe is not real: it is a fictitious company. In fact, any resemblance between any of the organizations or persons represented in this case and an any corporations or persons, living or defunct, is unintentional. However, if Cloneglobe has provided you with an experience that *is* real, an opportunity to be, albeit for a brief time, part of an experiment, it will for all its fictitious status have made a valuable contribution to understanding the totality that is biotechnology.

While managing a biotechnology company is a very real activity, it should be obvious from reading about Cloneglobe that there is no such thing as biotechnology management. Some of the present generation of biotechnology managers obtained their management degrees when there was no such thing as the biotechnology industry. Such is the speed of technological change in our world today that were someone to enter a management program today, the chances are that they too would practice their management career in a business that does not now exist. Management is a process designed to encompass the routine but also the unexpected, the unpredicted and even the unprecedented. Biotechnology, because it is new and still evolving, will continue to provide managers with learning experiences involving the new and the untried.

Managers also learn decision making through the experience of others. That is why mentors are important. Anyone interested in pursuing a management career should be on the lookout for an inspiring mentor, one who is a good manager but also a careful listener and a willing teacher. Managers who inspire excellence in others are performing the most important management task of all — they are exercising leadership.

Chapter 3

Financing Biotechnology Companies

Michael Ostrach

One of the most intriguing financial stories of the '70s and '80s has been the successful financing of independent biotechnology companies. Substantial amounts of capital have been invested in the companies that have pioneered the development of a group of technologies promising profound benefits to mankind and representing a powerful source of new commercial opportunities. Biotechnology ventures have been remarkably successful in raising capital on the basis of potential, rather than actual, operating results, primarily because they offer the possibility of huge returns.

Although not strictly an American phenomenon, the emergence of the independent biotechnology venture has been most pronounced in the United States. A peculiar mix of entrepreneurial spirit, availability of risk capital, extensive and sustained Federal support of basic research, a skilled and motivated work force and accessible capital markets led to the formation of numerous successful biotechnology companies in the United States and has enabled that country to establish its predominant position in the commercialization of biotechnology.

The perspective provided by this article is derived from the experience provided by the American environment which has proven to be extremely supportive of novel industrial enterprises and enterprise is a notable element of the American character. The freedom to try new approaches and the flexibility of the economic system has fostered and propelled the emergence of successful biotechnology companies in the United States.

When Cetus and Genentech went public in the early eighties, *The Economist* published an article implying that it was inappropriate for biotechnology companies to raise financing when they were not generating profits from product sales. The inevitable consequence of adopting that precept would be that innovation, if it were to occur at all, would depend on the efforts of established companies. Of course, it is now clear that the primary innovative force in the commercial development of biotechnology has been the publicly financed entrepreneurial firms.

The notion of taking financial risk to develop a nascent technology is culturally admired in the U.S. but is the subject of approbation in other parts of the world. Perhaps this is one reason why Great Britain has, with few exceptions, made a negligible contribution to the commercialization of biotechnology despite its acknowledged substantial contributions to the science itself.

In the U.S. risk taking is left to entrepreneurs because the established companies are reluctant to invest capital that does not have a probability of yielding fairly rapid returns. The fixation with quarterly financial performance discourages investments in innovation. By contrast, the relatively low cost of capital and the very long term, patient outlook of Japanese companies enabled them to participate in biotechnology at a very early stage of its emergence. Fortunately, the independent biotechnology companies have been able to finance their needs at a fairly low cost because the American public has continued to believe in the long term potential of the industry.

This article attempts to describe the typical financing processes and devices that have provided the foundation for this industry. This path is exemplary only in general terms as each biotechnology company has followed the path determined by its needs under the circumstances prevailing at the time. Although the general theoretical case is described, it is important to remember that only the general course is the same for all companies. A company starts with a group of people who have a dream, operates with private capital until performance, prospects and the external environment determine that public financing should be obtained. Each financial vehicle has a role in particular circumstances and any one might be appropriate at any given time.

FINANCIAL INSTRUMENTS

Biotechnology ventures have available for their financing all of the conventional devices developed in recent years by other high technology enterprises. Indeed, the biotechnology industry has employed most of the known vehicles and several hybrids, often in a dramatic fashion, to raise unprecedented sums for research on and, more recently, for development of, novel and valuable products. The array of financing mechanisms is limited only by the imagination and interests of the parties involved and the particular circumstances confronting the venture at the time financing is sought. External factors affecting the availability and cost of capital also help determine whether and when a particular device may be appropriate.

Economic conditions during the past fifteen years have been characterized by rapid change and relatively volatile financial markets. Interest rates and stock and bond prices have fluctuated wildly while market conditions have been unsettled by conflicting perceptions of the prospects for domestic and international economic growth and the future direction of exchange rates, budget deficits and trade imbalances. Investors have responded to this turbulent environment by seeking a higher return on their money and by attempting to minimize their investment risk. The desire for increased returns, continued changes in tax policy and the emergence of inflation have encouraged investors to shift assets from more traditional investments to investments in emerging new industries, thereby facilitating the emergence of the biotechnology industry.

The financial markets often are guided by a prevailing attitude, which often does not bear any relationship to fundamental reality, toward specific types of ventures (i.e. what is in vogue) and more objective considerations such as current interest rates and the health of equity markets and the general economy. For example, when interest rates are high (in relation to recent or historical levels) it becomes more "expensive" to invest in a biotechnology venture because the potential return, adjusted for risk, cannot compete with a relatively risk-free, higher return offered by alternative investments.

In addition to factors external to the particular operation to be financed, the peculiar characteristics of the industry in which it will compete must be recognized and addressed in every financing. In making an investment in an enterprise devoted to the commercial exploitation of biotechnology, investors will seek to determine that the enterprise has the capabilities required to succeed and will choose an investment vehicle that reflects the risks involved with a return commensurate with those risks.

One of the principal determinants of a biotechnology venture's success is its ability to raise capital at a reasonable cost at times and in amounts sufficient to meet its business objectives. The primary sources of financing for developing biotechnology companies include equity purchases by venture capital and other private investors, research and development and joint venture arrangements with, and equity purchases by, established companies, sales of equity in public equity markets, payments from research and development limited partnerships and debt financing. Each type of vehicle has one or more features that determine whether its use would be attractive to investors in view of the company's stage of development and the condition of financial markets at the time of the financing. The determination of when to effect a financing depends on many factors, including the financial status of the company, the cost of the capital, the prospects for future financing, the amount needed and the condition of the financial markets in general. Perhaps the most important factor, particularly for biotechnology in view of the substantial amounts of capital required and the extended period between investment and commercial return, is illustrated by the observation of Ronald Cape, founder of Cetus, that "The time to take the hors d'oeuvres is when they're passing them around."

The principal features of the basic investment vehicles, equity, debt and warrants are summarized in Appendix A.

PRIVATE FINANCING

In general, the stage of an entity's development has the greatest influence on the choice of investment vehicle, taking into account prevailing general financial market conditions. The typical sequence begins with startup financing through the issuance of common stock to founders and the sale of convertible preferred stock to venture capital investors.

There are, of course, many ways of raising capital to start a business. The founders may be lucky enough to have the necessary cash in their own bank accounts or their proposals may convince the bank manager to lend money on acceptable terms. But many biotechnology startups are not so fortunate. As they are often initiated on the basis of some good ideas and the technical skills to back them up but with an uncertain market appreciation, they may find it difficult to qualify for conventional bank loans. The venture capital industry is one avenue for funding startups of this kind. Specialist firms invest funds placed with them by individuals or institutions prepared to take a high risk for the prospect (but no guarantee!) of a high return.

Evaluation of commercial risk and putting together a financial structure to deal with it are all important. Venture capital investment of necessity must aim for a high rate of return in a relatively short time because the investors know that, in spite of their best efforts to spot the successes, they will often be wrong. Look at what happened to a collection of such investments (not only in biotechnology) reported for the U.S. by Venture Economics Inc. in 1981 (Table 1): because the risk of failure is so high, the return on the successes must more than compensate for the losses or the whole business of investing in high risk ventures is not going to be worthwhile. So a venture capitalist looks for proposals which plausibly offer the rate of return he needs as a target: something like a five- to tenfold increase in the value of his investment within a five year period. Table 2 shows the annualized compound rates of return implied by capital appreciation of that magnitude.

There follows a most important question: how is the increased value of the investment to be realized? In the parlance of the industry: "what will be the exit route?" If the venture capitalist is to sell his holdings at a great profit after a number of years, who will buy them? Will the company by then be a public one, with stock traded on the exchanges? Or will

Table 1
Return on Capital Investments

Average for 218 U.S. investments	
Multiple of original investment	Percentage of total invested
More than 10 times	3
5–10 times	8
2–5 times	20
Up to twice	29
Partial loss	25
Total loss	15
total	100

Table 2
Venture Capital Investment

Target rates of return and multiples of original investment

Compound rates of return ⟶	30%	40%	50%
Number of years before investment is realized			
3	2.2×	2.7×	3.4×
5	3.7×	5.4×	7.6×
7	6.3×	10.5×	17.1×

Reproduced by permission of Peter Laing

share ownership be restricted to a small private group and will they be willing to buy stock held by an original investor who now wishes to quit? The answer to that query is one of the factors influencing a willingness to invest. (Or, you may ask: "Why should he want to sell out if the investment is doing so well?" One answer might be that he does not think it will continue to appreciate as it had in the past and thus fail to meet his future investment targets. A second might be that he specializes in startups and wants to continue doing just that.)

Another investment consideration will be the perception by the potential investor of the risk/reward consequences of the investment. Table 3 shows one way of looking at that relationship but it is only one way out of many. Venture capital firms each have their own idiosyncrasies compounded of the experience, knowledge and understanding of their decision makers and their boards of management, the advice they receive from their panel of experts and an intention to confine their operations to a particular area of biotechnology.

Table 3
Investment Strategy in Biotechnology

unsuccessful biotechnology research companies		successful biotechnology research companies
high ←	Risk	→ low
established companies with low biotechnology exposure		established companies with high biotechnology exposure
high ←	Reward	→ low

Reproduced by permission of Peter Laing and the Economist Intelligence Unit

A firm with experience of investing in healthcare may be most reluctant to venture into, say, microbiological mining because of their unfamiliarity with both the technology and the markets.

The development of a startup investment in biotechnology is likely to go through several phases: Table 4 illustrates a typical series of events. In the beginning the venture consists essentially of the founders, the people who had the first ideas originating, perhaps, from a scientific or technical development ("technology push") or from an appreciation of what the market needs and will buy ("market pull"). Those people with ideas may also have some assets (a working system, or a patent) but often little or no money for equipment and expenses and may not have the enterprising friends willing to help. They will therefore need an initial injection of funds ("seedcorn investment") to help them get started and to both develop their ideas and build the business to the point at which it becomes more attractive to larger investors. A seedcorn investment may be no more a few hundred thousand dollars ($100,000 in the example in Table 4) to help the founders get to the next stage. One critical requirement of the seedcorn investors will no doubt include the appointment of a chief executive officer (managing director), particularly if the original founders are scientists without business experience: the investors will be very keen to ensure that their investment is in the hands of somebody who knows about running a business startup. Indeed, a sizable portion of the original tranche of funding many go to pay for the services of that important person and putting in place the basic structure of the business. Money for spending is generally going to be very tight at the beginning of the company's life. Notice that the initial investment is indeed very risky: more than 90% of seedcorn fundings end in failure of the venture. Note also that by year six in this model the original investors will still own 25% of the company.

Table 4
Investment Stages

Stage	Provides	Chance of failure (%)	Investment ($m)	% Control (year 6)	Cost/share at year 6 ($)
I: year 0 Founders	Original concept; patents	90+	0.1 No liquidity	25	
II: year 1 Lead venture investors	1st Round capital; helps to structure management team	65	0.5 Poor liquidity	30	0.17
III: year 2/3 Additional venture investors	More capital; possible board membership advice	40	2.0 Poor liquidity	25	0.80
IV: year 5/6 Public stock issue	Additional capital for expansion	20	10.0 Good liquidity	20	5.00

Reproduced by permission of Peter Laing

A year or so later the $100,000 will mostly have been spent but probably with no product or service yet ready for the market place: the firm will need more money. The chief executive and his technical colleagues will have been preparing a business plan which will map out the next stage of the company's development and prepare for first round venture capital funding. A lead investor is needed, a person or institution known and respected in the venture capital circle who will spend time scrutinizing the business plan, checking that all the claims and analyses are correct ("due diligence") and getting to know the people. When the lead investor acknowledges the promise of the venture and agrees to put up some of the capital funds being sought, others are likely to come in too, reassured by the lead given by the first. The funding may be several times greater than the seedcorn amount ($500,000 in the example in Table 4): those who invest at this stage will own about 30% of the company after six years (if it survives: the risk of failure is still 65%!) and they will have paid the equivalent of 17¢ for every share they own at year six. Money, alas, is still tight: no company cars yet for the senior executives but a more comprehensive management structure will start to develop.

By year two or three, prospects are looking brighter. For one thing, the company has survived, no mean feat when so many others do not. For another, the product(s) or service(s) the company is developing are nearer the market and the whole operation begins to look more real. But the funds raised a year or two earlier will be seriously depleted and more money is required to pay for the facilities to get some level of production going. At this point of second round funding one or more of the earlier investors may again decide to participate and new ones will join in, taking representation on the board. Perhaps $2,000,000 will now be raised, conferring 25% ownership after six years at a price equivalent of 80¢ a share. (As the company gradually becomes established its shares naturally are worth more. It is by this increase in share value that the early investors expect eventually to sell out at a healthy profit.) The risks are also gradually falling and only 40% or so of companies fail after this stage. But money remains limited: still no cars.

And so in year five or six the company may become a public corporation, offering shares for sale to the public. Product(s) and service(s) are now being marketed at least fairly successfully and the company is ready to expand on an altogether firmer footing. It might now seek to raise, say $10,000,000 at $5 a share; to do so it has to sell 20% of the ownership of the corporation to the subscribers. Those investors who bought shares at the equivalent of 17¢ in year one will have done very well and those who came in at year two/three at 80¢ will not have done badly, either. Liquidity is finally becoming reasonable (cars?) and the risks are falling fast: more than 80% of companies getting to this stage survive into the future and to all intents and purposes the venture has succeeded with the company permanently on the map. Let us look in more detail at how all this is achieved.

The availability of venture capital to support the early research efforts of biotechnology ventures has been crucial to the continued vitality of companies seeking to exploit these techniques. Venture capital funds have been formed to invest money provided by wealthy investors, corporations and financial institutions in high-growth enterprises because they provide an opportunity to enjoy unusually high returns as compensation for the unusually high risks involved in a start-up venture.

Basic Issues

Venture capital investments are made on the basis of the investor's assessment of the business prospects of the venture and the ability of its management team (see the following chapter). The financing process begins with a business plan. A thorough, thoughtful and realistic business plan is a prerequisite for any successful effort to obtain venture capital financing. The business must be described so that its potential can be recognized by investors and its projected financial performance must be demonstrated to be achievable in amounts and within a period of time that would provide a substantial return on investment.

Many entrepreneurs prepare business plans as a planning tool to chart the future course of their embryonic enterprise. Although this is a laudable exercise, a business plan must be crafted with the objective of providing the information necessary to convince investors that the venture will yield appropriate returns. The quality and perceptiveness of a properly prepared plan also functions to instill confidence in prospective investors that management has the ability to enable them to realize those potential returns.

If the initial review of the business plan is favorable, venture capital representatives discuss the plan with the founders to refine their understanding of the business and measure the ability of the persons to whom they will entrust their investment. This is the initial and most important phase of an extensive "due diligence" process in which the statements, assumptions and projections in the business plan are verified and tested by prospective investors. Key employees are interviewed, facilities are visited, products and technology are assessed and comparable businesses are analyzed. The interview process often extends to former employers of the founders, customers and suppliers; and professional advisors such as lawyers and accountants. If the attractiveness of the investment withstands this scrutiny, the venture capital investors and founders negotiate a term sheet that outlines the principal terms of the investment, which usually takes the form of preferred stock that is convertible into common stock. The determination of these provisions is often a difficult process, pitting the dreams of the entrepreneur against the desire of investors for substantial return and protection in the face of considerable risk.

The provisions most heavily negotiated include the percentage of the company that will be purchased by the investment, the amount of the investment, the level of control on management that will be imposed, the severity of anti-dilution provisions limiting the flexibility to issue securities in the future, conversion and redemption rights and the registration rights available for later resales of the securities. In addition, venture capital investors generally require as a condition to their investment the execution of long-term employment contracts by key employees. These agreements are intended to ensure that the efforts of these individuals will be available to the company during the expected term of the investment and to prevent them from engaging in competitive efforts.

A venture capital financing involves considerable attention to the financial terms of the investment, including fundamental issues such as the valuation of an undeveloped business and the percentage of the company purchased by the investment. The documents focus on accurately describing and assessing the company and its prospects through the analysis provided by the business plan and the information provided in the due diligence process and in the course of negotiating representations in the purchase agreement. Nonetheless, these transactions are relatively simple, inexpensive and rapid once a solid business plan has been developed and interested prospective investors are identified. The financing documents are standardized and not unduly complex or lengthy, and the number of individuals required to effectuate the transaction is limited. The entrepreneurs, a representative of the investors (generally the "lead" or largest investor) and their respective counsel are the principal players and the entire process of negotiation and closing usually can be completed within 60 days at a total cost of between $25,000 and $75,000.

Documents

After the term sheet is finalized, formal documents are prepared by the investor's counsel. The primary document is the purchase agreement, which describes the offering and the terms of the securities to be issued, contains representations by the issuer concerning its properties and financial position, provides warranties and covenants to the investor with respect to the business of the issuer and sets out the registration and other rights being granted to the investors. The principal standard conditions to the investor's purchase include confirmation of the issuer's representations and warranties on the date of purchase, receipt of all required government permits, particularly those relating to security issuances, the receipt of a specified minimum amount of proceeds, the delivery of a satisfactory opinion of legal counsel as to specified legal matters and the delivery of employment agreements by key employees.

The provision of representations and warranties is the legal equivalent in writing of the due diligence process. The purpose is to provide full disclosure of material facts to investors. Although some representations must be "flat", that is, without exceptions, others should be stated to reflect the actual facts and not those that the investor desires. In drafting the representations, the issuer should be careful to point out limitations on its rights or on its ownership of key assets, and any existing restrictions or liabilities to which the company is subject.

Specifically, the venture capitalists will expect a representation that the previously delivered business plan is complete, true and accurate in all material respects and that the financial projections in the document are reasonable and were made in good faith. Of course, it is unlikely that the projections actually will be achieved because a variation of any of the material underlying assumptions has a marked impact on the magnitude and timing of revenues and expenses, the size of markets, and the intensity of competition.

Other standard representations are provided as to the organization, good standing, subsidiaries, capitalization and basic corporate documents of the issuer, the corporate power to carry out its intended business, authorization to effectuate the financing, the financial statements and condition of the company, title to properties and assets, material liabilities and litigation, intellectual property rights, contracts and commitments, compliance with material agreements, governmental consents and tax and insurance matters. The legal fees of the investors generally are paid by the company out of the proceeds of the financing.

Several rounds of venture capital financing usually are required before the company's prospects have developed to the point where it can attract new investors to instruments other than common or convertible preferred stock. In the later stages of venture capital financing, the rights of the early investors generally are retained on a *pari passu* basis, that is, the rights of the old and new holders are on an equivalent basis, with changes in the company's prospects being reflected in the purchase and conversion prices. However, if prospects have been decidedly negative, later-stage investors often demand priorities over early investors, and in these cases the last dollar often speaks the loudest. Early investors can protect against this circumstance to some extent by obtaining preemptive rights ensuring they will have an opportunity to participate in future financings on a *pro rata* basis, but this protection is valuable only to the extent investors wish to continue to invest in the venture and to the extent that circumstances allow them to avail themselves of these rights. In cases where a substantial further infusion of capital is required and existing investors are reluctant to provide it, new investors "cram down" new terms on the original investors that vitiate the preemptive rights.

Venture capital and other early stage financings usually are "private" offerings that involve a distribution limited to persons and entities that meet suitability requirements imposed by state and federal law. Private offerings involve no or only a limited requirement of prior government review because they are restricted to investors who have the financial means and sophistication to evaluate an investment without the regulatory protections thought necessary for widespread offerings to the public. Thus the timing of the transaction and the documentation is more simple and flexible than public offerings. Extreme care should be taken to ensure that all legal requirements necessary to qualify for private offering exemptions from registration are met because the usual penalty for failure to do so is a right of rescission on the part of the investor.

Terms of Convertible Preferred Stock

A startup or early stage company does not often generate income from operations or have the prospects to do so with a certainty sufficient to attract debt financing. The security most frequently issued in venture capital financings is convertible preferred stock. The priority rights of convertible preferred shares provide a modicum of protection against complete loss of the investment and the conversion feature provides the means to participate in increases in the value of the common stock as the company prospers. The company is able to obtain funding for its operations, and because it is not in a position to provide a meaningful assurance of repayment, it "pays" for the funding in increased dilution of its equity if conversion occurs.

Convertible preferred stock is preferred stock that may be exchanged for common stock at the option of the holder, or that automatically converts into common stock on the occurrence of specified events or conditions. A company that expects the value of its common stock to increase significantly, but faces market resistance to a common stock investment at the time financing is sought, can use convertible preferred to attract investors who want a senior position over the short term but desire the unlimited profit possibilities of common stock in the future. In effect, the sale of convertible preferred stock is an early sale of common stock.

Convertible preferred shares have several features that favor their use by venture capital firms in early-stage companies. The terms of the securities provide investors with a preferential position in the event of a liquidation or merger and provide protection against dilution caused by subsequent issuances of securities to later investors at lower prices. Because the shares convert into common stock at the time of the company's initial public offering, the ability to sell the shares to the public provides potential liquidity to the investor. Preferred stock terms frequently provide some down-side protection for investors if the company's performance is less than optimal. These provisions might include mandatory redemption by the issuer or at the option of the holder, under specified circumstances. Preferred stock also votes separately from common stock holders on fundamental issues, including amendments to the company's articles of incorporation and mergers, and holders elect their own directors and may elect a majority of directors under specified circumstances, such as defaults on the securities.

The principal terms of convertible preferred stock include the number of shares offered and the price per share, dividend rights, liquidation preference, and redemption, conversion and registration rights. The size and pricing of the offering are based on the company valuation, which is determined by negotiation guided by comparisons with the valuation of similar companies and the perceived present value of the company's earnings stream, taking into account a discount rate appropriate to the probability of achieving those earnings and the time required to do so.

Dividends. The dividend rate varies according to the investor's objectives and the company's capacity to pay them. Often, venture capitalists do not expect to receive dividends on investments in development stage companies. Even if dividends are not required to be paid, they may nonetheless cumulate (that is, unpaid dividends cumulate at a stated rate and must be paid before dividends on common stock, and, possibly other series of preferred, are paid) and thereby increase preference and liquidation rights. Dividends also may be participating (that is, after payment of the stated rate, preferred stockholders participate in additional declared dividends under a specified formula). Participating dividend rights are not important if dividends are not expected. The dividend provisions must specify whether the dividend rights of an existing series of preferred will be prior to or on an equal basis with the proposed issuance. In all cases, the relevant state corporation law must be studied to ensure that restrictions on corporate dividend authority are not exceeded.

Liquidation. The liquidation preference represents the investor's right to a return of his investment prior to distributions to holders of common stock in respect of a liquidation of the company. In venture capital financings the liquidation price (i.e. the amount of the preference over common stock holders) usually is equal to the original issue price of the securities plus the amount of accrued but unpaid dividends, if dividends are noncumulative, and accumulated and unpaid dividends if dividends are cumulative. If the preferred is participating, there is a right to share in assets remaining after the liquidation preference is paid.

Redemption. The redemption provisions set out the right or obligation of the issuing company to repurchase the shares. Redeemable preferred stock refers to securities that may be repurchased by the company at its option at a specified price, usually after a specified period of time. Many investors dislike providing this right to the company because they may be forced to convert and lose their preferential status (if the common stock value exceeds the redemption price) prior to the full realization of the company's potential. Thus, the right to redeem is set to occur after a period of time during which investors would have sufficient time to determine if their investment will have future value. Usually a premium is required to be paid over the original issue price in order for the company to require a redemption.

Investors frequently require a company to redeem their shares at specified times at specified prices in order to provide some assurance that they will obtain a return on the investment. Although a means for the investors to exit at a profit is provided, the requirement can impose an unfortunate funding demand on the company if, at the time for redemption, it needs the funds for corporate development.

Conversion. Conversion of the preferred into common stock at the option of the investor usually may occur at any time after its original purchase. The stock automatically converts on the occurrence of specified events, such as an initial public offering at a minimum per share price with a specified minimum aggregate total offering, or achievement of particular sales or earnings goals. The conversion ratio initially is one-for-one, but the often heavily negotiated provisions on subsequent stock issuances that dilute the preferred stockholders' investment act to adjust the conversion ratio. The types of anti-dilution provisions vary widely. Minimal protection consists of an adjustment to the conversion price for stock splits, stock dividends and similar events. Greater protection is provided by the "standard" provision, which adjusts the conversion price if stock is later issued at a price lower than the original conversion price. The adjustment is based on the weighted average purchase price of outstanding stock and convertible securities. This provision normally permits a limited amount of issuances at lower prices without a resulting adjustment of the conversion price. Permitted issuances usually include stock issuable to employees or issuable on conversion of previously outstanding securities. The most severe adjustment occurs in the case of a "ratchetdown" provision, under which the conversion price is reduced to the price per share of the newly issued stock. If a merger is not treated as a liquidation, the holders of convertible preferred usually retain the right to convert their shares at a later time into equity in the surviving company at a ratio that would have applied at the time of the merger.

Voting rights usually are provided on an "as if converted" basis. Under state law, preferred stockholders also may have the right to vote separately under special circumstances, such as a proposed merger. Preferred stockholders may obtain the right to elect a specified number or percentage of directors. Usually supermajority voting rights, including the right to elect a majority of the board, are provided under specified adverse circumstances such as a default on redemption or dividend obligations or the failure to reach particular financial goals. Often major corporate actions will require a supermajority (e.g. 2/3) vote of the preferred. These actions might include amendment of the articles, issuance of new securities, the repurchase of securities, payment of dividends on common stock or the sale of the company or its assets. The voting provisions and rights of separate series of preferred should be consistent with each other and may or may not require separate voting series by series or class by class.

Registration rights. Registration rights are common in venture capital financings. Demand registration rights permit the investor to require the company to register the securities with the Securities Exchange Commission (SEC) in order to permit their resale to the public. The investor receives the right to demand one or two registrations, which may be limited in time (that is after the company is a publicly registered and reporting company and not more than a specified number of years after the financing). Other issues include the percentage vote of the investors required to exercise the right (often 50%) and a minimum size for each registration.

Piggyback registration rights consist of a right of investors to include their shares in a registration initiated by the company. Most commonly, these rights are limited in time rather than in number. The number of shares that may be included are subject to a cut back on a *pro rata* percentage basis if the company's underwriters determine that the inclusion of the investor's shares in the offering will adversely affect the amount that can be raised by the company.

Generally the expenses associated with registration of shares that carry registration rights are borne by the company, other than the underwriters' commissions and filing fees allocable to the investors' shares. The company also indemnifies the investors against liabilities arising out of misrepresentations or omissions by the company in the registration statement.

Other frequent provisions found in venture capital preferred stock placements include the requirement that the company provide investors with annual financial statements and budgets, a right for investors to purchase their *pro rata* share of future financings and a right to include their shares in any securities sales by the founders of the company.

LICENSE AGREEMENTS AND JOINT VENTURES

Most biotechnology companies have recognized that they must retain the rights to manufacture and market at least some of the products that emerge from their research laboratories in order to build stockholder value and justify a healthy market valuation for the company. However, the financial resources required to develop a product, build manufacturing capacity and establish distribution, marketing and sales capabilities often exceed the amount of equity capital available to the company on reasonable terms. In addition, the time required by a biotechnology company to establish a business capable of sustaining its operations through internally generated funds exceeds the time horizon for return on investment demanded by most venture capital investors. Finally, because biotechnology has the potential to generate profit in an almost limitless array of commercial applications, not all of them, or even many of them, can be exploited directly by one company.

Thus a principal limiting factor for the creation of meaningful stockholder value by biotechnology companies is the availability of capital to fund technology and product development efforts and to establish the infrastructure of a fully integrated company before profits from product sales are available. If equity capital is insufficient or unavailable, a venture must seek arrangements with other, more established companies to provide funding for research and to provide the means to reach the marketplace. In their simplest form, these arrangements consists of a contractual arrangement under which the biotechnology company performs specified research funded by the established company and licenses the sponsor to develop, manufacture, and market products that incorporate the research results in return for a royalty on net product sales. These arrangements provide funding for projects that the biotechnology company is unable to support or unwilling to risk its own funds on, and provide potential future revenues without any further investment in downstream capabilities. Of course, the return from such arrangements is more limited than would be obtained through direct exploitation of the research, reflecting the lower level of risk and investment required on the part of the developer. If the research company has performed substantial work or achieved significant results prior to obtaining outside support, it may be able to obtain a substantial, non-refundable payment on initiation of the license arrangement and thereby generate funds for projects that are retained for direct commercialization. Similarly, contract benchmark payments can be a significant source of lump sum cash payments.

Features of Joint Ventures

A biotechnology company can improve its share of the future returns from its research by attempting to leverage the value of its technology into a joint venture, rather than a license, arrangement with an established company. The establishment of research and joint venture arrangements with better financed and more experienced companies has been an integral element of the financing and business development plans of most biotechnology companies. A joint venture between the two companies is formed with the biotechnology company contributing its research results and capability and the established company contributing its financial, manufacturing, distribution or marketing resources. This vehicle permits the biotechnology company to retain a significant equity share in the ultimate commercial benefits yielded by its research efforts without the need to invest in and establish the operational infrastructure required for commercialization.

During the early stages of a venture's growth, these arrangements supplement the funding for research personnel and facilities obtained from equity investments and provide a commercial outlet for the company's initial products. The granting of commercialization rights to another company in return for funding is a form of financing, because the biotechnology company essentially is selling the right to reap the profits from its primary initial asset: its research results and technology. In addition to retaining a portion of those potential profits through the royalties, the biotechnology company is able to begin to build the foundation of a business that ultimately will have the capacity to directly exploit the products of its research.

Through a series of license arrangements over time, the biotechnology company can expand the scope of rights it retains according to its increased ability to handle them. This strategy begins with arrangements that grant all process development, manufacturing and marketing rights throughout the world to the established company. As the biotechnology company gains in strength, it negotiates to retain the right to develop its products and manufacture a portion of the licensee's needs for commercial product. It also seeks to preserve one or more countries as its exclusive territory for marketing and sales. For example, a biotechnology company might use its own funds to perform initial research on a potential pharmaceutical product, and based on its research progress, obtain further funding from European and Japanese companies in exchange for a license to exploit the results in those respective markets, and simultaneously use that funding to build its U.S. business.

For product areas or markets that the biotechnology company is unwilling to enter or incapable of developing on its own, a joint venture with an established company is a useful device to retain a significant share of the ultimate profits. The joint venture device enables the biotechnology company to devote its primary efforts and resources to the product areas it has chosen to exploit directly and to participate nonetheless in a meaningful way in commercial applications beyond its immediate resources or interest. The scope of a joint venture can be limited to a single product, but the usual scope is a group of related products or a broad commercial area or territory.

The established company can provide the venture with financing, manufacturing, distribution or marketing support and its commercial experience in the field of interest. If a company is judicious in its selection of venture partners, the venture can be a creative vehicle to accelerate the commercial introduction of the company's technology in a defined area or to build a foundation for the company's efforts in other areas. The partner obtains a "window on the technology" and creates or retains a market of interest to it more cheaply and rapidly that it could through its own efforts, assuming it has the ability to match the biotechnology company's expertise.

Joint ventures are an ideal mechanism for each company to learn from the other. However, they are difficult relationships to manage, especially when the partners are actual or potential competitors in areas outside of the scope of the partnership's field. The relationship must be structured to ensure a mutuality of interest and an equitable sharing of control and returns based on the value of the respective contributions of the partners.

Joint venture and license agreement terms

The determination of whether and when a particular product area is licensed or joint ventured is based on the biotechnology company's need for funding, the nature of the commitment required for completion and the potential acceleration to the marketplace or increased market share that might be realized through the efforts of the licensee or partner. In general, the value of a project increases in proportion to its degree of development. In some cases, the significant potential of a biotechnology project is sufficient to command payment of substantial value even at early stages of development.

The potential value of the research largely determines the nature of the terms that the developing company can obtain in its financing arrangements. A potential business partner will assess this value, just as an investor in the company would, on the basis of the market size of the potential applications, the stage of development, the additional resources required and the lead time or proprietary advantage that can be gained over competitors. In many cases the business partner or licensee will provide all or a significant share of the research and development expenses, payments on achievement of specified goals and royalties on sales or a share of profits. Another source of revenue or capital may be secured through retention by the biotechnology company of the right to supply the licensee with its requirements for marketing. The biotechnology company benefits from this arrangement through physical retention of its technology and the opportunity to gain the manufacturing expertise required by a fully integrated company.

The specific terms of joint venture and license agreements must be structured to be consistent with the long-term business objectives of the biotechnology company. Once the developing company has determined which applications and markets it intends to retain and those it intends to license, it must clearly delineate the rights granted to its business partners to ensure that it has fully exploited all applications of its technology without entering into overlapping obligations.

The particular agreements that are used to reflect a license or joint venture arrangement give rise to several common business concerns that must be resolved through negotiation. A biotechnology company that wishes to succeed as a fully integrated competitor in the markets it has chosen to exploit directly must retain in all of its license agreements the right to use the basic techniques it develops for application in retained areas and for licensing for other applications.

Technology rights. A fundamental distinction between two categories of technology – basic technology and product technology – must be recognized in each business arrangement to ensure retention of sufficient rights to permit a multiple licensing technology. Basic technology consists of those techniques and biological materials that have applicability to more than one end product. Product technology includes technology and material that is directly necessary or specific to a designated product. By retention of its basic technology, the biotechnology company is able to engage in a business development strategy that involves providing field of use licenses for specific fields or end products and thereby leverage itself into several areas through multiple simultaneous exploitation of its basic technology.

Field. The field of use must be defined clearly in order for a biotechnology company to exploit particular territories or applications through several business relationships. The most important concept that must be justified to licensees is that technology must be retained by the biotechnology company and not owned by the licensee.

The field definition should specify the product, the application and the territory being licensed. In biotechnology agreements, definitional matters are extremely complex. One of the most challenging issues is also the most basic; what is the product being licensed? The complexity of biology makes this task very difficult. A product can be defined by the techniques used to produce a particular protein, the protein itself, the protein responsible for the desired trait, or the DNA sequence coding for the protein. Additional consideration should be given to whether the product definition includes all developments and improvements by the licensor or licensee, and protection against the possibility that the definition is so narrow as to permit the licensee to make a trivial change and avoid payment of royalties.

The specification of the permitted uses of the product are somewhat easier to express. Examples are therapeutic v. diagnostic, human v. animal healthcare, health v. agriculture. However in some cases it is impossible as a practical matter to restrict the use of a product with closely related activity. For example, a microorganism developed as an inoculant for stimulation of soybean growth that also is effective for corn plants presents a situation where it is not practicable to determine where a product is used after it is purchased.

Most licensees who are new to biotechnology are initially quite reluctant to agree to field of use restrictions. If the licensee is substantially larger than the biotechnology licensor, it becomes extremely important and very difficult to explain to a potential client that it may gain only limited rights to a particular invention or development despite the fact that its funds may have supported the work.

Each party will have concerns about the breadth and narrowness of a field. The licensor wants to be free to exploit reserved areas in other future relationships and the licensee wants broad protection against competition from similar products. However, the licensee wants to have the right to exploit all applications of technology it funds, and the licensor wants to ensure that its product will not be designed around through use of the licensed rights to avoid royalty obligations. Often these conflicting motives result in a fairly narrow field with rights of first refusal on broader elements.

License grant. Generally the grant of rights describes the primary subject matter of the license as including the right to make, use and sell the product within the field throughout the territory, the right to practice under specified proprietary rights and the right to use specified know-how and biological materials, *all solely* in connection with the commercialization of the product. If the right to manufacture is granted, a licensor must be sure explicitly to retain ownership of the biological material to protect against unauthorized transfers of the material.

Improvements can have a great effect on the commercial success of a product. Improvements range from modifications of the product, identification of similar products or DNA sequences and development of more efficient production systems. The most difficult issue is to define the type of change in a product that would be sufficient to withdraw it from the field provided in the license. Assuming improvements are appropriate for inclusion in licensed rights, there should be a time period during which improvements will be included. The licensee and licensor should identify the types of improvements that automatically are included and those for which additional compensation must be paid.

Because much of the value provided to a licensee in this area inheres in the biological material and other know-how provided to it by the licensor, and often the patent situation is unclear at the time of the license grant, the royalty payments need not be tied to the issuance of valid patents. The primary value being provided to the licensee is a lead in development and a means to produce new products or enter new markets more efficiently, and this value is not always dependent on patent rights. At the time of the license however, it is not clear which of the rights being licensed will be the important commercial ones or whether any patents will issue. The antitrust implications of this position should nonetheless be carefully weighed.

Diligence. In addition to the grant of rights, a licensor generally obliges itself to develop a product or process in return for funding from the licensee. If a biotechnology company selects its licensees carefully, it may be able to commit the licensee to a development program that will supplement its own. The licensee has the obligation diligently to exploit the licensed rights. It is extremely important that protection is provided to the licensor against the possibility that the licensee will put the technology "on-the-shelf". Some solutions to this problem are termination of the license or payment of minimum annual royalties.

Termination. If the licensor is successful in retaining ownership of the biological materials and other licensed subject matter, it can insulate itself to some extent from the consequences of a termination by the licensee. The licensee's right to terminate should be limited to minimize the possibility of termination before payment of royalties is required, but nonetheless keep the technology off the market in the meantime and thereby limit its value to the licensor.

The licensee, of course, needs to have an ability to terminate under appropriate circumstances. One common termination right provided to licensees is the right to terminate the license if it is technically or commercially infeasible to continue. This determination must be made by both parties, with arbitration of this issue, if necessary. Another frequent termination issue resolves around the licensor's concern that it might "teach" its licensee so well that it can develop a product on its own outside of the license agreement. This concern is highlighted in this industry because it may be impossible to identify whether a licensee is actually employing rights it obtained from the licensor. Several solutions to this problem are available. In many cases, a licensor will agree not to compete in the field for a sufficient period after termination to ensure no licensed rights are used. Occasionally a licensor is able to obtain payments on sales by the licensee of any similar product, whether or not provided by the licensor, for a specified period of time.

Particular attention should be devoted by the biotechnology company to provisions that protect it from being squeezed out of the venture. Although these arrangements are intended to be long term relationships, issues such as the conditions under which a party may terminate and rights to partnership assets on termination must be addressed at the outset to avoid the possibility of overreaching by the stronger partner. If funding obligations are to be shared, the biotechnology company should negotiate the right to obtain financing from its partner or third parties, including the right to sell all or a part of its interest in the venture to the partner or a third party under appropriate conditions. At the same time, mechanisms must be provided to permit the biotechnology company to pursue projects in the partnership's field that the other partner is unwilling to support.

Patents. The licensor should retain the right to prosecute patent applications and enforce patent rights if a multiple licensing strategy is its objective. For example, the licensed patents for a technique to express foreign genes in microorganisms are likely to include claims of broad applicability to the business interests of the licensor in other products, markets, or territories. If the licensee is permitted the right to litigate against patent infringers, the entire licensing strategy of the licensor could be damaged. Licensors who have retained control over patent strategy may offer in return a reduced royalty if the failure by the licensor to enforce the patents in question results in increased competition for the licensee.

General terms. A licensor should obtain product liability indemnity from the licensee and should disclaim warranties, express and implied, including merchantability and fitness for a particular purpose. This is most appropriate in situations where the licensee has manufacturing rights. A licensor should nonetheless obtain the right to inspect the facilities to protect himself against potential claims in its capacity as licensor.

The licensor should obtain the agreement of the licensee that it will be responsible for compliance with all necessary governmental requirements, including regulatory, export/import rules, currency restrictions and governmental notice requirements.

THE INITIAL PUBLIC OFFERING

The initial public offering (IPO) is the first offering of company securities to the general public and in the United States accordingly requires registration under the Securities Act of 1933 (the "1933 Act"). The typical offering consists of shares of common stock newly issued by the Company (primary offering) and shares held by previous investors (secondary offering) such as venture capitalists whose convertible preferred stock automatically converts into common stock coincident with the primary offering.

Initial Considerations

Before embarking on the IPO process, management of a biotechnology venture must be cognizant of the consequences of this decision. The process is a lengthy and expensive one, requiring between two and six months and $200,000 to $1,000,000 in out-of-pocket expenses for legal and accounting fees and printing services. If the offering fails because the company and its financial advisors misjudge the demand for the offering or the market conditions that will prevail when the securities are offered, the incurrence of these expenses can cripple a company's ability to continue its operations. If the offering is successful, the company should expect to retain only 90% to 93% of the proceeds after payment of underwriters' fees. The level of the commission depends on the size and complexity of the offering, and companies should attempt to negotiate a fee equivalent to that charged by underwriters in comparable offerings.

The decision to go public is a pivotal event in the life of a developing company. By going public a company assumes a legal obligation to provide public disclosure of its business information on an ongoing basis. At the same time, the creation of a new stockholder constituency requires management to position the company to be responsive to the investment objectives of these stockholders. The glare of public scrutiny by financial analysts and the demands of public investors can severely limit the flexibility of a company in developing its business.

The principal motivation for going public is to obtain capital on terms more favorable and in amounts that are greater than may be available through other vehicles. Substantial amounts can be raised in public equity markets to fund working capital, research, development, marketing and manufacturing activities and facilities requirements. The public markets have been extremely receptive to investment in high technology companies with significant growth potential and investors have been willing to accept their returns through appreciation in the value of their stock rather than through the payment of dividends.

Thus, the traditional theoretical appeal of dividend-paying equities over those that do not offer that steady return is outweighed by the substantial capital appreciation that can be obtained by investing in a technology company which devotes its cash to innovation. The establishment of a public market for a company's stock enables it more easily and inexpensively to raise capital in the future through additional common stock offerings and creates a market priced security that can form the foundation for other types of financial instruments, such as warrants and convertible debt. Publicly-traded common stock also is a useful vehicle to expand the business through acquisitions. The existence of a public market provides liquidity for earlier investors, including management and employees, and an opportunity for them more easily to realize a return from the future success of the company through stock incentive or option plans for key employees.

In addition to allocating the financial resources demanded by an IPO, a company must divert the efforts of its key managers from the company's operations to the IPO process. Substantial management time is consumed in preparing and verifying the necessary documents and marketing the offering. A small company may have difficulty simultaneously managing its business and participating in the offering process, with the consequence that the results of each will be less than optimal.

Broadly stated, the periodic public disclosure and proxy information requirements of the federal securities laws require a company to disclose all information relating to its business and financial condition that an average investor would deem important in making an investment decision concerning the company's securities. These requirements may force a company to suffer the competitive disadvantage that results from disclosure of sensitive information such as the identity of products in research, methods and costs of manufacture, specific sales and profit results and the terms of material contracts. In most cases this is only a theoretical consideration because confidential treatment is available for competitive business information and the level of required disclosure does not, in most cases, affect the company's ability to compete. The public reporting obligation also has the effect of accelerating the release of important business information. Finally, the reporting requirements result in an increase in legal and accounting fees and a new demand on management time as reports are prepared on a quarterly basis.

A more subtle impact of going public is the temptation to operate the business to bolster the day-to-day market price of the stock. A publicly traded stock can exert significant pressure on management to make business decisions that will yield short-term gain at the expense of building stockholder value over the long term. Indeed, one unfortunate lesson learned from the continuing prominence of takeovers is that a long term emphasis at the expense of short term results makes a company considerably more vulnerable to a takeover.

Another consequence of going public is the loss of flexibility to take significant corporate actions. Major corporate events may require stockholder approval, and public companies usually are managed by a board of directors that include individuals who are independent of company management and therefore less likely automatically to endorse management decisions.

Underwriters and Underwriting Terms

If the company chooses to go public, it must select an investment banking firm to manage the offering. In return for a fee based on a percentage of the proceeds of the offering, the managing underwriters provide financial advice to the company in structuring the offering and organizing and managing the syndicate that will place the offering. A company with good prospects should be able to attract several firms to compete for its business, and often two, and sometimes three, are appointed as co-managers. In making the selection of managers, a company should assess the general reputation of the firm and its experience in similar offerings, the capacity of the firm to place the securities, including the number of its clients and brokers and the quality of its syndicate, its market-making capabilities and the perceived value of its investment banking services in the future. The investment bank's client base should be analyzed to determine the proportion of institutional, compared to individual, investors in order to determine the characteristics of the company's prospective investors. Some underwriters have strong retail sales organizations while others concentrate on sales to institutions. The traditional reluctance of institutions to invest in initial public offerings of high technology companies has dissolved in the face of the outstanding returns that have been available in recent years. Institutions such as pension and stock mutual funds have a significant influence on stock pricing and performance because of the size of their holdings and the herd instinct that drives their investment decisions.

The company also should consider whether the underwriting firm has a commitment to provide ongoing investment analysis and research reports on the company and its industry sufficient to create and maintain continued investor interest. This "after-market" support is vital to the performance of the company's stock price after the offering. Continued interest in the company can be generated among analysts and investors by reports on the company's business development and by the general facilitation of information dissemination. A deeper and broader following of the company's stock creates a liquid, stable and orderly market. Analysts who are knowledgeable, well known and followed can have a substantial impact on perceptions about the company's value.

The managing underwriters will be selected on the basis of the above factors and their willingness to accept an offering of the size and pricing consonant with the expectations of the company and its current investors. The determination of the amount of the funds to be raised is a function of the need of the company for the funds and the percentage of the company that will be obtained for that amount. The process begins with an analysis of the market value of the company based on the present value of its prospective earnings discounted for risk, the pricing of prior investments and the market evaluations of comparable publicly traded companies.

Another fundamental term of the arrangement is the nature of the underwriting commitment. Most often, a "firm commitment" underwriting is employed whereby the bankers agree to purchase the securities offered to the public after the offering is cleared by securities authorities. Occasionally, "best efforts" arrangements are chosen in which underwriters agree merely to use their best efforts to sell the securities.

When agreement on these and other basic terms are agreed upon, the underwriters are likely to request that the understanding be reduced to writing in a letter of intent. The letter of intent provides little benefit to the company because the commitment by the underwriters is tentative and subject to numerous conditions, yet it imposes several burdens, including an agreement not to engage other bankers and an obligation to reimburse the managers for their expenses if the offering does not proceed.

In determining the size of the offering the company will be interested in maximizing the number and price of shares sold by it and the underwriters will be interested in sizing a deal to match anticipated demand and that will create a stable and reasonably sized post-offering market. The selling intentions and registration rights of previous investors must be taken into account in the initial stages of planning the offering. Obviously, the desires of early investors to cash in all or a portion of their investment conflicts with the company's objectives to maximize its share of the offering proceeds.

The company and the underwriters will seek to accommodate the requests of existing stockholders to include their shares in the offering only if they believe this would not adversely affect the marketing of the shares required to be sold by the company. Often the registration rights granted in properly negotiated venture capital deals are subject to a provision permitting the underwriters to "cut back" on the number of shares selling stockholders otherwise would be able to include in a company registration if, in their view, a reduction is required for a successful offering. At the same time, the underwriters request officers, directors, selling stockholders and other large stockholders to agree to refrain from sales of their shares into the public market during the first 90 to 180 days following the offering. The purpose of these "lock-up" provisions is to ensure that there is an orderly and stable aftermarket for the shares. In addition, underwriters do not enjoy creating demand for an offering only to see a portion of it soaked up by stockholders who sell into the offering without bearing the cost of paying an underwriting commission.

The SEC Registration Process

The 1933 Act is designed to ensure that investors receive complete and accurate information necessary to make an informed investment decision concerning the offered securities. It is illegal to offer or sell securities to the public in the United States unless the securities have been registered with the Securities and Exchange Commission in a registration statement containing information specified in the Act and its regulations.

The period of time required to complete an IPO can range from three to twelve months, depending on the competence of the team of company personnel, underwriters and their lawyers, the complexity of the company's business and market conditions. The process includes preparation of a registration statement that contains the prospectus for the offering and an underwriting agreement, due diligence investigations, filing with and review by the SEC of the registration statement, information meetings with underwriters and prospective institutional investors and the offering of the securities and closing of the sale.

The Registration Statement

The first draft of the registration statement is prepared by the issuer's counsel, and is circulated for comment and redrafting among a working group consisting of company management, representatives of the underwriters and their counsel. The basic information for the registration statement is gathered through interviews with company managers and key personnel, review of company documents and perhaps the company's internal business plan. The underwriters seek to verify the statements made in the document through similar interviews and reviews, and through inquiries of customers, suppliers and business collaborators. Internal control systems are assessed and budgets, forecasts and strategic plans and financial prospects are reviewed. Lawyers for the underwriters and issuer examine company contracts, records, articles and by-laws, financing documents, minute books, stock records, product literature, reports to stockholders and market research studies.

Risk factors. The goal for the team drafting the prospectus is to furnish an accurate and fair presentation of the company's business, products, prospects and financial condition. A prominent portion of the document is devoted to setting out with specificity the particular risk factors that should be considered by investors prior to investing. Although management and underwriters may initially be reluctant to feature the reasons militating against the investment, a well written risk factors section protects the company against later claims by investors that sufficient information was not provided to them. The negative impact of the section is tempered by the fact that it is common in biotechnology offerings and does not constitute any disadvantage in marketing the offering.

Risk factors generally listed for a development stage biotechnology venture include the following:

1. *Development stage of the company.* Most biotechnology companies are still in the development stage. Profits from operations are not sufficient to fund research, development and general administrative expenditures. Revenues have been derived from research and development arrangements with established companies. Products are in early or intermediate stages of development and are several years from commercial introduction. Therefore, the company has no past performance upon which to judge future results or marketed products whose sales and earnings can be projected in a meaningful way. Revenues are unlikely to be sufficient to fund continued research efforts. Corporate licensing and similar relationships may be necessary for continued existence and the company may be dependent on the continuation of existing arrangements. Funds may not be adequate to finance production and marketing capacity and additional financing, which may not be available on acceptable terms, may be necessary in the future.
2. *Development risks.* Technology must be developed or refined to produce efficiently products that can be demonstrated to satisfy often difficult and uncertain regulatory standards. The rapid pace of technological developments may make the company's technology or products obsolete or uncompetitive. Marketing forces must be marshalled and targeted properly.
3. *Need for timely development.* The length of time required to develop and introduce a product to the market is critical to the commercial success of the product and the company. If the time frame is extended by technological difficulties, regulatory delay or manufacturing scale-up problems, competing or alternative products may occupy the niche intended for the company's product. Delays in marketing also negatively affect the return to investors by stretching out the time for return on investment.
4. *Unpredictability of patent protection.* Patent protection will be an important factor in the biotechnology industry. In addition to the uncertainty of the nature and scope of patent protection available in the field, the intense level of efforts throughout the world to develop similar products has created a complex pattern of patent positions that may take many years of expensive litigation to sort out.
5. *Competition.* Whether or not a genetically engineered product is completely novel or a replacement of an existing product, competition is fierce in each major area of activity. Large, established companies have embraced (somewhat belatedly) the technology and developed or acquired skills sufficient to compete with and, in some cases, surpass the efforts of smaller independent biotechnology companies. The established companies have greater financial resources, established manufacturing capability and experienced product development, regulatory and sales and service organizations.
6. *Dependence on key personnel, products or customers.* Many biotechnology companies, particularly those that are relatively small and undeveloped, have only a few key managers and scientists who are vital to its continued success. Similarly, in many cases the loss of a particular supplier, customer or product could cripple the company's operations.

SEC regulations and its staff appear to favor the inclusion of a risk factors section in the forepart of the prospectus for biotechnology prospectuses. The remainder of the prospectus contains a detailed description of the business of the issuer and the other disclosures required by SEC regulations.

Principal Items in Prospectus

The description of the company's business includes sections on the company's products, their stage of development and expected markets, the technology used to obtain and produce the products, marketing plans and capabilities, manufacturing capacity, patent position and competitive factors.

A regrettable aspect of the manner in which brokers market investments and investors choose them is their tendency to focus only on the summary of the prospectus that appears as its first textual item. The underwriters' primary concern is to tell a simple, compelling investment story and the company focuses on the accuracy and completeness of statements in the summary. It is difficult to do this in one or two pages.

Some of the specifically required disclosures include a use of proceeds section, a discussion and analysis of financial condition and results, dilution, executive compensation and transactions with affiliates.

The use of proceeds section describes the principal uses intended for the proceeds the company will receive from the offering. A discussion of the issuer's liquidity and cash expenditure needs is often required by the SEC, even if the proceeds are not immediately needed by the company. All known uses must be described, although the right to change the use may be reserved if specifically described contingencies occur.

A particularly important and difficult section of the prospectus to compose is the management discussion and analysis of the financial results and prospects. This section requires a textual analysis of the issuer's liquidity, capital resources and results of operations. In general the discussion centers on historical financial information and known trends, commitments and uncertainties that will affect future performance. The discussion is based on the financial statements included in the registration statement, including interim, quarterly and past two full years for balance sheet information and three full years for statements of operations.

Most IPOs involve a substantial disparity between the public offering price and the price paid by officers, directors, founders and other investors in the preceding five years. SEC regulations require a comparison between the relative amounts paid to the issuer by previous investors and their resulting percentage ownership compared to the amount to be provided by the public and its percentage ownership after the offering. The amount of dilution to new investors in net book value before and after the offering also must be disclosed. Although the value of this information is questionable, it is avidly and closely reviewed by state securities regulators, who frequently object if the dilution is large.

One of the consequences of being a public company is that all compensation payments and arrangements to executives must be disclosed. Many private companies have informal or unwritten policies that should be clarified or eliminated prior to going public. Loans to officers are abhorred by state regulators and should be repaid if possible (for example, out of proceeds from the offering if officers are permitted by the underwriters to be included in the offering). Often a stock option plan is adopted if one is not in place, as it is simpler to obtain stockholder approval prior to being owned by public shareholders.

Transactions between the issuer and its officers, directors and other affiliates also must be disclosed. Common examples include ownership by officers of properties leased by the issuer, loans or guaranties of loans to officers or directors, ownership by officers and directors of companies that do business with the issuer, registration and other rights of securities held by officers and directors and employment, consulting and similar agreements.

Compliance with general and specific disclosure requirements applicable to an IPO inevitably involves revealing information that for competitive or other business reasons the issuer desires to keep confidential. In particular, an issuer must describe new products or marketing plans that have a material bearing on its business plans if the issuer has not received revenue from operations for each of the prior three fiscal years. Specific disclosure of material product research and development to be performed during the period of the plan of operations is required. However, the status of a product or segment that has not been publicly announced need not be disclosed.

The name of each customer whose sales account for 10% or more of consolidated revenues must be disclosed. In some cases, however, the contract may specifically prohibit disclosure and permission to disclose must be obtained from the customer prior to the public offering. The requirement to disclose revenues, profitability and identifiable assets attributable to each of the issuer's geographic areas of operation could result in the loss of the business in that area as a result of disclosure.

Finally, the general requirement to disclose material information usually results in disclosure of competitive and other business information. There are procedures to keep this information confidential if disclosure would cause significant competitive harm to the issuer or if the information would lose its business value on disclosure. If confidential treatment is not granted, the issuer must either disclose the information or withdraw its registration statement. This is a serious problem for issuers who would not proceed if confidential treatment were not granted. The rules require the filing of the registration statement prior to the determination of confidential treatment, and thus after the expenditure of substantial time and money by the issuer.

SEC Review and the Waiting Period

After the registration statement is filed, the Division of Corporation Finance of the SEC reviews it and furnishes written comments to the issuer. In theory, the SEC has no authority to decide the merit of a particular offering and can only require the issuer to disclose all material facts. Because underwriters are anxious to commence the sale of the securities, in practice the changes in the registration statement suggested by the SEC usually are followed in order to effectuate an expeditious offering. Comment letters usually are received within 30 days of the initial filing.

Section 5 of the 1933 Act proscribes the making of public statements about the securities offered, other than those contained in the registration statement or prospectus, and requires the prospectus be made available to prospective and actual investors. Thus, the Act prohibits any offer to sell or offer to buy before the registration statement is filed. Discussions and agreements between issuers and underwriters are exempt from this prohibition.

The term "offer" is broadly interpreted by the SEC. In addition to formal offers, it includes any unusual publicity by the issuer or underwriters about the issuer's business or prospects that may condition the market or arouse investor interest in the issuer or its securities. This pre-conditioning is called "gun-jumping." If the SEC believes this has occurred, it may delay the offering to provide a "cooling-off" period to permit the effect of the publicity to dissipate.

If the notice includes only the name of the issuer, the total amount and basic terms of the offering, and a statement of the manner and purpose of the offering, the rules permit the issuer to provide a notice of the proposed offering without naming the underwriters together with a statement that the offering will be made only by a prospectus.

These rules make it important that an issuer take extreme care to ensure that its press releases and other information dissemination activities will not be construed as gun-jumping. The SEC does permit an issuer to issue factual press releases on business and financial developments, and to continue product advertising and stockholder communication if the disclosures (a) are consistent with prior practice, (b) do not contain projections and (c) based on the timing, content and distribution of the information, do not otherwise suggest a pre-conditioning effort is intended.

During the "waiting period" between the initial filing and the clearance or effective date of the registration statement, preliminary or "red herring" prospectuses may be distributed. The term "red herring" derives from the legend in red ink required by the SEC to be placed on preliminary prospectuses stating that the registration statement has been filed but has not yet become effective and that the securities may not be sold or offers accepted prior to the effective date.

During the waiting period the underwriters and company executives usually participate in a "road show" in which information meetings with prospective underwriters, analysts and potential institutional investors are held. Information beyond the prospectus is not permitted to be provided in these meetings. These meetings typically occur over a one to three week period and include visits to six to ten U.S. cities and three to six European cities. The meetings require the presence of the top two or three company executives and represent a considerable psychological and business distraction.

In addition to the federal securities laws, issuers and underwriters also must comply with the securities laws or "blue sky" laws of each state in which the securities will be offered or sold. Underwriters' counsel generally are responsible for preparing and filing the state applications and negotiating with the respective reviewers in each state for review and approval prior to or coincident with the federal review. In contrast to the 1933 Act which requires full disclosure to investors to achieve the goal of investor protection, many states have adopted a "merit" review system for securities offerings in which the state securities agency determines whether the investment is appropriate for its citizens. Merit review states provide several hurdles to lawyers attempting to register a high risk investment such as a biotechnology offering. State regulators frequently require justification of the initial offering price, benefits paid to managers, number of shares reserved for employee stock options and similar matters. Often the company is required to undertake to not make loans to officers and directors in the future and in some circumstances founders of the company must agree not to sell their shares for a specified period as a condition to gaining approval of the registration.

After clearance by federal and state regulators, the registration statement is declared effective and the underwriters commence their sales. Usually, one week after the effective date a closing of the sale occurs when documents effectuating the sale, including opinions of counsel, together with the stock itself are delivered to the underwriters in exchange for the proceeds of the offering.

RESEARCH AND DEVELOPMENT LIMITED PARTNERSHIPS

The research and development limited partnership provides an alternative to equity offerings as a source of substantial funding for developing biotechnology ventures. Unlike debt and equity, which are investments based on the earnings potential or growth of the enterprise generally, research and development partnerships are intended to provide a return to the limited partner investors through the commercial exploitation of specific products, projects or technology developed on behalf of the partnership by the sponsoring company. Research and development limited partnerships require several complex sets of agreements and involve substantial tax, securities law and financial sophistication.

Structure

The sponsoring company forms a limited partnership and provides a license to the partnership to use previously developed or "core" corporate technology solely for the purpose of designing, developing, making, using and selling specific products to be developed by the partnership. The development of these products is governed by a research and development agreement between the partnership and the sponsoring company. Investors fund the partnership through the purchase of limited partnership interests. In return for cost reimbursement funding by the partnership, the company for a specified number of years undertakes product research and development, the resulting products and technology becoming the property of the partnership. During this development period the sponsoring company has a license from the partnership to exploit the technology and, if commercial revenues are obtained during this interim period, the revenues are provided to the partnership through a joint venture or distribution arrangement with the company. The company also retains an option to purchase, at the expiration of the interim period, all of the partners' interests in the partnership or the partnership's interest in the products or project funded and owned by the partnership. If the purchase option is exercised, the investors receive an initial down payment and installment payments based on a percentage of the net sales of products incorporating partnership property.

Under applicable law, the general partner of a limited partnership has the exclusive responsibility for the management and control of the business of the partnership. If this requirement is ignored and limited partners participate in the partnership business, the limitation on liability ordinarily provided to limited partners will not be available. The sponsoring company usually incorporates an entity that acts as the general partner and provides its own employees to act as the directors and officers of the general partner.

The use of an incorporated subsidiary is intended to insulate the assets of the parent company from obligations that may be incurred by the general partner because the general partner is responsible for all obligations of the partnership that cannot be satisfied by partnership assets. Some general partners have board representatives who are not affiliates in order to provide independent scrutiny of transactions between the partnership and the sponsor. This practice provides hollow assurance when the business activities of the partnership are extremely technical and contributions of those who are not involved in them are unlikely to be meaningful. Sufficient protection against conflict of interest is provided by the fiduciary obligations of the employees when they are acting in their capacities as representatives of the partnership.

The recent prominence of the research and development partnership as a source of capital to biotechnology companies was propelled originally by accounting and tax rules. Under generally accepted accounting principles, a company's expenditures for research and development are charged as operating expenses that correspondingly reduce profits. A company that wishes to expend sums on a promising new project must face the unpleasant choice of reducing earnings (or increasing losses) by the amount of the projected expenditures required prior to realization of commercial returns, sharing it with a better financed company or foregoing the opportunity altogether.

Federal income tax regulations permit corporate research and development expenditures to be deducted as a business expense. This benefit is of little use to an independent biotechnology company that already has incurred substantial losses during its startup years and has accumulated large net operating loss carryovers for application against future tax obligations. The research and development partnership provided a means for a developing biotechnology company with little or no product revenues and profits to obtain the funding for research that ordinarily would be provided by profitable products and to transfer the concomitant tax deductions to investors who provided the funding and could utilize the deductions on a current basis. Funds received by the biotechnology company from the partnership for work on partnership projects are accounted for as contract revenues and offset the corresponding corporate expenditures.

The Tax Reform Act of 1986 vitiated the attractiveness of research and development partnerships as a vehicle to transfer tax deductions by limiting the availability of deductions by partners for partnership research and development expenditures. The elimination of this and other financial incentives such as favorable capital gains rates and favorable accounting treatment for stock options could have a considerable negative impact on continued U.S. competitiveness in biotechnology.

Although the tax benefits were an important motivation for investors to purchase research and development partnership interests, the vehicle has continued to be used when companies have been willing to provide additional "sweeteners" to investors to replace the value of the formerly available tax benefits. This has been accomplished by offering a higher potential return through higher purchase option exercise prices, including larger down payments and higher percentage installment payments, and the provision of warrants to purchase common stock of the sponsor to investors who purchase limited partnership interests. The availability of the "equity kicker" provided by warrants reduces the limited partner's investment risk. If the project is a failure and the purchase option is not exercised, but success in other projects drives the common stock above the exercise price of the warrant, the limited partner will obtain a return through exercise of the warrant. The warrants are a separate security that may be transferred for value and provide a return prior or in addition to that which might be obtained from the payments resulting from the Company's exercise of the option to purchase the partnership interests.

The availability of R&D partnership funding has enabled several biotechnology companies to continue the development of projects which they did not have the funds to finance and did not wish to license to larger, more established companies. The limited partner investors provide the risk capital, and the company obtains an option to purchase the project if it is successful in return for agreed upon payments. This mechanism enables a developing company to retain the right to enjoy a greater portion of the profits than would be yielded by the royalties paid by a company that finances the project and to which the project commercialization rights are licensed.

The activities funded by these partnerships generally have been development and clinical testing expenses for healthcare products. Specific products, a group of separate products and products in specified therapeutic categories are examples of the types of projects that have been financed by R&D partnerships.

Once the sponsor has selected the project, it must prepare a business plan. This plan is similar to the business plan developed for the entire business of the company in connection with its venture capital financing. The plan would detail the scope of the project, the overall operating budget and the potential return to investors. The plan also includes a product development schedule and a forecast of when funds will be required.

The business plan is set out in the offering document in order to explain to investors the nature of their investment and to induce them to make the investment. Central to the investment decision is the projection of revenues that might be yielded by the project and the returns projected to be paid to the investors. Projections are generated by examining the total market for the products, estimated adoption and penetration rates, expected pricing and market share and likely product life. Because the products often are novel, it is not a simple task to choose the appropriate assumptions necessary for a reasonable model of the potential returns.

The knowledge and expertise necessary to assess the validity of these assumptions often is too daunting a challenge for the investment bankers who act as placement agents for the offering. Their reaction to the challenge often is to hire a consultant who purports to be an "expert" in assessing technology and reviewing projections and development costs that are estimated by the biotechnology company. Investment bankers have to comfort themselves with the delusion that the use of these consultants will provide them with meaningful assurances that the company's estimates are reasonable and will reduce their liability to a charge that they failed to discharge properly their legal obligation to make "due diligence" inquiries.

R&D Partnership Offering Process

Biotechnology R&D limited partnership offerings generally have been made through investment banking firms acting as placement agents. Most of these partnerships have been sold under the private offering exemption under the 1933 Act and therefore are not subject to the SEC registration requirements and process. The use of a private placement in this context has several advantages over a public offering. Although a public offering will involve a much greater pool of potential investment funds, public investors are less sophisticated than private investors who, because they are wealthy, are more likely to be able to afford the loss of their investment. Because the project to be financed involves substantial risk, state regulators are reluctant to permit investors to participate in these complex investments unless they are "accredited investors" to whom the securities are offered privately. These investors are defined to have a net worth in excess of $1 million (including the value of the home, home furnishings and automobiles), and personal income greater than $200,000 in the current year as well as other requirements. Projections are not permitted by the SEC in public offerings. This might limit the marketability of the investment.

The disclosure requirements for private and public offering documents are generally the same except for the specific disclosures required by the 1933 Act, most of which are followed even though not required in a private offering document. In general, the elements of the offering document include the terms of the offering, suitability standards for investors, a description of the business of the partnership, the use of the proceeds, the estimated partnership cash flow, projected financial return and the assumptions underlying the model, a description of the general partner and the sponsor, potential conflicts of interest, risk factors, summaries of the technology, development, distribution, partnership and purchase option agreements, federal income tax considerations and descriptions of any warrants or other securities offered in connection with the partnership investment and of the company issuing them.

The process of negotiating the terms and preparing the documents for a R&D partnership is arduous and lengthy. Extreme tension is caused by the conflicting desires of the investment bankers to obtain as many rights as possible, and to be able to describe the potential return and the project in glowing terms, compared with the company's desires to retain as many rights as possible in the event the project fails and fairly and accurately to describe the project and its risks. Companies must be careful to ensure that the terms are structured properly in order that the desired accounting and tax treatment is available. The central requirement is that the partnership must bear the risk of project failure in order that the research payments received by the sponsor are treated as revenues.

A sponsor must be wary of acceding to unreasonable demands by the placement agents not only to preserve the desired accounting treatment, but also to preserve its ability to generate returns to existing investors in the event the project is unsuccessful and the company decides not to exercise its option to purchase the partnership's commercialization rights.

The agreements

The rights and obligations between the sponsoring company and the partnership are set out in agreements whose terms are negotiated by the company and the placement agents. The placement agents do not purport to represent the potential investors in this negotiation and often attempt expressly to disclaim in the offering document that they have any legal obligation to do so. However, the agents want to be able to sell the offering in order to pocket their substantial fees and commissions; they want the project to be successful so that the purchase option is exercised and investors will get a return of, and possibly a return on, their investment and thus buy other investments from the agents. These factors cause the agents to seek the best possible deal for the partnership.

The agreements generally include a cross license or background technology license, a development agreement, an interim license, distribution or joint venture agreement, a purchase agreement and the partnership agreement.

In the cross license agreement, the sponsor grants a license to the partnership, for the term of the research and development project, to use the sponsor's previously developed background or core technology solely for the purposes of designing, developing, making, using and selling the partnership's technology and products. This technology provides the foundation for the work to be performed by the sponsor on behalf of the partnership under the development agreement. The sponsor must ensure that it retains all rights to the background technology for activities outside the field of the partnership. The sponsor also should disclaim any representations that the background technology is adequate for the partnership's purpose.

The partnership licenses the sponsor to use the licensed background technology and the to-be-developed partnership technology for the purposes of providing research and development services to the partnership. The company also should receive an exclusive license to use any enhancements to the background technology for other than partnership purposes. If the company does not exercise its purchase option, the partnership must be free to exploit the developed technology on its own or through third parties. The background technology rights therefore end up in the possession of the sponsor's competitors, although the competitor should be limited by the license agreement to use of the technology only in connection with partnership products.

The development agreement specifies the terms under which the sponsor performs services on behalf of the partnership. The sponsor agrees to perform research and development activities to develop partnership technology and products in return for reimbursement of its expenses allocable to performing that work. The offering document will indicate the estimate and timing of these expenses and describe the general scope of the work to be performed. Some agreements provide for mandatory or optional payments by the sponsor for work that is required beyond the amount available from partnership finding. If the sponsor supplements the partnership finding it should receive a reduction in the payments it must make under the purchase agreement if the purchase option is exercised.

In projects that involve more than one program or product, the sponsor should be provided flexibility to reallocate partnership funds according to technical advances and changing circumstances.

Because the project represents only a portion of the sponsor's research activities, the personnel who perform services under the development agreement also perform services for the sponsor and its clients. The sponsor retains the right to allocate its facilities and personnel as it deems appropriate subject to an obligation to use its best efforts to undertake the specified partnership programs.

The interim license, marketing or joint venture agreement provides the sponsor with the right, during the period before the purchase option can be exercised, to exploit the technology and products developed for the partnership. Because the development period is often four years or more, this arrangement provides a mechanism for interim revenues if portions of the program can be commercialized during that period.

The purchase agreement provides the sponsor with an option to purchase all of the partnership's rights to the developed technology. Generally, the purchase price consists of an initial down payment, in the form of cash or stock of the sponsor and future installment payments based on a percentage of the net sales of products incorporating the technology. Payments received in return for licenses or other payments from third parties in respect to the technology are also subject to sharing with the investors.

As the above discussion indicates, R&D partnerships are complex vehicles for obtaining funding. The corresponding legal, accounting and printing fees often exceed $1 million, and the agents expect to receive at least a 9% share of the net proceeds of the offering. The payments to investors range from 6 to 10% of the ultimate sale price of the products. Despite these expenses, this vehicle is preferable to a research agreement with an established company in which the research company receives a royalty ranging from 10 to 20%, compared with paying a 10% "royalty" to its partnership investors.

CONVERTIBLE DEBT

Convertible debt securities are debt instruments convertible into common stock of the issuer at a specified price at the option of the holder. Features include an interest rate that is lower than would be obtained for debt without the conversion privilege, a conversion price higher than the market value of the common stock at the time of issuance and a right of repayment subordinate to other debt, permitting the company to issue senior debt. These features provide investors an assured income and added safety through a claim on assets senior to the underlying common stock. The ability to convert the repayment obligation into common shares permits the opportunity of participating in an increase in common stock values as the company prospers. Convertible instruments are particularly appealing during a period of rising stock prices because they provide the opportunity to benefit from stock price increases while retaining the relative safety of a debt or senior equity position. Convertibles frequently are employed by growth companies that prefer to offer lower than market dividend or interest rates. If the issuer is successful over the long term, the issuance of convertible debt serves the function of raising equity capital at attractive prices. If the market value of the underlying common stock increases, the issuer can force conversion of the debt into equity by issuing a notice it intends to redeem (repay) the debt. The result is to eliminate the debt obligation and the conversion option by the issuance of stock. Even if the market value of the common stock fails to rise sufficiently to force conversion, the issuer nonetheless will have received the benefit of the use of the debt proceeds at a relatively low interest rate.

Relatively few biotechnology companies have been able to finance their operations through the issuance of debt. In general, purchasers of debt require an existing and stable source of earnings to support repayment of the debt. However, in some cases the prospects of specific biotechnology companies to generate earnings in the future and to enjoy substantial equity appreciation has provided the foundation for successful convertible debt offerings.

Convertible debt offerings are fairly simple and rapid financial transactions for established companies. The offering document resembles a private offering memorandum or public offering prospectus. In addition, the terms of the securities are described. The principal terms include the aggregate amount, the interest rate, the maturity date, the conversion price and the redemption provisions. The conversion price (the exchange rate of the debt for stock) is set at a premium to the current market value of the stock, usually between 20 and 25%. The company usually has the option to redeem the debt at a premium if the price of the stock exceeds the conversion price for a specified period of time. This provides the company with the opportunity to "force" conversion through the call for redemption.

Convertible debt often is subordinated in right of payment to specified types of "senior debt." Senior debt includes existing and future bonds, notes and debentures issued for borrowed money, debt issued in connection with acquisitions and obligations under capitalized leases. Investors are willing to subordinate their priority of payment on bankruptcy in return for the conversion privilege.

A DOSE OF REALITY

Some of the above remarks are theoretical and do not necessarily describe accurately the real world practical aspects of financing biotechnology companies. Despite the enormous risk and daunting challenges facing the more than 300 independent companies formed in the U.S. to commercialize biotechnology, very few have gone bankrupt. The appeal of biotechnology's potential has continued to attract investors for many years during a period when financial markets have varied significantly. Capital has been available in many guises, ranging from public equity to convertible debt. Often a company does not have the luxury of weighing the theoretical considerations involved in a particular financial vehicle. Quite simply, it avails itself of the vehicle that appears most likely to be well received by investors. Finally, the ability of a company to sell the security that is in vogue at the time in the amount and at the price that it desires often depends more on the perception of analysts who purport to understand the company and its industry rather than on the fundamental reality of the company's situation and prospects.

APPENDIX A

Equity and Debt

The purchaser of equity receives a participation in the profits and growth of the entity as compensation for the investment. The entity does not promise to repay the investment. Thus a stockholder is really a stakeholder in the future of the company. Applicable law requires an entity to repay its debts before making distributions in respect of equity. In bankruptcy, the satisfaction of debt through liquidation of the entity's assets has priority over the distribution of any remaining assets to holders of equity. Equity therefore is most often utilized in situations where the entity does not have the capacity to provide an assurance of repayment but does have the potential for substantial growth and earnings. The startup and early stage capital needs of most ventures are obtained through equity investments. Because debt has priority over equity, the return on investment available to purchasers of debt is lower than that demanded by purchasers of equity, reflecting the greater certainty of repayment of debt.

A purchaser of a debt instrument receives a promise from the borrower to repay the amount of the investment, and prior to repayment to receive interest on the amount outstanding (whether at the end of a stated term or in periodic installments). Because the return to the investor is limited to invested principal and the stated interest rate, the holder of debt has no participation in the success of the entity.

Basic forms of equity

Common stock. The owner of a share of common stock has a share in the net income and net assets of the issuing company and the right to participate in the selection of management through voting rights. Dividends usually are paid only if earned and if declared by the directors of the company. Unlike a holder of debt, who has a fixed claim to the income of an entity and can take action in the event of a default, a stockholder has only a residual interest in income, sharing in the fortunes of the entity, good and bad, which are reflected in the value of the shares over time. Thus the value of common shares usually fluctuates in a much broader range than does debt, as the prospects of the enterprise to increase earnings and pay dividends is continually re-evaluated. However, interest rates and general market conditions also exert a powerful influence on the prices of common stock.

Preferred stock. Preferred stock is a hybrid of debt and equity. The owner of preferred stock foregoes a direct participation in the growth of the company's earnings in return for a fixed claim on the earnings and assets that is prior to common stockholders (but still subordinate to creditors). Preferred stock can have either a fixed or variable dividend rate, and dividends must be paid to holders of preferred stock before any dividends can be paid to holders of common stock. In either case, the payment of dividends is subject to earnings limitations provided by statute and to declaration by the entity's board of directors.

The market value of fixed dividend preferred stock varies inversely with interest rates. Because the claims of preferred stockholders are superior to common stockholders and subordinate to debt holders, negative prospects for the issuer first adversely affect the value of common stock, then the preferred stock, and finally the value of debt.

Types of debt

Debt securities are denominated as notes, debentures and bonds. A note is a short-term obligation, requiring payment in one year or less. Debentures and bonds have a longer repayment term, ranging up to 30 years. A debenture usually is an unsecured obligation and a bond is an obligation whose promise to repay is secured by specific property or assets. In bankruptcy, claims of debt holders have priority over those of common and preferred stockholders. The nature of the preference is specified in the instrument and may be preferred or subordinate to other debt ("senior" v. "subordinated" debt). The debt holder is entitled to receive a fixed interest rate and a return of principal at a specified date, but has no control over management because debt carries no voting rights. If the terms of the debt instruments are breached, the holder has the right to foreclose on pledged property, sue for damages or cause a liquidation of the entity to satisfy the obligation. The risk taken by a debt investor is lower than that of an equity investor due to the promise of repayment of principal and a fixed return and a priority over equity. Advantages to an issuer include the lower return required by debt investors compared with equity investors, the possibility of gaining leverage by borrowing at a rate lower than it expects it will be able to earn on reinvestment and the preservation of control.

Warrants

Debt and preferred stock issues with attached warrants are often used by development stage companies. A warrant is an option to purchase common stock (or other securities) of the issuer at a fixed price during a fixed period of time. A stock purchase warrant, unlike a convertible security, does not displace the initial security and thus provides benefits supplemental to those of the primary investment. After an initial period following issuance, warrants can be traded separately from the original security. The benefit to the issuer is the receipt of additional funds on exercise of the warrant while the benefit to the investor is the opportunity to purchase stock at a discount if the stock rises above the warrant price.

POSTSCRIPT: A VENTURE CAPITALISTS'S PERSPECTIVE OF BIOTECHNOLOGY

The mechanics of investing in biotechnology have been considered in detail. But why do people actually choose to invest in biotechnology rather than in something else? In the view of Robert F. Johnston, a venture capitalist from Princeton, New Jersey, the primary motivation is, of course, to make money. A venture capitalist is a professional investor: he invests funds on behalf of insurance companies, pension funds and wealthy individuals. His task is to make more profit for his clients than could be obtained from other forms of investment; if he fails his clients are unlikely to prolong their relationship with him. So all venture capitalists are under considerable pressure to perform well knowing that their investment decisions will be measured against possible alternatives. A decision to invest in a biotechnology company, with all the risks that such an investment might entail, must carefully balance the perceived risks against the prospective rewards. The fact that investments in those companies are indeed made clearly confirms that many venture capitalists do judge the risks to be worth taking.

Johnston sees the most important factor determining the success of a new venture as having the right president/chief executive officer for the particular company. While this may be true for any small company, it is particularly important in a young high-technology firm in which the fundamental factors affecting the company seem constantly to be changing. Not only will the technology be evolving rapidly but the company may itself be developing such new products that it is in effect creating new markets, adding to the uncertainty of its own future. Then there are regulatory agencies to deal with, corporate partners to massage and brilliant but no doubt individualistic scientists to keep happy, motivated, and focused on the business opportunities rather than their exploration of the pure science. To complicate matters, these new companies frequently have three or four different venture investors. Each has his own set of criteria and concerns about the company and the president has to do his best to keep all of them happy: the president/CEO of a small, high-technology company, particularly in biotechnology, has to be as close to the renaissance man as possible. He has to deal with the financial community, be a good public speaker, make presentations for public offerings, raise money, sell his company successfully to the investment analysts, educate and keep his employees motivated, and all this in addition to finding, selling, convincing, and making sure his corporate partners remain satisfied. To cap it all, he has to keep the technology on track towards the company's commercial objectives while sometimes helping to steer it in new directions in response to new discoveries or novel forms of competition. So perhaps the single most important decision the venture capitalist makes is the selection of the president for the company especially as it is often extremely difficult to find in one person an understanding of the technology coupled with both the requisite experience and good business instincts.

What then is the role of the venture capitalist in helping his biotechnology company grow? In Johnston's view he should be an active director, operating as a sounding board for the president, asking the right questions to make sure than the issues have been properly thought through as well as supplying introductions and entrées to the larger corporate partners and to the financial community. But that is not all: he must also make sure than the CEO himself understands and has thoroughly considered the fundamental issues, is on course to accomplishing them and, if he is not, help him to reorient himself. Not infrequently, Johnston observes, both the president and the venture capitalist tend to be too optimistic about their own projections and assumptions.

Chapter 4

Biotechnology Startups

George B. Rachmann

INTRODUCTION

Simmering through the 1970s, a series of key scientific discoveries would serve as the fuse to ignite an explosion of commercial biotechnology developments throughout the 1980s. As surely as the creative description of DNA by Watson and Crick in 1953 was the ignition spark, advances in gene manipulation, monoclonal antibodies, gene sequencing and gene synthesis unleashed the power to attract $3 billions in investment, thousands of scientists and hundreds of entrepreneurs and business executives. These efforts created a spectrum of products offering new hopes to the sick, the hungry, the young and the old. The biotechnology revolution of the 1980s emerged as a series of announcements of discoveries, financings, executive shifts, political and regulatory issues, patents, litigation and the marketing of products of extraordinary benefits to humankind. The macropicture was recorded in the monthly and often weekly announcements throughout the period. The micropicture can be viewed through the eyes of the scientists and business people who created Amgen, one of the several hundred biotechnology companies that formed and thrived by selling promises and then making them happen.

THE FUNDING AND GROWTH OF A BIOTECH COMPANY

Preparation (April, 1980 — September, 1980)

Biogen and then Genentech clone alpha interferon/U.S. Supreme Court upholds patent on life form/Genentech initial public offering — price soars.

Incorporation

The pace of biotechnology accelerated as the announcements of the first eight months of 1980 raised awareness throughout the world that something important was happening in biotechnology and the stage was set for the explosive progress to follow.

A virtually unnoticed event was the formation of Amgen, an acronym for "Applied Molecular Genetics", in April of 1980. Four venture capitalists, ten university scientists and a vice president of a major oil shale company felt that the power of biotechnology could support at least one additional company. Collaborative Research (founded in 1961), Cetus (1971), Genentech (1976), Biogen (1977), Genex (1977), and Molecular Genetics (1979) were then the major biotechnology companies. Cetus had broad projects in chemicals, pharmaceuticals and plants. Genentech was the only company to focus immediately on recombinant DNA and human pharmaceuticals. Biogen, with a network of scientific advisors, appeared well positioned from the breadth of their scientific base. Genex concentrated on chemicals. Molecular Genetics focused on animal health and to some degree plant genetics. In contrast to the other companies Collaborative Research had conventional product sales. Hybritech, Genetic Systems and Monoclonal Antibodies, all of them just formed, concentrated on diagnostics using monoclonal antibodies.

How biotechnology companies were started can best be analyzed through the roles of the founding participants. In the case of Amgen, the initial motivation came from venture capitalists who had previously participated in the founding, financing and management of Cetus and Biogen. As with any venture capitalist, their motives included significant potential economic gain. Most important for Amgen was their belief that such gain is maximized by building a strong company over the long term rather than solely by creating short-term stock appreciation. (These original venture investors, incidentally, have retained virtually all their initial Amgen stock although values have escalated 1000-fold since their founding purchase.)

The additional contributions of the venture capitalists included: focusing on finding a Chief Executive Officer a (CEO); identifying Dr. Winston Salser, Professor of Molecular Biology at the University of California at Los Angeles (UCLA) who organized a group of university scientists as the Scientific Advisory Board; confirming the commitment of Tosco as a key corporate investor; identifying the law firm of Cooley, Godward, Castro, Huddleson and Tatum to help in the incorporation of the company in April of 1980; and confirming the board participation of several individuals who would lend credibility and sound counsel to facilitate the first round financing.

The Scientific Advisory Board

Dr. Salser catalysed the formation of the Scientific Advisory Board. He used three major arguments to bring together a group of world class scientists. First, each candidate was advised that the other candidates were enthusiastic and would represent a powerful driving force for a new company; second, participating in the company would help to bring basic science and their own personal ideas to commercial reality for the benefit of society; and third, each member could participate in significant economic gain through major stock appreciation as had occurred with Biogen, Cetus and Genentech.

The ground rules for the Scientific Advisory Board were the same as they are today. A scientific advisory board member has no constraints on the publication of information from his research work, can limit his time commitment to the company to participation in six days of meetings each year and may have affiliations with other companies.

During the first six months, Scientific Advisory Board members met several times and the minutes of these meetings were summarized by Dr. Salser as a research plan which outlined product targets and project candidates. Through the Scientific Advisory Board, Amgen acquired no product rights or proprietary data but gained immediate credibility as a result of this prestigious board. Amgen has continually benefited from the wisdom, guidance and open discussion that has characterized the board's deliberation since the early days.

How valuable was the stock that was purchased at that time? Each board member was permitted to purchase 1200 shares of a restricted stock at 25¢ per share. This price was the same as that offered to the venture capitalists and to the first group of officers and scientists to be hired. At the time of the public offering, each share converted into 7.5 shares of common stock valued at $18 a share. Most scientific advisory board members have retained a high percentage of both those original shares and additional shares purchased at higher prices in subsequent distributions.

Chief Executive Officer

Early in April 1980, the author, then an executive at Abbott Laboratories, learned of the formation of Amgen and agreed in June to visit with members of the Scientific Advisory Board and the venture capitalists to explore a role in this company that was mutually interesting. A number of other candidates were being considered for the board of directors and for operating roles. In June, it was decided to offer the author the position of president and chief executive officer and to offer Dr. Joseph Rubinfield, who was then at Bristol Myers, a vice presidency. Dr. Winston Salser was selected to be Vice President of Research and Development and Chairman of the Scientific Advisory Board. Unresolved was the question of whether Dr. Salser would stay half-time at UCLA as professor in the Molecular Biology Institute or become a full-time Amgen employee. This would later prove to lead to Amgen's first crisis as an operating company.

Undoubtedly, the author's enthusiasm for recombinant DNA and involvement in a new biotechnology company was strongly stimulated by an article in *Fortune* (June 1, 1980) describing Biogen and the drama and excitement of world class scientists assembling a research organization at the cutting edge of biotechnology. However, Abbott Laboratories was at the time in the process of creating the world's leading diagnostic business. Budgets for research and development were generous and the scientific effort had expanded manyfold in the preceding five years. The original staff and the new scientists worked effectively together developing products at a pace unrivaled in the industry. By 1980, Abbott's Diagnostics Division had gained the respect of the entire organization. As Vice President of Research and Development, the challenges ahead would be stimulating and rewarding. On the advice of several executives at Abbott, several weeks were spent discussing alternative opportunities. Other biotechnology companies were forming and the Amgen opportunity could be more fairly evaluated in comparison to other situations.

All the discussions in the next few weeks were initiated by others as they learned of the author's plan to leave Abbott Laboratories. In this way, it was possible to become acquainted with the opportunities at both Harvard (which later became Genetics Institute) and the worldwide operation of Biogen. There were discussions with investment bankers and venture capitalists about their plans for forming new biotechnology companies. These plans would subsequently lead to the formation of California Biotechnology and Biotechnology General. Much of the author's confidence that the story of Amgen is typical of a young biotechnology company is based on the conversations and insights from that period.

In September, the difficult decision was made to pass up the opportunity to build a biotechnology company within Abbott Laboratories. With no particular basis for believing any of the outside opportunities were superior to Amgen, and with Amgen pressing for a final decision, the President, CEO and the first employee of Amgen was hired on October 1, 1980. Total compensation was roughly two-thirds of that received at Abbott Laboratories. Compensation would begin only after a successful first round financing.

Initial Financing (October, 1980 — February, 1981)

Monsanto invests $20 million in Biogen/Fluor makes major investment in Genentech/Genentech initiates clinical studies on human growth hormone.

The first day as Chief Executive Officer at Amgen was spent as a visiting scientist occupying a borrowed desk in Dr. Winston Salser's office at UCLA. The company's first objective was clear. Amgen had to raise money and do it fast. An audit of the "books" (a collection of personal checking accounts and various shoe boxes of receipts) was the first order of business and the Los Angeles office of Arthur Young was engaged as auditors. Amgen's "seed money" came to approximately $100,000 from stock sales to (and loans from) the venture capitalists, future board members, Scientific Advisory Board members and the three candidates for management positions. Checking accounts were consolidated into an Amgen account in Thousand Oaks, California, where the first laboratory space would be leased. The research plan, discussed by the Scientific Advisory Board and summarized by Dr. Winston Salser, was immediately restructured to be suitable for an offering memorandum. The law firm of Cooley Godward provided invaluable assistance in developing the required legal phraseology and the incorporation of the essential elements for a proper offering memorandum.

On October 10, Genentech went public and investors' appetites for the stock accelerated by the hour. Concurrently, Monsanto invested $20 million in Biogen. The timing of these events appeared to forecast a prompt and successful Amgen financing. Amgen's Offering Memorandum was sent to potential investors on October 23, 1980 and individual meetings were scheduled. One of the venture capitalist founders, William K. Bowes, selected Sutter Hill as a premier venture capital firm sure to be interested in the Amgen story. He would know by the end of the meeting whether or not Sutter Hill wished to reserve a position in the offering. During the recap of the meeting, he had sadly to advise his colleagues that Sutter Hill would not be investing. The Amgen group pressed hard to determine what had gone wrong. Bowes suggested changing the answer to the question "What will your sales be in five years?" He hoped we could find an encouraging and convincing answer.

The group were far from overconfident, but their initial presentations were still tragic disappointments. Although the offering memorandum gave relatively sophisticated discussions of the science, and even provided some rough market estimates, it was totally lacking the style and format of any recognizable type of business plan.

The following guidelines were subsequently agreed for future presentations:

1. There would be a business plan which generated a return to investors of *ten-fold* within 5–7 years.
2. The presentation would be much more formal.
3. The honest projection would be retained which, while indicating that there would be essentially no sales in five years, would nevertheless show the very high return on investment.

Techniques were used which are quite common today for evaluating biotechnology companies. Sales were projected for the year 1990 and discounted back to 1986. Such calculations are necessarily qualitative and subjective. To lend credibility, we defined four alternative approaches for estimating 1986 values and showed the same high rate of return for each. The group felt they had a convincing message.

It is interesting to note that in February, 1981 the first round investors paid $10.00 per share and by 1987 (corrected for stock splits) achieved roughly a seven-fold return.

Before the next presentation to executives of E.I. du Pont de Nemours, the Amgen group were advised that du Pont would be expanding their life sciences research and development from $100 million to $120 million during 1981. There was an enthusiastic discussion of the Amgen programs but very little interest in an investment in the company. (It was learned after the presentation that du Pont had just committed nearly $400 million for the acquisition of New England Nuclear.)

The following presentation was made to SmithKline and French, the third "assured" corporate investor. They also expressed considerable interest but felt that any type of capital investment would require at least a six-month review with their management. Amgen's goal was to close within sixty days. Since the Amgen strategy had called for three corporate investors including du Pont and SmithKline, these disappointments were potentially disastrous. At that point, the venture was assured of a $3 million investment by Tosco and a $200,000 commitment from Asset Management, a founding venture capital firm managed by Franklin P. Johnson. Efforts were accelerated to meet with each selected venture capitalist and arranged for a broad presentation to an executive group at Abbott Laboratories.

That presentation went well and Kirk Raab, then a Group Vice President, indicated that Abbott would be willing to purchase a $3½ million block of stock. Then after the next round of presentations, it appeared that New Court Securities (now N.M. Rothschild), Citicorp, Claremont Capital, Harrison Capital and Charles River would all participate in a significant way. Hoping to close by January 1, Amgen indicated both to Abbott and to Tosco the necessity to pursue more vigorously a third corporate partner, probably a pharmaceutical company. The Amgen management were anxious to close before any erosion of committed investors. Abbott suggested moving their purchase to $5 million if Tosco's purchase would also agree to an increase. They did, to $3½ million. The Amgen management then estimated $18 million in committed purchases. Surprisingly, a strong, late interest emerged from a number of investors including a major French company. However, in January, 1981, the French government took several steps that disturbed some of the already committed investors about a potential involvement of the French government. The company elected to forego the sale of additional shares and instead closed on February 2,

1981 for $18.9 million. In approximately four months, thanks to many favorable factors, and by giving up approximately one-half the company, Amgen had completed the largest initial financing in biotechnology.

Organization (March, 1981 — March, 1982)

Five or six new biotechnology companies forming each month/ Cetus raises record $120 million in initial public offering/ Chiron announces successful expression of hepatitis surface antigen and potential hepatitis vaccine/Genentech announces cloning and expression of gamma interferon.

Corporate Structure

How does a company start operations with $19 million in the bank, a Board of Directors, a Scientific Advisory Board and three members of the management team? In March 1981, as Amgen completed its first month after financing and its initial year as a corporation, a major operating problem developed.

Dr. Salser felt uncomfortable dedicating a large percentage of his time to organizing and managing the research and development at Amgen at the expense of his teaching and research responsibilities as a professor at UCLA. On the other hand, a part-time Vice President of Research and Development seemed totally incompatible with any reasonable business practice. Both positions were firm and the inevitable result occurred within 30 days when Dr. Salser resigned to devote full-time to his responsibilities in the Molecular Biology Institute of UCLA.

On an interim basis it was agreed that the president would assume responsibility as Chairman of the Scientific Advisory Board and as acting Vice President of Research and Development. With extraordinary assistance from the southern California members of the Scientific Advisory Board, including Dr. Arnold Berk, Dr. John Carbon, Dr. Martin Cline, Dr. Norm Davidson and Dr. Lee Hood, Amgen vigorously pursued hiring the best scientists that could be identified.

Two major organizational decisions were reached, one of which was to be reversed within 90 days. First, it was decided that Dr. Caruthers could organize a subsidiary in Boulder, Colorado for the purpose of proving that his synthetic oligonucleotide chemistry would be a practical basis for rapidly synthesizing genes. Dr. Caruthers would lease space away from the University campus and manage the activities on a very limited part-time basis. The specific goal would be to synthesize short genes for β-endorphin and calcitonin. His budget included six people to be hired before the end of the year. This corporation would be a wholly owned subsidiary of Amgen: to avoid future difficulties, only Amgen stock would be used for stock options and all employees would be treated as Amgen employees. The main purpose of the separate organization was to ensure that innovative, and perhaps even unpopular but novel, approaches could be investigated without overly restrictive control. The Boulder organization has continued to function to the present day and has expanded four or five–fold since the initial year.

The second decision for Amgen's new organization was to develop a subsidiary in San Francisco headed by Dr. William Rutter, a member of the Scientific Advisory Board. During the months of April and May, 1981, intensive negotiation led to definition of a subsidiary that would function as a primary part of the research and development of Amgen. A number of scientists and associates of Dr. Rutter appeared willing to leave the University of California, San Francisco to participate in a new biotechnology company. An option was obtained on laboratory space in South San Francisco and appropriate compensation and stock option details were worked out for six new employees to be housed in that space. However, a major concern of the group was whether they would be subordinate to the research staff (three scientists) in Thousand Oaks, California. It became clear that the Thousand Oaks staff was equally destabilized, fearing that headquarters might be moved to San Francisco. Dr. Rutter solved both of these problems by deciding to organize an entirely separate company and Chiron was born. This separation was accomplished with surprisingly little anguish as the missions for each of the research groups could be broadened and clarified.

These developments clearly established Thousand Oaks, California, as the primary site for Amgen's research and development.

Staffing

Recruiting became the highest priority item and virtually the only commitment of the first five or six employees. Each successful new hire facilitated recruiting and the president was able to concentrate his attention on hiring the Director of Research and Development.

Again, with the important assistance of the Scientific Advisory Board, candidates were suggested from across the country. Individual interviews were conducted with eight or nine candidates, all of whom had academic appointments or positions of a similar nature in research institutions. Because of this academic bias it seemed appropriate to consider one additional, officer level, research and development executive from industry. The first and only candidate considered for this position was Dr. Nowell Stebbing, Director of Biology at Genentech.

With no clear idea of how the organization structure would evolve, Amgen hired Dr. Daniel Vapnek, Professor of Genetics at the University at Georgia, as Director of Research and Development in the Fall of 1981. Shortly afterward Dr. Stebbing joined the Company as Vice President for Scientific Affairs. Both positions would report to the President, but it was understood that capital budgets, research plans and headcount requests for both the Boulder and Thousand Oaks laboratories would be reviewed by Dr. Stebbing.

Three additional key management positions were filled over a seven-month period. They included Dr. Phil Whitcome, Manager of Strategic Planning; Mr. Robert Weist, Vice President and General Counsel; and Mr. Gordon Binder, Vice President and Chief Financial Officer. These appointments would prove critical to Amgen's successful initial public offering one year later.

Amgen then set about hiring additional scientific staff including protein chemists, cell biologists, immunologists, virologists, pharmacologists, microbiologists, chemists, physical chemists, and fermentation specialists. All were necessary to support a core group of molecular biologists (genetic engineers). By the end of 1981, Amgen's staff numbered 42, expanding to 100 in 1982. Fortunately, it was not yet necessary to define Amgen's operating structure with a formal organization chart.

Turnover was virtually zero. The excitement of discovery, the comradery of young outstanding scientists and the prospects of rewards and recognition for making major contributions to society motivated the staff and welded the organization.

Initial Public Stock Offering (April, 1982 – June, 1983)

Schering-Plough purchases DNAX for $29 million/Johnson & Johnson makes investment and supports research with Enzo Biochem for $20 million/Genentech announces cloning and expression of tissue plasminogen activator/Financing opportunities for biotechnology dry up/Hybritech, Genex initial public offerings are disappointing/Dr. Robert Fildes leaves Biogen to join Cetus as CEO/Biogen initial public offering raises $53 million/Taniguchi announces cloning and expression of IL–2.

To compete with rapidly expanding budgets of the major biotechnology companies, Amgen doubled its pace of expenditures. By April 1982, management could foresee the need for major additional financing within one year. Amgen's first attempt at a five-year business plan was presented to the Board of Directors in the Spring of 1982. This plan was constructed in two weeks in cooperation with the controller who at that time was a part-time consultant to the company. The main goal of the plan was to show that Amgen could finance the programs necessary for success.

A preliminary analysis showed the Company would run out of money in September of 1983. There was absolutely no possibility of additional venture financing or a public stock offering in 1982 as articles in the business press were highlighting the "failure" of biotechnology to meet investor expectations. By the standards set in the electronics industry, a new company should be producing sales within 24 months, not forecasting five to seven years of investment. Any reasonable analysis would suggest the terrifying and inevitable prospect of either bankruptcy or slow attrition.

Amgen's five-year plan reassured both the Board of Directors and the Amgen staff. Corporate investors would be solicited and the expected funding levels "fortunately" matched the required cash needs over the next five years.

Three separate negotiating teams were organized to approach companies in the United States, Europe and Japan. Each team was prepared to present both business and scientific information to all prospective corporate investors in its geographic area. For the next nine months roughly 100 companies were contacted: the active list generally numbered 30–40, with 10–15 described as "likely" or "very likely" investors or corporate partners. As the candidate list dwindled with no corporate agreements concluded, periodic updates were continued to the Amgen organization and the Board of Directors in spite of the discouraging message. By December 1982, it was clear that no suitable corporate investor could be found without Amgen losing its autonomy by offering rights to all products, including future products not yet discovered.

In December of 1982 Amgen management decided to meet its financial needs by becoming a public company. In the climate of the period this proposal to the Board of Directors prompted one of them to say "An initial public offering is a pipe dream. What is your contingency plan?" Ninety days later, this same board would accept management's recommendation to become a public company.

During that crucial period between December 1982 and March 1983 a number of factors changed the climate for investment in biotechnology. Genentech's first limited research and development partnership for γ-interferon and human growth hormone was completed at the end of 1982. The final closing of this partnership was achieved only after some adjustments in the terms of the partnership, but the $55 million cash infusion was a positive sign for the future of biotechnology. Several companies, including Biogen, were moving toward initial public offerings and rumors suggested that these offerings would be "hot issues" and would be immediately oversold as Genentech's public offering had been in late 1980. Perhaps the most significant factor was the rebirth of excitement in the electronics industry with the successful launching of diverse new offerings including Televideo, Activision, Eagle Computer, Diasonics and many more. The parallel seemed clear. The electronics business had surpassed everyone's expectations and biotechnology was the opportunity to take an early position in the next wave of technological products.

In March of 1983 Amgen's Board of Directors gave approval for Amgen to proceed to retain three underwriters to complete an initial public stock offering.

A Public Company (1983–1986)

Genetics Institute completes private financing, becomes largest privately held biotechnology company/Genetics Institute and Genentech announce cloning and expression of factor VIII Amgen announces cloning and expression of erythropoietin/ Tumor necrosis factor cloned and expressed by Genentech/ Biogen initiates clinical studies on γ-interferon/Genentech initiates clinical studies of γ-interferon.

Amgen became a public company on June 17, 1983, with the sale of 2.3 million shares of stock at $18 per share. The market value of the Company on that date (market value equals total shares outstanding times price per share) approached $200 million. This was roughly seven times the sale price of DNAX just one year earlier and was 4½ times the stock price paid by Amgen's first round investors in January 1981. Most importantly, the 1982 business plan that had showed a requirement for $40 million of additional financing over the next five years moved from fantasy to reality in one day.

Amgen as a public company soon took its place among other major biotechnology companies with presentations at major investor meetings, publications in scientific journals and news releases highlighting the progress of science and business developments.

A word of explanation is needed about the motives behind such publicity and the problems of credibility that some early announcements have created. Critics often suggested that the financial doldrums facing biotechnology in 1982 and early 1983, and again in 1984 and 1985, were the direct result of irresponsible or premature announcements which were often labeled as "hype". Comparisons with the chemical and pharmaceutical industry suggested that biotechnology companies often made product announcements years before the product viability could be validated. The suggestion was made that a biotechnology company should not expose its early discoveries but wait until clinical data and the feasibility of scale-up or other commercial criteria were met. Accepting the desirability of this advice, it was still not practical for the biotechnology companies of the early 80s.

Not only did survival depend upon financing, and financing depend upon projections and promises, but once the company was public it had certain responsibilities to its shareholders. If 100 employees know of a new development and certain outside collaborators and academic or medical institutions are aware of the progress, there is a significant risk of premature disclosure. Security regulations require that a public company prevent selective disclosure of material events by prompt and effective publication.

In September 1982 Genentech disclosed plans for a limited R&D partnership long before there was any basis for confidence that it would be completed. Successful cloning and expression of a new protein was frequently disclosed by companies prior to the formal scientific publication that could be delayed by the scientific review process for six months or more. Initial promising clinical data, such as that obtained by Dr. Rosenberg on IL−2 or early data on TPA and erythropoietin, could not be suppressed until the formal publication of the results months later. The early release of such data occasionally had a significant impact on stock price but, in most cases, publication in a major, peer-reviewed journal prompted a more significant and sustained impact on investor confidence and stock price. For biotechnology companies all discoveries, contracts and regulatory actions can be regarded as material events requiring prompt disclosure. Since such actions would rarely represent a significant impact on the earnings of a large corporation as they are not regarded as material events and need not be announced.

And So to the Present

In 1988 Amgen's first product, erythropoietin, was approved in several countries in Europe and by June 1, 1989, the product had been approved in 15 countries including approval by the FDA on that date. Erythropoietin was cited by Scrip as one of the four breakthrough products approved in 1988. By January, 1990 over 80,000 patients were on the drug worldwide and over 150,000 transfusions had been avoided as a result of this therapy. That same month, the product was approved in Japan and was expected to be made available to patients by March.

A second product, NEUPOGEN, has been shown to be safe and efficacious for the treatment of certain white cell deficiencies. License applications to market the product in the United States were submitted by Amgen in December, 1989 and jointly in Europe by Amgen and its partner Hoffman-LaRoche in January, 1990. This product has been viewed as the first in a series of additional therapeutic breakthroughs from biotechnology that would be available in the early 90s.

GENERALIZED OPERATING ISSUES FOR INDEPENDENT BIOTECH COMPANIES

Missions and Strategies

For most startup biotechnology companies a mission and strategy statement was more important at financing times and investor presentations than as a guide to operations. Maintaining an integrated, consistent, detailed mission and strategy was not really compatible with the uncertainties and the rapid pace of discovery. However, there was generally a definable, broad mission which molded each company. Monoclonal antibody companies were clearly focused on operating at the leading edge of that science and technology. Hybritech, Centocor and several others adopted the stepwise goals of:

1. *in vitro* diagnostics,
2. *in vivo* diagnostics; and
3. therapeutics. Generally they expected that over five to ten years they would expand their technological and scientific base to include recombinant DNA. In contrast, Xoma adopted a mission which de-emphasized the first two steps and concentrated on therapies.

Conversely, companies such as Amgen that focused on recombinant DNA were highly motivated to operate at the frontiers of their own field. Monoclonal antibodies were developed as reagents to support the recombinant program but such research would not be funded at the levels necessary to lead to scientific and innovative discoveries. Genentech was the first to define its mission as being in human pharmaceuticals. This commitment focused their resources and permitted them to assume a dominant lead in becoming a fully integrated company.

For biotechnology companies, "strategy" is often a reconstruction of why a set of tactical moves were successful. Amgen's first public financing illustrates how such a strategy is used to attract investors. The investment bankers wanted to define a paragraph, or even a short phrase, that would differentiate Amgen from all other investment opportunities and most importantly from all other biotechnology companies. Should Amgen be "A BROAD BASED BIOTECHNOLOGY COMPANY"? This designation risked conveying a lack of business focus. Should Amgen be "THE BIOTECHNOLOGY INNOVATORS"? This seemed justified because of the novelty of discoveries such as bioproduction of indigo, active interferon analogs and chicken growth hormone. The underwriters rejected this statement because it reflected a technology driven rather than market driven strategy. A semi-serious suggestion was made that Amgen should be "A CHEAP GENENTECH"

For the first public offering the underwriters and management agreed that "AMGEN, THE SECOND GENERATION COMPANY" was the winning mission/strategy. Extraordinary gene synthesis technology had provided Amgen with unique capabilities which were being exploited. With new gene constructions, Amgen could rapidly produce multiple analogs of any new protein. These "second generation" products offered potential biological advantages over the natural molecule. Gene synthesis often afforded a rapid means to achieve production levels not commonly achieved with "first generation" technology. Amgen wanted to develop unique products and these methods afforded high yields of novel proteins. Indigo production also seemed to represent a new level of technology, combining complex biopathways from two organisms to develop novel biosynthetic methods.

In many ways Amgen had reconstructed a strategy after achieving successful results from opportunistic tactics. It is interesting to note that the company's direction, tempo and culture was totally unaffected when the "SECOND GENERATION" strategy was replaced three years later for second public stock offering. The new strategy became "AMGEN, A FULLY INTEGRATED HEALTH CARE COMPANY", which occasionally was rephrased as "FULLY INTEGRATED PHARMACEUTICAL COMPANY".

For a biotechnology company, strategy probably means primarily the establishment of a corporate culture or character. Virtually all biotechnology companies had a culture of informality that often led to vague or nonexistent organization charts with minimum constraints on individual freedom. Other trademarks of these small companies were frequent informal social events, broad-based stock options and stock ownership, free information flow at all levels and a clear commitment to the highest standards of scientific excellence. As demonstrated years before in Silicon Valley, small companies with such cultures could be highly results oriented, move dynamically to create and exploit opportunities, maintain high morale and produce extraordinary successes almost as a matter of course.

Very early, Amgen adopted some general business procedures and selectively integrated management practices borrowed from large companies. Accurate financial data and plans were biased toward actual results rather than forecasts. Periodic performance appraisals, formalized salary structures, approval levels for capital purchases, adherence to annual budgets and headcount plans, structured stock option distributions, product development teams, personnel training programs at all levels, and quarterly all-personnel, Scientific Advisory Board and Board of Directors meetings were all introduced into management practice. These activities were surveys were reviewed regularly with the Board of Directors and all were in place several years before the first organization chart was constructed.

This blend has worked well at Amgen, producing a continuing stream of new discoveries from a highly committed staff with essentially no turnover. Will biotechnology companies ever have executive dining rooms, designated parking spaces, executive offices in administration buildings, company cars or airplanes, and rigid company policies controlled by a six or seven-tiered hierarchy? Most importantly, will the time come when it is no longer appropriate to share virtually every scientific and financial dimension with every employee; to have stock options that do not extend to everyone in the company; or for any enthusiastic member of the staff not to hesitate to interrupt an executives' meeting with exciting new results?

The question often asked within biotechnology companies is "will success demand, or inevitably result in, some of the questionable benefits of being a big company?" Biotech executives are beginning to consider strategies for dealing with growth and success in a way that will maintain the spirit of these highly productive organizations.

Business Plans and Projections

The business plan is generally regarded as the one essential element of a successful financing. The requirements for such business plans were established and refined by the many electronics and computer ventures of the 1960s. It was accepted that such plans would include detailed market projections, costs and quantities of the items to be manufactured and a well-defined investment payout curve.

In the first years of the biotechnology industry, business plans, like missions and strategies, were rarely used as a detailed guide to business operations. Most biotechnology product targets had no counterparts in commerce. Yield and cost data, facilities requirements and potential market sizes were totally dependent on properties that could not be assessed for years. Extrapolation from conventional products and processes were often misleading. Predicted FDA approval times, product costs and market sizes for new genetically engineered pharmaceuticals were often unduly pessimistic. Projected market sizes for animal vaccines, approval time for animal growth promotants and public acceptance of the release of organisms were deceptively optimistic. As the information base for the industry expanded, and as embryonic companies developed, the planning process began to approach that of conventional businesses.

A new biotechnology enterprise forming in 1980 could propose project candidates with only vague projections of market size. As a result, the desire and credibility of the management, founders and scientific board were far more heavily weighted by investors than the data provided in business plans. The fever of excitement generated by new announcements often substituted for a definitive business plan or, for that matter, any business plan at all.

Amgen's Offering Memorandum in 1980 successfully raised nearly $19 million: it contained no expenditure data and only the crudest estimates of market size for a few of the proposed projects. To define the business outlook of the Company in presentations to the investors, each of the proposed projects was allocated a market value in 1986 based on discounting from projected sales figures for 1990. Other business plans at that time merely indicated the Scientific Advisory Board representation, the Board of Directors and the general fields of endeavor including how many Ph.Ds might be expected to be hired in the first year. Such generalities were made more intriguing by suggestions of proprietary new approaches, novel new vectors and expression systems, or the unique expertise of one of the scientific advisors or candidate employees. Plans of this nature were the vehicles for launching over 100 biotechnology companies from 1980 to 1982.

What did the business plans of biotechnology companies project in 1982? Most plans assured investors of major cash infusion from new corporate alliances. The Amgen plan showed that the Company would be sustained for five years by the influx of capital from corporate alliances. Two announcements in the spring of 1982 could be cited to justify this optimism. EnzoBiochem developed a corporate alliance with Johnson & Johnson with an equity investment and research and development funding totalling $20 million. DNAX, founded just two years earlier, was bought by Schering-Plough for approximately $30 million. Amgen had concentrated on internally funded programs and the early results of these programs seemed sure to attract comparable investments from large corporations.

History also justified such a plan. In the very early days of biotechnology, Cetus enjoyed major investments from oil companies who visualized prospects for enhanced oil recovery, novel biopathways to chemicals and even the biogeneration of energy to reduce dependency on fossil fuels. Lubrizol and Fluor made significant investment in Genentech for both technological and financial reasons. International Nickel had been a founding corporation of Biogen followed by Schering-Plough and Monsanto who made equity investments in attempts to gain product opportunities and a window on technology. Early product discoveries at Genentech were the basis of major contracts with Eli Lilly for insulin and with Hoffmann-LaRoche for α-interferon. Reportedly, Genentech also raised tens of millions of dollars selling certain product rights in Japan and Europe.

The pattern from the past was clear but few companies were able to develop profitable corporate partnerships during most of 1982. The logic and improved data of Amgen's 1982 plan, and probably those of other biotechnology companies at that time, did not assure the projected result. Why were the earlier, cruder plans more successful than the 1982 efforts? A frequently heard homily of venture capitalists succinctly explains this phenomenon: "The time to order peas is when they are passing the peas". The most lucid business plan cannot overcome investor apathy.

Corporate Alliances

It is apparent that corporate alliances have been pervasive in supporting biotechnology developments and have been essential to the levels of success achieved to date by all biotechnology companies. Yet such alliances frequently shifted the dominant share of a company's future profits to the partner. Those formed in the early days of a company contributed to credibility, cash flow, and financings and had a high probability of being viewed as beneficial over time. These early relationships were seen by investors as conferring validity to the technology and affording opportunities for synergy. In fact, the benefit to the small company was often exclusively money. The corporate partnerships formed after the company defined products with tangible results were very often marketing relationships. Such partnerships produced short and long term benefits to the small biotechnology company.

The most critical partnerships for any company are those formed between the two stages described above. For biotechnology companies in the early 1980s this was a particularly difficult period. The euphoria that biotechnology products were all in the billion dollar range had subsided. Interferons were viewed at worst as a mistake and at best as having some modest, future value. Animal products, that many had predicted would move rapidly through regulatory approval, were taking longer than human pharmaceutical products. Agricultural products based on genetically engineered microbes and even genetically engineered plants had encountered extensive delays before field tests could be authorized. Chemical applications of recombinant DNA were of less interest to chemical companies than patching up their short-term revenues and earnings and their deteriorating public image. In effect, the benefits of biotechnology were the least defensible just at the time when major new discoveries were virtually guaranteeing that biotechnology would live up to its early promise.

In the early 1980s, major corporations viewed biotechnology either as a curiosity or as a potential alternative technology that would be worth monitoring. They often approached biotechnology companies with a skepticism that was itself a powerful negotiating strategy. Pharmaceutical executives predicted FDA approvals were hundreds of millions of dollars and years away for any candidate genetically engineered pharmaceutical. Other business executives questioned the value of the new technology. The viability of new chemical processes by recombinant DNA might require tens of millions of dollars of plant investment with little assurance of success and questionable return on investment. Animal growth factors could take years to reach the market, would be highly competitive and might also require huge plant investments. No major diagnostic based on hybridization probes had been discovered and therapies based on monoclonal antibodies were more anecdotal than clinically significant.

The buoyant optimism of even the most enthusiastic biotechnology management team was not sufficient to change the perceptions of major corporations. If they were going to do deals, it would be on their terms. And the terms were painfully consistent. The biotechnology company must give up worldwide rights. The biotechnology company would be subjected to technology transfer as needed. If the biotechnology company retained manufacturing rights, it would soon find that it was obligated to build the plant to guarantee supply without any assurance of demand. Oftentimes, the partner's enthusiasm for the product would quickly wane as the product did not fully live up to expectations, or other priorities developed especially with the executive changes inevitable in large companies.

The rate of termination of agreements substantially exceeded the rate of their formation during the 1982 and early 1983 period. Genex, for example, had terminated all but two of numerous early agreements. One of those was the subject of litigation and the other was only a few months old. Genex used corporate alliances to gain credibility in its early years but ultimately encountered serious problems as they were unable to sustain them or operate successfully without them.

In later years, biotechnology executives were often seeking ways to recapture products at substantial premiums compared with what the company had received for them. In looking back, many biotechnology executives noted that the early corporate alliance deal that could *not* be made became one of the big success stories of their company.

Public and Legislative Policy Issues

Managements of biotechnology companies became increasingly aware in the early 1980s that public perceptions and government policies could seriously affect the growth and even the survival of a new biotech company. The organizations, goals and profiles of biotechnology companies had virtually no parallel in the history of American technology and business. Capturing, changing and exploiting the processes of life led to debates on new public policies to protect the public without disrupting the benefits and economic viability of a new industry. In addition to considering new legislation and regulation, existing policies and regulations required careful interpretation in light of the unusual nature of the inventions and perceived risks of the biotechnology industry.

Seven of these first biotechnology companies had foreseen these developments and in 1981 orchestrated the formation of the Industrial Biotechnology Association (IBA) to provide a united voice for informing the public and affecting government policy. This organization grew to over eighty large and small companies by 1986 and assumed an increasingly active role in public communication. Policy discussions with Congress and the Administration covered a broad variety of issues that assumed critical importance for virtually every biotechnology company. For executives of biotechnology companies, the agenda had shifted from internal developments and strategies to the public arena.

International Competitiveness

International competitiveness for the biotechnology industry has emerged as one of the major issues in the late 1980s. Large balance of trade shifts during that period highlighted the serious risk that although the United States might lead in science and innovation, companies in other countries were often more successful at commercialization. The Administration and Congress, concerned about preserving leadership in tomorrow's businesses, encouraged initiatives to support the development of biotechnology and to ensure that regulations and control were thoughtful and appropriate. These initiatives were often met by increasing concerns among environmentalists and other consumer advocates who feared that "international competitiveness" was a euphemism for businesses saying "get off my back".

Fortunately, several diverse biotechnology developments promised significant benefits to the environment. Developments underway included insect resistant genetically altered plants, potential reduced fertilizer demand for major crops, and microbial bioremediation of waste sites.

Responsible biotechnology companies began to address these viewpoints by channeling information to the public and to Congress concerning the benefits of biotechnology. In 1986, the Industrial Biotechnology Association, representing companies ranging from pure biotechnology companies to major corporations accepted this communications objective as a major part of its mission.

With increasing emphasis on the promotion of biotechnology rather than its control and regulation, and with increasing public support for biotechnology, the United States is likely to maintain a leadership role in this technology.

Intellectual Property Protection

The importance to this developing industry of intellectual property protection can hardly be exaggerated. In the U.S., for instance, the government invested several billion dollars over a ten year period to produce the scientific underpinnings and the trained researchers and teachers necessary for launching the biotechnology revolution. This information was published and made available throughout the world. The laboratories and institutions where the work was supported welcomed and trained scientists of all nationalities. The risk capital system funded more than $5 billion of technology in highly motivated, dynamic organizations operating at the leading edge of the science. The products and innovations of that investment have also been made public largely through the publication of patent applications throughout the world. If these investments are not given commensurate protection, any company anywhere can become fully competitive. Reverse engineering and targeting only the commercially successful products could duplicate the results of the U.S. biotechnology industry at greatly reduced investment.

The U.S. Patent Office and appropriate patent harmonization initiatives play a key role in the protection of intellectual property and the preservation of the leadership position established by U.S. companies. The motivation to conduct high risk research into the unkown and sustain prolonged development to commercialization requires that successful products will yield high returns. With reverse engineering even easier in genetic engineering than in other fields, intellectual property protection must be afforded to important discoveries. The keeping of notebooks and the prompt filing of patent applications was instituted in the early months of each biotechnology company. With high international interest in biotechnology, prompt, reliable, and consistent protection of intellectual property is needed throughout the world.

Regulation

Deliberate and appropriate relaxation of the regulation of genetic engineering research has proceeded consistently since 1976. Commercial release of microorganisms has raised new issues which are being addressed responsibly and cautiously by the Environmental Protection Agency. Stepwise procedures applied on a case-by-case basis should ensure that the benefits of biotechnology will not be unduly hampered by regulation. Virtually all biotechnology companies have active programs to provide information to the neighborhoods and communities where they are located so as to ensure an informed citizenry and avoid the fears that can be engendered by secrecy or evasion. Only with an informed public can the proper assessment of risk and benefit be developed and understood.

The therapeutic value of some of the newer products has already been recognized by the FDA. Streamlined regulations have accelerated the approval process for biotechnology products from an average time approaching ten years for conventional pharmaceuticals to a period of three of four years for the new pharmaceuticals based on recombinant DNA. This significant regulatory improvement has resulted in new genetically engineered pharmaceuticals requiring major plant investment and reaching marketable status before meaningful patent protection is obtained.

Reimbursal Policies

Faced with escalating health care costs around the world all governments have taken steps to control them. Those that exert major control over certain business segments are better positioned to provide incentives for biotechnology developments. Japan's medical reimbursement structure appears ideally suited to achieve this objective. In a sense this funding is affordable by the corresponding reductions in the funding of older products based on older technologies.

The U.S. in addressing accelerating health care costs has correctly identified technological advances as accounting for an increasing percentage of health care expenditures. Reimbursal of the newest products receives the most scrutiny. Congress has had a difficult time trying to assess whether these additional costs are fully justified by improvements in the quality fo health care and possibly even by reductions in other types of expenditures. In the absence of appropriate data to verify the situation on a case-by-case basis, congressional concerns have been focused on the newest products coming out of biotechnology. Although drugs represent only 7% of total health care costs, and biotechnology products represent a small percentage of these, the emerging products are a convenient but unfortunate focus for cost reduction initiatives.

A number of biotechnology products including tissue plasminogen activator, erythropoietin, human growth hormone and colony stimulating factors all represent levels of important therapeutic gain rarely matched by the conventional pharmaceuticals produced in the past five years.

The difficult issue facing reimbursement groups in the U.S. is how to provide affordable reimbursal without suppressing development of great therapeutic value. Congress is often hampered by public opinion which does not realistically link the profitability of today's products with the probability that such profits will stimulates additional investment and innovation. Biotechnology executives clearly feel that their companies will reinvest profits in the same type of effective research and development that has produced today's successes.

Export Controls

A number of years ago, regulations were passed to prohibit the export of pharmaceutical products from the U.S. until they had been approved by the FDA for sale inside the country. These restrictions originally came about because of fears that pharmaceutical products might be exported to less sophisticated societies and used inappropriately. Far more serious, such countries might be a channel for substandard U.S. products. The IBA recognized that any restrictions on exports must necessarily reduce the ability for U.S. companies to be competitive internationally. After intensive efforts to inform Congress of this problem by the IBA and other groups, Congress took a most significant step in 1986. They substantially reduced the export control of pharmaceuticals to be sold overseas prior to being licensed by the FDA in the U.S. Compromises produced appropriate safeguards to meet the earlier concerns. Another source of export regulations relates to security issues which until now have not affected the export of biotechnology products. Free trade, both import and export, in biotechnology as in other activities, is a most desirable goal.

Control of Technology Transfer to Foreign Companies

Concerns have been expressed publicly that biotech companies are giving away the U.S. leadership position in biotechnology by transferring technology to foreign companies. The earliest biotechnology developments appearing to have clear commercial potential were diagnostic products based on monoclonal antibodies, pharmaceuticals based on new human proteins that could be produced in bacterial cells, and viral antigens produced in yeast or bacterial cells for use in diagnostics and vaccines. During its early years, Genentech transferred human growth hormone technology to KABI in Sweden to receive royalties on sales outside the U.S. Hoffmann LaRoche was granted the worldwide license for α-interferon and developed a relationship with Takeda in Japan which eventually resulted in technology transfer to Japan. In all subsequent agreements, Genentech was apparently successful in negotiating satisfactory financial arrangements without the need to transfer technology.

Amgen, looking for financial support to accelerate the development of recombinant human erythropoietin, formed a relationship with Kirin Brewery Ltd. in Japan that involved complete technology transfer. The agreement assured, however, that Amgen would have exclusive rights to the patents and the technology in the U.S. This agreement was completed early in 1984. Companies with subsequent developments and those whose position was second or third on a particular product were generally required not only to complete a technology transfer but to provide U.S. rights to the foreign company. In general, these rights have been transferred to powerful large corporations since neither Europe nor Japan has small biotechnology companies similar to the U.S.

Was it visionary for these foreign companies to capture such relationships? Was it shortsighted for biotechnology companies in the U.S. to transport that technology to countries where delays or limitations in patent protection could lay the foundation for the type of competitive difficulties encountered in microwave ovens, television receivers, electronics and semiconductors? Was it shortsighted of major pharmaceutical companies in America to insist on total and exclusive U.S. rights which pre-empted the ability of small U.S. biotechnology companies from forming financial relationships in the U.S. that would have afforded them some domestic marketing opportunities?

One assessment of this situation is that technology transfer around the world is inevitable but, if that technology is properly protected, collaboration and transfer overseas need not result in the loss of a leadership position to the country pioneering the innovation.

THE FUTURE OF INDEPENDENT BIOTECHNOLOGY COMPANIES

The rapid attrition of independent biotechnology companies has been predicted yearly for the past four years. However, mergers, buyouts and bankruptcies have been minimal due to the periodic availability of capital through stock sales, limited R & D partnerships and corporate alliances. But what of the future? How many independent biotechnology companies will exist in 1990; in the year 2000; in the year 2010? Each year, from 1982 to 1988, one or two biotechnology companies elected to be acquired by larger companies (DNAX, Hybritech, Genetic Systems, Agrigenetics) and a very few went out of business completely. On February 2, 1990 Genentech and Hoffmann LaRoche agreed that Roche would acquire a 60% ownership of Genentech. At that time, Genentech was the largest independent biotechnology company and had developed four of the major biotechnological products that had been approved to date. The implicit evaluation of Genentech in the deal was in the vicinity of $3 to $4 billion, an unprecedented endorsement by an established drug company of biotech value previously recognized only by Wall Street. Many forecasts in 1988 call for significant consolidations and mergers with ultimately greatly reduced numbers of independent biotechnology companies. More and more such companies have instituted protection against hostile takeovers although these measures usually are limited to ensuring a deliberate decision and the involvement of the Board of Directors. Without question, hostile takeovers have been largely prevented by stock prices (market valuations) which fully reflect the intangible assets of the scientists, the management and the dynamics of small biotechnology companies. Hostile investors could scarcely expect to realize return on their investment in the absence of the assets "that go home each night in tennis shoes". In 1988, with products approaching the market for many companies and stock prices still suffering from the stock market collapse of October 1987, the managements and Boards of biotechnology companies are seriously addressing what will be the destinies of their companies.

For the pharmaceutical-based biotechnology companies the issue is likely to be "how big is a critical mass?" With the health care industry finding it appropriate to consolidate such major companies as A.H. Robins and Sterling Drug (and other consolidations rumored every day), is it realistic to believe that a biotechnology company can, without a merger, develop a critical mass? Agriculture-based biotechnology companies face the same issue. Delays in approval for the early release of organisms, and the extended regulatory process for animal health products, has postponed rapid commercialization. Molecular Genetics, one of the early leaders in biotechnology, has already elected not to pursue the commercialization of some of their animal products and may shift their focus significantly from the orientation of the past ten years. The monoclonal antibody based company, Centocor, has continued to grow its revenue base in diagnostics while achieving significant financing from three limited R&D partnerships. Whether their mission will be to become a leading competitor in diagnostics or to follow their strategy to become a pharmaceutical company they, too, can be faced with the issue of having adequate size to be competitive.

Consolidations of independent biotechnology companies have always appeared as an attractive alternative. Sales and marketing efforts would have an adequate portfolio from the combined products. It has often been speculated that ego problems among CEOs who have founded their own companies have probably inhibited such mergers. A more practical explanation could be that biotechnology companies are scarcely staffed with sufficient management depth to handle their ongoing science and business issues and can ill afford the time allocation for merger and acquisition discussion.

Whether biotechnology companies survive as independent entities, or are acquired by or merged with other companies, the extraordinary technology, products and character of these enterprises will leave their mark on worldwide health and economics of the 21st Century.

Chapter 5

Patents: Paradigms in Collision

Lorance L. Greenlee

The law is a creature of the society which makes it. Our labor laws are roughly adapted to real world labor/management disputes. Our commercial laws are generally adapted to the norms and expectations of actual business practices. In fact, one of the major strengths of the otherwise unwieldy system of Anglo-Saxon jurisprudence is its ability to adapt as society changes. Technology has driven much of the change of the late 20th century and some of the most rapidly evolving areas of law are those relating to issues involving science and technology: the patent law is no exception. This remarkable system has endured without radical change since the first statute of 1792, a tribute to the wisdom of its draftsmen and of the judicial system of precedents that has interpreted and adapted it since. Nevertheless, the patent system today is manifestly out of harmony with the science of such rapidly developing areas as biotechnology. This chapter will explore how the system became out of step, the effects on the biotechnology industry and what can be done to improve matters.

The patent law serves a public policy to stimulate innovation, "promote the progress of science and the useful arts."[1] It does so by providing a reward to inventors for making and fully disclosing their inventions. It is not the only system designed to stimulate scientific endeavor. An equally powerful academic system of grants and peer rewards has proved to be an even better generator of creative enterprise, particularly in basic science. The academic system does not directly stimulate commercial use of innovation while the patent system does. When scientific developments have commercial applications, their creators must turn to the patent system for protection against imitators.[2]

A major function of a patent is to define the scope of protection. This may seem fairly simple if the invention is a device or gadget, say a new kind of windshield wiper. The problem is exceedingly difficult if the invention is in the field of biotechnology, say a segment of DNA having promoter function.

The trouble begins when the inventor (or his attorney), mindful of competitors eager to benefit themselves by copying the new development, seeks to broaden his invention to include the basic features, however constructed, that approximate the same result. The inventor describes his invention in the patent claims which, like mining claims, stake out the territory of the invention and define the scope of the patent. The claims use terms that generalize and abstract the concrete features of the invention in an attempt to protect against imitators. The process of generalization and abstraction can extend quite broadly in the hands of a creative patent attorney, so far that they may embrace the basic idea or operating principle of the invention. However, the courts have put a limit to such practice by holding that patents are only granted for inventions and not for ideas or laws of nature on the ground that the latter should be available for all to use.[3] Nevertheless, patent claims can be broad enough to encompass embodiments of the invention that did not exist when the invention was made. Even outside the literal scope of claims, the courts will sometimes enforce a patent against an infringer whose device is deemed an equivalent of the claimed invention.[4]

Claims of broad scope are favored by inventors and patent owners while their competitors would prefer such claims to be narrow. The public interest lies somewhere in between, allowing sufficient scope to afford a meaningful commercial benefit for innovators, but avoiding claims that block competitors from related areas since the value of full disclosure promotes progress in science and the useful arts by providing ideas for others to build upon. The subject is byzantine in its complexity, having nuances within nuances which are a delight to patent practitioners.[5]

For the most part the patent system has worked well, serving its intended public purposes and providing substantial value for those with marketable inventions. In a mature industry, such as pharmaceuticals, a patent covering a new drug or antibiotic, broad enough to include some or most of its homologs, can be a gold mine. Several other factors have to be present, most notably that the patented compound has a unique and valuable function. Patents for the tranquilizer Valium and the herbicide Roundup[6] have been extremely valuable for their owners. Of course, a good market position does not begin and end with a patent but includes any and all forms of entry barriers to keep competitors out of the market, including federal regulations, trademarks, marketing and acquisition of customer confidence, and trade secrets for unpatented aspects of the product, all of which are used to reinforce an exclusive position.

For a new industry, such as biotechnology, the acquisition of patents can serve many purposes. The existence of pending applications can provide tangible evidence for potential investors of the research progress and intellectual assets of a company. A granted patent (or the existence of patents granted to others) may affect the early course of a company's development planning and future market strategies. Biotechnology companies are especially eager to obtain patents of broad scope to help carve out areas of exclusivity for their future development.

How have the biotechnology companies fared up to now as they have sought to obtain patent protection for a new and revolutionary technology? From the Olympian view-point of public policy, the development of the industry will be fostered if its products and processes are patentable and if the patents provide sufficient scope to provide a real market advantage for the patentee. If it is too easy for competitors to provide "me too" products, the incentive to innovate will evaporate; if whole areas of competitive activity are foreclosed by a few blocking patents, the benefit of a diversity of competing entities will be lost, both results being detrimental to the public.

Historically, the patent system has worked best for industries where developments are the result of empirical discovery, for example, in the agricultural chemistry the pharmaceutical industries. Developments in these areas often occur as a result of screening programs to search for chemical compounds with activity as insecticides, herbicides, antibiotics, tranquilizers, tumor inhibitors and so forth. Although discoveries in these areas often arise by accident, it is no accident that patents in the area are relatively easy to obtain and enforce.

The courts have always expressed a preference for inventions manifesting a "surprising" or "unexpected" result. Section 103 of the patent law[7] requires that an invention, to be patentable, must be "nonobvious." Here is a term with a highly specialized meaning, for decades the subject of court opinions and law review articles. Although introduced into the patent statute in 1952, the concept of nonobviousness and its criteria were first introduced in the 19th century case of *Hotchkiss v. Greenwood.*[8] To meet the requirement of Section 103, "the subject matter sought to be patented, taking into account the scope and content of the prior art must have been unobvious to one of ordinary skill in the art to which it pertains." Thus, there is a hypothetical person, a device also found in negligence law, against which the subject matter sought to be patented, and the "prior art" or body of available knowledge, are compared.

The person of ordinary skill in the art, sometimes called the "routineer", is charged with complete knowledge of all the prior art, and has the ability to apply known expedients to achieve a desired and *expected* result. A chemist who knows that application of a certain set of reactions will result in synthesis of a given compound, even if the compound was never before made, is a routineer. The new compound is unpatentable as being obvious to one of ordinary skill in the art. By a sort of symmetry of logic the converse, an unanticipated or surprising result, is deemed unobvious.

To a scientist such logic has a strange and uncomfortable feel to it. Asking the right question, designing the right experiment to test it and critical analysis of data are more highly valued by scientists than accidental discovery. To be sure, the patent law does not grant patents exclusively to accidental discoveries. Yet the cases abound with terms such as "unpredictable," "surprising," "unexpected," and "unforeseeable" when defining nonobvious subject matter. Alternative ways to demonstrate nonobviousness do exist. A combination of process steps or reactions that is "obvious" to try does not *prima facie* lead to a result.[9] Objective evidence, such as long felt need for the result achieved by the invention, an immediate commercial success for the invention, or widespread adoption of the invention, can be marshalled to support a contention that the invention must have been unobvious to routineers of the time.[10] Nevertheless, it remains a fact that unpredictable results lead to patents that are both easier to obtain and easier to sustain in subsequent litigation.

The emphasis on empiricism leads to difficulties both for biotechnologists in obtaining patents and for courts in interpreting their claims and articulating a rationale to develop a reasonable scope for claims. Molecular biology, in common with most 20th century science, is not an empirical science. It is structured on a framework of general operating principles, ranging from evolutionary principles to physical chemical principles. The thrust of academic science is to extend and further elucidate these principles or to amend them and develop new ones. The thrust of commercial technology development is to apply them toward a desired practical result. Progress, the development of new products or processes, is more often the result of incremental accretion of information following the application of known principles than the chance discovery of new phenomena. Truly new and unexpected phenomena are exceedingly rare. Thus, the process of innovation and the steps leading to new inventions in biotechnology are far removed from the 19th century empiricism embodied in the patent law.

Consider the hypothetical invention mentioned earlier: a promoter sequence having a useful property, say, of being induced by a certain compound. The promoter is useful in expressing a coding sequence under conditions that are particularly well suited for a fermentation process to make the expression product by inducing expression at a definite time. Such a development might well be valuable and worthy of patent protection. Assume the specific inducible properties of the promoter were learned in the course of biochemical studies on the timing and control of the gene it normally controls. It might be argued that properties of the promoter as deduced by the biochemical studies constitute a discovery of a new, "unobvious" phenomenon. Without further data a patent would be unlikely if it were based on properties of the promoter and the idea of using it to drive other genes. First of all, mere ideas and properties of nature are unpatentable. Secondly, a specific utility must be articulated[11] and, most importantly, the patent application must teach others how to make and use the invention,[12] which suggests that sequence data would be necessary. The latter requirement demands sufficient detail "as to enable any person skilled in the art to which it pertains ... to make and use the [invention]."[13] Presumably the same person of ordinary skill is the referent in both nonobviousness and enablement criteria.

If the biochemical data has not been published, the inventors could opt to wait until the promoter was cloned and sequenced, probably a matter of one to two years. If, however, the biochemical data is already published, the inventors must depend upon their cloning activities to prove the nonobviousness of their invention. A challenge to patentability could take the form of a general argument that the methods for locating, cloning and sequencing genes and their promoters are already known and understood. The inventors might counter that while one of several strategies might be expected to yield ultimate success, one cannot sit down beforehand and write a detailed protocol to be followed knowing that that exact protocol will yield the desired result. Alternatively, they might take a microscopic view that even though a cloned promoter could be the anticipated result, this particular nucleotide sequence could not have been anticipated as the sequence of the claimed promoter. This latter approach is dangerous since the invention may then be limited in scope to the exact sequence, making no allowance for silent base substitutions. Seeing such a claim, competitors will gleefully set about finding a sequence variant having the same promoter function and will have an imitative product on the market shortly thereafter, at minimal research cost. The inventors must then initiate litigation in the hope that a court will invoke the doctrine of equivalents to maintain their proprietary position.

Here we have a cross-section of the dilemmas faced by the biotechnologist, the courts and the Patent Office. A conservative course for the biotechnologist is not to disclose the original biochemical data until the promoter is cloned and sequenced, possibly even until it is known where base substitutions can be permitted. This course of action is undesirable from everyone's viewpoint: the public's legitimate interest in rapid publication and dissemination of information is injured; the inventors incur the risk that someone else will publish significant data blocking their patent,[14] and they also invest in base substitution data that is useless from a practical standpoint. Interpretations of the law that induce such behavior are clearly to be avoided. On the other hand, to rely on the subsequent activities of cloning and sequencing is to throw oneself open to tricky and inconclusive arguments about what the person of ordinary skill would know or would need to be taught. Since arguments couched in such terms are meaningless to most scientists, the stage is set for confusion and disarray.

That confusion and disarray have been the outcome of most decisions in the field of biotechnology is therefore not surprising. A brief review of some of the more interesting ones follows.

There was once a question whether microorganisms were even patentable subject matter. After a series of appeals, the Supreme Court finally held that a microorganism was not unpatentable merely because it was alive.[15] That the issue was litigated at all might be viewed as a last gasp for the vitalist fallacy. To be charitable, the question of patentability of a microorganism had seldom been presented to the Patent Office and the *Chakrabarty* case came along just as biotechnology was taking shape as a new industry in the late 70s. Later, when the Patent Office questioned whether plants were patentable subject matter, its own Board of Appeals ruled that the *Chakrabarty* holding applied to plants as well.[16]

Outside the U.S., patentability of plants has been difficult to resolve for various political and legal reasons. In *Pioneer Hi-Bred v. Canada*, an application claiming a new soybean variety made by conventional breeding was held unpatentable by the Federal Court of Appeal[17], and the decision was affirmed by the Supreme Court of Canada.[18] While the patent might have been denied on the basis of the facts of the case, the case has been viewed as a statement of Canadian policy.

In the European Patent Office (EPO), the opposite trend is discernable. The Technical Board of Appeal considered the meaning of "essentially biological" as excluding patentability of processes having that characteristic. While the exclusion had been enacted as a barrier to patents for plant breeding, there had been little guidance as to what it meant, apart from the standard requirements of novelty and inventive step. The Board considered the matter in the case of a plant breeding process that included laboratory cloning. Whether or not the process was "essentially biological" depended on evaluation of the qualitative and quantitative aspects of human intervention in modifying the natural process.[19] In a separate case, the EPO allowed claims to a vector for transforming plants and the resulting genetically engineered plants.[20] The EPO now seems disposed to grant patents for plants, particularly where genetic engineering or other significant technical intervention is evident.

The European and Canadian emphasis on technical intervention in natural processes seems almost bizarre considering that inventions are inevitably the application of laws of nature. For example, in *Pioneer*, the Supreme court said, "The intervention made by Hi-Bred does not in any way appear to alter the soybean reproductive process, *which occurs in accordance with the laws of nature*." (Emphasis added.) To add that seemingly superfluous and obvious statement suggests a factor of significance to the judge. That the laws of nature themselves are unpatentable is clear. However, both the

European and Canadian decisions imply a dichotomy between "natural" and "artificial" processes which is not encountered outside the biotechnology field.

In the U.S., patentability was extended for the first time anywhere to transgenic animals. The Patent Office acted on its own initiative, without seeking specific direction from an appeals tribunal.[21] The patent was controversial, but for reasons not based on patent law. Fears of economic dislocation in the farm economy have prompted legislative proposals to limit the scope of protection and to provide exemptions for farmers.

A puzzling case involving microorganisms was decided in *Ex parte Jackson*.[22] The applicant purported to have isolated a new species of microorganism, exemplified by three strains placed on deposit. The broadest claim included all strains of the species that synthesized a characteristic antibiotic. The Board of Appeals[23] held the claim too broad, stating that one of ordinary skill could not isolate the other strains without undue experimentation. The Board did not attempt to explain why this was so, relying on broad general statements about the unpredictability of microbial isolation and selection techniques. Such statements as "A unique aspect of using microorganisms as starting materials is that a sufficient description of how to obtain the microorganism from nature cannot be given" are scientifically debatable, although, in this instance they could have been justified. (The relevant facts were not discussed in the opinion.) The puzzling aspect of the case is that the Board's general statements cannot logically apply in all such cases since there are many instances where selections routinely yield the desired organism. But the Board's reliance on a generally worded rationale leaves one with an uncomfortable sense that it intended to establish a broad rule.

Subsequent decisions have tended to allay the worst fears inspired by *Jackson*.[24] Claims for a broader range of microorganisms or hybridomas than those deposited are allowed under the right set of circumstances. The disclosure must be detailed as to the source materials, perhaps even giving their location, and must describe in detail the screening or selection processes and means of identifying the desired organism. Some indication of the actual likelihood of finding the desired isolate must be given in order to permit an assessment of the amount of work, effort, or luck involved in repeating the isolation. Given the right set of circumstances, generic microorganism claims are patentable in the U.S.

Several monoclonal antibody cases have been decided at various levels of the judicial system. In *Ex parte Old*,[25] the Patent Office Board of Appeals held that a monoclonal antibody obtained by the conventional process using a known antigen was nevertheless patentably unobvious. The Board took the microscopic view that even though some sort of antibody might be expected "the routineer is unable to foresee what particular antibodies will be produced and which specific surface antigens will be recognized by them ... No 'expected' results can thus be said to be present." Inconsistent with its own rationale, the Board granted the broadest claims, not limited to the particular antibodies produced. Later, in *Ex parte Ehrlich*,[26] broad claims to monoclonal antibodies against human fibroblast interferon were rejected as obvious in view of the known method of Kohler and Milstein starting with the known antigen. According to this panel of the Board[27], "one would have approached this project with a reasonable expectation of success. . . ." There was no argument in the record of properties of specific monoclonals, so the microscopic view was not considered. In *Ex parte Goodall*,[28] the Board stated that a process for making a hybridoma and monoclonal antibody was not patentable even though the products were novel. One might conclude that the Board is evolving a position that where the general methodology is known, the substitution of reactants generating new products is unpatentable for obviousness, leaving open the possibility of taking the microscopic view of unobviousness for *particular* antibodies developed.

One's conclusion would be confounded by the Court of Appeals for the Federal Circuit's (CAFC's) decision in *Hybritech v. Monoclonal Antibodies*.[29] That case considered the validity of a patent claiming a sandwich assay method using monoclonal antibodies. Sandwich assays using polyclonal antibodies were known well before the patent's filing date. The CAFC overruled the trial court, which had held the patent invalid on the ground that the substitution of monoclonal for polyclonal antibodies in a known assay was obvious to those of ordinary skill in the art. The CAFC argued that the objective criteria such as "market impact" were sufficiently persuasive to outweigh considerations of the scientific obviousness of the invention. Getting a jump on the competition appears not only to be good business but good patent practice as well. The patent claimed monoclonal antibodies "having an affinity for the antigenic substance of at least about 10^8 liters/mole. ..." An issue of adequate description was raised because the patent did not disclose specifically how to screen for or measure antibodies having the requisite minimum affinity. The court concluded that those of ordinary skill would have been able to use known techniques of screening and affinity measurement to make the antibodies, measure their affinity and practice the claimed sandwich assay. Two different levels of skill seem to have been in mind, one for assessing obviousness and one for enablement. That monoclonals could substitute for polyclonals would be apparent to any immunologist at the time, since both are globulins. Yet, if the routineer were unable to accomplish this general result, how could the same routineer be expected to screen for antibodies having defined minimum affinities and measure these affinities? Further, the court used the "objective criteria" to outweigh considerations based on the level of skill in the art and the scope and content of prior art rather than as an alternative means of assessing the scientific or technical contribution. The policy of awarding patents for progress in science and the useful arts has been blurred.

The *Hybritech* decision is especially puzzling in the context of an earlier CAFC decision in *In re Durden*.[30] A claim to a method of making a compound was held obvious even though both starting material and product were unobvious, because the method steps were known using related compounds. In *Hybritech*, substituting a new reagent in an old process was held unobvious. The fate of *Durden* as precedent is clouded. Many processes in biotechnology such as immunization and gene expression in host cells are iterations of a basic process in which varying the inputs varies the result. Applied liberally, *Durden* has potential to cause mischief. Legislation has been proposed specifically to overrule *Durden*. Meanwhile, it remains to be seen whether its holding will be applied broadly or narrowly.

Cases involving hard-core genetic engineering have not yet been decided in the U.S.; however, two decisions in other countries are noteworthy. In the EPO a patent issued to Biogen was opposed and revoked in a decision of the Opposition Division.[31] The patent was based on the cloning of an α-interferon (IFNα) in Charles Weissmann's laboratory. The work was competitive with several other genetic engineering labs seeking to clone and express interferons. On the basis of cloning, sequence data and expression in *Escherichia coli*, the applicants claimed the gene and used various strategies to broaden the scope of protection to cover nucleotide sequence variants of the gene encoding IFN-α and amino acid sequence variants of the protein. The decision was based on complex and closely reasoned argumentation. The reasoning applied in various issues starkly illuminates the conflict between the paradigms of scientific and legal thought. For example, the Opposition Division ruled that claims to a cloned DNA segment coding for IFN-α were anticipated by a publicly available gene library. The Division constructed a plausible combination of known techniques (never carried out) that it supposed could have selected the desired clones from the gene bank. Here was empiricism reigning supreme: to be patentable, the invention must not only be unanticipated in fact but unanticipatable by hindsight. By such criteria, only accidents could be patented. The Division also resorted to a double standard of skill when dealing with inventive step compared with enablement. A reference (non-enabling due to non-availability of strains)[32] was nevertheless held to render the invention unpatentable for lack of inventive step. The EPO view, to the extent the Opposition Division was characteristic, seemed to tend toward an extreme microscopic view.[33]

While the Opposition Board's decision raised forebodings of an extreme microscopic view, the Appeals Board turned away from that course in a significant and far-reaching reversal. The Board stated that genes could be broadly claimed by a combination of structural and functional properties such as sequence, coding properties, and capability of hybridizing with a specified structure, provided these terms are clear in context. The Board specifically recognized that worthwhile protection would be lacking if such functionally defined features were not allowed. The novelty of the cloned gene over the prior known gene library was also recognized. Dirt does not anticipate an isolated bacterial strain. The decision in the *Biogen* appeal signified a trend in EPO decisions which make it the current world leader for quality, thoroughness and good sense in treating biotechnology issues.

The decision in *Genentech, Inc. v. Wellcome*[34] by the Patents Court of Great Britain revoked Genentech's patent covering tissue plasminogen activator (tPA). The opinion is probably the best reasoned one to date, dealing with the tricky issues of proper claims scope and the nature of an inventive contribution. Although the decision revoked broadly worded claims, e.g. to human tPA (however produced) essentially free of other proteins of human origin, the patentability of narrower claims was not ruled out. The justice broke new legal ground in departing from the 1977 Patents Act to incorporate a concept of the earlier Act that the claims should be supported by a description of commensurate breadth. On appeal, the patent revocation was affirmed, but on different grounds. The justices did not accept that lack of support could be incorporated into the new Act and struggled with various alternative grounds to reach the desired result. Consequently the decision contains a number of regrettable statements which are likely to confuse matters for future cases. For example, one justice stated the Genentech's work was mainly methodological diligence and, that lacking anything empirical, there was no inventive step. Another stated that since several other groups were able to achieve the same result at about the same time the result must be obvious. The view of the court seemed to elevate the status of discovery by accident or trial and error. The more extreme consequences of such a view will no doubt be avoided by future courts. Meanwhile, cautious patent draftsmen will take care to characterize their clients' good science as mere empiricism or blind luck.

In the U.S., the problem posed by research that follows a logical course has been treated by a general rule that something that may be "obvious to try" i.e., *via* a logical approach, is not necessarily unpatentably obvious. The distinction was brought into focus in *In re O'Farrell*.[35] O'Farrell and his coworkers were the first to obtain expression of a cloned gene in a transformed host cell by constructing a protein fusion. The coding region of the cloned gene was joined in reading frame phase to the coding region of an existing gene of the host. A convenient existing gene was the gene for β-galactosidase. Expression of β-galactosidase then resulted in synthesis of a fusion protein, beginning as β-galactosidase at the amino end, but continuing beyond the splice point with the amino acid sequence of the cloned gene. An experiment to test the feasibility of the idea proved successful. The "coding" sequence was not defined; however, the inventors were encouraged that some sort of large protein was detected on gels where the controls showed none. The result prompted the inventors to take the next step of using a defined and specifically identifiable coding sequence. Unfortunately, the results of the feasibility experiment were published and became citable as prior art against the patent application that was eventually filed. The Court of Appeals considered the feasibility result so encouraging that it considered the actual result, with a defined gene, unpatentably obvious. Here was where the line was crossed from "obvious to try" to "predictable". Not absolutely predictable, perhaps, but predictable to a confidence level of about 80–90%.

In summary, the small number of available decisions itself contributes to the confusion. Some cases present unusual facts and all are presenting technology that is unfamiliar to the decision makers. One can hope for more consistency as time goes on. Disturbing themes keep cropping up. The tendency to rely on blanket statements such as "that biotechnology is unpredictable" fails to take account of the many fundamental principles upon which the technology is based. There is a disturbing trends toward a double standard of skill: one for non-obviousness and one for enablement. The widespread adoption of a microscopic view will lead to patentability of almost anything novel but with narrow claims easily circumvented.

The process of bringing the paradigms of the law in line with modern scientific thought requires creative thought, debate and a keen sense of policy values. While the standard of ordinary skill is too useful to abandon, its misuse to favor empiricism over logical scientific progress must be avoided. The "objective criteria" can be useful, although they can mislead if courts fail to consider extraneous factors that may be responsible for the results. The courts should avoid decisions based on scientifically unsound premises. The approach of the EPO, thoughtful and mindful of the types of claims needed for worthwhile protection in biotechnology, seems to provide the best available reconciliation of the scientific and legal paradigms.

Meanwhile, biotechnologists will do what they can to protect proprietary developments. If the patent system fails to provide reasonable claim scope, or otherwise fails to provide the kind of protection that chemicals and pharmaceuticals enjoy, it simply will not be used. There will be a tendency to rely on trade secrets and economic entry barriers to the market, accelerating a trend toward greaters concentration of the industry into a smaller number of larger companies. It is to be hoped that future decisions will provide greater clarity than their predecessors.[36]

REFERENCES

1. U.S. Constitution, Article 1, Sec. 8, cl. 8.
2. A patent gives its owner the right to exclude others from making, using or selling the invention. 35 USC §154.
3. *O'Reilly v. Morse*, 56 U.S. (15 How.) 62 (1853).
4. *Graver Mfg. Co. v. Linde Co.*, 339 U.S. 605 (1950).
5. A patent for a chemical compound covers any use of the compound, but a patent for a method of making the compound does not, in the U.S., cover the compound made by a different method. A method of making a compound is infringed by sale of the compound in the U.S. over if the method is used outside the U.S. 35 USC § 271(g).
6. Valium, Trademark, Hoffman La-Roche Inc.; Roundup, Trademark, Monsanto Corp.
7. 35 USC §103.
8. 52 U.S. (11 How.) 248, 13 L.Ed. 683 (1851). Doorknob patent invalidated where "no other ingenuity or skill being necessary to construct the knob than that of an ordinary mechanic acquainted with the business, the patent is void . . .".
9. *In re Yates*, 663 F.2d 1054, 211 U.S.P.Q. 1149 (C.C.P.A. 1981); *Novo Industry A/S v. Travenol Laboratories*, 677 F.2d 1202, 215 U.S.P.Q. 412 (7th Cir. 1982).
10. The leading Supreme Court case on obviousness is *Graham v. John Deere*, 383 U.S.1, 15 L.Ed. 2d 545, 86 S.Ct. 684, 148 U.S.P.Q. 459 (1966).
11. 35 USC §101, *Brenner v. Manson*, 383 U.S. 519, 16 L.Ed. 2d 69, 86 S.Ct 1033, 148 U.S.P.Q. 689 (1966).
12. 35 USC §112.
13. *Ibid.*
14. In the U.S. an applicant can still obtain a patent if he can demonstrate he made the invention before the publication date, provided his patent filing date is less than one year after the publication date. However, outside the U.S. a publication by another is fatal if the publication date precedes applicant's filing date. Companies looking to international markets routinely file before publication.
15. *Diamond v. Chakrabarty*, 447 U.S. 303, 65 L.Ed. 2d 144, 100 S.Ct. 2204, 206 U.S.P.Q. 193 (1980).
16. *Ex parte Hibberd*, 227 U.S.P.Q. 443 (Pat. Off. Bd. App. 1985).
17. *Pioneer Hi-Bred v. Canada*, 3 F.C. 8 (Fed. Ct. App. 1987).
18. *Pioneer Hi-Bred v. Canada*, S.C.J. No 72 (Supr. Ct. of Canada 1989).
19. T 320/87 on European Patent Application No. 81.303287.7
20. European Patent Application No. 84302533.9
21. A patent was granted on a transgenic mouse carrying an oncogene to Leder, P., U.S. Patent No. 4,736,866.
22. *Ex parte Jackson*, 217 U.S.P.Q. 804 (Pat. Off. Bd. App. 1982).
23. Appeals from decisions of the Patent Examiner are heard by the Board of Appeals. Further appeal to the Court of Appeals for the Federal Circuit (CAFC) is possible. Beyond the CAFC, appeal can be taken to the Supreme Court but the latter seldom reviews patent cases.
24. *In re Wands* 5, 8 U.S.P.Q. 2d 1400 (Fed Cir. 1988); *Ex parte Hata*, 6 U.S.P.Q. 2d 1652 (PTO Bd. App. 1987).
25. *Ex parte Old*, 229 U.S.P.Q. 196 (Pat. Off. Bd. App. 1985).
26. *Ex parte Ehrlich*, 3 U.S.P.Q. 2d 1011 (Pat. Off. Bd. App. 1987).
27. Board of Appeal cases are usually heard by subsets, "panels" of the full Board. *Old* was decided by a five-member panel, *Ehrlich* by a three-member panel only one of whom also participated in the *Old* case.
28. *Ex parte Goodall*, 231 U.S.P.Q. 831 (Pat. Off. Bd. App. 1986).
29. *Hybritech v. Monoclonal Antibodies*, 802 F.2d 1367, 231 U.S.P.Q. 81 (C.A.F.C. 1986).
30. 226 U.S.P.Q. 359 (Fed. Cir. 1985).
31. European Patent No. 032 134, based on Application No. 81300050.2, in the name of Biogen N.V., opposed by Hoffman-La Roche and Co. *et al.* Decision of the Opposition Division.
32. Both in Europe and the U.S., microorganisms used to carry out or resulting from the processes disclosed in the application

must be placed in a public depository and be made available to the public to satisfy the enablement requirement unless it can be proven that the organisms are already available or can be reproducibly made following known or disclosed methods. Conversely, a publication cannot be enabling if the microorganisms it discloses are not publicly available.

33. European patent practice tends to favor narrow claims to the "core" of the invention. The courts may grant a broader range of equivalents than in the U.S. in specific instances arising during infringement litigation.
34. U.K. Patent No. 2,119,804 to Genentech, Inc. Petition to revoke filed by Wellcome Foundation Ltd., Patents Court, Chancery Division, High Court of Justice, July 7, 1987.
35. 7 U.S.P.Q. 2d 1673 (Fed. Cir. 1988).
36. The competent legal research and analysis of Barbara Gyure is gratefully acknowledged.

Chapter 6

Intellectual Property and Technical Know-How

D. Miles Gaythwaite

INTRODUCTION

There is a widespread belief that in biotechnology the most important form (if not the only form) of intellectual property is patents. Because of much of the publicity surrounding the protection of biotechnology, this view is understandable although there are other rights which require consideration by a person starting a new biotechnology business (or running an existing one).

This chapter is only intended as a general outline of how certain types of intellectual property work and how this applies to biotechnology. There is a general emphasis on the position in the United Kingdom and in Europe compared and contrasted with that in the United States. However each country has its own laws and, whilst the general overall picture is likely to be as described, there will be local differences. Accordingly anyone who intends to set up a new biotechnology venture needs advice from a practitioner in his own country, and preferably from one who has some experience in biotechnology. The present chapter is not intended to be used instead of such advice; its aim is rather to give the reader the necessary background for obtaining such advice.

INTELLECTUAL PROPERTY IN GENERAL

In order to understand the relevant intellectual property rights it is necessary to look at these rights in a little detail; each tend to have their own rules both as to how they arise and how they work.

Broadly speaking intellectual property consists of: -

(a) Design rights protecting aesthetic creations
(b) Trade marks
(c) Copyright
(d) Confidential information
(e) Patents
(f) Other special rights, including Plant Breeders' Rights

Design Rights

Of these rights the first are unlikely to be particularly relevant to biotechnology and will not be further discussed here.

Trade Marks

Trade marks tend to be important in all businesses, particularly those which sell goods or services to the general public. They are specially important in pharmaceuticals, where a trade mark can become so well established that once the patent has expired the patent holder continues to enjoy an enormous marketing advantage over third parties who will be selling the generic material. Although trade marks can be very valuable, indeed often more valuable than patents, there are no special considerations relating to biotechnology and again they will not be considered further.

Copyright

The next type of right, copyright, in the author's view, has little application to biotechnology. However as there are occasional suggestions to the contrary a few words on this topic are needed.

Copyright is intended to protect aesthetic creations, for example drama, music, painting, sculpture, works of literature and other products of the fine arts.

The boundaries of what may enjoy copyright protection become a trifle fuzzy in relation to drawings and literature because it would be inappropriate for some arbitrary aesthetic test to be applied to see whether the work in question was suitably "artistic": what is one man's masterpiece is another man's rubbish. In some countries (notably the United Kingdom) this approach had got totally out of hand and drawings of any sort, even purely functional blueprints, enjoyed copyright.*

Thus copyright protection is also afforded to computer

* This has now been reined back somewhat by the new Copyright, Designs and Patents Act 1988 and a new "unregistered design right" substituted.

software, provided that the work is embodied in a tangible form, even although it would be hard to say that sequences of 0s and 1s had any artistic or literary merit. It is not a long step from this to conclude that copyright should similarly be available for sequences of bases or amino acids. There may be something in this approach if the molecule in question has been consciously designed by someone on paper and then tailor-made. However in relation to naturally-occurring materials this is unlikely to work as a copyright work must be original. Moreover it needs an author and the person who elucidates the structure is not that author. Hence someone who has just determined some particular natural gene sequence (human or other) is in no position to think of "copyrighting" such a sequence. He is not the author of the work nor is the work original in the copyright sense.

If copyright were to exist, say, in a particular sequence of amino acids which have been designed by a person, the protection is only against copying. This means that access either to the sequence (or possibly to proteins embodying the sequence) would have to be proved; it would not be enough to show, for example, that the particular molecule being made by the competition had the same activity as the one which had been designed by the copyright owner. This is in contrast to the protection obtainable from patents where it is not necessary to show copying.

Furthermore, as will be discussed below, useful patent protection is more likely to be obtainable in respect of man-designed molecules rather than naturally-occurring products. Hence copyright does not fill in the gap left by patents and probably has little attraction except possibly as a cheaper method of protection. This is because copyright, unlike most of the other rights to be discussed below does not depend on formal registration and examination but simply comes into being when the copyright work is created; hence the official fees for filing and examination are not involved in copyright*.

The remaining three types of intellectual property rights are relevant and important in biotechnology.

Confidential Information

Confidential information is a general title covering, for example, trade secrets, other know-how and proprietary information. However one should remember that this is an area which goes rather wider than the purely technical and can also cover commercial information including pricing and marketing policies, names and attitudes of customers, etc.

There is no question of the registration of trade secrets and one simply takes the best precautions to prevent them from leaking out and becoming public knowledge. The precise way in which that can be done varies from country to country but in essence one has to ensure that employees and other persons who know the secrets are obliged to keep them confidential; this often involves confidentiality agreements between employers and employees. If the secrets are very valuable protecting them may require an active policing policy towards ex-employees or consultants and this can involve litigation.

Keeping something as a trade secret can, in some instances, be a good policy and it tends to be cheaper than obtaining patents, at least in the short term. Nevertheless, trade secrets often leak out over time and it would be rare to be able to keep one for, say, more than 10 years.

Additionally, keeping a trade secret does not prevent third parties from doing their own research work and from discovering the secret for themselves and, indeed, from publishing it too.

In a company in which trade secrets are important attention should be paid to pinpointing them accurately and preferably documenting them as such if this is possible. It is vital to regulate the number of persons who have access to the secrets, or at least to all of them, and ensure that such persons are aware of their obligations to keep them confidential.

Some types of material are inherently unsuitable for retention as trade secrets. For example, the deviser of an improved mouse trap has no possibility of keeping this secret for as soon as he sells one of the traps the purchaser will be able to see how it is constructed!. On the other hand a process for the annealing of a glass may well be capable of being retained as a trade secret as analysis is not likely to show how the annealing was carried out.

In biotechnology there are a number of areas where there is considerable potential for keeping trade secrets, e.g. in techniques of manipulation which often are developed in-house. Cell lines, soil isolates and other relatively inaccessible materials are also good candidates. A good example would be a hybridoma because the marketing of a monoclonal antibody derived from the hybridoma gives the purchaser no assistance in obtaining the hybridoma. Indeed there is already an established tradition of large pharmaceutical companies keeping as trade secrets the fermentation technologies which they use to make antibiotics and other valuable products.

Patents

Patents, on the other hand, are a way of encouraging inventors not to keep their discoveries secret. The basic idea is that in a detailed specification which is published the inventor discloses his invention and how it can be carried out. For a limited period (now usually 20 years) the inventor has a monopoly but after this period the invention may be freely used by the public.

A patent is a negative right which permits the inventor to stop third parties from using the invention. A patent is not a positive right in that it does not give to the inventor the right to do something which he would otherwise not be able to do. Thus when an inventor has made an invention there is no

* In the U.S.A. registration of copyright does exist.

obligation on him to patent it in order to be able to exploit it; and partly because of this it sometimes may be better to keep the invention as a trade secret.

The above statements are definitions of what patents are but they do not really tell you what practical use patents have and why they are worth obtaining.

The Popular Myth about Patents

Those who have had little to do with patents often believe that a patent is obtainable on demand by the inventor and that it acts as a kind of all-powerful magic talisman permitting the inventor to have the market for his invention all to himself and to stop all competition dead in their tracks. These beliefs are quite wrong, but are worth looking at more closely.

The Reality — Acquisition and Protection

As will be explained below, patents are not available at the whim of the inventor; rather they involve a lot of time and expense in negotiation with the issuing Patent Office and even after a patent has been obtained there is no guarantee that it is valid.

Furthermore the existence of the patent does not immediately protect the inventor either from regulatory or other constraints or from the possibility that the operation of his invention may infringe* another patent belonging to a third party. Nevertheless, the existence of a patent may have the effect of deterring rivals from infringement, it may cause the rival to find an alternative non-infringing process or product (this is called "engineering round" the patent) or it may prompt the rival to approach the patentee to ask for a licence.

But all these possibilities are no more than possibilities; if a rival decides to use the invention and to go ahead and infringe then the only way of actually enforcing the rights given by the patent are by commencing a law suit against him. Thus, policing of the patent is the responsibility of the patentee and the Patent Office does not do this for him. Patent litigation in any country tends to be lengthy and expensive and something best avoided if at all possible.

Despite this patents can be very valuable indeed, particularly if the patentee is prepared to invest the time and money necessary to police them. A striking example of the power of patents was seen a few years ago when the Eastman Kodak Company withdrew their instant developing cameras worldwide as a result of a successful patent action in Boston brought by Polaroid Corporation. However that was an unusually spectacular case and it worth noting that this result only came about after large scale litigation by Polaroid in policing their patents.

* In patent jargon the term "infringe" is used for the operation of the patented invention by a third party without a licence.

These have been mostly negative aspects of using patents but there is also the positive question of how the invention which the patent protects may be put into practice; this is touched on in greater detail in the section on Licensing.

Obtaining a Patent

Patents can be granted for most industrially applicable processes and devices. However here are certain exclusions which are particularly relevant in biotechnology and these are discussed below.

In order to obtain a patent it is necessary first to file an application, normally with the Patent Office of the country where the inventor works. Patent Offices are usually run by the governments of the countries in question.

This raises the question of who is entitled to apply for a patent. The short answer is the Inventor, or the Inventors if there have been more than one. However, many inventions are made by inventors as part of their normal employment; whilst their names will appear on the patent specifications as the inventors they will not usually own the patent. The way in which it is decided who does own the invention is a matter for the various national laws and therefore no simple generally applicable rules can be given.

There is a tendency to distinguish between two extreme cases which can be illustrated as follows: in the first, in which a research scientist who is employed by a pharmaceutical company to invent does indeed make an invention, that invention will normally belong to the company. At the other end of the scale is another employee of that same company who is employed as a car park attendant. He makes an invention in relation to his hobby, say model railway engines; in that case the invention will belong to the inventor himself. The difficult cases come when the employee has used the company's facilities in making the invention, or where the invention does have application to the company's business or where it is not clear whether the employee is employed to make the invention which he did make.

In some countries the ownership of employees' inventions will be dealt with by the employment contract although the extent to which the employer may seek to take all inventions from all employees may be proscribed by local national law.

In the United States virtually all patent applications have to be made in the name of the inventor(s) even though under their contracts of employment they belong to the employer. Customarily an assignment is executed which is then registered at the U.S. Patent Office so that the employer will ultimately be registered as the patentee, not the inventor(s)*.

* Because patents and patent applications are intangible, they cannot be sold or transferred like cars or houses. Instead an "assignment" is used, which is a document whereby one party transfers his rights in a patent to another. An assignment is to be contrasted with a licence which does not involve the transfer of the property.

In most other countries if the employer owns the invention then he will be the applicant, with the inventor being mentioned in his capacity of inventor.

Prior Art and Examination

Grant of a patent is not automatic and in practice an inventor is not entitled to a patent as of right. Thus to talk of "registering a patent" is usually a hideous oversimplification of what is involved. Normally no patent will be granted until an Examiner (who is a Patent Office employee) has made a search to find out what prior proposals in the same general area have been published. This material is normally referred to as the "prior art". After the Examiner has the search results he then considers how wide the patent should be, having regard to the inventor's contribution to the knowledge in the art. Naturally it is hoped that the Examiner has some experience in the technology which he is examining to be able to make a reasonably informed assessment. Frequently the precise form of the patent is the subject of much argument with the Examiner.**

The Format of a Patent Specification — Claims

A patent specification usually contains an abstract (which is of considerable help to searchers, but is not authoritative) followed by the detailed description of the invention (which may include drawings) and then finally some numbered statements called the claims**. *The claims are all-important in patent law as it is they which define the boundaries of the monopoly which the applicant is claiming. The drafting of the claims is a matter of considerable skill as what the draftsman hopes to capture in the claims is the essence of what the inventor has invented.

Thereafter, once the patent has been granted, any third party can look at the claims and, in theory at least, understand what is the "forbidden territory" of this patent. In theory, because often the draftsman will have used relatively vague terms (e.g. "means" for doing things) which may or may not cover a proposed activity depending upon how wide an ambit one gives to the language in the claims.

Whilst the draftsman is usually trying to widen the scope of the claims the Examiner on the other hand will normally try to ensure that the scope of the claims is commensurate with what he thinks the inventor has invented, and that usually means narrowing the claims.

After discussion with the Examiner some claims can often be agreed and the patent is granted or issued. However patentees are often dismayed to discover that even after all the discussion with the Examiner the patent which they have got (even one with a pretty official seal) is not guaranteed to be valid. Instead one can regard the Patent Office examination as being in the nature of a "coarse sieve" and validity (or invalidity) is ultimately only determinable by the Courts.

If the Examiner is intransigent then there is usually some right of appeal from his decisions to a type of Appeal Board and/or ultimately to the Courts. Whilst the Courts are usually the ultimate arbiters of whether a patent is valid or not there is frequently provision made for "Oppositions" before the Patent Office in which third parties may seek the revocation or amendment of the patent on the grounds that it ought not to have been granted, or not in its then existing form.

The process of obtaining a granted patent takes time, anything from 2 to 5 years being normal. However in some countries, for example South Africa, grant can be obtained in a year whereas in Japan, where examination is not carried out at once, 5 years would be optimistic.

An Invalid Patent?

The inventor is sometimes mystified as to how his patent can be invalid. This can arise in a number of ways. Firstly, no search is perfect and there may be other more relevant items of prior art which the Examiner did not find or know about. Furthermore the Examiner is only normally looking at published material and he has no knowledge of commercial operations which could amount to a prior use of the invention.

Nowadays it is common for Patent Offices to require the applicant to advise them of all the prior art cited* against a particular case world-wide; this has the effect of improving the overall width of the search although it has no effect on cases of prior use.

Width of Claim

Very often invalidity arises from the claims being too wide. The draftsman of the patent claims will not have slavishly

** There are many countries where patent applications are not examined, or are only given the most cursory inspection for formal defects. These are not, in general, economically important countries and it is very difficult to know whether any patent obtained is worth the paper it is printed on. Usually this is done by referring to the prior art which has been uncovered in other examining countries.

*** It is normally not necessary nowadays to submit to the Patent Office a sample or model of the invention, although in the 18th and 19th centuries that was quite common and incidentally served as a good way of weeding out patents for perpetual motion machines. The Smithsonian Museum in Washington has a fascinating collection of models submitted to the U.S. Patent Office. In one sense the current requirement that rare or inaccessible microorganisms be deposited (discussed below) goes against this trend.

* The terminology used for documents which form part of the prior art is that they are "cited" against the application and are often referred to as "citations".

followed the precise embodiments worked out by the inventor. If he had done so (and inventors who are foolish enough to do their own patent drafting often tend to do this) then the claims would probably have a better chance of being valid; but they would be unlikely to catch other competitors who, by making non-essential variations, can operate outwith the scope of the claim whilst still benefitting from the invention. On the other hand, if a very astute patent draftsman has made the claims very wide, and very general in their terms, he will undoubtedly have made it much easier to catch would-be infringers. At the same time he runs a greater risk of covering something which is old. Generally speaking the inventor of a completely new technology will be able to obtain very wide claims but as a technology develops the allowable scope of claims tends to become narrower and narrower. Thus, for example, if Köhler and Milstein had applied for patents before publishing their first article in *Nature* in 1975 (or at the least before the second in 1977) they could probably have secured very wide claims to the hybridoma technique and its application to the production of monoclonal antibodies. As it was those papers were prior art against all the relevant patent applications.

How Claims are Interpreted

It is worth noting that whilst the general rule in the United Kingdom and the U.S. is that the words of the claims have to be regarded as the absolute boundaries of what is protected, the courts in both countries are occasionally prepared to bend the rules a little and to hold that something which is not literally within the scope of the claims is nevertheless an infringement. This can be done by the doctrine of equivalents (where the infringer has used something equivalent to an essential feature in the claim to obtain the same result but to avoid literal infringement) or what was known as the doctrine of "pith and marrow"*. In Germany, however, the way in which claims are interpreted is much less tied to the precise wording of the claim and more on what the judge thinks the inventor has invented. This is helpful to patentees but makes it correspondingly more difficult for third parties to be sure if they have avoided infringement. There is a parallel here to the situation over the allowable breadth of claim as the courts are generally more sympathetic to the patentee of a really significant invention whereas with a minor improvement patent in an already well-tilled field the judge is much less likely to assist the patentee.

Novelty

A cardinal rule of patents is that whatever is claimed must be new and must also not be obvious. Hence if a claim, by being drafted too wide, covers something which is old then the claim is bad. The extent to which such invalidity taints the whole patent and the possibilities of amendment of the claims to save what is good, varies greatly from country to country. There usually is a superficial presumption of validity of a patent but it is no more than that, just as a criminal can be found to be guilty even although the law may initially presume him to be innocent.

Priority Dates

The question then arises as to the date at which "oldness" is to be judged. Normally this will be the date of application for the patent. Hence the inventor can file his patent application and the very next day announce with impunity the invention in the scientific press or by sale of an actual embodiment of the invention. This is because when the Examiner comes to do his search the "cut off date" will be the day before publication, i.e. the day of filing. In patents this date, at which novelty is judged, is known as the "priority date". If the inventor had, unwisely, announced his invention the day before filing then the priority date is too late and he will have invalidated his own patent.

Grace Periods

This invalidity often comes as a considerable shock, and an upleasant one, to inventors who feel instinctively (but wrongly) that disclosures which they themselves make ought not to count against their own later patent application.

Part of the confusion may stem from the situation in the U.S. where an inventor's own disclosure will not invalidate his U.S. patent provided it is made no earlier than 1 year before the date of filing in the U.S. This provision however (which is often known as the "grace period") only operates in the U.S.A. which means that the inventor will still not be able to obtain valid patents in most countries outside the United States.

Most other countries operate a rather harsher rule (known as "absolute novelty") which will count any disclosure or use anywhere before the priority date. This includes oral disclosures which are normally discounted in the U.S.

Despite the intellectual tidiness of the absolute novelty system there is a considerable swell of opinion which might ultimately lead to the introduction of grace periods in other countries similar to those in the U.S. However such changes are not likely to be made in the immediate future.

Paris Convention — Convention Priority — Early Publication

Going back to the concept of absolute novelty one may wonder how it is possible to obtain patents in countries

* Now renamed "purposive construction".

other than one's own because of this rather strict rule. This is where the Paris Convention plays a part. The convention, now over 100 years old, and to which most countries adhere permits an inventor to claim as the priority date the date of first filing in his home country (rather than the date of actual filing in the foreign country) provided that the filing in the foreign country has been made within 1 year of the first filing.

This means that the inventor first files his invention in his home country (often he *must* file in his home country, so that sensitive inventions e.g. those relating to defence may be made the subject of special treatment). Then the inventor has the period of a little less than 1 year to do further work on the invention and to decide whether he wants to proceed further and, if so, in which countries. Provided the foreign applications are on file within the period of 1 year of the original filing then any disclosures after the first filing will not count because the original filing date will be the priority date. However if the 1 year limit is missed he will often not be able to obtain a valid patent.

In many countries the patent application as filed will be published 18 months from the first filing (even though it is not known at that stage that any patent will be granted; this is called "early publication") which considerably restricts the possibilities of deciding to withdraw an application and do substantial further work before proceeding with a new patent application.

Most Patent Offices print the specification when the patent is granted and copies can then be bought by the general public. However some which publish early print a first version at that stage and then a second version (which may vary very little from the first, except possibly in the claims) on grant. In other countries the official file of the patent application is merely laid open to public inspection and the general public can then obtain photocopies of the specification. Although the printed specification is convenient it is the official file version which is authentic.

The official file also contains the Examiner's objections and the applicant's various responses and these, of course, are not printed. In the United States the whole of the official file, including the specification, search reports, and correspondence is referred to as the "file wrapper".

First to File — v — First to Invent

As indicated above, the priority date is normally the date of filing in a Patent Office. However in the U.S., when there is a dispute* between applicants as to who made the invention first, an inventor can obtain a date earlier than the date of filing if he can show by evidence that the invention was conceived and first reduced to practice at a date earlier than the filing date. This in principle permits the earliest inventor to benefit rather than the first inventor to file.

Each system has its advantages: the use of official filing dates is simple and allows a reader to know the earliest possible priority date for an invention just by reading the date off the printed specification. The U.S. system in principle may be fairer in that it does not penalise the earlier inventor who was not first to file; however it does involve producing documentary evidence to substantiate the earlier date. This is one of the reasons why U.S. corporations usually require their research workers to write up their work daily in special bound books and have these results or ideas witnessed. Furthermore it can mean that in establishing rights to the priority date one is involved in something akin to litigation in the production of documents and evidence.

At the present time the U.S. and Canada are the only significant countries to use the "first to invent" test. This means that the opportunities for reciprocity between countries is restricted. Nevertheless the way in which this has been implemented in the U.S. unfairly discriminates against foreign applicants as only happenings within the U.S. can be used to established an earlier date (which is done by a process alarmingly termed "swearing back"). This may be of enormous value to a U.S. corporation which can do this whereas, say, the earlier Japanese inventor is not permitted to establish a date earlier than his filing date in Japan. The implementation in Canada is much fairer as it takes a worldwide view.

Concurrent Conflicting Applications

We have already noted that the novelty of the invention is judged as at the priority date. That is relatively straightforward in the case of publications, whether patent specifications or articles, which have been published before the priority date. However, unless they are subject to early publication (at the 18 months stage) applications are not published until the patent is granted. This is particularly true for the U.S. where an application can remain pending and unpublished for 2 or 3 years before being published on issue*. Hence problems can arise with patent applications which are made at about the same time.

Assume that two corporations have been working on a project and have made essentially the same invention at the same time (which surprisingly frequently happens). The first files an application and the second, say, 1 month later. The second applicant knows nothing about the first application but, in effect, will be trying to monopolise the same ground. One can understand that it is undesirable to have two patents claiming essentially the same invention.

* Such squabbles between rival inventors in the U.S. are dealt with in proceedings of byzantine complexity called "interferences".

* The 2 to 3 year period can be much longer if there are appeals from the Examiner or if "continuation" applications are filed. These are explained below.

Prior Claiming – v – Whole Contents

Two rather different approaches have been used in different countries to try to solve this problem. The first, which can be called the "prior claiming approach", and which is now rather out of fashion, forbids granting two monopolies for the same piece of territory. This sounds fine in principle but is very difficult to apply in practice as it depends on one being able to map out effectively the territory which each proposed claim would in fact cover. Indeed, because of the different approaches or terminologies used by the two applicants it may not be easy to see whether there is a potential overlap between the two different claims and, if there is, what is its extent. Thus in two cases claiming similar compositions one may set the boundaries of what is within the claims by a viscosity measurement and the other by a carboxyl number. What the relationship is between viscosity and carboxyl number may well not be known to either party.

The other, called "the whole contents approach", treats the first application as being published at its filing date as against the second application: and the novelty of the second application is judged against this deemed publication. In some implementations of the whole contents approach the rigour of this rather artificial doctrine is muted slightly by saying that the earlier application shall only be used for the purposes of anticipation and not of obviousness. This means in practice that if the two inventions are precisely the same (in effect the first scoring a "bulls eye") then the second application will be refused. However if the inventions are not precisely the same, and the second one has a different twist, then something may be salvaged from the wreck of the second application although painful surgery may well be necessary to avoid the disclosure of the first application.

Novelty Includes Both Anticipation and Obviousness

So far no attempt has been made to analyse in detail what is meant by "novelty"; however, from the reference above it will be appreciated that this covers both "anticipation" and "obviousness".

Perhaps it will be best to illustrate this difference. Assume that the invention relates to a particular organic compound, a quaternary ammonium derivative of a certain base, prepared using trimethylamine. If the prior art discloses exactly that compound then the claim will lack novelty because it will be said to have been "anticipated". This may be so even if the earlier document has not spelled out in great detail the structure of this compound. (This is often a problem with literature dating from the 19th and the early years of the 20th centuries). If the nearest disclosure in the prior art is the same base quaternised with, say triethanolamine rather than trimethylamine, then the prior art has not scored a direct hit. In this sense the later claim to the trimethyl salt is not anticipated. However it may still fail as being obvious and this is a question of evidence from the relevant experts. Thus things look bad if the trimethyl salt is preparable in exactly the same way as the triethanolyl one, and has much the same properties. On the other hand if it can be shown that the trimethyl salt is an oddity produced in a rather unusual way which cannot be used for the triethanolyl salt then perhaps something can be claimed. The prior art position could have been even worse if the disclosure was of the triethyl salt. In some countries the replacement of an ethyl group by a methyl group would be regarded as inherently obvious (mere "Beilsteining") in the absence of convincing evidence to the contrary. In others the applicant might get the benefit of the doubt.

It will be understood that anticipation is something concrete which can be tested objectively, assuming the necessary background information. Obviousness is a subjective matter and therefore an area of much greater dispute. Furthermore the question of obviousness is one which must be tested by the fictional "skilled man in the art" *and sometimes it can be quite difficult to decide what skills, or combination of skills, this mythical being must have. Indeed in some relatively sophisticated technologies the notional skilled man is a composite of a team of relevant workers!

Before leaving the question of anticipation and obviousness it is worth remarking that some practitioners use the term "novelty" as not covering obviousness but as being synonymous with anticipation. Provided one is aware of these different usages they should not cause too much confusion.

Selection Inventions

There is also sometimes scope for arguing that what the inventor has invented is a "selection invention" in which he has made a particular selection from already known materials but for some particular and non-obvious utility. Thus there is no invention in merely screening a large number of compounds which are known for their surface-active properties to find out which are the best; however, finding out that a number of them have properties for accelerating the onset and resolution of *rigor mortis* in poultry could well be inventive. On the other hand many selection inventions seem to reside in selection of compositions which are alleged to have unexpectedly good properties not shared by the whole class*.

* It is to be doubted whether assertions in the patent specification that the alleged invention was "unexpected" (a word overused by patent draftsmen) really helps, except to show that the inventor was very dim.

* This sort of selection invention is endemic in insecticides and herbicides. Indeed they tend to bring the concept of "synergy" into ill repute.

Process Claims – v – Composition Claims

To return to the example given above, the type of claims which the inventor might get could be:

> "A method for dressing poultry carcasses which comprises applying to the carcass an effective amount of ... [here specify compounds]."

The nearest he could get to claiming the materials themselves would be;

> "A composition for treating poultry carcasses comprising at least one [here specify compounds] together with [specify at least one carrier, solvent or other constituent]."

This type of claim is risky if the carriers, etc., are not in themselves rather unusual.

The reason why one type of claim may be more advantageous than another often lies in the question of who would infringe. If the first type of claim were obtained then on the face of it only the poultry processor will infringe; the chemical company which supplies the composition may not infringe. On the other hand if the second type of claim is obtained then the patentee could more easily stop their competitors from selling the compositions for use by the poultry processors. In this sort of situation typically it is regarded as bad news to sue an actual or potential customer in relation to his use of the competitor's materials; a straight fight as between rival suppliers is preferable. (In some countries the supply of the composition may still be held to infringe the first type of claim. However if the compositions have other non-infringing uses then this would normally not work.)

There is another significant difference between these types of claim. It is much easier to prove that a claim to a compound, composition or article has been infringed. Thus if one can buy a can of a composition which is being sold by the competition for treating carcasses the proof of infringement comes down to a matter of analysis. On the other hand if the claim is to the method or process it is not at all certain that analysis of a dressed chicken will give enough information to establish proof of infringement. Indeed such proof may be available only if one can have inspection of the process and the ease of obtaining that sort of information varies greatly from country to country.

How to Read a Claim

The basic rule is that one should read the claim and simply give it the meaning which the wording bears. You may not find this very easy, particularly as by tradition a claim, no matter how long, is always in one sentence. In some cases you may be able to grasp what the claim is about but quite often you will have to refer to the specification even to begin to be able to understand what the claim seems to be saying. Such reference to the specification is generally permissible in trying to work out what the claim covers. If after reading the specification you still do not understand the claim then professional help is needed although it may well be the case that the claims simply are obscure and will be difficult to interpret even by a specialist.

Characterised in that ...

When you look at claims you will often find that there is a sort of preamble which sets the scene for the invention and then the word "characterised" followed by other features. This form of claim, originally of German origin, is intended so that all the features up to the "characterised" are being acknowledged by the applicant as being old and that everything which follows is what the inventor has invented. It is within this latter area that the court in Germany has flexibility to decide how wide the claim shall be. For some inventions this is very helpful but in other cases it is not so useful. Despite this, there is a modern tendency to require all claims to be in this form, whether appropriate or not.

Consisting and Comprising

Words which are frequently found in claims are "consisting" and "comprising". If you have a claim to a composition *consisting* of A, B and C, then this means that you must have A, B and C in order to infringe but that the addition of D (not mentioned in the claim) will probably not infringe. On the other hand if the claim is to a composition *comprising* A, B and C, then this means that you still must have A, B and C in order to infringe but that the addition of D will not have any effect of the question of infringement. This is likely to be so even if the ABCD combination is much better than the original. (As one judge put it "adding ingenuity to robbery will not avoid infringement".)

If there is wording in the claim to the effect that the composition comprises A, B and C but contains no E then on the face of it a composition comprising E as well will not infringe. However if, for example, the claim said that the composition comprised A, B and C but not more than 2% of E; it would be very dangerous to assume that a composition containing 2.1% of E would be held to be non-infringing.

Sometimes, mainly in chemical cases, you will see in U.S. claims wording like "an alkyl group selected from the group consisting of methyl, ethyl and propyl" which simply means "a methyl, ethyl or propyl group". This baroque wording arises from an allergy on the part of the U.S. Patent Office (USPTO) to the word "or" in claims!

Cascading Claims

You may also have noticed that patent drafstmen rarely content themselves with one claim but usually have a whole series, many of which refer back to earlier claims. Generally claim 1 will be found to be the widest and the additional limiting features introduced in the dependent claims (that is the ones which refer back to claim 1) make these narrower*.

One reason for doing this (particularly in the U.S.) is that if a limitation is found only in a dependent claim then that suggests that such a limitation should not be implied into the claim from which it depends. Thus, these additional narrower features reflect back on the scope of the main claim to try to keep that broader.

Another reason for having these dependent claims is tied up with the problems of drafting too widely and then finding that claim 1 is too broad. In some jurisdictions it is advantageous to have these narrower claims present so that if claim 1 has to be abandoned the patentee may nevertheless be able to rely on a narrower and valid claim. This is also related to the fact that once a patent has been granted the form of the specification, and particularly the form of the claims, can be regarded as being set in concrete. Although this varies from country to country it is generally difficult to start modifying the form of your claims after the patent has been granted; if it can be done it is often easier to delete than to rewrite, because in any case the claims cannot be widened only narrowed. Thus if the patentee can show that one of the dependent claims is valid and has been infringed then this is helpful even although the court may delete the earlier claims which are too broad.

Claim Types: *Per Se* Claims

As was seen above in relation to selection inventions the forms which claims can take are very numerous. They can include, for example, articles ("An improved mousetrap including ....") and processes ("A method for making an improved washing powder which comprises adding ...").

In the chemical field it is worth looking at the types of claims which can be obtained and what they protect. In many countries, but not in all, it is customary to be able to obtain what are known as "*per se*" for new compounds.

To take an example: the first person to have made aspirin would have been able to claim aspirin as such, either giving its full chemical name or merely characterising it as best as the inventor was then able. Once the patentee had obtained such a *per se* claim to aspirin he could then stop any third party from making selling or using aspirin, no matter how it was made, even though the original inventor has described only one method of preparation. Later inventors who devised improved ways of making aspirin were limited to claims to the process which they had invented (drafted as broadly as prudent). However these subsequent inventors had the additional problem that they would not be able to make use of their process (which might be completely different from and much better than the one described by the original inventor) without the licence of the original inventor because of his *per se* claim to aspirin. This is a further illustration of the point that the patent grants no positive rights to use. It is also worth noting that the above discussion on preventing two patent claims from covering the same ground does not mean that the operation of a particular process may not infringe more than one valid patent.

Product-by-Process Claims

One very often finds after method claims a claim that reads something like this:

> An acylation product of a hydroxy-substituted benzoic acid produced by a method as claimed in any of claims 1 to 14.

This is known as a "product by process" claim and only covers the product in question when produced by the claimed route; it is thus much more limited than a *per se* claim to the product itself.

Enablement

In order that the patent specification will actually be usable by third parties after the patent has expired, the applicant has to put sufficient detail into the specification to allow another skilled worker in the technology in question to be able to repeat the invention. The precise burden of this obligation varies somewhat from country to country and it is particularly stringent in the U.S. where the importance of a very full and detailed description can hardly be overrated. (This can frequently be seen in practice in U.S. originating mechanical specifications where one has very detailed drawings showing every last irrelevant nut and bolt lovingly numbered and described. Specifications originating elsewhere for the same invention might only have general sketches and those originating in Germany may content themselves with block diagrams or no drawings at all!)

In the U.S. there is also the "best mode" requirement; it means that the inventor is bound to disclose in his specification the best method which he had devised for carrying out his invention. This is a very reasonable requirement as it is not equitable for an inventor to obtain a monopoly by giving to the public only second-best methods of using the invention. It also used to be the law in the U.K. until 1978 but nowadays under the new law this is no longer a requirement (which is curious to say the least).

* However sometimes in U.S. patents you will find that the broadest claim is to be found, irritatingly, around claim 32. So beware!

Patents Valid only for One Country

Patents are distinctly national in character. A patent granted in one country has effect only in that country and if the patentee wants protection in a number of countries then, in general, a separate application has to be made in each country in which protection is desired; in addition the applications usually have to be filed within the 1 year priority period provided for in the Paris Convention. This means that a considerable investment in terms of filing and translation fees has to be made at a very early stage of an invention, before the prior art has been properly explored and perhaps before the actual commercial potential of the invention has been worked out.

International Patents

Sometimes one hears someone saying that they have obtained an "International Patent" but this is not something which yet exists. What it usually means is either that the patentee has obtained patents in many countries or alternatively that the speaker does not know what he is talking about. However, there have been some moves to try to simplify the job of obtaining protection in a number of countries.

Patent Applications — the Various Steps

One can break down the process of obtaining a patent into three separate phases:

1. filing of the application with the Patent Office,
2. search of the prior art and
3. substantive examination of the application in the light of the search results.

Until recently one had to go through all three stages in each country where protection was desired.

Certainly in the case of the search there is no obvious reason why a separate search needs to be done in each country; provided an adequately comprehensive search is done, once should be enough. Accordingly there is now a system called the Patent Cooperation Treaty (PCT) to which a number of countries adhere. Under the PCT the applicant files one application designating the various countries within the PCT where protection is desired. A single search is carried out by an internationally recognised searching organisation; thereafter the application papers together with the search report are forwarded to the various designated national Patent Offices. After that each national application proceeds separately and the various examiners carry out the substantive examination. The PCT system clearly has the merit of reducing the number of searches that need to be done, and paid for. The drawbacks are that not all countries belong to the PCT and the rules which govern the Treaty are appallingly complex and technical.

A more ambitious scheme has been set up by the European Patent Convention (EPC) and this is has now been running for nearly 10 years. The idea of the EPC is that a single supranational Patent Office, the European Patent Office (EPO) in Munich, deals with all three phases in the grant of a patent. Thus to use this system a single application is filed designating the various European countries which belong to the EPC in which protection is wanted. This is searched by the EPO and a single examiner deals with the examination. If successful, once the examiner in Munich decides to grant a patent the effect is that a separate national patent is issued in each of the designated countries. This is obviously simpler and avoids much duplication of work; additionally it avoids the expense of translation costs until the applicant knows that a patent is to be obtained. However, one is dealing with only one examiner who could be completely unreasonable and (subject to appeal) simply refuse to grant any patent at all. That might have a much more serious effect than a single awkward national examiner. So far, however, the system seems to have worked quite well, although the EPO do take rather academic views on obviousness.

There is provision for an even more sophisticated system for patents in Europe called the "Community Patent Convention". Under this system instead of a bundle of national patents one single patent will be granted covering all the designated states. This has not yet come into force and the idea appears to be becalmed at the present time.

Patent Litigation

If a third party is infringing in order to stop them it is necessary to commence a legal action. Usually it will be possible to stop infringement only after the case has got to trial (which can take some time) and the infringer can continue infringing in the meantime. But if the action is successful at trial, damages are likely to be awarded to cover the infringement.

In order to succeed the patentee not only has to prove that the infringer is in fact infringing but may also have to ward off a defence that the patent is invalid. Thus, the patentee has usually two hurdles to surmount, infringement and invalidity. Evidence is needed not only of what the infringer is making or doing but also expert evidence regarding the making of the invention, the significance of the invention and assessments of the prior art and related matters.

All this means that patent litigation tends to be some of the longest and most complicated of any and one can be quite sure that this will be true in biotechnology patents. Patent litigation tends to be very expensive, not only in terms of legal costs, but also (and often more importantly) in terms of the time which the inventors(s) and senior officials of the company need to devote to the prosecution. Hardly surprisingly, such actions are only for large companies with deep pockets. In Europe it is possible to obtain insurance to cover the costs of instituting or defending patent actions. Such cover does not extend to the U.S.; furthermore, as with all insurance policies, the small print needs careful thought.

The way in which such actions run varies greatly between the common law countries (those derived from English Law e.g. the U.S., England, Australia, etc) and civil law countries (which are those where Roman Law has been more formative e.g. France and Germany) because of the underlying differences in the legal systems.

It is always necessary to prove that the infringer is in fact infringing and that usually means showing that what he is selling or doing falls within the scope of the claims of your patent. If you have claims to a material *per se* this may simply be a question of buying a sample and then having the necessary analysis performed. However, if you only have process claims then you may have a difficulty as you need to show what the infringer is doing inside his factory and then to show that that amounts to infringement. It may be necessary to consider employing private detectives to try to find out more about what the infringer is doing. If you can show that there is no other way of making the infringing material, that may be helpful but it is in this sort of area that the differences between legal systems are particularly important.

In civil law countries patent actions tend to be begun by a "dawn raid", known as a "saisi". In this case you go to court first, with no warning being given to the infringer, and obtain an order that requires the infringer to permit you to inspect his process and to take samples of the allegedly infringing product. Hence, at least in theory, the infringer has had no warning when you arrive with a court order and demand to see the infringer's process and to take samples. Whether that is likely to give enough basis for an action will have to be considered case by case.

In common law countries it is normally possible to get "discovery", so that you can find out exactly what the infringer is doing. Discovery means that each side is obliged to give to the other facts and documents which are relevant to the dispute. The idea behind discovery is that it would be inequitable for parties to try to argue their cases in ways which are in effect artificial. To take an example: if the infringer, before the publication of the patent, had been trying vainly to get certain prior proposals to work, it would be inequitable to allow him to allege that the prior proposals anticipated the invention without also being required to disclose that he personally had had no success on that score.

Discovery may simply require the production of relevant documents, but in the U.S. in particular, it goes much wider and permits inquisitions on oath of the relevant personnel (called "depositions"), the answering of specified questions on oath and, even, a formal inspection of the infringer's factory. What may be theoretically justifiable on the grounds of equity can rapidly assume the form of a weapon of attrition which is all the more oppressive to the personal inventor or small company. Not infrequently the cost and inconvenience of discovery will be the factor which may force a settlement of the dispute even although neither party may very much like the result.

Another difference between common and civil law countries is that much is done in writing in civil law countries whereas at the trial of the action in a common law country it is usually necessary for all the witnesses to be present and to give their evidence in person; sworn statements will not do.

In civil law countries the tribunal not infrequently refers the technical aspects of the dispute to an independent expert, who prepares a report for the court and which tends to be unchallengeable in the later proceedings. In principle this can work well, provided the expert is in fact expert, is in fact independent and knows how to do his job. However the parties may end up with an expert foisted upon them that neither side particularly wants and both may be rather fearful of what wild conclusions he will dream up.

As discovery is practically unknown in civil law countries, and because the trial of the action does not require all the witnesses to appear in person, such proceedings tend to be cheaper and quicker than those in common law countries. The results achieved may sometimes be more rough and ready but that is the down-side of the speed and cheapness.

In most countries the questions of whether the patent is valid or invalid, and whether or not it is infringed, is tried by the same court. But this is not universally the case and, for example, in Germany different courts try these various questions.

The Position in the U.S.

Patent Law in the U.S. is substantially different from that in most other countries. The following is a very brief indication of some of the major differences in the U.S. compared with Europe:

1. Grace periods
2. Patent applications are not published at the 18 month stage but remain confidential until they are either issued, refused or withdrawn.
3. In Europe the date of the patent (from which the 20 years monopoly begins) is the date of filing and the examination period is taken out of the 20 years. In the U.S. the monopoly period which is 17 years begins only when the patent issues. (It is usually necessary to pay renewal fees to keep the patent in force for the full term.)
4. Normally in Europe it is not possible to add any further description to a patent application after the initial 1 year priority period. But in the U.S. this can be done relatively easily by filing what is known as a "Continuation in Part Application" (CIP) in which the material which was present in the original application takes as its priority date its own date of filing. The

more recent material benefits only from its actual date of filing. (However, once the basic application has been published after the 1 year grace period there can be complications with CIPs.) One may also encounter Continuations (not in part) which contain no new material but are, in effect, a new attempt to frame claims which the Examiner might accept.

5. Finally, there is a completely different philosophy prevalent in how patent applications are prosecuted in the USPTO and other Patent Offices. Outside the U.S. the applicant or his representative does his best to get the case allowed with the claims he desires; however once the patent is granted, the way in which the prosecution was carried out is substantially irrelevant (except when the patentee does a complete *volte face* over representations which were made to the Patent Office during prosecution). In the U.S., the applicant must be scrupulously careful in his dealings with the Examiner not to mislead him. This "duty of candor" is taken rather seriously and failure to discharge it can constitute what is known as a "fraud on the Patent Office". That can have the effect of making a patent which otherwise appears perfectly good to be unenforceable. It can only be supposed that it is the "ant-like persistence" (as it was once delightfully described by a U.S. federal judge) of those who prosecute patent applications before the USPTO which has caused this very spinsterish attitude to dealings with the U.S. Patent Office.

APPLICATION TO BIOTECHNOLOGY

Having tried to sketch the outlines of intellectual property we can now see how this applies to biotechnology. The important species of property to be considered are Confidential Information (to which no special considerations appear to apply) and patents. However, for reasons which will become clearer later, it is convenient first to deal with a rather special topic.

Plant Breeders' Rights

Plant Breeders' Rights allow a limited monopoly in newly developed plant varieties. In Europe the rights can be acquired by someone who has produced a new stable variety. Like patents, formal application for protection has to be made and generally a sample has to be deposited, but this sample is not made publicly available. Unlike normal patents, there is no obligation to describe how the new variety was produced. The protection obtained is more limited than that obtained with a patent as it allows the holder only to prevent the sale of propagating material without a licence. It does not prevent the buyer from doing further work and coming up with a new derived variety, which would not be covered by the registration, nor does it prevent a farmer from using left-over seed for re-planting.

In the U.S. the position over plant breeders' rights is rather complicated as there are, in effect, three separate systems in operation. The first, that of Plant Patents, was introduced in the 1930s by relaxing the disclosure requirements normally needed for ordinary patents ("utility patents") and extends only to asexually reproduced plants. The second system which deals with sexually reproduced plants was introduced in 1970 by the Plant Variety Protection Act (PVPA) but both systems specifically exclude tubers, hybrids, bacteria and fungi. These botanical entities, if they are to be protected at all, have to be covered by utility patent and that, of course, is possible only if an adequate description of the invention can be given. Perhaps as science develops it will become easier to give a full and precise description of a plant variety and in future the breeder might well prefer to apply for a utility patent which, although more difficult to obtain, confers more protection.

However there have been moves made by the USPTO to try to enforce a policy that if a particular plant variety is protectable under the Plant Patent provisions or the Plant Varieties Protection Act then it will not grant a utility patent. The position in this area remains unclear.

As in Europe, the protection afforded is much more limited than that obtained with a utility patent. Thus a plant patent, which may contain only one claim, permits the patentee to prevent third parties from asexually reproducing the specific variety covered and from selling or using such a plant. However this does not extend to parts of the plant, for example to the flowers or fruit. The rights conferred by a PVPA certificate are similar but neither can prevent third parties from experimenting with the plant for research or breeding purposes. Furthermore a farmer may save seed from the protected species and re-use such seed himself or even sell it without infringing.

Application of Patent Law to Biotechnology

Returning now to the question of the application of patent law to biotechnology there are 3 areas of particular interest:

A. Adequacy of description and deposit requirements

B. Limits on patentable subject matter

C. Extent of protection available

Adequacy of description and deposit requirements

A complication in the protection of microbiological inventions is that in more traditional sciences a description of the invention would normally be sufficient to allow anyone who wanted to to experiment in this area, or for the general public to make use of the invention after the patent has expired. It can be very difficult adequately to describe microorganisms but even if it can be done, mere description will not thereby permit the reader to obtain a sample.

As this ran so counter to the principles of the patent system certain special provisions now exist which require the deposit of samples of new or inaccessible microorganisms in recognised culture collections. There is now an international convention (The Budapest Convention) which sets up a system of internationally recognised depositories where inventors can deposit their samples and a single such deposit can be referred to in patent applications filed in all the countries which adhere to this convention for the purposes of ensuring that the description is sufficient. There are also various housekeeping provisions dealing with what happens if the original sample ceases to be viable and how this is to be replaced.

Although it is very helpful for the inventor to be able to supplement the description of his microorganisms by referring to a deposited sample, most inventors are profoundly unhappy about having to make available samples of their cultures, which they often regard as being "their inventions". They see this as being undesirable even if the collection agrees not to supply third parties with samples of their culture; however the rules relating to obtaining patents actually go much wider and require public access to the culture from the collection.

The question of access is currently one of considerable international debate. Probably the fairest rules are those applicable in the U.S. and Japan where the applicant is not required to authorise release by the culture collection until the grant of the patent; by that stage he knows that he will be getting a patent.

Under the European Patent Convention the rules are stricter and the culture must be made available as from the date 18 months after first filing (when the application is early published). It is possible for the applicant to restrict the availability of such cultures to certain nominated experts who act as a sample of the "general public" for the purpose of destroying novelty and being able to carry out experimentation for third parties, but they hold the cultures on conditions which preclude release to other competing companies. Once the patent application is granted such restrictions must be withdrawn. This is so undesirable that a number of companies now prefer to forgo patent protection in these countries or will try to argue that deposit in their particular case is not necessary. Fortunately this tends to be slightly easier in Europe than in the U.S. because in Europe there is no requirement that the inventor describes in his specification the "best mode" and if one can draft the claims to a wider generic class of substances one may be able to avoid deposit of the best ones.

Limits on patentable subject matter

In all patent systems there are certain "no go" areas designated in which, despite the inventor having satisfied all the other criteria for patentability, no patent will be granted. These normally are matters of public policy and, in general, arise out of three separate areas of concern:

1. Avoiding overlap with other intellectual property rights,
2. The product of nature problem, and
3. The living thing problem

In the first category the main area of potential overlap, so far as biotechnology is concerned, is Plant Breeders' Rights. The ways that this overlap has been handled in the U.S. and Europe are radically different and neither can be regarded as entirely satisfactory.

The second category is "the product of nature" exclusion which is intended to ensure that the public should be free to use things which are found in nature. Thus it would stop an inventor who has discovered for the first time a rare mineral at the top of a remote mountain from trying to monopolise the mineral which after all has thoughtfully been provided by Nature, albeit not in the most convenient of habitats.

The third category concerns moral questions of whether it should be permitted to patent living entities as well as ralated questions about to the extent to which medical and surgical discoveries ought to be patentable.

Unfortunately no coherent attempt has been made to frame exclusions which are referable to these different concerns; instead they have become rather muddled, with predictable results. Hence, whilst it is useful to keep these underlying concerns in mind one really has to look at the actual situation. We will begin with the European position. The relevant provisions of the European Patent Convention (Articles 52 and 53) are set out below. Most European Patent Laws have now been harmonised, although not perfectly, and take as their model the 1963 Strasbourg Convention from which these provisions come. Hence they can be considered as applying in most European countries.

Article 52

Patentable Inventions

(1) European patents shall be granted for any inventions which are susceptible of industrial application, which are new and which involve an inventive step.

(2) The following in particular shall not be regarded as inventions within the meaning of paragraph 1:
(a) discoveries, scientific theories and mathematical methods:
(b) aesthetic creations:
(c) schemes, rules and methods for performing mental acts, playing games or doing business, and programs for computers;
(d) presentations of information.

(3) [Omitted]

(4) Methods for treatment of the human or animal body by surgery or therapy and diagnostic methods practiced on the human or animal body shall not be regarded as inventions which are susceptible of industrial application within the meaning of paragraph 1. This provision shall not apply to products, in particular substances or compositions, for use in any of these methods.

Article 53

Exceptions to Patentability

European patents shall not be granted in respect of: —

(a) inventions the publication or exploitation of which would be contrary to "ordre publique" or morality, provided that the exploitation shall not be deemed to be so contrary merely because it is prohibited by law or regulation in some or all of the Contracting States:

(b) plant or animal varieties or essentially biological processes for the production of plants or animals; this provision does not apply to microbiological processes or the products thereof.

The exceptions set out in Article 52(2) probably are not strictly necessary as they do not appear to fulfil the basic criteria for patentability set out in Article 52(1). However in Article 52(4) one has exceptions which could well be argued to be "susceptible of industrial application". In this connection the lumping together of both human and veterinary medicine is curious, particularly when farming or at least animal husbandry can certainly be regarded as an industry. If methods for treating diseases in plants are patentable why not methods for treating diseases in animals?

Article 52(4) can be seen as arising out of the "living thing" concern. However it is to be noted that it does not forbid the patenting of living things themselves. Additionally the final sentence of Article 52(4) means that patent protection can be obtained for drugs and other compositions and implements which are used in the surgical and therapeutic treatment of humans even although such treatments are themselves not patentable. (This provision was new in some European states which had previously forbidden the patenting of compositions for medicinal use.)

Furthermore, and possibly even stranger, is that not all operations on or manipulations of the human or animal body are excluded from patentability. Surgery is specifically excluded and this would clearly include plastic surgery even for purely cosmetic reasons. Methods for harming the human body, or cosmetic operations (of no curative value whatsoever) provided they are not "surgery", could probably be patented. On this basis techniques of tattooing and ear piercing might be patentable. However methods of torture (which are quite plainly not therapeutic and probably not surgery) would probably be refused under Article 53(a) as being contrary to morality or ordre publique if for some reason they did not come within Article 52(4).

Another oddity of Article 52(4) is that whilst diagnostic methods when practiced on the patient are excluded, they are not if carried out externally of the patient. For example, if blood samples are first taken from the patient and then analysed in some way this can be patentable although the same analysis carried out on the blood whilst still in the patient is not. This also means that a particular technique for X-raying humans or animals is not patentable when used for diagnostic purposes but may be patentable when applied to Ming vases!

Article 53(b) touches on all three concerns at once by not permitting the patenting of varieties of animals or plants or of any essentially biological processes for the production of animals or plants, but then slightly illogically excepting microbiological processes and their products.

The term "microbiological processes" is construed widely, including not only traditional processes using microorganisms but also techniques of genetic engineering. However the reference to "microbiological processes" is not taken to override the earlier part of Article 53(b) so that products of such processes become patentable even if they are plant or animal varieties.*

Hence Article 53(b) certainly prevents overlap between patents and Plant Breeders' Rights. Unfortunately the exclusion goes much wider than is necessary to achieve that aim, for instance excluding methods of genetic engineering of animals of industrial importance. However there is a line of reasoning that Article 53(b) prohibits only the patenting of *individual* plant or animal varieties so that processes applicable to a wider range of plants or animals escapes the effects of this exclusion. Another line of reasoning is that Article 53(b) should be repealed as soon as possible.

Again Articles 53(b) (like 52(4)) does not deal with the fundamental question of whether it is permissible to obtain patent claims for living matter. This question first arose in the German "Red Dove" case in 1969 where it was decided that the question of whether the matter claimed was living or inanimate was irrelevant. Undoubtedly the most important case from the point of view of its public impact was Chakrabarty[1] where ultimately the U.S. Supreme Court held similarly. That should not have been entirely surprising as Patent Offices in many countries had for many years allowed claims to yeasts which are certainly living. Nevertheless Chakrabarty had an important impact not just on the patent law in the U.S. but almost world wide.

---

* The European Community recently issued a directive relating *inter alia*, to this question, It is in the nature of pious exhortations as to how the existing legislation ought to be interpreted rather than in actually trying to grapple with this problem by obtaining suitable alterations to the legislation.

It may be that the question of the importance of whether the matter being claimed is alive or dead is not entirely settled. Thus one could speculate that, for example, methods designed to regulate the production of human beings (say in order to suppress undesirable genetically transmitted diseases, or to select for some desired characteristic) even although obtained by essentially microbiological processes and not falling within article 52(4) might still be denied patent protection on essentially ethical grounds.

This would be possible under Article 53(a) which excludes the patenting of inventions contrary to morality or "ordre publique", a term perhaps untranslatable but certainly elastic.

It is worth noting that public perceptions of what would be ethically unthinkable do change and sometimes very rapidly. In the United Kingdom as recently as under the 1949 Patents Act claims to contraceptives were refused under a similar type of provision. Now with AIDS a major problem their use is the subject of Government propaganda. It will be interesting to see what claims may be permitted, perhaps first in animal eugenics and then possibly in the human field.

In the U.K. under earlier patent legislation (Patents Act 1949) there was a specific provision that claims to compounds did not extend to that compound when found in nature. The new European patent law does not have this express provision but relies instead on the argument that a product as found in nature is not new, and therefore not patentable. Additionally it could be regarded as a "discovery" and therefore excluded under article 52(2) (a).

On the other hand in the U.S. none of these three categories of exclusion is specifically dealt with by the relevant legislation. The definition of what is patentable in the U.S. is in 35 U.S.C. s 101 which is in very general terms:

> Whoever invents or discovers any new and useful process, machine, manufacture, or composition of matter, or any new and useful improvement thereof, may obtain a patent therefore subject to the conditions and requirements of this title.

Partly because of the very breadth of this basic provision the position in the U.S. is much more flexible in relation to obtaining patents in the biological sciences. Thus medical and diagnostic methods and the use of compounds or compositions in diagnosis, therapy and surgery are potentially patentable provided they are novel and not obvious, and can be described in sufficiently precise terms.

Until the Chakrabarty case the USPTO rejected claims to microorganisms as not falling within s 101 because (1) they were products of nature and (2) they were alive. In the Chakrabarty case the microorganisms (which had utility for degrading components of oil slicks) included two energy-generating plasmids. The U.S. Supreme Court held that the original living cell had been radically altered by human intervention, that it was a composition of matter or an article of manufacture within 35 USC 101 and was not a "product of nature" and therefore not subject to rejection on that ground; the fact that it was living did not prevent it falling within 35 USC 101.

Avoidance of the "product of nature" objection seems to require that there has been a substantial change wrought in the original product of nature to give it some new quality or property or form not present in the original. Thus in one case it had been discovered that the treatment of the rinds of oranges with borax made the fruit less susceptible to a type of mould. However it was held by the Supreme Court that the products were still oranges and there had been no change in their general character or appearance, and that the product of nature objection lay.

Although Chakrabarty has dealt authoritatively with the third concern, it will be interesting to see whether a newer case which claims a method for the selective culturing of oysters might still be followed in claims relating to human eugenics. From the purely patent law point of view there would seem to be no barrier. However recent calls in Congress for a 2 year moratorium on animal patenting suggests that ethical considerations as to the width of USC s 101 are now causing concern in the U.S. In seeking such a moratorium it seems to have been forgotten that obtaining a patent for a technique in human eugenics confers no right on the patentee to carry out the process; all it would do would be to permit him to stop third parties carrying it out without his licence. If both parties are equally constrained by other legal impediments then the existence of such a patent seems irrelevant.

The extent of protection available

It was explained above how in the past in chemical inventions it was common for the first person to make a new chemical compound to obtain a *per se* claim to that compound. As a matter of practice the claims usually went considerably wider than that.

To go back to the aspirin example, the first person to make that might just have claimed acetyl salicylic acid; more probably (depending on his preparative route, the enthusiasm of his patent attorney and the attitude of the Patent Office in question) he would have tried to obtain *per se* claims to acylation products in general, not only of ortho-hydroxy benzoic acid, but also of the meta and para isomers. That sort of claim potentially covers hundreds or indeed thousands of compounds and claims them *per se*. Although this meant that such a broad claim might well be vulnerable by including some already known compounds, such claims were very common and were perhaps encouraged by the ease with which in organic chemistry it is possible to draw out the structure of compounds on paper.

There are suggestions, arising from the attitudes being taken by the various Patent Offices (and more recently from one or two court decisions), that the same sort of approach will not be allowed in genetically engineered inventions. Thus the first person to produce a rare protein or a particular plasmid is not necessarily going to be able to obtain a claim to it at all.

The basic attitude currently being taken is that simply because the inventor has produced something which is formally novel does not mean to say that it was not obvious to try to make the entity in question. A much more stringent attitude is being taken to examining whether a particular entity is obvious rather than the old "first past the post" approach which prevailed in organic chemistry. (The position on this point may, however, be different in the U.S.; see the Hybritech decision discussed below). Even if the inventor can persuade the Patent Office that his protein is new and not obvious he may not be allowed to obtain wide *per se* claims to related proteins, even when these have the same desired activity. This result may arise partly from the fact that with proteins it is not possible to do creative paper chemistry with such ease. Indeed there are some pointers that the inventor will obtain, at most, a claim to the material in question when produced by the method or methods described by him.

There is also fundamental difference between the search for chemically produced drugs and other compounds, in that they tend to be new compounds, contrasted with work intended to elucidate the structure of rare naturally occurring materials and then to provide for their synthesis. One might wonder whether there ought to be a difference from the patent point of view between a material which has been isolated from nature with great labour or which has been genetically engineered. If one looks at the chemical cases the answer would be, "no"; it does not matter whether you make aspirin by a purely chemical route or using a custom-made microbe; aspirin is aspirin and that is that.

This matter received oblique consideration in the Scripps -v- Genentech case in the U.S. in which it was decided that genetically engineered factor VIIIc infringed a claim to factor VIIIc obtained by purification of the natural product. Although this was an infringement decision the logic means that a previously isolated natural product will deprive a subsequent inventor of the genetically engineered material of *per se* claims. On the other hand if the genetically engineered material is not the same as that found in nature, then *per se* claims may be obtained. If one assumes that the naturally occurring material is more likely to be efficacious than a slight deviant, then the result seems rather unjust.

In the case of naturally occurring products it is also necessary to think about the "product of nature" question. A claim to a naturally occurring product (e.g. insulin) as such can hardly be novel. However in the past there has been scope for claims which deliberately exclude the naturally occurring forms. Thus a claim to:

> "Insulin which is at least 90% pure."

at one stage might have been acceptable; another possibility might have been:

> "A preparation containing insulin which does not contain pharmaceutically unacceptable amounts of ... [list impurities normally found]."

Nowadays the attitude is often taken that if you know that something which is naturally occurring in minuscule percentages is desirable, it is obvious to try to produce the material pure, or at least in a pharmaceutically useful form. This means that any invention is likely to have to reside in the manner of extraction; purification or synthesis. This points in the same direction as before, i.e. in effectively denying *per se* protection and allowing nothing more than product-by-process claims.

In a case decided in 1987 on Genentech's patent relating to tissue plasminogen activator (t-PA)[2] in London the judge took a tough line with some very creative approaches of this sort used by Genentech. That decision was appealed and the original decision upheld for differing reasons which are not at all easy to follow. Seen from the point of view of the company which has expended a very large amount of effort in the production of the material, this is very unsatisfactory because when they try to police their patent it will not be enough to prove that the infringer is selling the same material but it will also be necessary to show that it has been made by the same method. (To make things worse in the case of naturally occurring materials the patentee may be met with the reply that the infringing material was indeed extracted from natural sources with great labour.) This, even with discovery of what the infringer is doing, may not be easy. If this trend goes too far it may have the effect of dissuading companies from obtaining patents and relying more on trade secret protection.

It is probably still rather early to make assessments of how patents in this area are likely to be treated. Some of the earliest ones, obtained in the heroic days of the early 1980s, often allowed enthusiasm to over-rule discretion and there are a number of patents with very wide claims which ought to be held to be invalid. Hence some early casualties would not be unexpected.

Another case of importance comparable with the Genentech t-PA decision in England is the Hybritech case in the U.S. In the Hybritech[3] case the patent in suit broadly claimed sandwich assays using monoclonal antibodies. The patent was alleged to be had for lack of novelty, obviousness, non-enabling disclosure and failure to disclose the best mode. This was, in a sense, a case of "grass roots obviousness" over the original Köhler and Milstein papers. The trial judge held the patent to be bad on the basis that given the disclosures of these papers the substitution of monoclonal antibodies (in accordance with the technique outlined in these papers) for polyclonal antibodies was obvious. On appeal this decision was reversed it seems primarily on the basis that significant commercial success (of the sandwich assays) could be used to neutralise this type of obviousness attack. It may however merely reflect a very pro-patent stance by the Court of Appeals for the federal Circuit. (Up until 1982 patent appeals went to the normal Circuit Courts of Appeals which tended to vary widely in their antipathy to patents; now with a single Court of Appeals a very positive pro-patent view has emerged.)

HOW IS PATENT LAW CHANGING TO ACCOMMODATE BIOTECHNOLOGY

This is a question which is frequently asked by biotechnologists. However the short answer is "It isn't"! Patent law has already changed (arguably for the worse) to require deposit of inaccessible microorganisms and has also, by one means or another, dealt with the "living thing" question. The problems of imprecise description had already been dealt with in the context of polymer chemistry where similar problems are encountered. Hence the existing rules apply quite reasonably (on the whole) to biotechnology. The major area for possible adjustments is in relation to deposit requirements, or more accurately to access thereto. There are also ragged edges in the definition of precisely what is patentable and what is not. However intellectual property is rarely uppermost in the minds of legislators, so it would be unwise to assume that major changes are just round the corner.

LICENSING OF RIGHTS AND EXPLOITATION OF TECHNOLOGY

The most obvious method of exploiting a new technology is to put it into practice and to sell articles or to carry out a process which makes use of the technology.

However that is not always the most practical method, particularly for a new venture, and especially if it involves heavy capital expenditure; nor is it necessarily the most remunerative. One of the major factors here is the size and financial strength of the inventor. For the purposes of this discussion it will be assumed that the inventor is either an individual or a small company, without the major financial resources of a large employer (for whom direct exploitation may be the preferred route).

In considering how to go about exploiting a new technology one of the major considerations is what protection is available. This is important for a number of reasons. Firstly, it will be much easier to obtain financial backing if protection is obtainable; indeed many venture capitalists would not look at a project for which no protection at all is available. Secondly, protection may offer the possibility of licensing which can diversify the ways in which the technology can be exploited. Thirdly, it should offer to the inventor some protection from competition by third parties.

Protection

The inventor merely having a brainwave in the bath is not enough. The brainwave may indeed be splendid and perhaps can be put straight into practice. However simply because the inventor had his brainwave does not entitle him to stop others making use of his idea. Generally speaking there is no property in ideas as such.

The question is therefore whether any intellectual property protection can be obtained. As we have already discussed the most likely possibilities in biotechnology are Confidential Information and Patents. Hence the brainwave should be examined at an early stage to see whether a patent might be obtained or whether it might be better kept as a trade secret.

It follows that if the first thing that the inventor does is to send off a communication to a scientific journal he may completely foreclose both of these options. A decision that it is better to keep the idea as a trade secret means that, for the moment at least, no papers can be published. On the other hand if a patent is to be applied for then a paper can be published but the patent application must be made first. Earlier in this chapter we set out the pros and cons of patents as against trade secrets. Cost is likely to be an important consideration. Obtaining patents is an expensive business and the filing fees and translation costs for all the various foreign countries are likely to be incurred within the period of about 1 year. Furthermore, if this road is chosen and patents are obtained, their policing and defence is also very expensive (see the comments on Patent Litigation). Both these concerns often suggest that a small inventor would do better not to try to do all this himself but rather to do some kind of deal with a much larger company who would be able to make the best of the technology in question. That type of approach is broadly termed "Licensing" and for the present discussion includes outright sale.

Licensing and Outright Sale

There are two major types of agreement which the inventor could make with the larger company; one involves outright sale of his technology, the other licensing the company to make use of the technology.

An analogy may help to explain the difference. If you sell your house then, after you have received the price, you will not have any further interest in the house; the benefits and the problems of the house will become those of the buyer. On the other hand if you lease your house to a tenant for, say 7 years, then you are still the owner of the house and many still have obligations to repair the roof and drains but will benefit from any capital appreciation in the house. Additionally, if the tenant misbehaves, or fails to pay his rent, then you would hope to be able to evict him quickly and recover your house. The question of whether you have rented your whole house to the tenant, or have merely rented part of the house, is a matter for negotiation between you and the tenant. Hence, if you have given the tenant the exclusive occupation of your house he can expect you to move out and to keep out of the house for the duration of the tenancy. The questions of the extent to which the tenant is obliged to keep the house in repair and how the rent is calculated and payable are also matters for negotiation.

This analogy should not be taken too far but it may help to illustrate the difference between outright sale and licensing. If the technology is sold outright then the inventor loses his security in the property but equally sheds the responsibilities of paying for it. Licensing, like renting a house, is much more complicated but allows the inventor to retain the security of the underlying rights.

Before considering outright sale as against licensing it must be stressed that the inventor must first have something to sell or licence. The brainwave is not enough. What is needed (as discussed above under Protection) is either a patentable invention or some confidential technology which has been devised by the inventor and which has not been published. Occasionally the inventor may have something tangible to sell (e.g. a valuable cell line) but the value to the buyer will still depend on what protection is available. If not patentable then as a trade secret the inventor will doubtless be required not to supply samples to third parties.

A further matter which often requires consideration is whether the inventor actually owns the rights to his brainwave. It is quite common for bodies which support academic research to attach strings to the funding and it may prove that the brainwave does not belong to the inventor; or at least that it cannot be exploited without the consent of the funding body.

The question or outright sale or licence is often a difficult one. A licence merely permits the licensee to do certain things which the licensor would otherwise be able to prevent. Typically the licence permits the licensee to operate within the scope of the licensed patent without thereby being subject to an action for infringement of the patent.

In the case of an outright sale the inventor will normally transfer all his rights to the buyer by means of an assignment and, after receiving the price payable, will no longer be involved with the exploitation of the technology except possibly as a consultant.

Normally when selling a house the whole price is payable when the deal is completed. That can also be done in the case of an assignment of the technology. However in the case of a house it is much easier to value what the house is worth on the market at the time of the sale. In the case of a new technology this can be virtually impossible; the technology may prove much more valuable and of much wider application than the inventor had appreciated. Alternatively it may prove to be a monumental flop. Hence putting a cash value on the assignment is a gamble.

There is no reason why all the price of the assignment need be payable on signing; it could be agreed that the buyer should pay the agreed price in, say, annual instalments. Furthermore there is no reason why part or all of the price cannot be taken in the form of payments geared to the actual use of the technology which is made by the buyer. Such geared payments are normally known as "royalties". Taking royalties as a price for the assignment means that some of the guesswork in how valuable the technology proves can be removed.

At first blush this appears a good way of proceeding but it does here two major problems. The first is that on assignment the inventor loses his rights in the technology as these have been transferred to the buyer. Hence he loses his security in case the buyer proves indolent, perfidious or insolvent. Indeed insolvency should be one of the major concerns here. If the buyer becomes insolvent the inventor has not only lost his rights but is left with a contrast with the buyer which is probably of no value when dealing with a liquidator. The other major problem in taking royalties for an assignment is one of definition of what royalties are payable, and on what goods and products. Whilst these problems can often be overcome, it is generally the case that if the inventor wants to obtain royalties he would be better to proceed by way of licence, rather than assignment, because of the greater security of the licence. On the other hand if he does go by way of licence he will normally be saddled with the responsibility and cost of prosecuting and maintaining patent applications; that, however, may be offset by down payments to be made on execution of the licence.

Generally speaking an assignment document is relatively simple: it identifies the rights to be transferred and the price payable and that is that. A licence is a much more complex business as it must deal not only with the rights to be licensed but also with the exact nature of the licence, how royalties are payable and the conditions under which it can come to an end.

It follows that there is no "standard form" for a licence as each deal tends to have its own peculiarities. A number of matters usually need to be considered. In theory the licensor (i.e. the inventor) can licence under whatever terms he chooses but this is a theory which breaks down easily. If the licensee is a larger entity with financial muscle and the inventor is not, the practicalities will result in the licensee substantially dictating the terms. Even between parties of comparable bargaining power negotiations may fail if the inventor is unreasonable. Finally there are certain competition law constraints (varying from country to country) which are imposed on licence agreements and which do not normally affect assignments.

The first question is what type of license is being given: exclusive, sole or non-exclusive. An exclusive licence is one which means that the inventor not only cannot grant any more licences but cannot even operate the technology himself. A sole licence is one where the inventor agrees not to grant any more licences but both the licensee and the inventor can operate the technology. A non-exclusive licence is one which means that the inventor can grant as many more licences as he wishes and he can operate the technology himself.

The value of a licence depends critically on this question of exclusivity as a licensee will not be willing to pay as much for a non-exclusive licence as for an exclusive or sole one. In the context of a new technology, where substantial capital investment is going to be made by the licensee, it is probable that the licensee will take nothing less than an exclusive licence.

Typically some down payment is made when the licence is signed and then royalties are payable on products which use the technology. We have noted above that the definition of what products attract royalty is an important and not an easy one. One of the major concerns of the licensor is that the licensee will not simply sit on the technology and do nothing. That is particularly disastrous if the licence is exclusive. Hence there must be provisions in the licence requiring some action by the licensee. These can take a number of forms, e.g. specified minimum royalties which are payable even if the licensee has sold nothing and provisions that if the licensee does not use his best efforts then the licence shall become non-exclusive or shall terminate.

Other matters require thought including the duration of the licence, whether or not the licensee is entitled to sub-licence, what happens to improvements made by either side, housekeeping provisions for payment, reporting and audit, what happens if the licensee fails to pay his royalties or commits other breaches; and the thorny problem of policing.

Thus a request from the licensee that the licensor will actively police, even to the extent of commencing and financing full scale patent litigation, needs very careful consideration. Usually it is better to leave such matters for discussion between the parties when the infringer makes his appearance.

Licensees sometimes ask for assurances that the patents are valid a request which well-adjusted licensors decline, particularly if the licensee is much larger and better able to look after itself than the licensor.

Licensing can have the advantage of permitting the licensor both to exploit the technology directly himself and at the same time have licensees who are also exploiting it and paying him royalties. This is often the case when a licensor will work the technology in his home country but will licence others abroad.

Sometimes one has two complementary technologies which leads to a "cross licence" between the owners so that each is authorised to use the other's technology. Cross licences are also useful for avoiding litigation between the owners of directly competing technologies.

The decision as to what type of licence to offer is primarily a commercial one and may vary from country to country. For example a company might well decide to grant non-exclusive licences (with no power to sub-licence) in their home territory where they are very familiar with the market and what acceptable royalty rates should be. But for a distant and unfamiliar market they may prefer a single exclusive licensee; preferably a large company who can then do their own sub-licensing and additionally deal with the problems of policing such sub-licensees.

It may be possible to divide up the rights into different market sectors. Thus, while a licensor with a patent for a new drug could licence one company for veterinary medical applications and another for human medical applications, this approach might be limited for reasons of competition law.

Licences can treat manufacture and sales in different ways. Quite commonly a patent licence would appoint an exclusive manufacturer for, say, the U.K. but the scope of the licence vis-a-vis sales is non-exclusive in all countries where patents subsist. Although that offers good export possibilities to the licensee, he must realise that while no-one else will be making the product in the U.K. he may not have the market to himself as his fellow licensees in Italy or Holland may choose to export to Britain. Hence before granting such licences consideration must be given to the likelihood of such parallel importation and the friction which this may cause.

Such freedom to the licensee to market anywhere is very helpful from the point of view of competition law because there is a doctrine called "exhaustion of rights" which means that a patentee is only permitted "one bite at the cherry" by way of royalties for use of his patented invention. Attempts to use a corresponding patent abroad, to prevent importation of goods on which the patentee or his licensee has already enjoyed royalty, is not permitted.

It is not very common to have "pure" patent licences and mixed patent and know-how licences tend to be commoner. These can have advantages if the strength of the patent protection obtainable is doubtful. This type of licence must include the necessary secrecy provisions to protect the confidential know-how.

It is important to gear the overall terms to the rights which are being licensed. For example, if a licence is to be granted under a patent, the licence should not continue after the patent expires (for there is nothing then left to licence, and to justify payment of royalties) and nor should it attempt to require the licensee to buy some other product (not patented) from the licensor or his nominees. Such "tie-ins" are regarded as objectionable.

It is in this sort of area where competition law is most important. This chapter does not pretend to cover such matters comprehensively; each proposed licence agreement ought to be considered in draft before any detailed discussions are attempted with potential licensees. Indeed, it is usually found that the provisions on which the licensor's marketing executives are keenest are precisely those ones anathematised by the competition law authorities!

DESIGNING A COMPETITIVE STRATEGY

Intellectual property is important in biotechnology both in trying to preserve a competitive edge over the competition and in having property which may be licensed to third parties.

The protection available from patents, particularly to naturally occurring materials and in cases in which the patent involves rare cultures, is not ideal and sometimes retention of the invention as a trade secret may be preferable. In the U.S. the very strongly pro-patent stance of the current law may suggest an alternative view and the Plant Breeders' Rights may also have a limited usefulness.

Nevertheless the tail should not be wagging the dog. The choice of a particular product (or research work which may lead to a product) is often determined in the first instance by factors which do not take account of protection available except perhaps when engineering round a patent held by someone else. In a choice between, say, identification and synthesis of a naturally occurring material and synthesis of some synthetic variant, the latter is preferable from the point of view of the protection currently available.

Most importantly the management of a company should take care to do the necessary legal good-housekeeping to protect the trade secrets their staff have developed, instruct their research workers not to talk about their work outside the company until after the patent applications have been made and to ensure that they have acquired all the rights they need to operate their business effectively.

REFERENCES

1. *Diamond -v- Chakrabarty* 477 U.S. 303, 100 S.Ct 2204, 206 USPQ 193 (1980).
2. *The Wellcome Foundation -v- Genentech Inc. and Böhringer Ingelheim Limited:* [1987] R.P.C. 553 and [1989] R.P.C. 147.
3. *Hybritech Inc. -v- Monoclonal Antibodies Inc.*, 227 U.S.P.Q. 215.

FURTHER READING

Beier, F.K., Crespi, R.S. & Strauss, J. (1985). *Biotechnology and Patent Protection: an International Review.* Paris: OECD.

Cooper, I.P. (1982). *Biotechnology and the Law.* New York: Clark Boardman Co. Ltd.

Crespi, R.S. (1982). *Patenting in the Biological Sciences.* Chichester: John Wiley & Sons.

Crespi, R.S. (1988). *Patents: a Basic Guide to Patenting in Biotechnology.* Cambridge: Cambridge University Press.

Grubb, P.W. (1986). *Patents in Chemistry and Biotechnology* (2nd ed.). Oxford: Clarendon Press.

Chapter 7

Public Perceptions of Biotechnology

Usher Fleising

INTRODUCTION

The translation of biological theory into engineering can obviate the need for dependency on oil and its petrochemical derivatives and holds much promise as well for waste disposal, health care products and enhanced food production. Government and private organizations have argued that by domesticating biological processes and microbiological organisms it is possible to maintain and continue economic growth and expansion. The petrochemical age must, and will yield, it is argued, to a BioSociety in which the power of life science research will become an important tool in the maintenance of human existence at a comfortable level.

The government of Japan has declared biotechnology to be an area of strategic importance in the next century and is organizing its industries and universities for a concentrated assault on biological technology. The United States is determined to maintain its lead in research and development of biotechnology and many governments both in the developed and the developing world are evolving policies and strategies for keeping pace with the potentials of biological engineering.

While there is disagreement within the biotechnological community as to whether they constitute a definitive industry or represent modifications of existing industries, the result is still an effort to redirect some of the production functions of society. Biotechnology is being presented to the public as an adaptive strategy for survival, a way of using and applying knowledge to maintain and improve the condition of our species.

In considering public perceptions of biotechnology it is important to assert that the intentions and motivations of the advocates for biotechnology are honest and well meaning. The application of technology for human benefit is as old as our species but so are disagreements about the social implications of the application of human knowledge. A consideration of public perceptions of biotechnology requires an understanding of the relationship between society and technology since biotechnology is but a special case of this more inclusive social dynamic. The objective of this chapter is, therefore, to convey a strategy for thinking about public responses to biotechnology that comes from our knowledge about the relationship between society and technology.

As a chapter in a textbook on the science and business of biotechnology this contribution on public perceptions is somewhat awkward. There is hardly any literature at all that deals specifically with public perceptions of biotechnology; there are mostly a series of incidents in which public awareness of biotechnology has been hightened. Thus in 1974 there was an informally imposed moratorium on recombinant DNA research that was initiated from within the scientific community and later, when decisions about the safety of proceeding with recombinant research and development was affirmed, these decisions were challenged. But the public challenges to biotechnology from, for example, *The Foundation on Economic Trends* and its director Jeremy Rifkin has its origin in the social dynamics of the environmental movement that predates a biotechnology industry. Rifkin's challenge in 1988, enjoining experiments involving oncogenes and transgenic mice, was tied to U.S. government requirements for environmental impact assessments. The literature on impact assessment, risk and cost/benefit analysis predates biotechnology as an identifiable target but it is this literature that must be accessed in order to consider and understand public perceptions of biotechnology.

Since biotechnology comes on board not in a vacuum but into existing structures for the assessment and public scrutiny of technology development, its public posture must be understood from the framework already in place and from experiences already encountered. Leaks from nuclear reactors and waste disposal sites, the thalidomide tragedy and concerns about car safety all feed into the building of perceptions of biotechnology. The nuclear, chemical, pharmaceutical and automobile industries did not fold up and go away, nor would the public want them to but it is probably the case that in general the public posture towards technology, or at least that of its educated spokespersons, has shifted as a result of the politicization of the environment.

The proposition that technology is morally neutral has become difficult to support. While some definitions of technology define it in strictly material terms as being composed of physical objects other definitions include the notion that technology involves the application of knowledge in the process of social production. Especially since concerns have been raised about the social consequences of the application of scientific knowledge in creating undesirable byproducts, the tendency has been to view technology and its development as having a strong political and, by implication, moral dimension. Decisions about using or not using a technology or the process of ascertaining risk/benefit is more and more being understood to contain value conflicts. Thus the socio-political arena in which public perceptions of biotechnology are being built must be seen in its larger context of society's relationship with technology.

TECHNOLOGY AND SOCIETY

Technological acts are social acts. The manufacturing of stone tools, the use of the plough, the building of a dam and the synthesis of insulin are human technological activities supported, dependent upon and integrated with systems of economy, politics, religion, education, and even music, drama, and art.

Technological activity is about making a living, transforming the environment in order to allocate and reallocate resources. Technology is about accumulating surplus and about the power and influence the results from differences in the ability to accumulate surplus capital. Technology and its application to make more technology and more stuff to keep in our bedrooms, mud huts and garages has also become a social problem. Many social scientists consider the technical means of production to be the core of a society's adaptive strategy from which other social behaviors are derived. How it is we feed ourselves and our children dominates our daily behavior: it organizes our time, determines a large part of our movement through space, gives us toys, mortgages and networks for interaction, whether these be kin based as in agricultural and pastoral societies, or contract based as in industrial societies.

Technology is also synonymous with social change. Shifts or transformations in productive technology are said to have the most significant impact on human social organization and Sgaramalla[1] cites industrial reorganization as the first in his list of four impacts from biotechnology. The others are on health and environment, the legal conversion of ethical norms and basic research into gene function.

The depth of intrusion across social sectors for biotechnology as an engine for social change is, according to the listed impacts, potentially wide ranging and significant. Many commentators have referred to biotechnology as a new industrial revolution and even some of its firmest detractors like Jeremy Rifkin[2] is rumored to have said that it is the greatest invention since the domestication of fire.

Public perceptions of biotechnology are important to know about because as a contender for consumer support and investment dollars biotechnology must establish an acceptable position in the sociopolitical landscape. A certain amount of turmoil and tension is certain to follow any novel attempt at restructuring and rethinking how it is that goods and services are bought and sold. New technologies and even modifications of old ones must be integrated into the cultural landscape and become a normal and accepted way of doing things. To be told that we are on the brink of an industrial revolution because we have domesticated DNA is not comforting news if you have to consider how it might affect your job or the image of the cozy world you have come to know. Let us illustrate with a bit of borrowed science fantasy.

Paleoanthropologists believe that the origin of sustained tool manufacture occurred together with a biological transformation to habitual bipedal locomotion. Standing up gave us weak backs but freed our arms of their locomotary function of grasping branches and vines. Human biology with its sociological potential embraced environmental manipulation and culture was born "all of a piece".

The origin details are of course shrouded in our species history, but men and women everywhere have consistently sought means to express and understand the duality of being a part of nature and apart from nature. Technological achievements invariably press this dilemma especially if it opens an uncharted frontier for exploitation and exploration. Societal decisions about whether or not to proceed are hedged about with debates about the natural or not natural quality of the technology.

In his science fantasy account of the adventures of *The Evolution Man*, Roy Lewis has Uncle Vanya looking down scornfully from his arboreal perch arguing with his brother Edward about the controlled manipulation of fire:

> . . . "I am prepared to accept simple trimmed pebbles as in the way of nature, provided one does not become too dependent on them, and no attempt is made to refine them unduly. I am not illiberal, Edward, and I will go as far as that. But this! This is quite another matter. This could end anywhere. It affects everybody. Even me. You might burn the forest down with it. Then where would I be?"
>
> "Oh, I don't think it will come to that, Vanya," said Father.
>
> "Won't it, indeed! May I ask, Edward, are you in control of the thing at all?"
>
> "Er — more or less. More or less, you know."
>
> "What do you mean, more or less? Either you are, or you are not. Don't prevaricate. Can you put it out, for example?"
>
> "If you don't feed it, it goes out of itself," said Father defensively.
>
> "Edward," said Uncle Vanya, "I warn you. You have started something that you may not be able to stop. So you think, it will go out if you don't feed it! Have you thought that it might decide to feed itself, sometime? Then where would you be?"
>
> "It hasn't happened yet," said Father crossly. "It takes me all my time to keep it going, as a matter of fact, especially on wet nights."
>
> "Then my most earnest advice to you is not to keep it going any longer," said Uncle Vanya, "before you get a chain reaction started."[3]

Africa is also the setting for this 21st Century exchange in Michael Crichton's *Congo*.

> ... "In Olduvai Gorge in Tanzania, there are traces of a house two million years old. The hominid creature wasn't satisfied with caves and other natural shelters; he created his own accommodations. Men have always altered the natural world to suit their purposes."
> "But you can't give up control," Elliot said.
> "We've been doing it for centuries," Ross said. "What's a domesticated animal — or a pocket calculator — except an attempt to give up control? We don't want to plow fields or do square roots so we turn the job over to some other intelligence, which we've trained or bred or created."
> "But you can't let your creations take over."
> "We've been doing it for centuries," Ross repeated.[4]

Is the application of genetic technology the next stage in giving up control? Are we in danger of starting a fire that cannot be put out? Disputes about the benefits and dangers of technology are as old as our species. So we should not be surprised about conflicts over the wisdom of shouting hallelujah for the controlled manipulation of biological processes. Especially so when the first red flags were waved from within the scientific community with the declaration of a moratorium on rDNA research in July 1974.

What are the mechanisms that can account for the shaping of beliefs about biotechnology? If technology is not morally neutral, as is emphasized in the research on culture and technology, what then is the interaction between culture and biotechnology that results in particular beliefs and attitudes?

WHAT ARE PUBLIC PERCEPTIONS?

What are public perceptions? You can't put it into a peptide synthesizer, you can't read it on gel, its not a glycoprotein and you can't get it from Celltech; but you can buy it! Public perceptions, or rather information on public perceptions, is a commodity, a child of the communications and information revolution. It is a commodity of the post-industrial state that has become as ordinary an item in the morning paper as milk and cookies after school. The technology that permits the calculation of daily interest on your bank book can be bought to tally interest in biotechnology.

The commodity value of public perceptions is why this chapter is in this book and why the American government's Office of Technology Assessment (OTA) undertook to read the publics' perceptions of biotechnology in 1987.[5] The information may then be used in strategic planning by government or the private sector with the goal of obtaining some net benefit from the purchased information. Whether operating at the level of radio talk-show surveys or methodologically rigorous commissioned studies, public perception information is marketed and factored into decision making. Public perceptions, therefore, have an economic and political function in the modern industrialized system.

Public perceptions are, in the technical language of sociology, a "social fact". They have an existence and meaning independent of particular individuals but they are yet capable of exerting constraints on individual behavior. In biotechnology one treads gingerly towards human germ plasm research while there is less constraint on the production of single cell proteins or monoclonal antibodies. Beliefs about parallels between field tests of "ice-minus" (see Chapter 23) and an Andromeda strain scenario were capable of delaying for a few years actual field tests. As social facts, public perceptions have a zeitgeist of power and control not housed in any particular individual: their effects on channeling behavior are emergent properties of a collective. These collective expressions are channeled and find a voice in the various organizations charged with implementing policy about how biotechnology is to proceed or not to proceed doing its business.

The control that common folk are capable of exercising over corporate production can be traced to the politicization of the environment in the late sixties and early seventies. In some countries, and especially in the United States, this took root in the growth of regulatory bureaucracies. The European manifestation of a cry from the margins is located in the Greening of the political landscape rather than in an elaborate structure for technology assessment and its mediation.

In addition to being a social fact public perceptions also imply individual mental activity. There is a psychological aspect with which we can individually identify and which describes a relationship between an external factor eg biotechnology, communism, abortion, immigration, the monarchy, etc. and one's feelings about this external social category. The business of biotechnology, insofar as it must be aware of public perceptions, is recognizing a phenomenon constructed in individual minds from a mixture of beliefs and experiences.

What individuals are expressing when public statements are glossed as public perceptions are beliefs. The statements collected in surveys, reified in the media, dissected in academia and fretted over for political leverage, are expressions of standards of conduct and fabrics of meaning that are a part of a society's culture, its system of symbols. Public perceptions are, as stated by the authors of the OTA survey, a collective expression of knowledge and opinion. This could be beliefs about the severity of the pollution problem, beliefs about what motivates the private sector, beliefs about progress, beliefs about safety, beliefs about risk and about benefit.

Surveys claiming to expose public perceptions are an operational device for eliciting attributes of culture in the sense that culture consists of values, beliefs, attitudes, or other ideational elements relating to behaviors. Public perceptions are an exposé of the fabrics of meaning that guide behavior, and the public opinion poll is an artifact in the cultural warehouse for taking the collective pulse. Since we cannot with a straight face divine the scapula of a caribou for strategic planning, we have invented the public opinion poll instead.

THE DEVELOPMENT OF PERCEPTIONS ABOUT BIOTECHNOLOGY

There are two levels of phenomena that have been defined for perceptions of biotechnology. At one level there are the day to day events and personal experiences of people that feed into their perceptions of the world around them. A parent with a haemophilic child will likely structure her/his beliefs about the dangers of genetic engineering differently from others. At another level of reality there are social institutions that have evolved to co-ordinate and organize our lives. These can be family and kin based groups, or larger bureaucracies of government and industry, all of which function to insure that as a species *Homo sapiens* continues to produce and reproduce.

Insofar as they project a slice of the mental images of a population, and because these images are built from different experiences, these public perceptions tell us about the conflicts that are present in society or potentially what is universally accepted. The perception that technology and its development is to be equated with progress is for example overwhelmingly accepted by industrial societies (both capitalist and non-capitalist) and is referred to by Leo Marx as progress ideology.[6]

Conflicts about what is appropriate or inappropriate, what is good or what is bad, or what is dangerous and what is not are constantly being negotiated and redefined. The fear of losing control will find a bung hole. As one fear is allayed, so another arises: Gorbachov pulled the plug on the fears of a nuclear holocaust so our fears are being refocused elsewhere-like the fear of contamination from technology. It would not be surprising if the fear of the military were replaced by a fear of the scientific. A recent study of high school students in Calgary showed that the majority believed that scientists were dangerous.

Public perceptions as a unit of observation and analysis are the end products of conflict. The authors of *The American Business Creed*[7] use the term "strain" rather than "conflict" but the operational mechanism is the same. The claim is made that American business ideology is the result of the strain that results from different social roles and agendas. The conflict can be a personal wrestling with the morality of patenting life, or alternative choices for a career. The conflict can be about the best use of our human and natural resources for effecting a high quality of life. In biotechnology the conflicts are about production and reproduction, and public images of biotechnology are constructed from the way in which these conflicts or strains are negotiated. The forum for settling alternative views about the use or non use of biotechnology were developed out of earlier experiences with attempting to manage technology and its impact on the environment. Difficulties experienced by biotechnology companies in getting approval for the testing and application of their products may in part be attributed to not recognizing the structures that had already been put into place to handle technology assessment. It was the successful utilization of these government structures by detractors of biotechnology that frustrated the industry in getting test or market approval for its products.

Conflicts about Production

With the politicization of the environment in the 1960s, and especially following the National Environmental Protection Act (NEPA) in the United States in 1969, there has emerged a more visible and active public sensitivity to the technology of production. The negative externalities associated with modern industrial activity — the withdrawal of resources and the addition of contaminating wastes — is a social problem that demands action and attention.

Biotechnology, as an industrial activity, must be viewed within the context of the alienation created by modern industrial technology. Social alienation as related to technology is a familiar theme for students of modernization and social change and under extreme circumstances can result in such divergent phenomena as cargo cults and the social anomie of Native American Indians. Usually questions of social alienation and technology are reserved for discussions of the impact of Westernization in developing regions of the world, but programs of technological assessment are revealing currents of social stress among Western populations. Public debates on, for example, car safety, pollution standards, and nuclear fuels are symptoms of the clash between systems of production and the alienation they have allegedly produced. The commodity value of this chapter for the biotechnology community is tied to a concern for the alienation of the consuming public from its products. As potential consumers one cannot afford to alienate the public.

Let us examine the matter a little further in order to identify the publics involved and the cultural theater in which perceptions are acted out. There is apparently a growing sense of loss of control and understanding of the human support systems and an accompanying loss of faith in the science that has generated (or is perceived to have generated) this situation. Philip Handler, as President of the National Academy of Sciences, made this point most forcefully:

> "Beneath the surface, the environmental and consumer movements may be an expression of anomie, a cry of

> protest for the sense of powerlessness of the individual educated citizen. The societal response has been attempts at examination of such matters by risk and cost/benefit analysis. Well, risk/benefit analysis can certainly inform the decision maker. But the decision must necessarily still turn on a value judgment, conditioned by social, economic, philosophic, and religious views. But that is the nature of the political process. The public acceptability of a given level of risk is a political, not a scientific, question."[8]

The creation of institutions to manage the environment was seen as a mechanism for negotiating society's relationship with the environment. Regulatory bodies were put in place to serve as a forum for the acting out of a cultural image. If we define institutions as organizations created to implement values then we get a better sense of the social functions of the technology assessment process and their role in creating perceptions.

The ethic of participatory technology was invoked as the acting out of democratic theory and the ordinary citizen, at least formally through NEPA in the United States, was thrust into the political process. The political opportunity was created for public input and industry ignored this opening at its peril. Rifkin's strategy for obstructing and frustrating the biotechnology industry was anchored to the technology management process that had been constructed to deal with environmental degradation and presumably with public alienation as well. The technology assessment legislation, again especially in the USA, gave opportunity for the implementation of public participation. But the claim from the public to be permitted to participate in the application of technology has been challenged by invoking scientific authority.

When scientific facts are seen to clash with public knowledge the claim is often made that the public is in need of education. Not only is the public in need of education but the judiciary is also sometimes singled out as requiring scientific expertise. The gulf between expert opinion and pedestrian knowledge about the risks of nuclear power generation is the worst case scenario feared by the biotechnology market. Anyone present at a meeting on Risk Assessment for the Industrial Biotechnology Association on the same weekend as the Chernobyl accident will know how readily the public extrapolates from a real perceived hazard to an imaginary one. The concern about public conceptions and the consequences for the industrial health of biotechnology are real and so they should be. The fear is about a public generalizing that all technology is bad.

Paul Slovic's work on the perception of risk shows how deep the chasm sometimes is between public and expert.[9] From a list of 30 activities and technologies, psychometric studies of risk reveal that while college students and the League of Women Voters rank nuclear power as the most risky activity, this is scored at the 20th rank by experts (genetic technology is not on the list). While there is no disputing a knowledge gulf between the public and the experts, the experts on risk perception are quite firm in asserting that lack of information is but one element, and not necessarily the most important one, in conceptualizing risk.

The insistence by members of the scientific elite that a properly educated public will make rational decisions about risk and benefit is simply not supported by the evidence. Statements such as those made by Danial Koshland in his role as editor of Science, insisting that regulatory decisions on risk must be based exclusively on scientific criteria to the point of enjoining the judiciary to be scientifically trained,[10] misses the point made by Philip Handler of the extremely political and value filled dynamic of public perceptions of risk.

The key is not content but process; thus Monsanto executives admit to having made a tactical mistake by neglecting to inform dairy cooperatives that they were receiving milk from bovine somatotropin (BST) studies. A situation was created in which anger, mistrust and perceptions of hidden agendas superseded any effort to deal with scientific and technical issues associated with BST. Similarly, an executive of Advanced Genetic Sciences (AGS) agreed that the company was sociologically naive when it came to having to interact with the public in a direct manner. Difficulties that arose with the Monterey County over field tests of ice-minus could have been avoided with sufficient sensitivity to local concerns rather than a blind fixation on the testing of a technology. For one thing it did not occur to the company that local strawberry growers felt that a successful test of the efficacy of ice-minus would put them at a competitive disadvantage compared with strawberry growers in Texas: in that state the growing season was shorter than in Monterey County and ice-minus would extend it.

The social impact assessment literature clearly demonstrates the significance of process in the development of perceptions and definitions of the situation. Raymond Gold's studies of surface coal mining projects in Montana, and the author's own experience with coal development projects in central Alberta, offer a litany of examples where tension conflict and misunderstanding are the products not of lack of education, but of neglect and blindness towards what it is that is important for the public. As Mary Douglas and Aaron Wildavsky note in their book *Risk and Culture*[11], all assessments are biased and subjective values take priority. So if a threat to personal and family welfare is perceived, as would be the case in the AGS example of undermining a competitive edge, the public posture becomes defined with this threat in mind and no amount of education and enlightenment about the evidence for a benign ice-minus will cool and placate fears. The fears are not about the technological details associated with a product, the fears are about the loss of control over what will happen to family and friends.

In a reversal of roles and a demonstration of how jumping to conclusions can undermine rational thinking, there is the frustration expressed by one Washington lawyer about how the biotechnology business community was unable to see the facts and their implications in Jeremy Rifkin's challenges to release of engineered organisms. The lawyer, who represented biotechnology interests, asserted that the litigation brought forward by Rifkin and the subsequent delays it generated were founded exclusively on technical matters of judicial process that related to legislation for impact assessment. Decisions were made not about the risks and/or benefits of release or evidence about the biology of recombinant engineering, but were based on procedure and due process in getting a licence. The reaction of the biotechnology community, that is their perception and construction of the situation, was one of being under siege and having to defend their science and its application and demanding that judges receive scientific education. The frustration for the lawyer was an inability to lift the fog and clear the glaze from the eyes of the business community as they would carry on about the naivete of those who were putting their science and their investments on trial.

The legal challenges of Rifkin amounted to a personal threat, an attack on a subjective edifice of beliefs that one should be able to go ahead and make a living to feed one's family and leverage investment to buy market opportunity. Government compliance with the validity of the legal challenge from Rifkin defined the situation as an attack on scientific credibility and on the worth of what these individuals were doing as proponents of biotechnology. That the litigation decisions had very little to do with the science of biological engineering was buried in the emotions of a threat to self and family. Why should this kind of reaction be different for anyone else? The concerns of the biotechnology lobby were legitimate within the framework of their lives and personal objectives. Paul Slovic summed the situation up as follows "... there is wisdom as well as error in public attitudes and perceptions. Lay people sometimes lack certain information about hazards. However, their basic conceptualization of risk is much richer than that of experts and reflects legitimate concerns that are typically omitted from expert risk assessments."[9]

The assertion that the key to public knowledge and acceptance of biotechnology is a matter of education is a false orientation. And even the supposed positive results of the OTA survey on perceptions of biotechnology shows a hidden hand. While it is true that the survey results show buoyant support for proceeding with genetic manipulation research and its application in the production of goods and services, the American public chose to retain its authority with respect to technology assessment. The report emphasizes a trend whereby Americans appear to favor greater regulation of scientific development. This result was not noticeably highlighted in biotechnology trade publications nor were the results about the relationship between technology and personal benefit emphasized.

The OTA document (chapter 4 and p61) notes that "the public expects science and technological developments to bring personal benefits for them and their families."[5] The juxtaposition of this assertion with a popular consensus for regulation and scrutiny should not be overlooked in considering public perceptions. Another important dynamic here is the consistent finding, in the OTA and earlier surveys of public opinion on genetic manipulation, of a positive correlation between levels of education and good thoughts about genetic tinkering. By and large those who will potentially benefit most from the fruits of biotechnology, either in direct employment or in being able to afford its commodities, support the science, technology and business of biological process engineering. However, these educated elites can also be and become the most vociferous and formidable opponents of the translation of biological theory into engineering.

Given a bureaucracy for technology assessment and an appropriate issue centered on actual or perceived threats to self and family, the educated elite might begin to challenge the legitimacy of the biotechnology industry. This could lead to demands for complete closure or greater community control. In fact we have already seen this happen in the early years of biotechnology growth and fears of accidental release of recombinant organisms when cities with high concentrations of academics, like Cambridge, Massachusetts and Ann Arbour, Michigan, organized citizen watch groups and were instrumental in passing unfriendly zoning restrictions and controls on biotechnology development. The publication *Genewatch* is an effort from educated professionals to monitor developments in genetic technology.

The lesson to be drawn from the OTA survey is that a balance needs to be struck between ends and means. The objectives and outcomes may be super but an inappropriate strategy for implementation can lead to despair if scientific authority tries to dominate interaction. Too narrow a focus on educating the public to scientific facts will drive a wedge between technocrats and the public. That the tables can be turned is demonstrated in the debate over the safety and desirability of nuclear technology. The argument has been made by Gary Downey[12] that it was the effective use of scientific authority by anti-nuclear power groups that molded public opinion on the use of nuclear power. The evidence from the technology assessment literature seems to assert that the use of scientific authority is an important ingredient in the shaping of public perceptions.

One can also with justice argue that the situation in Europe is not substantively different so far as perceptions being defined largely on the basis of perceived threat to self and family. Actually, Douglas and Wildavsky[11] essentially assert a pan-cultural bias in relation to technology as regards subjective values. The political expression of public beliefs is different in the European theater where issues of technology and environment are located in conflicts for control by political parties. The Greening of America is not likely to happen by electoral victory.

It is threats to kith and kin that drive conflict over control of nature. Social change is not a simple matter of moving into a new house. The transition from gathering and hunting to domestication was protracted and not at all pleasant. The reasons are not entirely clear but the image of the cornucopia of wealth and good life that came with the domestication of plants and animals has been shattered by archaeological and skeletal morphological data. Despotism, disease and death also flowed from the horn of plenty and the pollutants of the industrial revolution may be the unseen pestilence of our time. The fear of human production activities associated with technology are ancient and, it seems, quite legitimate.

Conflicts about Reproduction

The public, in truth, has no perception of biotechnology! In a common crowd the word lingers and dies unless you say what it means. There are no raised eyebrow flashes, no cues around the lips or in the posture that betrays awareness. The eyebrows actually lower and the nostrils flare slightly in puzzlement, but the affect becomes more animated as the pupils open to the sound of the key words — "genetic engineering".

In most lecture theaters and at the pub, "biotechnology" has yet to achieve the folk cultural status of "nuclear", "solar" or "petrochemical". Genetic engineering and even DNA (see Figures 1–4) has folk (or popular culture) status, but biotechnology is a blur and achieves meaning in the pedestrian theater by its association with specific key word components — "gene", "technology", "engineering", "science", "industry". For the business of biotechnology this is an important observation because it defines the level at which it becomes important to deal with public perceptions, i.e., reading the meanings others attach to words and to situations.

We all know that biotechnology is more than genetic engineering and often in a technical sense does not involve genetic manipulations at all. However, we have equally observed that as far as folk recognition is concerned the "genetic engineering" gloss achieves a level of awareness not elicited by other phrases. The technical label has become a generic label for fooling around with life in a test tube and to make a distinction between rDNA activity and the production of monoclonal antibodies is irrelevant. To insist on making a distinction can result in alienation, and the aggravation of social dialogue. The generic gloss of "genetic engineering" extends beyond the layperson even to the lawyers and brokers who engage on a regular basis in the biotechnology business.

Genetic engineering is what some cultural anthropologists would call a cover term which has acquired meanings beyond its original technical designation. Cover terms are like key words in that they symbolize an array of meanings and subsume a commonly understood category of implicit knowledge. The significance of "genetic engineering" as a meaningful stimulus, rather than "biotechnology", is underscored in the OTA study of public perceptions where "biotechnology" does not appear on a single survey question! The key word stimuli used are — "genetic engineering", "genetic manipulation" and "genetically altered".

The trade magazine Genetic Engineering News (GEN) further reinforces and energizes the pedestrian image of biotechnology as perhaps being as, we are often told, "not natural". This is ossified even more with the insertion of the double helix into the clip-art portfolio of the designers of biotechnology company logos. The symbolic relationship between DNA, its emblematic image as a double helix and the secrets of making life seems to have achieved a concreteness in folk taxonomy. The DNAgents (Figs. 1 and 2) make this point rather well. Tradition says that the first time we got curious about these things God threw us naked into the world.

The conflict between Genesis and biotechnology should not be dismissed as simple folk ignorance. The ethical and moral structure of the Western Industrial Democracies are the morals and ethics of the agriculturalists and pastoralists of the Testaments. There are no stories about how to deal with the industrialization of the body.

Culture and Nature

It would be remiss not to consider how perceptions of biotechnology are shaped by culture. While no systematic cross-cultural study of perceptions of biotechnology exist, there is good evidence to suggest that culture does shape the perception and use of technology. To demonstrate the relationship between culture and biotechnology, let us join the masses of Japan watchers and commentators and address certain features of Japanese culture by way of comparison with the west. Other societies will not be ignored but Japan will dominate the discussion much as they seem to dominate what is written in business. With some latitude for variation, these comments on Japan have parallels in other Asian countries.

There is much in the way of indirect evidence to argue that public responses to biotechnology in Japan are conceptualized and organized in a way that is consistent with tradition. It was a surprise to the author to see that, in the Genetic Engineering News 1990 Guide to biotechnology companies, Japan is tied for seventh position with Switzerland at 8 companies (two countries are in each of the second and fourth positions). In 1988 Japan was in ninth place with 6 companies. By way of contrast the United States smokes the rest of the pack with a listing of 524 companies in 1990, up from 390 in

Figure 1. DNAgents 1. (*Reproduced by permission of Eclipse Enterprises.*)

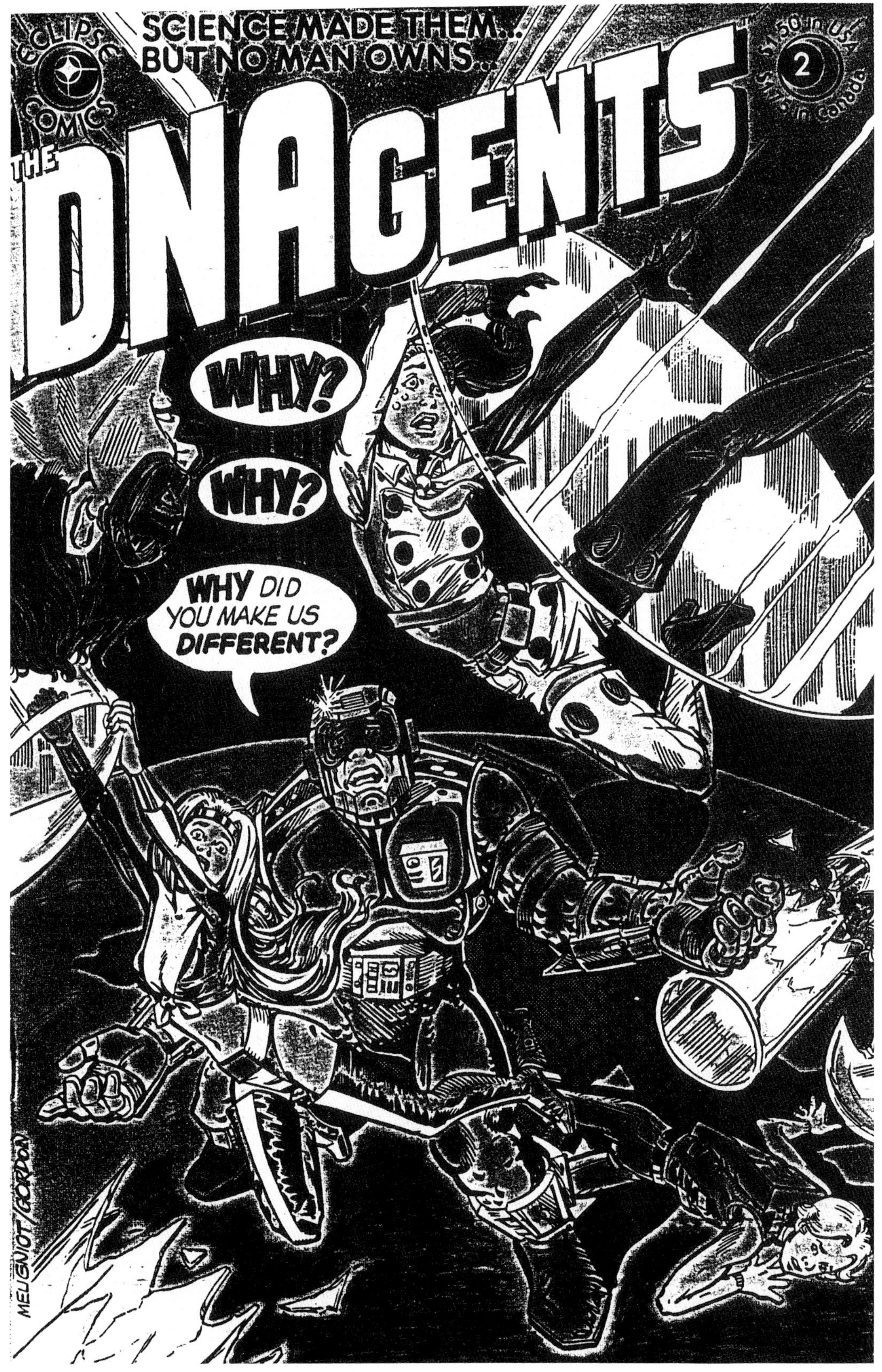

Figure 2. DNAgents 2. (*Reproduced by permission of Eclipse Enterprises.*)

VICTIM OF GENE REARRANGEMENT
chase

SCIENCE, VOL. 2..

Figure 3. Victim of gene rearrangement. (*Reproduced by permission of Science.*)

Possibilities of genetically improving human beings mean man is being tempted to play God as never before, say church l

Figure 4. Possibilities of genetically improving human beings mean man is being tempted to play God as never before, say church leaders. (*Reproduced by permission of The Gazette [Montreal].*)

1986. Canada and the United Kingdom share second place in 1990, not even close to the leader at 34 companies each. But even the distance between the Commonwealth allies and the Japanese is curious.

This disparity screamed for an explanation in view of the paranoia commonly expressed about actual or impending Japanese power in biotechnology. Where in Japan is Biotechnology? Obviously not in upgraded warehouses or on a shelf in some lawyer's office. At least at the level of formal organization, the context for doing biotechnology is different from that of the United States and Europe. Visibility of and identification with something called biotechnology must be differently construed and organized.

A student of Japanese language and culture, and for five years a resident of Japan, hypothesized that the biotechnology companies are probably hidden in fermentation and other industrial companies. Every neighborhood, he explained, has its tofu factory and very few households do not use or make fermentation products. In the West the making of beer, bread and pickles is more likely to be considered a hobby or to be associated with a rural farm tradition. In Japan the making of pickles, miso, and the culturing of bonsai are kinship oriented activities integrated with household economy and esthetics.

A biochemist of Asian origin, on the other hand, believed that the memories of watching his mother ferment tofu gave him a different perception of biotechnology than is the case for his Caucasian peers. At a biotechnology convention in London a British engineer said that "biotechnology needs more engineers, but engineers are afraid of anything living". Of course not all engineers share this perception but what is important is the distinction made and emphasized between living/not-living.

The art of shaking to nurture the growth of microscopic organisms is an ancient tradition in Japan that has a presence at every level of its social organization i.e. from family to corporation. Biotechnology would not be perceived as something new or dangerous because it is so everyday. This does not mean that there has been no opposition to biotechnology and genetic engineering for indeed there has been; but the effectiveness of the opposition even during the scientific catharsis over containment of recombinant viruses has had little impact.

The relative freedom with which biotechnology operates in Japan, recently emphasized in an article in the Financial Times (March 28, 1990), can be quickly stood on its head. When the mercury poisoning of fish was first described at Minamata in Japan, and the threat to the eating of fish was considered, the government acted swiftly and totally in restricting the potential hazards from mercury poisoning. The perceived threat to Japanese well being, symbolically represented in a highly valued food item, resulted in strong government action against polluters. But technology did not suffer and there has been no anti-technology bias except for some fringe groups.

Biotechnology is differently imbedded in Japanese culture than it is in Western and, in particular, American culture. The units of rights, duties and responsibilities that function to maintain a biotechnology industry are differently organized in Japan and in the West. This difference in structure can be functionally linked with differences in beliefs about nature.

The symbolic significance of fish brings us to a second point concerning a contrast between Japan and the West and its importance in forming perceptions of biotechnology. The point refers to contrasts in conceptions of nature and how this organizes beliefs and values. Perceptions of biotechnology must be seen in its broader context of being about the gonads and the meaning and organization of life. Biotechnology, and its association with genetic engineering, puts it into the same league as abortion issues and issues of reproductive technology.

In Japan an abortion is as easy to come by as a valium is in the United States. Organ transplants, on the other hand, are rarely performed and this medical procedure lags by about 20 years of experience in comparison with Western countries. Japan has no legal definition of death and the performance of services (*kuyō*) for the souls of aborted fetuses (*mizugo kuyō*) has become a booming business. The contrast with the West needs no amplification; the lens of culture through which nature is observed concentrates perceptions on different focal points.

Services for the souls of animals and objects are common in Japan. Many such *kuyō* for specific species began in this century — for slaughtered cattle by the butcher's guilds or for experimental animals and even bacteria sacrificed in research laboratories. The hayashibara biomedical laboratory in Okayama holds annual memorials for hamsters sacrificed to cancer research. The practice of services for the soul extends also to bicycles used on a pilgrimage, dancers' fans, tea bowls and flowers.[13]

In the Judeo-Christian tradition soul is a unique attribute of humans; in Japan it is an attribute of nonhumans as well, though the souls of nonhumans are not considered to be the same as human souls. There is therefore a socialization experience for the youth of Japan that has no parallel in the West. The extension of magical power to locker room socks and football jerseys does not have the moral and institutional sanction of normal behavior present in Japanese *kuyo*. Hemingway's typewriter was not burned, as are writing brushes, to release the spirit of the human with which it was associated.

Finally, a survey of Japanese and U.S. views on science published in 1987 as part of a National Science Foundation report showed that whereas between 43% and 47% of Americans expressed disbelief in human evolution only 12% of Japanese rejected evolution. The interpretation given the survey results pushes the argument that Japanese are more knowledgeable about science than are Americans. The alternative explanation is that the Japanese are not so constrained by the Book of Genesis as are Americans.

Perceptions of biotechnology in Japan are just as firmly rooted to the problems of production and reproduction as they are elsewhere. It is difficult to know exactly how Japanese conceptions of nature, or their pedestrian relationship with things that bubble and grow, colors their perceptions of biotechnology. At a minimum we can speculate that there is a functional relationship between Japanese culture, how the business of biotechnology is organized and even what kinds of questions Japanese scientists ask.

PERCEPTIONS FROM WITHIN

It will be instructive to devote some space to a consideration of what can be stated about perceptions from within the biotechnology business. There is a limited amount of empirical data to work from but some assertions can be made about self identification in relation to the outside world and identification and perceptions that people inside companies have of each other. The importance of these dynamics for public perceptions should be obvious since the image projected of oneself will help establish how others respond to you. In negotiating a position on the treadmill of production the absence of a clear identification of a biotechnology industry and internal conflicts between scientists and managers probably played a role in setting the public agenda for biotechnology.

Identifying as an Industry

There is little difficulty in accepting the science part of biotechnology but the business part seems a bit of a phantom. In 1985 there were still whispers being heard at biotechnology meeting-cum trade shows that biotechnology is not an industry. The service people in the booths were selling and it did not matter much what kind of show was going on next door at the scientific sessions. They were not, of course, selling biotechnology products, but products to make biotechnology products. For the service sector in the hardware end or the software end biotechnology was another [or, for some, just a renamed] market niche.

In terms of self identification the gap between the availability of marketable products and something called a "biotechnology industry" proved frustrating. After all there were dozens of government reports and ministerial studies from around the world extolling the potential benefits from biotechnology developments to convey to the layperson a sense of legitimacy and concreteness. In theory at least governments declared a willingness to embrace the latest instalment from industrialized science.

According to some analysts it was around 1970 that the global economic status began to shift toward the Far East. The traditional alpha position of Western economic clout began to drop in rank according to indicators of trade balance, budget deficits and sizes of banks. As manufacturing dominance slipped from West to East high technology enterprises were targeted by governments as a means for putting the breaks on economic slippage. Alpha status was to be regained, or alternatively captured, by outcompeting and out-innovating in high technology industries. Local and national governments were producing glossy brochures exclaiming the virtues and advantages of locating within their tax borders, but the number of companies out there was more apparent than real.

Much of what has happened to the development and evolution of biotechnology can be attributed to its being lumped with aerospace technology and computer technology as salvation enterprises in achieving economic success and by implication improving the quality of life. Alvin Toffler in his book *The Third Wave* includes biotechnology within his vision of the future.

The process of identifying a biotechnology industry was helped along in no small measure by these government perceptions of the value of supporting, at least in theory, a high tech venture and equally by the futuristic visions of academics about the potential for biotechnology as a way of coping with limited energy and food resources. Herbert Boyer appeared on the cover of Time Magazine in 1981 and some of the infant biotechnology companies received widespread coverage and public attention.

The image imposed on biotechnology from the outside and promoted from within was that of improving on the quality of life on two fronts. On the one hand there was the potential from biotechnology as an engine of economic growth and development while second there were the benefits to be gained from the social value of its products. It is in the latter that anxieties about self-identification were nurtured. It was a common occurrence to talk about how only the service sector for biotechnology was profiting and some came close to asserting that really "the emperor had no clothes".

The process of self identification seems however to have matured even though the number of marketable products is small: about a dozen according to the Industrial Biotechnology Association, but with a much larger number(just under one hundred) waiting for approval. Criteria for membership in trade associations have been established to the point where it is possible to exclude certain kinds of companies seen only as servicing the industry and in 1989 just over $500 million was targeted to something identified by the money markets as "biotechnology". This leaves no more than a few diehards to insist that the biotechnology business is but a dressed up version of industrial microbiology or pharmaceuticals. One no longer expects to hear from CEOs, as was common in 1985, that biotechnology is not really an industry.

That argument was based on the observation that something called industrial biotechnology has been around for a long time and, in the absence of an identifiable product, what was the point anyway! In 1982 Scientific American devoted an entire issue to Industrial Microbiology, not to Biotechnology as it would probably now be called. The majority of participants from the first International Conference on the Commercial Applications and Implications of Biotechnology (Biotech '83, London) were conspicuous by their lack of association with identifiable biotechnology companies. Clearly, however, there was an uncertain dynamic and future being nurtured. What was going on was neatly summarized by a British government official as follows:

DNA (makes) **RNA** (makes) **Protein** (makes) **Money**

Eventually this formula crystalized as a biotechnology industry but this maturity of self identification is recent and it must be recognized that a good deal of public posturing and negotiating was taking place during a period of doubtful or limited attachment to an identifiable group. What appears however to have been consistent is a belief in the value of the work being done for the general improvement of the human species and the adventure of uniting business and life science. The translation of biological theory into engineering pulled together a blend of individuals — bench scientists from microbiology, biochemistry, plant pathology, etc., as well as venture capitalists and entrepreneur business managers that created an uncertain dynamic and a hopeful future. Initially, and without some clearly identifiable products, the presentation of self as a unified and legitimate entity must have been difficult. This difficulty was compounded by the sometimes public disagreements and conflicts that developed between scientists and managers.

Taming Scientists and Managers

Frank Dubinskas[14] in an ethnographic analysis of biotechnology companies called attention to the "culture chasm" that can exist between scientists and managers in biotechnology companies. Dubinskas demonstrated that within biotechnology companies there is a distinction to the made between how managers and scientists use and perceive time and how this affects company operations. Simply stated Dubinskas argues that the quarterly statement has no counterpart in the lab report. Scientists cannot guarantee the conversion of an idea to a dividend within this or even the next fiscal year. One exasperated venture capitalist remarked that "scientists weren't real", by which he meant that their image of how the world turned, especially the business world, was naive at best; there were of course, he later remarked, some exceptions. It may be more difficult to find these exceptions than it is to find money.

The attribute of differences in time perspective identified by Dubinskas for scientists and managers is a function of differences in patterns of socialization during education. The structure of class projects, especially team-focused case studies for management students as opposed to individually oriented laboratory benchwork for science students, is said by Dubinskas to create tension and mis-communication between scientists and managers. Importantly the process of socialization creates for the scientist an emphasis on intellectual concern over economic concerns and one can hardly expect that loyalty to ideas would be quickly abandoned for loyalty to shareholders.

Many observations and questioning of scientists who have made the jump from the academic life to industry indicate a desire, if not an actual belief, that in the firm they could more freely pursue intellectual prizes than was possible within the university. Many companies have structured their working environment to give reign to basic research and sanction the pursuit of the intellect by encouraging journal publication. But differences of opinion over what a scientist can or cannot do vis-a-vis matters of intellect have resulted in the parting of ways in some cases. Thus the argument that [some] scientists are not real. Reality is for the private sector in the market, in prizing expression in things and services. Perceptions held of biotechnology companies as being something akin to research institutes clashes with the requirement for quarterly reports on corporate earnings. This phenomenon of a culture clash may be short lived since new recruits into biotechnology will not have had the academic experiences of their predecessors.

SUMMARY AND CONCLUSION

The aim of this chapter is to provide some tools for thinking about public perceptions of biotechnology. Rather than simply describing what it is we know about how different groups view the biotechnology business, the objective has been to confront the problem of defining public perceptions, to specify its social functions within the biotechnology industry and to examine what it is we know about how perceptions of biotechnology are formed.

This chapter has considered two components of public perception each of which addresses a different level of understanding and framework for explanation. The first is about macro issues — the big picture: it is about how perceptions of biotechnology are shaped by culture and social structure. The status a society gives its scientists, the allocation of capital, beliefs about the quality of life, the distribution of income and education will affect both how biotechnology is conducted as an activity and how it is perceived by the general population. This level of understanding is necessary for those whose interests are in the broader issues of social change, especially as this might impinge upon strategic planning.

The second division is about micro issues — the everyday activity of working to make biotechnology a legitimate way in which to earn a living. Here perceptions are shaped in face to face encounters where decisions are made about doing biotechnology. The encounters involve managers, lawyers, laypeople, salesmen, scientists, government bureaucrats, students, journalists, technology transfer officers, investment brokers and many others. Understanding this level of perception formation is more directly relevant for the participant in a biotechnology-related job, especially those that are removed from the solitude and craft of a laboratory bench. For the research biochemist who is thrust into the role of explaining to an agricultural community the mysteries of genetically engineered vaccines for pigs, or the benefits of engineering herbicide resistance into crops, the psychological dynamics of image formation are important. The social dynamics of image formation and definitions of the situation are critical in day to day operations and impact on morale and on the bottom line. In practical application then, knowledge about image formation enhances the ability to deal effectively with the public, government officials and business people.

Leo Marx[6] gives a vivid portrayal of the relationship between technology, social values and American culture in his now classic book on the tensions between the pastoral ideal and technological progress. He describes the value conflicts of technology in the American dream and exposes the contradictions that confront human behavior in relation to technology. Freud considered the search for the pastoral ideal as a cultural universal thereby creating by fiat a conflict between nature and culture. The conflict is both sociological and psychological inasmuch as technology is internalized and personalized but requires management in a larger social framework.

The human condition especially as presently constituted requires technological skill and creativity. The demands on the planet are great and the innovations developed and yet to come from biotechnology are being honestly applied to meet perceived human wants and desires. Yet, as with any technology, bringing the product to market is a political and value laden process and not a neutral event without impact. Public perceptions of biotechnology can be understood as a response to technology in general and importantly in recent years to the environmental additions and withdrawals that accompany technological development. In addition to this general response the special association between biotechnology and the mechanisms for reproduction and heredity make the industry particularly open to public comment.

REFERENCES

1. Sgaramella, Vitorrio. (1982) Why a Critical Transition? In Whalen, W.J. and Black, S., eds. *From Genetic Experimentation to Biotechnology — The Critical Transition*. New York: John Wiley and Sons.
2. Rifkin, J. (1983). *Algeny*. New York: Viking Press.

3. Lewis, R. (1960). *The Evolution Man*. London: Penguin.
4. Crichton, M. (1980). *Congo*. New York: Avon Books.
5. Office of Technology Assessment, U.S. Congress (1987). *Public Perception of Biotechnology (New Developments in Biotechnology, 2)*. OTA-BP-BA-45, U.S. Government Printing Office, Washington, D.C.
6. Marx, L. (1964). *The Machine in the Garden: Technology and the Pastoral Ideal in America*. New York: Oxford University Press.
7. Sutton, F.X., Harris, S.E., Kayson, C. and Tobin, J. (1956). *The American Business Creed*. New York: Schocken Books.
8. Handler, P. (1980). Public Doubts About Science. *Science*, **208**, 1093.
9. Slovic, P. (1987). Perceptions of risk. *Science*, **236**, 280–285.
10. Koshland, D. (1987). Ice Minus and Jobs Minus. *Science*, **236**, 761.
11. Douglas, M. and Wildavsky, A. (1982). *Risk and Culture*. Berkeley: University of California Press.
12. Downey, G.I. (1987). Risk in Culture: The American Conflict Over Nuclear Power. *Cultural Anthropology*, **1**, 388–412.
13. Asquith, P.J. (in press). The Japanese Idea of Soul in Animals and Objects as Evidenced by *Kuyō* Services. In Daly, D.J. and Sekine, T. (eds). *Proc. Japan Social Sciences Assoc. Canada*. Captus Press.
14. Dubinskas, F.A. (1988). Janus Organizations: Scientists and Managers in Genetic Engineering Firms. In Dubinskas, F.A. (ed). *Making Time, Ethnographies of High – Technology Organizations*. Philadelphia: Temple University Press.

FURTHER READING

Caldwell, L.K. (1987). *Biocracy: Public policy and the Life Sciences*. Boulder: Westview Press.

Carrol, J.D. (1973). Participatory Technology. In Barbour, I.G., ed. *Western Man and Environmental Ethics: Attitudes Towards Nature and Technology*. Reading, Mass.: Addison-Wesley. pp. 204–224.

Ellul, J. (1964). *The Technological Society*. New York: Alfred A. Knopf, Inc.

Freudenburg, W.R. (1988). Perceived Risk, Real Risk: Social Science and the Art of Probabilistic Risk Assessment. *Science* vol. 242, pp. 44–49.

Krimsky, S. (1982). *Genetic Alchemy*. Cambridge: M.I.T. Press.

Miller, J.D. (1982). Attitudes Towards Genetic Modification Research: An Analysis of the Views of the Sputnik Generation. *Science, Technology and Human Values*. Vol. 7, No. 39, Spring, pp. 37–43.

Pacey, A. (1983). *The Culture of Technology*. Cambridge: The MIT Press.

Ravitz, J.R. (1971). *Scientific Knowledge and its Social Problems*. New York: Oxford University Press.

Schmandt, J. (1984). Regulation and Science. *Science, Technology and Human Values*. Vol. 9 issue 1, Winter, pp. 23–38.

Schnaiberg, A. (1980). *The Environment: From Surplus to Scarcity*. New York: Oxford University Press.

Teich, A.H., Levin, M.A., Pace, J.H., eds. (1985). *Biotechnology and the Environment, Risk and Regulation*. Washington, DC: American Association for the Advancement of Science.

Toffler, A. (1980). *The Third Wave*. New York: Bantam Books.

Chapter 8

The Regulation of Biotechnology in the United States and Europe

Robert B. Nicholas and Brian Ager

INTRODUCTION

The discovery by Watson and Crick of the structure of DNA opened the way towards a greater understanding of the process of life. Flowing in turn from this came the ability in the early 1970s to alter more precisely an organism's genetic makeup. This improved ability to carry out genetic engineering (relative to more conventional methods of inducing genetic change, such as selection and mutation) brought the possibility of tremendous benefits for mankind. At the same time, the public proved to be ambivalent about genetic engineering. At first there were safety concerns focusing on conjectural risks to human health arising from microorganisms with novel genetic combinations. Latter concerns have been expressed about the ability of newly formed organisms to disrupt the ecological balance. Fears about the morality of genetic engineering have also surfaced. These range from concerns over interference with the natural order in microorganisms, plants and animals to the potential "engineering" of humans. It should not be surprising, therefore, that as the science has advanced, the development of a regulatory structure in the United States and elsewhere has been difficult and at times controversial.

The regulation of biotechnology from research through product marketing and disposal in many countries involves a complex series of laws. Many of these were enacted before rDNA and related technologies were considered to have commercial potential. The essential questions for those who write the laws are:

1. whether the new applications of molecular biology present risks that are not adequately addressed by existing laws and, if so,
2. whether an adequate system of regulatory oversight can be developed within the existing statutory framework.

The answers to these questions involve complex interactions among public perceptions, scientific unknowns and certainties, and political interest groups. This type of debate takes place, of course, against the political, social and legislative backgrounds in individual countries.

This chapter discusses the evolution of the regulatory framework for biotechnology in the United States and in Europe. An overview of the principal applicable policies, laws, regulations, and agency procedures is provided. The chapter is divided into three sections: Part I reviews the history of the regulation of rDNA research in the USA; Part II discusses the United States regulatory framework; and Part III reviews the European context.

THE HISTORICAL CONTEXT

The Environmental Decade

For decades the scientific community has been busy first by seeking to discover the structure of DNA, and thereafter, trying to understand how DNA is organized and how it functions. Knowledge about how to manipulate DNA and hence to begin to generate many new products by biological means has evolved as a direct result of the dramatic increase in scientific understanding about basic biology at the cellular level. Between the 1950s and the mid-1970s, a period when efforts to understand gene regulation were being made almost exclusively in university laboratories, the political community remained relatively unconcerned about the regulation of DNA research.

The change in political attitude towards the regulation of recombinant DNA (rDNA) research in the United States can be traced to concerns first expressed by the scientific community at the June, 1973 Gordon Conference. These concerns addressed the possibility that combining the DNA from a certain tumor virus with *Escherichia coli* (*E. coli*), a microorganism adapted for survival in the human intestine, potentially might prove hazardous to laboratory workers and to the public.

The significant points in the ensuing scientific debate are well-known to students of the rDNA controversies: they included a call by a committee of the National Academy of Science (NAS) for a moratorium on certain rDNA research in June, 1974; the convening of a major international scientific meeting at Asilomar, California in January 1975; and the establishment of the Recombinant DNA Advisory Committee, "RAC" (as the Committee came to be known), by the National Institutes of Health and publication of the draft "Guidelines for Research Involving Recombinant DNA Molecules" ("Guidelines")[1].

Public discussion and political reaction to the heated scientific debate led to numerous hearings before the U.S. Congress and resulted in various legislative measures being introduced and debated. Extensive lobbying by the scientific community largely defused congressional concern; however, establishment of RAC and adoption of the Guidelines generally shifted the focus of debate from Congress to NIH.

The Guidelines represented an astute political compromise between the public's expression of concern about the safety of recombinant organisms, should they be accidentally released into the environment, and the scientific community's concern about unnecessary and burdensome government control of science and scientific freedom. The Guidelines:

(a) provided explicit safety standards for experimentation, which set forth levels of biological and physical containment for experimentation;
(b) approved certain experiments while prohibiting others, including those involving the "deliberate release into the environment of any organism containing recombinant DNA;" and
(c) established an administrative structure to focus discussion and review of experiments and to allow quick changes in the Guidelines as new data became available.

The Guidelines were binding on all federal grantees, and privately funded industry voluntarily observed the Guidelines as well. This universal compliance provided public assurance (and, thereby, comfort to the political sector) that genetic engineering experiments were being actively reviewed by the Government. At the same time, because guidelines, rather than regulations, were issued and because oversight was to be conducted by the National Institutes of Health (a non-regulatory, scientific-research agency), the concerns of the scientific community about government interference were satisfactorily addressed. The non-statutory NIH procedures and peer-review approach of the RAC also conform more closely to the culture of the scientific community.

The fact that this voluntary system was politically acceptable was all the more extraordinary when viewed from the perspective of the prevailing general political climate. Concerns expressed about unbridled technological development and about nuclear power and public disclosures about environmental pollution from the chemical revolution led, during this same time period, to the passage of most of the landmark environmental legislation in the United States. Perhaps it was only the fact that during this time rDNA research was viewed as the province of university scientists, and not as the technology of an industry, that the voluntary system adopted by NIH was accepted by the political sector.

Several important lessons can be drawn from this period, lessons crucial to understanding the current structure and operation of the regulatory system in the United States:

First, public anxiety about recombinant DNA experimentation can be easily aroused. This concern can, and frequently will, lead to a political reaction in the bureaucracy, (which, in turn, will become more cautious in developing rules and approving products) and in the Congress, which will conduct oversight hearings and seek to pass new legislation.

Second, the scientific community can play a crucial role in providing input into the political process, and can help assure both public and political understanding of the technology.

Third, the speed with which products of rDNA research can enter the commercial marketplace will be dependent on maintaining the confidence of both the public and the business community.

The New Biotechnology

In the early 1970s, entrepreneurs formed the first companies in the United States specifically to develop the commercial potential in biological research. Biotechnology, the term coined to describe the new business, became big news, with frequent stories concerning extremely successful public stock offerings by the new companies. Today in the United States there are hundreds of new companies and countless established companies seeking to use biotechnology to improve production of old products and to produce new products for the pharmaceutical, agricultural and industrial markets.

As long as research was conducted in the laboratory, oversight of rDNA research remained the sole province of NIH. Even as biomedically oriented companies initially sought to develop biotechnology into the business of the future, the political sector paid it little attention. By voluntarily adopting the NIH Guidelines, industrial research was able to remain free of external federal regulation, with the RAC becoming the *de facto* reviewer of all rDNA research.

As genetic experimentation advanced, the NIH modified its Guidelines to permit field testing in limited circumstances. In 1978 NIH removed from the Guidelines the absolute prohibition on releases into the environment of genetically modified organisms. Experimental releases still were generally prohibited, but the Director of NIH was allowed to grant waivers on a case-by-case basis after public notice and review by the RAC. The NIH Director approved the first experimental release of a recombinant organism in 1981, a Stanford University field trial of a corn plant which had been transformed by corn DNA. In 1982, NIH further modified the Guidelines by completely removing the six-year prohibition on environmental release and classifying environmental release experiments as ones that "required RAC review and NIH and IBC[2] approval before initiation." During the next year, NIH approved applications by a Cornell University scientist to field-test tomato and tobacco plants transformed with bacterial (*E. coli* K–12) and yeast (*Saccharomyces cerevisiae*) DNA using pollen as a vector.

Although neither the Stanford nor Cornell plant experiments generated public attention, controversy did arise in late 1982 when NIH considered a similar request by researchers at the University of California at Berkeley to field test "ice-minus" bacteria on frost sensitive crops.[3] NIH approved the experiment in mid-1983; however, the resulting controversy, lawsuits filed against NIH by a public interest group, and reviews by other federal, state and local agencies, delayed the actual experiment until 1987. A nearly identical experiment proposed by an industrial concern was also held up until 1987; the morning before the test was to begin, vandals trespassed onto the field test site and uprooted the strawberry plants to which the bacteria were to be applied.

Thus, with time, the system of Guidelines and oversight by NIH came under increasing public and legislative scrutiny. Media attention, during the mid-1970s and early 1980s, to advances in basic science and to the application of science to the marketplace reawakened public interest in genetic engineering. Although much of the public attention focused on the possibility of new medical cures, questions about environmental impact and safety were soon raised, as well, precipitating a new round of regulatory discussions. Two factors accounted for the reawakening political interest: *first*, the shift from a near-total biomedical application of the technology to applications, including agricultural, environmental and industrial uses and, *second*, the shift from a spotlight on academic scientists working in the laboratory to industrial scientists working with a market orientation.

In Congress, the regulatory debate began in 1983 with hearings before the Oversight Subcommittee of the Science and Technology Committee in the House of Representatives. Although the initial focus of the hearings was the proposed introduction of genetically modified organisms into the environment, the hearings set off a broad examination of the laws applicable to the regulation of the products of biotechnology and the implementation of those laws by the Executive Branch.[4]

In early 1984, the Cabinet Council Working Group on Biotechnology, headed by the President's Science Advisor, was established to examine the applicability of existing laws to biotechnology and to sort out the varying responsibilities of federal agencies. The issues and questions raised in Congress and in the Executive Branch, each operating independently, were similar to those raised at the time of the initial debate in the 1970s and revolved around safety and scientific freedom. However, the question of commercialization and international competitiveness added new dimensions and additional actors to the political debate.

All of the questions that had been successfully avoided in the 1970s were to become central to the current discussions. Unlike most efforts to regulate, which are undertaken after an industry is well established and after problems are manifest, the congressional and Cabinet Council efforts to develop a regulatory program were undertaken without any demonstration of significant harm and before any products were on the market.

HOW THE BUREAUCRACY COPES: AN OVERVIEW OF THE U.S. REGULATORY FRAMEWORK

Regulation of research, development, and the commercialization of biotechnology is still in a formative stage. By 1989, however, many of the basic principles had been settled. Absent a major unfavorable event (such as a significant ecological disruption from a planned introduction) it is not likely that a new statute of broad application, nor a new agency will be established; the basic framework of statutes dividing agency jurisdictions and setting decisional criteria will not shift dramatically because biotechnology is involved. Indeed, there is a growing consensus that the technique of using rDNA is not itself a cause for special attention. Rather, any regulatory proceeding should focus primarily on the potential impact of the product and not on how it was produced.[5]

The basic framework for the federal agencies involved in regulating commercial biotechnology was set forth in June 1986 by the Office of Science Technology Policy (OSTP), headed by the President's Science Advisor.[6] Four general principles form the foundation of this regulatory Coordinated Framework:

Existing Authority

Although many of the applicable laws were enacted long before biotechnology was conceived, the existing statutes can be utilized to regulate biotechnology and neither a new agency, nor broad new statutory authority, is necessary.

Product Priority

Current statutes will be implemented so as to regulate the *product*, rather than the process used to develop or manufacture the product.

Individual Review

Regulation will be on a case-by-case basis until there is sufficient data with which to make broad determinations about safety.

Coordinated Framework

Coordination and cooperation will be developed among the agencies so that overlaps are avoided and multiple reviews, where statutorily mandated, can proceed concurrently.

The Coordinated Framework discusses specifically the laws and policies of five federal agencies:

1. the National Institutes of Health (NIH);
2. the Food and Drug Administration (FDA);
3. the Environmental Protection Agency (EPA);
4. the Department of Agriculture (USDA); and
5. the Occupational Safety and Health Administration (OSHA).

The major responsibilities of the five agencies are:

(A) *NIH*: federally sponsored rDNA research;
(B) *FDA*: human biologics and pharmaceuticals, animal drugs, animal and human food and food additives, medical devices, and cosmetics;
(C) *EPA*: chemicals and pesticides;
(D) *USDA*: animal biologics and plant pests; and
(E) *OSHA*: occupational safety and health.

A brief discussion of their regulatory programs follows. (In addition to the agency specific statutory mandates discussed, all Federal agencies are required to examine the potential environmental consequences of proposed actions.[7] (See also Table 1.)

Table 1
Agencies Responsible for Approval of Commercial Biotechnology Products

Biotechnology Products	Responsible Agencies
Foods/food additives	FDA,* FSIS[a]
Human drugs, medical devices, and biologics	FDA
Animal drugs	FDA
Animal biologics	APHIS
Other contained uses	EPA
Plants and animals	APHIS,[c] FSIS,[a] FDA[b]
Pesticide microorganisms released in the environment	EPA,[d] APHIS[c]
Other uses (microorganisms):	
Intergeneric combination	EPA,[d] APHIS[c]
Intrageneric combination:	
Pathogenic source organism:	APHIS
1. Agricultural use	
2. Nonagricultural use	EPA,[d] APHIS[c]
Nonpathogenic source organisms	EPA Report
Nonengineered pathogens:	
1. Agricultural use	APHIS
2. Nonagricultural use	EPA,[d] APHIS[c]
Nonengineered Nonpathogens	EPA Report

* Designates lead agency where jurisdictions may overlap.
[a] FSIS, Food Safety and Inspection Service, under the Assistant Secretary of Agriculture for Marketing and Inspection Services, is responsible for food use.
[b] FDA is involved when in relation to a food use.
[c] APHIS, Animal and Plant Health Inspection Service, is involved when the microorganism is plant pest, animal pathogen, or regulated article requiring a permit.
[d] EPA requirement will only apply to environmental release under a "significant new use rule" that EPA intends to propose.
SOURCE: 51 Fed. Reg. 23339.

A. National Institutes of Health (NIH)

NIH conducts an extensive intramural program of biomedical research and is the major government source of grants for biomedical research to the academic and nonprofit research institutions.

Under the Recombinant DNA Guidelines, NIH is responsible for overseeing all federally funded rDNA research. Until 1986, the Guidelines were also the *de facto* standard for industrially sponsored research, and the NIH exercised considerable informal control over all rDNA activities. However, the responsibility of NIH has diminished as other federal agencies developed regulations governing the conduct of field and other non-laboratory applications of rDNA and related technologies.

The Guidelines are intended to help insure the safety of research involving rDNA by classifying experiments according to the degree of perceived risk and subjecting them to varying degrees of biological and physical containment. Institutions covered by the Guidelines are required to establish Institutional Biosafety Committees (IBCs). These committees, composed primarily of persons affiliated with the sponsoring institution, review and make decisions on most experiments; decisions about higher risk experiments are made by the NIH.

B. Food and Drug Administration (FDA)

FDA's principal responsibilities include regulation of human and animal drugs, human biologics, diagnostic and other medical devices, human and animal foods and food additives, and cosmetics. The Federal Food, Drug and Cosmetic Act[8] and, for human biologics, the Public Health Service Act,[9] generally require that a drug, biologic or medical device developer establish safety and efficacy to FDA's satisfaction before marketing. Generally, the benefits of the product must outweigh the risks before the FDA will approve a product.

FDA has not established a new regulatory system for products produced by genetically engineered organisms, but has, where necessary, supplemented its extensive regulations for premarket, testing, manufacturing, and post-market monitoring of traditionally produced products. To date FDA has approved several rDNA produced drugs including: interferon, human insulin, human growth hormone, tissue plasminogen activator, hepatitis vaccine and erythropoietin or EPO. Dozens of drugs are in various stages of clinical investigation and hundreds of monoclonal-based diagnostic tests are currently being marketed.

Foods are not subject to premarket clearance by FDA. However, FDA has authority to insure the health of the food supply by taking legal action when a food is adulterated and by requiring premarket approval for "substances deliberately added to food" (food additives).[10]

Biotechnology companies are working to change the genetic characteristics of foods and to improve the processing of traditional foods. For example, corn, rape seed, sun flowers and other crops are being engineered to change protein content, increase oil production, and enhance taste, while microbes used to produce food enzymes, and yeast used to brew beer, have been engineered to improve processing characteristics. Potentially, all of these changes in food could be considered adulterations and require premarket clearance by FDA.

FDA has not yet issued guidance on how it will evaluate such products; however, it currently has under review petitions involving food enzymes produced by genetically engineered microbes and transgenic tomatoes.

C. U.S. Environmental Protection Agency (EPA)

EPA's authority encompasses regulation of chemicals, pest control agents, air and water discharges, and hazardous waste disposal. To date, EPA's regulation of biotechnology has focused on microbes introduced into the environment. Genetically engineered microorganisms are reviewed by EPA as chemicals under the Toxic Substance Control Act (TSCA),[11] based on the rationale that "DNA is a chemical." When used for pest control purposes, microbes are subject to the requirements of the Federal Insecticide, Fungicide and Rodenticide Act (FIFRA),[12] as biological pest control agents.

TSCA requires a manufacturer of a chemical not already in commerce to submit data to EPA before the chemical is placed on the market. EPA must allow the marketing of the chemical unless its use presents an unreasonable risk to human health or the environment. EPA has developed separate regulations under TSCA for genetically modified microorganisms that require review of new microorganisms (microbes containing genetic material from dissimilar source organisms), prior to any field trials.

FIFRA is a risk-benefit statute; before a pesticide or similar product can be registered, the registrant must submit data sufficient to enable EPA to determine that the product, when used in accordance with widespread and commonly recognized practice, will not cause, or significantly increase the risk of, unreasonable adverse effects to humans or the environment. EPA's 1986 regulations require that data be submitted to EPA prior even to small-scale field testing for pesticidal purposes of any nonindigenous microorganisms, including any genetically engineered microbes. To date, EPA has allowed several small-scale tests of genetically engineered organisms.

Field testing of plants engineered to enhance pesticidal properties are regulated by USDA, but there is continuing discussion about whether a pesticide registration will be required before such a plant can be marketed and whether EPA will set a tolerence level for pesticide residues allowable on raw agricultural commodities. It is possible that a developer of a food from a transgenic plant which has enhanced pesticidal properties may need to submit three applications: one to USDA for approval to field test the plant; one to EPA to have a tolerence set or waiver granted, if there is a pesticidal residue in the edible portion of the plant; and one to EPA for a pesticide registration.

Although EPA has yet to face these questions, with field trials of three dozen transgenic plants already approved by USDA, including several with pest or viral resistance, EPA will soon have to establish a regulatory policy. EPA is currently in the process of refining its regulatory approach and a proposal is expected by mid-1990. Among the issues EPA is expected to address are questions about taxonomy (e.g. when is an organism new?) and how to regulate small-scale field trials. (At present, EPA reviews all small-scale trials of covered organisms, yet there is concern that EPA will be unnecessarily overburdened, and that routine screening of microbes for research purposes will become prohibitively expensive and time-consuming for companies.) Significant other issues remain as to how EPA will handle large-scale field trials and registrations of genetically modified organisms.

D. U.S. Department of Agriculture (USDA)

USDA's responsibilities include authority over importation and interstate movement of plant pests, licensing of animal biologics, and inspection of meat and poultry. The Animal Plant Health and Inspection Service (APHIS) is the agency within USDA responsible for the regulation of genetically engineered plants, microorganisms and animal biologics. APHIS derives its authority from the Plant Pest Act,[13] the Plant Quarrantine Act,[14] and the Virus, Serum and Toxin Act.[15]

In June 1987, APHIS finalized a separate regulatory scheme that requires notification before importation, interstate movement or release into the environment of a "regulated article": an organism which

(a) is genetically engineered, and
(b) the donor, host or vector is from a plant pest source.

Notifications to APHIS must include data that:

1. identify the host, donor and recipient organisms;
2. identify the source of the organisms and method of movement;
3. include a description of the molecular biology of the system and the anticipated expression of the altered genetic material;
4. reveal the purpose, protocol and location of the field trial; and
5. describe the containment and mitigation measures.

APHIS will generally permit the requested action if it can be undertaken without risk to agriculture. As of July 1989, APHIS had approved approximately forty field releases of genetically engineered plants, but only a handful of microbes.

At the present time, no additional requirements have been established by APHIS for large-scale field trials or commercial marketing of plants or microbes. Discussions are ongoing between EPA, FDA, and USDA about how to regulate large-scale testing and commercial distribution of genetically engineered plants. The agencies are examining the regulatory mechanisms for transgenic fish and other animals as well.

APHIS regulates animal biologics under a premarket licensing program similar to that used by FDA for animal drugs. A license applicant must demonstrate purity, safety, potency and efficacy to obtain a product license and must also obtain a license for its production facility. APHIS has not developed separate regulations for genetically modified biologics. To date, APHIS has licensed only a handful of genetically engineered animal biologics.

E. Occupational Safety and Health Administration (OSHA)

OSHA is part of the Department of Labor, and has as its primary responsibility the protection of workers. The Occupational Safety and Health Act,[16] enacted in 1970, gives OSHA responsibility for insuring a safe workplace and provides OSHA with authority to issue safety and health standards, to inspect workplaces, and to insure enforcement with the Act.

In the June, 1986 Coordinated Framework, OSHA determined that no new regulations were necessary to protect workers in the workplace. OSHA noted several existing standards that established workplace exposure limits to various classes of substances, and that mandated employee protective equipment, recordkeeping and hazard communication which, though not specifically issued because of biotechnology, were applicable to biotechnology.

F. Conclusion

The debate about the regulation of biotechnology in the United States continues. Experience to date with transgenic plants and microorganisms is providing data confirming safety of specific applications and reports from scientific societies are generally confirming the approach taken in the Coordinated Framework. The public also appears to be becoming more accepting of some of the applications of biotechnology.

However, as scientific knowledge advances and as new applications of the technology are developed, new questions are being asked. For example, development of transgenic fish and other animals is causing a reexamination of the Framework. Increasingly, questions are being asked by public interest and other groups not about the potential environmental and safety concerns of the new applications, but about social and economic impacts. One example is the debate about the implications for small dairy farms of bovine somatotropin (BST), an animal drug which can be produced using genetically engineered bacteria, and which enhances milk production in dairy cows.

Increasingly, state and local governments also are becoming involved in overseeing field trials of genetically engineered organisms. Several states have passed new legislation, and others are examining their role. Academia and the commercial sector are concerned about the possibility of having to comply with fifty state regulatory regimes, in addition to the Federal Framework.

At the present time, it is likely that the Coordinated Framework will continue to evolve to meet new challenges. The pace of commercialization of biotechnology will, however, in all likelihood, continue to be affected by the complex interaction between public perceptions about the technology and the development of science.

THE EUROPEAN CONTEXT

Overview

In Europe regulatory reactions to genetic engineering took a similar course to events in the United States. The early debate in the United States, as witnessed by the Asilomar and Gordon conferences and the moratorium on certain experiments, was closely watched across the Atlantic.

Several European countries established oversight systems for all experimental work, usually with a non-mandatory notification requirement (except Great Britain, which has legally binding notification regulations). Furthermore, many countries developed detailed guidelines, often modeled on those from the United States. With experience, increasing knowledge, and the absence of any of the postulated adverse effects either to humans or the environment, these oversight mechanisms were relaxed.

Given that there were only postulated, rather than real risks, this was in many ways an unusual type of regulation. More commonly, regulations are in response to demonstrated harm or catastrophies. But with rDNA it has been a case of developing detailed guidelines and controls at the outset of the technology, and then adjusting the stringency of these controls with experience.

During the 1970s rDNA work was largely a research oriented laboratory activity. The establishment of risk assessment procedures meant that such work could be successfully assigned to an appropriate level of laboratory containment in a way that dovetailed long-standing research work with pathogenic microorganisms.

Towards the end of the 1970s several factors combined to allow a downgrading of controls, in general, and the degree of containment required for experiments, in particular. To begin with, increasing experience resulted in increasing confidence in the ability to assess potential risk. Indeed, there was a growing realization that early safety fears about the new biotechnology were exaggerated. Early fears had focused on the possibility of generating new pathogenic microorganisms from relatively harmless bacteria being used as cloning vehicles. A major initial point of debate concerned the introduction of genes from SV40, a virus known to be able to generate tumors in animals, into *E. coli*, a normal inhabitant of the human gut. The question was whether this could confer tumor-forming ability to *E. coli* and, in turn, lead to a new laboratory and public health hazard. This particular fear was dispelled by risk assessment research carried out in the United States. More general fears about the inadvertent creation of pathogens were calmed by the knowledge that pathogenicity is a multifactorial attribute dictated by the coordinated functioning of many genes. This could not be mimicked by the insertion and expression of single genes into an otherwise harmless organism.

In addition, the development and widespread use of technologies to prevent or reduce unintended gene transfer also helped minimize risk and apprehension. This methodology includes the use of disabled host/vector systems: bacterial host strains with reduced ability to survive outside the laboratory, or to colonize the human body, along with vectors (DNA molecules used to transfer engineered DNA into host cells) that are incapable of self-initiated transfer and have a decreased ability to be mobilized. For example, the use of a crippled strain of *E. coli* coupled with a non-mobilizable plasmid vector is considered safer than the use of non-disabled systems because it has reduced ability to transfer genetic material to bacteria indigenous to the human gastrointestinal tract, or other natural habitats.

Finally, increasing knowledge and experience was accompanied by an absence of any observed adverse effects to humans, plants and animals — a record of safety that rDNA work has continued to maintain. The general consensus began to develop that the technique of rDNA is not hazardous *per se*, nor does it give rise to any novel hazard. That is not to say that there is no hazard attached to this type of activity — it does, after all, involve work with microorganisms that may give rise to a hazard of infection, and that may also produce toxic or allergenic effects. But this is irrespective of any technique of genetic modification that may have been used and it arises from the nature of the organism itself. Thus, the realization that biotechnology may be carried out without any undue risk has enabled rDNA activity to be controlled in the same type of regulatory framework as work with micro-organisms, generally.

For the majority of European countries (except Great Britain), oversight of rDNA work and notification schemes remained largely non-mandatory into the early 1980s. In the Federal Republic of Germany, for example, as in the United States, federally funded research was covered by rDNA guidelines, with industry adhering to these laboratory rules on a voluntary basis. In Great Britain, which passed legally binding notification regulations for rDNA work in 1978, the Advisory Committee on Genetic Manipulation (ACGM) serves as the national watchdog body for genetic manipulation. Effectively, ACGM is one of a family of advisory committees under the Health and Safety Commission (HSC), along with other committees covering topics such as Dangerous Pathogens and Toxic Substances.

This relatively stable and relaxed regulatory picture was disrupted by the controversy over "deliberate release" — field trials with genetically engineered organisms. European regulatory agencies closely watched the U.S. debate and, in particular, the "ice-minus" controversy (discussed above). These events reawakened the rDNA debate and introduced a new dimension — concern over safety could not be underwritten with physical containment. For the first time, proposals for open field testing of organisms were being put forward. The concerns, broadened from being mainly oriented to human health and safety, to include the environment in a more direct way than before. Once again, European countries were faced with the need to review their regulatory positions to take this into account. It was in this context that the recommendations and conclusions of a report by the Organization for Economic Cooperation and Development (OECD) proved most useful in pointing the way forward on a broad internationally agreed basis.

The Role of the OECD

The Organization for Economic Cooperation and Development[17] took an important step towards international harmonization with the 1986 publication of "Recombinant DNA

Safety Considerations.[18] This landmark report established a scientific framework for the safe use of recombinant DNA organisms in industry and in the environment at a time when many national regulatory authorities were considering their approach in these areas. The OECD thus took the initiative towards harmonization of the scientific principles underpinning the regulatory approaches of its member countries. This, in turn, facilitates the development of safe biotechnology along common international lines and provides the basis of a consensus on protection of health and the environment. It also leads to the promotion of technological and economic development and the reduction of national barriers to trade in this field.

The principal recommendations in the OECD Report are as follows:

Industrial large-scale rDNA applications

The OECD acknowledged that the vast majority of cases to date have used organisms of intrinsically low risk. A corresponding level of control, based on established good industrial large-scale practice (GILSP), was recommended and criteria for the identification of organisms of low risk were established. The report also listed the basic principles of good practice that should underline this type of work, whatever the risk. Additional control and containment options were described for organisms of higher risk.

Environmental and agricultural applications

The report recognized that, at that time, the final establishment of internationally agreed safety criteria was premature. Accordingly, a provisional approach was recommended, incorporating independent case-by-case review of the potential risks of such proposals, prior to application. The report gave the factors that should be taken into account during risk assessment.

Three fundamental points underly the specific recommendations in the OECD Report. *First*, any risks raised by rDNA organisms are expected to be of the same nature as those associated with conventional organisms. Such risks may, furthermore, be assessed in generally the same way as non-rDNA organisms. *Second*, although rDNA techniques may result in organisms with a combination of traits not observed in nature, rDNA techniques will often have inherently greater predictability compared to conventional methods of modifying organisms. Third, there is no scientific basis to justify *specific* legislation for rDNA organisms, although the report did recommend an examination of existing oversight mechanisms to ensure that adequate control may be achieved.

There is little doubt that this major international report has had, and will continue to have, considerable influence on the development of regulations and guidelines worldwide. As noted in the following section, there are examples in several European countries where the OECD's recommendations and conclusions have been successfully incorporated into existing regulatory structures. As in the 1970s, increasing knowledge and experience will lead to improved ability to assess risks. A vital area for academia, industry, environmental and human safety, and for public confidence will be the follow-up work to the 1986 OECD Report which was initiated in 1988. Important components of this work are the elaboration of the GILSP concept and an attempt to identify further the scientific principles underlying the identification of low or minimal risk small-scale field trials. Both these concepts point the way forward in that they represent attempts to sort and categorize risk concerns on a scientific basis. This is analogous to moves in the 1970s to develop categorization schemes for laboratory work so that rDNA activities could be accommodated in the context of work with non-recombinant organisms.

Oversight of rDNA Activities in European Countries

The response to rDNA work in several European countries, with active research bases in the biological sciences, had clear parallels to United States events. Some examples:

Great Britain . . . published the "Report of the Working Party on the Practice of Genetic Manipulation" (the Williams Report) in 1976, giving detailed consideration of the safety issues raised by rDNA work. This led to the establishment of a national watchdog committee — the Genetic Manipulation Advisory Group (GMAG) in the same year. GMAG was a broadly based body, with representatives from the public, industry and trade unions, as well as scientific and medical experts. It was set up under the Department of Education and Science and its Secretariat was provided by the Medical Research Council. Like the U.S. RAC, in its early days GMAG reviewed proposals for every individual laboratory experiment. The experiments were initially notified to it under non-mandatory arrangements. In contrast to the U.S. situation, this notification obligation applied to all sectors — private industry and publicly funded institutions alike. From 1978 onwards these arrangements became compulsory under the Health and Safety (Genetic Manipulation) Regulations 1978.[19] As GMAG gained experience, detailed guidelines on risk assessment were developed and, echoing events in the United States, prior review obligations and containment requirements were then relaxed.

Interestingly, GMAG developed a risk assessment scheme for laboratory work different from that of the U.S. RAC. In effect, the GMAG scheme was a generic system for ranking any cloning project involving prokaryotic or lower eukaryotic host organisms. The scheme involves the assignment of a risk factor under each of three headings: "Access," "Expression," and "Damage."[20] The factors under each heading are then multiplied to give an overall score which, in turn, dictates the level of laboratory containment.

In 1984 GMAG was disbanded and replaced by the Advisory Committee on Genetic Manipulation (ACGM). This new body was set up under the Health and Safety Commission and Executive, but with terms of reference that allow it also to advise relevant government departments such as the Ministry of Agriculture, Fisheries and Food, and the Department of the Environment. As with its predecessor, ACGM is broadly based with representatives from employer and employee organizations, local authorities, scientists, and government officials. ACGM has continued to oversee contained applications (laboratory and large-scale work) and to issue detailed guidelines.

In 1986 ACGM also established a Planned Release Sub-Committee to review in advance all proposals involving field trials in the open environment. The committee's guidelines on this topic and on large-scale work closely followed the recommendations and conclusions of the OECD Report.

The primary legal foundation for ACGM's notification and review system is provided by the Health and Safety at Work 1974. This Act covers genetic manipulation and any other work activity, placing general duties on the employer for the maintenance of a safe place of work for both workers and the general public. It is under this Act that the specific notification regulations for genetic manipulation were made. Inspectors from the Health and Safety Executive are able to enforce appropriate standards in genetic manipulation facilities, as in all other workplaces.

Aside from the Health and Safety at Work Act, other legislation may be relevant, depending on the work in question. For example, the Wildlife and Countryside Act 1981 may have a bearing on certain field trials, the Plant Health Act is relevant for the genetic manipulation of plants involving plant pests, and there is a range of legislation for product classes, such as veterinary and human pharmaceuticals and pesticides.

There are important developments underway in Great Britain, with new regulations in 1989 extending the legal obligation to notify planned release and large-scale work. In addition, the topic has been studied by the Royal Commission on Environmental Pollution and its report was issued in 1989.[21]

Ireland ... took a similar course to Great Britain with the establishment in 1981 of a national oversight committee — the Recombinant DNA Committee — under the National Board for Science and Technology. It succeeded both an expert group, set up by the Irish Medical Research Council in 1974, and a broadly based advisory committee set up by the Royal Irish Academy. Non-mandatory notification of rDNA laboratory work is, in operation and detailed guidelines, modeled on the U.S. NIH Guidelines are available. This oversight system provides the regulatory focus for any large-scale and planned release applications. Consideration of such work would be guided by the OECD Report, as well as the NIH Guidelines.

In addition to the review mechanism that the rDNA committee provides, a number of Irish laws may be relevant to particular planned release applications: the Water Pollution Act 1977, the Dangerous Substances Act 1972, and the Destructive Insects and Pests (Consolidation) Act 1958.

France ... in 1975 established a "Commission Nationale de Classement" under the Ministry of Research and charged it with the major responsibility for assessing risks related to recombinant DNA work. The Commission used the NIH guidelines as a basis for its advice on classifying individual projects notified on a non-mandatory basis. Prior authorization for industrial use is required under the Classified Installations for Environmental Protection Act. An inter-departmental committee is preparing a set of regulations for such work.

In addition, there are plans to establish a commission to consider the categorization and level of precautions to be adopted for contained use of rDNA organisms. This new commission, to be established in the Ministry of Research and Higher Education, will replace the original committee. For planned releases, a Biomolecular Engineering Commission was set up in 1986 by the Ministry of Agriculture.[22] The Commission's remit is not restricted to organisms generated using rDNA technology; indeed, the Commission is considering how to define "biomolecular engineering" and the type of work that should be covered by its activities.

During 1987, the Biomolecular Engineering Commission advised on nineteen proposals although notification is, so far, voluntary. The Commission operates in the context of existing product regulations. Its opinion is presented to the body responsible for taking a decision on a particular class of product, such as food, pesticides or veterinary drugs.

In contrast to other similar bodies, the Biomolecular Engineering Commission does not believe that it is yet possible to provide specific evaluation guidelines and recommendations on organisms for release. It has recognized, however, that as experience and the outcome of relevant research accumulates, it will become possible to transfer accumulated competence to the bodies primarily responsible for product approval itself.

The Netherlands ... established an Ad Hoc Recombinant DNA Advisory Committee to provide the focus for regulatory oversight of rDNA activities. This committee has issued guidelines on laboratory work, large-scale use, and planned release. The guidelines for laboratory work largely follow the U.S. NIH-RAC approach. Guidelines for large-scale work and planned release follow the approach put forward in the 1986 OECD Report.

Notification of rDNA work is required prior to the issue

of a license by the local authority. Proposals are considered by the Ad Hoc rDNA committee as part of this review and license procedure. The legal basis of regulation of contained use of rDNA organisms in the Netherlands is currently based on the Nuisance Act.

New regulations for planned release are being prepared under the Chemical Substance Act. This will also involve the reconstitution of the rDNA committee with a broader scope and a statutory basis.

Germany ... has issued a code of practice on rDNA work[23] through the Federal Ministry of Research and Technolgoy (BMFT). Like the U.S. NIH guidelines, the BMFT code is mandatory for work funded directly or indirectly by the Federal Government. Private industry is also expected to follow the code of practice on a voluntary basis. The code covers laboratory work as well as large-scale fermentation, activities. Planned release is not permitted under the guidelines. In addition, a separate rDNA advisory committee (the ZKBS) operates under the Ministry of Research and Technology.

Other German regulatory features include the 1988 issue of national regulations on the protection of workers in rDNA plants and laboratories (Unfallverhütungsvorschrift Abschnitt Biotechnologie VBG 102). In addition, the fourth amendment of the "Law of Protection Against Intermission" issued in September 1988 provides for the obligatory approval of production plants using any type of genetically engineered cell. The approval procedure involves a public hearing of the production plans.

The German regulatory position is likely to be influenced by the 1987 publication of a wide-ranging report "Chances and Risks of Gene Technology" by the Enquète Commission of the German Parliament. Its recommendations include a five-year moratorium on the planned release of genetically manipulated microorganisms. The Parliament is expected to complete its debate of the Enquète report's recommendations in 1989.

The Federal Ministry of Health has drafted fresh legislation on gene technology. This may well result in a requirement for a permit or license before rDNA work is undertaken. In one sense this will put the existing BMFT rDNA guidelines on a sounder legal basis; but uncertainty as to the severity of the law remains, particularly with respect to the risk levels of laboratory work that will require prior authorization and the extent of public involvement in the authorization process. It remains to be seen whether any proposed new legislation moves to impose a ban on planned release, as recommended (at least for microorganisms) in the Enquète report.

Denmark ... is the only European country to date to have enacted a specific technique-based law for biotechnology. The Environment and Gene Technology Act 1986 covers the use of "gene technology" (defined as rDNA and cell hybridization techniques) in research, production and planned release. The Act requires advance permission before work is undertaken either for research or production. Planned release is prohibited under this Act although, in special cases, the Minister of the Environment may approve a release. Guidelines have been issued for research and production. Although initially restrictive, amendments to the Act have been passed in 1989. These specifically aim to exclude cell hybridization from the scope and to allow pilot plant work to be regarded as experimental rather than production. Also, 1989 saw the first approvals of planned release in Denmark. These covered field trials of genetically engineered sugar beets.

Other countries ... such as Spain, Italy and Portugal did not institute oversight mechanisms for rDNA work in the 1970s.

The Commission of the European Communities

Aside from the reaction of individual European countries, the rDNA regulatory debate also received attention from the European Commission. In 1979 the Commission proposed a Directive that, if agreed, would have forced Member States of the European Community to institute a national registration system for rDNA work. After lengthy negotiation, this eventually came into force in 1982 as a Council Recommendation, rather than a Directive, thus, reflecting the downward trend in concern over the technology at the turn of the decade. Implementation was not binding on members of the European Community, although most had, in fact, instituted similar oversight systems by then.

Largely triggered by the re-emerging debate prompted by the deliberate release issue, the Commission went on to issue three draft proposals for directives in 1988:

(1) *Proposal for a council directive on the contained use of genetically modified microorganisms*[24]

This proposal aims at harmonizing the regulations existing in the different Member States, in relation to the contained use of genetically modified microorganisms, i.e., laboratory and large-scale activities. It provides for a system of notification, the application of containment according to the type of microorganism used, and for measures relating to accidents and waste management. The Directive classifies genetically modified microorganisms into two groups, according to criteria in the OECD Report for good industrial large-scale practice (GILSP). When an installation is to be used for the first time, a notification is required to a national competent authority. Records have to be kept for low risk (GILSP) work and prior notification is required for work involving higher risk (non-GILSP) organisms. This directive is likely to be adopted by the Council early in 1990.

(2) *Proposal for a council directive on the deliberate*

release of genetically modified organisms to the environment[25]

This proposal focuses on the deliberate release of genetically modified organisms. It provides for a case-by-case notification and endorsement procedure. A distinction is made between the procedures for research and development release and releases involving finished products. In the latter case the endorsement procedure involves consultation with the Commission and other Member States. The product section of the draft directive does not apply to organisms already covered by Commission product legislation, if it has a similar risk assessment component.

Before carrying out a release, the responsible person has to notify the competent authority and provide details on the organisms proposed for the release, the conditions and the environment in which such release is to take place, and an assessment of the possible hazards for human health and the environment. This directive is likely to be adopted by the Council early in 1990.

(3) *Proposal for a council directive on the protection of workers from the risk related to exposure to biological agents at work*[26]

This proposal aims at protecting workers from the risks related to exposure to biological agents able to cause human disease, whether genetically modified or naturally occurring. The directive is divided into two main parts: a general section applying to all sectors of activities where workers may accidentally be exposed, and a second part applying only to those whose work involves the handling of pathogens. Activities involving genetic manipulation, included in the second part, require advance notification when they involve biological agents pathogenic to humans. Accidental releases that are likely to involve a danger for the health of workers also require notification. A list of containment principles are envisaged for health care facilities, diagnostic laboratories, industrial processes, laboratories and animal rooms. This directive began negotiation at the Council of Ministers in 1989. Once the directives are adopted, all twelve Member States of the European Community will have to implement their provisions in national law.

Conclusion

Many European countries in the 1970s implemented some type of oversight system for rDNA laboratory work. The reasons for this include:

1. the U.S. precedent, ranging from the influence of the early conferences and the moratorium, to the establishment of a specific oversight committee (NIH-RAC) and its detailed guidelines;
2. uncertainty over risk and the need to keep a watch on the new technology. These watch systems enabled national authorities and committees to learn with experience and, consequently, to adjust the stringency of their oversight. The key attribute in overseeing uncertain risk is flexibility — knowledge and experience must be allowed to influence the development of regulation;
3. recognition that rDNA has the capability to arouse public concern. This, in turn, can be alleviated by demonstration of a science-based, but balanced regulatory system overseeing both academia and industry. Interestingly, the reasons for continued oversight of this area have not yet included the demonstration of actual cases of harm.

With the arrival of the application of the new technology, first in large-scale fermenters and then in open field trials, countries sought to adapt their established oversight systems. Many found the work of the OECD valuable in this respect. Given the considerable trade implications, the way forward lies in further developing international harmonization to ensure common safety standards and to maintain free trade.

Summary and Conclusions

Almost from its inception, research and commercialization of the new biotechnology has generated public questions, questions about safety, as well as potential social and economic impacts. The public has also been excited about the potential products offered by biotechnology and fascinated by the efforts of science to unlock life's processes.

The development of a regulatory mechanism to oversee biotechnology in Europe and the United States has been an effort to reconcile expressions of concern with scientific realities and the tremendous potential benefit from biotechnology.

In the early period involving initial laboratory research, stringent regulations were put into place and, thereafter, based on experience, restrictions were greatly relaxed. Today the application of rDNA and affiliated technologies to the commercial market is in its infancy. Governments are moving cautiously in approving new applications and the regulations of biotechnology is again characterized by the restrictive approach, waiting for experience before any relaxation of regulations.

It is likely that there will continue to be parallels between the development of regulations in the United States and Europe. Indeed, it is vital that these two trading blocks keep closely in step as the new biotechnology begins to influence the type and range of products available to the public. During the coming years, governments worldwide will be working, individually and in concert, through bodies such as the OECD and EC to establish science-based regulatory structures that ensure a safe but optimum advancement of the new biotechnology.

REFERENCES

1. The RAC was established by the National Institutes of Health (NIH) in 1974, in response to the call of the NAS Committee. The NIH first proposed guidelines in 1976, which were finalized in 1977 (and modified numerous times since then). "Guidelines for Research Involving Recombinant DNA Molecules", 51 Fed. Reg. 16958 (May 7, 1986), *as amended* by 52 Fed. Reg. 31848 (1987), 53 Fed. Reg. 28819 (1988), 53 Fed. Reg. 43410 (1988), and 54 Fed. Reg. 10508 (1989).
2. IBCs, or Institutional Biosafety Committees, are review committees established under the Guidelines at institutions where NIH funded experimentation is being conducted.
3. These bacteria, *Pseudomonas syringae* and *Erwinia herbicola*, carry *in vitro* generated deletions of all, or part, of the genes involved in ice nucleation. The altered bacteria can then replace the normal bacteria that live on the leaf surfaces of crop plants and help reduce frost damage to crops.
4. U.S. Congress, House of Representatives, Committee on Science and Technology. 1984, The Environmental Implications of Genetic Engineering. 98th Cong., 2nd sess. Staff Report prepared by the Subcommittee on Investigations and Oversight. Washington, D.C.: Government Printing Office.
5. See for example, National Research Council, National Academy of Sciences, *Introduction of Recombinant DNA-Engineered Organisms into the Environment: Key Issues*, (National Academy Press; 1987). National Research Council, National Academy of Sciences, *Field Testing Genetically Modified Organisms: Framework for Decisions*, (National Academy Press; 1989); "Tiedje, J.M. et al., "The Planned Introduction of Genetically Engineered Organisms: Ecological Considerations and Recommendations." *Ecology* (Volume 70 (2):298–315).
6. Coordinated Framework for the Regulation of Biotechnology, 51 Red. Reg. 23339 (June 26, 1986). The OSTP Framework is not all inclusive; significant statutory mandates of the principal agencies are not covered and neither are other federal agencies with relevant responsibilities. For example, EPA's responsibilities under the air, water and waste disposal statutes are not addressed by the Framework; research and regulatory responsibilities of the Department of Energy, the National Oceanic and Atmospheric Administration, the Department of Defense, and the Department of the Interior are not discussed. Because the primacy of federal law has not been established in this field, in some instances, state and local governments have also passed laws or regulations.
7. 42 U.S.C. § 4331 *et seq.* The National Environmental Policy Act is a procedural statute requiring all federal agencies to examine the environmental consequences of proposed agency actions.
8. 21 U.S.C. § 301 *et seq.*
9. 42 U.S.C. § 262.
10. 21 U.S.C. § 201(s).
11. 15 U.S.C. § 2601 *et seq.*
12. 7 U.S.C. § 135 *et seq.*
13. 7 U.S.C. § 150aa *et seq.*
14. 7 U.S.C. § 151 *et seq.*
15. 21 U.S.C. § 151 *et seq.*
16. 29 U.S.C. § 651 *et seq.*
17. The Organization for Economic Cooperation and Development (OECD) is an intergovernmental organization comprised of 24 countries (19 European countries, Australia, Canada, Japan, New Zealand, and the United States).
18. Recombinant DNA Safety Considerations, OECD, Paris 1986 ISBN 92–64–12857–3.
19. Health and Safety (Genetic Manipulation) Regulation SI 1978, No. 752 London UK.
20. "Access" is a measure of the probability that a manipulated organism will be able to enter the human body and survive. "Expression" is a measure of the expression (anticipated or known) of the inserted DNA. "Damage" is a measure of the risk of a gene product resulting in ill-health of an exposed worker.
21. Royal Commission on Environmental Pollution. The Release of Genetically Engineered Organisms to the Environment. CM 720, HMSO, July, 1989.
22. Committee for the use of products from biomolecular engineering. Assessment of the first year's activity, Ministry of Agriculture, Paris, 30 June 1988.
23. Guidelines for protection against risk posed by new intro combinations of nucleic acids (5th revision), Federal Ministry for Research and Technology, Bonn, October 1986.
24. Proposal for a Council Directive on the contained use of genetically modified micro-organisms, Official Journal of the European Communities, C 198/9–18, 28 July 1988.
25. Proposal for a Council Directive on the deliberate release to the environment of genetic modified organisms, Official Journal of the European Communities, C 199–19–27, 28 July 1988.
26. Proposal for a Council Directive on the protection of workers from the risks related to exposure to biological agents at work, Official Journal of the European Communities, C 150/6–14, 8 June 1988.

Acronyms

ACGM	Advisory Committee on Genetic Manipulation (Great Britain)
APHIS	Animal Plant Health Inspection Service (U.S.)
BMFT	Federal Ministry of Research and Technology (Germany)
EPA	Environmental Protection Agency (U.S.)
FDA	Food and Drug Administration (U.S.)
FDCA	Food, Drug and Cosmetic Act (U.S.)
FIFRA	Federal Insecticide, Fungicide and Rodenticide Act (U.S.)
FSIS	Food Safety and Inspection Service (U.S.)
GILSP	Good Industrial Large-scale Practice
GMAG	Genetic Manipulation Advisory Group (Great Britain)
HSC	Health and Safety Commission (Great Britain)
IBC	Institutional Biosafety Committee
NEPA	National Environmental Policy Act (U.S.)
NIH	National Institutes of Health (U.S.)
OECD	Organization for Economic Cooperation and Development (International)
OSTP	Office of Science Technology Policy (U.S.)
PHSA	Public Health Service Act (U.S.)
PPA	Plant Pest Act (U.S.)
PQA	Plant Quarantine Act (U.S.)

RAC	Recombinant DNA Advisory Committee (U.S.)
TSCA	Toxic Substances Control Act (U.S.)
VSTA	Virus, Serum and Toxin Act (U.S.)
USDA	United States Department of Agriculture
ZKBS	Advisory Board for Biological Safety (Germany)

Chapter 9

Communication

Anita Crafts-Lighty

INTRODUCTION

Communication can be best described as the process of exchanging information. It is fundamental to the development of any new discipline such as biotechnology which is developed from the fusion of knowledge from many scientific specialisations applied commercially using business skills which, in many cases, have little in common with the technical basis of the industry. Biotechnology companies face a significant challenge in coordinating the priorities and goals of research and financial staff which is made even more complex by the need to integrate the disparate scientific resources involved. Computing and biochemistry are needed for protein engineering, microbiology and ecology for environmental release experiments, occupational health and virology to ensure workers' safety, pharmacology and molecular biology to produce therapeutic proteins, farming and electronics to develop biosensors for agricultural use, chemical engineering and immunology to produce monoclonal antibodies in cell culture. These are but a few examples of where good communication between specialists is critical to developing successful new products but not necessarily easy to achieve or frequently practised in academic circles.

Special Problems for Biotechnology

Communicating biotechnology information is difficult for many reasons but the main problems arise because the science is multidisciplinary in nature, it is in a very rapid phase of development both technically and commercially, is international in scope and is of great public interest and concern. As yet, biotechnology needs and uses no really novel techniques of communication. A few specialist software packages have been developed for applications such as a DNA sequence analysis and molecular modelling but they run on conventional computers which communicate between themselves in normal ways. The people involved read books and magazines, go to conferences, write letters, make telephone calls and have conversations as they do with any other topic. It is the information they communicate which is the concern of this chapter, the sources they use and the way the process is managed. It is, however, beyond the scope of this book to provide detailed listings of useful publications in biotechnology or very extensive instruction on how to use specific services but a good overview of these is provided in *Information Sources in Biotechnology* (1986)[1]. Biotech Knowledge Sources (BKS) a monthly updating service covering new books, market surveys and other documents plus forthcoming conferences which is published by BioCommerce Data, is a good supplement to this book.

SCIENTIFIC DATA

Every scientist knows that information gathering is a vital precursor to original research if only to check that someone else has not already verified or disproved the hypothesis about to be tested experimentally. Information is also needed to generate ideas for new work and for teaching purposes. A significant aspect of postgraduate education is training young researchers to organise the data they generate and to analyse the findings published by others. At school and university, the complex and piecemeal way in which scientific knowledge is built up is usually oversimplified in textbooks which concentrate on key discoveries and current theories: they present these as fact rather than the best current interpretation of many thousands of pieces of information. Science advances on many fronts simultaneously, with more than a few false starts along the way and intense controversy and competition often surrounds the most active areas. In biotechnology, this phenomenon is exacerbated by the opportunities for commercial exploitation of results, adding to the pressures of career advancements and the inevitable personality conflicts which affect scientists as much as anyone else, a need for secrecy and the potential for becoming rich.

Research Articles

Researchers today face an ever increasing volume of published information to use. The main sources consulted are, of course, scientific journals, most of which are published monthly by commercial publishers or learned societies. There are several hundred, perhaps a few thousand, such publications relevant to aspects of biotechnology including most biochemistry, genetics, microbiology, medical, veterinary and botany journals. However, most scientists will read only a handful on a regular basis and even the most conscientious find it hard to scan the contents of more than a hundred. Many rely on regular searching of secondary publications such as Current Contents (ISI) or Derwent Publications' Biotechnology Abstracts but this can be extremely time consuming to do manually. The modern approach is usually to set up a Selective Dissemination of Information (SDI) search on the computer database version of these services; this will regularly generate a printout of abstracts or titles of articles on a particular topic of interest. SDIs are very cost effective but they are limited by the coverage and processing time of the database producer, some of whom can take weeks or months to index a journal. Although such searches can be limited to papers in a particular language, or to review type articles, they cannot be judged by quality in any way and it is difficult to use them to monitor broad interests (e.g. significant advances in genetic engineering techniques).

A compromise approach for some researchers is thus to scan the output of SDI searches which provides a "first filter" of the literature, albeit after some delay. Another alternative is to scan the floppy disk version of Current Contents which has recently become available.

Other Documents

To supplement routine current awareness, general background overviews are often best derived from book series, such as annual reviews, and sometimes from conference proceedings. Although abstracts of the papers to be presented at scientific meetings are frequently circulated to participants before or at the event, the full length texts may not be published for many months. Information presented at poster sessions, designed to provide a discussion forum for research in progress, is rarely published in conference proceedings although titles and/or abstracts may be included in the abstracts book for participants. Monographs (books on one topic by one author) are still published in biotechnology but it is more usual to find a number of authors contributing articles to a book, as in this example. For many researchers, books are not a major source of new information once the use of textbooks to become familiar with a new subject is completed.

Technical reference books are used to some extent in biotechnology, including compendia of genetic engineering methods and genetic maps, lists of enzymes, handbooks of biochemical data and pharmacopeia but data are being accumulated so rapidly that such volumes are less useful than they might be in mechanical or electrical engineering.

Patents

Patents are an important source of technical information but few scientists are trained to monitor them. Increasingly, in subjects like biotechnology, patent applications are filed before the disclosure of research results at a conference or publication of a research paper. Although the full text of patent application may not be available for 18 months after its final filing because of the way the patent approval system works, it may nevertheless contain important details not included in other publications. Writing patent applications is an art. The necessary style is quite different from scientific articles and usually a patent agent is employed to assist with drafting the text of the claims and examples to ensure that useful cover will be achieved if the patent is granted (see Chapters 5 and 6).

Finding patents when doing SDI searches can be fairly difficult as the titles are often vague (e.g. "polypeptide composition") and a virtually identical application may be filed in 20 or more different countries. One useful tool to monitor patents is the World Patents Index (Derwent Publications) which groups these publications into "families", including all the equivalents in various countries, and augments the titles. The International Patent Classification (IPC) scheme is not a great help for biotechnology (most end up in the C12 section) and libraries commonly store patents numerically by country.

Culture Collections

Much of biotechnology is about creating new life forms through genetic engineering, recombining natural information in new ways by creating transgenic animals and plants and microorganisms carrying new genes. For many researchers in this field, keeping track of all the strains created is a formidable problem and for companies it is critical that commercially used cell lines and organisms can be kept constant. These requirements necessitate the maintenance of culture collections, often in the form of spores or seeds or more usually, freeze dried cells or embryos. Food and Drug Administration (FDA) rules in the U.S. require the maintenance of a master cell bank for production processes using mammalian cells (such as hybridomas for therapeutic monoclonal antibody production) and Good Laboratory Practice (GLP) and Good Manufacturing Practice (GMP) guidelines also recommend well organised culture collections. Some companies have published notes on their systems.[2,3]

Of course major public culture collections exist and are used as sources of new strains and to deposit patented microorganisms. The American Type Culture Collection (ATCC) is probably the best known but the U.K. has several important collections as do other countries including Germany and Belgium. Some Pan-European collections are being organised. As yet, only the MICIS system in the U.K. provides online data about the properties of organisms but there is a general trend for culture collections to computerise their printed catalogues in future. MICIS, originally run by the Department of Trade and Industry, is being merged with the Microbial Information Network in Europe (MINE) and will be moved to the Deutsche Sammlung von Mikroorganismen und Zelkulturen (DSM) in Braunschweig. MSDN, the Microbial Strains Data Network, is another important source of culture collection information though it is not itself a collection. MSDN also provides a useful electronic bulletin board service.

Research Results

At the moment most scientists still record the results of their daily experimental work in a handwritten laboratory notebook. This is usually a bound book in which are affixed printouts from machinery such as spectrophotometer traces, dried polyacrylamide gels, developed x-ray film and other demonstrative proof of experimental results. For patent and legal purposes, it is important that proof of discovery can be produced and so all work should be dated, in ink, corrections made in such a way that the original version is still visible and the apparent implications of the work written down. Most U.S. companies require each page to be "signed off" as read and understood by a supervisor and frequently notebooks are microfilmed to provide a backup copy.

In biotechnology companies notebooks are regarded as corporate property and are retained by the company when an employee leaves. Often each is numbered and must be surrendered at fixed intervals. In academe, practice is not nearly so strict but, with increasing awareness of the patentability of research and the increasing fear by senior team leaders of being held responsible for any allegations of fraud or infringement of safety regulations, this is changing. Another important trend is towards electronic notebooks where data files of results from computer controlled laboratory equipment can be integrated into a larger file describing the complete experiment. These will require much more sophisticated archiving procedures but appear likely to be commonplace within a generation.

Personal Computer Systems

Even if many scientists are still using paper notebooks as the final archival medium, an increasing number of researchers have access to microcomputers or larger timesharing computer systems for statistical analysis of data (curve fitting, sequence homologies, etc.). They also have the opportunity to use simple database packages such as Cardbox and DBase IV to keep track of important references to published articles and their own private collection of copies of articles. It is not uncommon for commercial scientists to be able to take their "reprints" (now largely photocopies) with them when changing jobs along with a disk recording the collection which replaces the handwritten cards many researchers used to keep. Of course, some companies have more sophisticated, permanent, centralised literature article collections (particularly on adverse drug effects) but it is still broadly true that a researcher's expertise is often believed to reside partially in the collection of specialist literature he or she has amassed.

Literature Database Searching

The increasing availability of computer systems is also making it feasible for many research scientists to set up SDI services and use online computer systems for themselves rather than asking librarians to do it. In universities, this trend is especially strong because the central libraries focus more on books for students while departmental libraries usually concentrate on journal subscriptions. There is often only a tiny university library budget for literature searching which can easily cost \$100 a time. This may not be a very significant cost to a large grant-aided project used to buying expensive laboratory chemicals so that accounting concerns alone encourage researchers to start searching for themselves.

Many scientists also feel they do better searches than information professionals because they know the subject being searched and the terminology involved and can instantly identify interesting papers when they are retrieved. This argument in favour of "end user" online searching is a powerful and substantially valid one but the counter argument is that the information specialist is more likely to know which database will be best (and there are hundreds to choose from) and will be fluent in the syntax required by all the major commercial systems (see Table 1). A more practised searcher will also be more likely to know the tricks of constructing a good strategy to maximise "precision" and "recall" in a cost effective way.

Table 1
Major Online Search Services

Data-Star
Dialog Information Services
ESA-IRS
Maxwell Online (comprising BRS and Orbit)
National Library of Medicine

There is more to searching than just typing in a few keywords. Precision refers to getting items only on the precise subject of interest (e.g. containing specified words in the title). Recall is a measure of how many of the references which are relevant are actually retrieved. When searching databases such as Biological Abstracts online (Biosis), which contains abstracts of over four million papers published since 1969, recalling too many documents can be a real (and expensive) nuisance so there is always a balance to be struck between these two aspects.

Table 2 lists some of the most popular scientific literature databases which are useful for biotechnology. One of the best specialist files is Derwent Publications' Biotechnology Abstracts which also includes patents linked to their World Patents Index file by a corresponding accession number. Current Biotechnology Abstracts includes patents although it is less up-to-date. Often, however, the best results for scientific articles will be found by searching the large general life sciences databases such as Chemical Abstracts, EMBase, Life Sciences Collection, SciSearch and Medline. A surprising number of technical references are also contained in the commercially oriented biotechnology databases, Biobusiness and BioCommerce Abstracts and Directory.

All that is needed to search these databases is some kind of terminal or personal computer, a modem or acoustic coupler and a telephone line. Searchers also need to obtain a user password for each computer bureau (also known as "spinners" or "hosts") so they can be billed, and an identification number for each telecommunications network used. The hosts all have telephone support as well as excellent training services and will advise on setting up the necessary hardware and telecommunications. Now that many people use microcomputers for this application some software is available to help with the somewhat tedious "logging on" procedures and to allow the temporary storage of retrieved references. Permanent storage in a local database is called "downloading" and is permitted by most database producers only if a special contract is signed because it may reduce future use of the main database. Some search assistance software can also help the inexperienced user to select a suitable database and to formulate questions in the correct way (using Boolean logic, truncation, etc.). At the moment, online charging is mainly

Table 2
Important Biotechnology Literature Databases

File	*Hosts*	*Producers*
Specialist		
Biobusiness	Data-Star, Dialog	BIOSIS
BioCommerce Abstracts and Directory	Data-Star, Dialog	BioCommerce Data
Current Biotechnology Abstracts	Data-Star, ESA-IRS, Maxwell Online	Royal Society of Chemistry
Derwent Biotechnology Abstracts	Dialog, Maxwell Online	Derwent Publications
General		
Agricola	Dialog, Maxwell Online	USDA
Agris	Dialog, ESA-IRS, Maxwell Online	FAO
Biosis Previews	Data-Star, Dialog, ESA-IRS, Maxwell Online	BIOSIS
CAB Abstracts	Dialog, ESA-IRS	CAB
Chemical Abstracts*	Data-Star, Dialog, ESA-IRS,	Chemical Abstracts
Chemical Engineering Abstracts	Data-Star, ESA-IRS, Maxwell Online	Royal Society of Chemistry
Current Awareness in Biological Sciences	Maxwell Online	Pergamon
EMBase	Data-Star, Dialog, Maxwell Online	Excerpta Medica (Elsevier)
Food Science & Technology Abstracts	Data-Star, Dialog, ESA-IRS	IFIS
Life Sciences Collection	Dialog	Cambridge Scientific Abstracts
Medline (Medlars)*	Data-Star, Dialog	NLM
National Technical Information Service	Data-Star, Dialog, ESA-IRS, Maxwell Online	NTIS
Pharmaprojects	Data-Star	PJB Publications
SciSearch	Data-Star, Dialog	ISI
World Patents Index	Dialog, Maxwell Online	Derwent Publications

* Also available direct from the producers.

monthly in arrears based on "connect hours" and the number of abstracts printed out. There is however a trend, led at present by Chemical Abstracts, to charge on the search strategy as well and this will probably be followed by other information providers.

Sequence Databanks

In biotechnology the importance of databanks of protein and DNA sequence information is considerable. Noticing sequence similarities (homologies) is very difficult and time consuming to perform manually but it can easily be done by computer programs and some very sophisticated matching algorithms have been developed. The main vendor of such systems have been IntelliGenetics which has made available the GenBank data compiled by the Los Alamos National Laboratory and the European Molecular Biology laboratory (EMBL) as well as the National Biomedical Research Foundation (NBRF) Protein Identification Resource (PIR) amino acid sequence database. These are all based primarily on published sequences. Several other protein databanks are also available and, although the overlap is considerable, it is not complete. Unfortunately, at the time of writing, a National Institutes of Health (NIH) grant to support the GenBank operation is due to expire and it is uncertain how the operation of this service will continue. The trend may be towards more distributed services. Many of the sequence databanks provide their information and software on magnetic tapes which can be mounted on local computers and EMBL has released a CD-ROM version of its data.

Future efforts to sequence the entire human genome will obviously lead to vast amounts of additional data. While this chapter was being written, several U.S. agencies including the Department of Energy were contesting the privilege of organising the project which may also involve international collaboration, particularly with Japanese companies which are developing low cost, rapid, automated equipment for sequencing. The scale of the task is immense and the costs will run into billions of dollars over a period of several years, probably necessitating government funding. Some commercial companies such as Genome Corp are also planning to become involved in this effort.

Compact Discs

Another important trend in databases is CD-ROM technology using compact discs which, when a player is connected to a micro, provide a local online service. Where heavy use (e.g., by students) is involved such systems are ideal, being relatively inexpensive and simple. The hardware is not yet widely available and most of the initial products released are ones with broad general appeal (encyclopedias, books in print, medicine, etc.). The publishing industry is still experimenting with CD-ROM pricing strategies having only recently adjusted to the impact of "traditional" online host services in addition to printed publications and many producers are viewing this medium with great caution and waiting for "mastering" costs to drop enough to enable volume production of low circulation, frequently updated products. Recently, however, the CD Biotech series has been announced by the International Association for Scientific Computing (IASC) which contains sequence databases and is reissued twice yearly.

Full Text

Another trend for future research data will be full text journals online and electronic bulletin boards. They already exist on a small scale but growth has been somewhat slower than expected, partly due to difficulties in handling graphics and half tone illustrations on computer systems.

BUSINESS INFORMATION

The primary technical data needs of a researcher employed in industry differ little from those of an academic scientist with the probable exception of a greater interest in patents. However, a research-based biotechnology company will have many other employees with important information requirements and often these personnel will have had less experience in information management than the scientists.

Market Data

One of the most difficult areas for biotechnology is market figures. Many of the potential products are completely new and it is therefore not possible to estimate future sales by extrapolation from the price and sales volume of existing products. Some biotechnology processes do have competitors of course, or will solve or prevent problems whose current cost can be estimated (e.g., how much hospital care is needed for certain incurable diseases or the cost of disposing of untreatable wastes). These are a little easier but generally the picture is very different from say, major consumer goods.

This situation has not gone unnoticed by publishing and consultancy companies and since 1980 at least 500 market surveys on various aspects on biotechnology have been published. They range in price from a few hundred dollars to over $25,000 depending on their scope. Some large consulting organisations, such as SRI International and Arthur D Little, have major multiclient programmes and several other firms, for example Frost & Sullivan, Biomedical Business International and Theta, have produced considerable numbers of lower priced reports ($750–2,000) on biotechnology topics.

The quality of available reports varies enormously and as most surveys are not sold "on approval" (to prevent illegal photocopying) it is advisable to obtain as much detail as possible about scope before ordering. Survey publishers will usually supply a detailed contents list to prospective purchasers and some will permit a copy of the report to be viewed at their premises. However, many offer significant discounts to clients who order before the report is actually compiled. Some survey producers use different experts for each report, others maintain the necessary personnel in-house.

In many cases, such published reports are too broad and many companies involved in biotechnology employ their own market research personnel to provide detailed data as required from their own surveys and/or other published materials. A considerable amount of market data appear in newsletters and other business oriented publications and can be retrieved by searching databases such as the BioCommerce Abstracts and Directory file.

Commercial News

The biotechnology boom has led to a corresponding explosive growth in specialist newsletter publications and increasing coverage of biotechnology in the trade press of affected industries (chiefly pharmaceuticals). A surprising number of articles on biotechnology are also found in general business publications such as the Wall Street Journal (U.S. European and Asian editions), the Financial Times (of London), Business Week, Fortune and The Economist.

Over 40 biotechnology newsletters exist and some of the best known ones are listed in Table 3. A few of these include original papers or significant review articles as well as shorter news items. Some also include lists of forthcoming conferences, book reviews and lists of recently published patents.

Over the last few years, as so many biotechnology companies have gone public, generating a flow of good news for the press and shareholders has become important to prevent excessive share price fluctuation and maintain investor confidence. Most companies now have a press officer or use a public relations firm to issue regular releases. The better newsletters will expand on such sources by interviews and will also draw on personal contacts, conferences, scientific papers (and sometimes other publications) for their articles

Table 3
Important Newsletters and Magazines

Title	Publisher
AgBiotechnology News	Freiburg Publications
Agricultural Genetics Report	Mary Ann Liebert
Applied Genetics News	Business Communications
BBI Newsletter	Biomedical Business International
BioEngineering News	D J Mycsiewicz Publishers
Bioprocessing Technology	Technical Insights
Bio/Technology	Nature
Biotech News	Springfield Information Services
Biotechnology Bulletin	IBC Technical Services
Biotechnology in Japan Newsservice	Japan Pacific Associates
Biotechnology Insight	LIBRA
Biotechnology Law Report	Mary Ann Liebert
Biotechnology Progress	AIChE
Biotechnology News	CTB Publications
Biotechnology Newswatch	McGraw-Hill
BioVenture View	Io Publishing
Changing Medical Markets	Theta Corp
Clinica	George Street Publications
Genetic Engineer and Biotechnologist	GB Biotechnology
Genetic Engineering Letter	Environews
Genetic Engineering News	Mary Ann Liebert
Genetic Technology News	Technical Insights
New Biotech Business	Winter House Scientific Publications
Process Biochemistry	Turrett-Wheatland
Scrip	PJB Publications
Trends in Biotechnology	Elsevier

but significant duplication is still a major problem in the business news literature leading to a law of diminishing returns as each additional publication is read. For managers in the industry, it is often critical not to miss competitor information and it can sometimes be important to read all the press coverage on a specific event but it is an impractical task to scan all this data manually, let alone organise it afterwards.

The most cost-effective service for monitoring biotechnology business news is Abstracts in BioCommerce (ABC) published by BioCommerce Data. ABC is a twice monthly digest covering most of the publications listed in Table 3 as well as many others. It indexes each major fact in any announcement, citing all similar articles on one abstract to remove any press duplication while allowing copies of the originals to be obtained where necessary. ABC abstracts are short and concise; a typical issue covers about 650 articles. These are mainly about biotechnology companies and their strategic partners: they include financial results, senior personnel changes, new startups, public offerings, joint ventures, mergers and takeovers. Also included are academic research collaborations and commercially important scientific work, national governments' funding and legislation, patent litigation, market size estimates and review articles.

ABC is usefully available as an online database, BioCommerce Abstracts and Directory, through Dialog Information Services (File 286) and Data-Star (file CELL). It may shortly also be available in the U.S. through the BioWorld online service (Io Publishing). As the printed ABC has no subject indexing but the text of the abstracts is searchable online, the database is the only way to find entries on a particular subject (e.g. interferon). The printed indexes in the quarterly cumulated issues of ABC can be used to find all entries about a particular organisation but if material over six months old is needed, searching these indexes becomes excessively tedious so this too is better done online. In addition, SDI searches may be set up to follow any defined topic (e.g., interleukin-2) or company of interest.

Other biotechnology databases which have significant commercial information include Biobusiness (which has no printed equivalent) and Current Biotechnology Abstracts.

Directories

The fast pace of change in the biotechnology industry has meant that often it is handy to have a "snapshot" view of the companies involved. There is also a strong demand for mailing lists for companies selling to the industry. These two trends have led to the publication of a number of directories, the most important of which are listed in Table 4. They range in price from $100 to $750. Most are annual and are arranged alphabetically by company name within each country, with some indexing. Generally the coverage of U.S. companies is best but inevitably such publications get out of date very quickly.

Some of the better known directories with broad coverage include BioScan, produced by Oryx Press and updated bimonthly, which offers considerable detail on about 00 companies, The International Biotechnology Directory (Macmillan) which has the most entries for the lowest price though early editions were not always very up-to-date or accurate and the winth edition of the Sittig and Noyes directory which has substantially expanded data on many of the entries. Publication of this reference is being taken over by Mega-Type Publishing from 1990. International directories (which actually cover mainly the U.S.) are also produced by the publishers of BioEngineering News (Bio1000), Biotechnology News and Genetic Engineering News.

As the biotechnology industry grows, many nationally organised directories have also been produced. The most detailed on the U.K. is the U.K. Biotechnology Handbook '90 (the second edition) which is endorsed by the BioIndustry Association (the British trade association for biotechnology). A much briefer book, the directory of British Biotechnology 1989/90, was published by Longman in 1988. Useful directories are also available on Australia/New Zealand, Canada, Japan, the U.S., France, Ireland and Germany.

A new trend is the publication of online directories. The first of these was the BioCommerce Abstracts and Directory file on Dialog and Data-Star in 1989. At the time of going to press this had about 1700 entries, roughly one third U.K., one third U.S. and one third elsewhere (mainly Canada, Australia and Europe). Io Publishing available the BioScan data on the private dialup service, BioWorld.

Publicity Information

The publicity value of an organised system of press release generation has already been mentioned but it is worth noting that companies will often send such releases to other companies and interested people on request (even to competitors). The same is true of the statutory financial information which they are obliged to produce and distribute to shareholders (annual and, in the U.S., quarterly reports). These are a very useful source of information as are share offering prospectuses which, by law, must describe all current projects with an "accurate" assessment of their chances of success. From the standpoint of competitor intelligence, other companies' catalogues and product data sheets are very useful and can often be obtained at exhibitions or through academic collaborators if they are not sent by direct mail.

In addition, many large companies in the industry (such as Monsanto) are bringing out general brochures about biotechnology aimed at the lay public. Trade associations for the industry, particularly the U.S. Industrial Biotechnology Association (IBA) and Association of Biotechnology Companies (ABC) are developing similar materials, including films and videos. Certain topics, such as the environmental

Table 4
Specialist Directories

Title	Publisher
Annuaire des Biotechnologies et des Bioindustries	ADEBIO/Biofutur
Australian and New Zealand Biotechnology Directory	ABA/Australian Industrial Publishers
Bio 1000	D J Mycsiewicz
BioScan	Oryx Press
BioTechnologie, Das Jahr- und Adressbuch	Polycom
Biotechnology Guide USA	Stockton Press
Biotechnology Guide Japan	Macmillan
Canadian Biotechnology Directory	Winter House Publications
Directory of British Biotechnology	Longman
Genetic Engineering & Biotechnology Related Firms Worldwide Directory	Mega-Type Publishing
Genetic Engineering and Biotechnology Yearbook	Elsevier
Healthcare Biotechnology Companies	PJB Publications
International Biotechnology Directory	Macmillan
International Biotechnology Industrial Directory	Biotechnology News
U.K. Biotechnology Handbook	BioCommerce Data

release of genetically manipulated organisms, the use of bovine somatotrophin (BST), human gene therapy and patenting animals have generated considerable public concern and have been badly handled by the popular press, especially newspapers.

Several surveys of public attitudes to biotechnology in the U.K. and Japan have indicated widespread support for some healthcare applications but also strong feelings that this industry should be more strictly regulated. Some religions oppose virtually all genetic manipulation not carried out by "normal" breeding, seeing it as "playing God", but a more serious problem for public awareness seems to be a generalised fear of science and lack of understanding of the most basic terminology involved (e.g. cell, molecule). Biotechnology is sometimes equated with nuclear power or electronics as a great technological revolution but both such parallels are dangerous as these industries are perceived as dangerous and dehumanising respectively.

Regulations

The next decade is certainly likely to see increased regulations and legislation for the biotechnology industry in major nations. Fortunately, on the advice of their researchers most of the countries involved have already set up voluntary systems which form a basis for more informed rules. Keeping track of regulatory information is an important information gathering exercise and involves knowing what is going on at a planning stage (to enable lobbying through trade associations, etc.) as well as obtaining copies of the published laws and guidelines. In the U.S., the National Institutes of Health (NIH) Recombinant DNA Advisory Committee (RAC) has had a dominant role in devising voluntary guidelines but the Environmental Protection Agency (EPA), the U.S. Department of Agriculture (USDA) and the Food and Drug Administration (FDA) play key roles in certain product sectors (EPA handles all pesticides, USDA plants and FDA human drugs and diagnostic tests). In the U.K., the Advisory Committee on Genetic Manipulation (ACGM) is the RAC's equivalent but part of the Health and Safety Executive (HSE). Many other countries have similar bodies. For further details see Chapter 8.

INFORMATION MANAGEMENT

Information management methods are very much a matter of personal taste and corporate style. There has long been a tradition particularly in science, that information should be freely available as evidenced by the existence of public libraries; Sadly, this has led many companies to regard published information as cheap and therefore unimportant. Fortunately, this trend is changing with the increasing use of computers, and many major U.S. companies are now appointing vice presidents of information. Nevertheless, these people are often primarily concerned with traditional data processing (DP) functions or "management information systems" (MIS) which deal primarily with financial performance against budgets, stock control, production schedules, etc. More strategic planning information and R&D data are often outside their scope as are records management systems to handle the enormous problems of filing paper which still plague us all, years after the supposed advent of the computerised paperless office.

A truly integrated information management programme will deal with all these sectors incorporating, of course, any conventional library and information department functions.

Managing Corporate Libraries

It is beyond the scope of this chapter to give detailed advice on library management for biotechnology companies, but the experiences of many suggest that the guidelines in Table 5 are well worth following. It is particularly important that a library is seen as a working tool, a growing collection of documents which provides information to generate knowledge and make decisions, not merely a book archive.

Table 5
Guidelines for Biotechnology Library Management

1. Senior staff need a relevant scientific degree.
2. Online search facilities are required.
3. Catalogues should be computerised.
4. Do not report to finance or personnel.
5. Provide services to commercial and research staff.
6. Integrate completely with "information department".
7. Liaise with patents, market research, records management, computing.

The exercise of document classification, circulation and storage can so easily become an all encompassing and somewhat futile exercise and it is partly for this reason that it is especially important to integrate information and library functions and to provide adequate financial and staff resources to the service. It is all too commonplace for companies to have no formal information manager anywhere in the organisation which is almost as irresponsible as having no accountant.

Setting up a library obviously creates an overhead but if well managed it can be a very good investment, saving staff time and thereby increasing efficiency, monitoring competitors, increasing the productivity of researchers and identifying new opportunities.

Managing Internal Communications

Many biotechnology companies are in a rapid growth phase and corporate communications is a key aspect in maintaining good employee relations. Generally, it is easiest to keep staff well informed about the company's progress when the firm is small enough for everyone to gather in one room. Many research based organisations also maintain a very academic atmosphere which incorporates a desire for a great deal of detailed information about what colleagues are doing but this can extend to the commercial progress of new products and the marketing of contract R&D projects. It is not unusual for R&D departments to have regular seminars and in some companies these involve all departments and are part of a generalised training programme to improve interdepartmental cooperation. Quarterly presentations of financial results and a general overview of company progress by senior directors are also widely used to keep staff aware of what is going on. It is important that employees are kept at least as well briefed as shareholders and usually they will be more aware of any problems or difficulties. Most biotechnology companies operate a fairly open style of management but inevitably some delicate issues must be presented in a way calculated to achieve a specific motivational effect.

Managing External Communications

Having a well-informed workforce is very beneficial but it can represent a serious risk if the channels for releasing confidential and proprietary information are not clearly laid down. Most companies therefore only allow certain designated people (usually senior officials) to speak to the press on an ad hoc basis and operate some sort of clearance procedure for all presentations being given outside by employees. It is critical that patent priority is not lost by too early disclosure of research results but if well managed such a policy need not be onerous or delay publication. Many people have expressed concern that such procedures will lead to great increases in the amount of secrecy in science but few of the researchers involved seem greatly concerned. Certainly there is no reason to suspect that biotechnology will be any worse than, say, pharmaceuticals in this regard but the employees concerned need to have a clear understanding of what is their expertise and what is their employer's data if they move to a direct competitor. Lawsuits over the theft of trade secrets in such circumstances have been known and are bound to continue.

Decisions on what information to make public are based on many criteria and are often designed to achieve one or several of the goals listed in Table 6. It is natural that these objectives will lead to more publicity for good news than bad but that is probably inevitable and in no way unique to biotechnology.

Table 6
Goals of Divulging Information

1. Meet statutory requirements.
2. Obtain scientific recognition.
3. Maintain/improve share price and investor confidence.
4. Publicise product/service/share offering.
5. Attract employees, customers, partners.
6. Discourage competition.
7. Secure patent protection.

The Press

The main channels for publicity are the press and conferences. Editorial press coverage is mainly achieved by issuing press releases to the specialist newsletters and sometimes to national or local newspapers. Important individual journalists can be given exclusive interviews (which is sometimes believed to encourage a more positive report) and of course will sometimes, phone companies to follow up tips or rumours. Most press officers prefer to be in control — feeding selected information to reporters rather than answering queries or allegations directly. Press conferences are sometimes used for particularly large announcements.

In addition to articles written by journalists, company staff prepare articles for some magazines which range from product reviews to original research papers and the press is, of course, used for advertising. Generally most biotechnology publicity focuses on the "quality" financial press, the newsletters and other publications aimed at target industries. Local and even national newspapers are used less and usually only for the general company public relations effort.

Quite a few biotechnology companies use public relations agencies but it is fairly difficult to find suitable firms with an adequate knowledge of the relevant basic science. Nevertheless, a PR company can be useful not just in the administrative aspects of issuing releases but also in advising on corporate image matters generally.

Conferences

Meetings and conferences represent another major route for disseminating information in public. The conference scene has been a very visible part of biotechnology, characterised by a growing involvement of commercial organisers supplementing, but not really replacing, learned societies in this role. Groups such as the American Society of Microbiology (ASM), the American Chemical Society (ACS), the U.K. Biochemical Society and Society for General Microbiology (SGM) have organised many small inexpensive seminars on biotechnology topics but these are largely aimed at R&D staff.

Conferences organised for profit by companies such as Conference Management Corporation and McGraw-Hill are primarily intended for business managers and senior executives. They deal with broad industrial issues (raising finance, market sizes, etc.) and are generally much more expensive ($500+ for 1–3 days). These meetings offer numerous opportunities for networking and gathering competitor intelligence but many people in this industry feel that there have been rather too many such events in the last few years with an excessive number of very general overview papers presented. After a boom in the mid 1980s in large biotechnology conferences, the trend now seems to be toward smaller more focused events which are now independently viable.

The same is true for exhibitions where the industry is having difficulty supporting several major international events each year. Exhibitions, when well managed, seem to be more profitable for the organisers than conferences but involve considerable financial risk and it is very expensive to participate. Space will often cost more than $1,000 per booth, plus utilities, transport, travel, hotel accommodation, etc. It is difficult to have even the most modest presence at an exhibition for less than $5,000.

Many specialist biotechnology companies do not exhibit because they are not sure that such expenditure would really generate sufficient new business. It is the equipment producers who mainly attend these events together with some reagent suppliers, a few publishers and, increasingly, regional authorities seeking to attract companies to a particular country, state or county.

INFORMATION IN PERSPECTIVE

Information is a critical resource for both science and business today. It is more than just raw data or collections of data. It is the building blocks of knowledge, the raw material for decision making, often the true source of competitive advantage.

Information handling is still a fast developing field. This is most evident in the startling increases in the price/performance ratios of modern computers and the flood of new hardware and software tools available. It must be remembered though that most such systems are really just smart filing systems and all rely on the input of good and necessary original information.

Information management is not easy. It is a moving target, continually pushed by new developments in technology but it deserves serious attention alongside other important concerns of biotechnology such as maintaining innovative science, environmental protection, product and employee safety, and obtaining finance. Information can help achieve all these. Its lack can be an insurmountable barrier.

REFERENCES

1. Crafts-Lighty, A. (1986). *Information Sources in Biotechnology* (2nd Ed.) London/New York: Macmillan/Stockton Press.
2. Scheirer, W. (1987). Laboratory management of animal cell cultures, *Trends in Biotechnology* Vol. 5, p. 261–265.
3. Belt, A. (1987). Establishing, organising and managing a culture collection in a biotechnology company, *SIM News* Vol. 37, p. 8–10.

Section II

Underlying Technologies and Economics

Chapter 10

The New Biology

Jennifer Van Brunt

INTRODUCTION

Just exactly what is the "new biology?" What distinguishes it from the "old biology?" The term has been bandied around now for well over a decade, so it may not seem so new anymore. In both instances, man has used other organisms for his benefit. Writers used to cite the ancient practices of animal husbandry, domesticating wild plants as crops, and brewing beer — usually introduced by the phrase "Biotechnology is not a new phenomenon..." The difference today is that we can control precisely what we wish these organisms to achieve. We can create tomatoes with improved solids content — without simultaneously selecting for other, usually negative, traits. And we can empower these organisms with capabilities they never had: bacteria that make human proteins, for instance. There is yet one other important difference between the old and the new: biology is now big business. Theoretically, at least, there are big bucks in biotech.

Contrary to popular wisdom, however, biotechnology is not an industry *per se*. It is instead a set of enabling technologies that are being applied across the board — from agriculture to human health care, from the chemicals industry to veterinary medicine. True, some companies were formed on the basis of commercializing these technologies, but many more have incorporated them as part of their R&D arsenal. The two most powerful technologies — the ones that made this all possible — are recombinant DNA technology and hybridoma technology.

Recombinant DNA

Genetic engineering is so straightforward today that "even a child can do it." (In fact, there are commercial kits available aimed at grade-schoolers.) It is "cookbook" to clone a gene. Determining its nucleotide sequence is straightforward and rapid, given the availability of instruments designed to do just that. There are many host/vector expression systems — well-documented — from which to choose. It is possible to alter the amino acid sequence of a given protein, to study structure/function relationships.

The cloned DNA is digested with a variety of restriction enzymes of different specificities. The digested fragments are separated by electrophoresis, generating a restriction map. This makes it easier to determine the nucleotide sequence of each fragment, and thus the whole gene (or genes). For eukaryotic DNA, which has introns that bacteria cannot recognize, the usual procedure is to use reverse transcriptase to make complementary DNA (cDNA) copies of the messenger RNA (mRNA) and then clone the cDNA.

In terms of gene expression, there are several factors that determine the final yield of a recombinant protein. These include: the efficiency of transcription (governed by the promoter); the number of copies of the gene; the stability of the vector that carries the gene; the efficiency of translation; and the stability of the polypeptide itself.

To be successful, gene cloning requires an understanding of the mechanisms of transcription and translation within the host cell, a way to transfer the engineered DNA into the host, an appropriate vector to carry and express the gene, and a reliable assay to determine if the transfer has worked.

The genetic engineering tools are there, but they still need some fine-tuning. For instance, maximizing the expression levels of recombinant proteins is still an issue, including choosing just exactly the right host, the correct controlling elements (including promoters), and secretion signals (if, indeed, the host cells actually secrete the recombinant protein into the medium). What about the glycosylation patterns of recombinant proteins? Does it matter to the molecule's therapeutic efficacy if it is glycosylated differently from the authentic version? Bacteria may be the least expensive to grow, but they do not glycosylate at all. As for structure/function relationships, the sequence databases are growing much more rapidly than our ability to predict how changing an amino acid sequence can influence either the way a protein folds or the way it works in three-dimensional space.

Expression Systems

There is no universal expression system for heterologous proteins. Choosing the best one requires evaluating the options — from yield, to glycosylation, to proper folding, to economies of scale. Bacteria, yeast, filamentous fungi, mammalian cells (including the human variety), and even insect cells or plant cells can end up in the manufacturing plant's bioreactors.

For each expression system, vectors have been developed for introducing the heterologous DNA into the host cell. Generally, these vectors consist of the gene itself (or its complementary DNA, synthesized from the messenger DNA), an upstream promoter for regulating transcription, and a downstream terminating sequence. Foreign genes can exist on autonomously replicating plasmids or integrated into the host genome. They may be present in single or multiple copies.

Bacteria and yeast cannot express genes that contain non-coding sequences, or introns, but researchers have developed ways of removing them — via cDNA techniques or straight chemical synthesis of only the pertinent sequences. It is also still somewhat of a feat to coax bacteria to secrete recombinant proteins into the culture medium: they are much more prone to secrete the product into intracellular inclusion bodies or the periplasmic space. And that adds another step — not to mention expense — to the downstream purification process.

Bacteria have the advantage in the absolute amounts of protein they can make, which can reduce the sheer volume to be processed, and perhaps save on overall product costs. Yeasts, on the other hand, tend to synthesize lower quantities of recombinant proteins than bacteria but they are better at making bioactive molecules, which again affects downstream processing considerations. Mammalian cells are still the poorest producers, often only milligrams of protein per liter per day. But they can perform a multitude of post-translational modifications that other hosts cannot. These modifications, which are often needed to turn a protein into a functioning entity, include phosphorylation, disulfide bridge formation, and glycosylation, to name a few.

Bacterial Systems

Traditional industrial fermentation and purification processes for producing pharmaceuticals have not translated well to those involving recombinant microorganisms. There are usually differences in scale (100,000 liters versus 10,000 or less), and a whole new set of issues involving containment of the organisms and their disposal. Plus, bacterial strains that have been engineered to produce heterologous proteins are suffering a metabolic burden: if they can find a way to get rid of that foreign genetic matter, they will certainly do it. The longer one cultures them, the greater the chances that wild-type cells will triumph — and there will not be any product to show for it.

Not all recombinant proteins emerge in their active form: some are denatured, and the steps that are necessary to convert them vary depending on the particular protein. It is fairly rare for *Escherichia coli*, the bacterial workhorse, to make functional versions of proteins derived from higher organisms since these usually require some sort of post-translational modification to achieve full — or even partial — activity.

Bacterial processes tend to employ batch or fed-batch culture modes. But each must be customized to the strain, its genetic stability, and the requirements of downstream processing (do the cells secrete product into the medium or must they be broken open to harvest crude product? Is the product sensitive to proteolytic digestion by one of the components in the culture fluid?). Developing cell lines and developing processes go hand-in-hand. In fact, to pass muster with regulatory requirements, the basic process steps should be well established before a potential therapeutic ever enters clinical trials.

For a therapeutic protein, produced intracellularly in batch mode operation, the process steps would include the following: culture and media preparation; fermentation; isolating the crude product from the cells and media; purification; concentration; and final purification to injectable form. Because the protein is fragile, the separation steps must be done under mild conditions, and the number of steps should be kept at a minimum. Along the way, Good Manufacturing Process Guidelines must be adhered to, Standard Operating Procedures followed to the letter, and quality control/quality assurance standards met with ease. Any deviations can be expensive, and they undoubtedly delay the time to market.

And operating costs must be taken into account. For a small volume, high value product (which includes most therapeutics), capital expenditures and labor are the frontrunners.

The exact means chosen for separations are critical, too, since downstream processing can make up 50–90 percent of the overall manufacturing costs. If the equipment is flexible enough, it can be used in different unit operations.

Experience has shown that the following separation procedures, used in some combination, will purify most therapeutic products: centrifugation; protein precipitation; liquid extraction; ion exchange chromatography; gel filtration chromatography; high performance liquid chromatography; affinity chromatography; and tangential-flow filtration. Other techniques available include dialysis and reverse osmosis.

Yeast and Fungal Systems

Yeast do not have an inherent means of DNA uptake. Genetic engineering in these organisms has been made possible by the development of transformation systems and cloning vectors that mediate the introduction of DNA. Yeast cells are surrounded by a thick wall of polysaccharides. It is necessary to remove this coating, forming spheroplasts, to introduce DNA.

Selecting transformants in yeast is somewhat of a problem, too. They are resistant to the antibiotics that are commonly

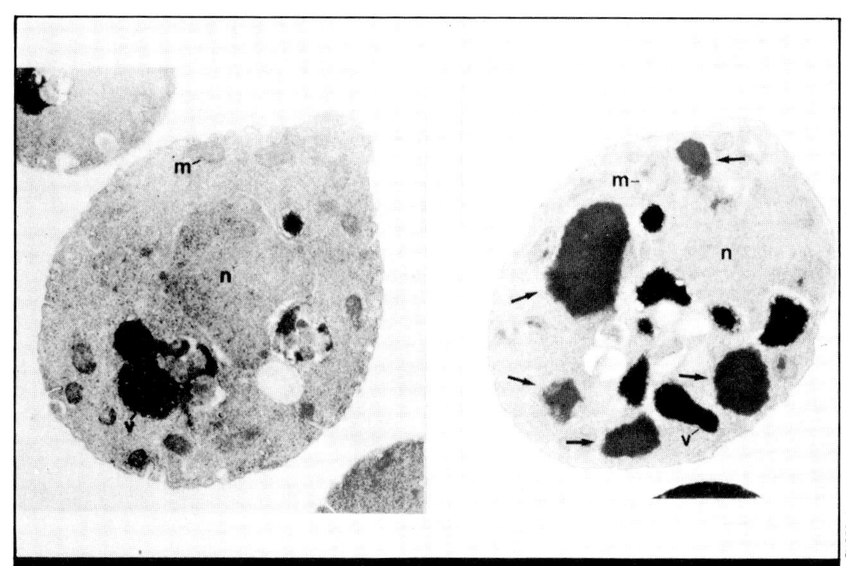

Figure 1. Electron micrographs of *Saccharomyces cerevisiae*, showing nuclei (n), mitochondria (m) and vacuoles (v). *Left*: Control. *Right*: A cell expressing human γ-interferon, which forms inclusion bodies (arrowed). Copyright *Bio/Technology*.

PHOTO COURTESY CHIRON CORP. AND U.C. BERKELEY, BIOCHEMISTRY

used to select transformed bacterial strains. Luckily, however, yeasts are sensitive to the antibiotic G418, an aminoglycoside that inhibits the growth of a wide range of prokaryotes and eukaryotes.

Most protocols for selecting and analyzing genes to be cloned in yeast start by first isolating the recombinant DNA sequences in *Escherichia coli*. This approach offers several advantages: transformation efficiency is high, there are very good screening methods available for identifying the clones and the bacteria amplify the cloned sequences, providing more material for introducing into the yeast.

Thus, yeast cloning vectors are composed of bacterial plasmids or phage DNA and yeast DNA sequences. These cloning vectors either integrate into the host genome, or replicate autonomously in the cytoplasm. Whichever type, the vectors all contain markers for selection in the host strain, an origin of replication for maintenance in *Escherichia coli* and several restriction endonuclease sites so that foreign DNA segments may be inserted.

There are two ways to produce heterologous proteins, either intracellular or secreted. One secretion system takes advantage of pheromones secreted naturally by haploid yeast strains to induce mating of the two sex types, "α" and "a". It is possible to modify the α-gene so yeast secrete proteins instead of mating factor. All of the expression vectors based on this modification are autonomously replicating plasmids. A typical vector might contain pBR322 sequences for amplification in *Escherichia coli*, the yeast two-micron sequences for replication in the host, and a few auxotrophic selectable markers. Use of the selectable markers allows for a high transformation efficiency as well as a high plasmid copy number — as many as 250 per cell. In practice, an expression cassette is inserted into these vectors. The cassette contains the heterologous gene of interest fused to a secretion leader sequence for secretion or a synthetic ATG for intracellular expression; it also contains yeast promoters and terminators.

As production vehicles, yeast are often considered superior to *Escherichia coli* because they can glycosylate, acetylate, fold, and perform many other post-translation modifications for functional eukaryotic proteins. And the related filamentous fungi naturally secrete vast quantities of enzymes. Glucoamylase, one of the largest bulk enzymes in the world, is produced by industrial strains of *Aspergillus niger*. From a single copy of the gene, they can make up to 20 grams per liter of the enzyme. The technology for gene expression in filamentous fungi is developing rapidly, but yeast have not been abandoned as production vehicles.

Saccharomyces cerevisiae, the "common" laboratory yeast, has been successfully engineered to express, and often secrete, a variety of potential therapeutic proteins. Its cousin, the industrial yeast *Pichia pastoris*, has also been engineered as a host for heterologous protein synthesis. Scientists have cloned the genes of the methanol utilization pathway and isolated the methanol-responsive regulatory regions of two of the genes. The levels of product expression can be controlled by switching the carbon source. The system offers two types of expression vectors, autonomous and integrated.

Traditional industrial yeasts such as those used in the brewing industry can also be engineered to improve existing properties or add new capabilities. One research group has developed plasmid vectors specifically for the wild type polyploid strains used in the fermentation industry. The selection procedures developed for transformation of haploid lab strains do not work for the wild type, but the yeasts are sensitive to the antibiotic G418 so it is possible to develop plasmid vectors based on resistance to G418.

The goal for engineering filamentous fungi is to get them to secrete vast amounts of a properly modified protein. These organisms already have a history of use in food products; they are acceptable from a regulatory and consumer viewpoint.

The problem comes in doing genetics on these organisms, not in growing the cells at a large scale.

As with any expression system, the bottom line is how much product can the system make. An exceptional system

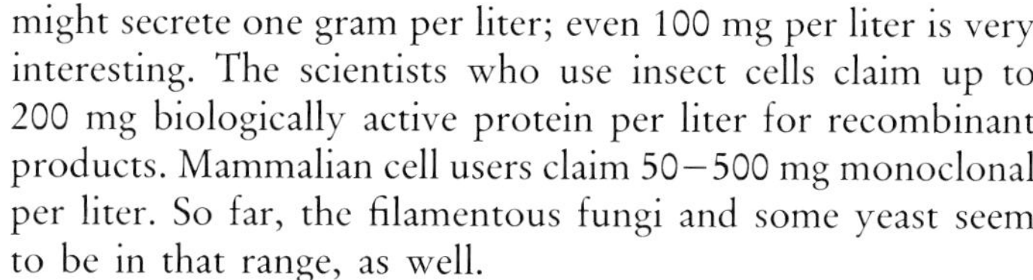

might secrete one gram per liter; even 100 mg per liter is very interesting. The scientists who use insect cells claim up to 200 mg biologically active protein per liter for recombinant products. Mammalian cell users claim 50–500 mg monoclonal per liter. So far, the filamentous fungi and some yeast seem to be in that range, as well.

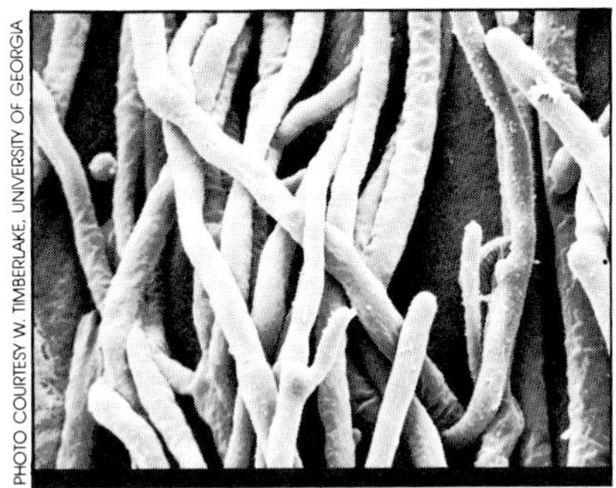

Figure 2. A scanning electron micrograph of *Aspergillus nidulans* hyphae. *A. nidulans* is the most "academic" of the *Aspergillus* species, and is well characterized genetically. Other species, including *A. niger* and *A. awamori*, are industrial organisms and are not being used to express and secrete heterologous proteins. Copyright *Bio/Technology*.

Figure 3. The bulging end of the *A. nidulans* stalk, the vesicle and support structures known as phialides ("bowling pin" shape). Copyright *Bio/Technology*.

Hybridomas and Mammalian Cell Expression Systems

There are currently a wide variety of animal cell systems used for the expression of recombinant and non-recombinant products. Primary criteria for the selection of a particular cell line or clone include fidelity of expression, specific productivity, and stability of expression. This selection may be made on the basis of a laboratory or pilot scale experiment.

However acceptable results at this scale do not necessarily scale up to a production level bioreactor. There are many areas of concern that must be addressed, namely, type of bioreactor, type of media used for cell selection, use of selective agents, stability of expression, longevity of cell line, and biosafety. The final choice of cell line/bioreactor system requires that these factors be weighed against the potential value of the product.

Monoclonal antibodies are produced by hybridomas, cell lines created by fusing an antibody-producing cell with an immortalized — usually transformed — one. Mouse/mouse hybridomas are the most common, and the easiest to produce. There are some human/mouse cell lines, but very few human/human.

Once one has mastered the genetic engineering required to make a monoclonal antibody, what kind should it be? Murine varieties have some real advantages over mouse/human or fully human ones: cell fusions are easier, the genetics are more established, and the yields are better. But they also have one big disadvantage: if used therapeutically, they will

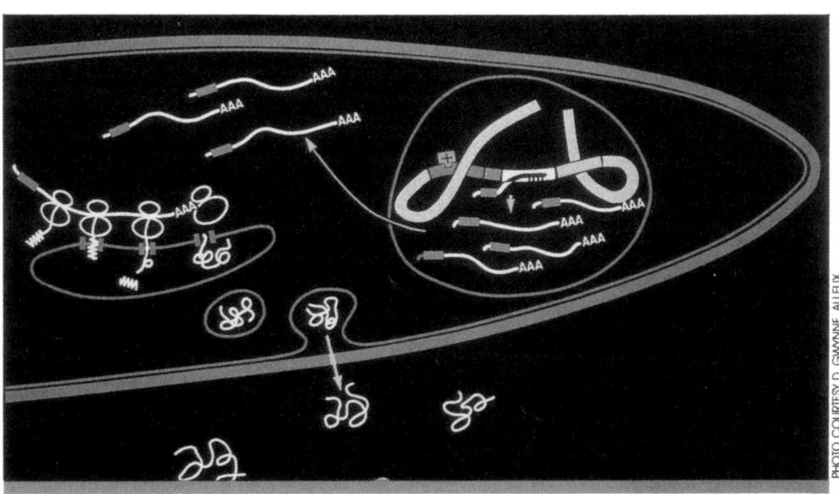

Figure 4. A fungal expression and secretion system. The vector contains the following regions: genomic DNA (brown); functional coding region (yellow); regulatory region (red); promoter/regulator (green); and secretion signal (blue). Copyright *Bio/Technology*.

induce an immune reaction, including fever and rash. The human anti-mouse antibody response prevents a mouse antibody from being efficacious if given a second time. Human cells are hard to culture, it is difficult to create continuous ("immortalized") cell lines that are not transformed, the yields are low, and the genetics are poorly understood.

An alternative, and being actively investigated, is to produce chimeric molecules — monoclonals engineered to be part mouse, part human. Research has shown that one can start with a mouse antibody and humanize it bit-by-bit until it is almost entirely human. (Most of this work has been done with the antigen-binding region).

Another variation is quadromas, bifunctional monoclonal antibodies (hybrid hybridomas). These engineered molecules have one binding site for the desired antigen and another for various agents of interest. In theory, this avoids the necessity for chemically modifying an antibody. Such bispecific antibodies could even crosslink effector and target cells. They can react with surface antigens and lyse target cells, or be used as an isotope delivery system for *in vivo* imaging.

The system of choice for producing commercial quantities of monoclonal antibodies is very much a function of the product's end-use. For *in vitro* diagnostic purposes in enzyme-linked or radio-immunoassays, gram quantities on a yearly basis might suffice. And because these antibodies are not injected into humans, they can be of mouse origin. *In vivo* diagnostics such as imaging agents, on the other hand, while still required in small quantities, should be at least partially "humanized" to avoid immune reactions. Therapeutic monoclonals present the biggest challenge: here, one needs kilograms per year; with a repeated dose schedule, immune reactions are a major consideration.

Currently, most monoclonal antibodies are still produced in mouse ascites fluid, rather than by cultured cells. Clearly, this is impractical if one needs a kilogram of product: that would require 20,000 mice. But hybrid cell lines — be they mouse/mouse or mouse/human fusions — are not so easy to culture. The most difficult of the lot are wholly human cell lines: if they yield continuous lines, they are usually transformed, as well, leading to future difficulties with the regulatory agencies. Researchers have even harnessed bacteria and plants in an effort to make these proteins on a large scale, and economically. *Escherichia coli* can now be engineered to secrete monoclonals, in most reported systems into the periplasmic space. The trick here is to coax the heavy and light chains to assemble into an active molecule.

There are almost no *in vitro* production systems available today that are capable of churning out kilograms of monoclonal antibody.

Cultured hybridoma cells, being mammalian, are extremely sensitive and often fastidious. Much work has gone into tailoring bioreactor design to fit their needs. Immobilizing the cells has its advantages, including lower reactor volumes and higher initial product purities. But such systems are often mass-transfer limited. Cells can also be grown in stirred tanks or airlift reactors, in batch, fed-batch, or continuous operation. Because mammalian cells grow slowly (often with population doubling time of 48 hours or longer), the danger of microbial contamination becomes high, and sterility issues of utmost importance.

To date, the highest cell densities and productivities seem to have been produced in continuous perfusion systems but, with the volume of medium required, this is a pricy choice for any commercial candidate monoclonal.

Developing the proper medium formulation is key also: not only to achieving maximal cell growth and productivity, but also to doing so economically. Traditionally, hybridomas require complex, serum-containing media. The individual components are ill-defined (harder to remove downstream); serum is expensive, and supplies can be unreliable. Major efforts are underway to resolve these problems though available defined media are still expensive and must be tailored to each cell line.

As with any potential product, scaling up to commercial production has its costs. To keep in mind are the following: the productivity and stability of the cell line; media costs; development issues; capital issues (e.g., facilities, overhead); and regulatory requirements. Of these, the testing and regulatory costs predominate.

A Matter of Scale

In the end, process efficiency and product demand determine the absolute scale of the production process. A cell line producing 50 mg/l/day in a laboratory reactor could handle 10–20 liters/day: this is suitable for producing monoclonals for *in vitro* diagnostics, for instance. On the other hand, if one were interested in producing therapeutic quantities from a cell line that produced 500 mg/ml, one would indeed need 10,000 liters/day.

Initially, off-target market predictions, coupled with old-line drug makers' preconceptions, generated estimates of product quantities that were usually too high or too low. Some products once thought to have a single potential application turn out to have three or four, resulting in initial underestimate of scale. So, too, does the realization that testing a product for safety, potency, efficacy, toxicity, and purity requires significant amounts of material. On the other hand, because many recombinant proteins are much more potent than anyone thought, the dosage was often overestimated. Conversely, the cell productivity was often underestimated. Optimized expression systems are better than ever: for mammalian cells, the yields are 4–5-fold better now than they were five years ago, largely due to new reactor configurations that pack cells into small volumes.

What a research scientist might define as large scale — a

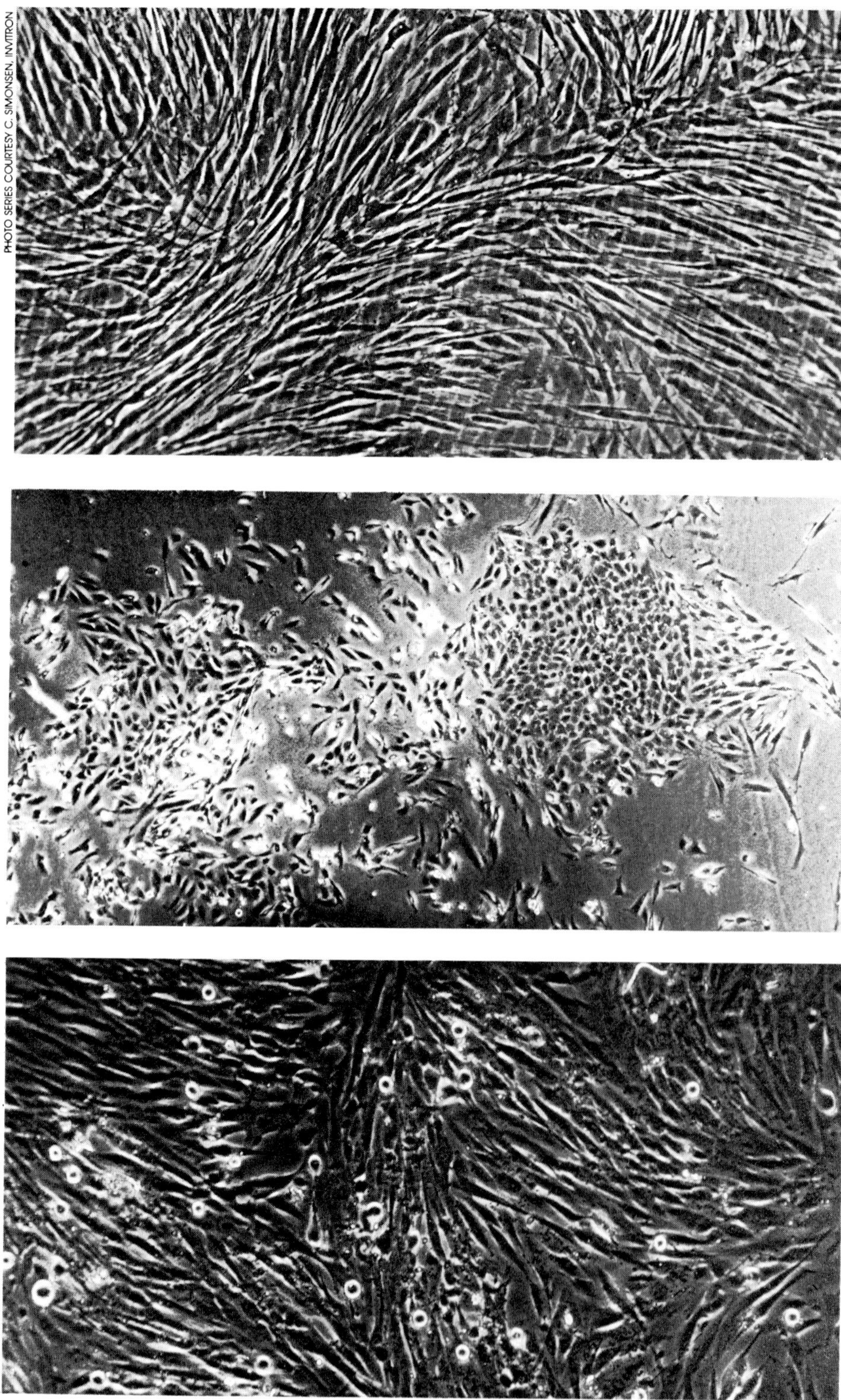

PHOTO SERIES COURTESY C. SIMONSEN, INVITRON

Figure 5. This succession of photomicrographs shows human colon fibroblasts before, during and after transfection with SV40 large T antigen gene constructs. Prior to senescence, the cells have a typical fibroblast morphology. As the cells emerge from the "crisis" period their morphology is altered and foci appear. Copyright *Bio/Technology*.

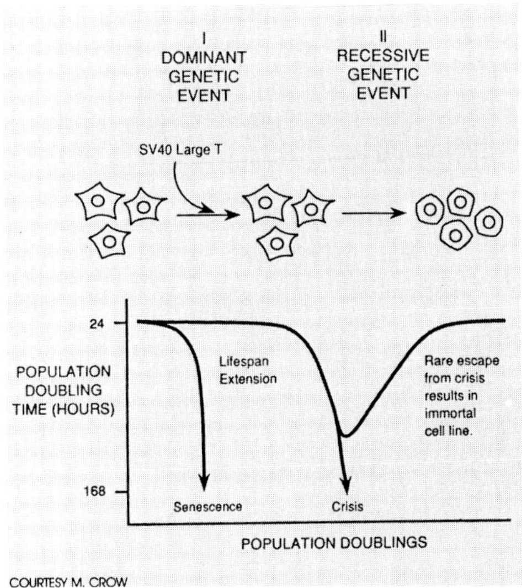

Figure 6. A summary of the events involved in human cell immortalization: at least two steps or events are required. The first (I) of these can be mimicked by the dominant genetic action of an exogenous oncogene such as the SV40 large T antigen. The oncogene confers life span extension on most, if not all, of the cells that express it. A second genetic event (II) occurs in only a few of the transfected cells, with a frequency that suggests a single genetic alteration. Based on cell fusion data by Pereira-Smith & Smith, this second genetic event is most likely recessive and probably involves the loss of anti-oncogene expression by the cells. Copyright *Bio/Technology*.

50 liter culture producing three grams of protein per week — would be lab scale to a biochemical engineer. When engineers talk large scale, they think in terms of industrial equipment, bulk flows, and logistics. Current industrial scales exhibit a bulk liquid capacity of 25–500 liters per day per reactor for continuous or semicontinuous processes; for batch runs, the flow is 500–5,000 liters over 1–3 weeks.

The purpose of scale up is to reproduce a process on a larger scale with a predictable increase in production capacity. And the scale has to satisfy the market needs. For biotechnology products these scales span several orders of magnitude.

Strain improvements and advances in reactor technology have gone hand in hand. For mammalian cell systems, increased culture densities have led to smaller equipment. Batch densities have risen to at least two million cells/ml and fed densities have come down tenfold, resulting in smaller reactor volumes. Although reactor capacities have changed, the amount of medium needed by each cell has not.

Process Development

Engineering yeast to produce recombinant hepatitis B vaccine, or a hybridoma to make a monoclonal antibody that prevents kidney transplant rejection is, however, just the beginning. If a company intends to commercialize that product, and have it pass muster with the Food and Drug Administration (or other appropriate regulatory authorities), it must develop a process for making that product — consistently and reproducibly, batch after batch. Moreover, if a company intends to make a profit (name one that doesn't), that process has to be economical. Adding milligram quantities of amino acids to a 10-liter culture is one thing; scaling that up to gram amounts for a 10,000-liter batch run is quite another.

Effective process development has to start early in the product development cycle. As one scientist succinctly puts it: "Work from the injection bottle backwards". The final therapeutic has to meet stringent regulatory requirements. It cannot contain stray viral particles or traces of antibiotics. The job of the quality control/quality assurance officers is to ensure that bench scientists never use an inappropriate host/vector system that will cause headaches down the line, or put something into the growth medium that only has to be removed later. Process development should be viewed as a series of interrelated steps, and viewed as a whole.

Until recently, research scientists and chemical engineers have not been able to talk to each other. Some still don't. But one thing that biotechnology has done is bring divergent disciplines together in an attempt to solve a whole new set of problems.

Bioreactors and Fermentors

Bacterial cultures are usually grown by batch fermentation. Many valuable therapeutics are present in low concentrations in the culture fluid or the bacteria themselves, often requiring that quite large overall culture volumes be employed.

To grow well, most bacteria require large amounts of oxygen: because the solubility of oxygen in the culture fluid is usually lower that what the bacteria demand, fermentation vessels are designed to maximize oxygen transfer. This is accomplished by bubbling air into the vessel and then breaking up the bubbles with an agitator (impeller). Unfortunately, this often results in foaming, which must be controlled either by adding anti-foam (remember, this has to be removed downstream), or leaving enough "head space" (as much as 25% of the reactor volume).

Conditions within the reactor need to be monitored and carefully controlled during the fermentation run itself. These include dissolved oxygen, pH, dissolved CO_2, and temperature. Most systems commercially available today offer built in controllers, to various degrees of sophistication.

Scaling up a fermentor configuration — from 100 liters to 5,000, for instance — is not just a matter of multiplication. The volume increases with the cube of the diameter, while the surface area increases with the square of the diameter. To complicate matters further, the impeller tip speed is directly proportional to the diameter. All of this, of course, affects

SCALE-UP:

FRED WARD PRODUCTIONS

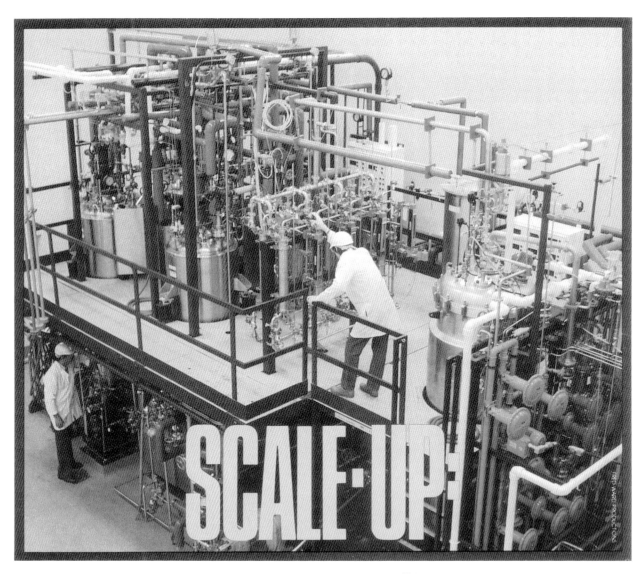

Figure 7. Cetus' pilot plant houses a 1,500-liter fermentor. Betaseron™ (human recombinant β-interferon) and IL-2 (human recombinant interleukin-2) were both produced in this facility. Copyright *Bio/Technology*.

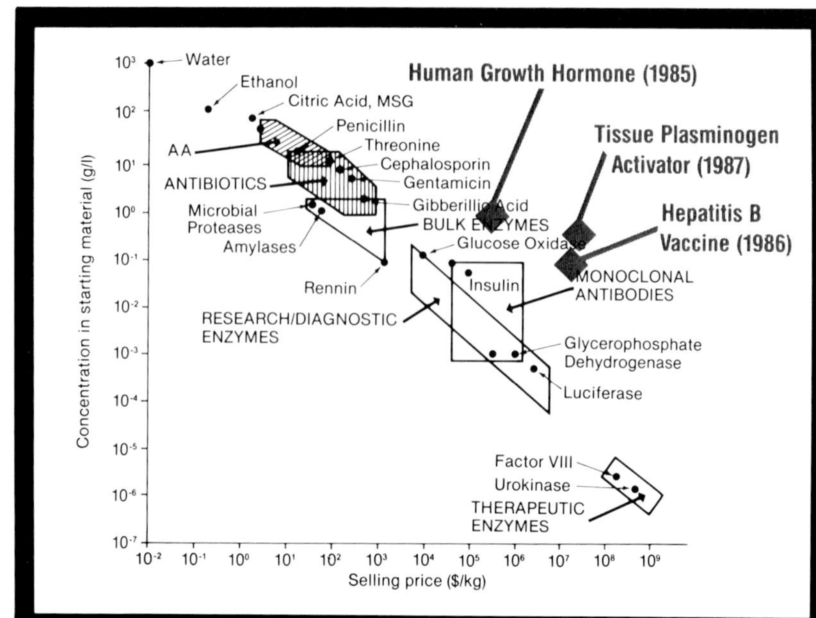

Figure 8. Concentration in starting material (prepurification) of various substances and their selling prices. This 1985 graph emphasizes the strong correlation between the crude product concentration and the products' production costs over a broad range of traditional products. The few biotechnology products now on the market lie outside this curve, commanding prices 100-1,000-fold higher than predicted. Copyright *Bio/Technology*.

Figure 9. Large-scale chromatography columns run in series. Each column holds 240 l of gel filtration medium. The system can purify 2.1 kg of protein in 12 hours. Copyright *Bio/Technology.*

Figure 10. A 25,000 l fermentor being lifted into position at Provesta's fermentation products plant site at the Phillips Research Center (Bartlesville, OK). Copyright *Bio/Technology.*

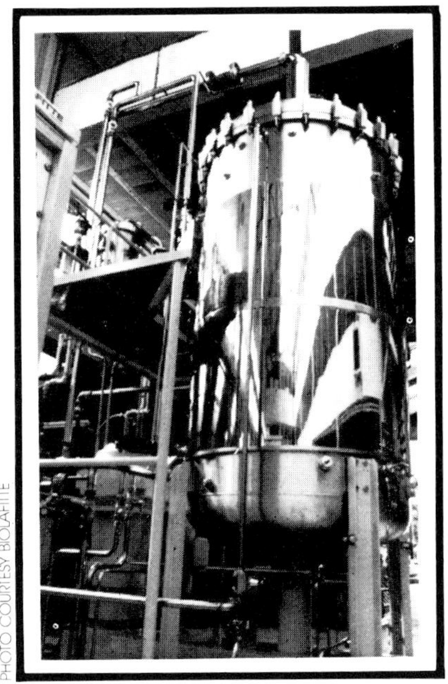

Figure 11. Copyright *Bio/Technology.*

the culture parameters and dynamics, as well.

When scaling up a process, it is more than the configuration of the culture vessel that needs addressing. Other issues include heat transfer, aeration, and sterilization — of the vessel itself as well as the culture medium.

While fed batch is the most common fermentation mode, there are other options. One is stirred tank, in which fresh broth continuously replaces that removed as the "product stream," with the overall culture volume remaining constant. Another option is an air lift, or suspension, reactor. Here, there is no physical agitation of the culture fluid: air is sparged into the vessel from the bottom, causing the fluid to rise up a central draft tube. Once it reaches the surface, gas is released and the fluid then descends down the outer edge of the vessel. The object is gentle mixing, especially important for fragile cells. Still, foaming may be a problem in this system.

One means of growing cells is to immobilize them on a carrier or retain them by some other means. Because there are often significant problems with oxygen transfer, this method is best for cells that make extracellular products in continuous culture. The advantage is that the cells are not growing, thus assuring their genetic stability.

Alternatively, one can grow cells in membrane reactors, the most popular being hollow fibers. The reactor is small, containing bundles of hollow fibers in parallel. The cells grow around the fibers, in the extracapillary spaces. Medium flows continuously through the fibers themselves, bringing fresh nutrients and removing waste products, as well as the desired, secreted recombinant protein. There are several advantages to such a system: for one, the cells can be packed to near tissue density, thus dramatically reducing the overall culture volume from what a culture vessel would require. Ideally, each cell has access to nutrients. Microenvironments (pockets of oxygen deprivation, for example) are eliminated. This is not always the case, however. Flow patterns and oxygen transfer may present problems.

Another configuration designed to address the special needs of fragile cells is the fluidized bed bioreactor. Here, the cells are immobilized on beads, which are suspended and mixed by medium flowing upwards through the bioreactor. The mixing is very gentle, but even so can produce enough shear force to rip the cells apart.

Figures 1–20 illustrate in a general way many of the points made in this chapter.

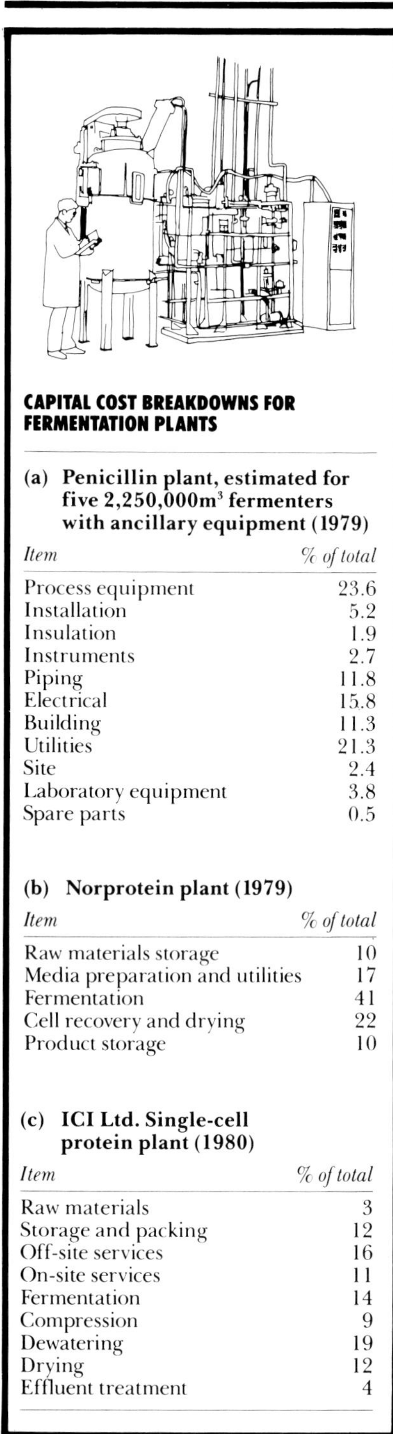

CAPITAL COST BREAKDOWNS FOR FERMENTATION PLANTS

(a) Penicillin plant, estimated for five 2,250,000m³ fermenters with ancillary equipment (1979)

Item	*% of total*
Process equipment	23.6
Installation	5.2
Insulation	1.9
Instruments	2.7
Piping	11.8
Electrical	15.8
Building	11.3
Utilities	21.3
Site	2.4
Laboratory equipment	3.8
Spare parts	0.5

(b) Norprotein plant (1979)

Item	*% of total*
Raw materials storage	10
Media preparation and utilities	17
Fermentation	41
Cell recovery and drying	22
Product storage	10

(c) ICI Ltd. Single-cell protein plant (1980)

Item	*% of total*
Raw materials	3
Storage and packing	12
Off-site services	16
On-site services	11
Fermentation	14
Compression	9
Dewatering	19
Drying	12
Effluent treatment	4

Figure 12. Copyright *Bio/Technology*.

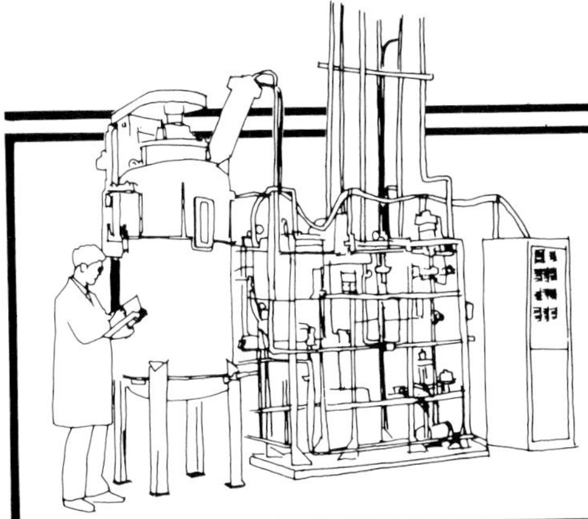

Costs for a low volume product are primarily capital and labor intensive; for a high volume product raw material and utility costs dominate.

Figure 13. Copyright *Bio/Technology.*

by Jennifer Van Brunt

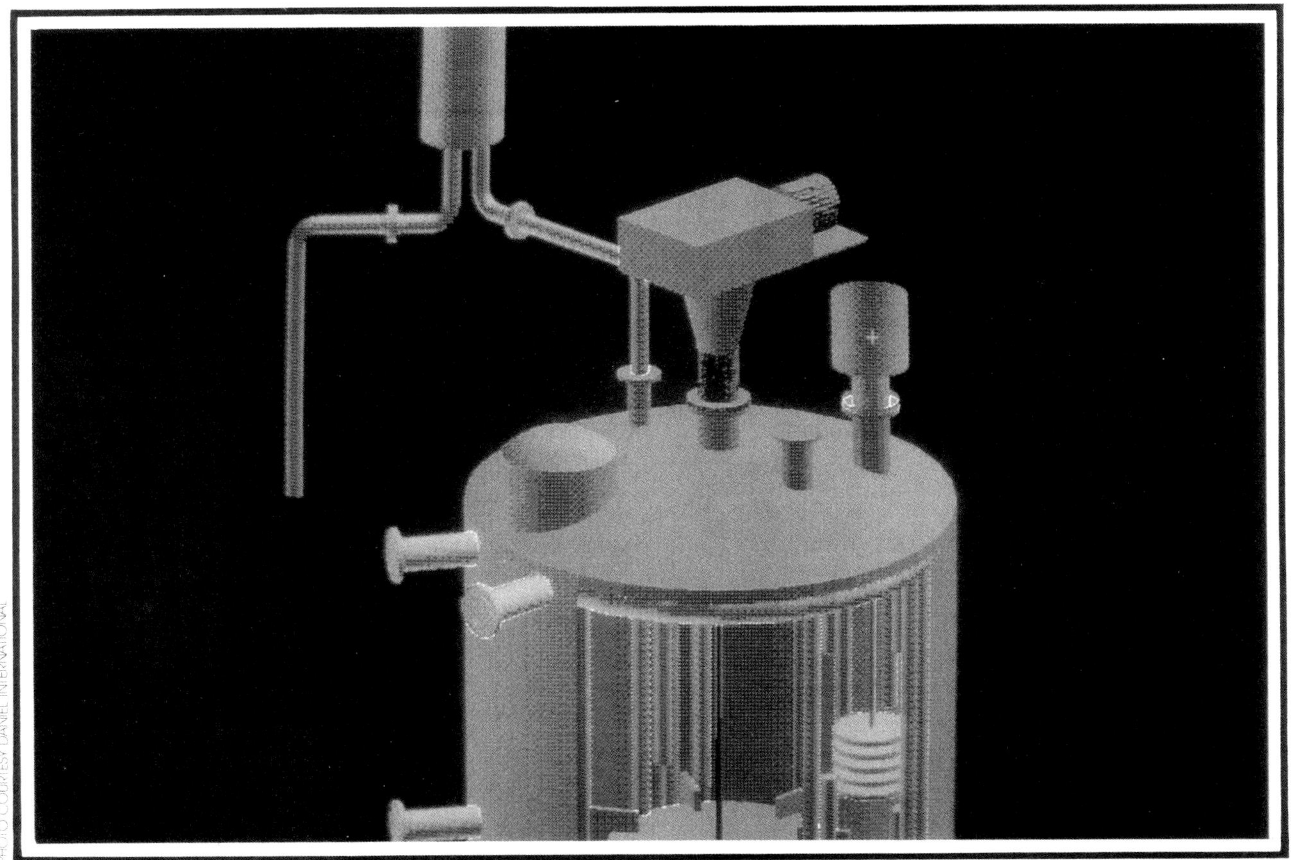

PHOTO COURTESY DANIEL INTERNATIONAL

Figure 14. The design process for the Daniel-Phillips fermenter uses computer-aided engineering. Copyright *Bio/Technology.*

Figure 15. End-on view of hollow fiber cartridge showing the uniform distribution of fibers within the cartridge. Copyright *Bio/Technology*.

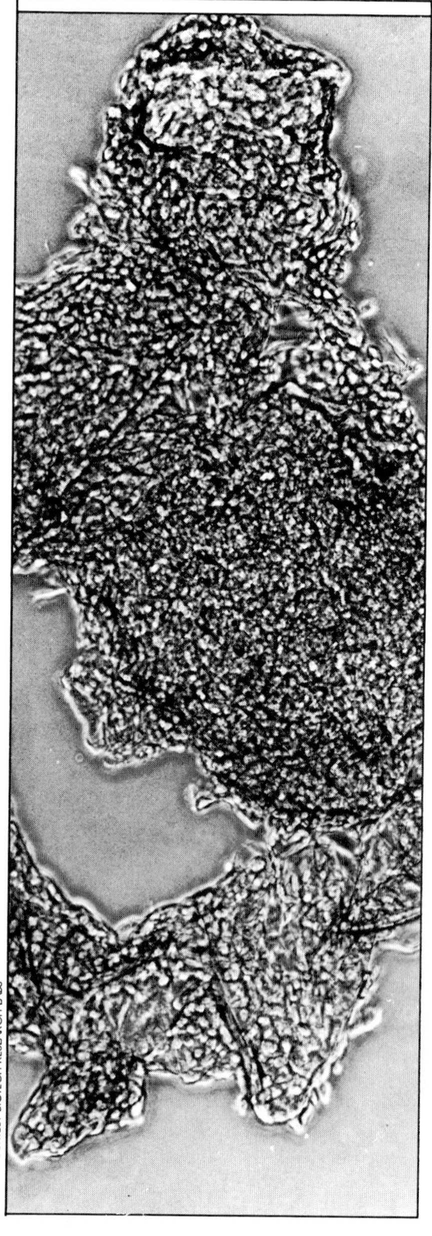

Figure 16. CHO cells growing in particles of a sponge matrix in stirred suspension culture. Copyright *Bio/Technology*.

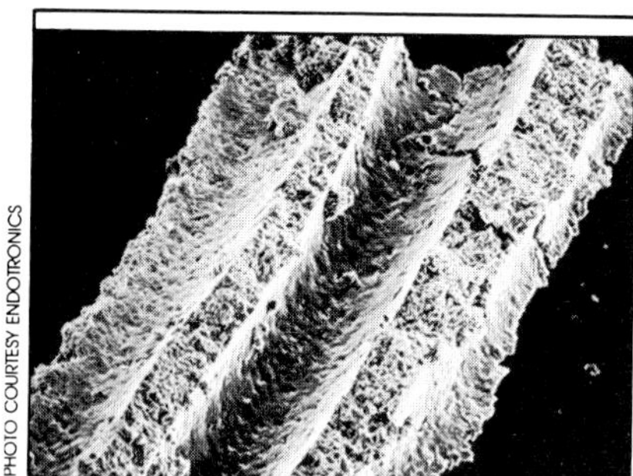

Figure 17. Electron micrograph of mammalian cells removed from a hollow fiber cartridge. The tracks are areas where single hollow fibers once lay. Copyright *Bio/Technology*.

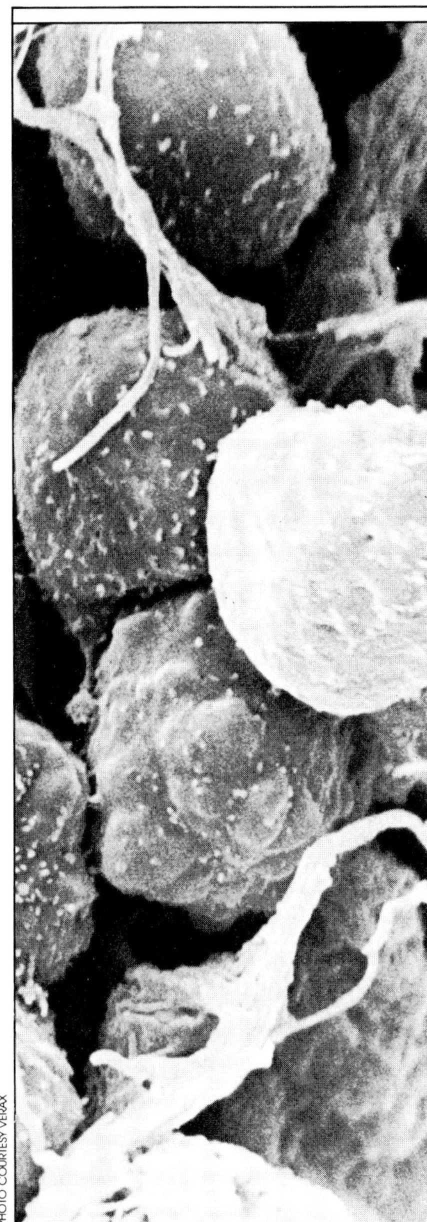

Figure 18. A colony of hybridoma cells immobilized in a weighted sponge matrix. Copyright *Bio/Technology*.

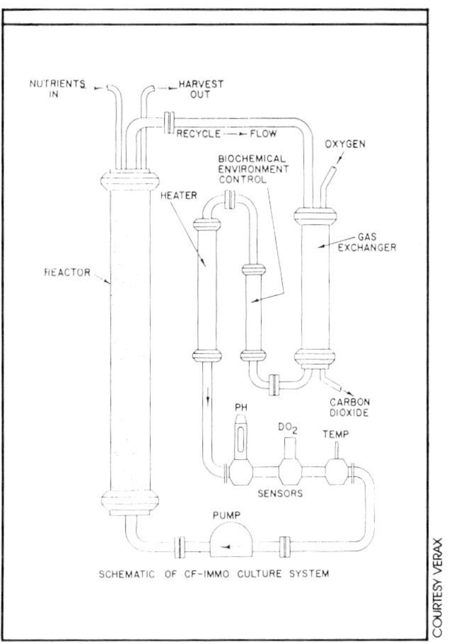

Figure 19. Schematic of a continuous flow fluidized bed bioreactor. Copyright *Bio/Technology*.

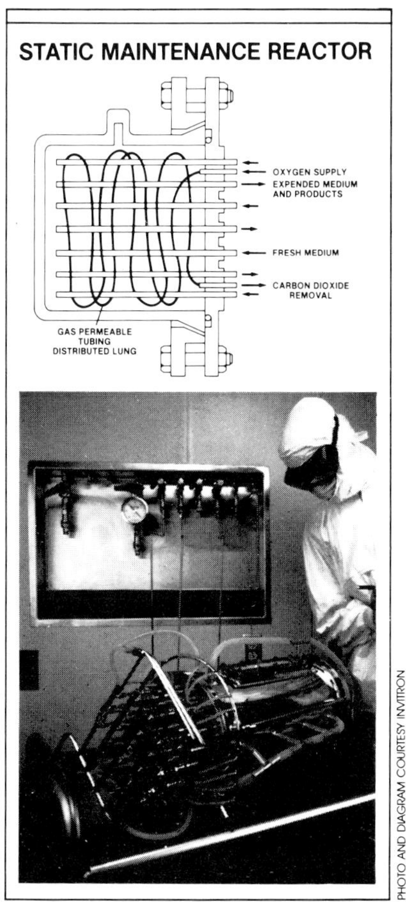

Figure 20. Static maintenance reactor in cross-section and in use. Copyright *Bio/Technology*.

Chapter 11

Polymerase Chain Reaction: Development of a Novel Technology in a Corporate Environment

Ellen Daniell

Kary Mullis conceived of the Polymerase Chain Reaction (PCR) while pondering certain problems in molecular biology from his position as chemist and head of the DNA synthesis group at Cetus Corporation. At the time of this writing (June 1989) three basic patents on PCR have been awarded to Cetus and thirty related applications submitted for approval in the U.S. alone; PCR is hailed as setting off a revolution in molecular biology equivalent to the discovery of restriction enzymes and their use in DNA cloning, and Cetus has a division of over seventy people dedicated to the technology. A joint venture with a major manufacturer of research instrumentation and a license agreement with a leading international pharmaceutical company are focussed on development of PCR-based products and services, and over a hundred other companies have requested rights to use PCR commercially.

This chapter chronicles the development of PCR at Cetus: how Mullis and then others were allowed time to work on PCR; the adoption of PCR in research programs at Cetus and elsewhere; the "marketing" of PCR to potential business partners, the recognition of PCR's value to a company focussed on the development of therapeutic drugs, and the formation of the Cetus PCR Division and current PCR-related business strategy.

WHAT IS PCR?

PCR is a method of amplifying a specific nucleic acid target sequence present in a complex template to produce a large amount of a specific DNA fragment of defined length and sequence. An analogy frequently used is that PCR locates a needle in a haystack and turns it into a new haystack composed mostly of needles. The method uses two oligonucleotide primers that hybridize to the ends of a target sequence. The primers anneal to opposite strands of DNA and are oriented towards one another so that a DNA polymerase will extend the primer on one strand in the direction of the primer on the opposite strand. As depicted in Figure 1, repeating cycles of denaturation of the template, annealing of the primers and extension by DNA polymerase result in the amplification of the segment defined by the 5′ ends of the primers.

The extension product of each primer can anneal to the opposite strand primer and serve as the template for another round of extension. With a molar excess of primers each cycle doubles the amount of the specific DNA fragment produced in the previous cycle, resulting in an exponential accumulation of the target fragment. Non-specific extension products of a single primer accumulate linearly and rapidly fall behind the exponentially amplified specific fragment.

Because DNA polymerases from common sources such as *E. coli* are inactivated by the temperatures required for denaturation of DNA, a thermostable DNA polymerase isolated from the thermophilic bacterium *Thermus aquaticus* (*Taq*) is used to avoid the necessity of adding fresh enzyme in each cycle.

The significant attributes of PCR for most applications are specificity, sensitivity and speed. The specificity of PCR stems from the specificity of DNA hybridization and the exponential amplification of the specific fragment; primers of a sufficient length are hybridized under conditions that favor the annealing of perfect complements. DNA synthesis, under appropriate conditions, has a high fidelity and is fast: after twenty-five cycles of three to five minutes each a single copy gene contained in a complex genomic DNA can be amplified several million-fold in a few hours (Fig. 2). The *Taq* DNA polymerase is moderately processive and specific fragments as long as ten kilobases can be produced. The requirement for sensitivity of the detection method used to identify the amplified target is much reduced because of the many-fold amplification that precedes detection. Furthermore, relatively crude DNA preparations serve as templates for PCR; because the amplification is so great, the resulting fragments are quite clean.

There are myriad variations of the basic PCR technique that expand its use. The addition of specific useful DNA sequences to the amplified product by including them in the primers at the 5′ ends produces fragments ready for cloning, or containing information necessary for expression of the

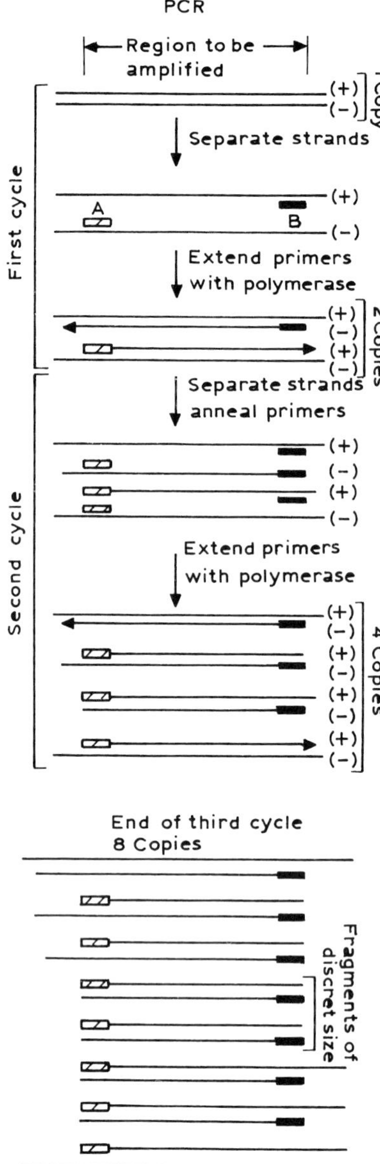

Figure 1. Diagram of the Polymerase Chain Reaction (PCR) process: at the end of three cycles of amplification, eight double-stranded copies of the specific region defined by the primers have been generated. Two of these copies are discrete sized fragments which are exponentially amplified in subsequent cycles.

Cycle	Relative Amount
1	2
2	4
3	8
4	16
5	32
6	64
7	128
8	256
9	512
10	1,024
11	2,048
12	4,096
13	8,192
14	16,384
15	32,768
16	65,536
17	131,072
18	262,144
19	524,288
20	1,048,576
21	2,097,152
22	4,184,304
23	8,388,608
24	16,777,216
25	33,554,432
26	67,108,864
27	134,217,728
28	268,435,456
29	536,870,912
30	1,073,741,824

Figure 2. The relative number of copies of specific PCR product generated during each successive cycle of amplification.

fragment in a bacterial host or in cell free transcription and translation systems. By using primer sequences that are conserved in evolution, or by using a mixture of primers that have sequence variations, DNA sequences that are related to known sequences but have not previously been isolated or characterized can be amplified and studied. PCR reactions using a lower concentration of one primer than the other can be used to generate single-stranded DNA ready for sequencing. By using tagged deoxyribonucleoside triphosphates of high specific activity, PCR has been used to prepare tagged probes for hybridization studies. Other modifications allow amplification of regions outside the defined region flanked by the selected primers, so that uncharacterized DNA which "flanks" a known sequence can be isolated and studied.

THE CONCEPTION OF PCR

Among Mullis' numerous ideas, PCR is the most innovative although many of the components such as primer extension. DNA polymerase and oligonucleotide synthesis were already available. Perhaps it took a chemist with imagination and a desire to do things faster and better than anyone else, working among molecular biologists, to put the pieces together. Mullis told story of the conception of PCR, presented as an after-dinner speech in 1989, which greatly enlivens its history.

Mullis, providing hundreds of nucleotide sequences for fellow researchers at Cetus, wanted to figure out "what else to do with all these oligonucleotides [we were making, because] the molecular biologists were so slow". An important scientific challenge in molecular genetics was how to distinguish quickly two alleles that differ from one another by a single base-pair. This was the key, for example, to detecting the mutation causing sickle cell anemia. Mullis considered synthesizing DNA across the site of the mutation by allowing DNA polymerase to extend an oligonucleotide primer placed upstream and very near the site. If the base encoded at that site were left out of the reaction, and the primer was positioned so that the critical site was the first place that particular base was needed in the extension, the reaction would stop, creating a band of a discrete size from the mutant allele, and one of a different size (determined by the next requirement for the missing base) from the wild type allele. However, there were lots of worries: maybe other oligonucleotides the same length as the critical one would result from primer hybridization and extension at other sites; also, when one deoxytriphosphate is missing from a polymerase reaction, the enzyme is capable of misincorporating a base, masking the base change sought after. So, thought Mullis, one could do the same thing from the other direction, with a primer positioned so the mutant would give another discrete size fragment and confirm the result. This is a key concept in PCR — the specificity results from the requirement that two primers hybridize specifically in order for exponential amplification to occur.

Mullis was "drivin' up to Mendocino, thinkin' about this stuff, and I hit Cloverdale and I thought what if the [primers] that got extended could bind to the other primer....... and I stopped the car". Because he had been doing computer programming, Mullis said, "I immediately knew you could do it several times. You see, no-one ever did that in biochemistry. In biochemistry you do it once and that's it. And you could do it just with an enzyme and deoxynucleoside triphosphates, which are cheap, soluble and legal....... I couldn't figure out why it wouldn't work, but I knew it couldn't because I hadn't heard of it...."

And so, returning to Cetus after the weekend, he had a computer search done and could not find any references to anyone trying such a thing. He talked the idea over with other Cetus scientists and began doing some experiments to show that it would work.

The Cetus scientific tradition is to foster creative new ideas without losing focus on product-related project goals. There were various opportunities for scientists to present their ideas to others, including "Blue Sky" sessions at which novel ideas could be presented without experimental evidence or proof of feasibility. Mullis was a frequent contributor to these sessions. He was regarded by his coworkers as a wild man, highly creative, undisciplined, quick to anger and occasionally combative, but to some endearing, his ideas worth listening to with some healthy skepticism. His enthusiasm for PCR was boundless and infectious.

DEMONSTRATING AND DEVELOPING A BASIC NEW TECHNIQUE

It was the responsibility of Tom White, then Vice President of Research at Cetus, to evaluate and select those exploratory ideas which would be pursued by the research division. With PCR, he had a new idea presented by a valued scientist who was known for interesting but sometimes unworkable ideas, and whose DNA synthesis operation provided support to critical therapeutic development projects at Cetus. White thought PCR was worthy of Mullis' time and he consulted with Henry Erlich and Norman Arnheim of Cetus' Human Genetics department to check out his assessment. They felt it was a longshot both theoretically, because of doubts that short oligonucleotides would prime with sufficient specificity, and practically, because of the inconvenience and expense of adding fresh DNA polymerase after every heating and cooling step. However, they also argued that if it did work it would revolutionize DNA probe diagnostics and therefore recommended that Mullis be encouraged and supported.

After the conception of PCR, White asked Mullis to give up his responsibilities as head of the DNA Synthesis laboratory, transfer to the Human Genetics department and have a year of freedom to work only on PCR. In addition, White allowed him some assistance from Fred Faloona, a talented young high school graduate who had been helping Mullis in the DNA synthesis lab. Since some key research projects were already understaffed, and Faloona's services were needed for DNA probe diagnostic work, only part of his time was given to Mullis. Mullis was naturally unhappy about this, believing it was ridiculous to require that an innovative and exciting new idea be proven workable before he could have more help. In reality, although enthusiasm for new scientific ideas was high among Cetus scientists, it was far from a trivial decision for White to allow Mullis full time to work on his new idea. There were many intriguing ideas and proposals being generated by the scientific staff and because of budget and staffing limitations, all decisions to undertake exploratory research were subjected to scrutiny by scientists and by management. Any project pursued meant that another could not, so the commitment of resources to a new concept by White and Jeffrey Price, head of Cetus R&D, was significant. Other successful exploratory projects selected during this time included studies on the function of *ras* oncogene proteins in cell transformation and the cloning and elevated expression of the gene for methionine amino peptidase, the enzyme involved in processing the initiating N-terminal methionine of proteins.

White felt that if Mullis could get preliminary data indicating that PCR would work, then further research and staff would be justified by the diagnostics program and other projects; he judged that Mullis assisted by part-time help was the appropriate starting level of effort.

RESULTS AND PUBLICATION

Mullis used a plasmid as a target for amplication. He designed primers that should produce a specific sized fragment and set to work with *E. coli* DNA polymerase (Klenow fragment) and two waterbaths, one for denaturation of DNA and one for primer hybridization and extension. He initially got some product of the correct size but the same product showed up in controls containing no target DNA which caused many scientists to doubt that success had been achieved. While preliminary results were encouraging, most Cetus scientists needed to see cleaner data to be convinced that the technique could work reliably.

At this time Erlich, Arnheim and their associates Randy Saiki, Steve Scharf and Glen Horn joined the PCR effort. To prove rigorously that PCR could amplify a specific gene from total cellular DNA, experiments were designed to demonstrate the amplification of both the β-S (sickle cell) and β-A (normal) alleles of β-globin from one microgram of total human DNA. The specificity of amplification would be assessed by using an independent analytical method previously described by Cetus scientists, oligomer restriction (OR). Throughout this period weekly meetings of all scientists working on PCR were held to exchange information. Work on plasmid templates continued in Mullis' group with the aim of proving the PCR concept by ethidium bromide staining of restriction enzyme digests of amplified products on agarose gels. Mullis was particularly interested in being able to demonstrate amplification of a particular genomic region without using hybridization (probe) techniques. He also told people he wanted to "make a kilogram of a specific gene".

When the scientists in Human Genetics had achieved their goal of obtaining publishable data demonstrating the diagnostic potential of PCR using oligomer restriction as the detection method, it was time to submit that work for publication. It was clear that Mullis' paper on the fundamental method should be published first. A patent had been filed and Mullis had participated in its preparation, but he preferred work in the lab to writing and delayed the task of putting together a manuscript. The technique was too important to delay publication. There was a risk that news of the method would leak out and someone outside Cetus would publish first. Also, scientists throughout Cetus were finding new uses for PCR and it would soon become unfair to keep those individuals who used the technique from publishing their results. White and Arnheim encouraged Mullis to write his manuscript on the fundamental method with the data from analysis of plasmid amplification and approval was also given by the Cetus management to reveal the application of PCR to the diagnosis of sickle cell anemia at the Human Genetics meeting in the fall of 1985. Following that presentation, the group working on sickle cell detection by PCR-OR would submit a manuscript for publication. The paper by Saiki, Scharf, Faloona, Mullis, Horn, Erlich, and Arnheim, entitled "Enzymatic Amplification of Beta-Globin Genomic Sequences and Restriction Site Analysis for Diagnosis of Sickle Cell Anemia" (1) was accepted by *Science* and published in December 1985.

To the dismay of everyone involved, a series of unforseen events ensued which resulted in Mullis' initial manuscript on PCR not being published until two years after the *Science* paper. Although Mullis did not have his paper ready in time to submit first, he and Faloona had submitted their manuscript on the fundamental method in December 1985; it included such key results and refinements as the detection of a single base change in a single copy gene by restriction enzyme cleavage and ethidium bromide staining of DNA fragments on an agarose gel, and addition of new useful genetic information (e.g. the T-7 promoter) to the 5′ ends of the primers. Everyone assumed the paper would be accepted by *Nature*, but it was rejected. It was quickly revised and resubmitted to *Science* with a cover letter explaining the significance of the differences between this and the Saiki *et. al.* paper (1) which had already been published, but it was rejected for lack of novelty! Dismayed, Shing Chang, Director of Microbial Genetics, and White arranged for its publication in a volume of *Methods in Enzymology*, whose editor (Ray Wu) was enthusiastic and accepted the paper in May 1986, although the deadline for submission had passed. The development of the technology continued. Mullis gave a brilliant talk at the Cetus scientific meeting in January 1986, and another in April at a Cold Spring Harbor Meeting on "The Molecular Biology of Homo Sapiens". After that talk both John Maddox of *Nature* and Dan Koshland of *Science* asked Mullis if he would consider submitting the PCR method paper to their journals, but he was unable to do so as the work had already been submitted to *Methods in Enzymology*. Although the Methods in Enzymology volume had been scheduled to appear by the end of 1986, its publication was unfortunately delayed and the Mullis and Faloona paper did not appear until late 1987(2).

DNA POLYMERASE FROM *THERMUS AQUATICUS*

The most significant chores in performing PCR reactions were (a) the necessity of moving tubes from water bath to water bath, and (b) of adding fresh DNA polymerase after each denaturation step, in which the high temperatures inactivated the *E. coli* DNA polymerase. As scientists interested in PCR met in biweekly meetings, the desirability of using a heat-stable DNA polymerase was much discussed. White encouraged David Gelfand, Senior Scientist in Microbial Genetics, to switch his own group's research efforts from the development of bacterial cloning vectors containing dominant selectable markers to the purification of a heat-stable polymerase. Mullis' literature search had suggested that *Thermus aquaticus*, a bacterium indigenous to the hot springs of Yellow-stone National Park, be chosen as the first source of enzyme. *Taq* DNA polymerase worked in PCR the first time it was used, and its use generated improvements in the method. The elevated temperatures used for *Taq* polymerase-mediated primer extension led to greatly enhanced stringency and significantly increased the specificity of primer hybridization. Soon all PCR work at Cetus was being done with *Taq* DNA polymerase, and many researchers outside the company were using the enzyme, which was provided to the research community by Cetus under materials transfer agreements. The cloning of the gene for *Taq* polymerase into an *E. coli* plasmid was subsequently accomplished by Gelfand's group.

APPLICATIONS OF PCR

The use of PCR to enhance the sensitivity of prenatal diagnosis of sickle cell anemia demonstrated the importance of the technique in human diagnostics. PCR-based assays have been developed for a variety of genetic diseases for which the molecular defect is known, and PCR has been coupled with classical linkage analysis to determine the likelihood of disease inheritance in cases where the disease is not known. The sensitivity of PCR allows the detection of infectious disease agents which are present at very low levels, and those which may not be detectable through immunological techniques because they are in a latent state, expressing no agent-specific proteins.

Highly polymorphic genetic loci have been for many years the basis for individual identification, used on criminal evidence samples and for determination of paternity. As methods for analyzing DNA became available, the greater variability detectable at the DNA level compared with the protein level (blood group typing) has led to the development of DNA typing methods. The capacity of PCR to amplify DNA from samples containing minute amounts of DNA or from damaged DNA makes it possible to type some biological samples from which no information can be obtained using other methods, and allows simpler methods of analysis to be used after the amplification step.

In another area, PCR is being applied to veterinary diagnostics, to sexing of livestock embryos, and to individual identification and lineage analysis of animals. In agriculture, use in detection of pests and of desirable genetic traits is under investigation. In many areas of biological research, PCR has made possible experiments which previously could not be done because of time or quantity constraints. Examples include the direct genetic typing of single sperm for purposes of linkage analysis, the study of transcription in small numbers of cells during organismal development and the ability to sequence and compare large numbers of mutations in a single gene without having to clone the DNA. Minute amounts of DNA from museum specimens of fossil remains have been amplified to demonstrate evolutionary relationships encompassing now extinct species.

PATENTS

At the time that PCR was conceived, the patent group at Cetus was housed close to Mullis' lab. Albert Halluin, Chief Intellectual Property Law Attorney, remembers numerous conversations in which Mullis questioned how one would patent such a basic idea and Halluin explained how process patents work. Mullis then filed an invention disclosure which described the basic method and, in March 1985, the first U.S. patent application on PCR was filed. As is frequently the case, this patent was later revised and subdivided into various continuations-in-part. The first two PCR patents were issued on July 28, 1987, (3, 4) and a third on January 24, 1989 (5). Cetus received the notice of allowance of its patent on *Taq* DNA polymerase, both native and recombinant forms, in June 1989.

JOINT VENTURE

In the winter of 1985–86, Cetus formed a joint venture in which PCR was to play a role, although how large a role could not have been predicted by either Cetus or by the venture partner. The agreement completed in December with the Perkin Elmer Corporation focussed on development of instrumentation for the biological research market and of reagents for use with those instruments. The existing instrument which Cetus brought to the venture was the Pro/pette liquid handler which had been developed by the Cetus engineering group in response to the needs of the scientists who needed to automate assays for Interleukin-2. PCR was not explicitly mentioned in the agreement. This venture is Perkin Elmer Cetus Instruments (PECI).

The first "thermocycling machines" were fashioned by Cetus' engineers to meet the requirements of the scientists working on PCR who wanted to be spared the tedium of moving tubes from water bath to water bath. There were several versions. The first was based on the Pro/pette and focussed on the need for liquid handling capability to add fresh *E. coli* enzyme to each tube after the denaturation cycle. This machine was dubbed "Mr. Cycle". As had occurred with the original Pro/pette, Cetus benefited from the presence of a responsive and talented engineering group who were ready to solve specific automation problems as they arose or to elaborate on prototypes rigged up by scientists. The interplay between science and instrument development was powerful.

With the purification of *Taq* polymerase, the ability to cycle rapidly among different temperatures became the primary requirement for PCR automation. The joint venture was looking for potential new products, the use of PCR by researchers was increasing and the idea of supplying an instrument to the emerging market of PCR users was attractive. Perkin-Elmer instrument engineers began to work with scientists and engineers at Cetus and the DNA Thermal Cycler became the venture's first new instrument. The GeneAmp^{tm} kit, which provides the necessary components of a PCR reaction (*Taq* polymerase, buffers, deoxynucleoside triphospates, and control templates) was the accompanying reagent product. PCR related instrumentation and reagents have since become the central focus of the PECI venture.

PCR DIVISION; ROCHE AGREEMENT

After considerable thought and discussion about how best to focus efforts on PCR, in November 1988, Cetus formed a PCR Division (PCRD) with two research units and a business group dedicated to PCR. The research groups were comprised of scientists who were already working principally or exclusively on PCR but who had been in various different departments in research and development. Bill Gerber, who had come to the company in mid-1987 to manage corporate ventures in non-therapeutic areas, became Vice President of PCRD. At the time the division was formed it had 70 employees, 60 of them Research and Development staff.

Meanwhile, the time was ripe for changes in funding of Cetus' diagnostic research. By the middle of 1988 Cetus had received more than fifty inquiries about licenses to perform PCR for commercial diagnostic purposes. Clinical researchers all over the world were using the technique, and the interested parties included some big players in the diagnostic field. A collaboration with Eastman Kodak in diagnostics expired in February 1989, and Cetus management sought to review a large number of options for commercializing PCR in diagnostics.

Final decisions were made as the year came to an end, and on January 15, 1989, Cetus and Hoffmann-La Roche announced their agreement to collaborate on the development and commercialization of *in vitro* human diagnostic products and services based on Cetus' PCR technology. A key aspect of the agreement is that Roche has capability both in the development of diagnostic kits and in providing diagnostic services through its reference lab network, Roche Biomedical Laboratories. This makes it possible to commercialize complex PCR tests and make them available to the medical community several years ahead of the kits, which require greatly simplified formats.

Under the agreement, Roche is funding research and development of PCR-based human diagnostics over a five-year period. Roche is also engaging in development and research directed toward *in vitro* diagnostic products with an option to receive exclusive rights to market the resulting products and services worldwide, paying a royalty to Cetus. Cetus has the right to supply reagents, most importantly *Taq* polymerase, used in the tests.

LICENSING

Before the Roche agreement was completed, two licenses in human *in vitro* diagnostics had been granted. Each allowed the licensee to offer the PCR-HIV test as a service in a clinical reference laboratory. In early 1989, licenses were offered to other potential licensees that had requested rights to perform certain PCR-based diagnostic tests on a fee-for-service basis. These included hospital laboratories and commercial reference labs wanting to use PCR in genetic disease testing. While it was important to maintain the exclusive position in the *in vitro* diagnostic field which gave value to the agreement between Roche and Cetus, both companies wish to encourage development of PCR-based tests, and value the beneficial results of such licenses for the advancement of technology and medical science. Some fifteen license agreements had been completed by Cetus under this program by late spring of 1989 and consideration of further diagnostic licenses are Roche's responsibility.

In fields other than human diagnostics, licenses from Cetus or from PECI, depending on the specific area of interest, have been negotiated with the aim of licensing to others those uses of PCR that Cetus or its partners do not intend to commercialize.

FORENSICS AND IDENTIFICATION BUSINESS

DNA typing for forensic analysis of biological specimens is the most important near-term PCR-related business opportunity which Cetus has decided to develop on its own. The use of PCR to analyze differences in the DNA of different individuals is a basic demonstration of the power of the technology and the advantages of PCR over other methods of DNA analysis are particularly appropriate to the needs of the forensics community. The ability to analyze old or degraded samples, the high specificity and sensitivity, rapidity of analysis, and the fact that non-isotopic detection methods are feasible are all critical to crime laboratories which are chronically short-staffed and frequently have no license to use radioisotopes. Cetus scientists have collaborated with the

FBI and other criminal investigation laboratories to develop PCR-based tests that meet their needs and to compare the methods with other methods of DNA analysis. The first PCR product for forensic analysis by PCR will be introduced in early 1990. In commercializing other areas of PCR, Cetus' licensees or partners manage the business aspects of these ventures; however, in the forensics business Cetus is the developer, manufacturer, and marketer of products.

IN CONCLUSION

Polymerase Chain Reaction is a powerful technique of molecular biology that is influencing both basic science and those businesses in which nucleic acid analysis has or may have a role. It is not simple to strike the right balance between caution about investing time and money in "wild" ideas and the risk of missing out on a truly revolutionary idea. The combination of inferential thinking with the critical but tolerant scientific attitudes that characterized Cetus' research division were key to the realization of PCR. The conception of PCR, its development, and its evolution as a business are unique histories much influenced by the individuals involved, by the scientific culture at Cetus, and the requirements of company management to conserve financial resources. The success of the idea and its scientific development are facts; the success of the business is just beginning to be demonstrated.

REFERENCES

No attempt has been made to reference all of the applications and refinements of PCR mentioned in the text. The article and books listed under "Further Reading" provide extensive references and chapters on recent technical developments.

1. Saiki, R.K., Scharf, S., Faloona, F., Mullis, K.B., Horn, G.T., Erlich, H.A. and Arnheim, N. (1985) *Enzymatic amplification of beta-globin genomic sequences and restriction site analysis for diagnosis of sickle cell anemia.* Science **230**:1350–1354.
2. Mullis, K.B. and Faloona, F.A. (1986) *Specific synthesis of DNA in vitro via a polymerase catalyzed chain reaction.* Methods in Enzymology **155**:263–273.
3. U.S. Patent No. 4,683,202, (1987) *Process for Amplifying Nucleic Acid Sequences, Kary Mullis, Inventor.*
4. K. Mullis, H. Erlich, N. Arnheim, G. Horn, R. Saiki and S. Scharf (1987) U.S. Patent No. 4,683,195, *Process for Amplifying, Detecting, and/or Cloning Nucleic Acid Sequences.*
5. U.S. Patent No. 4,800,159, (1989) *Process for Amplifying, Detecting, and/or cloning Nucleic Acid Sequences* (same authors as above).

FURTHER READING

1. White, T.J., Arnheim, N., Erlich, H. (1989) *Trends in Genetics*, **5**:185–189.
2. Innis, M.A., Gelfand, D.H., Sninsky, J.J., White, T.J., eds. (1989) *PCR Protocols: A Guide to Methods and Applications.* Academic Press.
3. Erlich, H., ed. (1989) PCR Technology: *Principles and Applications for DNA Amplification.* Stockton Press.

The views expressed in this article are solely those of the author and do not necessarily reflect those of Cetus Corporation or any other person.

Chapter 12

Protein Engineering

Dale L. Oxender and Thomas J. Graddis

INTRODUCTION

The U.S. market for biotechnology products based on engineered proteins has been estimated by various marketing consultants to exceed $1 billion by 1995. This economic potential has spawned numerous start-up companies and prompted the major pharmaceutical and chemical concerns to expend increasing percentages of their research and development funding on programs to develop protein engineering technology. International competition is increasing as governments and industry foresee the potential of protein engineering. Japan's Ministry of International Trade and Industry has catalyzed the formation of a consortium of 14 companies to develop a Protein Engineering Research Institute which has a 10-year research budget of over $100 million to develop new and improved proteins. Similar government-industry sponsored programs have emerged on a smaller scale in England. Corporate strategies are focusing on valuable biologicals and polypeptide hormones as well as "superior" enzymes for use as catalysts in the production of high-value speciality chemicals and pharmaceuticals.

Protein engineering is a new addition to the biotechnology revolution.[1,2,3,4] The primary goal of protein engineering is the rational design and construction of novel proteins with enhanced or unique properties. Rapid progress toward this goal has already provided several important products for market and promises to soon deliver many more. The birth of protein engineering is the logical consequence of the developments during the last decade in the methods for deoxyribonucleic acid (DNA) synthesis, recombinant DNA (rDNA) technologies, and significant improvements in protein structural analysis. In the late 1970s a technological breakthrough permitted investigators precisely and efficiently to alter genetic information coding for a protein. This technology is termed "site-directed mutagenesis". It allows investigators specifically to delete, add or replace amino acids in a protein structure at will. The success of protein engineering requires an interdisciplinary collaboration of scientists with expertise in biochemical, molecular genetic, protein structural analysis, enzymology, computational, and theoretical areas. An examination of the efforts currently being carried out suggests that studies of well established model systems that lend themselves to an interdisciplinary collaboration will be most effective for developing the genetic tools for protein engineering. Advances in protein engineering will have important applications to the fields of medicine, chemical industry, and agriculture.

Our intention in this chapter is to discuss methods of engineering proteins, principles governing prediction and design, and applications and future prospects of protein engineering in order to provide a conceptual framework by which the reader may better judge both the potential of protein engineering and its limitations.

STRUCTURAL ELEMENTS OF PROTEINS

The transfer of information in a cell from gene to protein is a multistep process that involves transcribing information from the DNA of the gene to a ribonucleic acid messenger (mRNA) and then translating this information into a linear sequence of amino acids referred to as the primary structure of a protein. The information or code for folding the protein into a three-dimensional structure is contained in the primary amino acid sequence. The information for the folding pathway has sometimes been referred to as the second-half of the genetic code, the determination of which would overcome a major bottleneck for the protein engineering field.

The architecture of a protein is a complex mixture of three-dimensional structural motifs. As mentioned above, the amino acid sequence is referred to as a protein's primary structure. Secondary structure, i.e. local formation of α-helices, β-sheets, or turns, is based on the most favorable conformation for the specific amino acid sequence. The helices, turns and β-sheet secondary structural motifs of each polypeptide chain are folded into a compact three-dimensional tertiary structure. Finally, quaternary structure refers to the shape of protein complexes that are composed of more than one polypeptide chain.

The tertiary structure of a polypeptide chain can often be subdivided into smaller functional units, called "domains". Domains are composed of sections of contiguous amino acid sequences that independently fold into defined structural units. Domains often represent functional units as well, containing intact binding and catalytic sites. These binding and catalytic sites are also often found at the interface between domains or at the interface between polypeptide chains of multimeric proteins. Nature has provided a set of functionally discreet structural domains which may be spliced together in unique combinations that either retain activity or in some cases produce new activities. A specific aim of protein engineering is the design and formation of functionally active chimeric proteins by combining domains of different proteins.

Analysis of protein functional families and divergence between families has begun to uncover some of the principles Nature uses in the natural evolution and design of functional proteins. Several generalizations can be made. Three-dimensional structures of proteins, either tertiary or quaternary, appear to be more conserved in evolution than the linear sequence of amino acids and considerably more conserved than DNA sequence. Secondary structure of α-helices and β-sheets of related or recently diverged proteins may often be superimposed while amino acid replacements, insertions or deletions tend to occur on the surface of the protein in loops between these secondary structures thus leaving the central globular core unchanged.

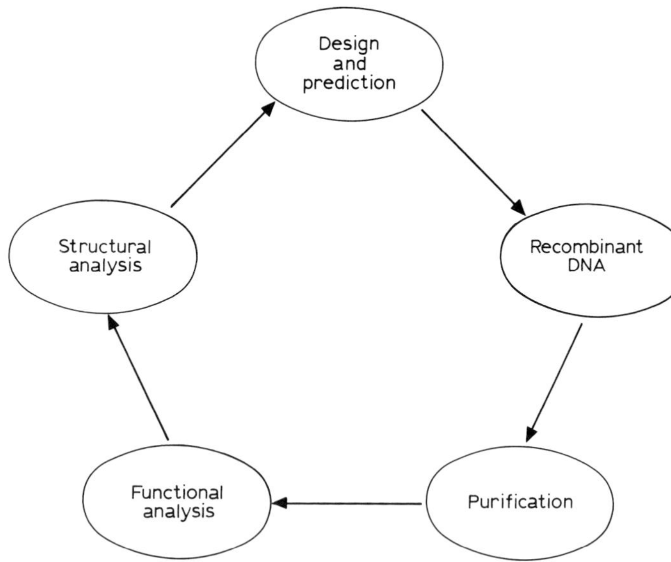

Figure 1. The cycle of Protein Engineering. Schematic representation of the five major paradigms comprising the field of protein engineering and the relationship between them.

ENABLING TECHNOLOGIES

The successful application of protein engineering requires an interdisciplinary approach dependent on a flow of information between the five disciplines or areas of expertise outlined in Figure 1. For purposes of this discussion we will start with the structural and functional analysis of an important hypothetical industrial enzyme. It is imperative to be able to obtain the three-dimensional structure of this enzyme so that structural features can be related to specific function. At the present time, the three-dimensional structure of over 300 proteins have been determined; however, structural analysis reamins one of the bottlenecks in the cycle represented in the Figure. From knowledge of the relationship between structure and function, predictions and design principles (next circle, Fig. 1) can be used to develop plans for modifying the structure of the enzyme to produce a new enzyme with improved catalytic activity or stability. Once the modification has been decided the tools of recombinant DNA and genetic engineering (Fig. 1) allow structural modification to be made. Using recombinant DNA technology it is now essentially possible to isolate the gene for any protein from the appropriate cell or tissue and modify its structure by site-directed mutagenesis to produce a specifically altered protein.

A large battery of techniques is available for overexpression and purification (Fig. 1) of the newly modified protein which can be subjected to a new round of functional and structural analysis. It is often possible to screen newly modified proteins by carrying out functional analysis prior to complete purification thus avoiding the more laborious structural analysis of modified proteins not considered useful.

The following section briefly describes the current status of the technologies necessary for the applications of protein engineering.

Recombinant DNA and Genetic Engineering

The isolation of a gene coding for a protein of interest, by cloning or by synthetic methods, is a prerequisite to protein engineering. A gene may be isolated based on its pattern of expression, its ability to bind a complimentary strand of DNA or its ability to code for a particular protein detected with antibodies. Once the gene has been isolated the nucleotide sequence can be translated by the genetic code to provide the amino acid sequence of the corresponding cloned protein product. The cloned gene will serve as the template for engineering the protein product.

Protein engineering has been aided by recent technological breakthroughs in both DNA sequencing, synthesis and splicing. A class of enzymes discovered in the early 1970s called restriction endonucleases will cleave DNA at unique recognition sequences. Today, several hundred of these enzymes are available commercially and are in wide use. Availability of these restriction enzymes permits isolation of a gene from one organism and splicing it into other organisms such as bacteria for efficient expression and production of the protein product. The wide array of procedures available for this type of manipulation are referred to as "recombinant DNA technologies" (rDNA). These technologies can be used to facilitate large scale, relatively low-cost production of proteins in plants, animals, and fast growing microbes. A chemical procedure for sequencing DNA, developed by Maxam and Gilbert, enjoyed wide spread use by the mid-1970s. In the early 1980s Fred Sanger developed an enzymatic means to sequence DNA that is amenable to automation. The chemistry of solid phase DNA synthesis has evolved to the level that it is now standard to generate synthetic DNA fragments of desired sequence in a matter of hours using a fully automated system. This technological advance also makes it possible to design and synthesize entire genes at a modest cost.

Once a gene has been cloned it is a relatively simple matter, through a variety of genetic engineering techniques, to edit information in that gene one base at a time and therefore specifically to substitute any amino acid in the protein structure with another. This makes it possible to examine the role of individual amino acids in the structure and function of a protein. Figure 2 presents the transfer of information encoded in the DNA sequence of a gene which specifies a protein. The DNA is a double stranded linear polymer of deoxynucleotide repeating units. The two complementary strands of DNA form a double helix. One strand of the helix contains regions of code called genes which direct the synthesis of cellular products such as hormones and enzymes. The first step in the information transfer is the transcription of the gene into a messenger ribonucleic acid, abbreviated here as mRNA. The information in the messenger is translated into a polypeptide or protein enzyme. The protein is produced as a linear polymer of amino acid units and the sequence of these amino acids is coded for by the sequence of nucleotides in the DNA. The functional enzyme is formed by specific folding into a unique three-dimensional structure. Folding of the nascent polypeptide may occur concomitant with translation or post-translationally. The folding pattern and unique structure is determined by the amino acid sequence. It is now possible to take advantage of this information transfer pathway to produce modified enzymes by changing the information in the gene coding for the enzyme. This process is referred to as "site-directed mutagenesis". The circle in the DNA structure at the top of the diagram represents a designed alteration in the nucleotide sequence of the gene which was accomplished by *in vitro* site-directed mutagenesis techniques. This change in the gene results in a change in the messenger and, ultimately, a corresponding change in the amino acid sequence of the enzyme. The altered amino acid sequence may produce a more stable enzyme or one with modified catalytic properties. Protein engineering techniques can be used for virtually any enzyme by first cloning the gene and then applying the appropriate gene splicing and engineering procedures.

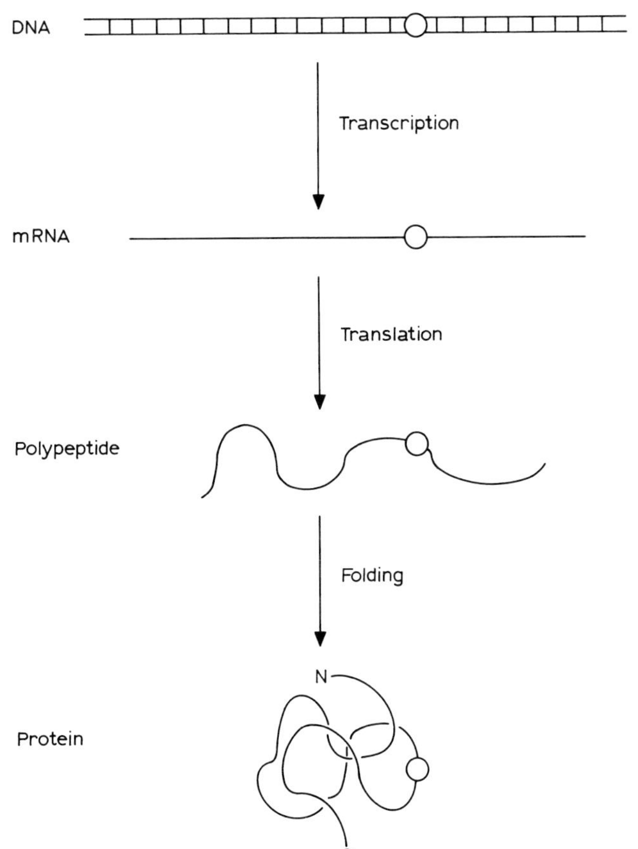

Figure 2. The transfer of information from gene to protein. The mutation in the DNA, represented here as a circle, is first transcribed then translated into the final folded protein structure.

Protein Purification

Cells normally contain several thousand different proteins as well as DNA, RNA, lipids, and carbohydrates. The challenge of protein purification is to isolate one protein from this complex mixture with reasonable efficiency, yield and purity, while keeping in mind that for each step of purification the yield decreases and the cost of producing the protein increases. Protein purification procedures depend on the properties of a protein and therefore must be optimized for each protein. Pharmaceutical use often requires highly purified proteins in small quantities while some industrial uses require larger quantities of somewhat less pure protein provided the remaining contaminates do not interfere with the reaction to be catalyzed. New protein purification techniques have emerged from advances in material sciences, such as ultrafiltration with highly specific membranes or high-performance liquid chromatography using new column resins. These methods complement classical approaches and give scientists a powerful set of tools for handling various protein purification problems.

Recombinant DNA techniques can be used to overproduce proteins so that in certain cases they represent as much as 50% of the total soluble protein of a bacterial cell. This degree of overproduction greatly aids the purification process. Some proteins when over expressed in bacteria are produced as soluble active proteins whereas others, such as interferon, form cytoplasmic inclusion bodies that precipitate inside the cell. Large quantities of protein can be sequestered in these inclusion bodies which may facilitate their isolation; however, sometimes there is a problem renaturing active proteins from these inclusion bodies. It is often possible to use special properties engineered into proteins to greatly assist their own purification. A cysteine residue engineered into subtilisin [3.4.4.14], a serine protease, allowed researchers at Genentech to use a thiol-specific-binding resin to isolate the modified protein. Sometimes it is possible to remove amino acid residues from a protein which interfere with the expression and purification of a fully functional protein. For example, expression in bacteria of properly folded β-interferon, a polypeptide hormone with antiviral activity, is hampered by the presence of an unpaired cysteine residue. This cysteine residue interferes with the proper formation of a disulfide bridge between two other important cysteine residues in the protein. Since the unpaired sulfhydryl group was not essential for activity, engineering a serine replacement for this cysteine residue resulted in improved yield of a more stable protein without significant loss in activity.

In some cases it may aid purification to have a protein secreted by cells into the culture medium. This is particularly true of proteins that contain several disulfide bonds. When proteins containing disulfide bonds are expressed in microorganisms, the reducing atmosphere inside the cells is not appropriate for disulfide bond formation and when the proteins are extracted they often form incorrectly folded aggregates. To get around this problem, the secretion of a protein may be controlled by genetically attaching cleavable bacterial signal sequences that direct a protein to be secreted from the cell. The extracellular location of the modified protein and oxidizing atmosphere will enable proper folding and disulfide bond formation.

Functional Analysis of Proteins

Specific and sensitive assays of protein function, whether it be catalysis, ligand binding, or stability, are essential to effective evaluation of the results of site-directed mutation steps in the cycle of protein engineering. The greater the sensitivity of such an assay the better the investigator is able to evaluate even small structural changes. A rapid assay will find greater utility in quantitating protein function. In addition, it is essential to have a means of monitoring the progress of purification of a protein. It is often necessary for an assay which monitors protein activity to be tailored to a specific protein or class of proteins. Binding assays for such proteins as ligand receptors or DNA binding proteins are often difficult to quantitate. Protein engineering has been used to facilitate binding assays in several of the following ways: chimeric proteins may be constructed so that the binding activity of interest is fused to an enzyme whose catalytic activity is easily determined. In addition, an indirect assay may be developed to evaluate DNA binding proteins. For example, β-galctosidase [3.2.1.23], an enzyme easily monitored in a colormetric assay, has been fused to a variety of proteins whose expression is dependent on the activity of a DNA binding protein. In this manner the DNA binding activity of the protein of interest may be determined by monitoring the enzymatic activity and thus the expression of the chimeric protein.

Structural Analysis

The heart of protein engineering lies in obtaining a broad range of structural information and this is usually the rate-limiting step in the cycle of protein engineering outlined in Fig. 1.

The three-dimensional structure of a protein determines its biological function whether it acts as an enzyme, a hormone, or serves some other purpose. It is important to have a high resolution three-dimensional structure of the protein available when designing new function for a protein. In addition, it is essential at this stage to acquire structural information of an engineered protein when testing design hypotheses so that the new structural elements can be related to altered function. With increasing computational sophistication we are better able to model three-dimensional structures of proteins based on their amino acid sequence analogies with other proteins of known crystallographic structure.

X-ray Crystallography

To date there are 300 plus refined protein structures in the Brookhaven Protein Data Base. These structures were acquired using X-ray diffraction of crystalline proteins. This technique requires substantial investment in time and dollars, sophisticated technology and highly trained personnel. Crystallographic techniques for determining protein structure have greatly improved in the last few years. Data acquisition taking hours by conventual means now has been reduced greatly by using more intense X-ray sources and modern two-dimensional area detectors coupled to a computer. This rapid data acquisition time permits transient phenomena to be captured in successive images, a sort of motion picture at atomic resolution. The intrinsic weakness of a crystallographic approach is that suitable protein crystals must be obtained. Protein crystallization is still as much art as science; however, emerging guidelines and improved techniques have yielded greater success. To obtain the initial three-dimensional structure of a protein it must be crystallized with a suitable heavy metal atom to serve as a reference point. Once a structure has been determined solving the structure of a series of mutant proteins is made easier by using the atomic coordinates of the first structure and looking for density differences. In this manner, for example, Brian Matthews and co-workers have obtained the three-dimensional structures of over 50 derivatives of T4 lysozyme [3.2.1.17].

NMR

Multi-dimensional Nuclear Magnetic Resonance (NMR) spectroscopy is a powerful technique for examining the structure of a polypeptide in solution. This method is used to look at dynamic structure of proteins in solution, bypassing the difficult crystallization step in X-ray diffraction. Three-dimensional structural information is gleaned from resonance patterns through complex computer assisted calculations. Multi-dimensional NMR techniques are expected to offer advantages for the study of protein folding since many of the intermediates in protein folding may be unstable and difficult if not impossible to crystallize. The major limitation to NMR is that it is currently only been useful for small proteins of mass less than 30,000 daltons. New 600 MHz instruments as well as improved techniques offer advantages by reducing the data collection time as well as providing the ability to study larger polypeptides.

Design and Prediction[5]

Mutational studies play a central role in identifying sites within protein structures critical to function, stability or structure, often uncovering surprising and unpredicted principles not immediately obvious from perusal of protein structure. For example, amino acid substitutions that increase conformational stability were identified in second-site revertant studies of staphylococcal nuclease [3.1.21.1], an enzyme that degrades DNA. The enzymatic activity of mutant enzymes, in which the mutations were remote from the active site, were restored by just a few key second-site suppressor mutations, termed "global suppression", of many different alleles. When only the suppressor mutations were present these proteins proved more stable to unfolding than the wild type protein.

The classical approach to obtain proteins with altered properties has been largely limited to proteins produced by microorganisms that have been subjected to chemically induced mutagenesis techniques followed by an appropriate selection or screening procedure. This "pot-luck" approach has produced a number of altered proteins and enzymes and still proves useful for identifying specific amino acid residues that are important for activity or structure. Since such methods primarily lead to a single amino acid substitution it is difficult to obtain altered forms of enzymes that may require several amino acid substitutions. Systematic design of proteins via site-directed mutagenesis offers advantages well beyond the reach of classical mutagenesis methods. It is possible to replace, delete or introduce single amino acids or large numbers of amino acid residues and radically alter the protein structure by eliminating or adding an entire domain.

It is premature to say we are designing proteins based on theoretical predictions; rather we are modifying existing structures in Nature to test hypotheses. There are two types of alterations obtained by site-directed mutagenesis that are most useful in defining the role of a particular amino acid residue. Isosteric replacement can alter amino acid function without changing shape: examples are the replacement of glutamic acid with glutamine or asparatic acid with asparagine, each of which removes a negative charge but maintains most of the hydrogen bonds. Substituting alanine for serine removes a potential hydrogen bond and somewhat increases hydrophobicity. A second type of change looks at dependence of function on structure. Replacing a glutamic acid residue with asparatic acid would change structure but not function. This mutation shortens the side chain carboxylate by less than an angstrom provided there are only minor structural oscillations. Since we do not have the rules defining an amino acid's contribution to protein structure it is imperative, at this stage, to obtain the structural information for mutant proteins so that the nature of a functional aberration may be assigned to a structural cause. While these types of mutations help define the role an amino acid plays in protein, changing both structure and function of a residue can lead to practical applications for proteins.

De Novo Design

The design of protein structures from first principles is at a primitive stage in development. It is clear that for the immediate future both *de novo* design and other approaches that begin with functional proteins are important to the progress of protein engineering. Realizing the full potential of protein engineering, however, will require rational *de novo* protein design and it therefore remains as an important long range goal.

Several successful examples of *de novo* protein design and construction involve only small polypeptides of 20–40 amino acids whose structures are entirely composed of either β-sheet or α-helices with clefts or pockets that can later be used to form binding and catalytic sites. Berndt Gutte of the Biophysical Institute, University of Zürich, has designed and chemically synthesized a 24-amino acid polypeptide with a binding site for DDT. This protein forms a β-sheet structure and binds DDT weakly but considerably better than if by chance. DeGrado and colleagues at du Pont laboratories have synthesized model amphiphilic α-helical peptides that aggregate within a lipid bilayer and form channels with ion permeability characteristics resembling those of the acetycholine receptor. The laboratories of Jane S. Richardson, David C. Richardson and David Eisenberg have designed protein structures "from scratch" based on first principles. These include structures assembled from four polypeptide α-helices that spontaneously self-associate to form a tetrameric bundle, and betabellin, a dimer of antiparallel β-sheets. The intent of these investigators is to build binding or catalytic sites into these structures.

Knowledge Based Structural Prediction

Knowledge based predictions represent one of the current approaches to design. Modeling the three-dimensional structure of a protein can be based on strong sequence homologies of other proteins of known structure, usually proteins within the same functional family. Aligning the homologous amino acid stretches of a protein of unknown structure with those of known structure permits identification of analogies in secondary structure motifs, domains or ligand interactions. The final stage is the assembly of a three-dimensional protein framework by borrowing bits and pieces of structure from homologous proteins closest in sequence to modeled proteins, preferably connecting chains at junctures between defined secondary structure. This procedure, coined knowledge based approach by J.M. Thorton and co-workers, primarily uses information from the 300 plus protein structures in the Brookhaven Protein Data Base.

With a knowledge based procedure researchers were able to model the serine protease domain of the mammalian protease, tissue plasminogen activator [3.4.21.31], using 17 pieces from the known X-ray structures of four serine proteases: trypsin [3.4.21.4], elastase [3.4.21.11], chymotrypsin [3.4.21.1], and kallikrein [3.4.21.8]. The success of this procedure has been promising. The variable domain of immunoglobulin was modeled and correlated with X-ray analysis. A high degree of accuracy was obtained for the main chain region and 4 out of 6 of the more difficult hypervariable loop regions were correctly predicted. T. Bundell and co-workers have used this approach to model the active site conformation of the angiotensinogen processing enzyme renin [3.4.99.19], an aspartyl protease secreted by the kidney that is involved in high-blood pressure. As a result of these models, successful design of renin inhibitors has led to valuable pharmaceutical products. These results reinforce the practical utility of a knowledge based approach. It is hoped that this procedure will be extended to cases of little sequence homology but suspected structural homology. The challenge is to identify amino acid sequence fingerprints that yield common structural motifs. A knowledge based approach in conjunction with advanced computer programs will have a profound effect on the ability to rationally design proteins for a given function.

CURRENT BOTTLENECKS TO PROTEIN ENGINEERING

It has been clearly established that the information for how a protein is folded into its unique three-dimensional structure is contained in the primary sequence of amino acids. The immediate challenge for the field of protein engineering thus is to understand the rules or code relating primary sequence to three-dimensional structure and then to determine how that structure is related to function. Though much progress has been made both experimentally and theoretically, our predictive powers are still largely limited to secondary structure for soluble globular proteins. As pointed out in an earlier section, knowing how proteins with similar sequences fold can be used with the aid of computers to make knowledge-based intelligent predictions.

A major bottleneck to efficient design using the knowledge based approach is the limited number of three-dimensional structures in the present data base. There is a significant backlog of proteins whose primary sequence is known but whose three-dimensional structures have yet to be determined. Advances in the techniques of structural determination, employing X-ray diffraction and NMR, and the increasing number of laboratories concentrating on structural analysis of proteins offers hope that this backlog will be decreased and more structures will soon be added to the data base. Another important bottleneck in protein design is the need for more sophisticated computational analysis of protein dynamics and energy minimization profiles. At present, huge stores of information regarding proteins are being generated by various university and industrial laboratories. As this body of information grows there is a critical demand for more efficient and innovative data base management as well as advanced algorithms capable of extracting important structure function relationships hidden in the data bases. Additional minor bottlenecks in the progress of protein engineering include the expression and large scale production of functional proteins. Further development of efficient host-vectors systems as well as determining the role of post-translational modification (methylation or glycosylation) in protein folding and activity must receive greater attention.

In the remaining portion of this section we will discuss in more detail these bottlenecks to protein engineering and design and provide examples where investigators are addressing these problems.

Protein Folding: Thermodynamics and Kinetics[6]

The forces governing protein folding are generally measured in thermodynamic terms — a decrease in free energy of the folded protein provides the driving force for spontaneous folding. Globular proteins in their water environments are more stable in the folded state than the unfolded state. The two predominant opposing forces contributing to protein folding are the cohesive and highly cooperative interatomic forces, primarily hydrophobic interactions, and the destabilizing entropic forces. Hydrophobic interactions serve to sequester apolar portions of the polypeptide side chains away from the aqueous solvent. The entropy of a folded protein relative to an unfolded protein contributes the major destabilizing component to the overall free energy of a protein conformation and unless stabilizing interactions outweigh the entropy term a protein will not fold. These forces acting in concert cause a net decrease in free energy by some 10–20 kcal/mol for most folded proteins. This value is small considering the enormous total energy input from stabilizing and destabilizing interactions of a polypeptide chain, 10^7 kcal/mol for a 100 residue polypeptide. As a result, overall protein stability may be disrupted by a seemingly minor loss of stabilizing interactions, whether they be van der Waals contacts, ion pairs, hydrogen bonds, or hydrophobic interactions.

The structure of a folded protein may be either the lowest free energy thermodynamic state or some kinetically accessible intermediate state. For many small single domain single chain proteins the native state is usually the lowest free energy state. For some more complex multidomain polypeptides there is evidence for a trapping of the active protein in some local energy-minima, intermediate state.

Protein folding may be thought of as initially consisting of numerous parallel and intersecting pathways that progressively converge to fewer pathways as the final structure becomes defined. For this reason the effect of a single amino acid replacement on folding efficiency may be masked by alternative folding pathways. This, however, is not always the case. Scientists at the Upjohn Company found that the rate of refolding of bovine growth hormone is reduced some thirty-fold when a lysine residue is replaced with leucine. Stabilization of a folding intermediate is believed by to be responsible for this decrease in the refolding rate. Kinetic studies complement thermodynamic studies of protein folding by looking at processes between the initial and final states. Protein dynamic studies, including NMR experiments, time-resolved fluorescence spectroscopy and hydrogen exchange help to quantitate the folding process and give a qualitative view of protein folding *in vitro*.

Recognized Steps in Protein Folding

As a random coil polypeptide begins to fold the secondary structure motifs quickly form into α-helices, β-sheets, turns and loops. The extended polypeptide then collapses into a compact globule in which the hydrophobic portions of a domain are buried in a solvent excluded core. Some proteins appear to collapse into a "molten state" with undefined tertiary structure but with considerable secondary structure that represents 60–90% of that present in the native protein. Further reshuffling of non-covalent and covalent interactions leads to an ordered three-dimensional native structure. This last step is often the rate limiting step.

In some cases it appears that the folding process might be mediated by other proteins. There is evidence for protein species, that trap intermediates in the folding pathway, such as secreted proteins or polypeptides of multimeric proteins. The biosynthesis of the heavy chain moiety of class I histocompatibility antigen has been shown to fold into a short lived intermediate. This high energy intermediate state must be stabilized by binding with a small chain polypeptide, forming an active oligomeric protein, or it will continue to fold into a lower free energy biologically inactive state. Some proteins, such as insulin, trypsin, pepsin [3.4.23.1], chymosin [3.4.23.4] and penicillinase [3.5.2.6], are synthesized as inactive precursors. Their precursors fold into a specific conformation that can be activated by enzymatic removal of a segment of the polypeptide chain. The common feature of these proteins is they become metastable after cleavage, having lost some of the stabilizing interactions required to reach that folded state.

The Structure-Function Relationship

The roles of individual amino acids in protein structure and function are beginning to be defined through site-directed mutagenesis studies of enzyme function which are fast becoming the method of choice in most laboratories, often complementing or supplanting classical chemical modification studies. Attempts to design new substrate specificities into enzymes has met with some success as well as surprises. Certain mutational studies designed to change an enzyme specificity by substituting residues thought to be involved in substrate binding, not catalysis, instead lead to a precipitous fall in enzymatic activity.

Computational Chemistry of Protein Structure and Function

Effective application of protein engineering necessitates a coupling of experimental data with theoretical studies for predicting the folded structure of globular polypeptides and for the development of models that anticipate the conformational effects of a given amino acid substitution. Deriving energy potential functions from energy minimization and molecular dynamic calculations demands the computational capacity of a main frame or supercomputer. Due to the current expense of computers and computational analysis it is not always practical to determine the global energy minimum of entire macromolecular systems and investigators must settle for regional or local energy minimization. Energy minimization and molecular dynamic procedures are constantly being improved and have exhibited considerable success in predicting protein secondary structure, yet their limitations painfully remind us that the prediction of tertiary structure remains a major bottleneck for progress in protein design. Any serious effort in protein engineering must develop a program for macromolecular computational chemistry. As a consequence of this demand a number of groups are presently dedicated to meeting this challenge.

Data Base Management and Computer Graphics

The impact of computer technology on the field of protein engineering is difficult to overstate. Despite rapid progress in data base management technology that permits storage and retrieval of vast amounts of information, this area remains a major bottleneck in protein design. Laboratories throughout the world are producing immense quantities of information from DNA and protein sequences in addition to studies of kinetic, thermodynamic and structural characteristics of native and mutant proteins. This ever increasing body of information presents a formidable task for experts in data base management. Its storage must be in an economical form readily accessible by a diverse field of researchers and in a manner that anticipates the development of new searching and comparison algorithms.

Dynamic programming methods using alignment algorithms to carry out a global comparison of DNA sequences, amino acid sequences and protein structures have proved invaluable in identifying homologies and analogies provided by nature. Numerous data banks have emerged world wide that are both commercially and governmentally sponsored: European Molecular Biology Laboratory (Heidelburg, Federal Republic of Germany); The National Biomedical Research Foundation (Maryland, USA) contains software to search, compare, align, and detect similarities and score and display the degree of similarity; GeneBank of Bolt, Beranach, and Newman Inc. contains some five million DNA bases in over 5,000 entries; Protein Information Resource Databank contains over 3,000 proteins; Brookhaven Protein Data Base, (Brookhaven, New York) contains the three-dimensional coordinates for over 300 proteins.

Advances in computer graphics technology allows three-dimensional models of proteins to be displayed and manipulated. Graphics modeling of protein interactions with substrates enables an educated guess to be made on the screen concerning possible changes in protein structure before going into the laboratory to make the real changes using gene splicing technologies.

Supercomputers can aid in the complex calculations of molecular dynamics and energy minimization of protein-solvent systems. The U.S. National Science Foundation has recently announced a multi-million dollar nationwide project to link six supercomputers (at San Diego, Boulder, Pittsburgh, Princeton, Ithica and Urbana-Champaign) and seven regional centers in one network called NSFNET. This "data highway" will provide greater access to information and computational power to a larger number of investigators thereby increasing the rate of knowledge expansion.

Protein Expression Systems

Functional proteins may be isolated from their natural sources, or from sources in which the foreign gene has been introduced by means of recombinant DNA technologies. In some cases proteins may be synthesized *in vitro*. For producing short polypeptides in small quantities, the *in vitro* chemical and/or enzymatic synthesis is proving to be competitive with other recombinant methods. For production of polypeptides in cells, the efficiency of gene expression is affected by both the structure of a particular gene and the physiology of the host cell. Factors such as promoters, enhancers, ribosome binding sites and codon abundance of transfer RNAs will effect the level of gene expression while host cell factors such as plasmid maintenance stability, gene copies per cell, secretion machinery, protease composition, tissue specificity and post-translational modification are all important for maximum gene expression. The optimum expression of a gene is often a unique combination of these factors and is not always transferable to a second gene.

Animal or human tissue has been used as a traditional sources of hormones for pharmaceutical purposes. Enzymes and hormones obtained from animal sources, however, sometimes induce immunogenic response in patients. Many hormones are species specific and must be isolated from human sources. The availability of human tissue is limited and hormone concentrations are vanishingly small. In addition, a persistent danger for products purified from human sources is contamination, particularly by viruses. Viral contamination of growth hormones, thyroid stimulation hormone and prolactin obtained from human pituitary glands has forced the U.S. Food and Drug Administration to ban proteins derived from this source. The advent of recombinant DNA technology has permitted the production of human proteins in either bacteria or mammalian cell culture where viral contamination and low concentration problems are avoided.

Protein Expression in Microorganisms and Mammalian Cell Culture

At present microorganisms are used to produce over 90% of the major industrial enzymes. Production of many proteins in bacteria can be advantageous since they can usually be scaled-up to synthesize large quantities in a relatively short time at a modest cost. *Escherichia coli* is the most common microorganism used for the production of a protein that remains in the cytoplasm. At the end of the fermentation, cells are harvested and homogenized in order to isolate the protein. A protein can be directed to be secreted into the periplasm of *E. coli* by attaching a signal sequence via gene splicing techniques. The advantage of secretion into the periplasm is that it can avoid problems for proteins which have complex folding pathways involving disulfide bonds. A continuous cycle of protein production can be achieved utilizing *Bacillus subtilis*, a bacterum able to secrete proteins into the medium via a signal sequence mechanism. The protein can then be isolated from the culture medium flowing through a bioreactor.

Bacteria can be at a disadvantage for production of proteins that demand post-translational modification for biological activity. Glycosylation, the attachment of carbohydrates to residue side chains of a protein, is a common feature of many proteins from higher organisms. In some cases it is possible to generate proteins in bacteria and modify them *in vitro* provided the modification enzymes are available and are not cost prohibitive.

Eucaryotic microorganisms such as fungi or yeast offer an alternative host for expression and modification of proteins. Yeast contain much of the protein modification machinery of higher organisms. One problem with yeast is that they tend to over-glycosylate proteins including some that are normally not glycosylated at all.

Production of mammalian proteins in mammalian cell culture such as hamster ovary cells overcomes the problem of post-translational modification associated with bacterial production. Cell culture methods, however, often require complex, expensive media that imitates the body environment of an animal. Despite the enormous research and substantial progress in improving cell culture techniques the high cost of production persists due to problems in keeping cells alive, preventing contamination and scaling-up.

An alternative approach to the production of mammalian proteins is the expression of these proteins in the body fluids of mammals, such as the milk of a mouse, goat or even a cow, where they are processed and modified as fully functional proteins for human medicinal use. The expression of tissue plasminogen activator in the milk glands of mice has been reported by researchers at Integrated Genetics Corporation. To obtain this expression system, the genetic information which directs the expression of a milk protein, such as casein, in the mammaliary gland and its secretion into the milk was attached by gene splicing techniques to the gene coding for tissue plasminogen activator. In this model system the tissue plasminogen activator was recovered from the milk as a fully functional protein without sacrificing the animal.

PROGRESS REPORT IN PROTEIN ENGINEERING

Surveying current knowledge of naturally occurring proteins and performing mutational studies on well defined model systems will address the gaps in our understanding of protein folding and structure-function problems. There are an estimated one million functionally different proteins in Nature. Over 3,000 of them have been characterized and 300 of these crystallized and spatially modeled. A number of examples, including proteases and their inhibitors, DNA binding proteins, immunoglobulins, aminoacyl-tRNA synthetases, triosephosphate isomerase [5.3.1.1], dihydrofolate reductase [1.5.1.3] and T4 lysozyme, are being developed as model systems for extensive enzymatic, folding, structural and thermodynamic analyses utilizing protein engineering. Considerable success has been achieved in altering the stability or the specificity of several important biologically active proteins.

In the following section we will highlight a few examples from investigators responsible for some of the present progress in the field of protein engineering.

A Study of Protein Stability

Extensive mutational and crystallographic studies carried out with bacteriophage T4 lysozyme by Brian Matthews and colleagues at the University of Oregon provides one of the larger data bases of temperature-sensitive mutational effects on protein structure. Currently, over 50 mutant proteins have been crystallized and analyzed by X-ray diffraction. Selecting temperature-sensitive mutations by genetic techniques has been an efficient method for identifying residues important to thermal stability. Site-directed mutagenesis was used to study the effect of other amino acid substitutions at these positions.

Matthews and co-workers identified a single substitution of isoleucine for threonine, located in a turn between two helices on the surface of T4 lysozyme, that disrupts a hydrogen bond network which in turn strongly diminishes protein thermal stability. A glycine substitution at this site yielded a mutant protein whose thermal stability was unexpectedly near that of wild type. Structural analysis of the glycine-containing mutant showed that a water molecule was located in the position normally occupied by the hydroxyl group of threonine so that the important hydrogen bonding network was maintained, underscoring the important role solvent can play in protein stability. In a separate study with the serine protease subtilisin, scientists at Genentech Corporation substituted serine for the native asparagine residue in order to improve hydrogen bond interactions in the protein core. This substitution resulted in improved thermal stability without loss of activity. These experiments indicate that single hydrogen bonds can contribute significantly to protein stability. Of the total population of hydrogen bonds in a protein structure only a small percentage would be expected to represent these potent stabilizing hydrogen bonds.

The role of disulfide bond formation in protein stabilization has been the subject of intense scrutiny. Matthews and associates were able to increase significantly the thermal stability of T4 lysozyme by introducing cysteine residues at sites suggested by theoretical calculations and computer modeling that would form disulfide bridges. At the same time they had to remove an unpaired cysteine residue to prevent intermolecular thermally induced thiol/disulfide interchange that could result in inactivation. In some cases, engineered disulfide bonds can diminish a proteins dynamic flexibility and cause a reduction of stability and activity. A disulfide bond engineered into dihydrofolate reductase, for example, resulted in a mutant protein whose activity was significantly diminished for the oxidized enzyme but not the reduced enzyme. Scientists at Cetus Corporation were able to introduce disulfide bonds into the peptide hormone, Interleukin II, which resulted in thermal stabilization of this commercially important protein. In general, attempts to stabilize protein structure by introducing cysteine residues in positions capable of forming disulfide bridges have met with mixed results.

Mutations that enhance the compactness of the protein core by increasing intra-helix packing interactions, such as changes of alanine for glycine, tend to improve the stability of proteins like T4 lysozyme. The common theme of antiparallel alignment of helices in folded proteins suggests that these helix dipoles serve to stabilize protein structure. The thermal stability of T4 lysozyme could be improved without decreasing catalytic activity by engineering amino acid replacements that are believed to decrease the conformational entropy of the unfolded state. Replacing an alanine residue with the more restrictive proline increased thermal stability of T4 lysozyme. Studies of chemical denaturation of tryptophan synthase [4.2.1.20], an enzyme involved in tryptophan biosynthesis from *E. coli*, show that substitution of a buried amino acid residue by each of the other 19 amino acids increased protein stability with increasing hydrophobicity of the replacement residue provided it did not introduce steric barriers. These studies suggest the possibility of numerous methods for achieving protein stability and clearly that there are energetic tradeoffs for a given alteration.

Increasing the thermal stability of a protein often correlates with increased stability in solvents, resistance to oxidative processes, and increased stability to protease digestion. Robert Saurer and colleagues at M.I.T. have shown that the thermal sensitivity of the N-terminal domain of mutant Phage *lambda* repressors, a DNA binding protein, correlates with resistance to proteolysis and may be compared with the activity of temperature-sensitive mutants *in vivo*. As a protein ages its integrity is destroyed by several irreversible chemical processes, including hydrolysis or rearrangement of aspartyl bonds, deamidation of asparagine and glutamine, β-elimination of cysteine, and oxidation of methionine to sulfoxide. In all cases, substitution of these amino acids in native proteins by chemically inert residues increases the longevity of the mutant proteins. For example, α-1 antitrypsin, a potent inhibitor of the protease neutrophil elastase [3.14.21.11], whose excess activity is believed to lead to emphysema, is inactivated by oxidation of a methionine residue located at a site that binds and inhibits elastase. Replacing this methionine with valine using site-directed mutagenesis techniques produced a fully functional protease inhibitor that was resistant to oxidative inactivation. As a result, the valine variant of antitrypsin may be used as a more stable alternative in the treatment of emphysema.

Proteins can often be profoundly stabilized by combining a number of selected mutations in one molecule. Investigators at Genentech Corporation screened a number of subtilisin mutant proteins in a thermophilic bacterium (which grows at 70C) and analyzed the thermal-stabilizing mutations. By incorporating a number of these amino acid replacements into a single mutant protein via site-directed mutagenesis they increased the thermal stability of this protein 50–fold.

Altering Enzyme Catalytic Activity

Alan Fersht and co-workers at Imperial College of Science and Technology have carried out extensive mutational and kinetic studies with tyrosyl-tRNA synthetase [6.1.1.1], an enzyme involved in the charging of tyrosyl-tRNA with tyrosine. Utilizing pre-steady state kinetic analysis of engineered enzymes, these investigators were able to quantitate the thermodynamic binding energies of individual amino acids with regard to the substrate, transition state and products in the catalytic cycle. These studies show that a single residue may effect either substrate binding (K_M) or the rate of catalysis (K_{cat}, transition state binding) independently or they may be inseparable, effecting both for a given amino acid change.

Fersht and associates improved the affinity of tyrosyl-tRNA synthetase for its substrate, adenosine 5'-triphosphate (ATP), without significantly reducing catalytic activity by substituting a threonine residue (which forms an energetically unfavorable hydrogen bond with substrate), with either alanine or proline (substitutions that remove this adverse hydrogen bond), or with cysteine (which is able to form a better hydrogen bond). Hydrogen bonds are thought to be a major determinant of specificity due to their directional nature. A single hydrogen bond may contribute a 2–20 fold increase in specificity ratio and the presence of two or more hydrogen bonds will greatly amplify this discrimination energy. The ability systematically to alter K_{cat} and K_M permits investigators rationally to tailor families of enzymes whose members are active at differing concentrations of target substrates.

Changing the substrate specificity of an enzyme may involve changing only a few residues or it can require the wholesale movement of an entire domain. J. Richards at the California Institute of Technology in Pasadena, working with carboxypeptidase from *E. coli* [3.4.17.1], an enzyme involved in protein degradation, excised the catalytic site in a 30 amino acid unit and spliced it into the catalytic site of the related enzyme, β-lactamase [3.5.2.6], an enzyme which degrades lactam antibiotics. This thermally stable chimeric protein with 18 amino acid substitutions had acquired 3% of the native carboxypeptidase and lost all its β-lactamase activity. This experiment provides evidence that functional domains can be grafted onto the scaffold of another protein either to replace function or to add function.

Charles Craik and associates at the University of California (San Francisco) performed structure-function studies with two hydrolytic enzymes, trypsin, which cleaves peptide bonds internal to proteins, and carboxypeptidase A [3.4.17.1], which cleaves aromatic and branched-chain amino acids from the carboxy terminus of proteins. The hydroxyl moiety of a tyrosine residue previously thought to be involved as a proton donor in the catalytic cycle of carboxypeptidase A was shown not to be essential when a phenylalanine substitution was found to exhibit wild type catalytic activity. These researchers altered the catalytic activity of trypsin in a discriminatory manner by replacing one of two key glycine residues with alanine. The mutant protein in one case displayed a preference for arginine substrates relative to wild type while the other mutant prefered lysine substrates. The role of an aspartate residue in the proton relay mechanism of trypsin catalysis was established by these authors by converting it to asparagine, an isosteric replacement. The aspartate residue was shown to be important for catalytic activity but not absolutely essential. The work emerging from this laboratory reinforces the necessity of a coordinated multidisciplinary approach to successful structure-function studies.

Peptide Hormones

Starting with functional polypeptides, investigators such as Emil T. Kaiser and William F. DeGrado systematically alter amino acid residues so as to improve the protein activity based on principles of secondary structure which, unlike tertiary structure, can be predicted with considerable accuracy. The secondary structure of intermediate sized hormones, particularly amphiphilic β-sheet and α-helices, appear to dominate receptor-hormone binding interactions. Thus, the design of intermediate size polypeptide hormones (10–30 residues) with enhanced biological activity is fast becoming a reality. The 31 amino acid rat hormone, β-endorphin, has potent opioid activity and serves as an animal model system for this important class of proteins. Fully active synthetic hormones were designed to have little amino acid sequence homology but to retain secondary structure homology with the native polypeptide. In one case a synthetic polypeptide made from enantiomeric D-amino acids was active.

Emil T. Kaisers' group at Rockefeller University has shown that it is possible rationally to design small novel polypeptides that have similar if not enhanced biological activity by mimicking the amphiphilic secondary structures of natural peptides. These investigators synthesized a series of short polypeptides that share little sequence homology to the structural unit responsible for biological activity of apolipoprotein. They found that some of these synthetic peptides were able to illicit biological activity by activating the enzyme lecithin-cholesterol acyl transferase [2.3.1.43], an important function of apolipoprotein. In another study with melittin, a toxin that causes the lysis of erythrocytes, these same investigators were able to enhance lysis activity by substituting a serine for proline in the middle of an important α-helix.

William F. Degrado and colleagues at du Pont laboratories designed and synthesized peptides that bind and inhibit calmodulin action. Calmodulin, a ubiquitous, small, acidic protein that interacts in a calcium-dependent manner with a number of regulatory enzymes, appears to play a central role in cellular regulation through modulation of calcium-requiring enzyme function. Features common to natural peptides known to tightly bind calmodulin, such as β-endorphin and melittin, are a cluster of basic residues and an amphiphilic α-helix. It appears that secondary structure motifs govern calmodulin's interaction with these peptides. The synthetic polypeptides produced by Degrado's group are the tightest-binding inhibitors of calmodulin thus far reported. By fine tuning the inhibitory polypeptide sequence combined with site-directed mutagenesis of calmodulin itself, these investigators are furnishing insights into the mechanism whereby calmodulin binds to target enzymes as well as providing a model system for examining protein-protein interactions.

Catalytic Antibodies

Early in this century Emil Fisher suggested that enzyme action depends on the geometric structures of both the enzyme and the substrate and that they must fit like lock and key. In 1948, Linus Pauling extended the lock and key model by suggesting that a reaction is accelerated if the catalytic site matches and binds the activated complex of the reaction more tightly than it binds substrate or product ground states. These observations have given scientists reason to wonder whether antibodies made to bind a transition state model would catalyze that chemical reaction.

Production of catalytic monoclonal antibodies was first reported by several groups in 1985. Richard Lerner's group at Scripps Research Institute generated antibodies to a series of tetrahedral phosphorus compounds that mimic the presumed transition state in the hydrolysis of a carboxylate ester. The antibodies produced were able to catalyze this reaction at a rate 1000 times greater than the uncatalyzed reaction. These catalytic antibodies exhibited properties of an enzyme, such as substrate specificity, saturation kinetics, and competitive inhibition. A catalytic antibody approach uses enzymatic mechanistic knowledge to provide new insights into the design of catalytic function and the use of such well established studies avoids many of the questions concerning structure-function correlation. By generating a host of antibodies to a single transition state analogue it is possible to catalog the structural motifs Nature uses to fashion catalytic sites.

APPLICATIONS AND CONCLUSION

Of the numerous biological activities performed by proteins those of greatest commercial interest are substrate recognition by antibodies, regulation of metabolism by hormones and enzymatic catalysis. The world market for commercial enzymes is well over $500 million a year. This market includes proteases for detergent additives, amylases used in starch degradation for the food and textile industries and the rennets used in cheese making. Two European chemical giants dominate the world market for supplying enzymes, Novo Industri of Denmark and Gist Brocades of The Netherlands, both of which have significant outlays for protein engineering research. It should be kept in mind that virtually any application presently using proteins can probably be profoundly improved through protein engineering by increasing a protein's utility and thus its dollar value.

Agricultural Applications

The food industry is the largest consumer of proteins, mainly hydrolytic enzymes such as amylases (which degrade starches in beer, bread, and fruit juices), chymosin and lactases (dairy processing), papain [3.4.22.2] (beer additive and meat tenderizer) and bacterial proteases. This market has remained relatively stable; only one major new enzyme-based industrial process — the production of high fructose corn syrup using glucose isomerase [5.3.1.9] and glucoamylase [3.2.1.3] — has emerged in the decade prior to 1985. This situation is likely to change dramatically as active research efforts in protein engineering yield valuable new products.

Casein micelles sequester calcium phosphate and protein in high concentration for effective nutrition of the young. A major portion of the dairy industry uses casein proteins, particularly, in the manufacture of cheese. The clotting of milk during cheese making involves cleavage of a specific casein peptide bond by the acid protease, chymosin. Cleavage of this bond releases a polar polypeptide which disrupts casein micell structure and causes coagulation to form cheese curd. Chymosin has been the subject of intense protein engineering efforts to improve its stability and protease activity to speed the aging process of cheese.

Increasing the biological value of proteins for human nutrition is a feasible goal or target for protein engineering. Plant proteins are the major source of amino acids in the diet for most of the world's population. Plant proteins are usually deficient in one or more of the essential amino acids: legume seed proteins lack methionine, cereal grains lack lysine, and tryptophan and threonine are often in low abundance. In general, breeding plants to improve essential amino acid composition has met with limited success. Breeding high lysine-containing maize resulted in decreased yields and proteins with different properties. Investigators at Purdue University have shown that maize storage proteins, the zeins, engineered to contain lysine and tryptophan and expressed in *Xenopus laevis* oocytes, assembled into structures similar to maize protein bodies. This model system suggests the possibility of creating high-lysine maize through protein engineering in such a way that it does not reduce crop yield nor introduce unwanted properties to the protein.

Accelerated growth of animals and plants has been achieved using specific growth hormones. Bovine growth hormone stimulates the milk production of dairy cows and increases the rate of maturation for cattle, thus reducing the feed cost. Porcine growth hormone produces animals with markedly leaner meat, again cutting the price of production. A modified porcine growth hormone gene has been incorporated into the genome of a pig, producing an animal with leaner meat, accelerated growth and whose traits are inheritable. The significant economic advantage of this and other transgenic animals has been recognized in the rush to patent these engineered animals. Protein engineering has been used to construct these genes for expression and may be further used to increase the serum clearance time of these hormones and to remove unwanted side effects.

Industrial Applications

Enzymes are active under mild conditions, permitting the synthesis of sensitive molecules that otherwise are unable to withstand the harsh conditions required for many classical catalysts. Despite an enzyme's speed, dependability and low energy needs, several economic shortcomings still prevent widespread use of enzymes in industrial scale chemical synthesis and materials manufacture. Protein fragility is one of the primary limitations. Enzyme denaturation is induced by changes in temperature, pressure, mechanical stress and by addition of chemical reagents such as acids and bases, oxidants, detergents and solvents. Enzymes are also susceptible to digestion by proteases secreted by bacterial contaminants, requiring sterile reaction conditions which introduce additional production cost. There is good reason to believe that a number of these factors, present in many industrial processes, can and in some cases have been overcome by practical applications of protein engineering. As a result of protein engineering entirely new enzymatic processes are being developed for cheaper, faster, and less hazardous chemical manufacture, waste treatment, and biomass conversion.

Medicinal Applications

The medical field, including biomedical research, acute and chronic patient care, disease prevention, and medical instrumentation, already uses many products of protein engineering. The health care field is and will continue to be for the foreseeable future the largest financial consumer of engineered proteins and products derived from engineered proteins. Protein engineering is able to augment the utility of a pharmaceutically-active protein by enhancing an activity, combining several activities, and/or increasing its stability and storage-life.

Production of traditional vaccines involves large scale culturing of dangerous viruses. The product vaccine is comprised of inactivated viruses that can be and have been contaminated by virulent particles or factors. Synthetic vaccines overcome the dangers inherent in traditional methods by producing only a single virus coat protein, not the virus, in bacterial culture. The main goal for generating synthetic vaccines is to mimic the immunogenic epitopes of the natural virus coat. Construction of hybrid proteins through protein engineering can facilitate the correct presentation of the immunogenic region. Hybrid synthetic vaccines constructed from the coat proteins of the Foot-and-Mouth virus have been successful in eliciting a protective immune response in farm animals against Foot-and-Mouth disease.

Practical medical application of immunogenic recognition is now possible through a combination of genetic engineering and hybridomia techniques used to produce monoclonal antibodies. The antigen binding sites of immunoglobulins (Fab fragments) have been produced in bacteria while cloned Ig genes have been expressed in mammalian cell culture. Monoclonal antibody diagnostic kits are now coming to market that are able to test for allergies, anemia, leukemia (Hybritech), pregnancy (Organon Technika), diabetes, blood groups, venereal diseases (Genetic Systems), hepatitis B (Centocor), breast cancer (Abbott), and genetic fetal defects, to name just a few. Construction of immunotoxins, proteins containing the Fab antigen binding fragment of immunoglobins and a covalently attached toxin, such as diptheria toxin or ricin, or an enzyme, such as a protease or nuclease, promises to provide a potent and specific weapon in fighting bacterial, parasitic and viral infection. The gene coding for Staphylococcal nuclease, an enzyme that degrades DNA, has been fused to genes coding for the Fab arms, producing a chimeric protein with dual function, the ability to bind a specific target and the ability to degrade DNA. Catalytic antibodies are being developed to catalyze hydrolysis reactions for synthesis of novel pharmaceuticals for clinical evaluation. Catalytic antibodies that cleave and form bonds with a high degree of specificity will have considerable utility in protein modification and analysis. The potential market value of both immunotoxins and catalytic antibodies is significant: not only will they serve as potent research tools but their potential to target and selectively modify molecules, such as by cleaving bonds in the proteins that form a viral coat, begins to approximate the long sought "magic bullet" for combating disease.

Growth Factors

The use of growth factors in wound repair promises to reduce healing time and thus cut costs for all involved. In early 1987 two firms, Chiron Corp. of Emeryville, Calif. and Ethicon of Somerville, N.J., initiated a joint study of genetically engineered growth factors in healing burn patients. The 1990 hospital sales of a protein, epidermal growth factor, known to promote healing of skin tissue is expected to reach $25 million. Fibroblast growth factor, another hormone, acts in the deep layers of a wound by stimulating both the growth of blood vesicle cells and the secretion of collagen which gives tensile strength to the healing tissue. A number of companies consider fibroblast growth factor an investment worth the gamble due to the impressive results with animal model systems. Another hormone, platelet-derived growth factor, induces fibroblasts to move into a wound and build new connective tissue. A combination of these growth factors may prove to be a potent cocktail in healing both trivial and severe wounds. Tissue engineering involves the introduction of a complement of genes, such as those coding for these growth factors, into the tissue genome of either animal or human fetal tissue. The prospect for using these augmented tissues in wound or burn repair is receiving great attention.

The Marriage of Electronics and Biology

The near term products of protein engineering will encourage the interface between the worlds of biology and microelectronics. Proteins are being used to construct biosensor electronic devices that utilize the unique catalytic and molecular recognition properties of proteins (see Chapter 20). Biosensors provide rapid, efficient, and extremely sensitive determination of concentrations of a wide range of molecules. The type of devices coming to market range from tiny implanted sensors for whole body monitoring to large scale flow sensors for industrial deployment. The use of these instruments presently focuses on hospitals and laboratories. A miniature biosensor has been developed which is able to measure micromolar concentrations of glucose in blood for treatment of diabetic patients. Bio-affinity sensors have been shown to measure the low concentrations of vitamins and a bioluminescence sensor utilizing immobilized luciferase [1.13.12.7], the light producing protein of fireflys, was able to measure micromolar concentrations of ATP. Prospects for designing biosensors that measure hormone levels and drug concentrations are encouraging. There is currently speculation about the development of a fast, extremely small biocomputer chip (see Chapter 21). The ability specifically to modify protein structure insures that the field of protein engineering will remain at the forefront of the union between electronics and biology.

The fusion of recombinant DNA technologies and new physical biochemical techniques has resulted in the emergence of the field of protein engineering. The enormous economic power of protein engineering to enhance the current use of proteins and introduce novel uses is propelling the development of this field at an astonishing rate. Protein engineering will profoundly extend our understanding of the molecular detail of the chemical world as well as produce products for the present and future fields of agriculture, industry and medicine.

REFERENCES

1. Oxender, D.L. and Fox, C.F., eds. (1987) *Protein Engineering*: Alan R. Liss, Inc., New York.
2. Oxender, D.L., ed. (1985–6). *Protein Structure, Folding, and Design*, Volumes I and II: Alan R. Liss, Inc., New York.
3. Antebi, E. and Fishlock, D. (1986). *Biotechnology: Strategies for Life*: The M.I.T. Press, Cambridge Massachusetts.
4. International Union of Biochemistry, Nomenclature Committee (1979). *Enzyme Nomenclature*: Academic Press, Inc., New York.
5. Degrado, W.F., Wassweman, Z.R. and Lear, J.D. (1989) Science 243, 622–643.
6. King, J. (April 10th, 1989) Chemical and Engineering News, 32–54.

Chapter 13

Fermentation Technology, Bioprocessing, Scale-up and Manufacture

Yusuf Chisti and Murray Moo-Young

The commercialization of biotechnology-based processes for the improvement of human life would be impossible without the supporting engineering disciplines. Chemical or process engineering taking into account the specificities of biological systems has developed into biochemical engineering which is already a rapidly growing branch of knowledge. Biochemical engineering has a crucial role in economically transforming the laboratory discoveries in biotechnology into large scale manufacturing. Process development time — the time between initial process conception and full scale manufacture of product for sale — may be considerably shortened by the earliest involvement of engineers in biotechnology research. The type and the quality of research data, for example, can lead to significant savings in resources in subsequent stages of bioprocess development.

This chapter is an overview of biochemical engineering base of biotechnology. The processing considerations common to many biological systems are examined. The bioreactors used in the production of biochemicals and biocatalysts (enzymes, microorganisms, cell cultures) and the fundamentals of design of these reactors and supporting systems are treated. Product harvesting, purification and other downstream processing operations are discussed with emphasis on newer developments. The associated process control technologies are considered. Finally, an overall process dimension is provided by examining a complete bioprocess.

BIOPROCESS: GENERAL ASPECTS

Any large-scale operation involving the transformation of some raw material (biological or non-biological) into some product by means of microorganisms, animal or plant cell cultures, or by materials (*e.g.* enzymes, organelles) derived from them, may be termed a "bioprocess". The "product" of such processes may be saleable (*e.g.* insulin, penicillin, SCP, enzymes) or they may have little commercial value (waste treatment). A bioprocess is typically made up of three steps shown in Figure 1. The raw material or feedstock (see Chapter 14) must be converted to a form which is suitable for processing. This is done in a pretreatment step which may involve one or more of the operations shown in Figure 1. Frequently, the well established chemical engineering operations suffice for the pretreatment stage and these will not be discussed further.

The pretreatment step is followed by one or more bioreaction stages where the desired biotransformation takes

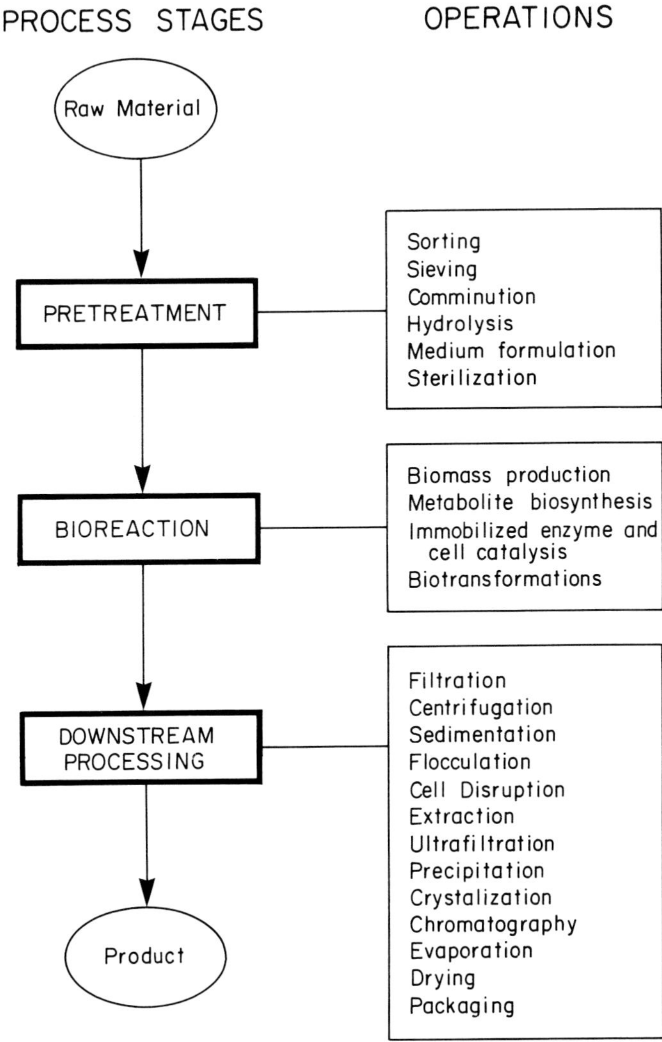

Figure 1. Bioprocess stages and the commonly used operations in them.

place. The transformation may involve the conversion of a substrate to biomass or biomass and some biochemical or enzyme. Alternatively, the conversion may use dead whole cells (immobilized or in suspension) or enzymes as the biocatalytic agency. Bioreactors form the core of the bioreaction step. The material produced in the bioreactors must usually be processed further in the downstream section of the process to convert it to a useful form. Downstream processing consists of predominantly physical operations which are aimed at concentration and purification of the product. The purified product may have to be in different physical forms (liquid, slurry, powder, crystalline) for different applications.

The properties of biological materials impose significant unique constraints on the bioreaction and downstream processing stages. These stages are treated more thoroughly later on in this chapter after a consideration of the characteristics of the biomaterials themselves.

PROPERTIES OF BIOLOGICAL MATERIALS

The design of a bioprocess and the engineering of the process equipment requires a careful consideration of the physical and chemical properties of the material being handled and a delimitation of the maximum processing stresses (temperature, pH, shear forces, contamination, pressure) that the material may safely tolerate. Typically a bioprocess must operate within the physiological ranges of pH and temperature (pH $\sim$ 7, temperature $\leq$ 37°C), the specific conditions being very process-dependent. The pressures which would normally be encountered ($\leq$ 2 MPa) in bioreactors do not seem to damage microorganisms or enzymes but carbon dioxide associated toxicity effects due to increased solubility of CO_2 at higher pressures may become important.

The sensitivity to shearing forces may vary widely. In general, bacteria and yeasts which grow as small individual cells are quite shear tolerant. Genetically engineered species and wall-less mutants are frequently susceptible to shear damage due to their weaker cell wall/membrane structures. Filamentous bacteria and mycelial fungi which have larger particle dimensions do show signs of mechanical damage in high shear fields. Similarly, plant and mammalian cells are more sensitive to shear. Enzymes, with the exception of multienzyme complexes and membrane associated enzymes, are not damaged by shear in the absence of gas-liquid interfaces.

Because nearly all processing operations must handle liquids and slurries a more in-depth treatment of biofluids follows.

Biological Fluids

Biofluids and slurries fall into two categories: (i) Newtonian fluids such as water, honey and most bacterial and yeast fermentation broths; and (ii) non-Newtonian media such as polysaccharide fermentations and the broths of *Streptomyces*, *Aspergilli* and *Penicillia*.

Newtonian fluids

At constant temperature and pressure, Newtonian fluids have a constant viscosity irrespective of the shear rate. For these fluids shear stress (τ) and shear rate are linearly related. In laminar flow

$$\tau = \mu_L \dot{\gamma} \tag{1}$$

Plots of τ vs. $\dot{\gamma}$ are straight lines of slope equal to the viscosity, μ_L.

Non-Newtonian fluids

Viscosity of these fluids is dependent on the rate of shear. This dependence is commonly described by the power law model:

$$\tau = K \dot{\gamma}^n \tag{2}$$

where K and n are the consistency index and the flow behaviour index, respectively, of the fluid. By analogy with eq. (1) an apparent viscosity (μ_{ap}) can be defined for the non-Newtonian fluids:

$$\mu_{ap} = K (\dot{\gamma})^{n-1} \tag{3}$$

For n = 1, eq. (3) reduces to constant viscosity form and the fluid is Newtonian. For n > 1, the fluid becomes increasingly viscous with shear and it is termed *dilatant* or shear thickening. When n < 1 the fluid is shear thinning or *pseudoplastic*. Many biological media display pseudoplastic behaviour.

The shear stress vs. shear rate plots for the various flow behaviours are shown in Figure 2. The slope of a line joining any point on these plots to the origin is the apparent viscosity. Clearly, the apparent viscosity increases (dilatant) or decreases (pseudoplastic) with shear rate for non-Newtonian fluids.

Certain fluids do not flow until the applied shear stress exceeds a minimum value (τ_o) known as the "yield stress". This type of behaviour may be described by the *Bingham plastic* flow model or by the *Casson* equation:

$$\tau = \tau_o + K \dot{\gamma} \text{ (Bingham plastic)} \tag{4}$$

$$\sqrt{\tau} = \sqrt{\tau_o} + K_c \sqrt{\dot{\gamma}} \text{ (Casson model)} \tag{5}$$

where K_c is a constant known as Casson viscosity.

Estimation of viscosity

For suspensions of yeasts and bacteria growing as individual cells suspended in a water-like medium, equations of Einstein

$$\mu_S = \mu_L (1 + 2.5\, \varepsilon_S) \tag{6}$$

and of Vand

$$\mu_S = \mu_L (1 + 2.5\, \varepsilon_S + 7.25\, \varepsilon_S^2) \tag{7}$$

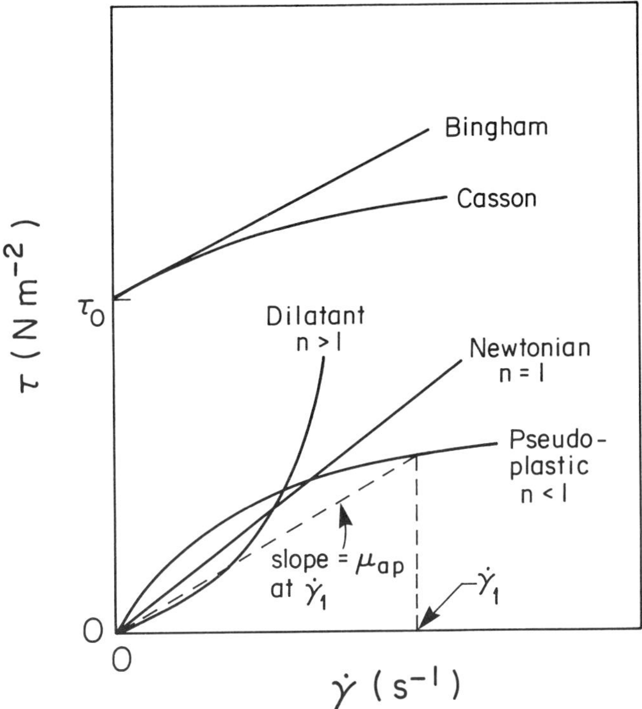

Figure 2. Shear stress vs. shear rate plots for various flow behaviours.

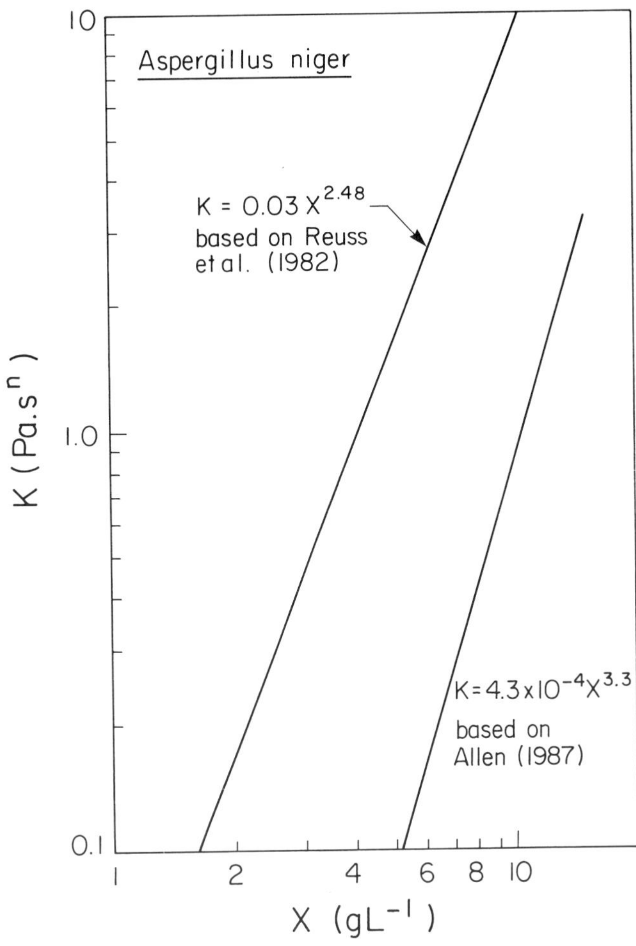

Figure 3. Dependence of consistency index (K) on solids concentration (X) in broths of *Aspergillus niger*.

may be used. For mycelial broths the power law model is often satisfactory. The parameters K and n are dependent on solids concentration; n generally declines with the concentration of solids, *i.e.*, the suspension becomes increasingly shear thinning, while K increases quite strongly with the solids content of the mycelial slurry. At present, however, no satisfactory quantitative relationships exist to describe the influence of mycelial solids on K and n of these fluids. For example, for broths of *Aspergillus niger* the dependence of K on solids concentration (X) according to two different correlations is shown in Figure 3. The agreement between these equations is not at all satisfactory. As a result, even though a flow model may fit the experimental data, the parameters obtained may have little value for bioreactor design. Furthermore, all the foregoing flow models and the parameters obtained on their basis apply strictly to laminar flow. Could such K and n have any real value for process design purposes under conditions of turbulent flow? This question is particularly important in many biological slurries in which the parameters K and n are not really constant but depend on the shear rate range used in their determination. Questions such as this remain to be answered. Alternative approaches which relate the design properties such as oxygen transfer, mixing and heat transfer directly to biomass content of a slurry are useful as discussed later.

PRETREATMENT OPERATIONS

Media Sterilization

The successful operation of most productive fermentations depends on the maintenance in culture of a single microbial species with which the fermenter was initially inoculated. To prevent contamination by other organisms the gaseous and liquid feeds to the fermenter have to be sterilized. Either physical elimination, for example by filtration, or destruction of microorganisms may be used to achieve sterile feed streams.

While ionizing radiation and chemical sterilents may be used, sterilization by filtration and heat treatment are by far the most common techniques. Liquids such as water and salt solutions can be inexpensively sterilized by passing them through absolute filters the pore size of which are smaller than the dimensions of any contaminating particles. This method is practicable only when the liquid is free of other suspended material and its initial microbial contamination is low. For some liquids such as blood serum filter sterilization may be the only viable technique if denaturation of its highly labile constituents is to be prevented. On the other hand, concentrated solutions of sugars and highly contaminated media (*e.g.* molasses, cornsteep liquor) are commonly heat sterilized. Thermal denaturation of contaminating organisms, when properly carried out, is among the most effective methods of sterilization.

Heat Sterilization

Thermal denaturation of one or more enzymes in the contaminating microorganisms is used to render them non-viable. The feed is brought to a sufficiently high temperature and held there for a certain time to ensure the destruction of the most resistant contaminant. The process may be conducted batchwise or continuously.

Batch sterilization

The rate of destruction of microorganisms follows the first-order kinetics:

$$-\frac{dN}{dt} = k_d N \tag{8}$$

where k_d is the specific death rate and N the concentration of the contaminating organisms at any time. The time (t) required to reduce the concentration of contaminants from an initial value N_o to some value N is obtained from the integrated form of eq. (8):

$$\frac{N}{N_o} = e^{-k_d t} \tag{9}$$

Typically, N_o is 10^5–10^9/mL. The final concentration N depends on the degree of acceptable fermentation failure since at some point the cost of further reducing the risk of contamination would exceed the expense of a lost fermentation. For a 250 m^3 fermentation with an acceptable failure rate of one in fifty fermentations the final level of contamination would be one microorganism in fifty fermenter volumes

$$N = 1/(50 \times 250) = 1/12500\ m^3 \equiv 8 \times 10^{-11} \text{ per mL}$$

The thermal death rate constant k_d is a function of temperature

$$k_d = A\ e^{-\Delta E/RT} \tag{10}$$

where ΔE is the activation energy for the destruction of a particular microorganism, A is its Arrhenius parameter and T is the absolute temperature. Bacterial spores such as those of *Bacillus stearothermophilus* and *Clostridium botulinum* are some of the most heat resistant, and sterilization processes are designed to be effective against them. The activation energy for destruction of these spores is $2.5-2.9 \times 10^8$ J $kmol^{-1}$ and A is $\sim 1.6 \times 10^{36}\ s^{-1}$. Because k_d increases with temperature, the higher the temperature the shorter the treatment time needed to achieve a given level (N/N_o) of destruction as illustrated in Figure 4. However, the processes which lead to microbial inactivation also cause destruction of heat labile essential nutrients in the feed. Denaturation of nutrients (k_n) is also temperature dependent

$$k_n = A_n\ e^{-\Delta E_n/RT} \tag{11}$$

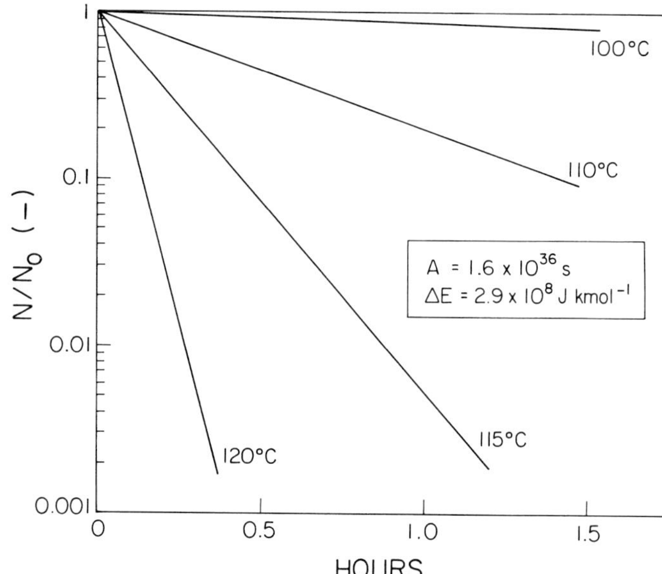

Figure 4. Time needed to obtain a given level of destruction (N/N_o) at various sterilization temperatures.

From equations (10) and (11) it follows that

$$\frac{k_d}{k_n} = \frac{A}{A_n} e^{(\Delta E_n - \Delta E)/RT} \tag{12}$$

The activation energy for the thermal deactivation of most nutrients (ΔE_n) is substantially lower than ΔE for microbial deactivation. For example ΔE_n for thiamine hydrochloride (vitamin B_6) is only 9.2×10^7 J $kmol^{-1}$. Hence, in order to maximize microbial destruction relative to nutrient loss (*i.e.* achieve higher k_d/k_n), sterilization at high temperature for a shorter time is indicated. This is the basis for HTST or high-temperature-short-time sterilization. Because of the short exposure times (of the order of seconds), HTST is best implemented in a continuous flow mode.

Either direct heat (steam injection) or indirect heat (coils, jacket) may be used to heat the fluid to the sterilization temperature where it is held for some time (holding time) followed by cooling. The time-temperature profile of such a process is shown in Figure 5.

In batch sterilization heating and cooling times are relatively long and some sterilization occurs during these periods. During heating and cooling k_d varies with time and the total sterilization is calculated by graphical integration of k_d vs. time profiles

$$-\ln\left(\frac{N}{N_o}\right)_{Total} = \int_{T_o}^{T_s} k_d\, dt + k_d\, t_{hold} + \int_{T_s}^{T_o} k_d\, dt \tag{13}$$

In continuous sterilization very rapid heating and cooling is obtained and the contributions of heating and cooling periods to sterilization is generally disregarded.

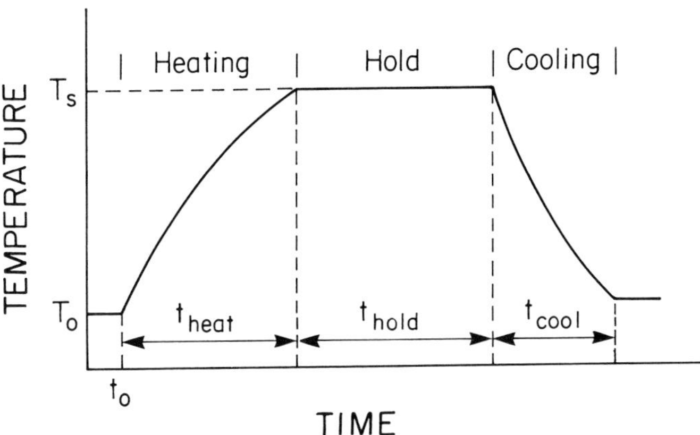

Figure 5. Time-temperature profile.

Continuous sterilization

Advantages associated with HTST sterilization, rapid heating and cooling and precise control of holding time makes continuous sterilization the preferred method whenever it can be employed. The kinetics of sterilization are identical to the treatment given in the previous section. The raw medium is heated to the sterilization temperature either by continuous steam injection or by a high efficiency heat exchanger (plate or spiral exchangers). This is followed by a holding coil where the sterilization temperature is maintained for a time equalling the residence time of the coil. Either flash cooling or indirect heat exchange returns the feed to the fermentation temperature. The steam injection and indirect heating schemes are illustrated in Figure 6.

For a continuous fermentation feed flow of Q m^3s^{-1}, N may be easily calculated for a given level of contamination, *e.g.*, one contamination during operation time t_{op}, as

$$N = 1/Q\, t_{op}. \tag{14}$$

Hence, the holding time necessary for a given N/N_o, and the length of holding coil may be determined.

The design of the holding coil requires careful attention. The velocity of flow is not uniform across the cross section of a pipe and the flow is always faster at the axis of a straight pipe. As a result, the residence times of different elements of fluid in the pipe can be different. A most conservative estimate of the residence time is obtained from the equation

$$t_r = \frac{L}{U_{max}} \tag{15}$$

where L is the length of the holding coil and U_{max} the centreline velocity of flow in the pipe. The maximum velocity U_{max} depends on the Reynolds number of flow

$$Re = \frac{\rho_L\, U\, d}{\mu_L} \tag{16}$$

where U is the average flow velocity through the pipe. Well-developed turbulent flow ($Re \gg 2300$) is desired in the pipe to minimize the difference between U and U_{max}. Values of U/U_{max} as a function of Reynolds number are given in Figure 7 for straight, circular pipes. In helical coils laminar flow persists to significantly higher values of Reynolds number than in straight pipes.

Air Sterilization

Aerobic fermentations require a continuous supply of large quantities of air or oxygen. The gas entering the fermenter must be free of contaminants such as bacteria, spores, bacteriophages and other microorganisms. Similarly, the exhaust gas from a fermenter must be treated to remove microorganisms and spray particles which can be potentially harmful to plant personnel and the environment.

Sterilization of fermentation inlet and exhaust gas is achieved predominantly by filtration on which depends the failure or success of a fermentation operation. The smallest particles which need to be removed from the air are bacteria and viruses. The smallest bacteria are ~ 0.1 μm in diameter; viruses are typically less than 0.3 μm and may be as small as 0.04 μm. Either depth filtration or absolute filtration may be used to free the air of unwanted particulates. Depth filtration depends on passing the gas through a bed of packing such as compressed glass wool or other fibrous material. The spaces between fibres are larger than the dimensions of the particles to be removed and particles penetrate the filter bed to various depths. The total filter depth is such that the required removal is achieved. Absolute filters, on the other hand, have openings which are smaller in size than the dimensions of the smallest particle to be retained. Particle removal is by a sieving action. Porous polymer membranes, ceramic and metal membranes are used as absolute filters. Polymer membranes in the very narrow pore size distribution can be produced by subjecting non-porous polymer films to bombardment by high energy nuclear particles. However, absolute membrane filters are easily fouled and produce relatively high pressure drops. Prefilters are used prior to the air filters to remove gross contamination such a dirt, oil and water droplets and foam to extend the operational life of the filter.

Depth filtration

Several different mechanisms of particle retention operate in a compacted bed of fibrous material: *direct interception* of

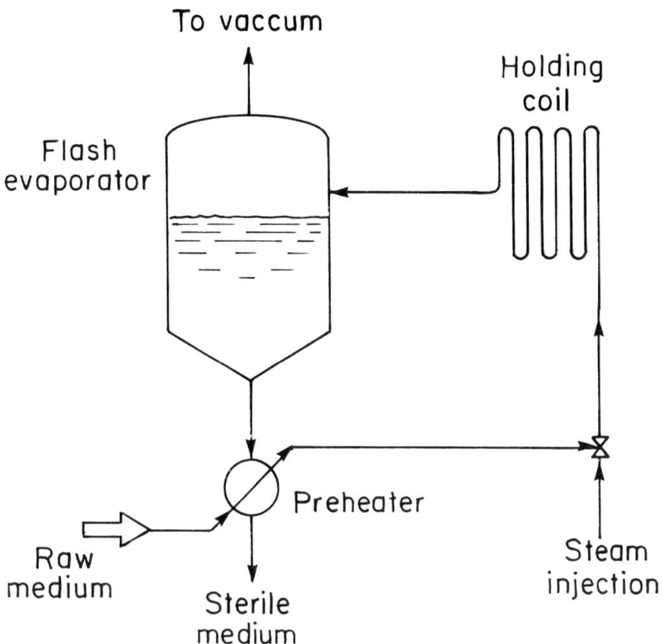

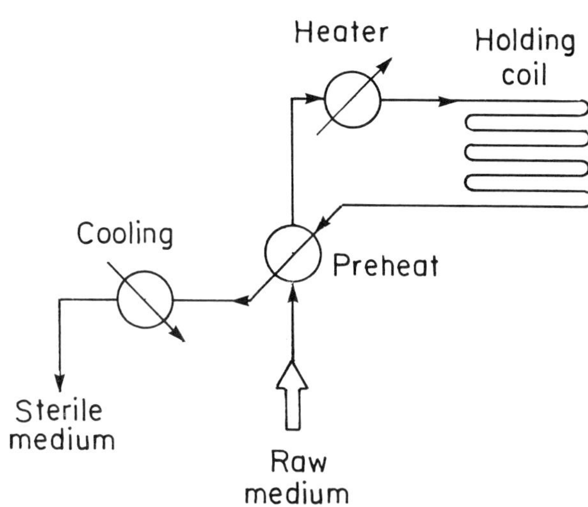

Figure 6. Sterilization processes: (a) direct steam injection; (b) indirect heating.

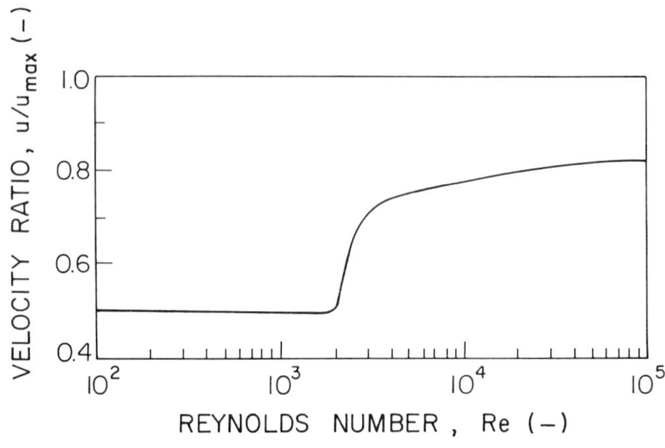

Figure 7. U/U_{max} vs. Reynolds number in straight, circular pipes.

particles by filter fibres; *inertial impaction* on fibres of particles with sufficiently high momentum that they are incapable of following the gas stream as it flows around to avoid the fibre and they impact on the fibre; small particles move around in the gas by *diffusion* and *Brownian motion*, they eventually collide and are retained on filter fibre. Other modes of particle removal mechanisms may occur to various degrees. The removal of particles with filter depth follows the equation

$$\ln \frac{N_o}{N} = k_f\, z \tag{17}$$

where N_o and N are, respectively, the initial and final levels of contamination in air, z is the filter depth to achieve N contamination level and k_f is the filter constant. k_f depends on bed void fraction, fibre diameter, velocity of flow and temperature. Formation of condensate affects filter performance and should be prevented.

The air filter is itself sterilized by direct or indirect steam heating. Chemical sterilization is also practiced.

A common test of filter performance is based on penetration of dioctylpathalate (DOP test) particles mainly of ≤ 0.3 μm size. A penetration of 0.003% or less corresponds to removal

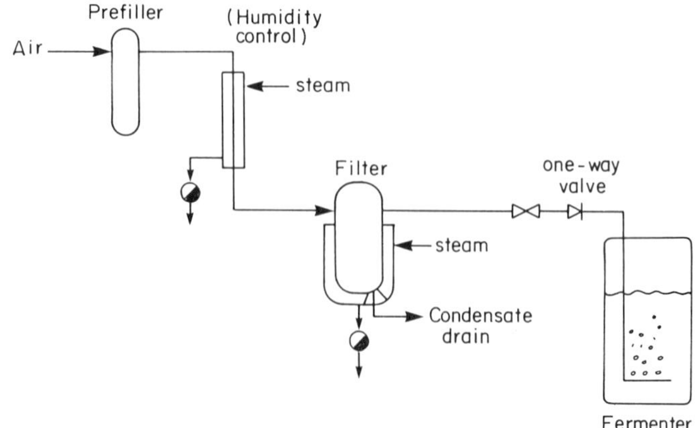

Figure 8. Air filtration using a packed filter.

of all viable organisms. In practice, each depth filter thickness may have a DOP penetration of 0.001% or less and since several layers are often used in series, the actual penetration is much lower. Hence, depth filters are an effective means for air sterilization. In some applications a depth filtration step may be followed by an absolute filter to gain additional confidence on air purity. A typical packed filter arrangement in fermentation application is shown in Figure 8.

BIOREACTION

Fermentation Process, Growth and Production

A sterilized batch fermenter containing a properly developed fermentation medium (C and N sources, micronutrients), sufficient aeration, supplies of pH control chemicals, antifoams and associated systems must be inoculated with the desired microbial species to initiate the fermentation. The inoculum consists of a microbial suspension in rapid exponential growth added at a concentration of 5–10% by volume to the fermenter. The slower growing the organism, the larger the volume of inoculum used to avoid having long fermentation times (costs) in the production vessel. Because industrial fermenters tend to be quite large, inoculum preparation from agar slants often requires several fermentation steps: shake flasks, seed fermenter and secondary (or tertiary) seed fermentation. In some instances quantities of spores for inoculation produced in a seed stage are blown directly into the larger scale vessel with the ingoing air.

Following inoculation the growth of the microorganism follows the typical pattern illustrated in Figure 9. Inoculation of cells into the fermenter often results in a period where there is no increase in cell number: this period is known as the "lag phase". The length of the lag phase is related to the growth history of the inoculum, the composition of the medium and the size of the inoculum. The composition of the media used in seed and production vessel should be identical to avoid or eliminate excessive lag. Additionally, as pointed out earlier, rapidly growing cells (late exponential growth phase) should be used for inoculation and the volume of the inoculum should be such that possible osmotic shock effects on dilution in the larger vessel are minimal. The existence of a lag phase should not be taken to mean lack of metabolic activity in the cells; in fact, the lag phase is preparatory to rapid exponential growth and is essentially an adaptation period. Nevertheless, the lag phase is unproductive with respect to fermentation time in the production vessel and fermentation optimization aims at reducing or bypassing the lag. The lag phase is followed by exponential growth during which the cell number (or mass) increases exponentially with time. The *cell mass* and *cell number* growth rates are not necessarily equal.

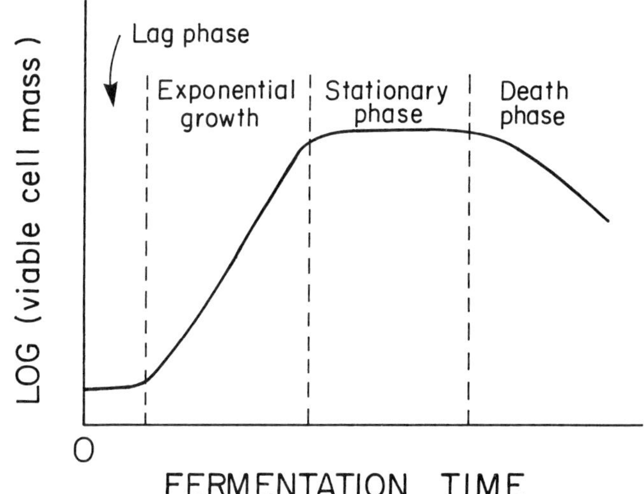

Figure-9. Typical progression of microbial growth.

Increase in cell mass (X) during exponential growth often follows the equation

$$\frac{dX}{dt} = \mu X - k_d X \qquad (18)$$

where μ is the specific growth rate and k_d the specific death rate. During exponential growth $\mu \gg k_d$ and eq. (18) reduces to

$$\frac{dX}{dt} = \mu X \qquad (19)$$

For a cell mass concentration X_o at the beginning of exponential growth (X_o usually equals inoculum concentration in the fermenter) and taking the time at which exponential growth commences as zero, eq. (19) can be integrated to yield.

$$\ln \frac{X}{X_o} = \mu t \qquad (20)$$

Hence, a biomass doubling time t_d can be shown to be

$$t_d = \frac{\ln 2}{\mu} \qquad (21)$$

Similarly, a cell number doubling time or mean generation time t_g is given by

$$t_g = \frac{\ln 2}{\mu_N} \qquad (22)$$

where μ_N is the specific cell number growth rate.

In bacteria, where cell division leads to two identical cells, μ_N and μ will be the same. For yeasts, moulds, plant cells and other organisms μ_N and μ are not always equal. The specific growth rate is characteristic of the microorganism and is a function of growth environment including temperature, pH, medium composition and dissolved oxygen levels. Some typical doubling times for different classes of microorganisms are given in Table 1. Exponential growth is followed by a stationary phase during which the growth and death rates are equal. Exhaustion of a growth-limiting nutrient in the medium or accumulation of toxic material are possible causes of onset of the stationary phase. Eventually the culture enters a death phase in which cell lysis or some other mechanism of loss of cell viability overtakes growth.

Table 1
Typical Doubling Times of Some Industrially Important Classes of Microorganisms

	t_d (minutes)
Bacteria	45
Yeasts	90
Moulds	160
Protozoa	360
Mammalian hybridoma	630–1260
Plant cells	3600–6600

Effect of temperature on growth

Depending on the optimum temperature for growth, microorganisms are classified as *psychrophiles, mesophiles* and *thermophiles*. Typical optimum growth temperature for these is given in Table 2. Actually, there is a range of temperatures near the values given in Table 2 over which these classes of organism grow; the exact optimum growth temperature depends on the microbial species and other growth conditions. The efficiency of conversion of the carbon source to cell mass is temperature dependent and declines with temperature. Maximum growth yield is obtained at temperatures lower than those for maximum growth rate. Furthermore, temperature optima for growth and product formation are not necessarily the same.

Table 2
Typical Optimum Temperature for Growth

	°C
Psychrophiles	~15
Mesophiles	~37
Thermophiles	~55

Substrate concentration effects on growth

The effect on growth of the concentration of a growth-limiting substrate, such as a carbon source for example, often follows the behaviour shown in Figure 10. The specific growth rate μ increases with substrate concentration until it is no longer growth limiting. The curve in Figure 10 is described by the Monod equation

$$\mu = \mu_m \frac{S}{K_S + S} \tag{23}$$

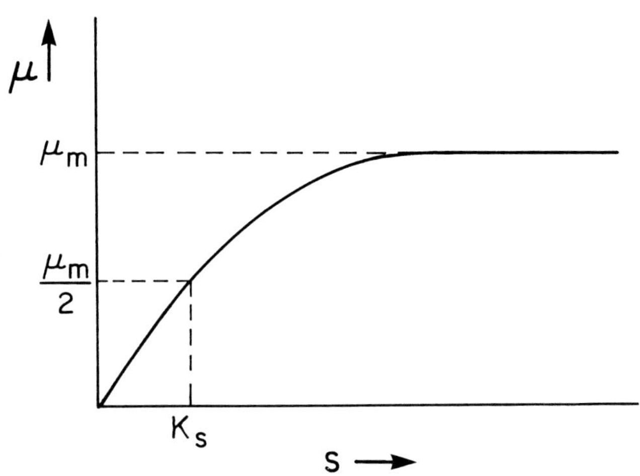

Figure 10. Effect of substrate concentration on specific growth rate. K_S is the substrate concentration at half μ_m.

where μ_m is the maximum specific growth rate and K_S is the saturation constant. Numerically, K_S is the substrate concentration corresponding to $\mu_m/2$. Thus, growth on a given substrate may be described by two constants: μ_m and K_S. However, at high substrate concentrations inhibition of growth due to substrate may be encountered. High substrate concentrations may adversely affect product formation in many fermentations.

Consideration of the relationship between cell growth and product formation is essential to the successful conduct of a fermentation. Two simple, extreme possibilities are growth-associated product formation (Figure 11(a)), in which case the product formation results from primary energy metabolism, and *nongrowth associated* production where product concentration is proportional to the quantity of biomass but not to growth rate (Figure 11(b)).

Growth Media

Careful formulation of growth and production medium is a prerequisite of successful fermentation. Microbial nutritional and environmental needs have to be met as well as several technico-economic constraints. Medium development aims to maximize product yield and concentration at minimum medium cost. Although traditional emphasis is on the fermentation step, the choice of medium affects downstream and upstream (pretreatment) activities and medium design should be carried out in an overall process context. The use

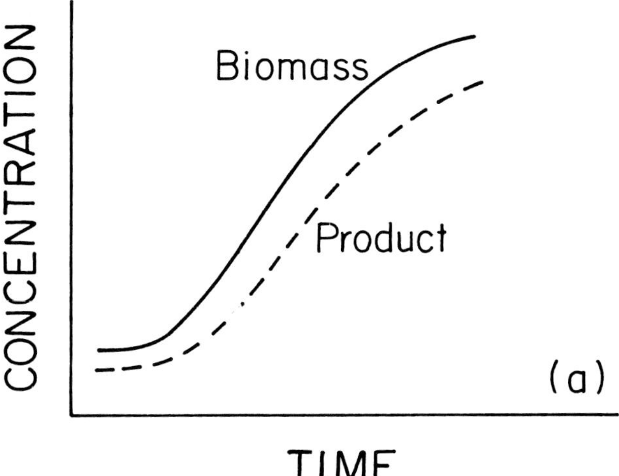

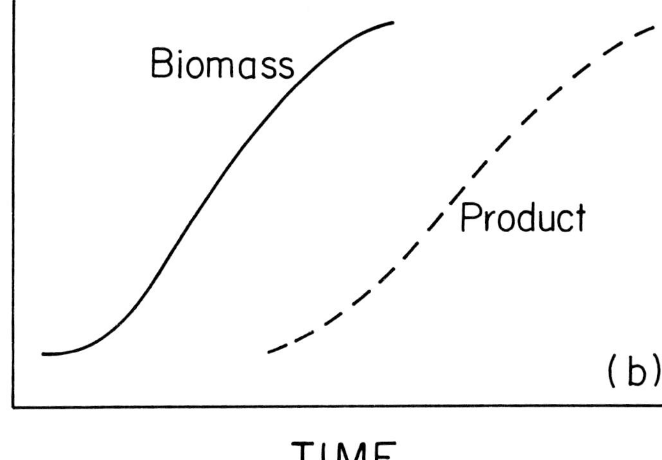

Figure 11. Relationship between growth and product formation: (a) growth associated product formation; (b) non-growth associated production.

of a purer carbon source such as glucose compared, say, with molasses may reduce purification problems and simplify pollution control and waste treatment.

The medium must provide sufficient carbon, nitrogen, minerals and other nutrients to yield the required amount of cell mass and product. Minimum requirements are estimated from the stoichiometry of growth and product formation. In general,

$$\text{C-source} + \text{N-source} + \text{minerals} + \underset{\text{(vitamins, hormones)}}{\text{specific nutrients}} + O_2 \rightarrow \text{cell mass} + \text{product} + CO_2 + H_2O \qquad (24)$$

Most nutrients are supplied at levels well above the minimal needs. Other considerations relating to fermentation feedstocks have been examined in Chapter 14.

Figure 12. Oxygen transport path from the gas bubble to the microorganism.

BIOREACTORS

Fundamentals of Mass and Heat Transfer

Transport of mass and heat are encountered not only in bioreactors but also in most other processing operations. Heat sterilization of fermenters and temperature control during a fermentation are both dependent on heat transfer phenomena. Similarly, the transfer of oxygen from a gas phase into a liquid and within the liquid to the biocatalytic particle are problems of mass transfer.

Gas-Liquid Mass Transfer

The transfer of oxygen from the gas-phase to the microorganism suspended in the gas-liquid dispersion takes place along a certain pathway. The most general transport route is depicted in Figure 12 which shows that eight resistances to oxygen transfer can exist:

1. in a gas-film inside the bubble;
2. at the gas-liquid interface;
3. in a liquid film at the gas-liquid interface;
4. in the bulk liquid;
5. in a liquid film surrounding the cell;
6. at the cell-liquid interface;
7. the internal cell resistance; and
8. the resistance at the sites of biochemical reaction.

Not all these resistances are significant. Thus, in practice bioreactors operate at such levels of turbulence in the fluids that convective transport dominates in the body of the liquid and hence the associated resistance (*i.e.* resistance 4 in Figure 12) can be ignored. Similarly, for single cells or dispersed mycelia the resistance due to the liquid film on the surface of the cell (*i.e.* resistance 5 in Figure 12) may be neglected. This is so in spite of the fact that the density differences between the microbial cells and the suspending fluid are very small and, consequently, there may be a stagnant liquid film surrounding the microbe. The minute dimensions of a microbial cell and its large surface area are the reasons for a negligible cell-liquid film resistance. The cell-liquid interfacial resistance and the resistance at the reaction sites (resistances 6 and 8, respectively, in Figure 12) can both be disregarded because of the active oxygen transport through the cell membrane as well as the rapid rates of biochemical reactions. An intracellular resistance (*i.e.* resistance 7 in Figure 12) can also be discounted since the enzymes for terminal respiration are located in the cell membranes rather than in the protoplasm, and again because of the small size of microbial cells. This eliminates all the transport resistances except those around the gas-liquid interface. The oxygen transport problem is thereby reduced to that of the gas-liquid interfacial mass transfer.

The mass transfer models

The region in the vicinity of the gas-liquid interface may be visualized as consisting of adjacent, stagnant, gas and liquid films of some finite thickness as depicted in Figure 13. According to this two-film model, the resistance to transfer in each phase is localized in the thin films close to the interface. The interface itself is assumed to offer no resistance to mass transfer; the interfacial concentrations are therefore determined by the equilibrium relationship. Mass transfer through the stagnant films is assumed to be solely by molecular diffusion and thus at steady state linear concentration profiles exist in the films (Figure 13). For this situation the mass flux (J_{O_2}) of the diffusing species is related to the concentration gradient (ΔC) in the film and to the film thickness (δ) in accordance with Fick's first law:

$$J_{O_2} = \frac{D}{\delta} \Delta C \tag{25}$$

where D is the molecular diffusivity of oxygen in the film. The ratio D/δ is known as the "mass transfer coefficient", k. Equation (25) may be written for each of the two films.

$$J_{O_2} = k_G (C_G - C_{Gi}) \tag{26}$$

$$= k_L (C_{Li} - C_L) \tag{27}$$

where k_G and k_L are the gas and the liquid mass transfer coefficients, respectively. Since the interfacial concentrations are in equilibrium, the flux may be expressed in terms of the overall concentration driving force as follows:

$$J_{O_2} = K_L (C^* - C_L) \tag{28}$$

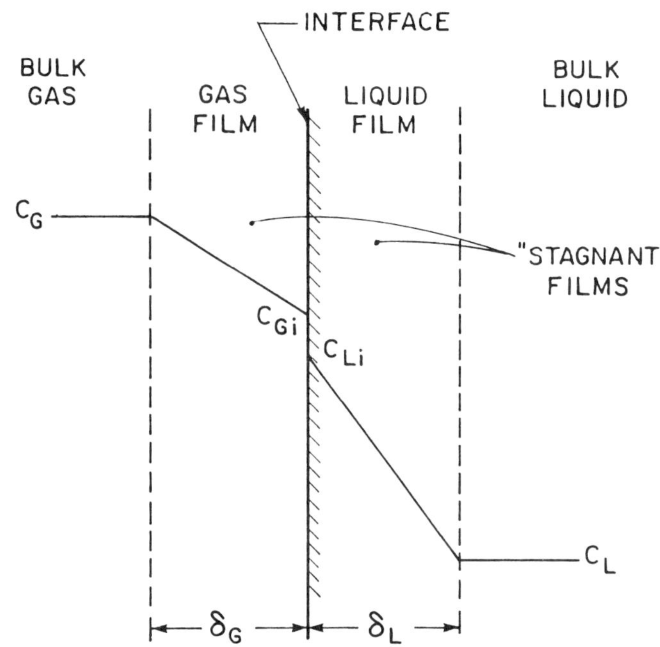

Figure 13. Oxygen concentration profile in the gas-liquid interfacial region.

where K_L is the overall mass transfer coefficient based on liquid film. C^* is the equilibrium concentration in the liquid, which, for a sparingly soluble gas such as oxygen, is related to C_G by the equilibrium relationship known as Henry's law:

$$C_G = \overline{H} C^* \tag{29}$$

where $\overline{H}$ is the Henry's law constant.

From equations (26), (27), and (28), and the knowledge that $C_{Li} = \overline{H} C_{Gi}$, it can be shown that

$$\frac{1}{K_L} = \frac{1}{k_L} + \frac{1}{\overline{H} k_G} \tag{30}$$

For sparingly soluble gases, such as oxygen, $\overline{H}$ is very much larger than unity. Moreover, k_G is typically considerably larger than k_L because the gas phase diffusivities are vastly greater than those in the liquids (cf. $D_{oxygen/air} = 10^4 D_{oxygen/water}$ at 20°C), and at the same time, the gas-phase film thicknesses are smaller than those of the liquid films. Under these circumstances the second term on the right hand side of equation (30) becomes negligible and the equation reduces to

$$\frac{1}{K_L} \approx \frac{1}{k_L} \tag{31}$$

This implies that essentially all the resistance to interfacial mass transfer of a sparingly soluble gas lies in the liquid film at the interface. In other words, the mass transfer is liquid film controlled.

For gas-liquid dispersions, the assumption of the two-film theory that turbulence disappears at the interface is probably valid only for the case when rigid interfaced bubbles form. In other instances the film may not be quite stagnant. Another limitation of this theory is that the mass transfer rate is presumed to be constant with time, which follows from Fick's first law. In transfer processes of practical interest, however, the contact between phases must at least partly involve a transient process.

Other models of mass transfer which are perhaps more appropriate for mobile interfaced dispersions and discontinuous contact between phases include the *penetration theory* of Higbie, the *surface renewal* or the *penetration-surface renewal* theory and the more general film penetration model. A masterly review of these is available elsewhere.[1] All these models relate the transport flux to a concentration difference driving force and a mass transfer coefficient expressed for the liquid, variously, as

$$k_L = \frac{D_L}{\delta_L} \quad \text{(two-film theory)} \qquad (32)$$

$$k_L = \sqrt{\frac{4\, D_L}{\pi\, t_e}} \quad \text{(penetration theory)} \qquad (33)$$

$$k_L = \sqrt{D_L\, r_s} \quad \text{(surface renewal)} \qquad (34)$$

Using the boundary layer theory with developed laminar velocity profiles, a separate analysis can be deployed to show that the laminar film mass transfer coefficient for particles with rigid, non-slip interfaces should be proportional to $D_L^{2/3}$. Because bubbles sometimes behave as rigid particles while sometimes they do not, the analysis of mass transfer and hydrodynamics becomes quite complex.

In a bioreactor the nature of the fluid and the operating temperature more or less fix the diffusivity of oxygen (D_L). Any improvement in k_L may then be achieved only by changes in the liquid film thickness, the exposure time and/or the surface renewal rate. All these are functions of fluid hydrodynamics in the reactor. Unfortunately, direct calculation of k_L using eqs. (32) through (34) is practically impossible because the film thicknesses, the exposure times and the surface renewal rates cannot be quantified in any realistic bioreactor configuration.

In summary, the mass transfer rate in the absence of bulk flow is directly proportional to the concentration difference driving force, and the oxygen mass flux may be expressed as:

$$J_{o_2} = k_L\,(C^* - C_L) \qquad (35)$$

Generally, k_L is proportional to D_L^m where m may take the value 1/2, 2/3, or 1, depending on the mechanism of mass transfer which predominates under given physical and hydrodynamic conditions.

Since the transfer rate and the flux are related by

$$a_L J_{o_2} = \frac{d\,C_L}{dt} \qquad (36)$$

in terms of the rate of oxygen mass transfer, eq. (36) may be rewritten as

$$\frac{d\,C_L}{dt} = k_L\, a_L\,(C^* - C_L) \qquad (37)$$

where a_L is the interfacial area per unit liquid volume, C^* is the saturation (*i.e.*, the equilibrium concentration) value of oxygen in the liquid in contact with air or pure oxygen and C_L is the oxygen concentration in the liquid at any time t.

For the design of bioreactors with predictable oxygen transfer performances and for the evaluation of existing oxygen transfer equipment, a knowledge of the product k_La_L is essential. The influences of various design (*i.e.* bioreactor type and geometry), system (*i.e.* fluid properties) and operation (*i.e.* liquid and gas velocities) variables on k_La_L must be evaluated so that design and operation are carried out to optimize k_La_L. This requires maximization of mass transfer with minimum total power input because, in general, the higher the biomass concentration which the reactor can support the higher is the reactor productivity. Improvement of k_La_L is not the only way of achieving better performance, however, and other alternatives exist for the enhancement of oxygen mass transfer in a bioreactor. For a fixed k_La_L, the oxygen transfer driving force, $(C^* - C_L)$, may be increased. In practice this may be done by increasing C^*; decreasing C_L is impractical since C_L must always be greater than or equal to the critical oxygen level for the given microbial species. The C^* can be increased either by increasing the gas phase mole fraction of oxygen (*e.g.* by the use of pure oxygen) or by increasing the total pressure (*i.e.* reducing the molal volume in the gas phase). Both these possibilities can be difficult to implement. The use of pure oxygen implies additional costs especially since only a small fraction of it is actually transferred to the liquid while increasing the total pressure may not only raise the capital and operation costs of a bioreactor but may not be feasible because of the increased solubility of carbon dioxide produced during the fermentation. The possibility of carbon dioxide-associated toxicity effects has to be considered. Very often the prediction and improvement of oxygen transfer is equivalent to the prediction and enhancement of k_La_L.

The prediction of k_La_L for various bioreactor types is treated in sections on those reactors. Here only a brief treatment of k_La_L measurement in actual fermentations is given.

Two relatively simple techniques are commonly employed in k_La_L measurements in bioreactors:

Gassing-in technique developed by Humphrey and coworkers is based on dynamic dissolved oxygen measurements using a dissolved oxygen probe. The oxygen concentration-time relationship in the bioreactor is

$$\frac{d\,C_L}{dt} = \underbrace{k_L a_L\,(C^* - C_L)}_{\text{mass transfer term}} - \underbrace{q_{O_2}\,X}_{\text{consumption term}} \qquad (38)$$

where q_{O_2} and X are the specific oxygen consumption rate (O_2/kg cells s) and cell concentration (kg cell/m^3) respectively. Interruption of the air supply to the reactor eliminates the mass transfer term (eq. 38) and the dissolved oxygen concentration declines linearly with time (Figure 14) due to oxygen consumption by the biomass. The slope of the C_L vs. t plot yields q_{O_2} X (Figure 14). The air supply is turned on before the dissolved oxygen concentration has dropped to the critical dissolved oxygen level for the microbial species so that the fermentation is not damaged. The overall volumetric mass transfer coefficient is determined using the C_L vs. t plot beyond the point of resumption of oxygen supply. Thus eq. (38) is rearranged to

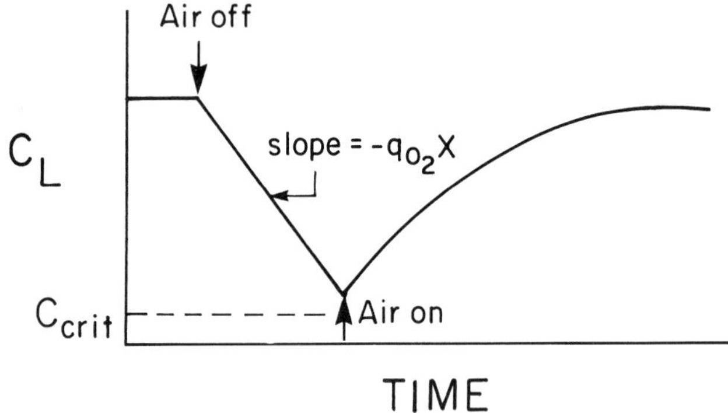

Figure 14. The dissolved oxygen concentration (C_L) vs. time.

$$C_L = C^* - \frac{1}{k_L\,a_L}\left(q_{O_2}\,X + \frac{d\,C_L}{dt}\right) \qquad (39)$$

and $k_L a_L$ is obtained from the slope of a plot of C_L vs. $\left(q_{O_2}\,X + \frac{d\,C_L}{dt}\right)$ (Figure 15). Rapid-response dissolved oxygen probes should be used to minimize the effect of electrode delay on the measurements.

Gas-phase oxygen balance technique depends on measurements of mass flow of aeration gas into and out of the fermenter. The mass fraction of oxygen in the inlet and outlet gas streams must also be determined (mass spectrometer, paramagnetic oxygen analyzer) as well as the steady state dissolved oxygen concentration (dissolved oxygen electrode). The $k_L a_L$ is obtained from the oxygen balance

$$M\,(\dot{x}_o - \dot{x}_i) = V_L\,k_L\,a_L\,(C^* - C_L) = V_L\,q_{O_2}\,X \quad (40)$$

where V_L is the broth volume, M the mass flow of gas and $\dot{x}$ is the mass fraction of oxygen in gas (o = outlet, i = inlet).

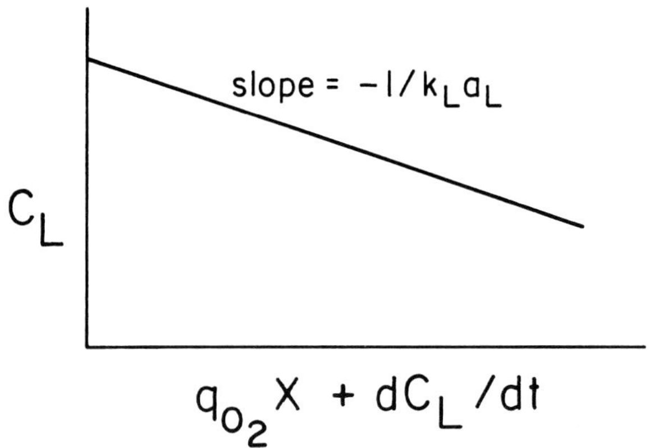

Figure 15. Calculation of $k_L a_L$.

Equation (40) assumes no evaporation and it does not correct for carbon dioxide production; however, the necessary corrections can be easily incorporated. With the steady-state method any possibility of affecting the fermentation by interruption of air supply is circumvented.

Heat Transfer

Most fermentations require careful temperature control. Heat generated by agitation and aeration power input and that generated by the fermentation itself needs to be estimated for design of sufficient cooling capacity. Sterilization operations also require knowledge of heat transfer and necessitate the provision of sufficient heating capability.

Typical fermentation heat generation for bacterial, fungal and yeast fermentations is of the order of 3–15 kW m^{-3}. The exact amount depends on the nature of the substrate and its rate of oxidation. A highly reduced substrate such as a hydrocarbon would release more heat per mole substrate on complete oxidation than a relatively less reduced carbohydrate. Methods for estimating the heat evolution have been discussed in Bailey and Ollis.[2]

Between 1 and 15 kW m^{-3} of heat input occurs due to agitation in stirred tank fermenters. In bubble columns and airlifts the contribution of heat due to agitation is usually less than 5 kW m^{-3}. Once the heat transfer rate (which equals the heat evolution rate *plus* the heat generation due to agitation at steady state) is established, the heat transfer area needed to obtain this rate is calculated from:

$$Q_H = U_H A_H\,\Delta T \qquad (41)$$

where A_H is the transfer area and ΔT is the mean temperature difference driving force. U_H, the overall heat transfer coefficient, is the sum of the resistances to heat transfer due to the fluid films on either side of the heating or cooling surface, fouling (corrosion, protein burn on) resistances on either side, and the resistance due to the metal wall through which the heat must pass. Hence,

$$\frac{1}{U_H} = \frac{1}{h_i} + \frac{1}{h_{if}} + \frac{1}{h_m} + \frac{1}{h_{of}} + \frac{1}{h_o} \quad (42)$$

where h's are the individual heat transfer coefficients and the subscripts, i, f, m and o refer to heating/cooling fluid film, fouling, metal wall, and the film between the fermentation broth and heating and cooling surface, respectively. Empirical correlations and methods of calculation for h_i, h_{if} and h_m abound in chemical engineering texts and works on heat transfer; h_{of}, the fouling coefficient between the broth and the reactor wall, is essentially constant and typical data given in handbooks should apply. The calculation of h_o, the film coefficient between the fluid and the heating/cooling surface, is one of the objects of research on bioreactors. Note that equation (42) applies to flat surfaces and it should be corrected for heat transfer through curved walls, particularly those which are thick.

For airlift vessels with very low rates of fluid circulation the heat transfer data obtained in batch bubble columns may apply. For air-water in industrial batch bubble columns (diameters > 0.45 m) Fair *et al.*[3] found the film coefficient h_o to increase with superficial gas velocity in the following way:

$$h_o = 8.85\ U_G^{0.22} \quad (43)$$

$$(\text{kW m}^{-2\circ}\text{C}^{-1})\ (\text{m s}^{-1})$$

indicating that the film coefficient was independent of column diameter. A correlation suitable for a greater range of fluids in bubble columns was provided by Deckwer[4] and took the form

$$\frac{h_o}{\rho_L C_p U_G} = 0.1 \left[\frac{U_G^3 \rho_L}{\mu_L g} \left(\frac{\mu_L C_p}{k_T} \right)^2 \right]^{-1/4} \quad (44)$$

which also predicted an increase in the film coefficient with gas velocity raised to a power of 0.25. In eq. (44) k_T and C_p are, respectively, the thermal conductivity and the specific heat capacity of the liquid in the reactor. For large fermenters the vessel surface area may be insufficient to handle the required heat transfer needs and additional internal heating surface in the form of baffles or coils becomes necessary.

It has been suggested that the heat transfer coefficient for non-Newtonian media in bubble columns may be calculated by equations for Newtonian fluids by using apparent viscosity in place of Newtonian viscosity. However, the calculation of apparent viscosities is not straightforward.

Compared to bubble columns, heat transfer coefficients in airlift reactors are more than two-fold higher due to higher liquid velocity in the latter. Heat transfer in airlift devices has been treated elsewhere.[5]

The presence of mycelial solids in an otherwise water-like broth may enhance or reduce heat transfer depending on the positioning of the heat exchange surface in the reactor.

For stirred tank reactors the heat transfer correlations developed in single phase liquid systems may be used for calculation of fluid/wall heat transfer coefficient in gas-liquid dispersions.

For heat exchange in jacketed straight tubes as used, for example, in continuous sterilizers the tube-side film coefficient can be satisfactorily estimated via the Seider and Tate equation

$$\frac{h_o d}{k_T} = 0.027 \left(\frac{\rho_L U_L d}{\mu_k} \right)^{0.8} \left(\frac{C_p \mu_L}{k_T} \right)^{1/3} \left(\frac{\mu_L}{\mu_{LW}} \right)^{0.14} \quad (45)$$

where μ_L and μ_{LW} are the fluid viscosity at bulk fluid and wall temperatures, respectively.

Stirred Tank Bioreactor

At present, of the aerated bioreactors used in industry about 93% (by value of product) are of the stirred tank variety. The standard stirred tank configuration shown in Figure 16 has been extensively investigated. The liquid height in the standard design equals the tank diameter and agitation is provided by a 6-bladed Rushton disc turbine of 1/3 the tank diameter located one impeller diameter from the base of the tank. Four equally spaced baffles ($d_T/12$) prevent vortexing and swirling. Gas (air or oxygen) is sparged via a sparger (often a single hole) placed below the impeller at the axis of the vessel. The turbine disc prevents channelling of gas up the impeller shaft. In many applications the standard stirred vessel makes an effective gas-liquid mass transfer and mixing device.

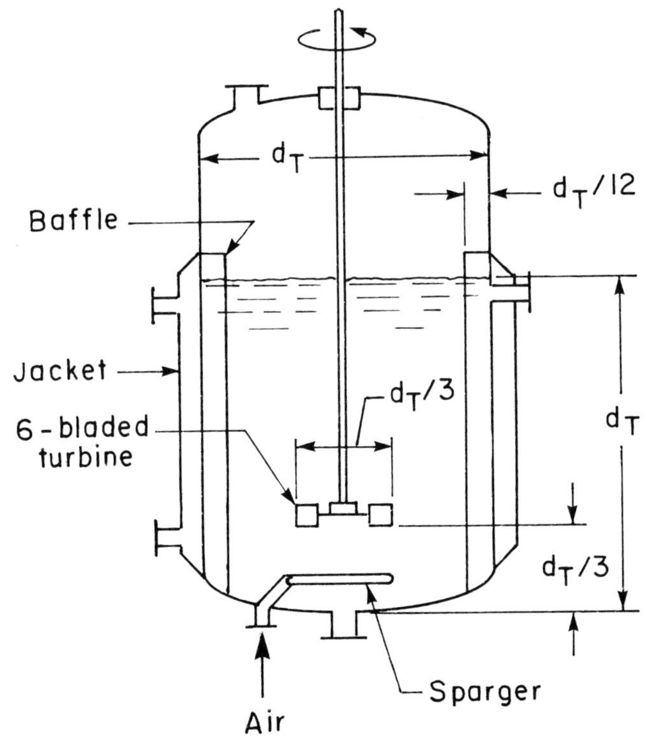

Figure 16. Standard stirred tank.

The mechanical power requirements of ungassed stirred tanks may be estimated using Power number (Po) vs. impeller Reynolds (Re_i) number plots, examples of which are shown in Figure 17. The Power number and the impeller Reynolds number are defined, respectively, as

$$Po = \frac{P}{\rho_L \overline{N}^3 D_i^5} \quad (46)$$

and

$$Re_i = \frac{\rho_L \overline{N} D_i^2}{\mu_L} \quad (47)$$

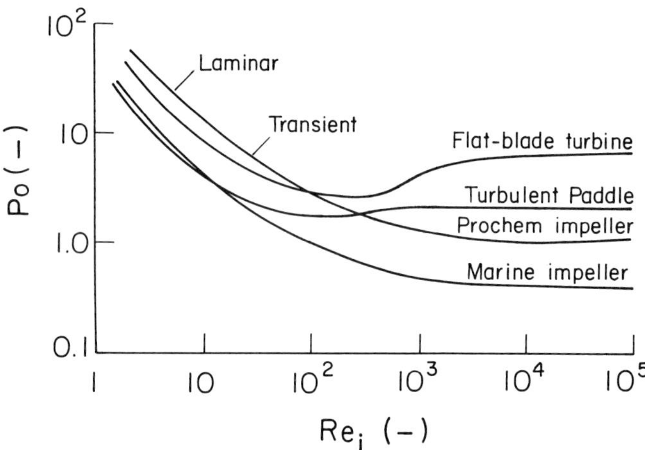

Figure 17. Power number vs. impeller Reynolds number for various impellers.

The exact nature of $Po - Re_i$ plots is dependent on impeller type and on the presence or absence of baffles. The power absorption by liquids in unbaffled tanks in turbulent flow ($Re_i > 10^2$) is significantly less than in baffled tanks. In laminar flow ($Re_i \leq 10$) the power number is inversely dependent on Re_i:

$$Po \propto Re_i^{-1} \quad (48)$$

with the constant of proportionality dependent to some degree on the type of impeller. Under developed turbulent flow conditions ($Re_i > 10^4$) the power number becomes independent of the impeller Reynolds number, but depends on the impeller type. Because most applications are likely to involve highly turbulent reactors, a compilation of constant Power numbers for various geometries is provided in Table 3. The values of the proportionality constant (eq. 48) are given in Table 4.

Introduction of gas into the mixing vessel always leads to a reduction in the power absorption relative to the ungassed situation. Once an estimate of ungassed power (P) is available, the power input in the presence of gas may be calculated using the Michel-Miller equation

Table 3
Turbulent Power Numbers in Stirred Vessels

Geometry (Baffled tank)	Po (−)
Propeller (square pitch, 3-blades)	0.32
Turbine (6-bladed)	6.30
Turbine (6-curved blades)	4.80
Flat paddle (2-blades)	1.70
Prochem impeller (5-blades, $D_i = d_T/2$)	1.0

$$P_G = 0.72 \left(\frac{P^2 \overline{N} D_i^3}{Q^{0.56}}\right)^{0.45} \quad (49)$$

This equation provides a good approximation in many applications but it should not be used for extreme values of gas volume flow (Q). Other design parameters such as the overall gas holdup (ε) and the volumetric mass transfer coefficient ($k_L a_L$) can be calculated on the basis of available correlations which have been summarized by Mann.[6] Some useful correlations are

$$\varepsilon = 0.52 \left(\frac{Q}{\overline{N} D_i^3}\right)^{0.5} \left(\frac{\rho_L \overline{N}^2 D_i^3}{\sigma}\right)^{0.65} \left(\frac{D_i}{d_T}\right)^{1.4} \quad (50)$$

and

$$k_L a_L = 1 \times 10^{-3} \frac{d_T}{V_L} P_G^{0.58} U_G^{0.75} \quad (51)$$

Numerous other equations are available which may be more suitable for specific situations.

Table 4
The Values of c in $Po = c\, Re_i^{-1}$ for Various Impellers

Impeller	c (−)
6-Bladed standard turbine (unbaffled tank)	~100
Helical ribbon (unbaffled tank)	~380
Propeller (3-bladed, square pitch, baffled tank (4-baffles))	~40

Non-Newtonian media

For non-Newtonian media the impeller Reynolds number is based on the apparent viscosity of the fluid:

$$Re_i = \frac{\rho_L \overline{N} D_i^2}{\mu_{ap}} \quad (52)$$

For the often observed power law behaviour the apparent viscosity is given by

$$\mu_{ap} = K\,\dot{\gamma}^{n-1} \qquad (53)$$

while the average shear rate ($\dot{\gamma}$) in the stirred vessel is often approximated by the equation

$$\dot{\gamma} = k_i\,\overline{N} \qquad (54)$$

Substitution of equations (53) and (54) in equation (52) leads to a modified Reynolds number:

$$Re_i = \frac{\rho_L\,\overline{N}^{2-n}\,D_i^2}{K\,k_i^{n-1}} \qquad (55)$$

The Power number-Reynolds number behaviour for non-Newtonian media is similar to that described for the Newtonian fluids. The constant k_i in eq. (54) is dependent on the system geometry and to some extent on the rheology of non-Newtonian media. The dependence of k_i on the flow index (n) of non-Newtonian fluids has been reported to be

$$k_i = K'\left(\frac{4n}{3n+1}\right)^{\frac{n}{n-1}} \qquad (56)$$

where K′ is impeller-tank geometry dependent. Some typical values of k_i are given in Table 5.

Table 5
Values of k_i (eq. 54) for Various Impellers

Impeller	k_i (−)
6-Bladed turbine	11−13
Paddles	10−13
Propeller	~10
Helical ribbon	~30

Quite distinct from an average shear rate in the tank, a maximum shear rate on the impeller also exists. Considerations of maximum shear to which a fermentation culture may be exposed without harm are particularly important for fragile biocatalysts which also tend to have large particle sizes (animal cells, plant cells, filamentous organisms). The maximum shear rate on a Rushton turbine in Newtonian media has recently been expressed as

$$\dot{\gamma} = 3.3\,\overline{N}^{1.5}\left(\frac{D_i^2\,\rho_L}{\mu_L}\right)^{1/2} \qquad (57)$$

which applies for Re_i = 100 to 29,000.

Other Stirred Tank Configurations

The "standard" configuration of stirred tanks is not the commonly used geometry in bioreactor applications; instead tanks with height-to-diameter ratios of 3:1 and 4:1 are more common because they permit better utilization of the expensive sterile air. These bioreactors employ multiple impellers, usually Rushton turbines. With some modifications the design methods developed for the standard reactor can be usefully employed for other geometric configurations. Multiple impellers are located on a single shaft with a minimum distance of one impeller diameter between impellers. Two different types of impellers may be used on the same shaft and are in fact beneficial in some cases. For example, a combination of radial flow Rushton turbines and axial flow propellers is sometimes used to provide improved mixing in vessels with $H/d_T > 1$. Recent investigations into other impeller designs have shown that impellers such as Prochem hydrofoils and InterMIG provide higher mass transfer at lower power consumption than Rushton disc turbines. Some of these newer impeller types are depicted in Figure 18. In many cases existing stirred tank bioreactors are known to have been upgraded by changing the Rushton turbine in favour of the newer impellers. The lower shear characteristics of the latter are an added advantage.

Pneumatically Agitated Bioreactors

Although traditionally in extensive use, the mechanically stirred bioreactors have several significant limitations when compared to pneumatic bioreactors which are agitated by gas injection. A comparison of pneumatic bioreactors (airlifts and bubble columns) with stirred vessels is provided in Table 6. Numerous advantages of the gas-agitated reactors have led to a clear preference for them particularly in the newer biotechnology applications involving fragile material. The following sections examine some of the design considerations for bubble column and airlift bioreactors.

Bubble Columns and Modified Bubble Columns

Bubble columns are among the simplest of gas-slurry bioreactors. A gas-sparged pool of liquid with height-to-diameter ratio well above unity constitutes a bubble column (Figure 19). Several modifications to the basic design are possible, however, and Figure 19 illustrates some possible configurations.

The energy input to the fluid in the bubble column arises predominantly from isothermal expansion of the injected gas and depends on the superficial gas velocity

$$\frac{P_G}{V_L} = \rho_L\,g\,U_G \qquad (58)$$

The main reactor performance characteristics — gas holdup (ε), specific gas-liquid interfacial area (a_L), overall volumetric mass transfer coefficient (k_La_L), mixing, axial dispersion (E_L) and heat transfer — are controlled by gas flow and hence also by the energy input. A wide range of gas velocities may be used; however, the maximum velocity should be less than the

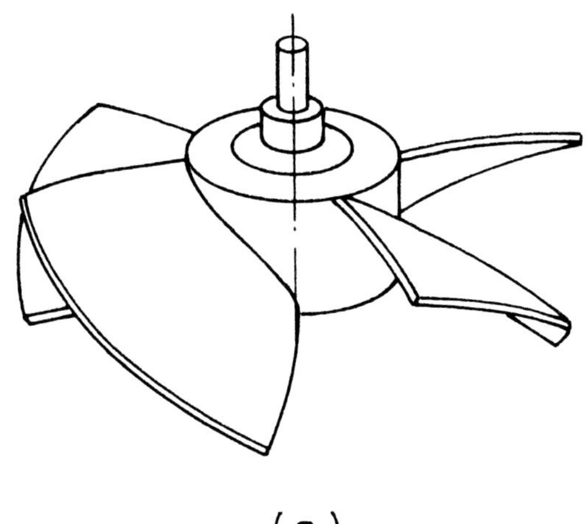

(b)
Hydrofoil impeller

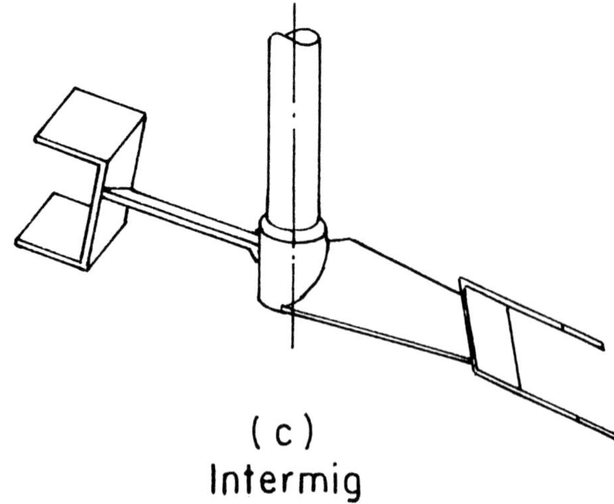

Figure 18. Some newer impellers.

Table 6
A Comparison of Mechanically and Pneumatically Agitated Bioreactors

Mechanical Agitation (Stirred Tank)	Pneumatic Agitation (Airlifts, Bubble Columns)
1. Mechanically complex (stirrers, shaft, seals, bearings)	Mechanically simple and robust
2. Often high shear	Gentle, low shear levels (suitable for tissue culture, plant cells, fragile genetically engineered microorganisms)
3. Gas throughput limited by impeller flooding	High gas throughputs possible (particularly in airlift devices)
4. Difficult to clean due to mechanical complexity; greater possibility of contamination over extended operation	Easy to clean. Extended asceptic operation possible (useful in continuous operation)
5. Turbulence confined to impeller zone in viscous non-Newtonian media. Gas channels through the impeller zone while the rest of reactor remains stagnant	More uniform distribution of turbulence
6. Operationally flexible (controlled by impeller speed and by gas flow rate)	Limited operational flexibility. Require more careful design

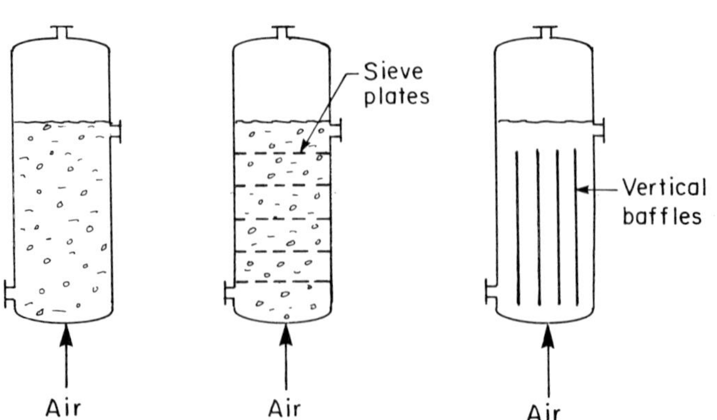

Figure 19. Bubble columns.

"blow out" (spray formation) condition. The maximum liquid velocities that may be used tend to be quite low because of the long residence times typical of bioreactors.

The hydrodynamic regime of operation influences column performance. At low gas velocities ($\lesssim 0.05\ ms^{-1}$) in water-like fluids, bubbles have spheroidal shapes and rise uniformly with no interaction. This is the *bubble flow* regime (Figure 20) which is also known as "homogeneous" or "unhindered bubble flow". As the gas velocity increases the bubble motion becomes unstable and chaotic, and the column becomes more turbulent. Larger bubbles with little definition to their shape coexist with many small bubbles. This is the *churn-turbulent* regime (Figure 20). The transition from bubbly to churn-turbulent flow is gradual and it occurs over a range of gas flow depending on the properties of the fluids and on reactor geometry. Further increase in gas flow rates leads progressively to increased bubble coalescence, slugging and annular film flow; however, these other flow regimes are generally not encountered in bioreactor applications.

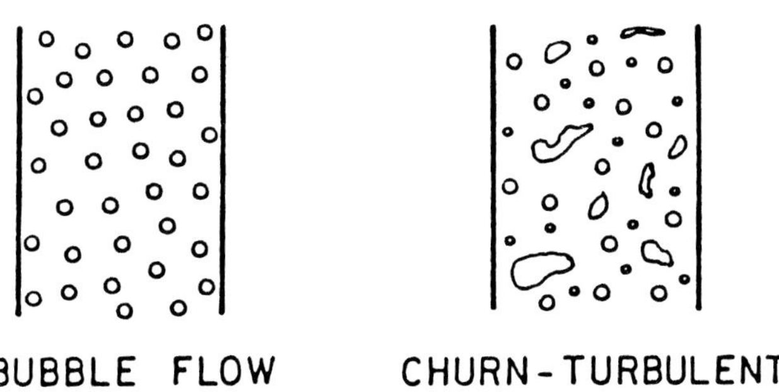

Figure 20. Bubble and churn flow regimes.

Gas holdup.

The volume fraction of gas in dispersion, or "gas holdup" (ε), is an important characteristic of bubble columns and other gas liquid reactors. By definition,

$$\varepsilon = \frac{V_G}{V_G + V_L} \tag{59}$$

The reactor must be able to accommodate the gas holdup produced under various conditions. Furthermore, the residence time of gas in liquid and hence the efficiency of utilization of gas depend on gas holdup

$$t_G = \frac{h_L\ \varepsilon}{U_G\ (1 - \varepsilon)} \tag{60}$$

For columns larger than $\sim$0.1 m diameter, gas holdup is independent of column diameter and the overall gas holdup is independent of the height of liquid (h_L). Hence, for a given U_G the gas phase residence time increases with column height. Height-to-diameter ratios of four or higher are not uncommon in bubble column bioreactors.

The specific gas-liquid interfacial area for mass transfer is controlled by a combination of gas holdup and mean bubble diameter

$$a_L = \frac{6\varepsilon}{d_B\ (1 - \varepsilon)} \tag{61}$$

where d_B is the diameter of a sphere having the same surface-to-volume ratio as the gas bubble. In practice a distribution of bubble sizes is encountered and d_B is calculated using

$$d_B = \frac{\sum_{i=1}^{N} n_i\ d_i^3}{\sum_{i=1}^{N} n_i\ d_i^2} \tag{62}$$

where n_i is the frequency of occurrence of bubbles with a diameter d_i. Bubble size and frequency distribution may be measured, for example, by electrical resistivity and other similar probes. Alternatively, a_L may be determined by one of the direct measurement techniques such as sulfite oxidation.

In bubble columns gas holdup shows the following general dependence on gas velocity

$$\varepsilon = a\ U_G^{\ b} \tag{63}$$

The parameters a and b have been found to be 2.47 and 0.97, and 0.49 and 0.46, respectively, for bubble ($U_G < 0.05\ ms^{-1}$) and churn-flow ($U_G > 0.05\ ms^{-1}$) regimes in air-water for broad ranges of bubble column geometries. Addition of inorganic salts to water enhances gas holdup by a few percent up to an ionic strength corresponding to $\sim$ 0.15 M NaCl. This effect is due to coalescence inhibition which results from electrical repulsion between like ions at the surfaces of bubbles. For any given ionic strength, the type of inorganic salt does not influence gas holdup.

Numerous other gas holdup correlations are available in the voluminous literature on bubble columns (see Reading List). One example is the correlation[7]:

$$\frac{\varepsilon}{(1 - \varepsilon)^4} = c \left(\frac{g\ d_c^2\ \rho_L}{\sigma}\right)^{1/8} \left(\frac{g\ d_c^3\ \rho_L^2}{\mu_L^2}\right)^{1/12} \left(\frac{U_G}{\sqrt{g\ d_c}}\right) \tag{64}$$

where c is either 0.20 (non-electrolytes) or 0.25 (electrolytes). Equation (64) covers column diameters d_c = 0.152 – 0.60 m and U_G = 0.004 – 0.33 ms^{-1}. It applies to Newtonian media such as water, glycerol and methanol.

In homogeneous non-Newtonian systems the following equation may be employed

$$\varepsilon = 0.207\ U_G^{0.6}\ \mu_{ap}^{-0.19} \tag{65}$$

which was developed by Godbole *et al.*[8] using aqueous carboxymethyl cellulose (CMC) solutions (n = 0.440 – 0.697; K = 7.683 – 0.095 Pa s^n). Equation (65) applies to churn-turbulent flow with U_G not exceeding 0.25 ms^{-1}. A higher coefficient of 0.255 has been reported for eq. (65) in presence of 0.8 M sodium sulfate.

The shear rate ($\dot{\gamma}$) expression commonly employed for the calculation of apparent viscosity of fluids in bubble columns (see eq. (3)) is

$$\dot{\gamma} = 5000\ U_G \quad (66)$$

which is due to Nishikawa and coworkers.[9] This expression [eq. (66)] is used for the calculation of μ_{ap} in eq. (65). However, there is a considerable degree of uncertainty on the mean shear rate in bubble columns.

According to some recent work,[10] the simple holdup equation (eq. 63) should apply to non-Newtonian media also. The parameters a and b now depend on the properties of the fluid as well as on the flow regime. The parameter b has been empirically correlated with the flow index according to

$$b = 0.564\ n^{-0.354} \quad (67)$$

Equation (67) disregards any flow regime effects, but it is based on data on a variety of fluids including fermentation broths of fungi *Chaetomium cellulolyticum* and *Neurospora sitophila*. Other gas holdup data on slurries which simulate fungal media is available elsewhere.[11,12]

Gas-liquid mass transfer

Two of the correlations for the overall volumetric mass transfer coefficient in Newtonian fluids are:

$$k_L a_D = 3.31 \left(\frac{D_L\ \varepsilon}{d_B^2}\right) \left(\frac{\mu_L}{\rho_L\ D_L}\right)^{1/3} \left(\frac{d_B\ \rho_L\ U_G}{\mu_L}\right)^{0.5} \quad (68)$$

and

$$\frac{k_L a_D d_c^2}{D_L} = 0.6 \left(\frac{\mu_L}{\rho_L\ D_L}\right)^{0.5} \left(\frac{g\ d_c^2\ \rho_L}{\sigma}\right)^{0.62} \left(\frac{g\ d_c^3\ \rho_L^2}{\mu_L^3}\right)^{0.31} \varepsilon^{1.1} \quad (69)$$

These equations were developed by Fair[13] and Akita and Yoshida[7], respectively. For air-water, a simple equation is

$$k_L a_L = 2.39 \times 10^{-4}\ (P_G/V_L)^{0.86} \quad (70)$$

which has been shown to apply up to a height-to-diameter ratio ~ 24. Notice (eqs. (68)–(70)) that the overall volumetric mass transfer coefficient may be based either on the liquid volume ($k_L a_L$) or on the volume of gas-liquid dispersion ($k_L a_D$). These two are related as follows:

$$k_L a_D = k_L a_L\ (1 - \varepsilon) \quad (71)$$

The mass transfer work on non-Newtonian media in bubble columns is less extensive. Some equations which may be useful in estimation of mass transfer performance are

$$k_L a_D = 8.35 \times 10^{-4}\ U_G^{0.44}\ \mu_{ap}^{-1.01} \quad (72)$$

due to Godbole *et al.*[8] and

$$k_L a_D = 3.15 \times 10^{-3}\ U_G^{\ 0.59}\ \mu_{ap}^{-0.84} \quad (73)$$

due to Deckwer *et al.*[14]. For additional information on non-Newtonian systems the work of Schumpe and Deckwer[15] should be consulted. Gas-slurry systems have been treated[11,16] elsewhere.

A vast amount of literature on bubble columns is available; some of the main sources are listed in the Reading List.

Airlift Bioreactors

Airlift bioreactors consist of a liquid pool divided into two distinct zones only one of which is usually sparged by gas. The different gas holdup in the gassed and ungassed zones results in different bulk densities of the fluid in these regions which causes circulation of fluid in the reactor by a gas-lift action. The part of the reactor containing the gas-liquid upflow is the "riser" and the region containing the downflowing fluid is known as the "downcomer". Figure 21 shows the schematic of an airlift reactor.

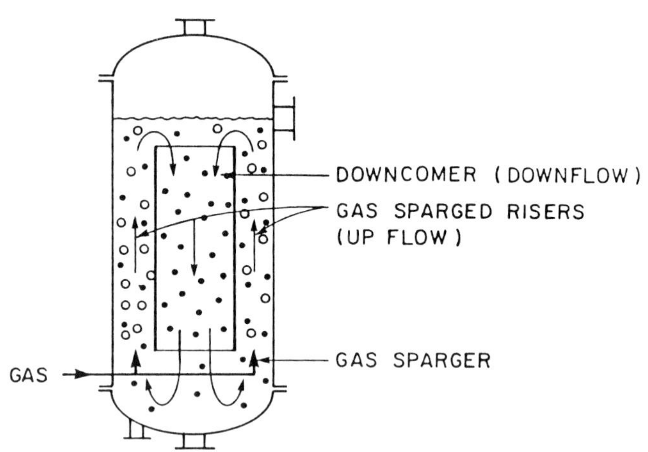

Figure 21. Schematic of an airlift reactor.

Airlift reactors have been successfully applied to almost every type of fermentation. Many examples have been cited in other works.[5,17] Recent applications include hybridoma cell culture for monoclonal antibody production on a commercial scale.

Airlift reactors are available in two basic forms: (i) the internal-loop airlifts in which the riser and the downcomer are contained in the same reactor shell, and (ii) the external- or outer-loop reactors where the riser and the downcomer are two quite separate tubes which are linked near the top and the bottom. The external- and internal-loop configurations are shown in Figure 22. Modifications to the basic airlift design have been used to produce other sub-types of airlift reactors, some of which have been discussed by Chisti and Moo-Young.[5]

Estimation of such essential airlift reactor design parameters as the overall gas holdup (ε), volumetric mass transfer coefficient ($k_L a_L$) and the magnitude of induced liquid circulation velocity using most of the available correlations is limited only to specific reactor geometries over narrow ranges of scale. Only recently did a more general airlift design procedure become available as discussed later in this section.

The induced liquid circulation is an important distinguishing characteristic of airlift reactors. In other types of bioreactors, such as the bubble columns and the stirred tanks, the general requirement of long residence times severely limits the maximum linear flow velocity through the reactors unless recycle flow is employed. In airlifts, high linear liquid velocities are attainable without recycle and these lead to improved turbulence and good mixing, heat and mass transfer. The liquid circulation in an airlift reactor originates from the difference in the bulk densities of the fluid in the riser and the downcomer. The fluid circulates along a well defined path: upflow in the riser, downflow in the downcomer. A mean circulation velocity ($\overline{U}_{LC}$) is defined as

$$\overline{U}_{LC} = \frac{x_c}{t_c} \tag{74}$$

where x_c is the circulation path length and t_c is the average time for one complete circulation. The circulatory flow is clearly revealed by injection of a tracer such as an acid pulse into the downcomer (or riser) and following the tracer flow at some downstream location. The characteristic decaying sinusoidal tracer response depicted in Figure 23 is observed: the time difference between adjacent peaks is the circulation time.

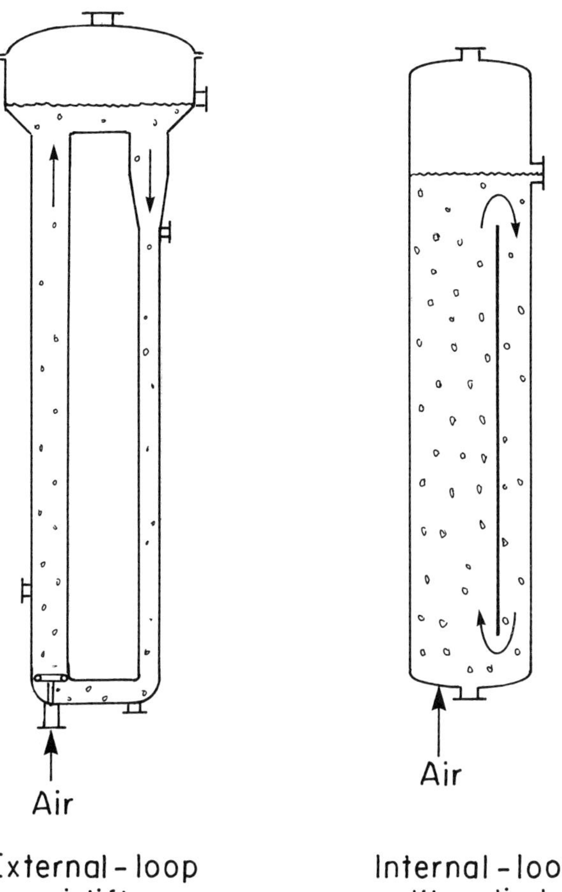

Figure 22. External- and interal-loop airlift reactors.

Unlike an overall, average, circulation velocity ($\overline{U}_{LC}$), values of a superficial velocity measured either in the downcomer (U_{Ld}) or the riser (U_{Lr}) are more meaningful. The continuity criterion leads to the following relationship between the liquid velocities in the riser and the downcomer:

$$U_{Lr}\, A_r = U_{Ld}\, A_d \tag{75}$$

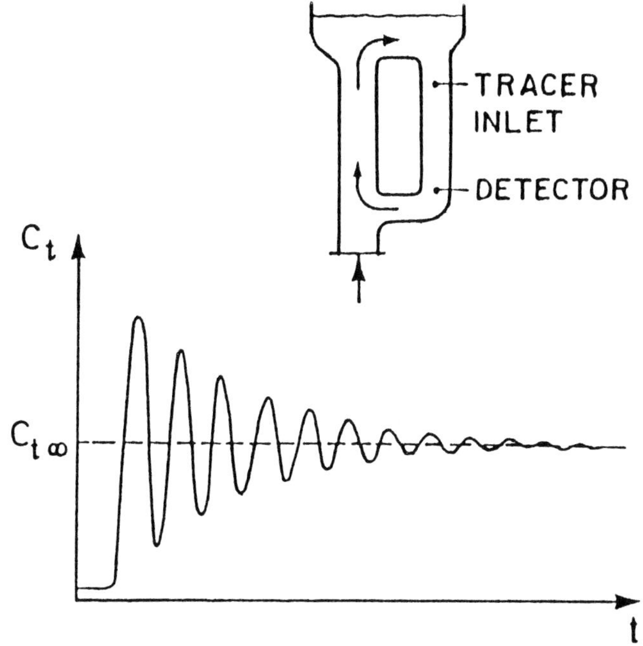

Figure 23. Tracer response in an airlift reactor.

The superficial velocity must be distinguished from the "linear liquid velocity", also known as the "interstitial velocity", because in reality the liquid flow occupies only a part of the flow channel, the rest being taken up by the gas. The interstitial velocity ($\dot{V}_L$) and the superficial velocity are related as follows:

$$\dot{V}_{Lr} = \frac{U_{Lr}}{1 - \varepsilon_r} \tag{76}$$

and

$$\dot{V}_{Ld} = \frac{U_{Ld}}{1 - \varepsilon_d} \tag{77}$$

The velocity of liquid circulation, while itself controlled by the gas holdups in the riser and the downcomer, in turn affects these holdups by either enhancing or reducing the velocity of bubble rise.

Airlift reactor design

Probably the first question faced by the designer of airlift bioreactors for a particular application would be one of choice of configuration: external-loop or the internal-loop. Table 7 compares the performances of these two distinct geometric types of airlifts; such a comparison could form the basis of a preliminary choice. Generally internal-loop reactors have better mass transfer characteristics. On the other hand, in fluids in which very high viscosities necessitate greater turbulence and shear for adequate mixing and mass transfer, the external-loops may be preferable.

An energy balance over the circulating airlift loop can be used to obtain the following equation for the superficial liquid velocity in the riser:[18]

$$U_{Lr} = \left[\frac{2g\, h_D\, (\varepsilon_r - \varepsilon_d)}{\dfrac{K_T}{(1-\varepsilon_r)^2} + K_B \left(\dfrac{A_r}{A_d}\right)^2 \dfrac{1}{(1-\varepsilon_d)^2}} \right]^{0.5} \tag{78}$$

Equation (78) is for low viscosity water-like fluids and it ignores wall friction losses in the riser and the downcomer. The equation applies to external- and internal-loop configurations of airlift reactors.

The parameters K_T and K_B are the frictional loss coefficients for the headspace and the bottom of the airlift reactors. For typical internal-loop airlift the term containing K_T (eq. 78) can be ignored, while K_B is dependent on the bottom geometry:[18]

$$K_B = 11.4 \left(\frac{A_d}{A_b}\right)^{0.8} \tag{79}$$

Equation (79) applies over an A_d/A_b range of 0.2–1.8; A_b is the free area for flow between the riser and the downcomer. In external-loop reactors $K_B \approx K_T$ and a K_B of 5 may be used for design purposes for the following approximate geometric ranges: $A_b/A_d = 1-2$, $A_b/A_r = 0.25-1$ and $L_{cp}/d_{cp} = 2-7$.

Recent research[19] has shown that for non-Newtonian, pseudoplastic fluids, for which eq. (78) is unsuitable, the following may be used for U_{Lr} calculation:

$$U_{Lr}A_r\,(\Delta P_{Fr} + \Delta P_{Fd}) - \rho_L\, g\, h_D\, U_{Lr}A_r\,(\varepsilon_r - \varepsilon_d) + \frac{1}{2}\rho_L\, U_{Lr}^{\,3}\, A_r \left[\frac{K_T}{(1-\varepsilon_r)^2} + K_B\left(\frac{A_r}{A_d}\right)^2 \frac{1}{(1-\varepsilon_d)^2}\right] = 0 \tag{80}$$

The ΔP_{Fr} and ΔP_{Fd} in this equation are the frictional pressure drops in the riser and the downcomer, respectively. The in-depth procedure for the determination of these pressure drops is described elsewhere.[19] Equations (78) and (80) assume that the riser and the downcomer gas holdups are known; these parameters are interrelated:

$$\varepsilon_d = 0.89\, \varepsilon_r \tag{81}$$

for internal-loops without a gas-liquid separator *per se*, and

$$\varepsilon_d = 0.79\, \varepsilon_r - 0.057 \tag{82}$$

$$\varepsilon_d = 0.46\, \varepsilon_r - 0.024 \tag{83}$$

for external-loop airlifts. Equation (82) is suitable for water-like fluids while eq. (83) is more appropriate for slurries encountered in fermentations of such fungi as *Penicillia* and *Aspergilli* and in the cultivation of filamentous microorganisms like *Streptomyces*.

The calculation of riser holdup for reactor design and scale-up requires some experimental investigation, particularly when new applications are involved and the fluids are rheologically complex. Equations of the type

$$\varepsilon_r = \frac{U_{Gr}}{\alpha + \beta\,(U_{Gr} + U_{Lr})} \tag{84}$$

need to be established by independent variation of gas and

Table 7
Relative Performance of External- and Internal-Loop Airlift Bioreactors

Parameter	Reactor	
	External-loops	Internal-loops
Mass transfer (k_La_L)	lower	higher
Overall holdup (ε)	lower	higher
Riser holdup (ε_r)	lower	higher
Downcomer holdup (ε_d)	lower	higher
Liquid velocity (U_{Lr})	higher	lower
Circulation time (t_c)	lower	higher
Liquid Reynolds Nos. (shear)	higher	lower
Heat transfer	probably higher	probably lower

liquid flows in a vertical pipe using either the fluid of interest or a reasonable simulation of the fluid. The experimentation is very simple and straightforward. For example, for air-water the following applies

$$\varepsilon_r = \frac{U_{Gr}}{0.24 + 1.35\,(U_{Gr} + U_{Lr})^{0.93}} \tag{85}$$

when $U_{Lr} > 0.3\ \text{ms}^{-1}$.

Knowledge of the riser and the downcomer holdups enables the calculation of overall holdup (ε):

$$\varepsilon = \frac{A_r\,\varepsilon_r + A_d\,\varepsilon_d}{A_r + A_d} \tag{86}$$

and hence the height of gas-liquid dispersion:

$$h_D = h_L/(1 - \varepsilon). \tag{87}$$

In equation (87) h_L is the unaerated liquid height.

Design at the hydrodynamic and mass transfer level would involve the prediction of U_{Lr}, ε, ε_r, ε_d and h_D for any given operating conditions (U_{Gr}, fluids) and given reactor geometry (A_r, A_d, A_b and h_L). A design flow chart for internal-loop airlifts has been published.[12]

Gas-liquid mass transfer

The measurement of the overall volumetric mass transfer coefficient and gas holdup in a given fluid in a small bubble column enables the calculation of the ratio k_L/d_B:

$$\frac{k_L}{d_B} = \frac{(1 - \varepsilon)\,k_L a_L}{6\varepsilon} = \psi \tag{88}$$

This ratio has been found to be constant (ψ) for any specific fluid over broad ranges of gas flow rates. Thus k_L/d_B which has been experimentally determined in a bench-top model reactor may be used for estimation of $k_L a_L$ in larger production vessels. An estimate of the gas holdup in the reactor is first obtained using the procedure described earlier; $k_L a_L$ is calculated as follows:

$$k_L a_L = \frac{\psi 6\varepsilon}{(1 - \varepsilon)} \tag{89}$$

For air-water the parameter ψ is ~0.053 s^{-1}. For fluids made up of filamentous or fibrous solids suspended in a water-like medium $\psi(s^{-1})$ depends on the concentration C_S (dry wt./vol.%) of solids:

$$\psi = 5.63 \times 10^{-5} \left(\frac{g\,\rho_L{}^2 D_L\,\sigma}{\mu_L{}^3}\right)^{1/2} e^{-0.131\,C_S^2} \tag{90}$$

where ρ_L, μ_L, D_L and σ refer to the properties of the suspending fluid.

Other considerations

Substrate injection. The problem of location of substrate feed points in an airlift vessel becomes particularly significant in continuous and fed batch operations. For rapidly utilized substrates, the concentration of which must be kept low for reasons such as substrate toxicity or substrate inhibition, the microorganisms in a tall airlift may be starved of the substrate only a short distance downstream of the point of substrate injection. Thus, multiple substrate feed points may be necessary axially up a reactor if product yield reduction due to substrate starvation is to be avoided.

The substrate balance for a differential volume of the riser may be written as

$$E_{Lr}\frac{\partial^2 S}{\partial z^2} - \dot{V}_{Lr}\frac{\partial S}{\partial z} - R_S = 0 \tag{91}$$

where S is the substrate concentration at any vertical position z, $\dot{V}_{Lr}$ is the interstitial riser liquid velocity, E_{Lr} the riser axial dispersion coefficient of the liquid phase and R_S the rate of substrate consumption. When the substrate concentration must not fall below a critical minimum value S_{min} and it should not exceed a maximum of S_{max} because of inhibition considerations, then eq. (91) may be solved with appropriate reaction kinetic expression to determine the axial distance at which fresh substrate addition becomes necessary.

Gas sparger

Perforated plate gas spargers are often used in airlifts and, in keeping with the practice in bubble columns, these plates are located at the base of the riser in the airlift. However, this type of sparger positioning is inappropriate in airlift devices because the recirculating flow from the downcomer leads to a maldistribution of gas (Figure 24(a)). The use of perforated pipe ladder type gas spargers located just above the point where the flow from the downcomer meets the riser leads to improved gas/liquid flow (Figure 24(b)). Perforated pipes are recommended for bioreactor applications.

Immobilized Enzyme Reactors

Immobilized enzyme (and immobilized whole cell) catalysts (see Chapters 17 and 18) can be employed in a variety of reactor configurations. Catalyst particles may be used in suspension as in stirred tank and fluidized bed reactors (Figure 25) or they may be held in place in fixed or packed bed devices. Hollow fibre reactors containing catalyst immobilized either throughout the thickness of the fibre wall or confined to one side of it (*e.g.* perfusion systems) are possible. Flat polymer membranes containing immobilized catalyst have been used in spirally wound configurations. Immobilized particulate biocatalysts can, of course, also be used in airlift and bubble column reactors so long as the solids loading and density are not excessive. In such reactors a compressed gas provides the necessary agitation in the fluid and gas-liquid mass transfer is not the main consideration.

Reactor efficiency is measured by the quantity of substrate transformed per unit time per unit mass of immobilized

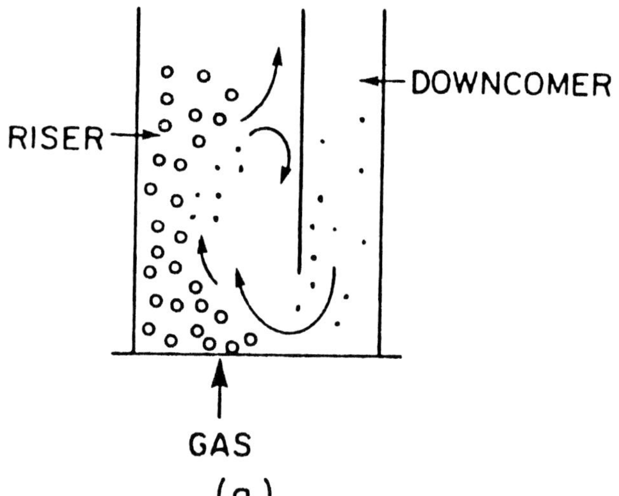

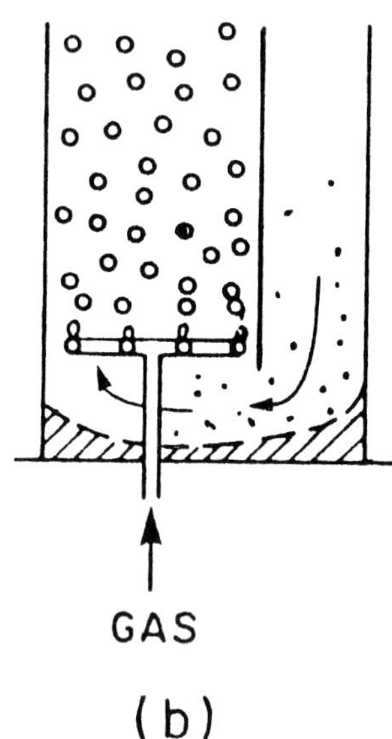

Figure 24. Positioning of gas spargers in airlift reactors: (a) poor gas distribution; (b) improved gas injection.

catalyst for specified initial concentration of substrate (S_o) and its desired conversion $\overline{X} = (S_o - S)/S_o$. The conversion characteristics of different reactor configurations can be calculated from a knowledge of the kinetics of reaction. Thus, for a reaction which obeys Michaelis-Menten kinetics

$$-\frac{dS}{dt} = \frac{k_r \, e \, S}{K_S + S} \tag{92}$$

(e = enzyme concentration, K_s = Michaelis constant, S_o substrate concentration), we have for various reactors:

Batch stirred tank

Change in quantity of substrate in the reactor = Rate of substrate consumption by reaction (93)

or

$$-V_L \frac{dS}{dt} = \frac{k_r \, E \, S}{K_S + S} \tag{94}$$

where E is the total amount of catalyst in the reactor. Equation (94) may be integrated for $S = S_o$ at $t = 0$ and $S = S$ at $t = t$, to

$$\frac{k_r \, E \, t}{V_L} = S_o - S - K_S \ln \frac{S}{S_o} \tag{95}$$

which can be rewritten in terms of conversion $\overline{X}$ as

$$\frac{k_r \, E \, t}{V_L} = \overline{X} \, S_o - K_S \ln (1 - \overline{X}) \tag{96}$$

Continuous stirred tank

The substrate concentration in the inlet stream is S_o and because the reactor is well-mixed the substrate concentration in the exit stream (S) is the same as in the volume of the reactor. A steady state substrate balance in the reactor can be written as

Substrate flow into reactor = substrate flow out of reactor + substrate consumption due to reaction (97)

or

$$Q \, S_o = Q \, S + \frac{K_r \, E \, S}{K_S + S} \tag{98}$$

which can be rearranged and written in terms of $\overline{X}$:

$$\frac{k_r E}{Q} = S_o \, \overline{X} + \frac{K_S \overline{X}}{1 - \overline{X}} \tag{99}$$

Packed bed

Following the procedures outlined in the earlier examples, the appropriate equation for a packed bed system with feed flow rate Q is

$$\frac{k_r E}{Q} = S_o \, \overline{X} - K_S \ln (1 - \overline{X}) \tag{100}$$

Because Q is the volume processed in time t in a continuous flow reactor and V_L is the corresponding volume for a batch reactor, comparison of eqs. (96) and (100) shows that the performance of batch stirred tank and plug flow systems is identical. This is a general conclusion, irrespective of reaction kinetics. However, kinetics alone do not determine reactor choice and operational considerations are important. For example, control of pH is operationally easier in stirred reactors.

For reactions which display Michaelis-Menten kinetics, continuous stirred tank and packed bed reactors operated such that $S \gg K_S$, eqs. (99) and (100) reduce to an identical

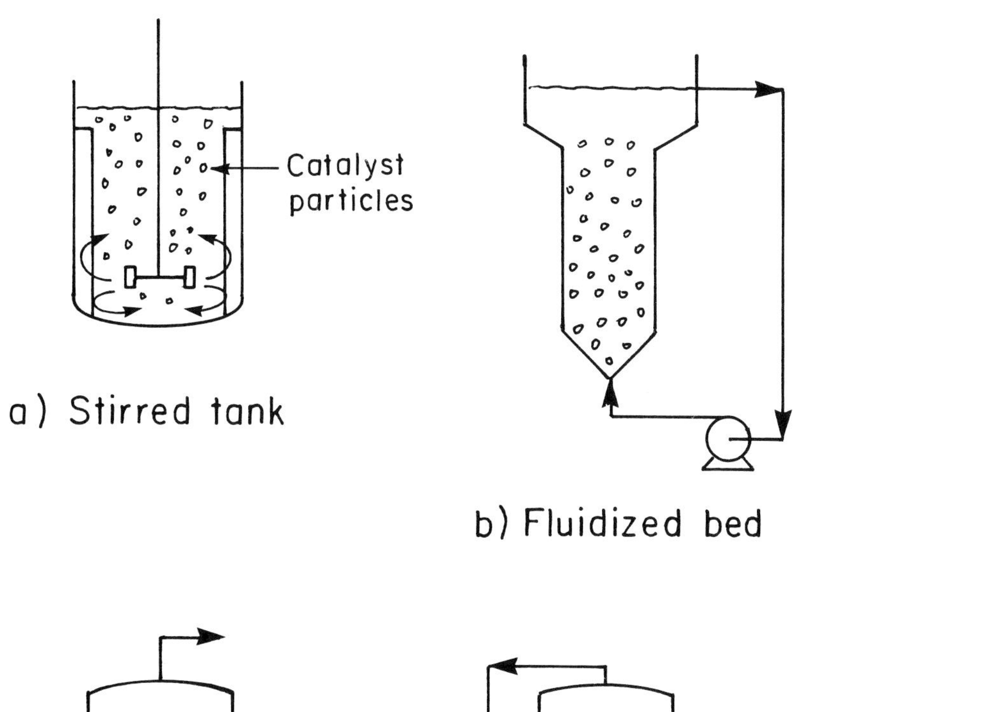

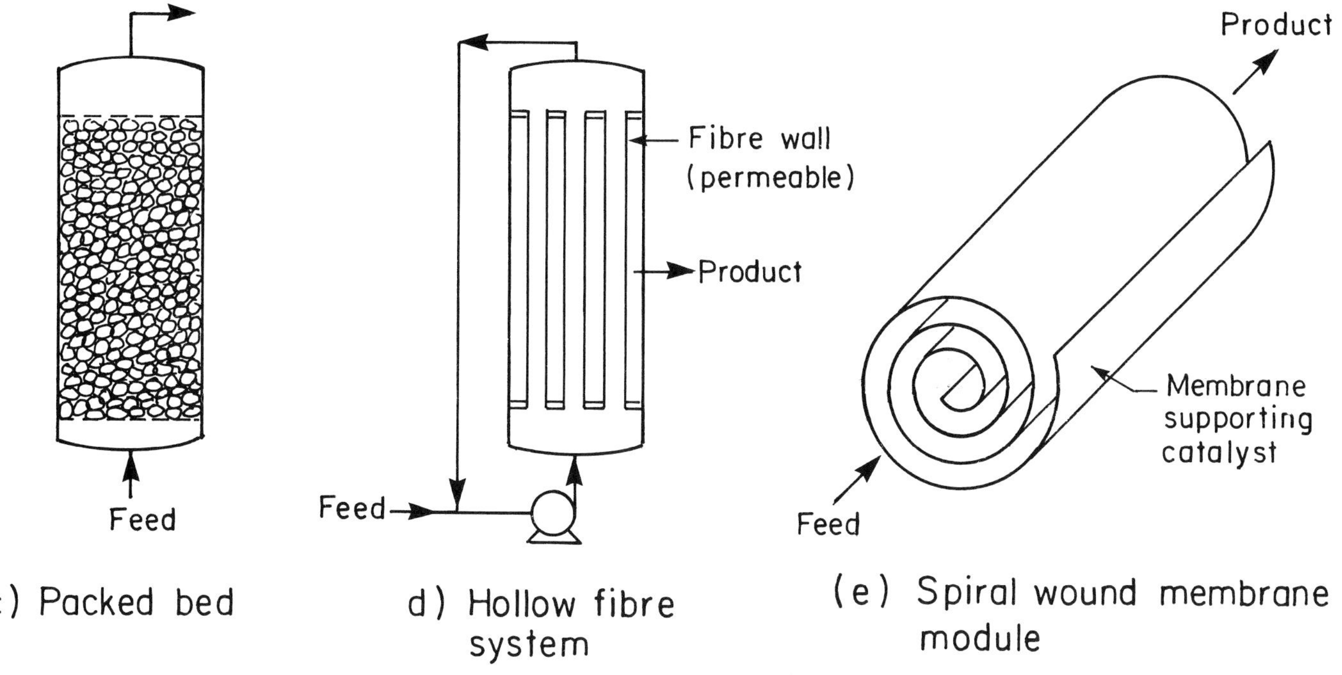

Figure 25. Deployment of immobilized catalyst: free suspension in stirred tank (a) or fluidized bed (b); fixed catalyst in packed bed (c), hollow fibre (d) or spiral wound membrane (e).

form which is indicative of equal performance of the two reactor systems in this regime. However, when $S \ll K_S$ the reaction rate is first order in substrate (eq. 92) and the plug flow system gives a better performance than the continuous stirred tank. In the latter, all the catalyst would be exposed to a low substrate concentration and this can be utilized advantageously in continuous stirred tanks when the reaction is inhibited by substrate.

The theoretical efficiency of other types of reactors is between the two extremes of the packed bed and continuous stirred tank flow geometries.

Mass Transfer Effects

Heterogeneous catalysis has its associated mass transfer considerations. Mass transfer resistances at the interface of solid support and the bulk liquid and within the solid matrix often reduce the effectiveness of the immobilized form. Advantages of immobilization should be weighed against possible disadvantages in the process of choosing a particular form of biocatalyst.

Analysis of the interfacial and intraparticle mass transfer and catalyst performance is illustrated for a spherical catalyst particle. For a substrate (*e.g.* oxygen or glucose) diffusing into the catalyst particle the general substrate balance on the particle is

Rate of diffusion into particle = rate of consumption (101)

since at steady state there is no accumulation. Solution of the appropriate balance equations leads to

$$D_e\left(\frac{d^2S}{dr^2} + \frac{2}{r}\frac{dS}{dr}\right) - R_v = 0 \tag{102}$$

where S is the substrate concentration at any radius r in the spherical particle of effective diffusivity D_e; R_v is the volumetric reaction rate. Equation (102) may be solved, either analytically or numerically, using the applicable kinetic expression (R_v) to obtain the positional variation of substrate concentration inside the particle. For example, for a first order reaction with rate constant k_r, the expression for concentration at any radius r in the catalyst bead is

$$\frac{S}{S_i} = \frac{R_P}{r}\frac{\sinh[(k_r/D_e)^{0.5}\, r]}{\sinh[(k_r/D_e)^{0.5}\, R_p]} \tag{103}$$

Equation (103) applies in the absence of interfacial mass transfer limitation, *i.e.* when concentration in the liquid at the solid/liquid interface (S_i) is the same as the bulk liquid concentration. The total rate of reaction in the particle (R_vV_p) is obtained by equating the total rate to the total diffusive flux at the surface of the particle:

$$R_vV_p = -4\pi\, R_p^2\, D_e \left.\frac{dS}{dr}\right|_{R_p} \tag{104}$$

dS/dr at the surface being calculated by differentiation of eq. (103) followed by replacement of r with R_p. The diffusional resistance in the particle gives rise to a concentration profile within the particle, the intraparticle concentration being less than in the bulk fluid. Hence, the average volumetric reaction rate is lower in the catalyst compared with a homogeneous bulk liquid reaction. The ratio of the reaction rate observed in the catalyst (presence of diffusional resistance) to the hypothetical rate for the same reaction in the absence of diffusional mass transfer resistance (*i.e.* liquid phase reaction) is the catalyst effectiveness factor η:

$$\eta = \frac{\text{Rate of reaction with mass transfer limitation}}{\text{Reaction rate in the absence of mass transfer limitation}} \tag{105}$$

For the example of a first order reaction, the maximum possible reaction rate (no mass transfer limitation) is

$$(R_vV_p)|_{S_i} = -\frac{4}{3}\pi\, R_p^3\, k_r\, S_i \tag{106}$$

Generalized plots of the effectiveness factor (η) for any *n*th order reaction can be found in the literature. Figure 26 shows the effectiveness factor plotted against a Thiele modulus φ which for any particle shape (sphere, cylinder, slab) is

$$\phi = \frac{V_P}{A_p}\left(\frac{n+1}{2}\frac{k\, S_i^{n-1}}{D_e}\right)^{1/2} \tag{107}$$

when n > −1. Figure 26 is for a spherical particle and first order reaction (n = 1). Clearly, for spherical geometry and first order reaction the mass transfer limitation is negligible (*i.e.*, η = 1) for 0.3 ≤ φ (Figure 26).

The effect of mass transfer external to the particle (solid-liquid interfacial mass transfer) on its effectiveness needs also to be evaluated. Use of the boundary conditions

$$\text{at } r = R_p,\ \frac{dS}{dr} = -\frac{k_S}{D_e}(S_i - S) \tag{108}$$

$$\text{at } r = 0,\ \frac{dS}{dr} = 0 \tag{109}$$

in the mass balance equation (eq. 106) leads to an equation which includes the external mass transfer. The mass transfer coefficient k_S is calculated from the well-known correlations applicable to a particular hydrodynamic regime. For example, for stagnant fluid around a spherical particle (*i.e.* negligible difference between the density of the particle and that of the suspending fluid), we have

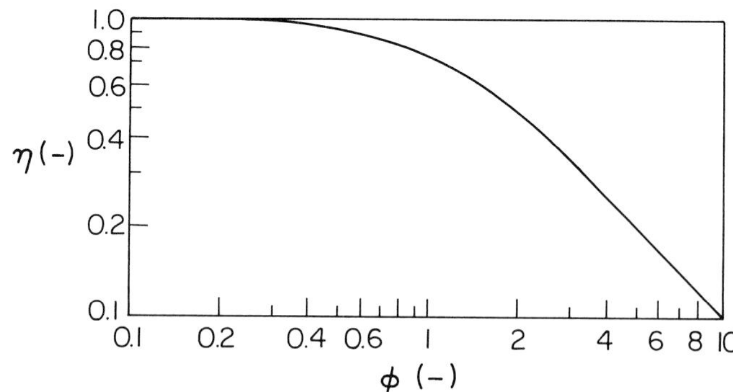

Figure 26. Effectiveness factor (η) vs. Thiele modulus (φ) for spherical particles and first order reaction.

$$Sh = \frac{k_Sd_P}{D_L} = 2.0 \tag{110}$$

where Sh is the Sherwood number and for forced convection, the Frössling equation

$$Sh = \frac{k_Sd_P}{D_L} = 2.0 + 0.552\, Re^{0.5}\, Sc^{0.33} \tag{111}$$

where Re and Sc are the Reynolds and the Schmidt numbers, respectively.

Several other equations for k_S are available for particular applications such as particles in fluidized beds and slurries in stirred tanks.

Bioreactor Scale-up

Laboratory scale bioprocess development identifies the optimal fermentation conditions for the process. Oxygen transfer requirements, maximum tolerable levels of shear, pH and temperature control needs should become known at this point. The object of scale-up is to reproduce on pilot or production scale the successful fermentation results achieved in the laboratory. The results are often specified as production rate per unit fermenter volume.

In practice scale-up is quite complex. It is not generally possible to reproduce exactly on the production scale all the various parameters from laboratory or pilot scale units. For example, at equal specific power inputs two geometrically similar stirred reactors do not have identical mixing times. As a result scale-up is based on the strategy of holding constant only one or two of the several possible parameters at different fermenter scales. The parameter(s) held constant are those which are considered to have the greatest impact on the fermentation; furthermore, the criterion of geometric similarity (*i.e.* keeping the ratios of corresponding lengths equal on production and pilot-scale units) is not always rigidly adhered to so that small geometric variations may be utilized to advantage as long as they do not result in unpredictable behaviour.

The scale-up methods which have been most often proposed are as follows:

1. scale-up based on equal power input;
2. scale-up based on equal mixing times;
3. scale-up based on equal oxygen transfer (k_La_L);
4. scale-up based on equal shear rates (or impeller tip speed).

The list is not exhaustive. For highly aerobic fermentations scale-up based on maintaining a constant oxygen transfer rate is a reasonable approach but in other fermentations, limitations such as those on shear rate may be equally important.

The following comments on scale-up apply to stirred tank type of fermenters. Considerations for scale-up of pneumatic reactors, particularly the airlifts, were examined earlier in this chapter.

Scale-up based on equal P_G/V_L ratio

The criterion of equal P_G/V_L on pilot-plant and production units has been employed for certain antibiotic fermentations. The available evidence indicates that the necessary power requirements decrease with increasing fermenter volume approximately as

$$\frac{P_G}{V_L} \propto V_L^{-0.37} \tag{112}$$

Consequently, keeping P_G/V_L constant in scale-up may not be an energy efficient approach. Furthermore, it may not be a satisfactory strategy for shear sensitive fermentations since the impeller tip speed and Reynolds number scale-up by factors of > 1 when P_G/V_L is held constant for geometrically similar vessels. Table 8 shows some of the effects of geometrically similar scale-up of a 20 L reactor to 2.5 m^3 plant vessel. Effects of keeping P_G/V_L constant (*i.e.* $P_G/V_L = 1$ arbitrary unit for both reactors) on impeller rpm ($\overline{N}$), tip speed ($\overline{N}D_i$) and Reynolds number (Re_i) is shown in Table 8. These parameters scale-up by the respective ratios of 0.34, 1.7 and 8.5. Table 8 also shows the effects of maintaining constant rpm ($\overline{N}$), constant tip speed ($\overline{N}D_i$) and constant impeller Reynolds number (Re_i).

Table 8
Effects of Scale-up Based on Constant P_G/V_L (or Constant $\overline{N}$, $\overline{N}D_i$, Re_i) on Other Parameters

Parameter	Laboratory reactor 20 L	Plant reactor 2.5 m^3			
P_G/V_L	1	1	25	0.2	0.0016
$\overline{N}$	1	0.34	1	0.2	0.04
$\overline{N}D_i$	1	1.7	5	1	0.2
Re_i	1	8.5	25	5	1

Scale-up based on equal shear

The maximum shear rate is related to the impeller tip speed which is held constant on scale-up. However, the shear rates in the fluid which are governed by fluid turbulence or Reynolds numbers do not scale-up proportionately because the impeller Reynolds number does not remain constant (Table 8).

Scale-up based on equal oxygen transfer

Maintenance of an equal overall volumetric oxygen transfer coefficient (k_La_L) is often taken to ensure equal oxygen transfer on scale-up. This is true only when the oxygen transfer driving force also remains unchanged on scale-up.

For stirred tanks

$$k_La_L = k_1 (P_G/V_L)^{k_2} U_G^{k_3} \tag{113}$$

where k_1 is dependent on geometry and k_2 and k_3 are scale-dependent.

More complex scale-up methods rely on estimation of k_La_L as well as the spatial oxygen concentration profiles in the reactors to yield a value of oxygen transfer rate. Operating and scale-up parameters are adjusted until the desired transfer rates are obtained for realistic operating conditions.

DOWNSTREAM PROCESSING OPERATIONS

General Considerations

The output of a bioreactor usually undergoes one or more downstream separation, purification, stabilization and packaging operations to produce a saleable product. This section examines some of the more common unit operations employed in downstream bioprocessing.

Overall process design involves consideration of interactions between various downstream and upstream stages and the bioreactor. In general, the smaller the number of processing steps necessary the more attractive the process.

Solid-Liquid Separations

All bioprocesses involve one or more solid-liquid separation steps. Following fermentation the biomass may need to be separated from the broth, or the cell debris may have to be removed following cell disruption. Purification of enzymes and biochemicals by precipitation and crystallization also employs solid-liquid separation processes.

The well established solid-liquid separation technologies such as sedimentation and filter presses are not treated in this section even though they find numerous applications in the biotechnology industry. Excellent treatments of these subjects can be found in the chemical engineering literature. Here only the operations of particular interest in bioprocessing are examined.

Centrifugation

Advances in structural steels have made possible the use of high-speed, corrosion resistant centrifuges for large scale bioprocesses. Attention to ease of cleaning, containment and aerosol suppression, and the availability of sterilizable machines have made centrifugation a very important separation operation in biotechnology industry.

Operational principle

A centrifuge is basically a sedimentation tank with enhanced gravitational force to increase the rate of sedimentation. A particle enters the cylindrical bowl of the centrifuge (Figure 27) with the feed flowing at some constant velocity. The centrifugal force drives the particle outwards towards the walls of the bowl. A particle initially at radius r_i (Figure 27) would be at some position r after time t. If the residence time of the liquid in the centrifuge is such that the $r \geq r_B$, the particle will reach the wall of the centrifuge and it will sediment. For particles in Stokes' law regime ($Re_p \ll 1$), the terminal settling velocity at radius r is

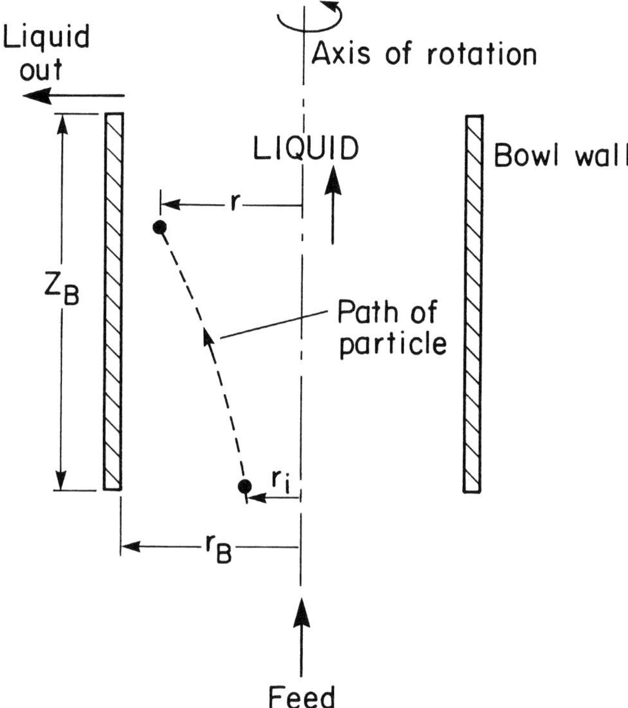

Figure 27. Particle motion in the bowl of a centrifuge.

$$u_t = \frac{\omega^2 r\,(\rho_S - \rho_L)\,d_p^2}{18\,\mu_L} \qquad (114)$$

where ω is the angular velocity of the centrifuge. Since $u_t = dr/dt$, equation (114) may be rewritten and integrated between the limits $r = r_i$ at $t = 0$ and $r = r_B$ at $t = t_r$ (the residence time) to give

$$t_r = \frac{18\,\mu_L}{\omega^2(\rho_S - \rho_L)\,d_p^2}\ln\frac{r_B}{r_i} \qquad (115)$$

Note that r_i cannot be zero and the feed must enter the separating zone some distance from the axis of rotation.

The acceptable volume flow rate through the centrifuge which will allow the particle of diameter $\geq d_p$ to separate may be calculated as

$$Q = \frac{V_L}{t_r} = \frac{\omega^2(\rho_S - \rho_L)\,d_p^2\pi\,(r_B^2 - r_i^2)\,Z_B}{18\,\mu_L\,\ln(r_B/r_i)} \qquad (116)$$

The design of the centrifuge and strength of construction materials limit the maximum rotational speed.

Performances of different centrifuges are compared on the basis of the sigma concept which is also the commonly used basis of scale-up. The parameter Σ is defined as

$$\Sigma = \frac{Q}{2\,u_t} \qquad (117)$$

Because u_t (eq. 114) is dependent on the geometry of the centrifuge (via Z_B, r_B, r_i), Σ (m^2) is dependent on centrifuge geometry. The value of Σ represents the area of a gravity settling tank which is capable of the same separating ability for continuous flow operation as the centrifuge. For appropriate equipment selection the separation requirements have to be defined. It is uneconomical to specify equipment for more stringent separation duty than is really necessary. Clearly, from eq. (114) the particle diameter and the density difference between the particle and the suspending fluid are important factors which affect separation.

Selection of a centrifuge for any new application would almost always involve expensive pilot scale evaluations. A few simple laboratory tests can, however, provide an indication of whether or not the pilot run is even worth pursuing. If a sample of the slurry does not settle on standing under the influence of gravity over several days, it is unlikely that a separator can achieve very much. However, change in sample characteristics such as particle size which may be achieved, for example, by the addition of flocculating agents or by alteration of pH may improve the likelihood of separating difficult to settle solids. The flocs should be strong enough to withstand the accelerational forces which are experienced as the fluid enters the centrifuge and comes up to the same rotational speed as the bulk of fluid. If the flocs formed are easily disintegrated there is little advantage to adding flocculation chemicals.

A slight shaking of a bottle of gravity-settled solids can provide an indication of how light the particles are. Other solids properties such as the particle size and density need also to be known. Here the density refers to solids as they are in suspension and not dry. This difference is of particular importance for biological solids which contain a high proportion of water and swell when more is added. The solids may be fibrous (fungal mycelia) or slimy, or may occur as pellets. These properties impact upon the choice of centrifuge. For example, some fibrous materials settle as mats under the high centrifugal force and may cause de-sludging problems in certain automatic solid-discharging centrifuges. Solid packing characteristics and ease of settling can be easily judged by spinning a test tube sample in a laboratory centrifuge at ~3000 rpm for 3 to 5 minutes.

Equipment

Several types of centrifuges are available; the more common ones are:

(i) tubular bowl;
(ii) multichamber bowl;
(iii) disc-stack;
(iv) scroll discharge decanter centrifuge.

The particle size ranges for which these configurations are suitable are shown in Figure 28.

Tubular bowl centrifuge. Shown schematically in Figure 29, the tubular bowl is the simplest centrifuge configuration.

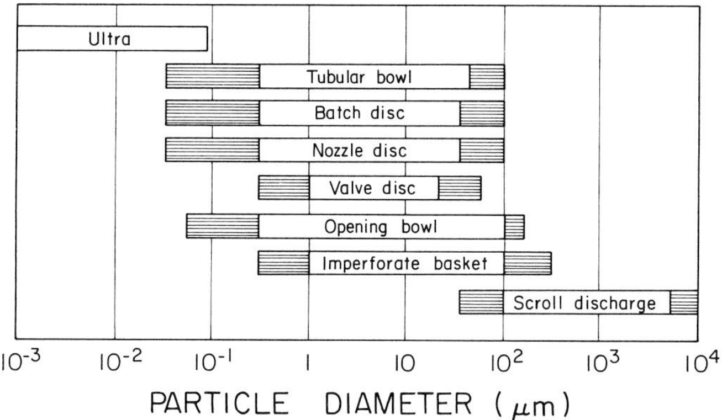

Figure 28. Particle size range for different types of centrifuges.

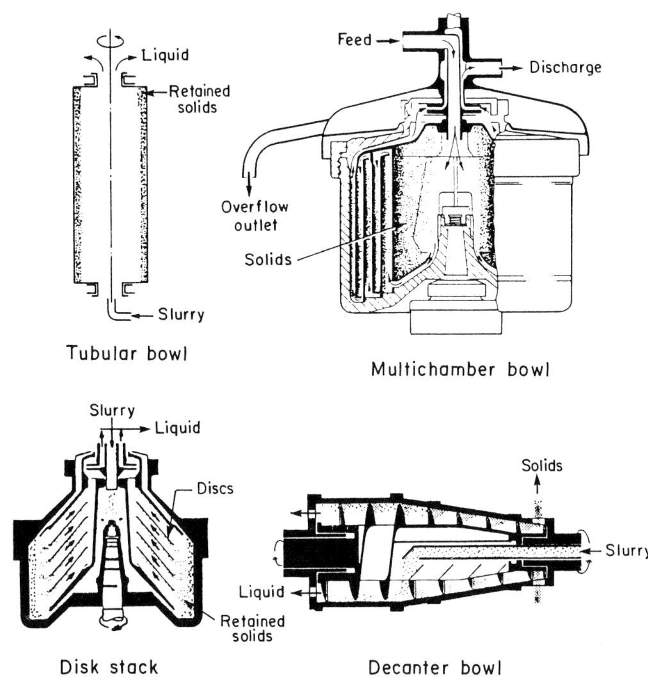

Figure 29. Centrifuges.

High 'g'-forces do permit good solids dewatering but the operation is batch with respect to solids. The solids-handling capacity is limited and solids recovery is labour intensive. Consequently, only slurries with low solids concentrations can be economically dewatered.

Multichamber bowl centrifuge. This configuration (Figure 29) is basically a tubular bowl centrifuge with increased solids handling capacity. Efficiency is maintained up to complete filling of the chambers. Other operational characteristics are nearly the same as for the tubular bowl machines.

Disc-stack centrifuges. Disc-stack centrifuges come in several types depending on whether the solids are retained or discharged and on the mechanism of discharge of solids. All disc-stack machines (Figure 29) contain a set of conical plates or discs separated by flow channels. The thin flow channels mean a reduced "depth" for solids to settle and hence better performance. The feed is introduced to the rotating bowl by a stationary inlet pipe and passes into the zone between the discs where separation takes place. Under the influence of centrifugal force, the particles travel radially outwards until they strike one of the conical discs. The particles then slide down the under side of the disc and are thrown into the space outside the disc stack. The solids may either accumulate here (solids-retaining disc centrifuge), or discharge from the bowl continuously (nozzle discharge) or intermittently (solids ejecting with peripheral or axial discharge).

For further details of these devices the literature mentioned in the bibliography should be consulted.

Decanter centrifuge. The decanter bowl discharge centrifuge (Figure 29) is suitable for slurries with high solids contents. Solids are continuously discharged by the helical screw mechanism. Only relatively low centrifugal forces are feasible.

Filtration

Rotary vacuum (or pressure) filters

Rotary vacuum drum filters appear to be the most commonly employed type of filters in biochemical industry, particularly in antibiotics manufacture and the production of such chemicals as citric acid by *Aspergillus niger* fermentations. Rotary filters are available either for suction (or vacuum) operation as in a Büchner funnel or for pressure operation. In the latter the liquid is forced through the filter by the application of pressure on the liquid surface. These filters have the advantage of continuous operation and are useful when sterility and containment requirements are not stringent.

A rotary vacuum filter consists of a drum frame covered with filter cloth (canvas, nylon, Dacron, metal or glass fibre). The internal volume of the drum is divided into radial chambers (Figure 30) to which vacuum may be applied. The drum rotates (0.1–2 rpm) partly submerged in an agitated trough of the slurry to be filtered. Application of vacuum (250–500 mm Hg) to the submerged chambers (~30% of filter area) of the drum results in the slurry being drawn through the filter cloth; the initial layer of solids deposit acts as the filter medium. Continuation of suction as the solids-coated drum surface emerges from the slurry bath leads to dewatering which may be followed by spray wash. Before the drum re-enters the slurry the solids cake is taken off the filter surface by a knife scraper (doctor blade). Other solids-discharge mechanisms may be used such as strings which can be lifted off the filter surface. In some cases the filter cloth itself is passed over small diameter rollers to crack the solids cake which then drops off before the cloth returns to the drum surface. The type of solids discharge used depends on the properties of the solids. In the cake removal stage the suction is discontinued; in some designs the suction chamber may be under positive air pressure to assist cake removal.

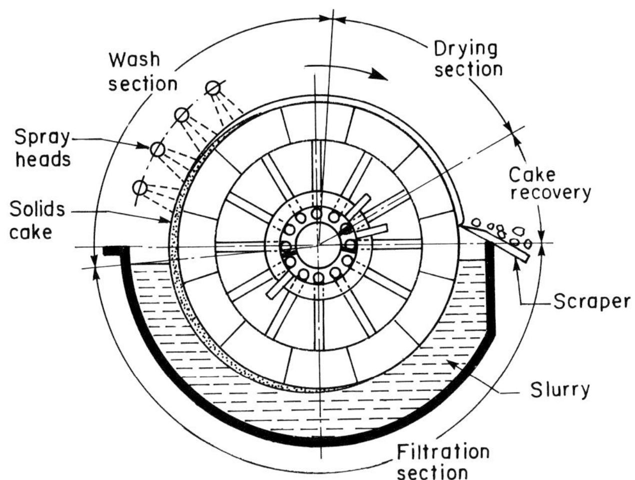

Figure 30. Rotary vacuum filter.

When high filtering capacity and no washing are desired, filter drums with 60 to 70% submerged filter area may be used. Filtration of fine or gelatinous solids which form impermeable cakes cannot be carried out effectively with a bare filter cloth which is readily plugged. For such cases a precoat filtration scheme employing filter aids can be used. Filtration of *Streptomyces* broths often requires filter aids. In this type of operation a slurry of a filter aid such as diatomaceous earth or cellulose fibres is filtered through the filter cloth to form a porous cake of the filter aid. Subsequently the broth is filtered through this cake and as a layer of solids deposits on the cake it is scraped off together with a thin layer of the filter aid thereby exposing fresh filtration surface. Suction is maintained throughout the entire cycle to keep the bulk of the filter aid material firmly attached to the filter drum.

Precoat filtration is usually limited to cases in which the solid is not the desired product. Filter aid can be difficult to recover and it may have to be discarded together with the filtered solids. Many biological products are adsorbed to the filter aid material and this loss can be significant particularly when the product is expensive. Laboratory trials are indispensible to satisfactory filtration performance for any new application. The broth pretreatment conditions can radically alter its filtration characteristics; changes in pH and temperature, for example, and the length of holding time at these conditions lead to large changes in filtration properties of *Streptomyces* broths. Proper pretreatment conditions have to be found experimentally. The flux of filtrate, *i.e.* the volume of filtrate (V_L) collected per unit time (t) per unit filter area (A_f), is related to the pressure drop driving force (ΔP), the viscosity of the continuous phase (μ_L) and the flow resistance (R_F) by the Hagen-Poiseuille type equation:

$$\frac{1}{A_f}\frac{dV_L}{dt} = \frac{\Delta P}{\mu_L R_F} \qquad (118)$$

The flow resistance R_F is the sum of the resistance due to filter medium (r_m) and that due to accumulated biomass:

$$R_F = \dot{\alpha}\frac{\bar{w}}{A_f} + r_m \qquad (119)$$

where $\dot{\alpha}$ is the mean specific resistance of the biomass cake and $\bar{w}$ is the dry weight of accumulated biomass. At constant pressure (ΔP) plots of t/V_L vs. V_L for incompressible filter cakes are linear, with slope and intercept dependent on conditions of operation. However, biological materials usually produce compressible cakes and experimental determination of filtration volume vs. time relationship is necessary.

Microfiltration and ultrafiltration

Microfiltration and ultra-filtration rely on porous membrane filter media. The basic difference between the two operations is the "particle" size range handled. Microfiltration membranes retain suspended solids down to ~0.05 μm. Bacteria, yeasts, fungi and tissue cells are readily removed while proteins and enzymes pass through the filter membrane at high flux. Ultrafiltration membranes have much finer pores (1–20 nm) which allow retention of proteins, enzymes and carbohydrates of various molecular weight cutoffs. The following discussion places emphasis on the microfiltration of bacterial cells. Note that industrial ultrafiltration and microfiltration systems are physically and operationally similar; the theoretical fundamentals of these two operations are equivalent. A recent review[20] on ultrafiltration should be consulted for further details. In practical processing operations microfiltration is usually employed in a cross-flow mode. The fluid to be filtered flows parallel to the filter surface (Figure 31). The cross-flow of feed with respect to the filtrate flux generates shear forces which help to sweep the filter surface of excessive solids buildup. However, in most cases the buildup of a thin layer of solids (concentration polarization) cannot be entirely prevented.

The filtrate flux (J) through the membrane depends on the transmembrane pressure ΔP_{TM}, the viscosity of the suspending liquid (μ_L) and the hydraulic resistance of the membrane (R_M) and the deposited solids (R_C):

$$J = \frac{\Delta P_{TM}}{\mu_L (R_C + R_M)} \qquad (120)$$

The resistance of the solids layer depends on its thickness (δ_S), voidage (ε_S) and the particle size:

$$R_C = \frac{180\,(1 - \varepsilon_S)^2\,\delta_S}{d_p^2\,\varepsilon_S^3} \qquad (121)$$

Biological solids from compressible cakes: the porosity (ε_S) of the solids layer decreases with increasing transmembrane pressure and the flux does not increase linearly with ΔP_{TM}. A typical relationship between filtrate flux and the transmembrane pressure is depicted in Figure 32. While for pure liquids the flux varies linearly with ΔP_{TM}, for slurries increasing ΔP_{TM} beyond a certain point produces no additional benefit. As shown in Figure 32, for fixed ΔP_{TM} and other operating parameters, an increase in cross-flow velocity enhances the permeate flux due to reduced solids layer thickness at higher flow rate. Reliable theoretical prediction of the behaviour of a solid deposit is not possible and experimental evaluation is necessary to determine suitable operating conditions. The flux usually increases with temperature (reduced viscosity) and with increasing flow rate parallel to the membrane. In biological applications the upper temperature limit would be determined by consideration of product stability (usually < 40°C). The choice of cross-flow rate would be a balance between the pumping costs and the higher filtration rate. The flux depends also on the concentration of solids in the bulk fluid since it affects not only the rate of transport of deposited solids back into the bulk flow (hence δ_S) but also the turbulence intensity on the retentate side. The flux decreases with solids concentration in the feed.

The process equipment consists of polymer membrane filters mounted in various ways. Ceramic membranes are now avail-

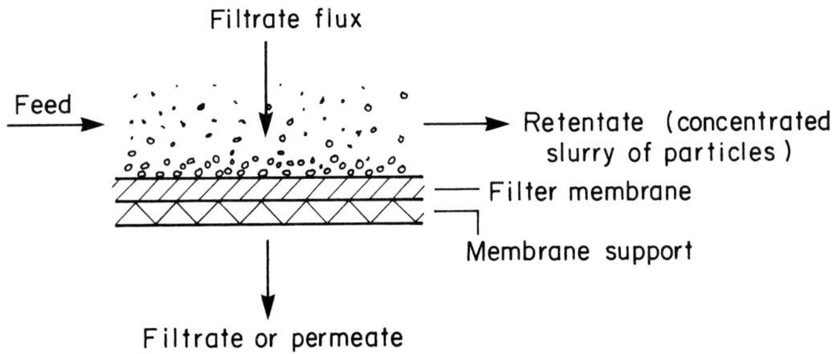

Figure 31. Principle of cross-flow filter.

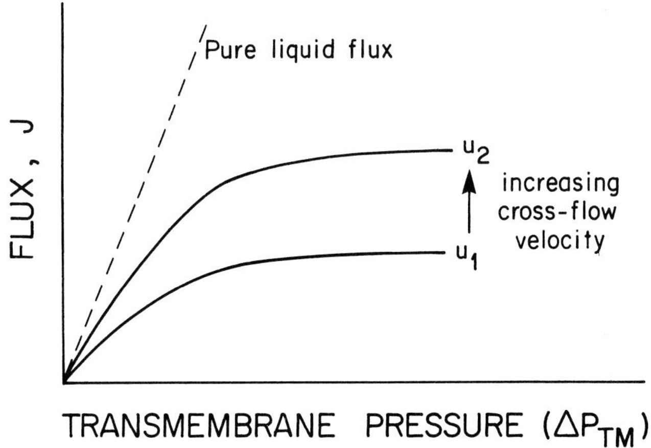

Figure 32. Typical relationship between filtrate flux and transmembrane pressure.

able but have a much lower porosity (number of pores per unit area of membrane) than the polymer membranes. Flat sheets of supported membrane clamped in a plate and frame structure are available. Membranes formed into hollow fibres provide large filtration areas in small volumes. Multiple cartridges of hollow fibres piped in parallel provide a straightforward way of filter scale-up. The feed flows inside the fibre and the permeate is collected in the shell-side of the casing.

Filtration equipment have been developed consisting of microfiltration or ultrafiltration membranes mounted on the adjacent surfaces of two porous concentric cylinders. The inner cylinder can rotate at high speed and the resulting Taylor vortices in the liquid in the narrow gap between the cylinders keep the membrane surfaces clean of solids buildup. Compared with flat plate units, the rotating filters allow significantly enhanced filtrate flux but compared with hollow fibre cartridges of similar dimensions they have only limited membrane filter area. Shear damage to cells in the annular gap (~ 4 mm) does not seem to be a problem. The ability to vary the shear at the membrane surface by rotational speed (as opposed to variation by liquid flow rate alone) provides an additional and independent means of controlling filter performance.

In most equipment configurations either continuous or batch filtration schemes can be employed. Additional process requirements are incurred due to the need for periodic filter cleaning (backflush, chemical and enzymatic cleaning).

Cell Disruption

Nearly all products of microbial origin in current use are of the extracellular type *i.e.* they are produced within the microbial cell but are then excreted into the surrounding environment. A much larger proportion of the potentially useful microbial products is retained within the cells. Most enzymes, for example, are intracellular. The isolation of such intracellular material requires disintegration of the cell wall structures by physical, chemical or enzymatic means to release the cell constituents into the surrounding medium: this is the reason for the cell disruption. Although the additional cell disruption step adds to the cost of production of intracellular substances relative to extracellular products, this need not be a drawback. For the manufacture of high value products the added expense is of little importance; furthermore, production costs may be reduced by such strategies as simultaneous isolation of a number of products following cell disruption. Extracellular product isolation may preceed the isolation of the intracellular product from the same fermentation batch.

Cell Disruption Methods

A classification of cell disruption methods is shown in Figure 33. The non-mechanical techniques are at present of little

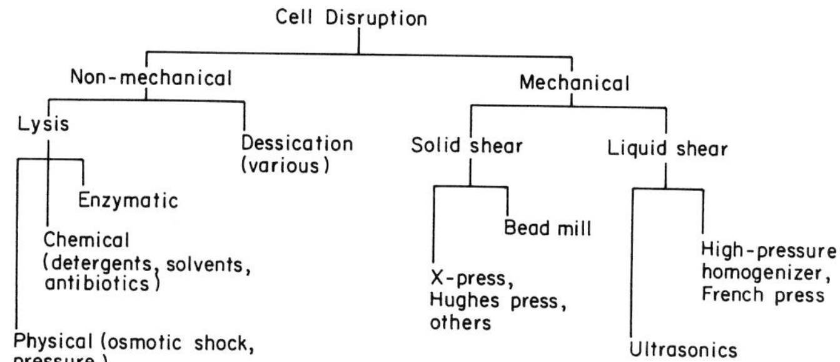

Figure 33. Cell disruption methods. See reference 21.

commercial significance. For example, the cell lytic enzymes presently available are expensive and the quantities obtainable are insufficient for large-scale use. In addition, enzymes and chemicals used in cell lysis are lost in the product, possibly as undesirable contaminants and indeed chemicals such as acids, alkalis, surfactants and lytic enzymes are themselves known to damage the desired products. Autolysis, the self-lysing ability of many microbial species under the right environmental conditions, may be a useful alternative.

The mechanical cell disruption methods are more generally applicable and are expected to remain the workhorse of the large-scale disruption technology. Both solid shear (*e.g.* bead mill) and liquid shear (*e.g.* high pressure homogenizer) based methods have proven commercially successful. The solid shear methods may involve either a grinding action (as in a ball mill) or may involve extrusion of frozen cells, either alone or as a cell-ice (or other abrasive) mixture, through narrow gaps or orifices under high pressure. Liquid shear disruption devices rely on shear fields within the cell suspension undergoing large pressure drops and on impact of cell slurry jet on a stationary surface. Only the bead mill and homogenizer types of disruption equipment will be discussed here because of their value in industrial disruption operations.

The bead mill

Bead mills consist of either a vertical or a horizontal cylindrical chamber with a motor-driven central shaft supporting a collection of off-centred discs or other agitating element (Figures 34 and 35). The chamber is filled to the desired level with steel or ballotini glass beads to provide the grinding action. Horizontal mills do not require a bead retention mechanism at the fluid inlet which is located above the level of the beads in the chamber (Figure 35). At the fluid exit port, three main types of bead retention systems have been employed: a sieve-plate, a disc rotating in very close proximity to a plate with a central exit port in it (Figure 35) and a vibrating slot. The latter two types of bead retention devices reduce fouling problems. The smallest bead should be at least 1.5 times the gap in the bead retention system. The horizontal configuration of the mill has superior disruption performance relative to the vertical one because the upward fluid flow in vertical

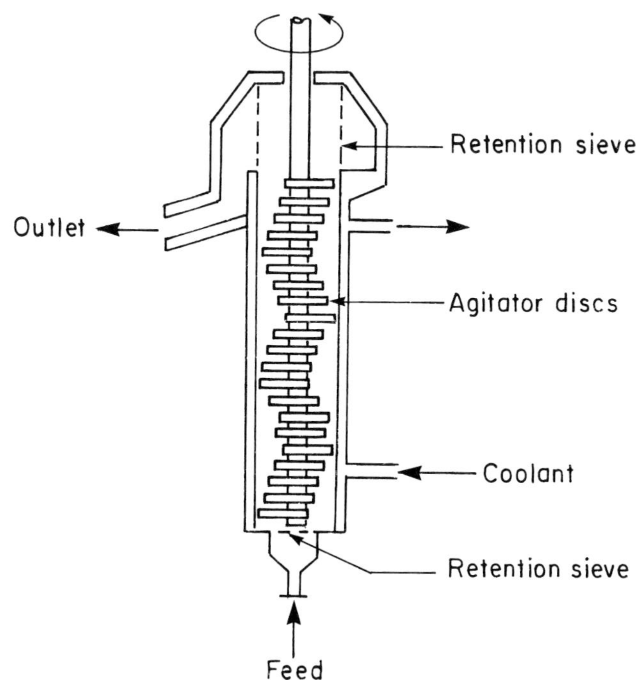

Figure 34. Bead mill (vertical chamber).

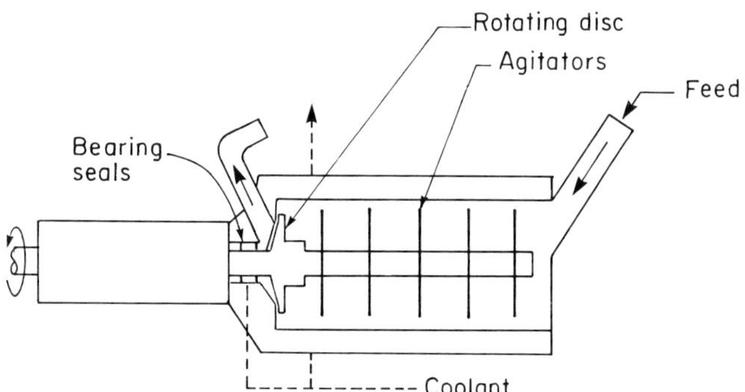

Figure 35. Bead mill (horizontal chamber).

machines tends to fluidize the grinding beads to some degree thereby reducing grinding efficiency.

The kinetics of cell disruption in bead mills depend on the construction of the mill. First-order disruption kinetics have been found in machines with predominant plug flow, whereas in machines in which the rotor design (Figure 36) permits significant backmixing the disruption deviates from the first order behaviour. For first order batch disruption the rate of protein release by cell rupture is directly proportional to the amount of unreleased protein:

$$\frac{d\dot{R}}{dt} = k_D(\dot{R}_m - \dot{R}) \qquad (122)$$

where $\dot{R}$ is the weight of protein released per unit weight of cells, and $\dot{R}_m$ is the maximum measurable release of protein. Equation (122) may be integrated for batch time (t) to give

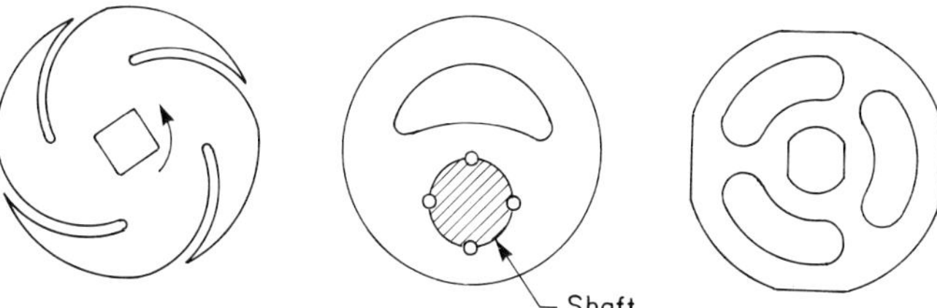

Figure 36. Some rotors for bead mills.

$$\ln\left(\frac{\dot{R}_m}{\dot{R}_m - \dot{R}}\right) = \ln D_f = k_D t \qquad (123)$$

where D_f is the reciprocal of the fraction of unreleased protein.

For continuous disruption in mills in which the flow may be described in terms of the continuous stirred tank in series (CSTR) model the disruption kinetics follow the equation

$$D_f = \frac{\dot{R}_m}{\dot{R}_m - \dot{R}} = [1 + (k_D t_r/j)^j] \qquad (124)$$

where t_r is the mean residence time and j is the number of CSTRs in series. The value of j may be obtained experimentally from residence time distribution studies, whereas t_r is given by

$$t_r = \frac{V_C}{Q} \qquad (125)$$

The disruption rate constant, k_D, is a function of several parameters: temperature, impeller rotational speed, bead loading, bead size and cell concentration. In addition, the density of bead material is expected to affect k_D although little has been written on this subject.

Within limits, the disruption rate constant, k_D, increases with the agitator tip speed, U_T:

$$k_D = K_y U_t \qquad (126)$$

the practical upper limit on the impeller tip speed being $\sim 15-16\ ms^{-1}$. The power consumption increases with agitator speed according to

$$P = c\,\overline{N}^3\, d_i^5 \qquad (127)$$

where $\overline{N}$ and d_i are the rotation speed (rps) and the agitator disc diameter, respectively. The constant c is a function of the agitator design, suspension viscosity and the density of suspension. Heat production and the associated cooling requirements increase with increasing agitation as also does the wear on the beads, agitator and the chamber walls. A certain amount of wear is unavoidable and bead material must be carefully selected in cell disruption applications. Beads are available in various types of glass, ceramics and steels; note that some materials (leaded glass, for example) will not be acceptable with products intended for pharmaceutical or food applications. The kinetic energy of the beads is an important factor in disruption; it may be calculated as

$$\text{K.E.} = \frac{1}{2}\, m\, u_b^2 \tag{128}$$

which indicates high density beads and high agitator tip speeds (for higher bead velocity, u_b) for good disruption. The optimum density of the bead material is dependent on the apparent viscosity of the cell slurry inside the mill because the viscous drag tends to reduce the bead velocity. The optimum density of bead material may be estimated using the equation.

$$\rho_S = 1016 + 183\, \mu_{ap} \tag{129}$$

for $1 \leq \mu_{ap} \leq 20$ Pa s. Bead diameter and bead loading are other important considerations in a disruption operation. Generally the disruption increases with increasing bead loads and so does the power consumption and the production of heat. Experience shows that bead loading should be 80 to 95% of the void volume of the disruption chamber. Lower loads lead to poor disruption efficiency.

In general, more rapid disruption is achieved with smaller beads, the optimal bead size being dependent on the size of the microbial cells being disintegrated: the smaller the cell size the smaller should be the bead diameter. For fungal hyphae, for example, bead sizes > 1 mm may be satisfactory. For animal and plant cells and for yeasts the bead size should be < 1 mm. The lower practical limit on bead size is about 0.3 mm and for small bacteria the cell disruption on a single passage through the mill may not produce satisfactory disruption performance. Typically, two or more passes may be needed to cause sufficient disruption of bacterial slurries whereas a single pass may be enough for the larger yeast cells.

Other factors such as the concentration of cells, the location of the desired enzyme within a cell and the strength of the cell wall affect product release by disruption. The cell wall strength depends on the growth environment and the growth stage at which the cells are harvested for disruption. Some of these considerations have been reviewed elsewhere.[21]

The high pressure homogenizer

The high-pressure Manton-Gaulin APV type homogenizer is among the most widely used liquid shear disruption devices. The high pressure homogenizer consists of a positive displacement piston pump with one or more plungers. The cell suspension is drawn through a check valve into the pump cylinder and, on the pressure stroke, is forced through an adjustable discharge valve (Figure 37) with a restricted orifice. As the cell slurry passes between the valve and the seat its velocity increases rapidly to approximately 290 ms^{-1} with a corresponding decrease in pressure so that cavitation bubbles form. The product velocity decreases again as the suspension leaves the valve seat area causing the bubble to implode. The shock energy released together with the associated turbulence cause the disintegration of cell wall. The impingement of cell slurry on the impact ring (Figure 37) possibly contributes to disruption. Because both cavitation and impingement processes are velocity associated, the pressure drop across the valve (*i.e.* the difference between the operating and the atmospheric pressure) influences both of them and affects the rate of disruption. The protein released by disruption depends on the pressure difference (ΔP) and the number of passes (N_p) through the valve as follows

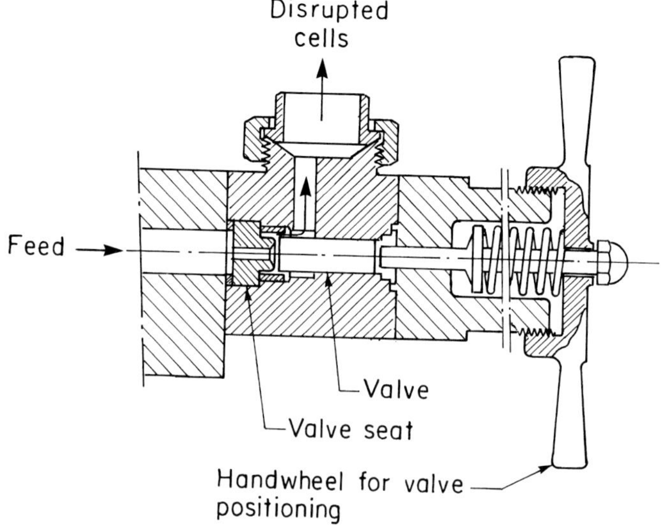

Figure 37. High pressure homogenizer valve assembly. See reference 21.

$$\frac{d\dot{R}}{dN_p} = k_D\, \Delta P^a\, (\dot{R}_m - \dot{R}) \tag{130}$$

where $(\dot{R}_m - \dot{R})$ is the amount of protein remaining to be released. Equation (130) can be integrated for $\dot{R} = 0$ at $N_p = 0$ and $\dot{R} = \dot{R}$ at $N_p = N_p$, to

$$\ln [\dot{R}_m/(\dot{R}_m - \dot{R})] = k_D\, N_p\, \Delta\, P^a \tag{131}$$

The exponent a in the pressure term in equation (131) depends both on the microbial cell being disrupted and on its growth history; cells grown on simple synthetic media are generally less robust. For *Saccharomyces cerevisiae* and *Escherichia coli*, a values of 2.9 and 2.2, respectively, have been found. Within limits, the disruption process is independent of the concentration of cells in suspension. The optimum slurry viscosity and solids concentration ranges tend to be narrower for the high-pressure homogenizers than for the bead mills. The maximum slurry viscosity should normally not exceed 1 Pas for the homogenizer although more viscous material may be processed in some circumstances. Similarly the maximum acceptable particle size is about 20 μm; a lower size (~ 2 μm) is preferable. The homogenizer is not suited for fungal broths such as those of *Aspergilli* or for clumps of plant cells. The disruption rate constant is sensitive to the design of the valve seat and some designs are shown in Figure 38. While most of the available disruption data applies to valve seats type (a) in Figure 38, recent work has shown that valve seat (c) is significantly better than other designs in cell disruption applications.

From equation (131) it can be seen that the operating pressure is the major influence on disruption rate. Typically the operating pressure does not exceed 50–60 MPa but higher pressure (~ 130 MPa) equipment is available. An optimal choice of operating pressure is important because the power consumption during disruption is a linear function of the operating pressure, corresponding to about 3.5 kW per 100 MPa of operating pressure. The operating pressure also affects heat generation: at operating temperatures higher than 40°C, protein denaturation during disruption may occur. Since the temperature rise across a homogenizer due to adiabatic compression is about 2°C per 10 MPa, inadequate precooling, or failure to cool between multiple passes, can result in temperatures above 40°C and consequent denaturation. Although the degree of disruption is increased by the number of passes through the homogenizer, a minimum number is desirable in practice. Multiple passes not only reduce the machine throughput but also cause further disintegration of already broken cell debris which leads to separation problems further downstream.

A "microfluidizer" high pressure homogenizer which relies on complex interactions between multiple liquid jets, cavitation and impingement has recently become available. For bacteria such as *E. coli* and *Bacillus subtilis* this device gives a performance similar to the more traditional homogenizers but 95% breakage of yeast (*S. cerevisiae*) required 30 passes in one case compared with a residence time of only 3.3 minutes in a bead mill.

Other considerations

A unit operation cannot be considered in isolation from the rest of the process and the overall process must always be kept in mind. For example, the cell disruption operation affects the physical properties of cell slurry such as viscosity, density, particle size and settlability of suspension which in turn affect the subsequent processing.

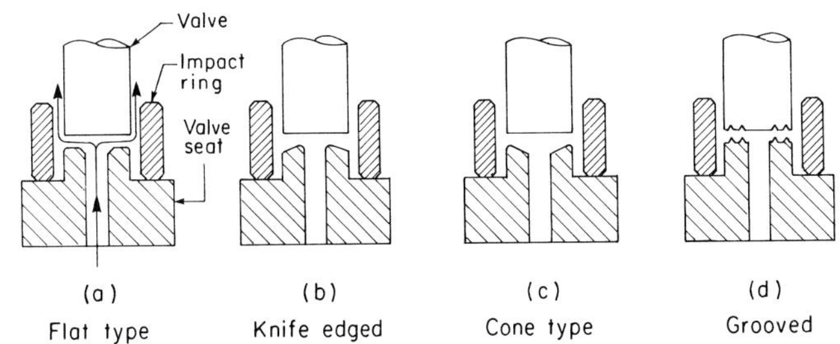

Figure 38. Valve seats for high pressure homogenizer.

Precipitation

Purification of enzymes and other biologically active proteins is often a multistep process. A single purification may involve cell disruption, debris removal, fractional precipitation, ion-exchange chromatography, gel filtration, affinity chromatography and crystallization. The smallest possible number of separation steps is desirable for reasons of economy. Generally, no more than seven are used; many industrial processes make use of relatively crude preparations of enzymes and one or two purification stages may be sufficient. The purification scheme may be configured to produce several products from a given mixture so reducing the unit cost of purification.

Selective precipitation of proteins from a solution of several proteins is among the oldest of purification and concentration techniques. Purification factors of 3–10-fold are relatively modest compared with chromatographic methods. However, precipitation methods can deal with large quantities of material which may be quite crude (cell debris, suspended solids, contaminants). Furthermore, continuous operation can be effectively employed. Precipitation is encountered frequently in protein purification schemes, predominantly as one of the early purification stages. Additional steps may be used downstream to polish further the product obtained at the precipitation stage.

The process of precipitation converts the soluble protein to an insoluble form by altering the solute-solvent interactions. Protein molecules carry positive and negative charges, the net charge being dependent on the solution pH, At the *isoelectric* pH the protein molecule carries zero net charge and is least soluble in a polar solvent such as water. The isoelectric pH of different proteins is usually different. Hence, by stepwise variation of pH of a protein solution different protein fractions may be precipitated and collected but exposure to extreme pH values may denature proteins and cause the loss of their biological activities. Protein precipitation by pH variation is employed in the food industry (*e.g.* in milk coagulation).

Unwanted, heat-labile protein may be coagulated out of solution of relatively thermally satable components by heating.

Water is a strongly polar solvent (with high dielectric constant $K_\Delta \simeq 80$ at 20°C) which interacts with the charged protein molecules to keep them in solution. The addition of less polar solvents such as methanol, ethanol and acetone ($K_\Delta \simeq 21$ at 20°C) reduces the dielectric constant of the solution and protein solubility accordingly declines. Fractionation by organic solvents is sensitive to temperature, pH, ionic strength and the presence of other metal ions. Manipulation of these parameters provides flexibility in the selection of separation conditions. However, organic solvents have a tendency to denature proteins and temperatures as low as −10°C may have to be used to reduce denaturation in a less polar environment.

Probably the most widely used protein precipitation technique is salting-out. Addition of salt (either as crystalline solid or concentrated solution) to protein solutions reduces protein solubility. This effect is apparently brought about by a reduction in water activity or water availability for protein hydration although the exact mechanics of salting-out remain uncertain.

The effectiveness of anions and cations in protein salting-out depends on ionic charge — in general, the higher the charge the more effective the ion. Based on this observation some common ions may be arranged into a salting-out efficiency series, the Hofmeister or lyotropic series of ions (Table 9). Table 9 is not a complete listing of possible ions. Commonly used salts are ammonium sulfate, sodium sulfate, potassium and sodium phosphates. Ammonium sulfate is cheap, and has high solubility at low temperatures; however, it is also corrosive and releases ammonia in alkaline environment. Protein salting out is controlled by the ionic strength, I, of solution which is calculated as follows

Table 9
Lyotropic Series of Ions

Anions	Cations	
Citrate^{3-}	Al^{3+}	
Tartarate^{2-}	Ba^{2+}	Decreasing
PO_4^{3-}	Ca^{2+}	effectiveness
SO_4^{2-}	Mg^{2+}	in precipitation
Acetate^{-}	NH_4^{+}	
Cl^{-}	Na^{+}	

$$I = \frac{1}{2} \sum_{i=1}^{n} c_i z_i^2 \qquad (132)$$

where c_i and z_i are the concentration and charge of the *i*th ion. Typical plots of protein solubility (S_p, kg m^{-3}) vs. ionic strength of solution follow the pattern shown in Figure 39. The linear portion of such plots is described by the Cohn equation

$$\ln S_p = \beta - K_{SL}\, I \qquad (133)$$

where K_{SL} is the salting out constant. The constant β depends on pH, temperature and protein, but is little affected by the salt.

The characteristics of protein precipitates depend significantly on such factors as the method of contacting the salt and the protein solution, the nature of mixing and the magnitude of shear fields in the precipitation reactor and on aging effects. Low shear, helical ribbon impeller agitated mixing vessels (Figure 40) have been found useful for contacting the reagent and protein solutions.

The operations of protein precipitation and precipitate processing have been examined in depth in an excellent review by Bell, Hoare and Dunnill.[22]

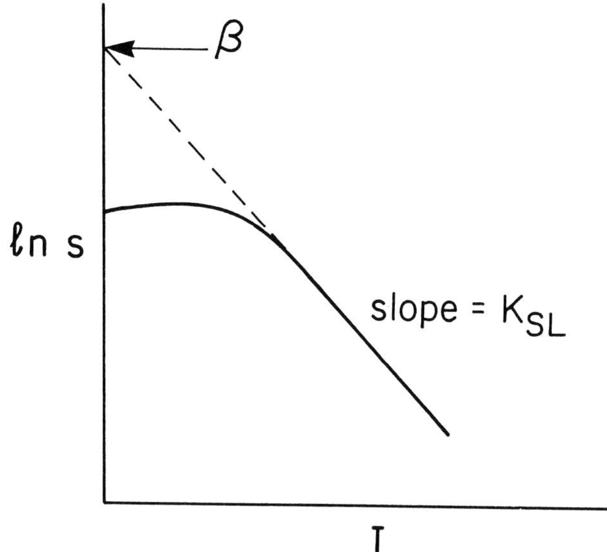

Figure 39. Protein solubility as a function of ionic strength of solution.

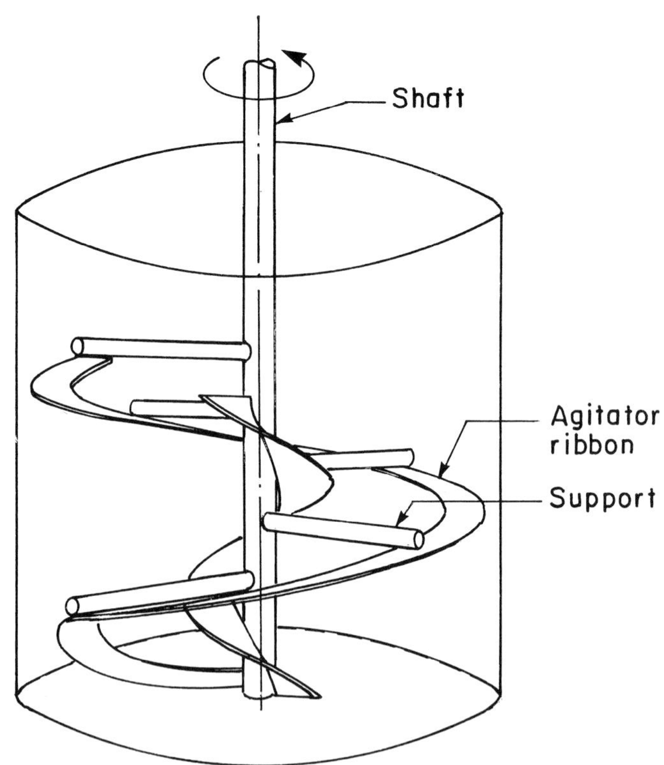

Figure 40. Helical ribbon impeller mixer.

Liquid-Liquid Extraction

Liquid-liquid extraction is a method of selective removal of a desired substance from a liquid phase mixture into a second immiscible liquid. The solute (*e.g.* antibiotic, organic acid) which is usually in aqueous solution (fermentation broth or liquor), when contacted with an immiscible solvent (extractant), distributes or partitions itself between the two phases. The extent of partitioning is determined by the partition coefficient, k_p, defined as

$$k_p = \frac{C_{solvent}}{C_{broth}} \qquad (134)$$

For organic acids and bases such as penicillins, benzoic acid, citric acid, erythromycin, k_p is strongly pH dependent: the salt forms of these compounds (*e.g.* sodium benzoate) have preferential solubility in aqueous media, while the acid (*e.g.* benzoic acid) or base (erythromycine) forms show higher solubilities in less polar, organic solvents. Variation of pH is thus used to alter k_p for the desired extraction. Addition of inorganic salts, fatty acids, detergents, etc., can be used to manipulate k_p which is also affected by temperature. Organic phases composed of mixtures of two or more organic solvents have been employed and in these cases k_p can be altered by changing the solvent composition.

The ratio of the total amount of solute in the two phases is known as the "degree of separation" (G) and depends on the volumes of the solvent and the broth:

$$G = \frac{C_{solvent} \cdot V_{solvent}}{C_{broth} \cdot V_{broth}} = k_p \frac{V_{solvent}}{V_{broth}} \qquad (135)$$

Equations (134) and (135) are equilibrium relationships.

Various types of extraction equipment are available and have been discussed in chemical engineering literature. In the antibiotic industry centrifugal extractors such as the Podbielniak extractor are commonly used for very rapid extraction. Excessive exposure of the antibiotic or other product to extraction conditions which may be deliterious (*e.g.* low pH in penicillin extraction) is avoided and because of the high centrifugal fields the formation of stable emulsions is reduced. Either whole broth or clear liquor may be extracted but the extraction of whole broth can lead to problems with blockages due to solids. The extractors consist of several perforated concentric shells attached to a central shaft which acts also as the inlet and outlet for the fluid streams. The shaft and the shells rotate; the dense liquid is fed to the innermost shell through the shaft and moves radially outward under the action of centrifugal force. A light liquid fed at the periphery of the outermost shell moves inward counter current to the flow of heavy liquid. The continuous circular interface (major interface) between the two liquids lies somewhere between the inner and outermost shells and its position can be controlled by varying the operating conditions. Selection of optimal operating conditions for any new application requires appropriate laboratory trials.

Proteins and other biopolymers which show reasonable solubility only in aqueous solutions, or are denatured in organic solvents, may be purified by liquid-liquid extraction between two *aqueous* phases. Immiscible aqueous phases for such applications are produced by dissolving high concentrations of two different polymers or a polymer-salt combination in water. The reading list should be consulted for additional information on this technique.

Chromatography

Industrial application of chromatography as a separation technique is a recent phenomenon, but already large scale production chromatography has proven itself particularly valuable for protein purifications. The production of insulin, hormones and medicinal enzymes makes use of this technique while blood plasma fractionation by chromatography is also rapidly developing. Very complex mixtures can be separated or resolved into their components.

Operating principles

All chromatographic separations depend on physicochemical interactions between the dissolved components of a mixture and a stationary phase. The latter is usually a solid (or a liquid supported on a solid) contained in a packed column. The mixture is applied to the column as a small volume of solution. The column is then washed or eluted with a solvent which constitutes the mobile phase. Different components of the mixture move down the column at different rates depending on how strongly a particular component interacts with the stationary phase. The components which associate strongly with the stationary phase flow down the column at a slower rate than those which do not bind strongly to the solid packing. As a result of their different velocities the different components of the mixture separate as they move down the column and can be collected as separate components. The phenomenon is analogous to what happens on a racing track: all contestants are at the starting position in a single line: part way down the track, however, they have separated and are at different distances from the starting position and from each other because of their different average speeds.

In industrial biological separations the mobile phase is always a liquid, usually an aqueous solution. However, the nature of the interactions between the mixture components and the stationary phase can be very different leading to different types of chromatography: they include affinity, ion exchange and hydrophobic chromatography as well as gel filtration. While all these are useful in biotechnological separations, ion exchange is widely used for protein purification and affinity chromatography is an especially powerful technique for biologically active substances. Beginning from the time a mixture is applied to a chromatographic column and the flow of eluting solvent is started, a concentration vs. time plot of the components emerging from the column can be plotted as in Figure 41. The peaks correspond to the two components the mixture, A and B. The extent of separation

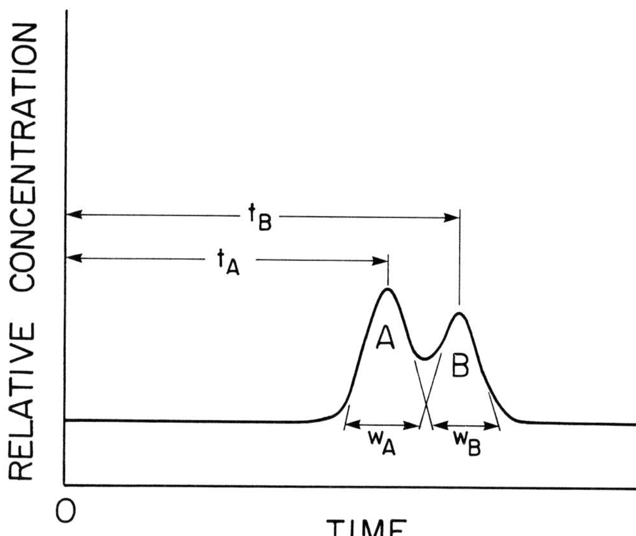

Figure 41. A chromatogram.

is measured in terms of the peak resolution, R_z, defined as the difference between the retention times (t_A and t_B) of the components divided by the average peak width:

$$R_z = \frac{2(t_B - t_A)}{W_A + W_B} \tag{136}$$

the peak widths being expressed in time units. When $R_z = 1.0$ the area of overlap of the two peaks is about 2% of the total area of peaks. To reduce the amount of overlap to 0.1% the resolution must be 1.5 or better.

The separation efficiency of a column is measured in terms of H the height equivalent of a theoretical plate (HETP) which is a concept common to all equilibrium stage operations conducted in packed columns. A theoretical plate can be considered as a contacting device on which the distribution of a component of a mixture between the stationary and mobile phases is determined by the equilibrium relationship. The greater the number of theoretical plates to which a given height of the column corresponds, the more efficient the column. The number of theoretical plates available for the separation of a component A is given as

$$N_A = 16 \left(\frac{t_A}{W_A}\right)^2 \tag{137}$$

where t_A is the retention time (see Figure 41) and W_A is the basal peak width. For a column of height L, HETP is

$$H_A = \frac{L}{N_A} \tag{138}$$

For a given column N_A and H_A are dependent on the component being separated.

For optimum separation minimum H is desired. The dependence of H on the eluent flow rate (U_L) which is the principal operating parameter is given by Van Deemter equation:

$$H = \frac{A}{U_L} + B\,U_L + C \tag{139}$$

which is plotted schematically in Figure 42. The minimum HETP is given by

$$H_m = A + 2\sqrt{BC} \tag{140}$$

and the elution velocity for H_m is

$$U_{Lm} = \sqrt{\frac{B}{C}} \tag{141}$$

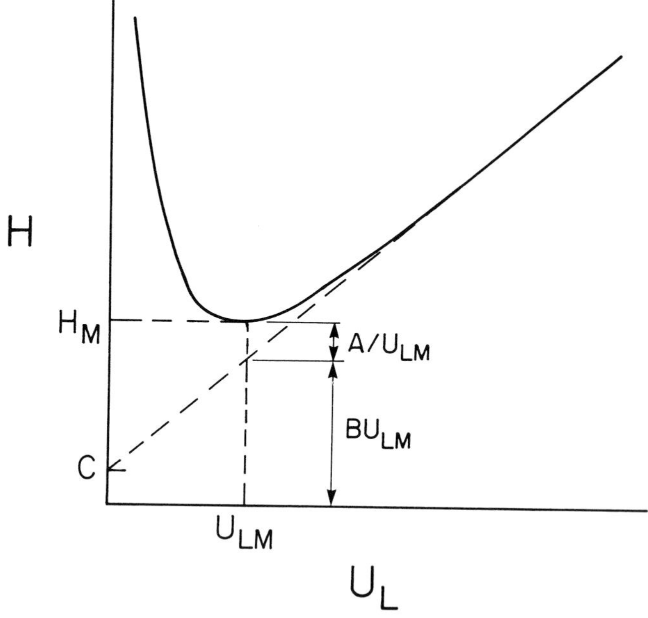

Figure 42. Height equivalent of a theoretical plate vs. the flow velocity.

The parameters A, B and C in eq. (139) represent, respectively, the effects of forward and backward diffusion of the components in the axial flow direction, the effects of mass transfer of the solute between the eluent (carrier solvent) and the stationary phase, and the channelling effects through the packing. Because in most biotechnological separations liquid eluents are employed the axial diffusional effects (parameter A) can be ignored even for low molecular weight species and when quite low ($< 1 \times 10^{-3}$ ms^{-1}) linear eluent flows are used. Low flow rates are desirable to reduce B and allow sufficient time for the solute to distribute itself between the mobile and stationary phases in each differential element of the column. As the molecular weight of the species being separated increases (as in the cases of enzymes and proteins in general) mass transfer becomes poorer and B increases with molecular weight.

In a well packed column the channelling effects (parameter C) are independent of flow and are minimized by using small spherical particles with a narrow size distribution as the packing material. Although theoretical reasoning indicates that a bed of small particles would give better separation efficiency, the operational requirement of acceptable pressure drop through the bed places lower limits on the size of bed material. The flow rate through a packed bed of rigid particles for a given pressure drop is calculated using the Kozeny-Carman equation

$$U_L = \frac{k_x\, d_p^2\, \Delta P}{L\, \mu_L} \cdot \frac{\varepsilon_S^3}{(1 - \varepsilon_S)^2} \qquad (142)$$

which applies for the laminar flow which normally occurs in chromatography columns. This equation is useful because it indicates the effects of bed voidage (ε_S), pressure drop (ΔP), bed height (L), eluent viscosity (μ_L) and the particle size (d_p) on the superficial velocity of the eluting solvent. The packing particle size (d_p), the eluent velocity (U_L) and the molecular diffusivity (D_L) of the solute in the eluent can be combined into a dimensionless reduced velocity (V_r) given by

$$V_r = \frac{U_L d_P}{D_L} \qquad (143)$$

For good separation performance U_L and d_p should be selected to give a reduced velocity in the range 3–10. This criterion, however, yields quite low values of U_L and in commercial practice the separation performance is often sacrificed to attain reasonable process throughputs.

Packing material

Selection of the column packing is the most important step in chromatographic separations. Properties of the components of the mixture and the operational requirements determine the most appropriate column packing for the given separation needs. Many of the chromatographic packing materials used in bioseparations are porous, hydrophilic substances (cross-linked polyacrylamide, agarose, cross-linked dextran, cellulose) which give rise to deformable particles. This restricts both the maximum pressure drop that may be used across the column and the column height to relatively low values to avoid the bed compressibility problems. Although packing materials with improved mechanical properties are becoming available the practical solution to avoiding bed compressibility while maintaining satisfactory separation performance is the use of stacked columns. These consist of several packed sections, typically no more than 30 cm thick, arranged in series in a stack to give the necessary column length (Figure 43); each section of the stack is a self-contained packed bed. Because the loading capacity (amount of mixture sample that may be handled in a single batch operation) is dependent on the amount of packing material, and because of the restrictions on height of any packed section, the commercial columns tend to have large diameters. Flow distribution, collection and redistribution of flow between packed sections require careful specialist design so that separation achieved is not lost by remixing of components during these transferring operations. Column chromatography as currently practiced is a batch separation technique: a batch of mixture is applied to the column followed by elution with a continuous solvent flow. However, column designs which allow continuous application of mixtures are being developed. The literature in the reading list should be consulted for details.

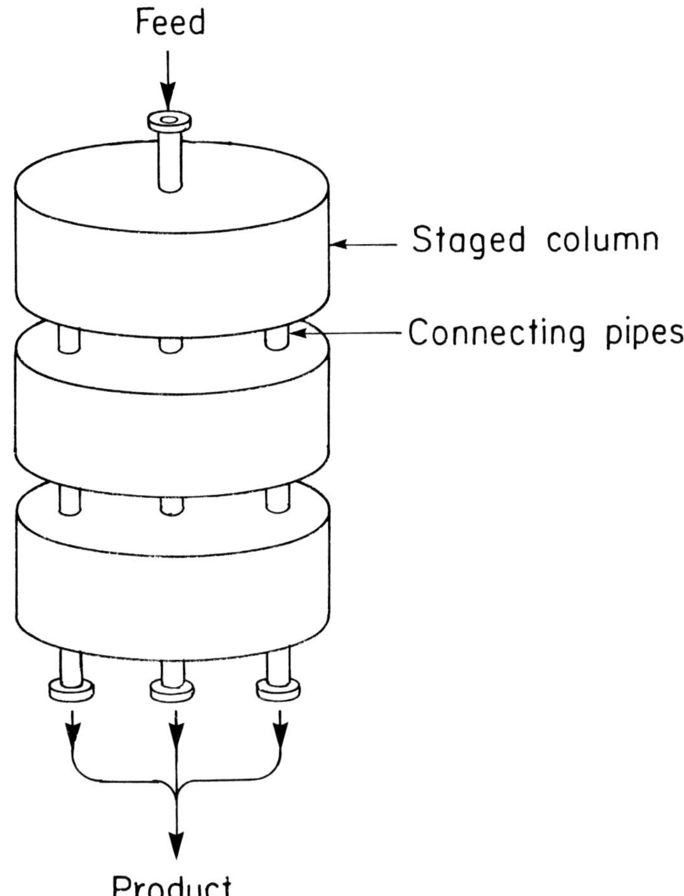

Figure 43. Stacked chromatography column.

Drying

Many products of the biochemical industry such as vaccines, enzymes, pharmaceuticals, etc. have to be dehydrated for preservation. Dry products keep well and are easy to package and transport. Several types of drying operations are employed; spray and freeze drying are particularly important for thermolabile, biologically active products.

Spray Drying

Spray drying is a method for rapid, continuous, drying of solutions, emulsions and slurries. Pressure or centrifugal atomizers or gas-liquid jets are used to generate a fine spray of solution droplets which are brought into continuous contact with hot air in a large chamber (Figure 44). Large droplet surface area and small droplet size ensure high evaporation rates so that drying times are but a few seconds. The flow of air is usually cyclonic. The dimensions of the drier must be such that the droplets do not reach the walls until sufficiently dry to prevent sticking and burn-on. A drying chamber tends to be quite large: 1–10 m in diameter being common. The dry powder settles to the bottom from where it is removed either pneumatically or mechanically, or by a combination of these methods.

Advantages of spray driers are: continuous operation, powdered product requiring no further size reduction and rapid drying which leads to good product quality particularly for heat-labile materials but relatively low thermal efficiency is a limitation.

Aseptic spray drying equipment is available. All the air used is filter sterilized and the drying and solids-handling chambers operate under slight positive pressure. The installations can be operated leak-tight and are sterilizable. Antibiotics such as streptomycine sulfate for direct injection can be spray dried. Highly heat-labile products like some enzymes and blood sera can be successfully spray dried. Microorganisms may be spray-dried for preservation and use as SCP.

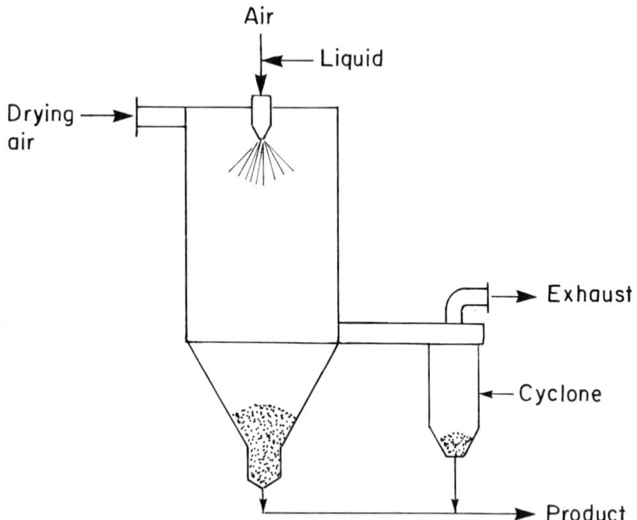

Figure 44. Schematic of a spray drier.

Freeze Drying

Freeze drying is the most gentle of the drying methods. The material to be dehydrated is frozen and the ice crystals sublimed by slight warming without thawing. The process may be carried out at atmospheric pressure or under vacuum and sublimation assisted with infrared or microwave radiation, or by contact heating. About 2800 kJ of heat needs to be supplied for each kg of ice removed. Freeze-dried products are easy to reconstitute (rehydrate) for use; thus, vaccines, blood plasma, hormones and enzymes are often freeze-dried but a disadvantage of the technique is the long processing time.

BIOPROCESS CONTROL

In order to ensure optimal functioning of a bioprocessing plant several processing parameters need to be monitored and controlled. Temperature, pH, product and substrate concentrations, dissolved oxygen, and material flows are a few of those which may have to be followed over time and manipulated in some predetermined way so as to obtain the desired product yields at minimal cost.

Computer-based control systems are increasingly encountered in biochemical processing plants and operations such as in-place cleaning, filling, sterilization sequences are often fully automated. Control of the biochemical reactor or fermenter is generally limited to control of pH, temperature and dissolved oxygen. A typically instrumented fermenter is shown in Figure 45. More extensive control of fermentation processes is desirable but it is restricted by two main factors: (i) the availability of online sensors to measure the biological and physicochemical parameters needed to follow the progress of fermentation remains limited; and (ii) our limited ability to interpret the available information in the context of the biological system so that the information obtained can be used as a basis for control. Substantial research effort is underway in overcoming these limitations.

Sophisticated control of fermentation systems presupposes the existence of a mathematical description — or model — of

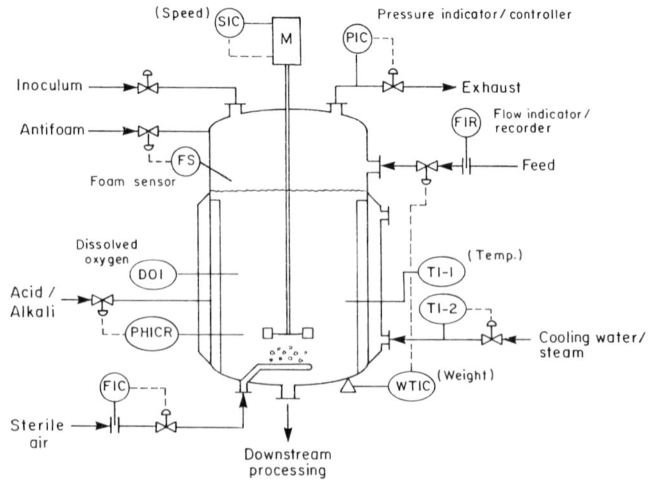

Figure 45. Typical fermenter instrumentation.

the process. The kinetics of growth and product formation in combination with the physical system characteristics form a set of equations which constitute the process model. One of the aims of control is optimisation of the process. In batch or fed-batch cultures, profiles of progressive changes in environmental conditions (temperature, pH, dissolved oxygen, substrate concentration) are determined for maximization of product yield. In continuous cultivation, optimisation is used to select an environmental regime for maximum biomass or product formation.

A series of chapters in *Comprehensive Biotechnology* (see Further Reading) provide in-depth insight into bioprocess control and control instrumentation.

THE OVERALL PROCESS

6-Aminopenicillanic Acid

Penicillins are among the most widely used antibiotics. About 10,000 tonnes of benzyl penicillin (Penicillin-G) are produced per annum by fermentation with *Penicillium chrysogenum*. Penicillin-G (PEN-G) itself is of limited use and most of it is converted to 6-aminopenicillanic acid (6-APA) which is a precursor for the manufacture of semi-synthetic penicillins (Figure 46). Although complete chemical synthesis of 6-APA is possible, it is economically not feasible on an industrial scale and an enzymetic method is commercially used for the conversion of PEN-G to 6-APA. The enzyme responsible for the transformation is penicillin acylase (EC 3.5.1.11) produced by the bacterium *Escherichia coli*. Several process varients may be used: (1) *E. coli* cells grown separately are killed and brought into contact with a solution of PEN-G at 37°C in a batch slurry reactor. After one use, however, the cells lose most of their enzyme activity due to lysis and have to be replaced. This is obviously a drawback. (2) Live, immobilized *E. coli* cells may be brought in contact with a continuous flow of PEN-G solution. Either packed bed or suspension reactor modes may be used. Side reactions and contamination by substances required to sustain the cells are some possible problems. (3) The enzyme penicillin acylase may be extracted from *E. coli*, immobilized and used in a continuous reactor. Scheme (1) has certainly been used commercially and the other two routes probably have been, too. The immobilized enzyme route is examined further in the following section.

The overall process schematic flow sheet[23] is depicted in Figure 47. A high yielding strain of *E. coli* grown in a batch stirred tank is used to obtain the enzyme. The cell slurry is concentrated by centrifugation and the cells disrupted in a high pressure homogenizer. The enzyme penicillin acylase is isolated by a two stage salt precipitation in a low-shear helical ribbon impeller vessel. The first step precipitates the nucleic acids which are removed by centrifugation along with

$C_6H_5CH_2C(=O)-NHC$ ... S ... N ... CO_2H

Penicillin - G

NH_2C ... S ... N ... CO_2H

6 - Aminopenicillanic acid

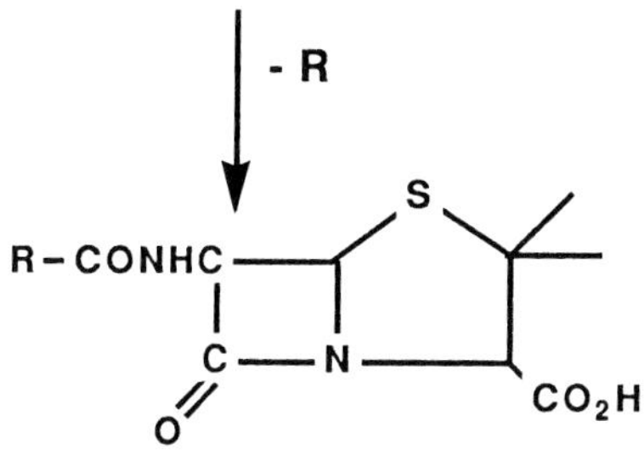

Figure 46. Semi-synthetic penicillins from benzylpenicillin (Penicillin-G).

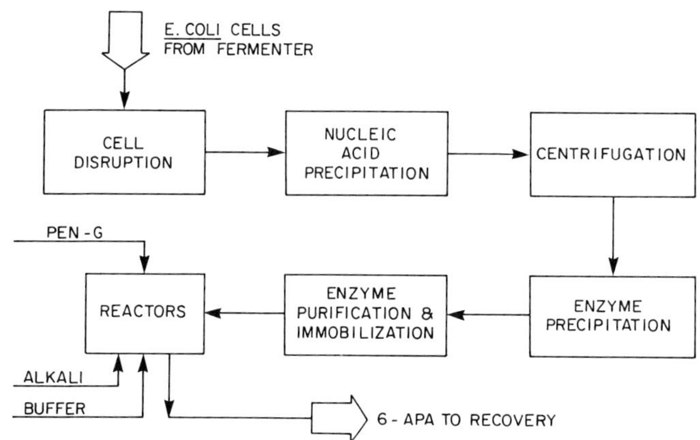

Figure 47. Schematic process flow sheet for production of 6-aminopenicillanic acid.

the cell debris. The enzyme precipitate undergoes some further separation to a relatively pure form which is immobilized on amberlite beads. The immobilized catalyst has a half-life of the order of several months under the normal reactor conditions of 37°C and pH 6–8, long enough for industrial purposes.

The kinetics of the deacylation reaction are such that it is strongly inhibited by 6-APA and is also susceptible to some substrate inhibition. Detailed calculations indicate a packed bed plug flow reactor for the conversion. However, as the deacylation reaction proceeds, the pH of the reaction medium drops and good pH control is necessary to avoid damage to the product, substrate and enzyme catalyst. Control of pH is difficult in packed columns and in this reaction is achieved by the addition of alkali to a buffered reaction medium. Rapid and uniform mixing is necessary throughout the reactor in order to avoid high local pH values which significantly reduce the half-life of the enzyme. To satisfy the operational requirement of good reactor mixing and at the same time to approximate the reaction system to a plug-flow type, a battery of four continuous stirred tank reactors (CSTRs) in series is used for the reaction. The use of four CSTRs is about optimum and a PEN-G conversion of more than 95% is theoretically possible. Addition of a fifth reaction stage in series would increase the conversion only slightly since the productivity of the catalyst in this stage would be low because it would be subject to inhibition by the reaction products which reach their maximum concentration in this last stage. A fifth stage would, of course, increase the capital and operation costs.

The process plant for even a relatively simple process such as the production of 6-APA can be surprisingly complex when in continuous operation. The requirements for automatic cleaning and catalyst replacement as well as the need to accommodate the associated flow schemes leads to extensive pipework, valves, pumps and other ancilliaries while the whole plant has, of course, to be built to hygienic standards.

CONCLUSIONS

This overview of bioprocessing and bioprocess engineering has naturally been limited to basic considerations and a selection only of processing operations has been presented. While very many factors combine to influence the final outcome, it is quite clear that the design of both equipment and operating protocols demands an integrated approach to the process under consideration.

NOMENCLATURE

Roman Symbols

A	Arrhenius parameter (s^{-1}); parameter in eq. (139) (m^2s^{-1})
A_b	Free area for flow between riser and downcomer (m^2)
A_d	Cross sectional area of downcomer (m^2)
A_f	Filter area (m^2)
A_H	Heat transfer area (m^2)
A_n	Arrhenius parameter for nutrient denaturation (s^{-1})
A_p	Surface area of particle (m^2)
A_r	Cross sectional area of riser (m^2)
a	Parameter in eq. 63 ($(m^{-1}s)^b$)
a_D	Gas-liquid interfacial area per unit dispersion volume (m^{-1})
a_L	Gas-liquid interfacial area per unit liquid volume (m^{-1})
B	Parameter in eq. (139) (s)
b	Parameter in eqs 63 and 67 (−)
C	Parameter in eq. 139 (m)
ΔC	Concentration difference ($kg\ m^{-3}$)
C^*	Saturation or equilibrium concentration ($kg\ m^{-3}$)
C_{broth}	Concentration in broth ($kg\ m^{-3}$)
C_{crit}	Critical oxygen concentration ($kg\ m^{-3}$)
C_G	Concentration in bulk gas ($kg\ m^{-3}$)
C_{Gi}	Interfacial concentration on gas side ($kg\ m^{-3}$)
C_i	Concentration of species i ($kg\ m^{-3}$)
C_L	Concentration in bulk liquid ($kg\ m^{-3}$)
C_{Li}	Interfacial concentration on liquid side ($kg\ m^{-3}$)
C_p	Specific heat capacity ($J\ kg^{-1}\ °C^{-1}$)
C_S	Concentration of solids (dry wt./vol.% (g/100 mL))
$C_{solvent}$	Concentration in solvent ($kg\ m^{-3}$)
C_t	Tracer concentration ($kg\ m^{-3}$)
$C_{t\infty}$	Equilibrium tracer concentration ($kg\ m^{-3}$)
c	Constant (eq. 64, 127) (as appropriate)
D	Diffusivity (m^2s^{-1})
D_e	Effective diffusivity in catalyst (m^2s^{-1})
D_f	Reciprocal of fraction of unreleased protein (−)
D_i	Impeller diameter (m)
D_L	Diffusivity in liquid (m^2s^{-1})
d	Diameter (m)
d_B	Sauter mean bubble diameter (m)
d_c	Column diameter (m)
d_{cp}	Connecting pipe diameter (m)
d_i	Diameter of the *i*th bubble (m)
d_T	Tank diameter (m)
E	Total amount of enzyme in reactor (kg)
ΔE	Activation energy ($J\ kmol^{-1}$)
E_{Lr}	Liquid phase axial dispersion coefficient in riser (m^2s^{-1})
ΔE_n	Activation energy for nutrient denaturation ($J\ kmol^{-1}$)
e	Enzyme concentration ($kg\ m^{-3}$)
G	Degree of separation (eq. 135) (−)
g	Gravitational acceleration (ms^{-2})
H	Height equivalent of a theoretical plate (HETP) (m)
$\bar{H}$	Henry's law constant (−)
H_A	H for component A (m)

H_m	Minimum HETP (m)
h_D	Dispersion height (m)
h_i	Heat transfer coefficient (inside film) ($J\ s^{-1}m^{-2}{}^\circ C^{-1}$)
h_{if}	Heat transfer coefficient (inside fouling) ($J\ s^{-1}m^{-2}{}^\circ C^{-1}$)
h_L	Unaerated liquid height (m)
h_m	Heat transfer coefficient (metal wall) ($J\ s^{-1}m^{-2}{}^\circ C^{-1}$)
h_o	Heat transfer coefficient (outside film) ($J\ s^{-1}m^{-2}{}^\circ C^{-1}$)
h_{of}	Heat transfer coefficient (outside fouling) ($J\ s^{-1}m^{-2}{}^\circ C^{-1}$)
I	Ionic strength (−)
J	Flux ($kg\ m^{-2}s^{-1}$ or $m^3m^{-2}s^{-1}$)
J_{O_2}	Oxygen flux ($kg\ m^{-2}s^{-1}$)
j	Number of CSTRs in series (−)
K	Consistency index ($Pa.s^n$)
K′	Constant (eq. 56) (−)
K_B	Frictional loss coefficient (bottom) (−)
K_C	Casson viscosity (Pa.s)
K_L	Overall mass transfer coefficient based on liquid film (ms^{-1})
K_S	Saturation constant, Michaelis constant ($kg\ m^{-3}$)
K_{SL}	Salting-out constant (eq. 133) ($kg\ m^{-3}$)
K_T	Frictional loss coefficient (top) (−)
K_y	Constant (eq. 126) (m^{-1})
K_Δ	Dielectric constant (−)
k	Mass transfer coefficient (ms^{-1})
k_D	Disruption rate constant (s^{-1})
k_d	Specific death rate (s^{-1})
k_f	Filter constant (m^{-1})
k_G	Gas film mass transfer coefficient (ms^{-1})
k_i	Constant (eq. 54) (−)
k_L	Liquid film mass transfer coefficient (ms^{-1})
k_n	Specific nutrient denaturation rate (s^{-1})
k_p	Partition coefficient (eq. 134) (−)
k_r	Rate constant (as appropriate)
k_s	Solid-liquid mass transfer coefficient (ms^{-1})
k_T	Thermal conductivity ($W\ m^{-1}{}^\circ C^{-1}$)
k_x	Constant (eq. 142) (−)
k_{1-3}	Constants (eq. 113) (as appropriate)
L	Length (m)
L_{cp}	Connecting pipe length (m)
M	Mass flow rate of gas ($kg\ m^{-3}$)
m	Mass of bead (kg)
$\underline{N}$	Microbial concentration (m^{-3} or $kg\ m^{-3}$)
$\overline{N}$	Impeller speed (rps)
N_A	Number of theoretical plates for component A (−)
N_o	Initial microbial concentration (m^{-3})
N_p	Number of passes (−)
n	Flow behaviour index (−)
n_i	Number of bubbles with diameter d_i (−)

P	Power (ungassed) ($W\ m^{-3}$)
ΔP	Pressure drop (Pa)
ΔP_{Fd}	Frictional pressure drop (downcomer) (Pa)
ΔP_{Fr}	Frictional pressure drop (riser) (Pa)
P_G	Gassed power ($W\ m^{-3}$)
Po	Power number (−)
ΔP_{TM}	Transmembrane pressure (Pa)
Q	Volume flow rate (m^3s^{-1})
Q_H	Heat transfer rate ($J\ s^{-1}$)
q_{O_2}	Specific oxygen consumption rate (kg O_2/kg cell·second)
R	Gas constant ($J\ K^{-1}\ kmol^{-1}$)
$\dot{R}$	Protein concentration ($kg\ m^{-3}$)
R_c	Resistance due to solids cake (m^{-1})
Re	Reynolds number (−)
Re_i	Impeller Reynolds number (−)
R_F	Total flow resistance (m^{-1})
R_M	Resistance of membrane (m^{-1})
$\dot{R}_m$	Maximum releasable protein ($kg\ m^{-3}$)
R_p	Particle radius (m)
R_s	Rate of substrate consumption ($kg\ s^{-1}$)
R_v	Volumetric reaction rate in catalyst ($kg\ s^{-1}m^{-3}$)
R_z	Resolution (−)
r	Radial distance (m)
r_B	Radius of bowl (m)
r_i	Initial radial position (m)
r_m	Resistance of filter medium (m^{-1})
r_s	Rate of surface renewal (s^{-1})
S	Substrate concentration ($kg\ m^{-3}$)
Sc	Schmidt number (−)
Sh	Sherwood number (eq. 110) (−)
S_i	Concentration in bulk liquid or concentration in liquid phase at solid/liquid interface ($kg\ m^{-3}$)
S_o	Initial substrate concentration ($kg\ m^{-3}$)
S_p	Protein solubility ($kg\ m^{-3}$)
T	Absolute temperature (K)
ΔT	Temperature difference (°C)
T_o	Initial temperature (°C)
T_s	Sterilization temperature (°C)
t	Time (s)
$t_{A,B}$	Retention times of peaks A and B (s)
t_c	Circulation time (s)
t_{cool}	Cooling time (s)
t_d	Mean doubling time (s)
t_e	Exposure time (s)
t_G	Gas phase residence time in liquid (s)
t_g	Mean generation time (s)
t_{heat}	Heating time (s)
t_{hold}	Holding time (s)
t_o	Zero time (s)
t_{op}	Operation time (s)
t_r	Residence time (s)
U	Average flow velocity (ms^{-1})
u_b	Bead velocity (ms^{-1})

U_H	Overall heat transfer coefficient (W m^{-2}°C^{-1})
$\underline{U}_L$	Liquid velocity (ms^{-1})
$\overline{U}_{Lc}$	Mean liquid circulation velocity (ms^{-1})
U_{Ld}	Superficial liquid velocity in downcomer (ms^{-1})
U_{Lm}	U_L at H_m (ms^{-1})
U_{Lr}	Superficial liquid velocity in riser (ms^{-1})
U_{max}	Maximum velocity (centreline velocity) (ms^{-1})
U_G	Superficial gas velocity (ms^{-1})
U_{Gr}	Superficial gas velocity based on riser (ms^{-1})
U_T	Tip speed (ms^{-1})
u_t	Terminal settling velocity (ms^{-1})
V_{broth}	Volume of broth (m^3)
V_C	Chamber volume (m^3)
V_G	Volume of gas in dispersion (m^3)
V_L	Liquid volume (m^3)
$\dot{V}_L$	Interstitial liquid velocity (ms^{-1})
$\dot{V}_{Ld}$	$\dot{V}_L$ in downcomer (ms^{-1})
$\dot{V}_{Lr}$	$\dot{V}_L$ in riser (ms^{-1})
V_p	Volume of particle (m^3)
V_r	Reduced velocity (eq. 143) (ms^{-1})
$V_{solvent}$	Volume of solvent (m^3)
$\overline{w}$	Dry weight of accumulated biomass (kg)
W_A, W_B	Basal width of peaks A and B (s)
$\underline{X}$	Solids concentration (dry) (kg m^{-3})
$\overline{X}$	Conversion (−)
X_o	Initial concentration of solids (dry) (kg m^{-3})
$\dot{x}$	Mass fraction of oxygen (−)
$\dot{x}_i$	Mass fraction of oxygen (inlet) (−)
$\dot{x}_o$	Mass fraction of oxygen (outlet) (−)
x_c	Circulation path length (m)
z	Filter depth, axial distance (m)
Z_B	Bowl length (m)
z_i	Charge on species i (−)

Greek Symbols

α	Parameter (eq. 84) (ms^{-1})
$\dot{\alpha}$	Mean specific cake resistance (m kg^{-1})
β	Parameter (eq. 84) (−); constant (eq. 133) (kg m^{-3})
$\dot{\gamma}$	Shear rate (s^{-1})
δ	Film thickness (m)
δ_G	Gas film thickness (m)
δ_L	Liquid film thickness (m)
δ_S	Thickness of solids layer (m)
ε	Overall gas holdup (−)
ε_d	Downcomer gas holdup (−)
ε_r	Riser gas holdup (−)
ε_S	Void fraction of solids (−)
η	Effectiveness factor (−)
μ	Specific growth rate (s^{-1})
μ_{ap}	Apparent viscosity (Pa.s)
μ_L	Liquid viscosity (Pa.s)
μ_{LW}	Fluid viscosity at wall temperature (Pa.s)
μ_m	Maximum specific growth rate (s^{-1})
μ_N	Specific cell number growth rate (s^{-1})
μ_S	Suspension viscosity (Pa.s)
ρ_L	Liquid density (kg m^{-3})
ρ_S	Density of solids (kg m^{-3})
Σ	Sigma factor (eq. 117) (m^2); summation
σ	Interfacial tension (N m^{-1})
τ	Shear stress (Pa)
τ_o	Yield stress (Pa)
ϕ	Thiele modulus (−)
ψ	Constant k_L/d_B (eq. 88) (s^{-1})
ω	Angular velocity

Abbreviations

6-APA	6-Aminopenicillanic acid
CMC	Carboxymethyl cellulose
CSTR	Continuous stirred tank reactor
DOP	Dioctylpathalate
HETP	Height equivalent of a theoretical plate
HTST	High temperature and short time sterilization
PEN-G	Penicillin-G (benzylpenicillin)
SCP	Single cell proteins

REFERENCES

1. Coulson, J.M. and Richardson, J.F. (1977). *Chemical Engineering*, **vol. 1** (3rd ed.) Oxford: Pergamon Press.
2. Bailey, J.E. and Ollis, D.F. (1977). *Biochemical Engineering Fundamentals*, New York: McGraw Hill.
3. Fair, J.R., Lambright, A.J. and Andersen, J.W. (1962). *Heat transfer and gas holdup in a sparged contactor.* Ind. Eng. Chem. Process Des. Develop., **1**, 33–36.
4. Deckwer, W.-D. (1985). *Bubble column reactors.* In Biotechnology, **vol. 2**, p. 445. Ed. by H.-J. Rehm and G. Reed. Weinheim: VCH.
5. Chisti, M.Y. and Moo-Young, M. (1987). *Airlift reactors: Characteristics, applications and design considerations.* Chem. Eng. Commun., **60**, 195–242.
6. Mann, R. (1983). *Gas-Liquid Contacting in Mixing Vessels*, Rugby: Institution of Chemical Engineers.
7. Akita, K. and Yoshida, F. (1973). *Gas holdup and volumetric mass transfer coefficient in bubble columns.* Ind. Eng. Chem. Process. Des. Develop., **12**, 76–80.
8. Godbole, S.P., Schumpe, A., Shah, Y.T. and Carr, N.L. (1984). *Hydrodynamics and mass transfer in non-Newtonian solutions in a bubble column. AIChE J.*, **30**, 213–220.
9. Nishikawa, M., Kato, M. and Hashimoto, K. (1977). *Heat transfer in aerated tower filled with non-Newtonian liquid.* Ind. Eng. Chem. Process Des. Develop., **16**, 133–137.
10. Chisti, M.Y. and Moo-Young, M. (1988). *Gas holdup in pneumatic reactors.* Chem. Eng. J., **38**, 149–152.
11. Chisti, M.Y. and Moo-Young, M. (1988). *Hydrodynamics and oxygen transfer in pneumatic bioreactor devices.* Biotechnol. Bioeng., **31**, 487–494.
12. Chisti, M.Y. (1989). *Airlift Bioreactors*, London: Elsevier Applied Science.

13. Fair, J.R. (1967). *Designing gas-sparged reactors.* Chem. Eng., **74** (July, 3), p. 67.
14. Deckwer, W.-D., Nguyen-Tien, K., Schumpe, A. and Serpemen, Y. (1982). *Oxygen mass transfer into aerated CMC solutions in a bubble column.* Biotechnol. Bioeng., **24**, 461–481.
15. Schumpe, A. and Deckwer, W.-D. (1987). *Viscous media in tower bioreactors: hydrodynamic characteristics and mass transfer properties.* Bioprocess Engineering, **2**, 79–94.
16. Moo-Young, M. and Kawase, Y. (1987). *Bioreactor design for slurry fermentation systems.* In Horizons of Biochemical Engineering, p. 281, Ed. by S. Aiba. Tokyo: University of Tokyo Press.
17. Merchuk, J.C. and Siegel, M.H. (1988). *Air-lift reactors in chemical and biological technology.* J. Chem. Tech. Biotechnol., **41**, 105–120.
18. Chisti, M.Y., Halard, B. and Moo-Young, M. (1988). *Liquid circulation in airlift reactors.* Chem. Eng. Sci., **43**, 451–457.
19. Chisti, Y. and Moo-Young, M. (1988). *Prediction of liquid circulation velocity in airlift reactors with biological media.* J. Chem. Tech. Biotechnol., **42**, 211–219.
20. Flaschel, E., Wandrey, C. and Kula, M.-R. (1983). *Ultrafiltration for the separation of biocatalysts.* Adv. Biochemical Engineering, **26**, 73–142.
21. Chisti, Y. and Moo-Young, M. (1986). *Disruption of microbial cells for intracellular products.* Enzyme Microb. Technol., **8**, 194–204.
22. Bell, D.J., Hoare, M. and Dunnill, P. (1983). *The formation of protein precipitates and their centrifugal recovery.* Adv. Biochemical Engineering, **26**, 1–72.
23. Chisti, M.Y. (1982). *A new process for the production of 6-aminopenicillanic acid from Penicillin-G.* The Polytechnic Ibadan Journal, **1**(1), 88–92.

FURTHER READING

1. References 2, 4–6, 12 and 20–22.
2. Bailey, J.E. (1980). *Biochemical reaction engineering and biochemical reactors.* Chem. Eng. Sci., **35**, 1854–1886.
3. Bjurstrom, E.E. (1985). *Biotechnology: Fermentation and downstream processing.* Chem. Eng. (18 February), pp. 126–158.
4. Brown, D.E. and Kavanagh, P.R. (1987). *Cross-flow separation of cells.* Process Biochemistry (August), pp. 96–101.
5. Erickson, R.A. (1984). *Disk stack centrifuges in biotechnology.* Chemical Engineering Progress, **80** (December), pp. 51–54.
6. Fiechter, A. (Editor, 1982). *Adv. in Biochemical Engineering,* **25**. Berlin: Springer-Verlag.
7. Karel, S.F., Libicki, S.B. and Robertson, C.R. (1985). *The immobilization of whole cells: engineering principles.* Chem. Eng. Sci., **40**, 1321–1354.
8. Keshavaraz, E., Hoare, M. and Dunnill, P. (1987). *Biochemical engineering aspects of cell disruption.* In Separations for Biotechnology (M.S. Verrall and M.J. Hudson, Eds.). Chichester: Ellis Horwood. pp. 62–79.
9. Konecny, J. (1977). *Theoretical and practical aspects of immobilized enzymes.* In Survey of Progress in Chemistry, **8** (A.F. Scott, Ed.). New York: Academic Press. pp. 195–251.
10. Kroner, K.H., Nissinen, V. and Ziegler, H. (1987). *Improved dynamic filtration of microbial suspensions.* Bio/Technology, **5** (September), pp. 921–926.
11. Mackay, D. and Salusbury, T. (1988). *Choosing between centrifugation and crossflow microfiltration.* The Chemical Engineer, April. pp. 45–50.
12. Moo-Young, M. (Editor, 1985). *Comprehensive Biotechnology,* **vol. 2.** Oxford: Pergamon Press.
13. Moo-Young, M. and Chisti, Y. (1989). *Considerations for designing bioreactors for shear-sensitive culture.* Bio/Technology, **6** (November), pp. 1291–1296.
14. Oldshue, J.Y. (1989). *Fluid mixing in 1989.* Chem. Eng. Progress, **85** (May), pp. 33–42.
15. Ripperger, S. (1988). *Engineering aspects and applications of crossflow microfiltration.* Chem. Eng. Technol., **11**, 17–25.
16. Schügerl, K., Lücke, J. and Oels, U. (1977). *Bubble column bioreactors.* Adv. Biochemical Engineering, **7**, 1–84.
17. Siegell, J.H., Dupre, G.D. and Pirkle, Jr., J.C. (1986). *Chromatographic separations in a cross-flow MSB.* Chem. Eng. Progress, **82** (November), pp. 57–61.
18. Tutunjian, R.S. (1985). *Scale-up considerations for membrane processes.* Bio/Technology, **3** (July), pp. 615–626.
19. Webb, C., Black, G.M. and Atkinson, B. (Editors, 1986). *Process Engineering Aspects of Immobilized Cell Systems,* Rugby: Institution of Chemical Engineers.
20. White, M.D. and Marcus, D. (1988). *Disintegration of microorganisms.* In Advances in Biotechnological Processes (A. Mizrahi, Ed.). New York: Alan R. Liss, Inc. pp. 51–96.

Chapter 14

Feedstocks

Geoffrey Hamer and Thomas Egli

INTRODUCTION

Irrespective of the scale of operation, the technology employed and the product produced, all commercial manufacturing processes have requirements for either a single feedstock or a range of feedstocks. The fundamental concept of commercial processing ventures is the generation of profit by risking capital investment in a processing plant. That plant, with an input of both know-how and energy, can transform or convert feedstocks by chemical, biological, mechanical or physical means into products of enhanced economic value relative to that of the feedstock utilized, such that after deduction of all costs, charges and taxes incurred, net profit generation results.

In this context, feedstocks represent the major material inputs into processing operations. In the case of microbially mediated processes, feedstocks will include only the major substrates and nutrients required by the microbes, i.e., carbon and energy sources, oxygen in the case of aerobic processes and a nitrogen source. All nutrients required in relatively smaller proportions to those specified above are generally excluded and simply considered as chemical additives required by the process.

One of the most fundamental of concepts in microbiology is the classification of microbes as either heterotrophs or autotrophs. Heterotrophs are those microbes that exhibit an obligate requirement for their growth for organic compounds, i.e., combined carbon energy substrates. Autotrophs on the other hand are able to use carbon dioxide as their carbon substrate for growth and either light (in the case of the photoautotrophs) or energy derived from the oxidation of reduced inorganic chemicals (in the case of the chemoautotrophs) as separate energy sources, respectively. Those autotrophs that can additionally utilize organic compounds as combined carbon energy substrates are described as "facultative autotrophs".

As far as combined carbon/energy substrates are concerned, these can be water soluble solids and water miscible liquid organic compounds (generally preferred for laboratory studies) water immiscible liquid and insoluble solid organic compounds (which are frequently encountered in industrial fermentation processes) and slightly water soluble organic gases and vapours which rarely provoke widespread interest in either the laboratory or as industrial process feedstocks.

Most of the carbon/energy substrates commonly used for the growth of microbial cultures in the laboratory are either water soluble or water miscible compounds. They vary from complex, ill-defined protein hydrolysates in the case of the cultivation of many microbes of medical and veterinary significance to supposedly pure organic compounds, most commonly sugars, that are used for the growth of bacteria in defined media. In general, so called pure substrates, of the quality grades used in microbial growth media, frequently contain trace concentrations of impurities that can also serve as secondary substrates. In fact, genuinely pure substrates are sufficiently expensive as to be virtually unknown in microbiology.

In the fermentation industry there is general acceptance that feedstocks contain significant concentrations of impurities. However, the consequences of these impurities on the physiology of the process microbes, particularly on their product forming ability, are frequently neither questioned nor understood. The production of many traditional fermentation products is based on the use of mixed microbial cultures which are often superior in their utilization of either impure or mixed substrates to microbial monocultures. Even so, virtually all modern biotechnological processes are based on pure monocultures or, in exceptional cases, the use of monocultures in sequence. Defined mixed process cultures comprizing a single primary species and a restricted number of secondary species offer numerous possibilities for the complete utilization of impure carbon energy feedstocks. Frequently the lack of fastidiousness exhibited by defined mixed cultures can be attributed to their ability either to utilize impurities present in commercial feedstocks or to make use of traces of inhibitory byproducts.

In any commercial process it is clear that feedstock costs play an important role in overall process economics and hence in process attractiveness from the commercial viewpoint. Clearly, the products of biotechnology can be divided into a number of categories based on their value: bulk products, which in general command relatively low prices, medium volume products, which command markedly higher prices than do bulk products and products that can be considered as essentially fine chemicals or biologicals, which command very high prices. For fine chemicals or biologicals it is usually the case that either product purity or efficacy is critical; their market prices are very largely divorced from the costs of the primary production operation but more closely related to both downstream processing costs and product quality testing costs.

In general, both bulk and medium volume products are produced commercially from low price feedstocks whilst, in the case of fine chemical products, medium cost feedstocks are widely utilized for production processes. In any discussion of feedstocks it is very important to examine both the criteria that dictate the price of any particular feedstock and those that control the prices of feedstocks that in either the medium or longer term might become realistic alternatives to the original feedstock proposed.

In the case of production processes mediated by heterotrophic microbes, carbon feedstocks must clearly also be energy sources. Such feedstocks include compounds or materials that have an alternative use for thermal energy production, derivatives of primary fuels, agricultural products used as food and feed ingredients and byproducts derived from agricultural product processing.

Two major criteria for the selection of a biotechnological process feedstock are its carbon content and its energy content; in other words, its relative state of oxidation and reduction. Until only a decade ago the question of the carbon and energy contents of carbon/energy substrates that were utilized by aerobic heterotrophic organisms was totally disregarded. The concept of either carbon excess but energy deficient, or carbon deficient and energy excess, substrates had not been recognized. Linton and Stephenson[1] exposed this failure when they demonstrated that, for microbial biomass production, the maximum attainable biomass yield coefficient on a carbon-carbon basis was proportional to the heat of combustion of the carbon/energy substrate on a carbon basis, provided the carbon/energy substrate in question did not exceed the heat of combustion of the dry microbes produced on a carbon, but ash free, basis. All carbon/energy substrates that exhibited higher heats of combustion (essentially higher degrees of reduction) than does the microbial biomass produced are utilized inefficiently by microbes; both inordinately high levels of low grade heat production ensues and, in high intensity, high productivity systems, oxygen transfer requirements are difficult to satisfy at a realistic cost.

Virtually any carbonaceous compound that is biodegraded by heterotrophic microbes can be considered as a potential process feedstock. However, the simple fact that it can be utilized by microbes does not automatically make the compound an attractive process feedstock. As far as microbial process feedstocks are concerned the definition of the term "attractive" depends upon who is responsible for the definition. There are many cases of compounds that are scientifically and/or technologically attractive feedstocks yet commercially unattractive, while many feedstocks that may appear idealistically and/or emotionally desirable suffer a similar fate when viewed in the harsh light of commercial reality. Among the latter, one of the major issues concerns the respective merits of renewable feedstocks, essentially either agricultural or forest products or feedstocks derived from them, on the one hand and non-renewable feedstocks, essentially fossil fuels or feedstocks derived from them, on the other. The idealistic/emotional view is that the former are clearly attractive while the latter are equally clearly unattractive. However, as far as the industrialized countries are concerned, the advantages frequently attributed to renewable feedstocks are for the most part myths.

Perhaps the most important question concerning the choice of feedstock is the number of degrees of freedom available. As Miall[2] has pointed out, it was only during the early 1960s. with the publication of production routes for single-cell protein (SCP) from gas oil and n-alkanes by Champagnat *et al.*[3], that evidence became available which effectively contradicted the hitherto universally accepted belief that industrial fermentation processes would always be based on carbohydrate feedstocks. In spite of the fact that some 10 years earlier Just *et al.*[4] had reported on the possibilities offered by various n-alkane fractions by Fischer-Tropsch synthesis as feedstocks for fermentation processes, this new view of carbohydrate feedstocks dramatically altered basic thinking with respect to potential feedstocks for biotechnological processes. In the past 25 years various liquid hydrocarbons, gaseous alkanes, hydrogen/carbon dioxide mixtures, vegetable oils, animal fats, alcohols, carboxylic acids and solid substrates such as cellulose and lignin have all attracted significant attention and have been subjected to evaluation as feedstocks for the production of a wide range of products. Today the basis for feedstock selection enshrines the concept of interchangeability of feedstocks in accordance with a complex matrix of technological feasibilities, product quality criteria, monetary efficiencies and politico-strategic policies. As far as fermentation products are concerned, very few processes with specific feedstock requirements exist. Provided a feedstock can be biodegraded, the potential for microbial product formation exists. However, as far as commercial processes are concerned, it is the rate at which the feedstock is utilised and the completeness of the overall process that are critical.

For biotechnological processes successful long term feedstock selection depends on effective planning based on realistic predictions of the future. Until a few years ago, single-line forecasts were the basis for most predictions and, provided time horizons were short, such forecasts seemed to provide an acceptable basis for planning. However, frequent failures occurred, particularly in the industrial sector of many national economies, although they were largely camouflaged until the end of the 1960s by rapid economic growth[5].

The most important sequence of events affecting planning in the last 25 years has been the series of steep price increases for crude oil that occurred from 1973 onwards. Prior to 1973, there had been considerable argument about whether the price of crude oil would ever exceed US$2 per barrel. These oil price increases, together with the exposure of similar failures in forecasting concerning many other important matters and the discovery that even the surrounding assumptions upon which most forecasts were based were wrong, clearly demonstrated the impossibilities of realistic planning on the basis of single-line forecasts.

As far as bulk product microbial biotechnology is concerned, the three ventures that have dominated the last three decades were:

1. Single-cell protein;
2. Fluid fuels (ethanol and methane);
3. Biopolymers;

To a very considerable extent, all three have become victims of failures in planning based on single-line forecasting. The best alternative that has been proposed to replace single-line forecasts is an approach involving the construction of a series of conceptual futures or scenarios. The effectiveness of applying scenario planning techniques to energy supply and demand was very clearly demonstrated as early as 1979 by DuMoulin and Eyre[6] when many of the real issues involved became clearly evident but were totally ignored in planning concerning biotechnological process ventures.

ENERGY ANALYSES AND FEEDSTOCK SELECTION

Energy analyses represent what has been the single most damaging factor as far as the realisation of bulk microbial product production processes are concerned. After the initiation of OPEC-mediated step price increases for crude oil in 1973, a worldwide obsession with future energy prices and availability ensued: virtually any approach that resulted either in alternative supplies of energy or energy saving was received with unabated enthusiasm. In pursuit of this objective, many basic assumptions were made, including the acceptance that rapid depletion of world reserves of fluid fossil fuels would occur, that in the future OPEC would continue its escalation of cartel-mediated crude oil price increases *ad infinitum* by restricting production quotas, that irrespective of capital investment requirements all energy saving and energy trapping proposals would be economically attractive, that energy efficiency and monetary efficiency are compatible concepts, that neither politically mediated differential regional and/or national pricing policies nor restrictions to free international trade would occur with respect to either energy or agricultural commodity products and that, through accelerated and unrestricted renewable agricultural and forestry resource exploitation, a bioresource-based global economic order could be established in the short term.

Subsequent examination of the validity of these assumptions have shown most of them to be insustainable. For example, estimates of total world crude oil reserves show a significant increase between the mid-1970s and the mid-1980s although this does not apply in all producing regions. Furthermore, during the mid-1980s, OPEC was not able to sustain crude oil prices by restricting production and prices fell markedly compared with earlier attained price maximums.

The first published example of an evaluation of bulk microbial production routes on the basis of their estimated gross energy requirements was by Lewis[7] and concerned single-cell protein. The results effectively demolished the concept of producing single-cell protein from fluid fossil fuel-derived feedstocks and emphasized the apparently more energetically favourable potential exhibited by materials of agricultural origin as microbial process feedstocks. Such an approach is an extension of single-line forecasting and assumes that an invariant ratio exists between the exploitable energy content of different carbonaceous feedstocks, irrespective of the mode of exploitation of the energy content, that a fix ratio exists with respect to different feedstock prices and that a global price exists for each specific feedstock. Such assumptions are clearly invalid. Microbial processes exhibit marked variations in yield coefficients and even when these are optimized, conversion coefficients are frequently dependent on the physical form of the feedstock and/or the type and mode of operation of the bioreactor employed. Further, data presented by Drozd[8] clearly demonstrates both marked fluctuations in the ratios of the prices of various potential microbial process feedstocks with respect to time and equally marked changes in feedstock prices from region to region; these result primarily from political interference in the pricing of agriculturally produced commodity products which dissociates production costs from product prices, thereby disrupting the supply versus demand relationship. A further dimension serving to invalidate the energy analysis approach is that many microbial process feedstocks have no alternative use as fuels; hence, pricing on an equivalent fuel value basis is largely irrelevant.

With the demise of single-cell protein production from fluid fossil fuel-derived feedstocks and the subsequent obsession with renewable energy sources, the emphasis of bulk microbial product research and development was reoriented to fluid fuel (ethanol and methane) production both from crops grown specifically for the purpose and from various agro-industrial wastes. Single-line forecasts based on energy analysis concepts clearly encouraged projects involving the conversion of agricultural products into fluid fuels and soon after 1973 massive efforts in process research and development for an industrial-scale production of ethanol and methane (biogas) were established throughout the developed and the developing world. Essentially what occurred, virtually overnight, was a complete change of direction as far as the objectives of bulk product microbial biotechnology was concerned, i.e., instead of producing food and feed ingredients from fossil fuels and/or their derivatives, a new direction requiring the production of fossil fuel substitutes, specifically ethanol, from so called energy crops such as maize (corn) and sugar cane was initiated. As far as ethanol production was concerned, the relative failure that occurred in the industrialized countries such as the U.S. must be contrasted with the relative success that occurred in some developing countries, with Brazil, undoubtedly, the best example.

Essentially, the problem that most countries faced as a result of the OPEC-mediated crude oil price increases was a potential shortfall in supplies of liquid fuels, particularly automotive fuels. In the specific case of the U.S., the combination of events that stimulated the development of "gasohol", a 10 percent ethanol/90 percent gasoline blend, were several. First, even prior to any step changes in crude oil prices, legislation requiring a reduction in lead-based octane enhancers was enforced. This, together with the question of indigenous liquid fossil fuel resource depletion, associated strategic attitudes concerning the security of supply of liquid fuels, a marked overproduction of corn resulting in seriously depressed corn prices and a strong agricultural lobby that sought a reverse in corn prices combined to enhance enthusiasm for gasohol production from corn. As Phillips and Humphrey[9] have pointed out, under most favourable case conditions for gasohol production in the U.S., the overall energy balance was clearly positive, but under worst case conditions it was marginal, although on a liquid fuel energy balance basis it still remained potentially attractive. However, the conflict between crop use for either fuel or food was never clearly resolved. By 1979 it had become obvious that fuel ethanol production economics were dependent on the by no means fixed ratio that exists between OPEC-mediated crude oil prices on the one hand and corn production cost which depend on the vagaries of productivity (yield) dependent factors, particularly climatic factors, on the other hand.

In the case of Brazil, where large-scale fuel ethanol manufacture is a commercial reality, motivation for the initiation of ethanol production ventures was distinctly different from that which existed in the U.S. As a result of the step changes in crude oil prices, virtually all developing countries devoid of their own oil resources experienced a similar problem: an inability to pay for their liquid fuel requirements in U.S. dollars, the currency in which crude oil is priced and traded. This was often exacerbated by the non-convertability of their own national currencies and it further compounded their balance of payments difficulties. For those countries such as Brazil with extensive land resources, suitable climatic conditions for high agricultural productivities and appropriate expertise in process plant design and construction, indigenous fuel ethanol production, with no significant requirement for either imported equipment or technology, was an obvious solution for counteracting deficits in liquid fuel availability. The Brazilian National Alcohol Programme (PROALCOOL) was established in 1975 to increase the indigenous output of ethanol destined for industrial and automotive uses. The initial objectives of PROALCOOL were to lessen Brazil's vulnerability to external politically mediated events, to make Brazil a world leader in fermentation ethanol production technology, to produce a cost-effective substitute for imported oil and to generate employment in the agricultural sector. Whilst initially it was intended to aim for automotive fuels comprizing 20 percent ethanol/80 percent gasoline, the subsequent target involved complete substitution of gasoline by ethanol. The success of PROALCOOL can be measured in terms of the increase in ethanol production from 6×10^5 m^3 in the 1975–76 crop year to 9.2×10^6 m^3 in 1984–85, with the projection for 1987–88 being 14.3×10^6 m^3[10]. However, on the basis of PROALCOOL's own evaluation, fermentation ethanol can only compete when crude oil prices exceed US$29 per barrel. One of the most fundamental problems concerned with crude oil substitution is that its market price is dissociated from production costs; it is essentially a compromise between a price that the market will accept and one which generates a satisfactory income for the members of OPEC such that individual OPEC members will not significantly exceed their production quotas, thereby creating fragmentation and, ultimately, the collapse of the cartel. Further, the price is also set so that no significant market opportunity exists for substitute liquid fuels and feedstocks from alternative sources.

The subject of liquid fuels and feedstocks from renewable feedstocks produced by agriculture has been addressed by Andrew[11] who has sought to explain on the basis of the very great differences in the energy efficiencies of the human operators involved the apparent contradiction between the relative success of ethanol for automotive fuels in Brazil with the almost total disenchantment with the concept that has occurred in the U.S. Essentially, the energy efficiency of an agricultural labouring populace with a relatively low standard of living, as is the case in Brazil, compares extremely favourably with the energy efficiency of workers in the U.S., such that the true energy efficiency of ethanol production in the two countries differs primarily in the differing human energy efficiencies involved.

The maintenance of low standards of living amongst agricultural labouring populations is inconsistent with development and it has been one of the primary objectives of the agricultural policy of the EEC to eliminate such inequities. However, an emerging concept within the EEC is one in which biotechnological processes are being sought for the utilization, as feedstocks, of surplus agricultural commodity products[12]. Clearly such proposals can only be supported on either protectionist or strategic grounds rather than on the basis of realistic economics.

Methane (biogas) production is a concept that has also

been widely proclaimed since 1973. It is nevertheless most important when considering this matter to differentiate between the potential of biogas in the energy deficient regions of developing countries compared with industrially developed country situations and to differentiate between by-product biogas production from either anaerobic waste sludge digestion or landfill sites and biogas production from solid biomass produced by energy-cropping.

Interest in biogas production is worldwide and includes programmes in both the industrially developed and developing countries. Village- and community-scale production has many obvious advantages in developing countries and advances in China and, to a lesser extent, in India, bear witness to this. In both Europe and North America, very extensive biogas research programmes have been established. Such programmes have been directed towards both farm-scale production with on-site use and commercial-scale gas production coupled with distribution networks.

Evaluations of biogas production projects in industrially developed countries frequently fail to incorporate the costs of the bioreactor and ancillary process plant in an economically realistic manner, thereby over-emphasizing the potential benefits of such processes. Important factors that must be considered when evaluating biogas production processes for introduction in industrially developed countries are: the consistency of composition and maintenance of the fuel value of the biogas produced; the attainment of distributed gaseous fuel quality criteria, particularly with respect to hydrogen sulphide concentration; and economic and acceptable treatment and disposal techniques for residual liquid and solid wastes from such processes.

In industrially developed countries, it is already clear that biogas production from large landfill sites offers commercially attractive possibilities as investment costs for such systems are confined to collection, purification and storage. With this exception, biogas production ventures are without commercial interest in industrialized countries with unrestricted economies.

WATER SOLUBLE/MISCIBLE CARBON ENERGY FEEDSTOCKS

Mono- and Oligosaccharides

Mono- and oligosaccharides represent two of the three groups of compounds that comprize carbohydrates, i.e. compounds composed of carbon, hydrogen and oxygen, which correspond to the general composition $C_n(H_2O)_m$. Essentially, mono- and oligo-saccharides are readily water soluble while the polysaccharides, which comprize the third group of carbohydrates, are water insoluble and frequently form colloidal suspensions in water when they occur in a relatively pure form. The best known monosaccharides are glucose and fructose, while the best known oligosaccharides are sucrose, maltose and lactose; all of them are natural products. Examples of polysaccharides include starch, glycogen and cellulose.

Monosaccharides, depending on their chemical nature are either hydroxyaldehydes (aldoses) or hydroxyketones (ketoses) and, according to the number of oxygen atoms present in the molecule, are described as bioses, trioses, tetroses, pentoses or hexoses. Glucose and fructose are fairly widespread in Nature as constituents of sweet fruits although monosaccharides occur naturally to a much greater extent as monomers in the molecules of both oligosaccharides and polysaccharides.

For the most part, any monosaccharide that finds application as the carbon/energy feedstock for either a medium or bulk volume microbially-mediated production process will be derived from either an oligosaccharide or a polysaccharide; with the exception of the aldohexose D-glucose, the aldoketose D-fructose, and possibly the pentose D-xylose, they are rarely available in either sufficient quantities or of appropriate purity to be considered as essentially single compound process feedstocks that can stand alone for evaluation.

By far the most widely utilized fermentation process feedstocks are either an oligosaccharide, specifically sucrose, in an essentially pure form, or fluid byproduct streams from oligosaccharide production, specifically molasses (sucrose) and whey (lactose), that remain relatively rich in their oligosaccharide concentration.

As has been pointed out by Coombs[14] the range of sucrose-containing fluids available for use as process feedstocks depends on the crop used for sugar production, the technology adopted and the product or by-product stream selected for use. The two crops used for sugar production are sugar beet in temperate regions and sugar cane in sub-tropical and tropical zones. Although the processing methods used for each crop differ, the ultimate objective of processing is the same: the production of white crystalline sugar. The main products and intermediates available from sugar processing able to serve as process feedstocks are:

(i) refined white sugar (>99.7% sucrose) derived from either sugar cane or sugar beet;
(ii) raw cane sugar (containing >99.5% by weight sucrose) on a dry basis;
(iii) molasses, of which several distinct types may be identified, i.e., blackstrap (cane factory) molasses, refinery molasses, beet molasses and high test molasses;
(iv) intermediate process streams;
(v) cane juice or beet juice.

The world production of sugar varies between 90 and 100 M metric tonnes per annum whilst consumption is generally a few percent below production. However, sugar production could easily be increased if a demand existed.

For each metric tonne of sugar produced, approximately 300–360 kg of molasses are produced as byproduct, suggesting that the total world availability of molasses as a feedstock is between 30 and 40 M metric tonnes per annum. Molasses is the traditional carbon energy feedstock for many fermentation processes. However, the concentration of sucrose in residual molasses depends on the degree of optimization achieved in the sugar refining process and modern process technology is tending to reduce sucrose concentrations to values where molasses looses its attractiveness as a potential feedstock. Because of this, intermediate process streams such as high test molasses, from which no sugar has been removed, or refined sucrose are presently considered much more attractive feedstocks from a technical viewpoint. The fundamental problem with either sucrose or concentrated sucrose streams as feedstocks is economic in nature with the major question being what price or range of prices of sugar should be used for the economic evaluation of processes which might not become fully operational for almost a decade?

Raw sugar, as with many agricultural products, is traded as a commodity so, when either demand or forecast demand slightly exceeds either supply or forecast supply, dramatic price increases occur; in the reverse situation, prices plummet. An examination of raw sugar prices during the mid-1980s is particularly illustrative of these movements. In August 1984, the price of raw sugar fell to only one third of that pertaining in August 1983, with a fourteen year low of US$100.50 per tonne being reached in mid-December 1984. The price of raw sugar remained relatively depressed at below US$150 per tonne until August 1987 but by July 1988 peaked to US$400 per tonne, but fell back by August 1988 to US$270 per tonne. In spite of the above prices being quoted in US $ of the day rather than corrected to a standardized base, fluctuations have clearly been dramatic in spite of relatively little change in either production or real demand. To predict raw sugar prices ten years hence is obviously not without pitfalls but as far as commodity trading is concerned such an objective is without interest; what matters is the crop year and the agricultural support policies of regional political alliances or cartels such as the EEC.

The impact of pre-1986 EEC regulations on the price of sucrose as a fermentation feedstock has been discussed by Gray[13] in a paper in which the policies of EEC pricing are explained and where it was admitted that biotechnological industries within the EEC faced a major handicap: whereas in an EFTA country, industry could purchase sucrose of EEC origin at a world price of between 150 and 200 ECU per tonne, in an adjacent EEC country, the price of sucrose from the same source would be 550–580 ECU per tonne. Furthermore, products such as citric acid produced from the sucrose in an EFTA country were not subject to discrimatory duty when sold in an adjacent EEC country. In order to overcome the disincentive both with respect to investment in the biotechnological process industries in the EEC and the use of sugar and starch as feedstocks new regimes based on world prices for industrial feedstocks were introduced in mid-1986.

In some parts of the world, specifically those with extensive dairy industries, whey represents a potentially important oligosaccharide-containing feedstock. Whey is a byproduct of cheese manufacture and, in the form in which it is produced, is relatively dilute for use as a feedstock. In many countries production is widely distributed but where centralized production occurs quantities of between 500 and 1500 metric tonnes per day can be produced and concentration of whey results in its availability in several forms: whey molasses (containing ca. 70% solids), whey permeate (containing between 35 and 50 kg m^{-3} of lactose) and whey powder (a dried solid material). Whey can be readily demineralized and/or deproteinized. Just as with beet sugar production, whey is also a feedstock that is subject to the vagaries of political decisions on European agricultural policies.

Mono- and Polyhydric Alcohols

Certain alcohols have the unusual distinction of being both fermentation process products and fermentation process feedstocks. However, from the viewpoint of application as commercial process feedstocks, the range of alcohols requiring consideration is relatively restricted. Primary candidates as process feedstocks are the monohydric alcohols methanol and ethanol and the trihydric alcohol, glycerol. The monohydric alcohols are essentially hydrocarbon molecules in which a hydrogen atom has been replaced by a hydroxyl group so that their general formula is $C_nH_{2n+1}OH$. In the case of methanol $n = 1$ and in ethanol $n = 2$. Glycerol is a C_3 molecule comprising five hydrogen atoms and three hydroxyl groups. All three alcohols occur naturally. Traditionally, methanol is produced by the destructive distillation of wood, ethanol by the fermentation of carbohydrates and glycerol by the hydrolysis of fats. Today methanol is usually produced on a very large scale from either natural gas or a liquid hydrocarbon fraction such as naphtha, although production from coal is equally feasible. Both ethanol and glycerol are still produced in significant quantities by the traditional technologies mentioned above. As far as its use as a fermentation process feedstock is concerned, fermentation ethanol is clearly a non-starter because the carbohydrate feedstock used for its production would inevitably substitute for it. However, where ethanol is manufactured via a petrochemical route from ethylene, its potential as a fermentation process feedstock depends on the economics of its production. For many years petrochemical ethanol was cheaper to produce than was fermentation alcohol, but today respective prices are clearly controlled by the complex politics and strategic arguments surrounding agricultural commodities and oil (energy). Glycerol is also produced on a large scale by petrochemical process routes from propylene either via allyl chloride or via allyl alcohol. The former process is extreme with respect to its resultant pollutant load and in this respect the latter process has clear operating advantages. An alternative biological route for glycerol production has also been suggested and involves production by osmophilic species of unicellular green microalgae of the genus *Dunaliella* which are able to synthesize very high intracellular glycerol concentrations when growing photoautotrophically under conditions of high salinity. If glycerol is to become a major fermentation process feedstock in the future, its most likely source will nevertheless be via a petrochemical, rather than a biological route unless strategic policies invalidate conventional economic principles. From the technical viewpoint, glycerol represents an ideal substrate for microbial biomass production because its carbon and energy contents are essentially balanced.

Methanol was first considered as a potential fermentation process feedstock only some 20 years ago although methanol-utilizing microbes were first discovered 55 years earlier. Even in the laboratory, the use of methanol as a carbon energy substrate was very largely ignored until about 1960. However, the realization in the late 1960s that methanol was, at that time, one of the cheapest and most abundant water-miscible carbon energy feedstocks available for fermentation processes prompted prodigious efforts aimed at its effective utilization, particularly with respect to SCP production. Clearly, methanol became markedly less favoured as a potential carbon/energy feedstock during the series of step price increases for crude oil in the years after 1973 but, in fact, its price did not follow oil prices quite as closely as might have been expected; the reasons included its production from natural gas in regions where natural gas demand and/or export possibilities were restricted together with massive over capacity for its production in very large-scale single process line plants that were unsuited for operation at reduced capacities. Present day (end 1988) crude oil prices of ca. US$13 per bbl represent no more than a doubling of real prices compared with 1970. One of the primary effects of the oil price escalation was to stimulate the development of alternative energy sources and the realization of one such activity, the production deep earth gas[15], could mean a secure supply of methane, and therefore of methanol, for several centuries to come.

Methanol has been criticized as a fermentation process feedstock on several grounds. These include the fact that it is an energy excess feedstock and, as such, its utilization results in excessive heat production; that it is a very simple molecule so that product formation depends on synthesis rather than breakdown to an intermediate and subsequent synthesis; it is inhibitory, even to many methanol-utilizing microbes; and even at relatively low concentrations uncoupling of growth and respiration occurs, thereby depressing biomass yield coefficients and wastefully converting feedstock to carbon dioxide. However, as has been pointed out by Dijkhuizen *et al.*[16], very considerable potential still exists for methanol as a biotechnological process feedstock provided a better understanding of the regulation of those metabolic fluxes leading to useful products in methylotrophs can be gained. Further, increases in the spectrum of characterized methylotrophic microbes to include strains that grow optimally on methanol up to 55°C[17] further enhances the possibility of more widespread use of methanol as a commercial process feedstock.

To date, the primary application of methanol as a feedstock has been for the production of SCP where very considerable success was achieved. Its potential as a feedstock for exopolysaccharide production has also been extensively investigated and evaluated but, compared with glucose, it is markedly inferior both with respect to the product oxygen-based yield coefficient and high levels of heat dissipation, features that would make process routes based on methanol both technologically and economically unattractive.

Provided crude oil prices remain low and more closely associated with production costs, ethanol produced by petrochemical routes must also be considered to be a potential major feedstock for fermentation processes in the future. It possesses clear advantages over the initial feedstock (crude oil) and the intermediate (ethylene) as a fermentation feedstock, being a water miscible liquid rather than either a water-immiscible liquid or a moderately soluble gas. Clear advantages that ethanol possesses as a feedstock are the very broad spectrum of both eucaryotic and procaryotic microbes capable of growth on it and the fact that it is an approved food ingredient thereby rendering any food products produced from it essentially more acceptable and less subject to criticism on a regulatory basis. Disadvantages include its inhibitory nature if encountered in significant concentration to those microbes that can utilize it for growth and, as with methanol, it is an energy excess substrate so that its use exacerbates process cooling problems. During the era of SCP a number of major companies devoted very considerable efforts to the development of an ethanol based route for production.

Carboxylic Acids

The shorter chain length carboxylic acid are also both microbial substrates and microbial products. Carboxylic acids, which have the general formula C_nH_{2n+1} COOH, can be regarded as either carboxylic derivatives of hydrocarbons or derivatives of water in which a hydrogen atom has been replaced by the $C_nH_{2n+1}CO$- radical. With increasing chain length, the odour of short chain carboxylic acids becomes increasingly obnoxious, but in spite of this, acetic, propionic, butyric and valeric acids can all be considered to be either actual or potential fermentation process feedstocks. Formic acid, the first member of the carboxylic acid series, cannot be regarded as a potential process feedstock because it is one of the most energy-deficient carbon substrates commonly encountered.

The carboxylic acids are, of course, natural products with acetic acid being the most widely available for potential utilization as a feedstock. It was traditionally produced either by the microbially-mediated oxidation of ethanol or by recovery from pyroligneous acid produced by the distillation of wood. More recently, with the development and growth of the petrochemicals industry, the traditional production routes have been supplemented by synthetic acetic acid.

At first sight, the use of synthetic acetic acid as a fermentation process feedstock would seem unrealistic unless it were produced from liquified petroleum gases (LPGs), primarily propane and butane. However, acetic acid (acetate) has been very widely used as a commercial feedstock in Japan for amino acid and 5'-nuceotide manufacture. Such products are frequently produced from molasses as a feedstock but throughout the 1960s the Japanese fermentation industry was subject to a politico-strategic quota system with respect to molasses importation from all sources other than Okinawa and the Ryukyu Islands, where production was restricted. This caused a search for alternative process feedstocks, including the evaluation of various liquid hydrocarbon fractions, but acetic acid (acetate) was found to be the most technically and commercially attractive alternative feedstock.

Acetate, although slightly inferior with respect to its carbon:energy balance than either glucose or glycerol, is ubiquitous substrate in Nature and therefore utilized by a very broad spectrum of microbes. However, acetic acid (acetate) has not found significant acceptance as a fermentation process feedstock outside Japan which suggests that in most situations it is less attractive than more conventional alternatives.

GASEOUS CARBON AND ENERGY FEEDSTOCKS

Gaseous Alkanes

The gaseous alkanes are hydrocarbons with the general formula C_nH_{2n+2} and differ from each other by CH_2 or a multiple thereof. As potential biotechnological process feedstocks the group comprises only 5 compounds, methane, ethane, propane, n-butane and iso-butane of which methane has been widely studied and iso-butane has been very largely neglected with respect to their potentials as carbon energy substrates for microbes. When evaluating any of the gaseous alkanes as potential process feedstocks several very important factors have to be borne in mind.

The first is that these feedstocks, in their commercially available forms, are likely to contain very significant concentrations of contaminating components. For example, methane as an economically realistic feedstock is available only as natural gas or biogas. Natural gas can be placed into one of two groups depending on the source of production. Associated gas is that natural gas produced from oil fields simultaneously with the crude oil. It contains significant concentrations of other gaseous hydrocarbons, particularly ethane, propane, and n-butane. Both propane and butane are condensed from associated gas prior to its transportation and utilization and the condensate is marketed separately as liquified petroleum gases (LPG). However, ethane remains associated with the methane and associated gas, as commercially available, comprises predominantly methane but with a significant fraction of ethane and traces of propane and butane. As far as methanotrophic bacteria are concerned these impurities exhibit adverse effects. Unassociated gas is produced from gas fields rather than from oil reservoirs and although frequently comprising ca. 90% methane, is usually substantially free from any significant contamination by other gaseous hydrocarbons with the possible exception of ethane. The predominant components that make up the remaining 10% of unassociated gas are nitrogen and carbon dioxide in various proportions. While the former can be regarded to be physiologically innocuous if unassociated gas is to be used as a biotechnological process feedstock, the latter, because of its relatively high solubility, could impact adversely on the performance of process cultures. This will be particularly important in large-scale high aspect ratio bioreactors with considerable hydrostatic pressures, especially during high intensity process operations generating large amounts of carbon dioxide. The final source of methane as a commercial feedstock is biogas, the product of anaerobic digestion of biodegradable waste solid matter, produced and collected from land-fill sites. Biogas is a mixture containing about 67 volume % of methane and 33 volume % of carbon dioxide, together with traces of hydrogen and hydrogen sulphide. Quite apart from the high levels of carbon dioxide, the possible physiological effects of the non-methane components of biogas cannot be ignored.

In feedstock terms ethane is not generally commercially available and will not be discussed further. However, under certain circumstances, such as the transmission of natural gas by pipeline, liquified petroleum gases (LPG), specifically n-propane and n-butane, might be available process feedstocks at gas production locations.

In virtually all respects methane and other gaseous alkanes are much less preferred feedstocks than is the methanol which is manufactured directly from them by chemical means.

Carbon Monoxide

Carbon monoxide is a colourless, odorless, toxic gas that is produced deliberately and incidentally as a result of burning carbonaceous matter in the presence of insufficient oxygen to allow complete combustion. For use as a potential biotechnological production process feedstock it is the carbon monoxide which is a principal constituent of manufactured fuel and/or synthesis gases that is of particular interest.

Carbon monoxide as a substrate for microbial growth has been relatively little studied in the laboratory because its potentially flammable and toxic properties are incompatible with conventional microbiological techniques. Even so a reasonably large number of carboxydotrophic bacteria have been isolated. Most are capable of utilizing hydrogen as well as carbon monoxide as their source of energy and are facultative autotrophs. Most data on the growth of carboxydotrophs have been obtained using batch culture techniques and there is very limited information with respect to carboxydotroph process performance. Discussion of carbon monoxide as a commercial process feedstock must necessarily be hypothetical rather than based on experience.

Undoubtedly the most interesting aspect of carbon monoxide as a commercial feedstock is that it provides an indirect method of utilizing solid feedstocks such as coal but, because carbon monoxide is a gas, the question of effective conversion must arise as with all gaseous feedstocks. One particularly intriguing feature of carboxydotrophs is their ability to fix carbon dioxide. This permits the judicious selection of carbon monoxide/hydrogen ratios in feedstocks such that all the carbon supplied to the process is contained in products rather than some of it being released to the atmosphere as surplus carbon dioxide. Such release of surplus carbon dioxide is presently a topic of intense debate.

Hydrogen/Carbon Dioxide Mixtures

When hydrogen/carbon dioxide mixtures are used as substrates for microbial growth, the energy for growth is derived from oxidation of the hydrogen while the carbon for cell and product formation is provided by the carbon dioxide; if the ratio of hydrogen:carbon dioxide supplied can be varied at will, an optimum balance with respect to carbon and energy requirements is possible.

The use of microbial processes based on the utilization of hydrogen/carbon dioxide mixtures by "Knallgasbacteria" was first proposed more than 20 years ago by Schlegel[18] when he introduced the concept of food production from electricity via the electrolysis of water. During the decade that followed the autotrophic route for single cell protein production from hydrogen and carbon dioxide was further researched. However, it was not single cell protein but rather polyhydroxybutyrate that was to prove to be the commercial product of greatest potential that could be produced from hydrogen by "Knallgasbacteria". Polyhydroxybutyrate can be produced from a range of substrates, including lower alcohols, lower carboxylic acids, sucrose, dextrose and hydrogen and as far as laboratory studies are concerned, hydrogen is clearly the least convenient. But judged on the basis of feedstock cost per tonne of product, hydrogen could prove to be the cheapest feedstock if it were available as a pipeline distributed fuel; if not, methanol would be the most cost-realistic.

Carbon Dioxide/Light

Photosynthetic production systems employing both green algae and cyanobacteria (bluegreen algae) have been extensively studied as a basis for biotechnological product production. In the liquid/gaseous fossil fuel-limited economy which might exist in the future in the developed countries and that already prevails today in some developing countries, such approaches must clearly be of major interest. However, little progress towards any extensive commercialization seems to have taken place.

Photosynthetic production process are only very rarely subjected to stringent process evaluation and this has tended in the past to relegate such processes into a category where they can be considered to be emotionally attractive, but economically unattractive. Furthermore, such process proposals usually depend on the use of aquaculture.

Considerable controversy exists about both the efficiency and dynamics of photosynthetic growth; this has recently been reviewed in a biotechnological process context by Pirt[19]. If the potential offered by photosynthetic bioreactor systems is to be fully exploited it will also be necessary to optimize solar energy utilization by employing some of the concepts discussed by Manassah[20] a few years ago.

IMMISCIBLE LIQUID CARBON ENERGY FEEDSTOCKS

Mineral Oils

For the second part of the present century mineral oil has been the major feedstock for chemicals production. Discontinuities with respect to mineral oil prices during the mid- and late-1970s cast doubt on the wisdom of its continued use but for the present and for the medium term future few economically realistic alternatives for its replacement exist. Mineral oil is, of course, a highly complex mixture of a broad spectrum of hydrocarbons; before refining it is a totally unrealistic microbial process feedstock.

The first report of microbial hydrocarbon oxidation appeared in 1895 but it was not until 1951 that any hydrocarbon was considered as a potential fermentation process feedstock. In fact, the first example concerned n-alkanes produced from coal or coke via the Fischer-Tropsch synthesis.[4] Subsequently, it was to be mixtures of waxy n-alkanes (C_nH_{2n+2}) between carbon numbers 14 and 20 that were to prove the most potentially interesting mineral oil-derived feedstock.

Initial industrial interest in the microbial oxidation of waxy n-alkanes concerned an application in oil refining, specifically a process for dewaxing gas oils used for heavy road vehicles, in which the yeast cells that were produced represented a potentially saleable by-product. The waxy n-alkane content of crude oil varies with its source. In the early 1960s the supply demand position for n-alkanes, which are themselves important chemical process feedstocks, was in imbalance such that supply exceeded demand and oil refiners without tied petrochemical industries suffered from the vagaries of the spot market for n-alkanes.

British Petroleum Co., where the microbial dewaxing process was developed by Champagnat[3] were, at that time, in exactly that situation. In due course they diversified their activities so that, in addition to concomitant dewaxing and protein production, a process was developed utilizing a purified waxy n-alkane fraction exclusively for protein production. This latter B.P. process technology was copied by many other organizations but without improvement upon it. In Western Europe plants with capacities up to 100,000 tonnes per annum were constructed but sustained production was never achieved for a variety of non-technological reasons[21]. However, in the U.S.S.R. n-alkane and other feed-stock-based SCP production was until recently practised on a very large-scale under the different politico-economic regime that applied in that country.

As Miall[2] pointed out, provided they are available at competitive prices, n-alkanes can be used as substitute feedstocks for a wide range of conventional fermentation products; the only difficulty lies in the need for process cultures to produce appropriate intermediates that can be incorporated into the tricarboxylic acid cycle.

Because of their immiscibility with water, n-alkanes require emulsification prior to their effective uptake by microbes. However, most hydrocarbon-utilizing microbes in fact produce such emulsifying agents thereby facilitating utilization. Nevertheless, with n-alkanes there is always a potential danger of feedstock residues being associated with products, particularly if the product is either biomass or a product derived from it. Such potential residues are the main problem with respect to n-alkane feedstock acceptability although one that has been very much overplayed in the past. It is serious only when either feedstock mixtures comprising a utilizable and a non-utilizable fraction are employed, or when incomplete carbon energy substrate utilization is sought.

In most proposed fermentation processes involving n-alkanes the substrate is present as the dispersed phase, with water as the continuous phase. However, it is conceivable that the phases might be reversed. Such an approach would allow markedly higher saturation concentrations of dissolved oxygen in the continuous phase and hence enhanced driving forces for oxygen transfer. In addition, heat transfer for effective cooling might also be facilitated but product separation and purification might be markedly more difficult and expensive.

Vegetable/Animal Oils and Fats

The terms "oil" and "fat" as they apply to either vegetable or animal products are essentially interchangeable; both consisting entirely of glycerides, i.e., esters of the trihydric alcohol glycerol with higher and intermediate fatty acids. The general formula of triglycerides is:

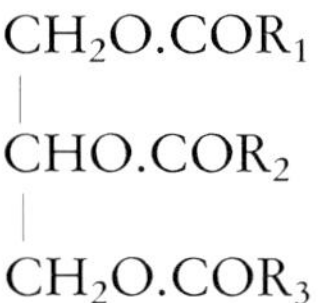

$$\begin{array}{l} CH_2O.COR_1 \\ | \\ CHO.COR_2 \\ | \\ CH_2O.COR_3 \end{array}$$

where R_1, R_2 and R_3 are either the same or different saturated $(CH_3(CH_2)_n)$ or unsaturated $(CH_3(CH_2)_aCH{=}CH(CH_2)_b)$ groups. The general formula given in the unsaturated case represents a mono-unsaturated group but such structures can also contain more than one double bond.

The best known fats and oils of animal origin are tallow from cattle and/or sheep, the traditional raw material for soap and candle manufacture, lard from swine, butter, whale oil and a range of fish oils. Their counterpart vegetable oils are derived from soyabeans, palm, rapeseed, sunflowers, olives, cottonseed, corn and, more recently, saf-flowers. Both animal and vegetable oils are widely used in foodstuffs and are frequently referred to as "edible oils". To make a raw material like rapeseed oil into an edible oil has required important advances in plant breeding.

Vegetable oil production has increased dramatically in recent decades but the EEC, for example, remains deficient with respect to indigenous production and the import/export trade remains significant in both North/North and South/North trade. Soyabean oil is dominant among edible oils and like all commodity products is subject to major price fluctuations depending on the supply and demand. However, soyabean oil is cushioned by the interlinked supply and demand position for soyabean meal which is the major protein ingredient in many compounded animal feeds.

The acceptability of any particular oil for inclusion in human foods has, in the past decade, been very strongly influenced by its polyunsaturated nature; polyunsaturated oils are widely believed to less likely to raise the level of cholesterol in the blood, thereby reducing the risk of heart attacks. Such a hypothesis, although perhaps not well founded, does favour the use of soyabean, rapeseed and sunflower oils in human food. It discriminates particularly severely against palm oil, depressing its price and thereby making it a potentially attractive fermentation process feedstock. Some other plant oils are in an analogous position.

In some eyes the polyunsaturated/saturated argument represents yet another false trade barrier against the South. Palm oil is a product from developing countries, particularly Malaysia and Indonesia; soyabean, rapeseed and sunflower oils are products of the North. In the specific case of soyabeans, for which the U.S. is the principal producer, it should be remembered that soyabean cultivation was introduced on a significant scale into the U.S. only in 1930. Since then, the Soyabean Producers Association have made soyabeans a major crop and the political lobby they have established knows no bounds with respect to the protection of soyabean derived products.

The potential for both animal and vegetable oils as carbon energy feedstocks for antibiotic fermentations has been reviewed by Stowell[22] where not only the advantages but also some technical disadvantages of such feedstocks are identified and discussed. In general, the potential of edible oils as fermentation process feedstocks exceeds that of all but the most pure fractions of mineral oil.

INSOLUBLE SOLID CARBON ENERGY FEEDSTOCKS

Lignocellulose

Lignocellulose, particularly lignocellulosic waste material, has attracted widespread attention as an interesting carbon energy feedstock for biotechnological processes. A quarter of a century ago, cellulose, hemicellulose and lignin, the major components of lignocellulose, were identified as potential feedstocks for the future and much the same sentiments are still being expressed today[23], suggesting that relatively little progress has in fact been made in the interim with respect to realizing the potential offered by lignocellulose as a biotechnological process feedstock. Without doubt, both lignin and cellulose have proved challenging carbon/energy substrates in laboratory studies.

Lignocellulose is a product, byproduct or waste product from both the agricultural and forest product industries and as such is a renewable resource. It is, in fact, the predominant renewable resource. Although its composition varies with source, lignin, cellulose and hemicellulose are always present as major components.

Cellulose molecules are unbranched chains of D-glucose linked by $\beta-1-4$ glucosidic bonds. The average number of glucose residues in a cellulose molecule is about 8000 and the repeating unit in cellulose is cellobiose, a disaccharide comprising two glucose units. Hemicellulose is not, as was originally thought, a cellulose precursor but differs from cellulose both with respect to its chemical composition and its structure, consisting of xylans, mannans and galactans. The chemical composition of hemicellulose varies markedly depending on its source. Lignin is composed of a group of closely related high molecular weight polymers whose main building unit is a phenylpropane residue. Lignin composition is also source-dependent and the chemical residues resulting from its hydrolysis differ markedly. Thus, even when dealing with cellulose, hemicellulose or lignin as separate materials essentially mixed feedstocks are involved. Clearly, unfractionated lignocellulosic materials can be regarded only as highly heterogeneous as far as any potential feedstock value that they might have is concerned.

The main lignocellulosic products are sawn timber, wood chips for pulping and wood for fuel. For biotechnological processing the most widely available feedstocks in this category are (and will continue to be) either the byproducts and waste products of sawn timber and wood chips or those of agricultural origin such as cereal straw and bagasse. At the present time, very large quantities of lignocellulosic wastes are subjected either to natural decay or to wasteful combustion. However, processes do exist that make use of lignocellulosic wastes: they include sensible combustion (e.g., bagasse by the cane sugar industry), pulping (e.g., waste paper and a small fraction of the cereal straw produced) and reconstitution (e.g., sawdust and waste chips conversion into artificial board).

Considerable research has been undertaken on the thermochemical conversion of lignocellulosic matter (pyrolysis, gasification and catalytic lignifaction) but has yet to make significant impact. Biological technologies that have been proposed for the utilization of lignocellulosic wastes include composting, methane generation by digestion in either anaerobic bioreactors or in appropriately constructed land-fills and, in specific cases, either utilization as ruminant feeds or as feedstocks for SCP production. Research has also been directed to saccharification. This involves the production of fermentable sugars from lignocellulosic materials to yield either glucose syrup for direct consumption as a food-grade product or as a fermentable feedstock stream for bulk chemicals or fuel ethanol production.

The key for introducing lignocellulosic wastes as technologically realistic and economically attractive feedstocks for the biotechnological process industries depends upon the effective chemical or enzymic hydrolysis of the original waste raw material. Until this is achieved lignocellulosic materials will remain potential rather than actual biotechnological process feedstocks.

Microbial Biomass

Microbial biomass is generally considered to be a product rather than a feedstock. However, very large quantities of waste microbial biomass are produced by the fermentation industry, in which waste mycellium from antibiotics production is frequently cited as presenting disposal problems, and from municipal sewage and industrial wastewater treatment, where secondary sludge is a major byproduct presenting complex treatment and/or disposal problems particularly after mixing with primary sludge.

Waste microbial biomass can be considered as a potential process feed both for processes where other microbes grow on the waste biomass and for those involving the refining of an individual fraction, i.e. the separation of components present in the waste biomass. In the former context, microbial cells clearly represent a relatively unfavourable substrate for microbial growth especially as they are particulate. But their mineral composition and overall carbon and energy contents makes them ideal substrates for aerobic, heterotrophic growth, exhibiting neither energy deficiency nor excess provided all of their components can be utilized simultaneously. In any biotechnological processes involving whole microbial cells as the process feedstock it is important to differentiate between the process microbes which grow, but are also subject to death/lysis and "cryptic" growth mechanisms, and the non-growing feedstock (substrate) microbes which are subject only to degradative processes. Unlike lignocellulosic materials, which are either continuous or porous solids, microbes as process feedstocks comprise a complex essentially fluid cytoplasm surrounded by a rigid cell wall and membrane which maintain the physical and chemical integrity of the cell. When microbial cells are biodegraded the cell wall/membrane is punctured or burst. Both readily soluble matter and cell wall fragments are released. The cube root pattern of hydrolysis applicable in the case of lignocellulosic materials is appropriate only so far as cell wall fragments are concerned. Even so, as for lignocellulosic feedstocks, the use of microbial cells in process feedstocks presents problems of realistic conversion.

Starch

Starch is a naturally occurring highly-polymeric carbohydrate. It is the most important carbohydrate reserve material present in plants where it is found in roots, tubers and seeds. The approximate formula is $(C_6H_{10}O_5)_n$, where n is probably greater than 1,000. Starch occurs in the form of white granules insoluble in cold water, comprising on organized mixture of a linear polymer (amylose) and a branched polymer (amylopectin), oriented and associated in a crystal-like lattice. Starch is sparingly soluble in hot water, forming a viscous liquid which, upon cooling, becomes a gelatinous paste. As a traditional fermentation process feedstock, starch in the form of barley has been used for malting and brewing beer since ancient times.

In the temperate regions of the world, the primary sources of starch are cereal grains, such as wheat and maize, and potatoes: in the specific case of beer, barley remains the preferred source. In subtropical and tropical regions primary sources are rice, sorghum and manioc or cassava. The last is best known in the form of tapioca starch and flour which are essentially hydrocyanic glucoside-free materials that are widely used as foodstuffs.

Cassava is one of the crops considered to be of primary interest in the production of "food crops" specifically for industrial purposes and it clearly has potential as a feedstock for fuel ethanol production after it has been hydrolysed.

One of the more interesting developments of the SCP era was the Symba Yeast process which used native rather than hydrolysed starch as the process feedstock. The procedure was originally developed for operation on a waste starch feedstock from potato processing but would function equally well with tapioca. The basis of the process[24], was the use of a symbiotic mixed culture of *Endomycopsis fibuliger*, which produced amylases for starch hydrolysis, and *Candida utilis*, which grew on the hydrolysis products; feedstock hydrolysis as a separate activity was thereby circumvented. The process could be operated in a continuous flow mode and when evaluated for operation on tapioca as feedstock quality problem arose. During its production, tapioca is sun-dried on sand-beds and becomes contaminated with sand particles. If the sand is not removed during feedstock preparation it can cause serious equipment damage and malfunction during the production process for which it is used.

Feedstocks such as starch might become more attractive in the future if the efforts of plant breeders and of those who run the political and economic cartels which protect indigenous agricultural production combine to make them so.

COMMERCIAL ATTRACTIVENESS OF FEEDSTOCKS

Feedstock conversion is a feature of biotechnological processes that is very frequently ignored during process research studies and assumes prominence only during process development and evaluation of process economics. A major reason is that in the laboratory the importance of yield coefficients is often overemphasised. For any microbial process the yield coefficient for product formation is defined as the weight of anhydrous product produced per unit weight of feedstock or nutrient utilized. The yield coefficient concept in biotechnology should not be confused with the yield concept in agriculture where yields are quoted in terms of the weight of crop produced per unit area of land each year or growing season. In biotechnology, the analogous term for such agricultural yields is "productivity", defined as the weight of anhydrous product produced per unit bioreactor operating volume and unit time.

The microbiological yield coefficient concept completely ignores the critical economic consideration of conversion, usually expressed on either a fractional or on a percentage basis: it is either the fraction or the percentage of a substrate (or nutrient) that is utilized compared with the total quantity of the particular substrate or (nutrient) supplied in the feed. Some years ago it was proposed that for industrial-scale biotechnological processes conversion coefficients, defined as the weight of anhydrous product produced per unit weight of each particular feedstock or nutrient supplied, rather than utilized, would be an important descriptor. Such conversion coefficients are the products of the appropriate yield coefficients and the particular fractional conversion achieved.

In the case of either readily water soluble or miscible substrate and nutrients which are growth limiting, yield and conversion coefficients are virtually coincident. For insoluble, solid or gaseous substrates and nutrients yield coefficients approaching theoretical maxima might be achieved with correspondingly poor conversion coefficients. Further more, irrespective of their solubilities, all nutrients and substrates that are not process rate-limiting will also exhibit conversion coefficients markedly inferior to corresponding yield coefficients.

Although most aerobic processes do not incur raw material costs by using air as their oxygen source, very considerable capital and operating costs do accrue to processes because of the need to both compress and sterilize the air prior to use. In commercial processes it is most important to minimize such costs by achieving maximum conversion of the oxygen supplied provided the resultant costs for maximization do not impact adversely on the overall process economics or on product quality.

The fractional conversions achieved for either oxygen or gaseous carbon and/or energy substrates only slightly soluble in water (methane, carbon monoxide, hydrogen, etc.) rarely exceed 0.3 in high intensity laboratory bioreactors while in conventional large industrial-scale bioreactors fractional conversions for oxygen are typically about 0.15 when air is used as the source of oxygen. Even with such low fractional conversions, gaseous substrates or nutrients frequently become limiting with respect to process rate and whereas this might be technologically desirable in some cases for carbon and/or energy substrates, oxygen limitation in aerobic processes can seriously affect overall process performance. A further unfortunate feature is that high fractional conversions of gaseous substrates and nutrients are frequently inconsistent with the maximization of respective transfer rates and clearly a techno-economic optimum must be sought to ameliorate the conflict between transfer rate and conversion. The operating mode of the bioreactor will also markedly affect gaseous substrate or nutrient conversion and the superiority of systems where the gas phase can be maintained in essentially plug flow should be noted in this respect. One of the most frequently proposed means of enhancing fractional conversions in bioreactors is the introduction of recycle, an approach of equal applicability to either the gaseous or the liquid (aqueous) phases in biotechnological processes, but one that is not without numerous ramifications.

Unlike the conversion of oxygen present in process air supplies, the conversion of gaseous carbon and/or energy substrates, as well as oxygen when supplied as a relatively pure gas derived from either cryogenic or pressure swing adsorption processes, must approach completion for such raw materials to be used effectively from an economic viewpoint, making bioreactor design and process integration dominant requirements. In the case of fuel gases and processes with heat requirements for some ancillary processing operations such as drying, possibilities in the direction of process integration genuinely exist. Even then the matching of individual unit process requirements might well require the attainment of fractional conversions in the bioreactor of 0.7–0.8. Such values will only be attainable either in an elevated pressure bioreactor with the gaseous phase in plug flow and recycling (if realistic bioreactor productivities are to be maintained) or by the employment of multiple high pressure completely mixed bioreactors operating in series with interstage flow of the process gases.

As with gaseous feedstocks, both solid and immiscible feedstocks suffer similar problems with respect to the achievement of near complete conversion, such that either water soluble or water miscible feedstocks will always exhibit an intrinsic technological advantage as far as conventional fermentation processes are concerned. Gaseous and immiscible liquid feedstocks show potential for non-aqueous phase process systems that might be developed in the future. Nevertheless, a major key to commercial attractiveness for a feedstock is high potential conversion.

FUTURE PROSPECTS

Biotechnology is intimately related to both the agricultural and energy sectors of the global, regional and national economies, in that the feedstocks used, the operating costs involved in adding value and the products they generate are all either derived from or controlled by costs from one of these two sectors. Relationships are most evident when bulk biotechnological products are under consideration, but many medium volume and even fine chemical products also have an impact on these same economic sectors. Without doubt, the fundamental reason for this is that biotechnological processes are essentially accelerated natural processes for food (feed), energy and bioactive product production on the one hand, and for either complete or partial biodegradation and/or biomodification on the other.

When considering biotechnology, it is not the *status quo* that is usually considered but rather the prospects that can be envisaged for the future. A factor in this attitude is the relatively small contribution that biotechnological products, with the exception of potable alcohol, currently make to the overall Gross National Product (GNP) of most countries. The question of forecasting future developments has already been discussed from a business planning point of view but it is also necessary to consider global change over a much more extended period in order to evaluate the contributions that will be needed from biotechnology in the future.

Today, dramatic differences in economic status exist between the developed countries, exemplified by the majority of the member countries of the Organization for Economic Cooperation and Development (OECD), i.e. the North, and most developing countries measured on the basis of both

GNP and per capita income, i.e. the South.

Demographic trends, by no means uniform throughout the world, will undoubtedly have a very marked bearing on future development. The population in the OECD countries is aging fast, whilst population in the South will continue to expand unabated for many decades to come in spite of declining fertility rates. This implies not only population growth, but a young, outward-looking South facing an old, inward-looking North.

Similar differences are fast becoming evident with respect to international trade, governed by the rules of the General Agreement on Tariffs and Trade (GATT). Although GATT might be expected to facilitate trade, it has certainly become a serious impediment to free trade because of its inability to resolve protectionist issues.

For more than a quarter of a century biotechnology has been seen to offer immense potential for facilitating development in the South. The protectionist attitudes of the North may result in greater South/South trade; the availability of a wide range of potential fermentation process feedstocks in the South could make fermentation products important candidates for such trade.

Irrespective of where future development occurs, a clear objective of the fermentation industry must be a more judicious use of available process feedstocks. In the case of heterotrophic process cultures this will most probably best be achieved by using better balanced carbon energy feedstocks in the form of specifically designed mixtures.[25] However, such objectives will not be attainable without considerable advances in microbial physiology. In the case of autotrophic process cultures, the major questions concern efficiency in the case of photoautotrophs and conversion for chemoautotrophs, both of which depend on bioreactor design and require major advances for their solution.

REFERENCES

1. Linton, J.D., and R.J. Stephenson: *A preliminary study on growth yields in relation to the carbon and energy content of various organic growth substrates*; FEMS Microbiol. Lett., **3**, 95–98 (1978).
2. Miall, L.M.: *Organic acid production from hydrocarbons*; In — Hydrocarbons in Biotechnology, D.E.F. Harrison, I.J. Higgins & R. Watkinson (Eds.), Heyden/Inst. Petroleum, London, 25–34 (1980).
3. Champagnat, A.: *Protein — the BP adventure*; Petroleum Rev., **25**, 419–426 (1971).
4. Just, F., W. Schnabel and S. Ullmann: *Submerse Züchtung von kohlenwasserstoffe zehrenden Hefen und Bakterien*; Die Brauerei, **4**, 57–60 (1951).
5. Beck, P.W.: *Corporate planning for an uncertain future*; Long Range Planning, **15**, 12–21 (1982).
6. DuMoulin, H., and J. Eyre: *Energy scenarios — a learning process*; Energy Econ. **1**, 76–86 (1979).
7. Lewis, C.W.: *Energy requirements for single cell protein production*; J. Appl. Chem. Biotechnol., **26**, 568–575 (1976).
8. Drozd, J.W.: *Hydrocarbons as feedstocks for Biotechnology*; In — Carbon Substrates in Biotechnology, J.D. Stowell, A.J. Beardsmore, C.W. Keevil and J.R. Woodward (Eds.), IRL Press, Oxford, 119–138 (1987).
9. Phillips, J.A., and A.E. Humphrey: *Microbial production of energy: liquid fuels*; In — Biotechnology and Bioprocess Engineering, T.K. Ghose (Ed.), United India Press, New Delhi, 157–186 (1985).
10. Hamer, G.: *Impacts of economic strategies on biotechnological developments*; Trends Biotechnol, **3**, 73–79 (1985).
11. Andrew, S.: *Liquid fuels from alternative feedstocks*; Chem. Engnr., 28–29, Jan. 1984.
12. Munck, L., K. Bang-Olsen, L. Elin, A. de Francisco, L. Hallgren, K. Johansson, K.G. Jörgensen, R. Leah, J. Mundy, B. Pedersen, L.H. Pedersen, B. Petersen, P.B. Petersen, F. Rexen, B. Stilling and P. Vaag: *Biotechnological production and use of new plant raw materials*; In — Proc. 4th Europ. Cong. Biotechnol, Elsevier, Amsterdam, 79–90 (1987).
13. Gray, P.S.: *Impact of EEC regulations on the economics of fermentation substrates*; In — Carbon Substrates in Biotechnology, J.D. Stowell, A.J. Beardsmore, C.W. Keevil & J.R. Woodward (Eds.), IRL Press, Oxford, 1–12 (1987).
14. Coombs, J.: *Carbohydrate feedstocks: availability and utilization of molasses and whey*; In — Carbon Substrates in Biotechnology, J.D. Stowell, A.J. Beardsmore, C.W. Keevil & J.R. Woodward (Eds.), IRL Press, Oxford, 29–44 (1987).
15. Gold, T.: *The origin of natural gas and petroleum and the prognosis for future supplies*. Ann. Rev. Energy, **10**, 53–77 (1985).
16. Dijkhuizen, L., T. Hansen and W. Harder: *Methanol, a potential feedstock for biotechnological processes*; Trends Biotechnol., **3**, 262–267 (1985)
17. Al-Awadhi, N., T. Egli, G. Hamer and E. Wehrli: *Thermotolerant and thermophilic solvent-utilizing methylotrophic aerobic bacteria*, System. Appl. Microbiol., **11**, 207–216 (1989).
18. Schlegel, H.G.: *From electricity via water electrolysis* to food; In — Fermentation Advances D. Perlman (Ed.), Academic Press, N.Y., 807–832 (1969).
19. Pirt, S.J.: *The thermodynamic efficiency (quantum demand) and dynamics of photosynthetic growth*; New Phytol., **102**, 3–37 (1986)
20. Manassah, J.T.: *Basic bioenergetics and the solar spectrum*; In — Advances in Food Producing Systems for Arid and Semiarid Lands, J.T. Manassah & E.J. Briskey (Eds.), Academic Press, N.Y., 85–103 (1981).
21. Ellingham, J.: *The BP single cell protein summary of experience*; In — Proceeding of OAPEC Symposium on Petroprotein, OAPEC, Kuwait, 61–75 (1980).
22. Stowell, J.D.; *The application of oils and fats in antibiotic processes*; In — Carbon Substrates in Biotechnology, J.D. Stowell, A.J. Beardsmore, C.W. Keevil & J.R. Woodward (Eds.), IRL Press Oxford, 139–159 (1987).
23. Broda, P.M.A., B.S. Hartley and P.J. Senior: *Technology in the 1990s: Utilization of Lignocellulosic Wastes*, Royal Soc., London, (1987).
24. Jarl, K.: *Symba yeast process; Food Technol.*, **23**, 1009–1012 (1969).
25. Egli, T., and W. Harder: *Growth of methylotrophs on mixed substrates*; In — Microbial Growth on C_1 Compounds, R.L. Crawford & R.S. Hanson (Eds.), ASM, Washington, D.C., 330–337 (1984).

Chapter 15

Process Economics

Nicholas J. Haritatos

INTRODUCTION

Developing and commercializing a new or improved process for manufacturing any product can be a very risky enterprise. It can be risky to make and market a new product; and it can be risky to develop a new process for making an already-commercialized product. For every new process that makes it to the marketplace, there are dozens of others that did not meet the economic requirements. The economics of a process must be evaluated at a very early stage in its development. Then, as the process is moved from bench-scale to pilot plant to design and construction, the economics must be re-evaluated at timely intervals.

General Guidelines

Many an overzealous chemist has come up with a novel reaction mechanism — only to discover that the cost of the raw materials exceeds that of the final product. Or, he may have included in his process a reagent which is not an article of commerce and is, therefore, not available in commercial quantities.

An example involving flagrantly-expensive raw materials is the proposed production in the United States of ethylene from corn syrup via fermentation to ethanol. A great deal of research could be devoted to improving the fermentation process, but with corn syrup at 14 cents per pound (100% solids basis), and even assuming 100% of theoretical yields for the fermentation of dextrose to ethanol followed by the dehydration of ethanol to ethylene, the cost of raw materials is 43 cents per pound of ethylene. With ethylene derived from petroleum available in the United States for about 25 cents per pound, this project would not be profitable. It may well be, however, that in a third world country, where ethylene is probably much more expensive and corn syrup or molasses less expensive, the conversion of corn syrup or molasses to ethylene would be a cost-effective process.

A process using a triazine in one of its key steps could not be commercialized because the triazine was not available in commercial quantities. This triazine is available in small lots for laboratory use, but it is a shock-sensitive material. To determine how to produce this shock-sensitive material in large quantities would have required a major research project. Unfortunately, the scientists were not able to find a commercially-available substitute, and the project was terminated.

Preliminary Evaluations

Estimates carried out early in a project are often too rosy. The scientist involved in the project is invariably an optimist — and wants the project to succeed. Thus, the engineer making the economic evaluation has several key objectives:

* Prepare as realistic an estimate as possible
* Identify areas which have a significant effect on cost (To reduce costs most effectively, research needs to be directed specifically to these areas.)
* Add a large allowance for contingencies (to allow for problems which have not yet been identified)

As the project matures, and more and more problems are identified and solved, the estimated investment and operating costs for the project will tend to rise. On the other hand, the allowance for contingencies can be reduced. If the project still looks good, project management needs to make a key decision. Should the project be commercialized immediately, even though there is room for improvement? Or, should the research effort be continued with the aim of improving the economics still further? At this point, additional marketing input is needed. Potential savings in the process need to be balanced against the cost of delay in entering the market.

Final Economic Analysis

When the decision is made that the project has matured to the point that it can be commercialized, the final economic analysis is carried out. It involves input from process engineers, cost-estimating engineers, marketing staff and management staff to prepare an appropriation request for plant construction. Some of the questions that need to be answered to aid the decision-making are:

* How large will the plant be? How large is the market for a new product, or how large a market share do we expect to capture for an already-commercialized product?
* Where will the plant be located? Is infrastructure available, or will we have to build roads, houses and electrical-generation facilities?
* How much of a risk in the design is management willing to take? Does the plant have to be conservatively designed so that it will reach design rate within a few weeks, or should the engineers take some process risks and plan to make any required equipment-modifications during start-up? Should plant equipment be built to last for five years, ten years, or twenty years? How much extra should be paid in order to build in increased reliability?

After these questions are answered, the plant investment and manufacturing costs can be estimated and an appropriation request can be prepared for building the plant. If top management approves the request, a project manager is appointed and the project is underway.

DEFINITIONS OF TERMS USED IN ECONOMIC EVALUATION

By-product credit is the value of any products, other than the major product, made in the plant. In a plant making one major product and small quantities of by-products, this item poses no serious problems. By-products which are articles of commerce can be sold. Other by-products may have fuel value. If a by-product has to be sent off-plot for disposal in a dump, then the by-product credit will be negative.

In a plant, such as an ethylene plant, making more than one major product the situation becomes more complex. If the propylene, butylene, and other by-products are given high by-product credits, then the manufacturing cost of the product ethylene will be reduced. Alternatively, one can relate the by-product value of the propylene and of the other major by-products to the manufacturing cost of the ethylene. For example, if the price of the propylene has averaged at about 90% of the price of ethylene for the past five to ten years and it is expected that this relationship will continue, then the by-product value of the propylene can be taken as 90% of the manufacturing cost of the ethylene. Then a trial and error (or algebraic) method will be required to calculate the values of all the by-products and the manufacturing cost of the ethylene.

Catalyst and chemicals cost includes not only the major chemicals and catalyst required for the process, but also items such as water-treating chemicals, antifoulants, antifoam agents, and corrosion inhibitors.

Contingency allowance is an allowance for problems which have not yet been identified. The amount allowed for contingencies can cause a great deal of argument on a project because it can have a large effect on the economics. Early in the project, when the technology is still being developed, a high contingency allowance (such as 20% to 40% of the identified operating costs) can be justified. As the project matures, and the technology and economics are better-defined, the contingency allowance can be dropped to the range of 0% to 10%.

Depreciation is used for tax purposes as a method of recovering the on-plot and off-plot cost of a project. The method of depreciation allowed by the federal and state governments in the U.S., and national and regional governments in other countries is subject to frequent changes and needs to be checked before a detailed economic evaluation can be carried out.

Development costs — Depending on the tax laws, these can be either expensed or included in the capital cost of the new project.

Feedstock cost can be either the cost of an article of commerce or the cost of an intermediate material made for the plant. In the case of the latter, it will be necessary to negotiate a "transfer price" as the intermediate material crosses the plant boundary.

Incremental overhead includes the cost of support facilities required at the site — such as accounting, central office, cafeteria and security personnel. A great deal of judgement and experience is required to estimate it accurately. Two common estimates are 1)10% to 15% of the sum of maintenance, labor, utilities, catalyst, and chemicals or 2)50% to 75% of maintenance and labor. (In the examples shown in Tables 4 and 5, either method would give a reasonable value.)

Investment cost is the total amount of money (capital) required to build and start up a facility employing the process. It includes: on-plot investment, off-plot investment, working capital and (sometimes) development costs.

Labor includes the direct cost of the operators, their supervisors, and benefits (including vacations). In the United States this can vary between $125,000 and $200,000 per shift position. Clearly, different numbers will prevail elsewhere.

Local taxes and insurance are typically 2% to 3% of the total of on-plot and off-plot investment.

Maintenance costs typically vary between 2% and 8% of the total of on-plot and off-plot investment. For a simple process with very little fouling and corrosion, 2% to 3% is typical. But as the plant gets more complex, or if the process service is corrosive or prone to fouling, then a higher percentage will be required.

Manufacturing cost is the sum of the operating and feedstock costs minus any by-product credits.

Off-plot investment is the capital cost of all facilities outside the boundary limits of the new process plant required to support it. The off-plot facilities typically include a steam boiler, cooling tower, electrical distribution facilities, treatment facilities for waste streams, feed tankage and product tankage. If the plant is in a remote location they could also include infrastructure requirements, such as roads and housing for plant personnel.

On-plot investment is the capital cost of all of the process facilities within the boundary of the plant. It includes reactors, distillation columns, heat exchangers, pumps, piping, instruments, foundations and the like.

Operating costs are defined as all out-of-pocket costs of manufacturing the product except for the cost of the feed and the credit for the by-products. They include: maintenance, labor, utilities, catalyst and chemicals, incremental overhead, local taxes and insurance, running royalties, and a contingency allowance.

Present value is the value today, at a specified interest rate, of money which will be received in the future.

Rate of Return (ROR) is the interest rate (or discount rate) at which the present value of a project's future profits equals the present value of the project's investment. If the capital is generated internally (out of past and current profits) then the value of the capital is related to the value of its other possible uses, to the risk of the project and to the strategic importance of the project. For example, management may be willing to accept a rate of return only 5% above the prime rate if the project is deemed necessary to its business plan and if the technology is well demonstrated. However, for a new project based on poorly-demonstrated new technology and/or entering a new market, management may require values of at least 40% to 50%.

Running royalty — If any of the steps in the process are licensed, a royalty payment will be required by the licensor. This can be either in the form of a one-time payment or as a payment per unit of production. The latter is called a "running royalty".

Sales expenses are the cost of marketing the product; they include salesmen, offices, storage costs, and transportation.

Utilities costs include the cost of all utilities crossing the boundary limits. For example, if a new plant is located at an existing site, the steam and cooling water it requires may be available from other plants at the site (at a price to be negotiated). On the other hand, in a grass-roots (green-fields) location, the new steam boiler and new cooling tower will be included in the off-plot investment. Here, the utilities would include fuel and feedwater for the boiler and electricity to drive the cooling water system pumps.

Working capital is the value of all materials — raw, partially-processed, and product — in the plant and in associated storage. It represents those funds, in addition to on-plot and off-plot investment, which must be provided to carry out a plant start-up and meet subsequent obligations as they become due.

TOOLS NEEDED FOR PROCESS ECONOMICS

What Needs to Be Done

The first step is to prepare a process flow diagram, showing heat and material balances, pressures, temperatures and equipment sizes. Preparing the flow diagram requires a co-operative effort among the scientists and engineers working on the project. The basic chemistry or biochemistry has to be defined, then each step in the process has to be identified and quantified.

The flow diagram is then used to prepare an on-plot investment estimate, an off-plot investment estimate and a utilities summary. These serve as the major input for the manufacturing cost and for the economic evaluation.

Process Flow Diagrams

Process flow diagrams for two plants — one in operation and one for a speculative process — are described below.

Refinery amine plant

The process flow for an amine plant in an operating refinery is shown in Figure 1. In this plant a sulfur-containing gas (in this case, a mixture of hydrogen sulfide (H_2S), hydrogen, methane, ethane and ethylene) is sent first to a knockout drum [AV-1] to remove any entrained liquid. The dry gas is then contacted with 25 weight-% monoethanolamine (MEA) in the amine-gas contactor [AV-2]. The gas leaving the contactor contains less than 32 ppm (by volume) of H_2S. After passing through a final knockout drum [AV-5], where any amine which has been entrained in the gas can be removed, the gas can be sent to the refinery fuel gas system or to sales. Sulfur-containing liquefied petroleum gas (liquefied propane and butane, known as LPG) is sent to a separate contactor [AV-100], where it is also contacted with 25 weight-% MEA.

The rich MEA containing the absorbed H_2S is then sent to a rich-solution flash tank [AV-4], where any hydrocarbon vapors which dissolved into the rich solution can be flashed off at a reduced pressure. The rich solution is next sent to the amine still [AV-3] where the H_2S is driven off by heating and depressuring the MEA solution. The overhead vapor from the amine still is cooled, and the condensed water is separated from the acid gas (H_2S) in AV-6 and recycled. The acid gas is sent to a sulfur recovery unit where the H_2S is converted to sulfur. The bottoms from the amine still are cooled and then recycled to the two absorbers. Slipstreams of amine solution are purified by 1) passing through a filter [AF-1] and 2) boiling overhead in the reclaimer [AE-5].

The feed gas rate is 5.45 million standard cubic feet per day (MM SCFD), or 154,000 cubic meters per day. This is separ-

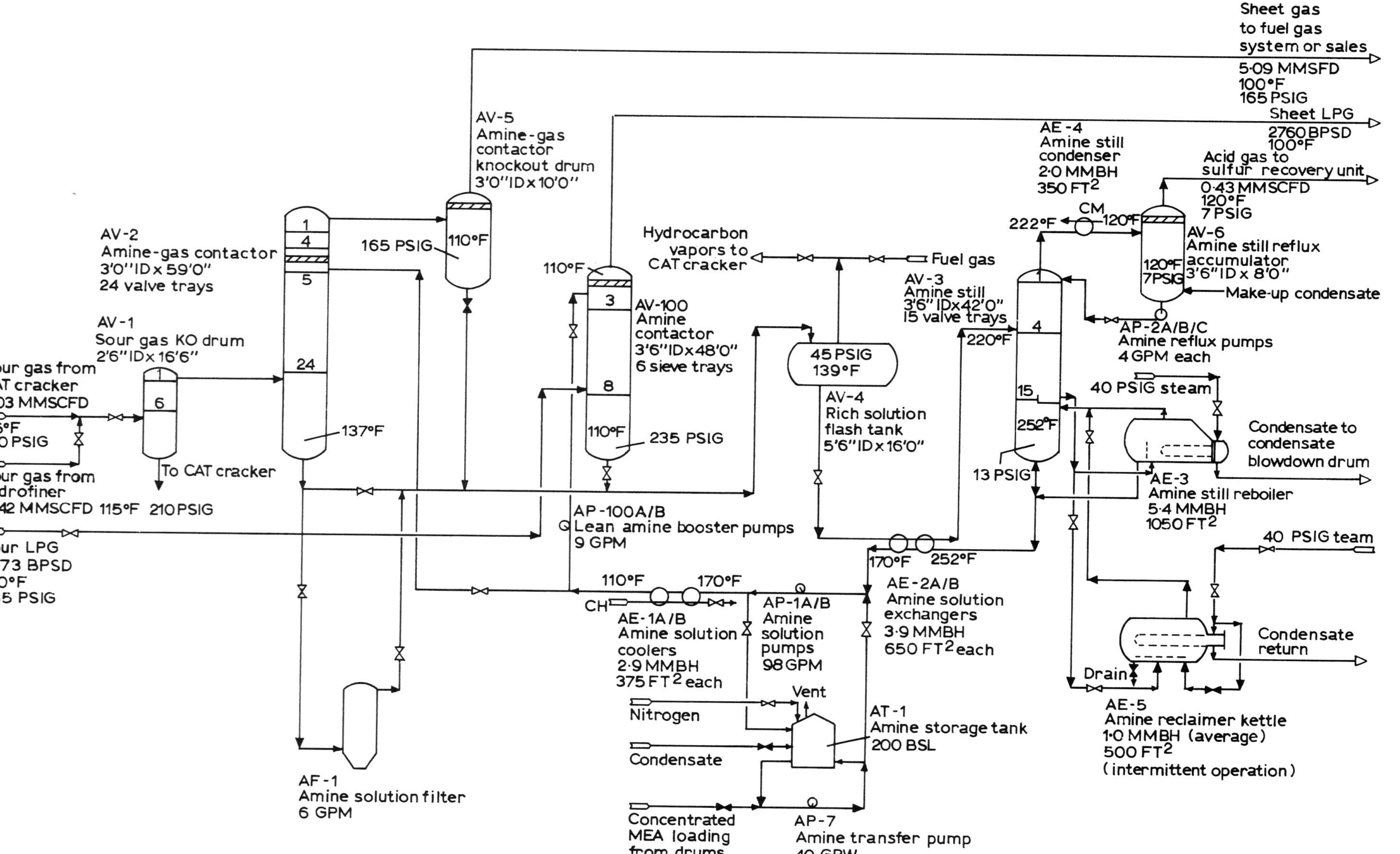

Figure 1. Process flow diagram: amine plant.

ated into 5.09 MM SCFD of sulfur-free gas and 0.36 MM SCFD of H_2S. The LPG feed rate is 2773 barrels per standard day (BPSD), or 440,800 cubic meters per day. This is separated into 2760 BPSD of sulfur-free LPG and 0.07 MM SCFD of H_2S.

Fructose plant

Figure 2 shows a conceptual flow diagram of a process for producing fructose from glucose. Feed to the plant is a glucose solution diluted with water to a concentration of about 10%. In the reactor the glucose reacts with oxygen over a supported enzyme catalyst to form glucosone. A second catalyst in the reactor decomposes the by-product hydrogen peroxide. The solution leaving the oxidation reactor is concentrated to reduce the size of the downstream hydrogenation reactor. In this reactor, the glucosone is selectively hydrogenated to fructose. The resulting fructose solution is concentrated and purified by carbon treatment and ion exchange. The purified solution is further concentrated in a multi-stage evaporator system. Wet fructose from the evaporators is dried and packaged for sale.

The material balance is based on producing 600 MM pounds per year of fructose. At an operating rate of 8000 hours per year, a feed rate of 78,125 pounds per hour (35,437 kilograms per hour) of glucose is required. Also required are about 5000 thousand standard cubic feet per hour (5000 MSCFH) of air and 170 MSCFH of hydrogen.

On-plot Investment Cost

Detailed estimate

Preparing a detailed investment estimate for a new plant can be very expensive. For example, an estimate good to within plus or minus 10% can cost up to 5% or 6% of the total plant investment. This degree of accuracy cannot be obtained until the process design and the piping and instrument diagrams have been completed, quotes have been obtained for most of the equipment items, the off-plot facilities have been defined and sized, and a portion of the detailed project engineering has been carried out.

Factored-type estimate

A factored-type estimate, good to about plus-or-minus 25%, requires less work, but could easily cost $100,000 in engineering charges. For this type of estimate, quotes are obtained for the major equipment items and estimates are made for all other process-equipment items. The bulk materials (such as piping, electrical, and structural) are factored as a percentage of equipment costs. These factors are based on historical data for the same type or similar plants. Estimates of construction costs, engineering fees, cost of the initial charge of catalysts and chemicals, and the cost of spare parts are then added.

Another item which needs to be added to the estimate is the plant owner's project-management expense. This includes all items, in addition to the actual cost of building the plant,

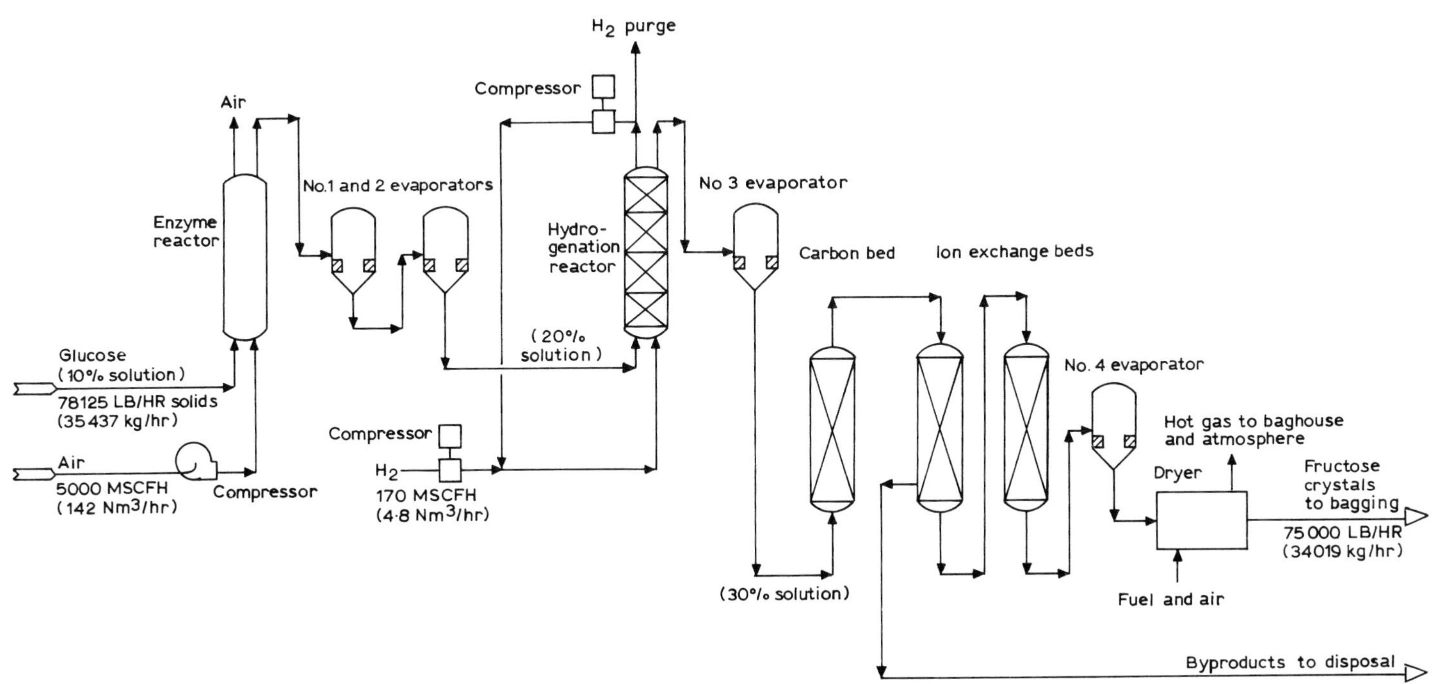

Figure 2. Speculative process flow diagram: fructose process.

required to insure that the plant is built well and the start-up is smooth. Typical project-management items include:

* Preparation of an invitation to bid — or of project specifications
* Choosing a contractor
* Review of contractors' and vendors' designs
* Inspection of equipment and of the progress of construction
* Preparing operating and analytical manuals
* Training operators
* Process and mechanical support during start-up

These costs can run between 3% and 6% of the plant investment.

Order-of-magnitude estimate

For a preliminary evaluation of a new project or process, an order-of-magnitude estimate is usually satisfactory. How to obtain this type of estimate for the amine process shown in the flow diagram (Figure 1) is outlined below:

The first step is to cost all pieces of process equipment. There are several good books which describe how to do this.[1,2,3] This example is based on the procedures in Peters and Timmerhaus,[2] and uses costs as of January 1979.

Vessels

AV-1, sour gas knockdown drum
2 ft 6 in. (76 cm) diam. × 16 ft 6 in. (5 m) tall
Operating pressure = 170 psig (11.7 bars)
Design pressure = 200 psig
Carbon steel construction
Welds are spot-radiographed.
Corrosion allowance (C.A.) = 1/8 in.
Thickness
= (pressure) (radius)/[(stress) (efficiency)−0.6 pressure]+C.A. = 200 (15)/[13,700(0.85)−0.6(200)] + 0.125 = 0.385 in.
Use 7/16-in. plate.
Weight of carbon steel vessel
= 10.68 (diam. in inches) (thickness in inches) (ht in ft)

= 10.68 (30) (7/16) (16.5)	= 2313 lb
Weight of ellipsoidal heads	= 350 lb
Allowance of 15% for nozzles	= 400 lb
Total weight	= 3063 lb
Cost of vessel	= $ 12,000
Similarly for:	
AV-4 (6760 lb)	= $ 19,500
AV-5 (2510 lb)	= $ 10,000
AV-6 (1405 lb)	= $ 7,500
Total cost for all vessels	= $ 49,000

Columns

AV-2, amine-gas contactor
3 ft 0 in. diam. × 59 ft tall
Operating pressure = 165 psig
Design pressure = 195 psig
Carbon steel construction
Welds are spot-radiographed
Corrosion allowance = 1/8 in.
Column has: 3 18-in. manways, 3 8-in. nozzles, and 10 2-in. nozzles
Thickness = 195 (18)/[13,700 (.85)−0.6 (195)] + 1/8 in. = 0.304 + 0.125 in. = 0.429 in.
Use 7/16-in. plate.
Weight of column shell

= 10.68 (36) (7/16) (59)	= 9,925 lb
Weight of ellipsoidal heads = 2 (250)	= 500 lb
Weight of platforms, ladders, and handrails	= 3,175 lb
Total weight of column	= 13,600 lb
Cost of shell	= $ 27,000
Cost of 3 18-in. manways = 3 (18) (70)	= $ 3,780
Cost of 10 2-in. nozzles = 10 (2) (41)	= $ 820
Cost of 3 8-in. nozzles = 3 (8) (41)	= $ 980
Cost of stainless steel valve trays = 24 ($400)	= $ 9,600
Cost of column	= $ 42,180
Similarly for:	
AV-100 8 trays	= $ 37,420
AV-3 15 trays (stainless steel clad)	= $ 34,300
Total cost for all columns	= $ 113,900

Heat exchangers

AE-2A/B, amine solution exchangers
2 shells, 650 ft^2 (60.4 m^2) each
Floating-head with 3/4-in. tubes
Stainless steel tubes and carbon steel shell
300 psig design

Cost of one carbon steel shell	= $ 13,500
Relative cost with alloy tubes	= 1.6
Heat exchanger cost	= $ 43,200
Similarly for:	
AE-1A/B	= $ 28,500
AE-3 (Monel tubes)	= $ 45,000
AE-4	= $ 11,700
AE-5 (Monel tubes)	= $ 34,600
Total cost for all heat exchangers	= $163,000

Pumps and motors

AP-100A/B, lean amine booster pumps
Normal rate = 9 gpm
Design rate = 10 gpm

Head = 165 ft (50 m) of liquid (70 psi)
Use cast steel. (Factor for cast steel = 1.5 × castiron cost.)
Cost of cast-iron pump = $1360
Cost of two cast steel pumps
= 2 (1.5) ($1360) = $ 4,080
Cost of two 1.5 hp motors
= 2 ($240) = $ 480
Cost of pumps and motors = $ 4,560
Similarly for:
AP-1A/B = $ 11,200
AP-2A/B/C = $ 2,940
AP-7 = $ 1,000
Total cost for all pumps and motors = $ 19,700

Tank (AT-1)

200 barrels = 8400 gallons
Cost of tank = $ 13,000

Filter (AF-1)

6 gpm cartridge filter
Cost of filter = $ 1,500

MAJOR MATERIALS

Vessels	= $ 49,000
Columns	= $113,900
Heat exchangers	= $163,000
Pumps and motors	= $ 19,700
Tank	= $ 13,000
Filter	= $ 1,500
Total cost of major materials	= $360,100

To these costs are added:
- Direct costs
  - Installation of the equipment, including foundations
  - Instrumentation, control, computer(s)
  - Piping and insulation
  - Electrical system
- Indirect costs
  - Control house and/or other buildings
  - Land and site preparation
  - Engineering and supervision
  - Contractor engineering and drafting costs
  - Contractor's fee
  - Owner's costs
- Contingency allowance
- Estimated escalation

For an order-of-magnitude estimate of the on-plot investment, the cost of major equipment is usually multiplied by an installation factor. (A detailed estimate of the direct and indirect costs is much more expensive to make.) For most petrochemical plants, installation factors between three and six are reasonable. If we use a historical factor of five for this type of plant, the on-plot investment for the amine plant is calculated at $1,800,000 on a January 1979 basis. This investment can now be up-dated to a January 1991 basis by using the Marshall and Swift cost index (Table 1).

Table 1
Marshall and Swift Cost Index[a]
(1926 = 100)

1969	285.0	1977	505.4	1984	780.4
1970	303.3	1978	545.3	1985	789.6
1971	321.3	1979[b]	570.0	1986	797.6
1972	332.0	1979	599.4	1987	813.6
1973	344.1	1980	659.4	1988	852.0
1974	398.4	1981	721.3	1989	895.1
1975	444.3	1982	745.6	1991[c]	950
1976	472.1	1983	760.8		

[a] All indices, unless otherwise indicated, are mid-year.
[b] January
[c] Estimate for January

Cost (Jan. 1991) = $1,800,000 (950/570) = $3,000,000

Similarly, for the plant shown in Figure 2, the investment cost for each section of the plant is:

	$ Millions
Oxidation reaction section	25
Intermediate concentration	5
Hydrogenation	20
Purification	10
Product concentration and drying	10
Total on-plot investment	70

Here, as in the first example, the cost of most equipment items was determined using one of the standard texts. For specialized equipment, such as the multiple-effect evaporators, quotes were obtained from suppliers.

Off-plot Investment Cost

The major off-plot items include:
- Utilities support
  - Steam generation facilities
  - Cooling tower
  - Electrical distribution facilities
- Storage facilities
  - Tanks
  - Warehouses
- Administrative services

The cost of the off-plot facilities depends both on the

process and on the location of the plant. A grass-roots location — with little or no infrastructure — will require a much larger off-plot investment than will a plant which is located at an already-established plant site — with utilities and storage facilities available.

For a preliminary evaluation, off-plot investment estimates are usually taken as a percentage of on-plot investment. A typical range for off-plot investment would be 25% to 60% of on-plot. If a plant is to be located at an existing site where infrastructure and some utilities are available, then the low end of the scale, say 25%, is appropriate. However, in a grass-roots location, values of up to 60% may be required. Also, if an extremely large amount of tankage is required for feed, intermediate product, and/or final product storage (or if most of the required infrastructure is not available) even higher values may be appropriate.

Table 2 shows a detailed breakdown of the off-plot (as well as the on-plot) investment for a commodity-petrochemical project on the Gulf Coast. This breakdown was obtained from a plus-or-minus-25% cost estimate. Much of the infrastructure (including utilities) for this project was already available.

Table 2
On-plot and Off-plot Investment for a Gulf Coast commodity-petrochemical plant

	$ Millions
ON-PLOT	
Feed preparation section	1.8
Oxidation section	30.1
Recovery section	3.3
Purification section	3.1
Catalyst	1.8
Subtotal for on-plot	40.1
OFF-PLOT	
Waste-gas disposal section	3.7
Utility connections	0.6
Boiler feedwater treatment	0.6
Cooling tower addition	0.3
Electrical distribution	1.1
Butane feed system	0.3
Tanks and loading facilities	0.9
Control house extension and lab. facilities	0.5
Sewers and drains	0.3
Oxidation-pond aerators	1.0
Relief system	0.2
Site preparation	0.4
Subtotal for off-plot	9.9
TOTAL INVESTMENT	50.0

Utilities Summary

The process flow diagram also serves as the basis for the utilities summary. Typical utilities are:

* Fuel — for furnaces
* Steam — for reboilers, other heat exchangers, and steam stripping
* Cooling water — for heat exchangers
* Electricity — for compressors and pumps

For the amine plant (Figure 1), the utilities required are 40 psig steam for the reboiler and reclaimer, cooling water (CW) for the amine-still condenser and the amine-solution coolers, and electricity for all of the pumps.

Calculations for the utilities are shown below:

40 psig steam

Reboiler and reclaimer duties: 6.4 MM Btu/hr (6.75 MM kilojoules/hr)
Latent heat of 40 psig steam: 919 Btu/lb (510 kcal/kg)
40 psig steam required: 6964 lb/hr

Cooling water

Condenser and cooler duties: 4.9 MM Btu/hr
Cooling water temperature rise: 20 deg. F. (11.1 deg.C.)
C_p of cooling water: 1.0 Btu/lb deg.F. (1.0 cal/gm deg.C.)
Density of water: 8.33 lb/gal (1 gm/cc)
Cooling water required

$$= \frac{4.9 \text{ MM Btu lb deg.F. gal hr}}{\text{hr (1) Btu 20 deg.F. 8.33 lb 60 min}}$$

= 490 gal/min (1855 liters/min)

Electricity

Pump	*gpm*	*Approx. pump press. drop (psi)*	*Approx. pump efficiency (%)*	*Horsepower*
AP-100	9	70	40	1
AP-1	88	240	50	25
AP-2A/B	8	40	20	1
AP-7	40[a]	—	—	—
Total horsepower				27

[a] normally 0 gpm

Kilowatts used by pumps = 0.746 (27) = 20 kw
Allowance for lighting and miscellaneous = 15 kw
Total kilowatts used = 35 kw

For the fructose plant (Figure 2) the corresponding utilities were calculated as:

Medium-pressure steam 215,000 lb/hr
Cooling water 24,000 gal/min

Power	9,900 kw
Fuel	0.85 MM Btu/hr

Manufacturing Cost

After the investment costs and utilities requirements for a plant have been established, the manufacturing cost of the product can be calculated. The basis for calculating the manufacturing cost includes the investment costs, utilities requirements, utility unit costs, cost of proprietary chemicals and catalyst, feedstock requirement, and unit cost of that feed. Also included are the factors for calculating maintenance, incremental overhead, local taxes and insurance. As an example, the basis for the calculation of the manufacturing cost of a commodity petrochemical is shown in Table 3 and the calculation of the manufacturing cost is shown in Table 4. Since the process for the commodity-petrochemical plant used in this example is very well developed, no contingency allowance has been included. The total estimated manufacturing cost is $17.57 million per year, or 22 cents per pound of product.

The manufacturing cost for producing fructose from glucose (via the process illustrated in Figure 2) was calculated on the basis of the utility requirements shown above (see Utilities Summary) and on these unit costs:

Medium-pressure steam	$2.95/M lb
Cooling water	$0.15/M gal
Power	$0.03/kwh
Fuel	$3.00/MM Btu

A contingency allowance of 40% has been included in the calculation of this cost (see Table 5). This allowance is for unanticipated problems which are likely to arise as the process is further developed in the laboratory and then in the pilot plant.

ECONOMIC EVALUATION

Once investment and manufacturing costs are estimated, the economics of the project can be evaluated. Three of the most common criteria for evaluating the economics are payout period, rate of return and maximum net present value.

Payout Period

Payout period is the amount of time (number of years) required until the profits from the project are equal to the capital cost invested. Usually, the time-value of money is not taken into account in this calculation.

The payout period can be calculated on either an after-tax or a before-tax basis. As an example, consider the Gulf Coast commodity-petrochemical plant used as an example in Tables 3 and 4. The plant requires an on-plot plus off-plot investment of $50 million. It also requires $4 million of working capital. It takes two years to build, goes on stream at the beginning of year three and begins to make a profit. Assume that the gross income is 52.5 cents per pound (selling price of 55 cents per pound minus sales expense of 2.5 cents per pound) times 80 million pounds per year, or $42 million per year. The manufacturing cost (from Table 4) is $17.6 million per year. During the first five years of operation the plant is being depreciated (using the simplifying assumption of $10 million straight-line depreciation per year) and the part of the profit which would otherwise be taxable is reduced by the amount of the depreciation. In the succeeding years, the plant profits are fully taxable. For these calculations we have used a tax rate of 40%. (The combined federal and state corporation tax in the U.S. for 1987 was 41%. This rate dropped to 35% for 1988. It may increase again in the future.)

During the first five years of operation the taxable income is the gross income minus the manufacturing cost and minus the $10 million per year of depreciation, or $14.4 million per year. In subsequent years the taxable income is $24.4 million per year.

Cash flow on a project will start out in a negative direction because investment is required to build the plant. After the plant starts up, profits are generated and the cash flow moves in a positive direction. Cash flow (on an after-tax basis) is shown for the commodity-petrochemical plant in Figure 3. Assume that $30 million of the on-plot plus off-plot investment cost is spent in year one and the balance, $20 million, in year two.

In year three the plant has an income of $42 million. Expenses are the $17.6 million of manufacturing costs and taxes of $5.8 million (40% of the taxable income of $14.4 million), for a total of $23.4 million. The profit is the difference — $18.6 million. The cash flow for year three is the profit minus the working capital of $4 million, which is

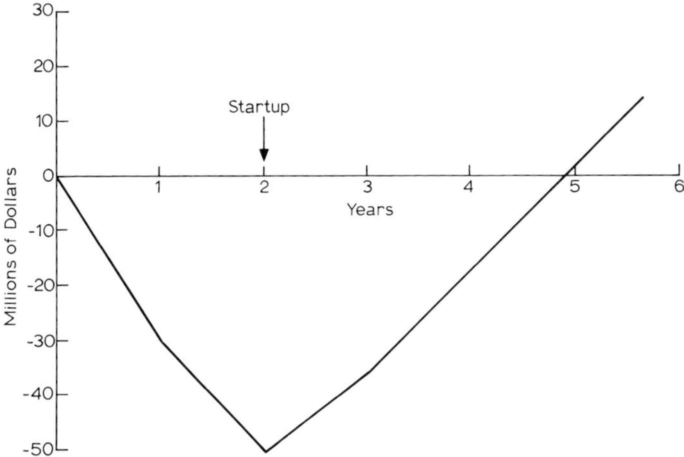

Figure 3. Cash flow on an after-tax basis.

Table 3
Basis for Calculating the Manufacturing Cost of a Commodity Petrochemical

Plant size	80 MM lb/yr	
On-plot investment	$40 MM	
On-plot plus off-plot investment	$50 MM	
Operating hours	8000/yr	
Utilities required:	*Number of units*	*Cost per unit*
High-pressure steam (export)	52,400 lb/hr	$3.70/M lb
Medium-pressure steam	24,100 lb/hr	$2.95/M lb
Low-pressure steam	12,500 lb/hr	$0.30/M lb
Cooling water	835 gal/min	$0.15/M gal
Power	670 kw	$0.03/kwh
Fuel	172 MM Btu/hr	$3.00/MM Btu
Labor	2 shift-positions at $150,000/position	
Catalyst and chemicals (proprietary)	$2.6 million/yr	
Maintenance	3% of total investment	
Incremental overhead	50% of maintenance and labor	
Local taxes and insurance	2.5% of investment	
Feed (butane)	0.216 gal/lb of product	
Butane cost	44 cents/gal	
Contingency allowance	None required	

Table 4
Calculation of Manufacturing Cost for a Commodity Petrochemical

Operating Cost	$ Thousands per year	Cents/lb of product
Maintenance	1500	1.87
Labor	300	0.38
Utilities:		
Fuel	4130	5.16
High-pressure steam (credit)	(1550)	(1.94)
Medium-pressure steam	570	0.71
Low-pressure steam	30	0.04
Power	160	0.20
Cooling water	60	0.08
Chemicals	1100	1.38
Catalyst	1500	1.87
Incremental overhead	900	1.13
Taxes and insurance	1250	1.56
TOTAL OPERATING COST	9950	12.44
Feedstock cost (butane at 44 cents/gal)	7620	9.53
By-product credit	0	0.0
TOTAL MANUFACTURING COST	17,570	22.0

Table 5
Calculation of Manufacturing Cost for a Speculative Process to Convert Glucose into Fructose

Production (design rate) = 600 MM lb/yr of crystalline fructose

Investment	*$ Millions*	
On-plot	70	
Off-plot (assumed to be 35% of on-plot)	25	
TOTAL INVESTMENT	95	
	$ Thousands per year	*Cents/lb of product*
Operating cost		
Maintenance (assumed to be 3% of investment)	2,850	0.5
Labor (at $150,000 per shift position)	600	0.1
Utilities		
Medium-pressure steam	5,070	0.8
Cooling water	1,730	0.3
Power	2,380	0.4
Fuel	20	0.0
Catalyst, chemicals and hydrogen	6,200	1.0
Immobilized enzyme	12,000	2.0
Incremental overhead (assumed to be 50% of maintenance and labor)	1,725	0.3
Taxes and insurance (assumed to be 2.5% of investment)	2,375	0.4
TOTAL IDENTIFIED OPERATING COST	34,950	5.8
Contingency allowance (assumed to be 40% of identified operating cost)	13,980	2.3
Feedstock cost (corn syrup at 14 cents/lb, dry basis)	87,500	14.6
TOTAL MANUFACTURING COST	136,430	22.7

spent in year three. In years four through seven the cash flow is $18.6 million per year. As shown in Figure 3, the accumulated after-tax profits equal the original $54 million investment in ($54 million/$18.6 million per year), or 2.9 years after start-up.

The depreciation rates most commonly used are not straightline and they will be different each year until the plant is completely depreciated. Also, tax rates and depreciation schedules are likely to change. Therefore, it is much simpler to calculate the cash flow on a before-tax basis and the before-tax basis is frequently used for preliminary economic evaluations.

Cash flow (on a before-tax basis) is shown for the commodity-petrochemical plant in Figure 4. During the first two years the $50 million of on-plot plus off-plot investment is spent. At the end of year two the cumulative cash flow is a negative $50 million. In year three the plant has a before-tax income of $24.4 million ($42 million minus $17.6 million). Year three cash flow is then $24.4 million minus the working capital of $4 million, which is spent that year. In subsequent years the cash flow is $24.4 million per year. The accumulated before-tax profits equal the original $54 million investment in ($54 million/$24.4 million per year), or 2.2 years after start-up.

Still another way to consider the economics is to calculate the payout period based on the long-term net income after taxes — using the period (in this case year eight and later) after the plant has been fully depreciated. In year eight or

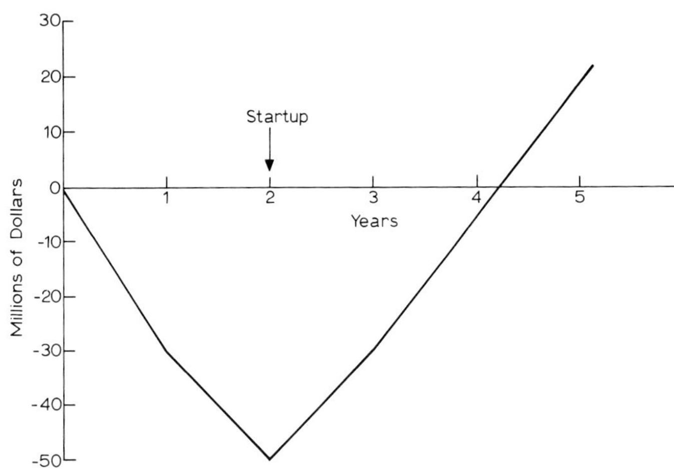

Figure 4. Cash flow on a before-tax basis.

later, the plant still has an income of $42 million per year. Expenses are the $17.6 million per year in manufacturing costs plus taxes. The taxable income is the difference between $42 million and $17.6 million, or $24.4 million per year. At a tax rate of 40%, taxes are $9.8 million per year. Then the after-tax income is $24.4 million minus $9.8 million, or $14.6 million per year. The payout period is ($54 million/$14.6 million per year), or 3.7 years.

The before-tax payout period and long-term after-tax payout period are related by the factor 1-(%tax/100). With a 40% tax-rate and having calculated the long-term after-tax payout period to be 3.7 years, then 1 − (40/100) = 0.6; and 0.6 × 3.7 years = 2.2 years, which is the before-tax payout period.

Table 6
Rate of Return for a Commodity Petrochemical at a Selling Price of 55 Cents per Pound

Basis:

Production rate = 80 MM lb/yr On-plot plus off-plot investment = $50 MM Working capital = $4 MM Construction period = 2 years	Manufacturing cost = 22 ¢/lb ($17.6 MM/yr) Selling price = 55 ¢/lb ($44 MM/yr) Sales expenses = 2.5 ¢/lb ($2 MM/yr)	Depreciation is 5-yr straight-line Tax rate = 40% Project life = 15 years

	$ Millions					at 25% discount rate			at 30% discount rate		
							$ Millions			$ Millions	
Year	Capital cost	Gross Income	Manufacturing cost	Taxes[a]	Net Income	Present value factor	Present value	Cumulative value	Present value factor	Present Value	Cumulative value
1	(30)	—	—	—	—	0.8000	(24.00)	(24.00)	0.7692	(23.08)	(23.08)
2	(20)	—	—	—	—	0.6400	(12.80)	(36.80)	0.5917	(11.83)	(34.91)
3	(4)	42.0	17.6	5.8	18.6	0.5120	7.48	(29.32)	0.4552	6.65	(28.26)
4	—	"	"	"	"	0.4096	7.62	(21.70)	0.3501	6.51	(21.75)
5	—	"	"	"	"	0.3277	6.10	(15.60)	0.2593	4.82	(16.93)
6	—	"	"	"	"	0.2621	4.88	(10.72)	0.2072	3.85	(13.08)
7	—	"	"	"	"	0.2097	3.90	(6.82)	0.1594	2.96	(10.12)
8	—	"	"	9.8	14.6	0.1678	2.45	(4.37)	0.1226	1.79	(8.33)
9	—	"	"	"	"	0.1342	1.96	(2.41)	0.0943	1.38	(6.95)
10	—	"	"	"	"	0.1074	1.57	(0.84)	0.0725	1.06	(5.89)
11	—	"	"	"	"	0.0859	1.25	0.41	0.0558	0.81	(5.08)
12	—	"	"	"	"	0.0687	1.00	1.41	0.0429	0.63	(4.45)
13	—	"	"	"	"	0.0550	0.80	2.21	0.0330	0.48	(3.97)
14	—	"	"	"	"	0.0440	0.64	2.85	0.0254	0.37	(3.60)
15	4	"	"	"	"	0.0352	0.65	3.50	0.0195	0.36	(3.24)

[a] For years 3 through 7, taxes = 0.40 (42.0 − 17.6 − 10) = $5.8 MM/yr
For years 8 through 15, taxes = 0.40 (42.0 − 17.6) = $9.8 MM/yr

By interpolation, rate of return = 25.0% + (3.50) (5%)/(3.24 + 3.50) = 25% + 2.6% = 27.6%

Rate of Return

Rate of return is a more-sophisticated criterion for evaluating a project. Effects of time-value of money and of inflation can each be figured into this evaluation.

Capital is usually scarce; there are many places to use available capital in order to generate profits. Because of this, alternative projects are evaluated — both with regard to economics and to degree of risk. Which projects are chosen depends to a great degree on management philosophy. For example, suppose there are two competing projects: Project A, with a high degree of risk and a 60% rate of return; and Project B, with a low degree of risk and a 20% rate of return. A risk-taking management would probably opt for Project A, while a more-conservative management would probably choose Project B.

The rate-of-return calculations for the Gulf Coast commodity-petrochemical project used in Tables 3 and 4 (and Figures 3 and 4) are shown in Table 6. The first column shows the project life; in this case it is a fifteen-year project.

The second through sixth columns show the items which make up the cash flow for a project. The second column shows the capital cost (investment) per year. As before, it is assumed that the plant takes two years to build and that $30 million is spent on it in year one and $20 million in year two. The working capital of $4 million is spent in year three and recovered in year fifteen. The third column shows the gross income (after selling expenses) of $42 million per year. The fourth column shows the manufacturing cost of $17.6 million per year (see Table 4). The fifth column shows the taxes paid. As discussed above, the taxes are $5.8 million per year while the plant is being depreciated and they then rise to $9.8 million per year. The sixth column shows the net income, which is the gross income minus the manufacturing cost and minus taxes. As discussed above, the net income is $18.6 million per year in years three through seven and $14.6 million per year in years eight through fifteen.

The seventh through ninth columns show the effect of the time-value of money. The seventh column shows present value factors at a 25% discount rate (from Table 7). What this represents is the value today — at a 25% discount rate — of money which will be received in the future. For convenience, it is assumed that money received during a period of time is received at the end of that period.

The eighth column shows the product of the present value factor times the income during that period. It represents the value — today — of income to be received in future years. At a 25% discount rate the $30 million invested in year one (and assumed to be spent at the end of the year) is worth only $24 million at the beginning of the project. Similarly, the $20 million investment in year two is worth only $12.8 million. In year three there is a net income of $18.6 million less the $4 million of working capital spent that year. Thus the present value of the cash flow in year three is 0.512 times $14.6 million, or $7.48 million. In years four through fourteen the present value in each year is the product of the present value factor and the net income. In year fifteen, at the end of the project, the working capital is recovered. Therefore, the present value is the product of 0.0352 and the sum of the net income plus working capital. It is apparent here that income received in the fifteenth year has very little value today. The $4 million in working capital recovered in year fifteen is worth only 0.0352 times $4 million, or $0.14 million today.

Table 7
Present Value Factors

n	i = 5%	10%	15%	20%	25%	30%	40%
1	0.9524	0.9091	0.8696	0.8333	0.8000	0.7692	0.7143
2	0.9070	0.8264	0.7561	0.6944	0.6400	0.5917	0.5102
3	0.8638	0.7513	0.6575	0.5787	0.5120	0.4552	0.3644
4	0.8227	0.6830	0.5718	0.4823	0.4096	0.3501	0.2603
5	0.7835	0.6209	0.4972	0.4019	0.3277	0.2593	0.1859
6	0.7462	0.5645	0.4323	0.3349	0.2621	0.2072	0.1328
7	0.7107	0.5132	0.3759	0.2791	0.2097	0.1594	0.0949
8	0.6768	0.4665	0.3269	0.2326	0.1678	0.1226	0.0678
9	0.6446	0.4241	0.2843	0.1938	0.1342	0.0943	0.0484
10	0.6139	0.3855	0.2472	0.1615	0.1074	0.0725	0.0346
11	0.5847	0.3505	0.2149	0.1346	0.0859	0.0558	0.0247
12	0.5568	0.3186	0.1869	0.1122	0.0687	0.0429	0.0176
13	0.5303	0.2897	0.1625	0.0935	0.0550	0.0330	0.0126
14	0.5051	0.2633	0.1413	0.0779	0.0440	0.0254	0.0090
15	0.4810	0.2394	0.1229	0.0649	0.0352	0.0195	0.0064

The ninth column shows the cumulative sum of all of the items in the two previous columns. Initially, there is a large negative number which represents the cost of building the plant and the working capital required to run it. As the plant generates profits, the cumulative value becomes less and less negative, until it finally reaches zero. With a 25% discount return, at the end of year fifteen the cumulative value has become positive, namely $3.50 million. This indicates that 25% is low, and that the actual rate of return is larger than 25%.

The same procedure is now repeated with the present value factors at 30% (tenth through twelfth columns). In the twelfth column we note that at year fifteen the cumulative value is now negative, minus $3.24 million. Thus, the rate of return is between 25% and 30%. By interpolation we find that the rate of return is 3.50/(3.50 + 3.24), or a little over halfway between 25 and 30. The actual value is 27.6%. This project would probably be approved if the risk of not selling all of the product is low.

Sensitivity analysis (effect of other factors on rate of return)

The rate of return is usually calculated on what appears to be the most likely set of assumptions regarding investment and income. However, it is usually prudent to run a sensitivity analysis. In other words, determine what the effect would be on the rate of return if certain of your assumptions are not correct. Some of the factors which should be investigated are changes in: selling price, investment, amount of working capital and rate of sales buildup.

Table 8
Effect of a 15-Cent-per-Pound Decrease in Selling Price on Rate of Return for a Commodity Petrochemical

Basis: (same as Table 6 except that selling price is 40 ¢/lb)

Production rate = 80 MM lb/yr	Manufacturing cost = 22 ¢/lb ($17.6 MM/yr)	Depreciation is 5-yr straight-line
On-plot plus off-plot investment = $50 MM	Selling price = 40 ¢/lb ($32 MM/yr)	Tax rate = 40%
Working capital = $4 MM	Sales expenses = 2.5 ¢/lb ($2 MM/yr)	Project life = 15 years
Construction period = 2 years		

						at 10% discount rate			at 15% discount rate		
	$ Millions						$ Millions			$ Millions	
Year	Capital cost	Gross income	Manufacturing cost	Taxes[a]	Net Income	Present value factor	Present value	Cumulative value	Present value factor	Present value	Cumulative value
1	(30)	—	—	—	—	0.9091	(27.27)	(27.27)	0.8696	(26.09)	(26.09)
2	(20)	—	—	—	—	0.8264	(16.53)	(43.80)	0.7561	(15.12)	(41.21)
3	(4)	30.0	17.6	1.0	11.4	0.7513	5.56	(38.24)	0.6575	4.87	(36.34)
4	—	"	"	"	"	0.6830	7.79	(30.45)	0.5718	6.52	(29.82)
5	—	"	"	"	"	0.6209	7.08	(23.37)	0.4972	5.67	(24.15)
6	—	"	"	"	"	0.5645	6.44	(16.93)	0.4323	4.93	(19.22)
7	—	"	"	"	"	0.5132	5.85	(11.08)	0.3759	4.29	(14.93)
8	—	"	"	5.0	7.4	0.4665	3.45	(7.63)	0.3269	2.42	(12.51)
9	—	"	"	"	"	0.4241	3.14	(4.49)	0.2843	2.10	(10.41)
10	—	"	"	"	"	0.3855	2.85	(1.64)	0.2472	1.83	(8.58)
11	—	"	"	"	"	0.3505	2.59	0.95	0.2149	1.59	(6.99)
12	—	"	"	"	"	0.3186	2.36	3.31	0.1869	1.38	(5.61)
13	—	"	"	"	"	0.2897	2.14	5.45	0.1625	1.20	(4.41)
14	—	"	"	"	"	0.2633	1.95	7.40	0.1413	1.05	(3.36)
15	4	"	"	"	"	0.2394	2.73	10.13	0.1229	1.40	(1.96)

[a] For years 3–7, taxes = 0.40 (30.0–17.6–10) = $1.0 MM/yr
For years 8–15, taxes = 0.40 (30.0–17.6) = $5.0 MM/yr

By interpolation, rate of return = 15.0% – (1.96)(5%)/(1.96 + 10.13) = 15% – 0.8% = 14.2%

Selling price decrease

A large decrease in the selling price will have a very negative effect on the rate of return. The effect of a fifteen cent decrease, from 55 cents per pound to 40 cents per pound, is shown in Table 8. In this case the income after taxes in years three through seven drops from $18.6 million per year to $11.4 million per year; in years eight through fifteen it drops from $14.6 million per year to $7.4 million per year. The calculated rate of return drops from 27.6% in the base case (Table 6) to only 14.2%. This rate of return is normally considered too low for a project to be approved. However, the project might be approved if it is considered to be important for the company's long-range strategic plan, or if the prime rate is so low that 14% interest is considered attractive.

Unexpected increase in investment. The effect of an unexpected 20% increase in on-plot plus off-plot investment on the manufacturing cost and on the rate of return is shown in Tables 9 and 10. When the investment increases, the manufacturing cost also increases because some of the items included in the manufacturing cost are functions of investment. As shown in Table 9, the maintenance cost, local taxes, and insurance each increase by 20%. The incremental overhead increases, but not by as much as 20%, because it is a function of both maintenance (which increases) and labor (which does not). The net result is an increase in the manufacturing cost from $17.6 million per year (in Tables 4 and 6) to $18.3 million per year in this case.

The 20% increase in on-plot plus off-plot investment has a large effect on the rate of return because the money is spent early in the project, when the present value factors are still high. This effect can be seen in Table 10. For this case the rate of return drops to 23.2%, compared to the base case rate of 27.6%. This decrease is substantial, but it would probably not be enough to stop the project if it appeared — early in the project — that a substantial overrun in investment might be expected.

Increase in working capital. Table 11 shows the effect of including an additional $10 million of working capital in the calculations for the case shown in Table 6. In the base case, the working capital was assumed to be $4 million. In Table 11 the working capital is assumed to be $14 million, or about 28% of on-plot plus off-plot investment. (This amount of working capital might be appropriate for a remote location where long-term storage of feed and product is necessary because of limited infrastructure, or for a case where payment for product may be delayed.) Even though the $14 million of working capital is recovered in year fifteen, at the end of the project, its present value is only $0.91 million at a 20% discount rate and only $0.49 million at a 25% discount rate. Adding $10 million of working capital has almost the same effect as increasing the on-plot plus off-plot investment by $10 million because it is required early in the project. However, unlike an increase in investment, it does not affect either the manufacturing cost or taxes. Also, it is spent in year three, rather than in the first two years. Thus, a $10

Table 9
Effect of a 20% Increase in On-plot and Off-plot Investment on the Manufacturing Cost for the Commodity Petrochemical in Tables 4 and 6

Plant size		80 MM lb/yr
On-plot plus off-plot investment		$60 MM
Operating cost	*$ Thousands per year*	*Cents per lb of product*
Maintenance (20% higher)	1,800	2.25
Labor	300	0.38
Utilities	3,400	4.25
Chemicals	1,100	1.38
Catalyst	1,500	1.87
Incremental overhead (50% of maintenance and labor)	1,050	1.32
Taxes and insurance (20% higher)	1,500	1.88
TOTAL OPERATING COST	10,650	13.33
Feedstock cost	7,620	9.53
TOTAL MANUFACTURING COST	18,270	22.9

Table 10

Effect of a 20% Increase in Investment on Rate of Return for a Commodity Petrochemical Selling at 55 Cents per Pound

Basis (same as Table 6 except that the on-plot plus off-plot investment has increased from $50 million to $60 million)

Production rate = 80 MM lb/yr
On-plot plus off-plot investment = $60 MM
Working capital = $4 MM
Construction period = 2 years

Manufacturing cost = 22 ¢/lb ($17.6 MM/yr)
Selling price = 55 ¢/lb ($44 MM/yr)
Sales expenses = 2.5 ¢/lb ($2 MM/yr)

Depreciation is 5-yr straight-line
Tax rate = 40%
Project life = 15 years

	$ Millions					at 20% discount rate			at 25% discount rate		
							$ Millions			$ Millions	
Year	Capital cost	Gross Income	Manufacturing cost	Taxes[a]	Net income	Present value factor	Present value	Cumulative value	Present value factor	Present value	Cumulative value
1	(36)	—	—	—	—	0.8333	(30.00)	(30.00)	0.8000	(28.80)	(28.80)
2	(24)	—	—	—	—	0.6944	(16.67)	(46.67)	0.6400	(15.36)	(44.16)
3	(4)	42.0	18.3	4.7	19.0	0.5787	8.68	(37.99)	0.5120	7.68	(36.48)
4	—	"	"	"	"	0.4823	9.16	(28.83)	0.4096	7.78	(28.70)
5	—	"	"	"	"	0.4019	7.64	(21.19)	0.3277	6.23	(22.47)
6	—	"	"	"	"	0.3349	6.36	(14.83)	0.2621	4.98	(17.49)
7	—	"	"	"	"	0.2791	5.30	(9.53)	0.2097	3.98	(13.51)
8	—	"	"	9.5	14.2	0.2326	3.30	(6.23)	0.1678	2.38	(11.13)
9	—	"	"	"	"	0.1938	2.75	(3.48)	0.1342	1.91	(9.22)
10	—	"	"	"	"	0.1615	2.29	(1.19)	0.1074	1.53	(7.69)
11	—	"	"	"	"	0.1346	1.91	0.72	0.0859	1.22	(6.47)
12	—	"	"	"	"	0.1122	1.59	2.31	0.0687	0.98	(5.49)
13	—	"	"	"	"	0.0935	1.33	3.64	0.0550	0.78	(4.71)
14	—	"	"	"	"	0.0779	1.11	4.75	0.0440	0.62	(4.09)
15	4	"	"	"	"	0.0649	1.18	5.93	0.0352	0.64	(3.45)

[a] For years 3 through 7, taxes = 0.40 (42.0−18.3−12) = $4.7 MM/yr
For years 8 through 15, taxes = 0.40 (42.0−18.3) = $9.5 MM/yr

By interpolation, rate of return = 25.0% − (3.45) (5%)/(3.45 + 5.93) = 25.0% − 1.8% = 23.2%

million increase in on-plot plus off-plot investment decreases the rate of return from 27.6% to 23.2% (Table 10), while a $10 million increase in working capital reduces the rate of return to only 24.3% (Table 11).

Slow sales buildup. The effect of a slow sales buildup on the manufacturing cost and on the rate of return is shown in Tables 12 and 13. It is assumed here that only half of the product is sold in the first year after start-up (year three) and only three-fourths in the second (year four). All of the product is sold in year five and in subsequent years.

The major effect of a slow sales buildup is to increase the cost per pound of product because many of the expenses of manufacturing the product will be independent of the amount of product made. For example, maintenance costs have been assumed to be 3% of on-plot plus off-plot investment, or $1.5 million per year. If only 40 million pounds of product are produced in the first year of operation (year three), the cost of maintenance will be 3.75 cents per pound of product (see Table 12). In the third year of operation (year five), when 80 million pounds of product are produced, the maintenance cost will drop to 1.87 cents per pound of product. Similarly, labor, incremental overhead, insurance, and local taxes will increase on a per pound of product basis.

Normally, the amount of feedstock and utilities required per pound of product will remain constant even though the production rate changes. This will not be strictly true at very low production rates, because at such low rates some of the

Table 11
Effect of an Additional $10 Million in Working Capital on Rate of Return for a Commodity Petrochemical Selling at 55 Cents per Pound

Basis: (same as Table 6 except that an additional $10 million of working capital is included in the third year)

Production rate = 80 MM lb/yr On-plot plus off-plot investment = $50 MM Working capital = $14 MM Construction period = 2 years	Manufacturing cost = 22 ¢/lb ($17.6 MM/yr) Selling price = 55 ¢/lb ($44 MM/yr) Sales expenses = 2.5 ¢/lb ($2 MM/yr)	Depreciation is 5-yr straight-line Tax rate = 40% Project life = 15 years

	$ Millions					at 20% discount rate	$ Millions		at 25% discount rate	$ Millions	
Year	Capital cost	Gross Income	Manufacturing cost	Taxes[a]	Net income	Present value factor	Present value	Cumulative value	Present value factor	Present value	Cumulative value
1	(30)	—	—	—	—	0.8333	(25.00)	(25.00)	0.8000	(24.00)	(24.00)
2	(20)	—	—	—	—	0.6944	(13.89)	(38.89)	0.6400	(12.80)	(36.80)
3	(14)	42.0	17.6	5.8	18.6	0.5787	2.66	(36.23)	0.5120	2.36	(34.44)
4	—	"	"	"	"	0.4823	8.97	(27.26)	0.4096	7.62	(26.82)
5	—	"	"	"	"	0.4019	7.48	(19.78)	0.3277	6.10	(20.72)
6	—	"	"	"	"	0.3349	6.23	(13.55)	0.2621	4.88	(15.84)
7	—	"	"	"	"	0.2791	5.19	(8.36)	0.2097	3.90	(11.94)
8	—	"	"	9.8	14.6	0.2326	3.40	(4.96)	0.1678	2.45	(9.49)
9	—	"	"	"	"	0.1938	2.83	(2.13)	0.1342	1.96	(7.53)
10	—	"	"	"	"	0.1615	2.36	0.23	0.1074	1.57	(5.96)
11	—	"	"	"	"	0.1346	1.97	2.20	0.0859	1.25	(4.71)
12	—	"	"	"	"	0.1122	1.64	3.84	0.0687	1.00	(3.71)
13	—	"	"	"	"	0.0935	1.37	5.21	0.0550	0.80	(2.91)
14	—	"	"	"	"	0.0779	1.14	6.35	0.0440	0.64	(2.27)
15	14	"	"	"	"	0.0649	1.86	8.21	0.0352	1.01	(1.26)

[a] For years 3 through 7, taxes = 0.40 (42.0−17.6−10) = $5.8 MM/yr
For years 8 through 15, taxes = 0.40 (42.0−17.6) = $9.8 MM/yr

By interpolation, rate of return = 25.0% − (1.26)(5%)/(1.26 + 8.21) = 25% − 0.7% = 24.3%

equipment items in the plant could function at lower than design efficiency. In this case the utility consumption per pound of product would increase.

If feedstock and utilities do remain constant, then the manufacturing cost will be 26.9 cents per pound in year three and 23.6 cents per pound in year four; then it will drop to 22 cents per pound in year five and subsequent years.

Since the slow sales buildup has its major effect at the beginning of the project when the present value factors are still high, the rate of return drops from 27.6% to 23.6% (Table 13).

Inflation

The effect of inflation can be complex because the investment cost and the components of the manufacturing cost will each probably inflate at a different rate. If we assume that all components increase at the same rate, then the rate of return in constant dollars (which are dollars corrected by the inflation rate to the base year) is essentially equal to the rate of return in current dollars minus the inflation rate. For example, the rate of return for the case shown in Table 6 is 27.6% in current dollars. With an inflation rate of 3%, the rate of return in constant dollars would be 24.6%, and the project would have a good chance of being approved. If, however, the inflation rate were 30%, management would require a much higher rate of return that 27.6% before a project could be approved.

Table 12
Calculation of Manufacturing Cost for a Commodity Petrochemical Project with a Slow Sales Buildup

Basis:

Plant design rate	= 80 MM lb/yr
Sales, first year of operation	= 40 MM lb/yr
Sales, second year of operation	= 60 MM lb/yr
Sales, third year and later	= 80 MM lb/yr

Manufacturing costs	Cents per pound of product		
	First yr	*Second yr*	*Later yrs*
Maintenance	3.75	2.50	1.87
Labor	0.76	0.50	0.38
Fuel	5.16	5.16	5.16
Steam (credit)	(1.19)	(1.19)	(1.19)
Power	0.20	0.20	0.20
Cooling water	0.08	0.08	0.08
Chemicals	1.38	1.38	1.38
Catalyst	1.87	1.87	1.87
Incremental overhead	2.26	1.50	1.13
Taxes and insurance	3.12	2.08	1.56
Feedstock	9.53	9.53	9.53
TOTAL	26.9	23.6	22.0

Maximum Net Present Value

The rate of return is a measure of the efficiency of an investment; the net present value is a measure of the amount of profit that a project will generate. If two projects with different lives are being compared, both the rate of return and the net present value per unit of investment should be calculated for each project.

As an example, compare Project A (illustrated in Table 6) with Project B. For Project A the net present value (called Cumulative value in the table) is \$3.50 million at a 25% discount rate and a negative \$3.24 million at a 30% discount rate. Assume that Project B is similar to Project A — except that (1) it has a project life of only seven years and (2) the net income per year in years three through seven is \$25.0 million (instead of \$18.6 million).

The rate of return for Project B is 29.7%, compared to a 27.6% rate of return for Project A. Thus, on a rate of return basis, Project B is a better project. However, because it has a much shorter life than Project A, Project B will generate less revenue. At discount rates of 15% and 20%, which are reasonable for a period of low inflation, the net present values for the two projects are:

	Project *A*	Project *B*
At a 15% discount rate:		
Net present value, \$ millions	28.43	21.03
Ratio: Net present value/Investment	0.53	0.39
At a 20% discount rate:		
Net present value, \$ millions	13.33	11.83
Ratio: Net present value/Investment	0.25	0.22

At a 15% discount rate, the net present value for Project A is \$28.43 million, which is considerably greater than the net present value of \$21.03 million for Project B. So, using the criterion of maximum net present value, Project A is a better project. Note that at a 20% discount rate, the difference in the net present values of the two projects has narrowed considerably. This shows that at a lower discount rate, the longer project is more desirable because it generated profits over a longer time period. However, at higher discount rates the project with the shorter life may become more attractive because the profits generated in later years are less valuable.

The net present value can be used to compare projects having the same investment. If the investments are not the same, which is the usual case, the comparison is made on the

Table 13

Effect of a Slow Sales Buildup on Rate of Return for a Commodity Petrochemical Selling at 55 Cents per Pound

Basis: Same as Table 6 except that sales are 50% of product the first year, 75% the second year, and 100% in later years)

Production rate = 80 MM lb/yr	Manufacturing cost = 22 ¢/lb ($17.6 MM/yr)	Depreciation is 5-yr straight-line
On-plot plus off-plot investment = $50 MM	Selling price = 55 ¢/lb ($44 MM/yr)	Tax rate = 40%
Working capital = $4 MM	Sales expenses = 2.5 ¢/lb ($2 MM/yr)	Project life = 15 years
Construction period = 2 years		

	$ Millions					at 20% discount rate	$ Millions		at 25% discount rate	$ Millions	
Year	Capital cost	Gross income[a]	Manufacturing cost	Taxes	Net income	Present value factor	Present value	Cumulative value	Present value factor	Present value	Cumulative value
1	(30)	—	—	—	—	0.8333	(25.00)	(25.00)	0.8000	(24.00)	(24.00)
2	(20)	—	—	—	—	0.6944	(13.89)	(38.89)	0.6400	(12.80)	(36.80)
3	(4)	21.0	10.8	0.1	10.1	0.5787	3.53	(35.36)	0.5120	3.12	(33.68)
4	—	31.5	14.2	2.9	14.4	0.4823	6.95	(28.41)	0.4096	5.90	(27.78)
5	—	42.0	17.6	5.8	18.6	0.4019	7.48	(20.93)	0.3277	6.10	(21.68)
6	—	″	″	″	″	0.3349	6.23	(14.70)	0.2621	4.88	(16.80)
7	—	″	″	″	″	0.2791	5.19	(9.51)	0.2097	3.90	(12.90)
8	—	″	″	9.8	14.6	0.2326	3.40	(6.11)	0.1678	2.45	(10.45)
9	—	″	″	″	″	0.1938	2.83	(3.28)	0.1342	1.96	(8.49)
10	—	″	″	″	″	0.1615	2.36	(0.92)	0.1074	1.57	(6.92)
11	—	″	″	″	″	0.1346	1.97	1.05	0.0859	1.25	(5.67)
12	—	″	″	″	″	0.1122	1.64	2.69	0.0687	1.00	(4.67)
13	—	″	″	″	″	0.0935	1.37	4.06	0.0550	0.80	(3.87)
14	—	″	″	″	″	0.0779	1.14	5.20	0.0440	0.64	(3.23)
15	4	″	″	″	″	0.0649	1.21	6.41	0.0352	0.65	(2.58)

[a] Income after sales expense of 2.5 ¢/lb

By interpolation, rate of return = 25.0% − (2.58)(5%)/(2.58 + 6.41) = 25% − 1.4% = 23.6%

basis of the ratio of net present value to investment. In the cases illustrated above, the net present value was divided by the total investment of $54 million.

USES OF ECONOMIC EVALUATIONS

Economic evaluations are valuable tools for management but they are *no* substitute for business judgement. Two of the ways that they can be used are to monitor the progress of research and to help determine the size of a new plant.

Monitoring Progress of Research

Preliminary economic evaluations may serve either to determine whether a project is attractive enough that research and development should be continued — or to determine areas of the process where substantial improvements are required for the process to be economically successful.

An example of the "continue or stop" evaluation is shown in Table 14. Here the goal was to convert glucose, from corn syrup at 14 cents per pound, into crystalline fructose which had a projected selling price in the range of 40 to 50 cents per pound and a projected market of at least 600 million pounds per year. As shown in Table 14, at a selling price of 40 cents per pound, the payout period before taxes is calculated to be 1.1 years. Similarly, at a selling price of 50 cents per pound, the payout period before taxes would be only 0.6 years. These values are considered to be reasonable for a speculative (high risk) process.

An example of the procedure for determining where to improve a process so that it will be more economical is shown in Tables 15 and 16. Table 15 lists the process par-

Table 14
Speculative Economics for Process to Convert Glucose to Fructose

Total investment (from Table 5)	\$95 MM
Projected market	600 MM lb/yr
Manufacturing cost (from Table 5)	22.7 cents/lb
Estimated selling expenses	2.3 cents/lb
Estimated price of product	40 to 50 cents/lb

At 40 cents/lb:
Income before taxes
= 600 MM lb/yr (40 cents/lb − 22.7 cents/lb − 2.3 cents/lb)
= \$90 MM/yr
Payout period before taxes = 1.1 years

At 50 cents/lb:
Income before taxes
= 600 MM lb/yr (50 cents/lb − 22.7 cents/lb − 2.3 cents/lb)
= \$150 MM/yr
Payout period before taxes = 0.6 years

Table 15
Design Basis for Development of an Immobilized Enzyme Catalyst

	Start of Project	*End of Project*
Enzyme properties		
Soluble activity; units/mg enzyme	5	5
Coupling efficiency; %	20	35
Half-life, hr	135	135
Fermenter process parameters		
Enzyme production required (1×10^{11} units/yr)	7	4
Fermenter cell density (gm/liter)	5	6
Fermenter cycle time (days)	10	8
Fermenter productivity (units of recovered soluble activity/liter-day)	15	75
Enzyme recovery process parameters		
Buffer before homogenization (kg buffer/kg cell)	150	150
Buffer after homogenization (kg buffer/kg cell)	25	25
Filter aid (kg filter aid/kg cell)	8	8
Precipitant used (Both are proprietary.)	type 1	type 2
Total precipitant added to crude extract (kg precipitant/kg crude extract)	0.2	0.4
Number of times support is used	1	1
Loading (units/gm support)	2	25

ameters for producing an immobilized-enzyme catalyst. It then shows both the original and final values for each of these parameters.

The impact of each of these process parameters on the project economics is shown in Table 16. The research results demonstrated at the start of the project are clearly unacceptable when compared to the goal of about 2.5 cents per pound of product.

The value of this approach is to highlight where the major expenses are so that research can be directed toward achieving the goal of 2.5 cents per pound. In this case, the highlighted items are costs of feed for cells, of precipitant, and of the enzyme-support. Once these expenses are identified, it becomes possible to focus research so as to achieve the goal.

Deciding Size of New Plant

Before deciding what the capacity of the new plant should be, many factors must be considered. If the plant's capacity is too low, the investment will be high relative to the profits and the payout period will be long; the rate of return will be low. On the other hand, if it is too large, the product from the plant will either be not completely sold, or it will be sold for a lower price than planned. At a lower price either there will be a greater demand for the product, or competitors who have higher manufacturing costs will be driven out of the market.

The effect on project economics of large changes in the size of a new plant is shown in Table 17. The base case (first column) shows the investment and manufacturing cost for the commodity-petrochemical plant illustrated in Table 4. Here the payout period before taxes is 2.2 years, which is equivalent to a rate of return of 27.6% (see Table 6).

The second case (second column) shows similar values for a plant with a capacity of only 40 million pounds per year, half the size of the first. In this case the investment is reduced, but not halved; therefore, investment cost per pound increases. (Investment costs for different-size plants are related by the formula $I_2 = I_1[Size_2/Size_1]^{0.6}$.) The same number of people are needed to run the plant so that the labor cost on a per pound basis doubles. The utilities, catalyst and chemicals, and feed-stock costs are typically independent of the size of the plant. Overall, the payout period increases to 3.1 years for this small plant, and it would not be competitive with the larger plant.

If the capacity of the proposed plant is doubled to 160 million pounds per year, the manufacturing cost decreases from 22 cents per pound to 20.6 cents per pound. If all of the product could be sold at 55 cents per pound, the payout period (before taxes) would be only 1.6 years. However, because the capacity of this plant is so large (slightly greater than 30% of the projected worldwide demand of 500 million pounds per year for the product) it is unreasonable to believe that the market can absorb all of this new product in a short period of time without a substantial decrease in price. If the price per pound drops by 10 cents to 45 cents, then the payout period will be 2.4 years — which is higher than the 2.2 years in the base case. Therefore, management's decision on the size of the plant should depend very heavily on its analysis of the market in addition to its analysis of the payout period or rate of return calculations.

Table 16
Manufacturing Cost Estimate for Immobilized Enzyme Production

	Cents per pound of product	
	Start of project	*End of project*
Feed for cells	10.5	0.1
Buffer salts	0.5	0.1
Filter aid	5	0.7
Precipitant	25	0.3
Support	15	0.8
Utilities	0.5	0.2
Maintenance and labor	0.5	0.1
Overhead, contingency, taxes, etc.	5	0.2
TOTAL	62	2.5

Table 17
Effect of Plant Design Rate on Economics for the Commodity Petrochemical in Tables 4 and 6

Plant design rate (MM lb/yr)	*80*	*40*	*160*
On-plot plus off-plot investment ($MM)	50	33	76
Working capital ($MM)	4	2	8
Manufacturing cost		*Cents per pound of product*	
Maintenance	1.87	2.48	1.42
Labor	0.38	0.76	0.19
Fuel	5.16	5.16	5.16
Steam (credit)	(1.19)	(1.19)	(1.19)
Power	0.20	0.20	0.20
Cooling water	0.08	0.08	0.08
Chemicals	1.38	1.38	1.38
Catalyst	1.87	1.87	1.87
Incremental overhead	1.13	1.62	0.81
Taxes and insurance	1.56	2.06	1.19
Feedstock	9.53	9.53	9.53
TOTAL	22.0	24.0	20.6
Projected demand, worldwide = 500 MM lb/yr			
Payout calculation			
Estimated price of product (cents/lb)	55	55	45
Sales expense @ 2.5 cents/lb ($MM/yr)	2.0	1.0	4.0
Income, after sales expense ($MM/yr)	42.0	21.0	68.0
Manufacturing cost ($MM/yr)	17.6	9.6	33.0
Net income before taxes ($MM/yr)	24.4	11.4	35.0
Payout period, before taxes (years)	2.2	3.1	2.4

REFERENCES

For Sizing and Costing Equipment:

1. Institut Français du Pétrole. (1981). *Manual of Economic Analysis of Chemical Processes.* [Translation of *Manuel d'évaluation économique des procédés.* (1976)]. New York: McGraw-Hill.
2. Peters, Max. S and Timmerhaus, Klaus D. (1980). *Plant Design and Economics for Chemical Engineers.* (3rd ed.) New York: McGraw-Hill.
3. Popper, Herbert, ed. (1970). *Modern Cost-Engineering Techniques.* New York: McGraw-Hill.

FURTHER READING

Stermole, Franklin J. (1984). *Economic Evaluation and Investment Decision Methods* (5th ed.) Golden, Colo.: Investment Evaluations Corp.

Tyler, Chaplin and Winter, C.H., Jr (1959). *Chemical Engineering Economics.* (4th ed.) New York: McGraw-Hill.

Section III

Biotechnology and Industry

Chapter 16

The Established Industries

Derek G. Springham

INTRODUCTION

The history of the earliest microbial technology will never be written for it began too long ago, much of it before the first written records. Beer was brewed by the Babylonians and Sumerians around 6000 B.C.; cheese was produced from milk in the region which is now Iraq in about 6000 B.C.; records of baking in Egypt date back to 4000 B.C.; the Babylonians were manufacturing vinegar from palm juice and date syrup in 3000 B.C.; sewage treatment in septic tanks is known from Pakistan and the Baghdad region from around 3000 B.C. and vinegar was used as an antibiotic on wound dressing in Biblical times. By contrast, it was not until the 17th century that van Leeuwenhoek first observed microorganisms under the microscope and the recognition of the role of microbes in fermentation and the development of cell-free systems had to wait until the late 19th century. The practical applications of microbiology thus pre-date the beginnings of scientific understanding of the processes by several thousands of years and it is instructive to consider why brewing could be performed by the ancients with apparent ease and success whilst the production of penicillin caused so many problems less than fifty years ago.

The development of microbial biotechnology can conveniently be regarded as having taken place in four phases (Table 1), each representing a stage in technological development. The scheme inevitably oversimplifies the real developments and, in particular, ignores the considerable overlap between phases.

The first phase includes the products whose origins predate written records. Unlike processes in the later phases, their production does not depend on an understanding of the principles of microbiology and biochemistry nor even on a knowledge of the existence of microorganisms. What they have in common is that they are all highly robust from the microbiological point of view: inoculation with a culture is not required, although a starter of active material may be necessary or advantageous, and the operations are naturally resistant to the excessive growth of contaminating organisms provided that appropriate conditions are maintained.

The earliest products are made using (mainly) fast-growing facultative anaerobes which are strongly selected under the conditions employed; low levels of contaminants have little effect and the growth of competing organisms is discouraged by the absence of oxygen, by the accumulation of metabolic products such as ethanol, carbon dioxide and lactic acid and, in cheese, by the reduction of water content. Success is thus dependent on fairly simple, empirical procedures.

All of these methods have been subjected to substantial technological improvement using techniques characteristic of the later phases but are still practised on a small scale using phase 1 technology in third world countries, often alongside large-scale highly modernised versions of the same processes.

The development of phase 2 processes required application of the rapidly advancing knowledge of biochemistry, microbiology and genetics which started in the 19th century. Phase 2 includes operations which are not naturally resistant to the growth of competing organisms, such as the commercial production of baker's yeast. They thus required an appreciation of the specific role of the microbes concerned, the ability to prepare and maintain pure cultures, to sterilise media and plant and to exclude competing organisms. Conscious selection to improve strains was practised, as in the acetone-butanol fermentation, and the composition of growth media was manipulated to divert metabolism in the desired direction, as in the production of citric acid and glycerol.

The production of penicillin and other antibiotics in phase 3 posed new problems. Vigorous aeration was required and the fermentations proved highly susceptible to contamination so substantial advances in fermenter engineering were required to enable large volumes of fluid to be agitated vigorously without permitting the entry of contaminants through the points at which stirrer shafts entered the vessels. Pure cultures were essential. Extensive programmes of development were undertaken to improve yields by selection coupled with a variety of mutagenic techniques. Strains which had been subjected to that mutagenesis and selection were often highly unstable and had to be subjected to constant checking to avoid reversion. Satisfactory yields were dependent on close control of fermentation conditions. Sophisticated methods were developed for downstream processing to attain the required degree of product purity. Increasingly stringent re-

Table 1
Phases in the Development of Biotechnology

Phase 1 (Prehistoric times onwards)
Technology: robust technologies, developed and carried out without understanding of scientific principles.
Examples: alcoholic beverages; bread; cheese; fermented foods e.g. yoghurt, tanning of hides, purification of sewage.

Phase 2 (Mid 19th century-1940)
Technology: operations dependent on near-sterility. Manipulation of media to increase product yields. Specific processes of strain selection. Use of pure cultures.
Examples: acetone and butanol; glycerol; citric acid; gluconic acid; lactic acid; yeast in pure culture for food, fodder, baking, alcoholic fermentations; crude enzyme preparations e.g. takadiastase; first microbial (fungal) insecticide.

Phase 3 (1940–)
Technology: microbial processes highly susceptible to competition or leading to pharmaceutical products: very high standards of sterility required. Pure cultures and extensive strain development essential. Sophisticated process control and quality control.
Examples: antibiotics; single cell protein; vaccines.

Phase 4 (Late 1970s–)
Technology: identification, isolation, controlled alteration and generation of specific gene products.
Examples: production of pharmaceuticals by gene transfer e.g. human growth hormone, insulin; prenatal screening for genetic disease e.g. sickle cell anaemia; identification of individuals for forensic purposes from blood or semen samples; use of gene manipulation for strain improvement.

quirements for quality control and product testing were imposed by regulatory authorities for pharmaceutical and food products.

Phase 4 involves the isolation and manipulation of specific genes. The technology permits product yields to be enhanced, protein products to be modified at will and the genetic characteristics of organisms to be redesigned. The benefits of this technology are only just beginning to flow.

This chapter is about traditional microbiological industries and is concerned with processes which fall into phases 1 and 2. To avoid overlap with other chapters some processes, which might have fallen within the scope of the title, have been omitted e.g.; single cell protein (Chapter 25); enzymes (Chapter 18); biomass conversion (Chapter 28); amino acids, vitamins, some organic acids and antibiotics (Chapter 17).

ALCOHOLIC BEVERAGES

Alcoholic beverages are of many types and are produced world-wide except where this is prevented by religious considerations. In terms of value they are by far the most important microbial products with a value in world markets estimated to be £23 billion ($37 billion) in 1981, comfortably exceeding the estimates for cheese (£14 billion; $22 billion) and antibiotics (£4.5 billion; $7 billion).

Alcoholic beverages can conveniently be considered in three classes according to ethanol concentration. Wines and beers are produced directly by fermentation and product inhibition limits their ethanol concentration to a maximum of about 18% (v/v), and usually much less. Spirits are produced by distillation of wines or beers: their concentration could thus be as high as 95%; at that concentration ethanol and water form a constant-boiling mixture which cannot be further concentrated without special processes such as co-distillation. In practice, spirits are sold at much lower concentrations (generally 35–50%), representing the maximum ethanol concentration generally acceptable for drinking undiluted. Spirits offer *inter alia* the advantage of indefinite keeping whereas wines and beers usually have a limited shelf life and must be consumed soon after the container is opened. Fortified wines, such as sherry and port, are produced by adding spirits to wine and share the advantage of stability. Compounded spirits are products which derive their flavours, a least to a major degree, from herbs ("botanicals").

The prime requirement for ethanol production is a suitable source of carbohydrate. Fermentable sugars, mainly glucose, fructose and sucrose, are derived from fruits, especially the grape, from honey and from plant storage organs such as sugar cane or sugar beet. Polysaccharides, mainly starch, are derived from gains such as barley, corn (maize), wheat, rice, millet or from root crops such as potatoes. Carbohydrates from animal sources are used less often although the large quantity of lactose available as a waste product of cheese manufacture is an attractive target for the production of industrial ethanol.

Characteristics of Alcoholic Beverages

Alcoholic beverages are retail products. Sales thus depend on the reactions of individual customers and the manufacturer must pay careful attention to consumer preference. The appeal of alcoholic beverages is due only partly to ethanol and the pleasant intoxication which, under ideal circumstances, follows consumption. With the exception of a few spirits such as vodka, the attraction depends to a substantial extent on the flavours, aromas and colours of the product. Several hundreds of trace compounds have been identified in alcoholic beverages. Many of them have distinctive flavours and aromas and are known as "congenerics". The most important classes are alcohols, organic acids, esters, carbonyl compounds and sulphur compounds. They originate in several ways, including entry from primary raw materials, production by yeast metabolism and that of other microorganisms, from herbs added for flavour, by extraction from wooden barrels used during maturation processes, from chemical reactions occurring during fermentation or catalysed by copper surfaces in the stills during distillation, or from substances added as preservatives or to improve colour, flavour or ethanol yield.

Most people find it surprisingly difficult to assess accurately the ethanol content of a beverage: thus, although two beers made to different ethanol concentrations by the same process will be distinguished easily, the obvious differences are due less to the ethanol than to the congenerics, the minor products of yeast metabolism. Advantage has been taken of this phenomenon to produce non-alcoholic low alcohol beers and wines by distillation to remove the ethanol, usually with the return of the ester fraction. These products possess many of the attractions of the real thing without the intoxication. In a recent trial, conducted with eighteen social drinkers, the success rate in identifying three beer products containing respectively 5.0%, 3.7% and 0.5% ethanol was less than the chance expectation.

Other properties may also be important in determining acceptance of the final product by the consumer. Perhaps the most complex product in this respect is beer where, in addition to flavour and aroma, consumer preference may depend on clarity, the absence of any tendency for beer to gush out suddenly when the bottle is opened, beer colour, foam colour, the amount of foam formed when beer is poured into the glass, the stability of the foam which must not collapse too rapidly and the way in which the foam clings to the side of the glass. The shelf life, i.e. the period of time before the beer becomes unacceptable due to changes in flavour or appearance, is also of substantial importance. It should thus be clear that the production of an acceptable alcoholic beverage involves far more than making a dilute ethanol solution.

Flavour Components

The use of gas chromatography (GC), especially with the increased resolution of capillary columns, and of gas chromatography-mass spectrometry, has permitted the identification of large numbers of volatile components in alcoholic beverages. Thus over 550 volatile components have been identified from wine, including aliphatics, aromatics and heterocyclics containing oxygen and nitrogen.

Flavour Assessment

The human palate is capable of recognising some eight different tastes: they include sweet, sour, salty, bitter, astringent and metallic. The sense of smell is both highly sensitive and highly complex: many important flavour components have aroma thresholds in the parts per million range or even lower and the number of discernable aroma sensations is large. For convenience, taste and aroma will be considered together as "flavour" in the remainder of this section. The perception of flavours is notoriously subjective and normal language is insufficiently precise to permit detailed and useful descriptions of the aromas of alcoholic beverages. (This is easily confirmed by comparing the descriptions produced by two or more acknowledged wine experts after tasting the same wine.) Moreover, the effects of different components are not independent: mixtures may have synergistic or antagonistic effects, or one component may modify the effect of another in a qualitative sense. Despite the obvious problems, producers of beverages on a large scale need reliable methods of flavour assessment for quality control purposes and to test the acceptability of new raw materials and new production methods.

The identification of the compounds responsible for particular flavours is difficult but considerable progress has been made. Components identified in beverages can be added to pure alcohol solutions for aroma assessment. A useful analytical technique is to split the effluent stream from a GC column, one part going to the detector the other part being sniffed by the operator to determine the aromas associated with particular peaks. In one recent report, the volatile components from a lager-type beer, brewed from experimental malt, were resolved into 96 peaks by GC-mass spectroscopy: 90 peaks had an aroma, identified by sniffing, 30 of these were provisionally identified[1].

At present, only a limited understanding of the aroma characteristics of beverages is possible in terms of measurable components. Analysis can show that a particular batch of product is unacceptable because of deviation from normal values but cannot be used to conclude that a batch *will* prove acceptable. To achieve this, recourse must be made to organoleptic evaluation, i.e. appraisal of taste and smell by a trained taste panel. Such panels have an essentially negative function: they cannot predict the acceptability to the consumer of a new and different product but are used for quality control purposes to detect unwanted changes in produt aroma and taste. They can also be used to test whether changes in production methods, for instance the substitution of continuous for batch fermentation or the introduction of a new raw material, have any detectable effect on product quality.

Taste Trials

Taste trials are widely used in the alcoholic beverage and food industries and detailed methods for their organisation have been developed. To be of any value they should satisfy several criteria:

(i) Double blind methods are essential, i.e. neither the taste panel nor the person providing the samples and collecting the results should know the identity of the samples.
(ii) If the trials are intended to assess flavour they should be conducted in such a way that extraneous factors such as colour cannot affect the results. This is usually achieved by conducting trials in subdued red light and, if necessary, using black glasses to conceal the appearance of the contents.
(iii) The design of the trial must permit the results to be evaluated by statistical methods so that objective conclusions can be reached.
(iv) The panel should be selected from people who have shown their ability to discriminate in previous trials. Ideally, they should be trained to describe flavour differences in terms of standardised descriptors, each corresponding to a reproducible flavour standard, preferably a pure substance.

The third requirement is satisfied by using an experimental design such as a three-way trial with forced choice. Each taster is presented with three glasses in random order, two of which contain the same sample whilst the other contains a different sample, and is required to identify which glass is the odd one out. This design permits the results of a trial to be expressed in terms of the usual statistical probabilities. Having identified the difference, if any, the taster is asked to describe it as precisely as possible in the standard terminology.

Williams[2] described a standard terminology developed for use in wine assessment, involving fourteen general characteristics and thirty-four specific descriptors. Several other such schemes exist, designed for use with beer, cider, whisky, various types of wine and various foods. Clapperton *et al.*[3] described a library of 35 reproducible reference standards corresponding to the majority of terms in their scheme. A further refinement is to train the panel to estimate relative intensities of aroma components, describing each in terms of five categories of intensity. This permits a beverage sample to be assigned a flavour profile[2].

Specific Gravity Measurements

One of the most widely-used analytical parameters in the alcoholic beverage industries is specific gravity (S.G.). Sugar solutions have specific gravities greater than 1.000: thus a solution containing 100 g/l sucrose has an S.G. of 1.040. The mixtures of sugars commonly present at the start of fermentation are difficult to analyse by conventional chemical methods. Specific gravity measurements are used to measure the initial sugar content. These values serve as a check on the quality of raw materials and on the correct operation of the early stages of production such as the mashing process in brewing. By experience, the final ethanol concentration can be predicted, even where substantial amounts of non-fermentable carbohydrate are present; in the U.K., S.G. measurements before fermentation are used to assess the excise duty payable. The progress and end point of fermentations can also be assessed. Ethanol solutions have S.G. values less than 1.000, pure ethanol having an S.G. of 0.794. By S.G. measurements on distillates, ethanol content can be assessed. Most commonly S.G. values are measured by hydrometer. Where corrections are made for temperature and, if appropriate, for dissolved carbon dioxide, the results can be surprisingly accurate. Specific gravity bottles and electronic methods can be used for more critical assessments. The measurements are not specific: they do not distinguish between fermentable and non-fermentable carbohydrates and other substances can also contribute. Ethanol and carbohydrates influence the measurements in opposite senses. Despite this, the ease of measurement, the degree of precision and the wealth of experience in interpreting the results make S.G. the most useful analytical parameter in almost any alcoholic fermentation.

Health and Social Aspects

The physiological effects of ethanol, including intoxication, aggressive and criminal behaviour, alcohol dependence and long term physical damage, are well-known. They pose problems for society and for companies involved in the alcoholic beverage industry. Attempts to ban production and consumption in the U.S. during the prohibition era from 1919 to 1934 were unsuccessful, and led to the proliferation of organised crime. The bans instituted on religious grounds by many Moslem societies appear to be more successful due to a much greater measure of public support and to the more drastic legal remedies available to their governments. Further attempts to ban alcohol in western nations seem unlikely but increasing government and public concern may well lead to the progressive imposition of taxation as a means of discouraging excessive consumption. The alcoholic beverage industry is thus to be regarded as mature and many companies involved are actively seeking diversification into other areas.

Biochemistry of Yeast Fermentations

The vast majority of yeasts used for alcoholic fermentations are classified either as *Saccharomyces cerevisiae* or as *S. uvarum*. *Saccharomyces* is one of 39 yeast genera and over 40 species are recognised. The taxonomy of yeasts is complex and has been subjected to recent changes so that the literature frequently includes references to a particular species under different names. The changes have affected yeasts important in alcoholic fermentation: *S. carlsbergensis* and *S. uvarum*, once recognised as separate species, are now combined under the latter name and a proposal has recently been made to merge *S. uvarum* with *S. cerevisiae*. Much of the confusion is due to the fact that the species concerned are interfertile. The situation will become even more complex in the future due to forced interspecific and intergeneric crosses and to gene manipulation. More than 1000 distinct strains of *S. cerevisiae* are recognised.

Starch

Most yeasts used for alcoholic fermentation have little or no amylase activity and cannot utilise starch. Where starch is the carbohydrate source, this must be degraded to fermentable sugars by enzymes from some other source. Starch is a high molecular weight polymer of glucose which exists in two forms. Amylose is a helical structure formed by a linear sequence of α-1,4-linked glucose residues. In amylopectin, α-1,4-linkages predominate but branch points are introduced by α-1,6-linkages, resulting in a tree-like structure. Most sources of starch contain a mixture of the two forms. In plant materials starch is organised into microscopic granules, surrounded by protein coats. To permit rapid enzymic attack the native starch granule must be gelatinised by heat treatment. The temperature required differs from one type of plant material to another within the range 65–80°C. Barley starch has a low gelatinisation point which makes it attractive for alcoholic fermentation as the gelatinisation can be brought about without destroying the barley amylases.

Amylases from plant sources are of three types. α-Amylases hydrolyze amylose or amylopectin molecules at internal α-1,4-linkages, releasing smaller products. β-Amylases hydrolyze the penultimate α-1,4,-linkages at the non-reducing ends of molecules, releasing maltose. The two types of activity are referred to respectively as "solubilisation" and "saccharification" and together result in the rapid breakdown of starch to fermentable sugars and limit dextrins. The latter products arise because neither α- nor β-amylase can hydrolyze the α-1,6-linkages which are numerous in amylopectin and hydrolysis stops a few residues from a branch point. A third type of enzyme, α-1,6-glucosidase (also known as limit dextrinase or debranching enzyme), can hydrolyze the branch points and permit complete transformation of starch to a mixture of glucose, maltose and maltotriose. Amyloglucosidases from fungal or bacterial sources remove glucose residues from non-reducing ends and can also hydrolyze the α-1,6-linkages. They can thus hydrolyze starch completely to glucose.

Utilisation of Sugars

The principle fermentable sugars encountered by yeasts in alcoholic fermentations are sucrose, fructose, glucose, maltose and maltotriose. Maltotetraose and the higher linear products of starch breakdown, together with branched products, are not usually fermented by yeasts and are loosely referred to as "dextrins". Separate transport systems exist for the entry into the cells of glucose, fructose, maltose and maltotriose. A cell wall invertase rapidly hydrolyzes sucrose and, until recently when a sucrose transport system was demonstrated, was assumed to account entirely for sucrose metabolism. The permease systems for maltose and maltotriose are subject to repression and destruction by glucose and sequential utilisation of sugars is normal. Inside the cell, maltose and maltotriose are hydrolysed by α-glucosidase (maltase).

Aerobic and Anaerobic Metabolism

S. cerevisiae and related yeasts can generate energy for growth by oxidizing glucose via glycolysis and the tricarboxylic acid cycle. This is an energy-efficient process as 38 molecules of ATP can be generated by the oxidation of one glucose molecule. Both respiratory enzymes and mitochondria are subject to catabolite repression and the access of oxygen is usually prevented. Thus, in the presence of the substantial sugar concentrations found in alcoholic fermentations, metabolism is almost completely anaerobic. The major route of glucose catabolism is the glycolytic (Embden-Meyerhoff-Parnass) pathway. Energy generation is inefficient by comparison with aerobic metabolism, the breakdown of one molecule of glucose to two of pyruvate being accompanied by the formation of only two ATP molecules (Figure 1). Two molecules of NADH are generated for each glucose molecule converted to pyruvate. To permit continued metabolism these must be reoxidised

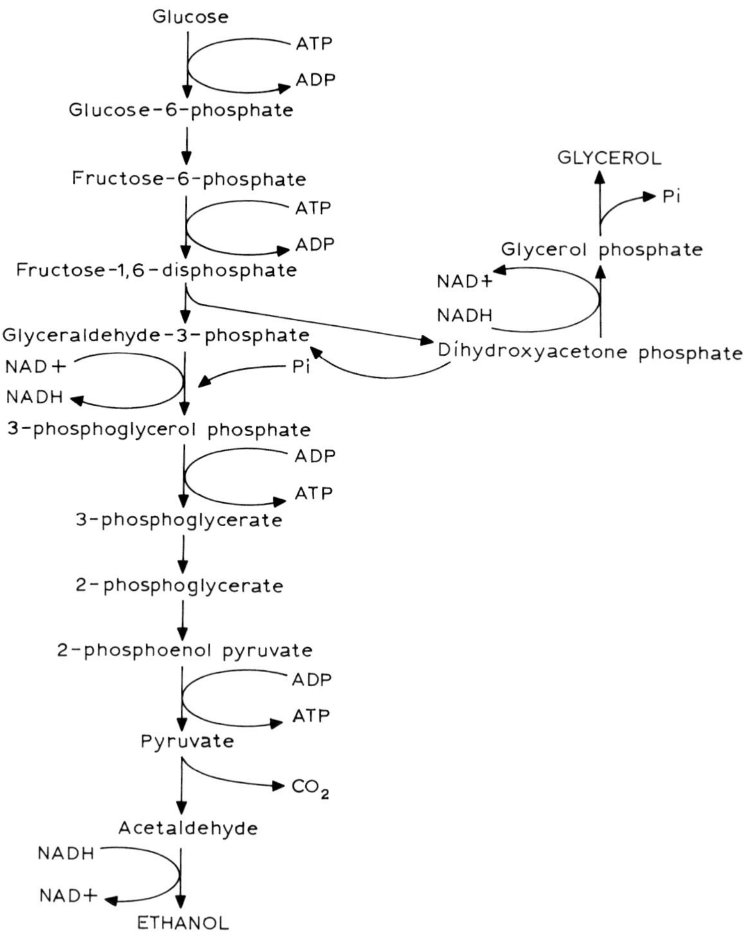

Figure 1. Reactions leading to the formation of ethanol, ATP and glycerol by yeast under anaerobic conditions.

to NAD^+. This is accomplished by the decarboxylation of the pyruvate and reduction of the resulting acetaldehyde to ethanol. The overall equation:

$$C_6H_{12}O_6 + 2ADP + 2Pi \rightarrow 2C_2H_5OH + 2CO_2 + 2ATP + 2H_2O$$

predicts the formation of two molecules of ethanol for every hexose molecule consumed, equivalent to 51% conversion by weight. Due to the diversion of carbon to form yeast cells and minor metabolic products, the actual conversion yield is a few percent less. A small proportion of hexose is metabolized via the pentose phosphate pathway, serving to generate pentoses and reduced NADP for biosynthesis.

Since a proportion of the pyruvate molecules generated in glycolysis are used for biosynthesis, some NADH molecules are reoxidised instead by concomitant reduction of dihydroxyacetone phosphate to glycerol phospate: glycerol, an important flavour component of alcoholic beverages, is produced by the action of a specific phosphatase.

The inefficiency of anaerobic metabolism as an energy-generating process is important because it maximises ethanol production: ethanol is a by-product of yeast energy metabolism and the less efficient the process, the higher the ratio of alcohol to yeast cells. It might be expected *a priori* that there would be a tight linkage between the production of ethanol and energy utilisation for growth because ATP is formed stoichiometrically during glycolysis. This is certainly not the case since substantial alcohol production can occur in the absence of growth. The selection of yeast strains for efficient conversion of carbohydrate into ethanol has applied pressure for inefficient utilisation of energy for growth.

Alcoholic fermentations are usually highly anaerobic after the first few hours because, even in open top fermenters, carbon dioxide forms a protective layer preventing the access of oxygen to the medium. Although yeast metabolism during alcoholic fermentations is essentially anaerobic, yeast is not a true anaerobe because it requires molecular oxygen for the synthesis of the unsaturated fatty acids and sterols which are important membrane components. The yeast is thus unable to synthesize these components during fermentations, and the molecules present in the initial inoculum are shared out with the daughter cells. Membrane composition accordingly changes progressively and sets a limit to the maximum amount of growth possible. Prolonged anaerobic growth is feasible if sources of sterol (ergosterol) and unsaturated fatty acid are present in the medium. When yeast is recycled from one fermentation to another, success is dependent on oxygen pickup between fermentations. For continuous fermentation a small but regular supply of oxygen is required; this can most conveniently be provided by aerating or oxygenating the inflowing medium.

Nitrogen Metabolism

Yeasts have little proteolytic activity although the media for most fermentations contain complex mixtures of amino acids and peptides. In brewing fermentations, amino acids fall into four groups which are absorbed in a regular sequential order. Arginine, asparagine, aspartic acid, glutamic acid, glutamine, lysine, serine and threonine are absorbed first, followed by histidine, isoleucine, leucine, methionine and valine. Alanine, ammonia, glycine, phenylalanine, tyrosine and tryptophan are absorbed more slowly whilst proline is virtually unused.

Organoleptic Compounds in Alcoholic Beverages

The relative importance of trace compounds in the flavour of alcoholic beverages is not simply related to their concentrations. Thus ethanol, present at the highest concentration, has an extremely high taste threshold. Some of the higher alcohols are present in the next highest concentrations but make a relatively small contribution due to their high taste thresholds, roughly ten times higher than those of esters, and a thousand times higher than that of 2,3-butanedione (diacetyl). Interpretation of these values is not simple as flavour compounds show both synergistic and antagonistic effects. Groups of alcohols, esters or carbonyl compounds, each below the taste threshold, may combine to give a detectable taste. Ethanol modifies the thresholds of several other compounds. Acetaldehyde below the taste threshold depresses the aroma of other compounds and introduces a sweet estery note. During beverage production the pattern of organoleptic compounds must be maintained within certain ill-defined limits since this will mainly determine the character of the product. The required levels and balance will differ for each type of beverage. Individual components will usually be beneficial or neutral below certain limits but detrimental if present in excess. The yeast strain used will play a major role in determining the balance between different components. Various fermentation conditions are also known to have a major influence but the exact biochemical basis for most of the effects is not well understood since most experimental work has been done on batch culture in complex media where firm conclusions on control mechanisms cannot easily be made.

Higher Alcohols

Numerous higher alcohols are known to occur in alcoholic beverages: some 45 have been detected in beer. The most important are n-propanol, 2-methyl propanol, 2-methyl butanol, 3-methyl butanol and 2-phenyl ethanol. They can be formed by either of two routes. Both involve the decarboxylation of an oxo-acid to produce an aldehyde which is in turn reduced to the corresponding alcohol by alcohol dehydrogenase (Figure 2). In the route originally described by Ehrlich, the oxo-acid is derived by aminotransfer of an amino acid present in the medium. In the alternative (biosynthetic) route the oxo-acids originate as intermediates during the synthesis of amino acids from carbohydrate.

Increased levels of readily-metabolized carbohydrates, or amino acids or ammonia in the medium, and higher fermentation temperatures, have all been reported to increase the levels of higher alcohols produced. Fermentation under increased pressure has the opposite effect. In continuous culture using defined medium, increasing the growth rate decreases levels of higher alcohols.

Glycerol

Glycerol is a normal component of alcoholic beverages, contributing to the taste sensation known as "mouthfeel" and playing a role in the perceived impression of smoothness. It occurs at levels up to 10 g/l in wines; levels in beers are rather lower. It is formed from dihydroxyacetone phosphate, an intermediate in glycolysis (Figure 1).

Organic Acids

Over 100 organic acids have been identified in alcoholic beverages. Some originate from the raw materials used, many are synthesized by yeast. One group includes pyruvate and the acids formed from it by the reactions of the tricarboxylic acid cycle. The most important members are acetate, citrate, α-oxoglutarate, malate, pyruvate and succinate. Together they are of some importance in influencing flavour and the pH of the beverage. Pyruvate is known to contribute to mouthfeel. Acetate and lactate (also formed from pyruvate) are produced in small amounts by the yeasts used for fermentation but can be produced by contaminating organisms in quantities sufficient to cause spoilage.

Of the remaining acids some, such as 2-methylpropionate and 3-methylbutyrate, probably originate from amino acid biosynthesis or degradation but most are produced from acetyl conezyme A by the fatty acid synthase pathway. Un-

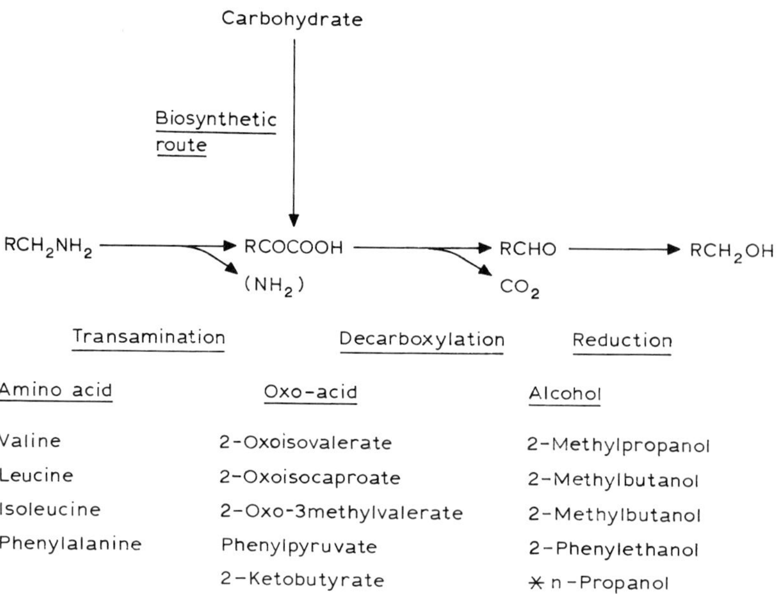

Figure 2. Formation of higher alcohols by yeast.
* (Propanol is formed only by the biosynthetic route).

saturated acids are produced from the corresponding saturated acids by a desaturase reaction requiring molecular oxygen. The principal fatty acids of medium chain length are hexanoate, octanoate and decanoate. When large amounts are released by yeast autolysis they can produce "soapy" or "fatty" off-flavours in beer. Normally the majority of the long chain fatty acids remain in the cells but they can be released if distillation of a fermented medium is performed without removing the yeast. In general, factors which increase fermentation rates decrease the amounts of fatty acids released. In brewing, lager yeasts produce more fatty acids than ale yeasts.

Esters

These are the most numerous organoleptic components in alcoholic beverages. They have penetrating fruity flavours and low taste thresholds. The majority are formed by yeast during fermentation by enzymic reactions between alcohols and acyl coenzyme A compounds but some arise from copper-catalyzed reactions during distillation. The relative amounts of each are related to the abundance of individual alcohols and acids. Ethanol is the major alcohol involved and acetic the major acid; ethyl acetate is the single most abundant ester. The importance of an ester is not necessarily determined by its abundance because there is considerable variation in taste threshold levels.

The concentration of nutrients in the medium is of great importance in controlling ester formation: when beers are brewed with higher strength worts, the concentrations of esters in the beers increase out of proportion and are an important influence in determining the character of strong beers. The effect of medium concentration does not appear to be a simple one and the relative levels of carbohydrates and amino acids are not critical. Increased aeration and an increase in the level of unsaturated fatty acids in the wort both reduce ester formation.

Carbonyl Compounds

More than 200 carbonyl compounds (along with the related acetals and ketals) have been reported in alcoholic beverages. They are extremely important flavour compounds because some have very low taste thresholds. Most originate from raw materials such as hops or fruit, or are produced by chemical reactions during thermal processing operations such as pasteurisation and distillation. Some, especially aromatic aldehydes, are extracted from wooden casks during maturation processes. An important off-flavour in beer is caused by 2-nonenal, generated by oxidation reactions resulting from bottling in the presence of excessive air.

Aldehydes are produced by yeast by decarboxylation of oxo-acids, small amounts leaking into the medium rather than being reduced to alcohols. Like many of the other compounds in this group, the aldehydes released during the main stage of fermentation are frequently removed by the yeast later on. The lower alcohols are responsible for flavours described as "grassy", "green leaves" and "fruity"; but the longer chain compounds have unpleasant "cardboard" or bitter flavours. Excessive levels of acetaldehyde can arise if too much air is supplied to the fermentation or if beer is bottled with too much air in the headspace. Excessive levels of a

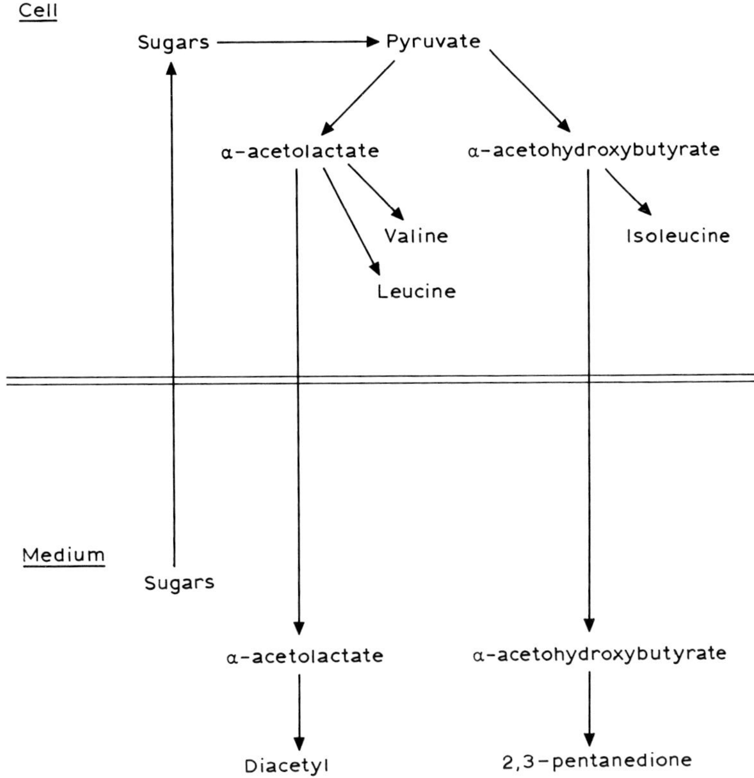

Figure 3. Formation of vicinal diketones by yeast.

acetaldehyde are produced by *Zymomonas anaerobia*, a bacterium which can be a troublesome brewery contaminant.

Two vicinal diketones, 2,3-butanedione (diacetyl) and 2,3-pentanedione, are important in a number of beverages. The taste threshold for diacetyl is about 0.4 mg/l in ales and 0.1–0.2 mg/l in lagers. Both compounds have a "buttery" aroma which is definitely desirable in small amounts in some drinks notably rum, whisky and red wine, but detrimental in excess. It is considered offensive if detectable in white wine and lager.

The two diketones originate respectively from pyruvate and 2-oxobutyrate formed in yeast metabolism. The oxo-acid forms an acetohydroxy acid by condensation with a molecule of "active acetaldehyde" (2-[α-hydroxyethyl] thiamin pyrophosphate) which leaks out of the cell and undergoes a non-enzymic oxidative decarboxylation to form the corresponding vicinal diketone. Later during fermentation the amounts of vicinal diketones are normally decreased by reduction within the cell to the 3-hydroxy-2-ketones (Figure 3). The final concentrations of the two compounds depend on the balance between formation and removal. The acetohydroxyacids are intermediates in the synthesis of valine and isoleucine and their synthesis is inhibited if these amino acids are present in the medium. High levels of α-amino nitrogen are also inhibitory. The effects of aeration are complex as both the oxidative decarboxylation reactions and the removal of the diketones by reduction are probably affected. Excessive levels of diacetyl can also be due to contamination with strains of *Lactobacillus* or *Pediococcus*.

Sulphur Compounds

Over 50 volatile sulphur compounds occur in beverages. Most are not produced by yeast but come from raw materials such as malt and hops. Sulphur dioxide is added to wine as a preservative. Sulphur compounds are responsible for a variety of unpleasant aromas: descriptors include "onion", "garlic", "rubbery", "burnt", "catty", "rotten egg" and "rotten fish". Some aroma thresholds are very low (<2 μg/l for mercaptans and 0.4 μg/l for diethyl sulphide). The most important compounds formed by yeast are hydrogen sulphide and sulphur dioxide, both of which are by products of the pathways which synthesise sulphur-containing amino acids from sulphate. Yeast can also form sulphide by reduction of exogenous sulphur dioxide.

Miscellaneous Compounds

Various phenolic compounds occur in beverages: the most important originate from raw materials. Thus the peaty aroma of scotch malt whisky is due to phenols introduced via the peat smoke which is used in kilning the malt. Some yeasts can transform phenolic compounds derived from the raw materials into significant flavour components. An example is *S. diastaticus*, a wild yeast which can convert phenolic acids to volatile phenols which produce a phenolic off-flavour. Ferulic acid, for instance, is decarboxylatd to 4-vinyl guaiacol which is reduced to 4-ethyl guaiacol. Numerous terpenes have been identified in beverages. Most originate from raw materials and it has been suggested that they could provide a means of identifying the grape cultivar used to produce a particular wine. Yeasts can also produce terpenes and the flavor of champagne is partly due to terpenes released into the wine by autolysis of the yeast used for secondary fermentation.

Beer

Beer is an alcoholic beverage usually made from malt and flavoured with hops. Two main variants of the production process exist: top fermentation, the original process which produces ales, and bottom fermentation, a more recent variant which has supplanted top fermentation in most countries and which gives rise to lagers. The production of lager as a separate type originated in Central Europe where, before refrigeration, it was not possible to brew in the summer because of the high ambient temperatures. As a result the practice grew up of brewing during the cool months and storing the beer in cool cellars. With time, lager brewing diverged from ale brewing in several respects. Barley grown in the hot continental climate produced malt with a high nitrogen content which was more difficult to malt; hence the adoption of the more complex techniques of decoction mashing (see below). The lagering or storing process resulted in the precipitation of proteins and polyphenols; this became important with the fashion for clear, light coloured beers. Different yeast strains were adopted and fermentations were conducted at lower temperatures. In recent years, some of the distinctions between the two types of process have disappeared.

Malt

Barley, the raw material for malt manufacture, is a particularly suitable source of carbohydrate for alcoholic fermentations. Its starch gelatinisation temperature (52–59°C) is lower than that of the other important cereal grains so starch granules can be softened by heat treatment without too much denaturation of malt enzymes. It has a high level of β-amylase and the tough husk protects the grain against fungal infection and assists filtration in the traditional mashing process. The barley grain consists of an embryo adjacent to the much larger endosperm, a reserve tissue packed with starch grains. The embryo contacts the endosperm by an absorbing organ, the shield-shaped scutellum. A sheath of living cells, the aleurone layer, surrounds the endosperm and connects with the embryo. The whole grain is surrounded by the husk, a tough impermeable protective layer (Figure 4).

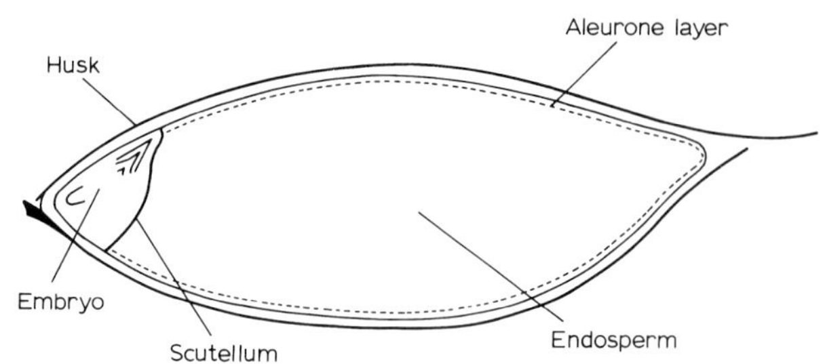

Figure 4. Structure of barley grain.

For brewing purposes specially-bred strains of barley are used. To avoid excessive amounts of protein being extracted, barley with a low nitrogen content is required. Germination is induced by soaking the grain in water. Water is absorbed and the embryo produces gibberellic acid, a plant growth hormone which migrates into the aleurone layer. The aleurone cells secrete various hydrolytic enzymes, notably amylases, proteases and endo-β-glucanases which break down the endosperm cell walls. About 40% of the nitrogen compounds are solubilised during malting to produce a complex mixture of amino acids and peptides. Some of the polypeptides released have beneficial effects as they are involved in stabilising beer foam; others can react with polyphenols and produce troublesome hazes. Some breakdown of starch occurs and sugars are absorbed by the embryo through the scutellum but, as soon as the correct stage of development is reached, the process is terminated by kilning.

Exogenous gibberellic acid is frequently added to speed germination and penetration of water may be aided by mechanical abrasion of the grain. The addition of gibberellic acid tends to produce excessive proteolysis: this can be controlled by the addition of bromate. Improvements in malting technique have shortened the time required from about eleven days in 1940s to as little as 3–4 days currently.

Kilning

Kilning, the final stage in malt manufacture, consists of drying the malt with hot gases to kill the embryo, to prevent further utilization of reserve carbohydrates, and to stabilize the malt for storage. Certain changes in flavour compounds also occur: beers produced with unmalted barley have a characteristic "green-malt" flavour. The Maillard reaction between amino acids and carbonyl compounds leads to the production of coloured aromatic melanoidins and certain compounds which contribute to the malty flavour of beer are formed, including the 1-valino-, 1-alanino- and 1-glycino-derivatives of 1-deoxyfructose.

The bulk of malt used is pale malt: here the water is removed by heating as rapidly as possible to minimise colour formation. Other malts are used in smaller quantities to produce certain colours and flavours in the beer. Crystal malt is produced by holding the malt at 50–55°C in moist air to encourage the enzymatic breakdown of starch to sugar and maximise colour formation. Added to beer in small quantities, crystal malt contributes some colour and a sweet nutty flavour. Black malt is produced by raising the temperature high enough to char the grain. It contributes no carbohydrate but is used to colour stouts and to produce a bitter flavour. Some stouts use roasted barley for the same purpose.

Mashing

The function of the mashing stage is to convert starch to fermentable sugars and to extract them from the malt together with other nutrients. After screening to remove foreign objects, malt is milled by passing it through large rotating rollers set at a precise distance apart. The aim is to break the husk and permit easy extraction of sugars and other nutrients from the malt. Care is taken not to allow the grain to disintegrate as the release of fine particles make filtration more difficult. The crushed grain is known as "grist".

Two variants on the mashing process are in wide use. Infusion mashing is used in the United Kingdom for the production of ales. Grist and hot water (known as liquor) are mixed together by an Archimedian screw and delivered to the mash tun, a squat, cylindrical vessel where mashing takes place. The water temperature is chosen to produce the required temperature in the mash after mixing with the grist. This will be very close to 65°C and is a compromise between the optimum temperatures of the various enzymes involved. Lower mash temperatures decrease the amount of carbohydrate extracted; higher temperatures decrease the proportion of fermentable sugars because β-amylase is more thermolabile than α-amylase. The mash is incubated for 1–2 hours with no external heating.

The combined actions of the amylases during mashing break down starch to a complex mixture of sugars and dextrins. The fermentable sugars, which constitute 70–80% of the total carbohydrate, consist of maltose, maltotriose, glucose, sucrose and fructose in decreasing order of concentration. Substantial breakdown of proteins occurs in malting; this process continues during mashing and a complex mixture of soluble proteins, peptides and amino acids is extracted along with vitamins, organic acids, inorganic ions and breakdown products of nucleic acids. The solution of sugars and nutrients formed in mashing is known as "wort". It is separated from the malt grains by allowing it to drain off through the false floor of the mash tun which contains numerous fine slits to act as a filter. Sparging, spraying hot water onto the top of the mash, assists the removal of sugars and permits further enzyme activity by elimination of the end products. The spent grain which remains after mashing is sold for use in compounding animal feed.

Decoction mashing, a more complex process than infusion mashing, is used for the production of lagers. Three vessels are used: a cooker for heating the grist, the converter where enzyme activity takes place and the lauter tun, a special vessel used for filtration. The mash starts at a much lower temperature, perhaps 45°C, the optimum for protein breakdown. This is gradually increased by removing a portion of the mash to the cooker, boiling it to assist starch gelatinisation and returning it to the converter. A period at about 65°C to maximize sugar formation is followed by an increase to 70°C to complete the solubilization of starch. A more finely divided grist is produced at the milling stage; this aids extraction but makes filtration more difficult. The lauter tun has a false floor for filtration like a mash tun but rotating rakes cut through the layer of fines to aid run off of the wort. Decoction mashing, because it is not limited to a single temperature, allows the brewer more flexibility in his choice of conditions.

With the two traditional systems wort separation is slow and limits the number of mashes to four per day. Improved filtration systems have been developed to increase the surface area available for filtration; these permit twelve or more mashes per day.

Water

The quality of the water used in mashing is of critical importance and breweries were traditionally located to exploit particulary suitable water supplies. In the U.K. the town of Burton-on-Trent owed its fame as a brewing centre to the possession of an underground water supply ideal for the brewing of pale ales. Nowadays the special character of a local water system is of less importance since unwanted components can be removed by ion-exchange or boiling and additions made to produce an ideal composition. Bacteriological standards are the same as for drinking water. Nitrate is deleterious to yeast and may be a sign of pollution. Calcium ions in the water cause precipitation of phosphate during mashing, lowering the pH by about 0.6 units and producing various desirable effects including enhanced activity of amylolytic enzymes during mashing. Bicarbonate ions have the opposite effect as carbon dioxide is lost at mashing temperature and the pH rises. Water for mashing is therefore treated, if necessary, to remove bicarbonate and the appropriate amount of calcium sulphate is added. The concentration and balance of salts used will vary according to the type of beer being produced.

Malt Substitutes

Malting is a slow, energy-intensive process and substantial cost savings can be attained by mashing with a proportion of unmalted cereals (adjuncts). The most common are various preparations of rice, corn (maize), wheat and barley. Corn and rice require precooking to gelatinize the starch. Apart from cost, advantages have been claimed for the use of adjuncts. Thus, because of their low nitrogen content they may allow the brewer to use malt produced from cheaper barley with a high nitrogen content. Beers produced using corn as adjunct have been reported to have a longer shelf life due to lower levels of haze-forming proteins. The use of moderate amounts of adjuncts is said to have no detrimental effect on flavour although filtration may be more difficult.

The availability of cheap preparations of amylases and proteases suggests the possibility of dispensing entirely with malt and using bacterial enzymes to breakdown cheaper sources of carbohydrates. Systems have been described to achieve this using wet milling of the barley, mixtures of bacterial pullulanase (α-1,6-glucosidase) and α-amylase which act in conjunction with the β-amylase present in unmalted barley and proteases to degrade proteins. This option has been used on a commercial scale but has not been widely adopted.

Boiling

After combining wort fractions collected at different stages the wort is boiled together with hops for 1–2 hours in a vessel known as the "copper". Boiling has several functions. It sterilises the wort, precipitates proteins which would otherwise produce haze in the beer, inhibits further enzyme activity, extracts the flavouring components of hops, removes some unwanted flavour components by evaporation and reduces the wort volume. The colour of the wort also intensifies. Extra fermentable carbohydrate, in the form of glucose, sucrose, invert sugar or starch hydrolysate may be added at this stage. The final wort pH will be in the region 5.2–5.4.

Hops

The vast majority of beer is flavoured by extracting components of the female hop plant *Humulus lupulus*. The plants are perennial and grow each year to a height of 5–6 metres. Only the flower cone is used. This consists of a cluster of leaf-like bracteoles, each having at its base a small lupulin gland containing the resins and oils which are to be extracted. The chemistry of hop components is complex and not fully understood[4]: only the most superficial account will be attempted here.

The bittering potential of hops is due almost entirely to the α-acids; the content of this fraction, which can be measured by conductometric titration, polarography or HPLC, is a useful guide to bittering power. The α-acids, principally humulone, cohumulone and adhumulone, are sparingly soluble and are not themselves bitter but on boiling they are converted to the corresponding iso-α-acids which are soluble and bitter (Figure 5).

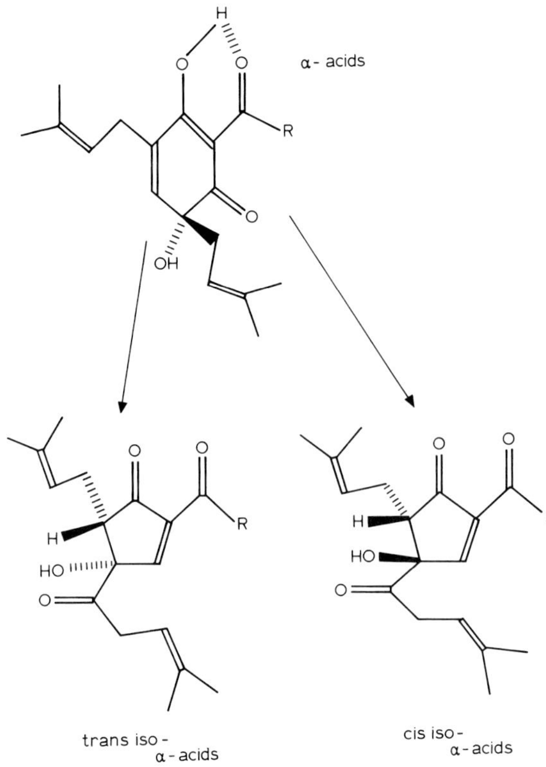

Figure 5. a-Acids and iso-a-Acids.
Humulone R = $-CH_2CH\ (CH_3)_2$
Cohumulone R = $-CH\ (CH_3)_2$
Adhumulone R = $-CH\ (CH_3)\ CH_2CH_3$

During fermentation iso-α-acids adsorb to the surface of the yeast cell: as a result of this, together with inefficient extraction and isomerisation during boiling, only about one third of the hop α-acids are converted into beer bitter substances. On storage, the content of hop α-acids declines steadily although the bittering power is reduced less than predicted by analysis because of the formation of different bitter substances from another group of hop components, the β-acids.

To reduce the cost of storage, hop powders can be prepared which consist mainly of material from the lupulin glands. Hop extracts, prepared using organic solvents, are even more economical in terms of storage space and permit more efficient extraction of α-acids. However, brewers have become concerned at the possible effects of traces of solvents remaining in the extracts. The use of extracts prepared with liquid carbon dioxide overcomes these fears and offers improved selectivity of extraction with minimal unwanted reactions. The use of chemically isomerized extracts by addition to the beer after fermentation offers the prospect of even greater efficiency but so far this approach has met with little commercial acceptance. In 1983 hop powders accounted for 34% of hops used throughout the world with hop extracts accounting for another 27%.

Another important group of compounds is the essential oil fraction which is responsible for the "hoppy" aroma of beers. Over 200 compounds have been identified, the main components being terpenes, especially myrcene, humulene and caryophyllene. These compounds are a more important part of the character of top fermented beers than of lagers. Because of their volatility they are lost at the boiling stage and a proportion of the hops is often kept back to be added a few minutes before the end of boiling to ensure a hop aroma in the beer. In some cases hops are added to the beer in the final casks to achieve the same result. Extracts of hop oil are commercially available but the problems involved in their use do not seem to have been fully overcome.

Various polyphenolic compounds are present in hops and are extracted into the wort at boiling. These can polymerize and react with proteins, giving rise to beer hazes. In the preparation of hop extracts the aim is to avoid extracting these substances.

Fermentation

After cooling the wort and removing hops and precipitated protein, fermentation is started by pitching (inoculation) with yeast at about 10^7 cells/ml. The inoculum is normally obtained by harvesting yeast from a previous fermentation but after several successive fermentations the yeast performance tends to deteriorate and it is usual to start again with a fresh inoculum grown up from a laboratory culture. For ale production, strains of *S. cerevisiae* are used whilst *S. uvarum* (formerly known as *S. carlsbergensis*) is used for lagers. Yeasts of the *S. cerevisiae* type are known as top fermenters because a substantial part of the yeast rises to the surface during fermentation. Bottom fermenting strains (*S. uvarum*) sink to the bottom of the vessel. Although the distinction is a traditional one it is not absolute: under certain circumstances top fermenting yeasts can behave as bottom fermenters and changes in behaviour easily arise by mutation. The yeasts used are brewing strains, the results of many years of selection (much of it unconscious) for the required characteristics of flavour and fermentation behaviour. Usually a single yeast strain is used at a particular brewery but a survey in the 1960's found that many ale breweries in the U.K. were using stable mixtures of strains. Different pitching (inoculation) rates and fermentation temperatures are used for ales and lagers. Ales are pitched with about 3–4 g/l yeast and fermented at temperatures of 15–21°C, the fermentation taking 3–7 days. Lagers are pitched with yeast at 2.5 g/l and fermented at 5–15°C with fermentation times of 7–15 days.

Yeast is an excellent oxygen scavenger and the oxygen present in wort disappear within an hour or two. Thereafter, metabolism is entirely anaerobic as carbon dioxide formed by metabolism forms a blanket over the wort surface. During the lag phase, which may last several hours, amino acid absorption starts and the pH drops by about 0.5 units.

Wort sugars are taken up rapidly by yeast. Most yeast strains absorb the main sugars in the order glucose, maltose, maltotriose. The phases are not distinct; the uptake of one sugar overlaps that of another. The sequence is due to the inducibility of maltose and maltotriose permeases and their repression or destruction by glucose. Inside the cell maltose and maltotriose are hydrolyzed by α-glucosidase. Yeast growth and the removal of sugar and formation of ethanol take 3–4 days in an ale fermentation, longer in a lager fermentation. After this the beer may be left in the fermenting vessel for a few days more to allow yeast to separate out.

Yeast flocculation, defined as the reversible clumping of non-dividing cells, is an important part of many beer fermentation processes; it aids removal of yeast from the beer by speeding its sedimentation to the bottom of the vessel or rising to the top. The stage at which flocculation occurs is important. Early flocculation will slow or stop the fermentation before it is complete, late flocculation will make it difficult to separate the yeast from the beer . Flocculation is under mutational control and care must be taken to guard against changes in yeast behaviour. In top fermentations flocculation is usually triggered by the disappearance of maltose. The mechanism is not fully understood but involves interaction between the outer cell wall layers, aided by the formation of calcium bridges.

In traditional top fermentations the yeast head is removed by skimming, a process which involves drawing the yeast foam to one side of the fermenting vessel and removing it by suction. Centrifugation has now replaced natural separation to a large extent. It substantially shortens the cycle time in the fermenting vessel and, because a non-flocculent yeast is employed, eliminates the risk of incomplete fermentation due to premature flocculation.

Fermenting Vessels

The traditional open-top fermenting vessels which permitted ale brewers to remove their yeast from the top of the beer by skimming it off the surface are now fast being replaced for both ale and lager production by a variety of more sophisticated enclosed vessels. Amongst other advantages these permit the evolved carbon dioxide to be collected for later sale or use. They also permit the use of cleaning-in-place systems for spraying the inside of the vessel with detergent solutions, acids and biocides to minimise the labour requirement.

One widely-used type is the Nathan, or conical-bottom fermenter (Figure 6), first patented in 1908 but not widely adopted until many years later when engineering developments, especially in cleaning-in-place systems, made it more attractive.

This design has several advantages. The tall narrow shape reduces the requirement for floor space and a vigorous natural

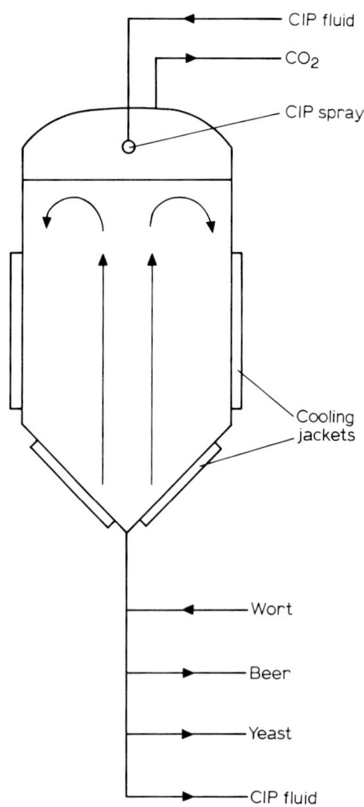

Figure 6. Conical (Nathan) Fermenter.

circulation, set up by rising carbon dioxide bubbles, increases the rate of yeast growth and fermentation. The mechanical strength originating from the narrow section, together with a curved top, facilitates the application of a top pressure of carbon dioxide to control foaming. Cooling jackets are used to control the rise in temperature caused by heat of fermentation liberated in a large vessel. Because of the fluid circulation no internal cooling coils are required, making the vessels easier to clean.

When fermentation has reached the required stage, the beer is rapidly cooled to stop metabolism and to induce the yeast to sediment into the cone whence it can readily be run off as a separate phase. The increased fermentation rate, together with the more rapid removal of most of the yeast from the beer at the end of fermentation, substantially shorten the cycle compared with a traditional vessel in which little natural circulation occurs. The same vessel can be used for maturation of the beer if required and yeast can be stored in the cone. Nathan vessels up to 400 m^3 have been constructed but many brewers favour the greater flexibility and reduced emptying and filling times of smaller vessels of around 150 m^3.

The tall, narrow Nathan vessels have a small volume: surface ratio and are therefore somewhat expensive to construct. An alternative trend in fermenter design is towards vessels with a more favorable volume to surface ratio. Several designs of this type have been used in the U.S., Japan and Spain. The vessels are squat cylinders with sloping bottoms to aid yeast and fluid removal, or spheres with conical bottoms. They sacrifice the advantages of natural circulation and easy cooling for reduced capital cost. Vessels of up to 550 m^3 have been constructed.

Continuous Fermentation

Continuous fermentation appears at first sight to offer certain advantages in commercial brewing operations. Given an extended period of continuous operation, most of the time taken to empty, clean and refill the vessel is eliminated. Fermentation proceeds at a constant high rate reducing the number of fermenters needed for a given capacity. Continuous rather than intermittent processing permits the capacity of ancillary equipment such as centrifuges to be reduced. Steady-state operation will, it is claimed, produce a more uniform product.

The first semi-continuous systems for beer production were described in 1906 but continuous culture was not used on a commercial scale until the late 1950s when several breweries in New Zealand adopted the system patented by Coutts, consisting of two fermenting vessels and a yeast separation vessel in series, and reducing fermentation time to 35 hours. In the U.K., Watney-Mann pioneered a system with two stirred tanks in series. Wort was oxygenated before entering the first vessel and a fermentation time of 15 hours was claimed.

The continuous stirred tank reactor (CSTR), the large-scale equivalent of the laboratory chemostat, allows cells to escape freely with the spent medium. As a result, the throughput is limited by the properties of the organism: the maximum dilution rate is, in theory, equal to μ_{max}, the maximum growth rate of the organism, but in practice rather less. If the escaping cells are separated from the spent medium and some are returned to the fermenter, the dilution rate can exceed μ_{max}. This principle can be used to reduce the fermentation time for beer by building up a very high yeast concentration inside a continuous fermenter. A similar effect is obtained if the escape of yeast cells is restricted.

The tower fermenter (Figure 7) exploits this principal. It consists of a tall narrow cylinder with provision for feeding in a continuous stream of wort at the bottom. A series of perforated horizontal baffles prevents free circulation of the fermenting wort. A highly-flocculant yeast strain is used which sediments rapidly to the lower part of the tower and builds up a semi-solid plug. Incoming wort, forcing its way through the plugs is rapidly fermented. An expansion chamber at the top separates the gas bubbles from the liquid and permits most of the yeast in suspension to drop back into the tower. It was claimed that beer could be fully fermented with a mean residence time of four hours and that a product of

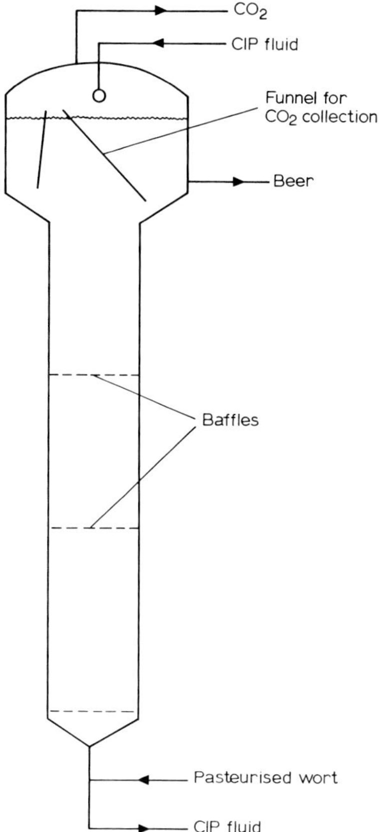

Figure 7. Tower Fermenter.

normal commercial quality could be obtained. Runs of several months were possible before it was necessary to shut down for repairs and servicing and to replace the yeast strain. In short, the technical problems appear to have been overcome but, in the words of one luminary of the industry, "the operation was a success but the patient died".

A number of breweries installed tower fermenters and for a while it appeared that the innovation might become standard. However, in several respects continuous culture has proved disappointing. The operating complexity of continuous systems requires the close attention of skilled staff and high labour costs are incurred. Continuous fermenters can take some time to reach a steady state with acceptable product quality; the dilution rate must generally then be maintained constant. As a result neither the production rate nor the beer being produced can easily be changed. The advantages of continuous fermentation do not apply to the other parts of the brewing process so the reduction on overall costs is small and the use of continuous fermentation seems to have died out in most countries.

It has recently been shown that modifications to the tower fermenter, notably the controlled recycling of yeast back into the base of the vessel, permit the dilution rate to be reduced during a run without serious consequences, thus increasing production flexibility. Moreover the current interest in the possibilities of improving fermentation performance by computer control are clearly easier to apply to continuous systems. It may thus be premature to conclude that continuous fermentation has no future in the brewing industry.

Maturation

After fermentation, beer is matured by storage for anything up to 9 months at about 5°C, the traditional "lagering" process, or for 1–2 weeks at 12–20°C for ale fermentations. A slow secondary fermentation takes place at the expense of added sugar or of residual sugar from the primary fermentation. Yeast metabolism decreases the levels of some undesirable volatiles such as acetaldehyde, hydrogen sulphide and vicinal diketones, and generates carbon dioxide to dissolve in the beer. At the same time proteins and polyphenols are removed, either by precipitation or by adsorption to the yeast cells; amino acids, peptides, nucleotides and other organic and inorganic phosphorus compounds leak from the cells. Finings, a solution of collagen extracted from fish swim bladders, is sometimes added to aid clearing of the beer. The origin of the process is obscure but it depends on the electrostatic interaction between positively-charged, high molecular weight collagen aggregates and negatively-charged yeast cells to form large, rapidly-sedimenting complexes. The effect of all these changes is to improve the flavour and clarity of the beer. Nowadays increasing use is made of accelerated maturation techniques which use higher temperatures and a top pressure of carbon dioxide in the absence of yeast.

Before final packaging in bottles, cans or metal kegs, or loading into bulk tanks, beer is usually filtered to remove residual yeast and precipitated protein and pasteurized to prevent growth of bacteria or yeast. Beer is served from kegs by applying a top pressure of carbon dioxide from a cylinder to force out the beer and prevent the access of air.

In the U.K., some beer is still matured in the traditional manner by carrying out a secondary fermentation in wooden, aluminium or stainless steel casks, (so-called "naturally conditioned" beer). Casks differ from kegs in having no provision for applying external gas pressure; the beer is thus pressurised only by the carbon dioxide resulting from secondary fermentation. The cask is filled with beer which has not been pasteurized or filtered; sugar is added if necessary, usually along with a solution of finings. Hops are frequently added at this stage so that the hop oil is extracted to flavour the beer. After delivery to the customer, the cask must be allowed to stand for about 24 hours without disturbance to allow the yeast to settle. Careful temperature control is necessary because of the presence of live yeast and, since the design of the cask permits air to enter as beer is withdrawn, the growth of acetic acid bacteria soon begins to spoil the product. It is easy to see why this process is relatively unpopular but it can produce beer of superior flavour. A small amount of beer is also matured by secondary fermentation in bottle.

Manufacture of Table Wine

Wine making developed several thousands of years ago as a typical Phase 1, low technology operation (see Table 1) carried out on a domestic scale and dependent upon purely empirical technology. At one extreme, practised as a part-time operation by farmers in country areas, it has changed little whereas in the major wineries of California, Portugal, Spain and Australia it has developed into an impressive modern industry, operating on the million gallon per-year scale. Wine is produced in substantial quantities in over forty countries. In 1985 world production was 30×10^9 litres split between Europe (78%), North and South America (15%), Africa (4%), Oceania (1.5%) and Asia (<1%). Two countries, France and Italy, accounted for 44% of the total.

Grapes

Most wine is produced from berries of the European grape, *Vitis vinifera*, which has been grown around the world. In nearly all parts this is cultivated by grafting onto the rootstock of American vines, a practice which originated in the late nineteenth century. Early settlers in the U.S. found abundant wild vines growing but the wines they yielded were considered vastly inferior to those of the European vine. The latter could not be grown in much of the U.S. because of the presence of a soil aphid, *Phylloxera vastatrix*, which attacked the roots and killed the plants; the native American species *V. aestivalis*, *V. riparia* and *V. labrusca* were resistant. In the late 1860s *Phylloxera* appeared in France, presumably transported with vines imported for hybridisation. It devastated crops and spread rapidly throughout Europe and other parts of the world including California which was originally free from infestation. The situation was saved by grafting European vines onto American rootstocks, combining the winemaking characteristics of the former with the resistance of the latter to *Phylloxera*. *V. vinifera* survives on its own rootstock only in Chile and in isolated places such as the Colares region of Portugal near Lisbon where the grapes are grown in dune sand 3–10 metres deep, rooted into the underlying clay, and *Phylloxera* cannot survive. California wines are produced from European vines on American rootstocks although wine of a different character is produced in other parts of the U.S. from American vines and from European-American hybrids. Such hybrids are also grown in other areas where high humidity makes *V. vinifera* susceptible to fungal infection.

Some hundreds of cultivars of *V. vinifera* are in use. Important examples are Pinot Noir (red Burgundy), Pinot Blanc (white Burgundy), Sauvignon (red Bordeaux), Riesling and Sylvaner (German white) and Palomino (sherry). Commonly a wine will contain a mixture of grape varieties: some forty are used for the production of port wine.

The grape, the main raw material in winemaking, is also the most critical variable determining the quality of the finished product: whereas it is easy to make bad wine from good grapes, the best wines are made only from the best grapes and technology has made only limited contributions to correcting any deficiencies.

The regional climate determines the general possibilities. The growth of grapes for wine is considered to require a mean annual temperature in the range 10–20°C and the major wine-producing regions lie within these limits in the northern and southern hemispheres. A long growing season is required, with summer temperatures and light levels high enough to produce the required sugar levels in the grape. At the warmer end of the climatic range (for example in southern California, Cyprus and southern Spain) there is a danger that grapes may lack the required levels of acidity. At the other end of the range it may be necessary to add sugar to the must. Other factors are the amount and seasonal distribution of rainfall and the onset of late-season frost, which limit the latest date for harvesting.

For the individual vineyard the height above sea level, aspect and shelter are all important factors determining the microclimate. The nature of the soil is vital: the best grapes are generally produced on poor soils, low in humus, often based on sand, gravel, slate or chalk. Two vineyards close together may produce wine of greatly differing quality due to local variations in soil and microclimate.

Other vital factors are the care taken to exclude underripe or rotten berries and to avoid damage during picking and handling, and the selection of the optimum time for harvest. As the grape ripens the sugar content increases, whilst that of acids, especially malic acid, falls. The skin pigmentation of black grapes increases. The correct time for harvesting is decided on the basis of appearance and flavour, aided by objective measurements on the juice from random samples of 100–200 berries: sugar content is estimated by measuring specific gravity and acid content by titration.

If the sugar content at harvest is too low it may be permissible to add sugar to make up the deficiency (Chaptalisation). This is permitted with restrictions in France, where it is often necessary in a poor season, but not in California where sunshine is more reliable. Conversely, in warm climates the acidity may be too low; the addition of organic acids to restore the balance is frequently permitted.

Red and *rosé* wines depend for their colour and flavour on the extraction of materials including red anthocyanin pigments from the grape skins so highly-pigmented grapes are used for their production. White wines are produced either from non-pigmented grapes or from pigmented grapes by minimising the extraction of pigments from the skins.

Harvesting, once started, has to be as rapid as possible. In Europe hand picking, using knives or shears to cut off the bunches, still predominates although mechanical pickers have been developed and are used in California. The ease of harvesting depends on the methods used to prune and train the vines: bushes may be allowed to reach a height of only three feet or, at the other extreme, as in the *vinho verde* district of Portugal, may be trained up tall trees and require the use of long ladders for picking.

The grapes are crushed immediately after picking. Any delay is disadvantageous because broken grapes become infested with fruit flies which introduce undesirable micro-organisms giving rise to uncontrolled fermentations. Large amounts of bitter polyphenolic compounds are readily extracted into the juice if the pips are damaged so the aim is to crush all the grapes but to minimize damage to the pips. Frequently the stalks are removed during the same process. Traditionally the grapes were heaped into tubs where they were trodden repeatedly by the bare feet or hobnailed shoes of the workers until crushing was judged to be complete; grapes are now crushed mechanically. Since iron and copper are soluble in grape juice these materials are avoided as much as possible in the construction of the crusher: wood, plastic and especially stainless steel are the preferred materials. In one type of crusher the grapes pass between two serrated rollers; other types involve a hollow, perforated, rotating cylinder. Paddles rotating within crush the grapes against the cylinder, the pulp, juice and pips being forced out through the perforations.

The crushed grapes, known as "must", contain large numbers of yeasts and bacteria. Sulphur dioxide (100–300 mg/1) is normally added to suppress the growth of acetic and lactic acid bacteria and undesirable yeasts, mainly of the genera *Brettanomyces*, *Candida*, *Hansenula*, *Kloeckera* and *Pichia*. Sulphur dioxide may be supplied as the liquid under pressure, as a solution or in the form of potassium bisulphite or metabisulphite. Although initially very effective (100 ppm sulphur dioxide has been reported to reduce viable counts by a factor of a thousand) the effect soon declines as the concentration declines due to evaporation, oxidation to sulphate and the formation of bisulphite addition compounds.

For the production of red wine the entire must is fermented. Fermenting vessels may range in size from a few hundred litres up to tens of thousands and may be open rectangular or circular tanks of wood, stone, or concrete lined with epoxy resin, wooden casks, or stainless steel cylinders. The nature of the material has no known effect on flavour, although stainless steel, because it can be fabricated with a very smooth surface, is much easier to clean.

If no inoculum is added fermentation will be carried out by those yeasts introduced with the grapes which have survived the treatment with sulphur dioxide and a complex succession will occur involving several yeasts which change in relative numbers as the fermentation passes through its different stages. The species involved and their relative importance differ from one region to another and this influences the individual flavour of the finished product. Some producers rely on this natural succession, believing that greater complexity and subtlety of flavour thereby results compared with fermentations inoculated with a single cultured strain.

The use of pure starter cultures, pioneered by Muller-Thurgau between 1880 and 1890 soon after their adoption in brewing by Hansen, is universal for large-scale production and is gaining ground with even the smallest producers. Pure cultures make it easier to eliminate undesirable organisms, give more reproducible behaviour and, because the balance of congenerics differs from one strain to another, permit some control of product flavour. The inoculum, usually a strain of *S. cerevisiae* var. *ellipsoideus*, may be propagated on the premises or may be purchased in compressed or dried form. Continuous fermentation is little used: in the Torres Vedras region of Portugal it is employed for the production of inexpensive red wines but batch methods are used for wines of higher quality.

Satisfactory red table wines may be produced over a wide range of fermentation temperatures. The range from 17–33°C was traditionally considered suitable but recent practice has been to use closely-controlled temperatures at the lower end of the range. Where necessary, cooling is performed by heat exchangers; in hot climates cooling towers and refrigeration are often required. As fermentation begins, bubbles of carbon dioxide become attached to the grape pulp and skins which rise to the surface of the liquid. To encourage extraction of tannins and pigments, and to prevent the growth of aerobic bacteria, the crust is pushed back down into the liquid either by breaking it up mechanically or more often by pumping liquid up from the vessel and discharging it onto the surface. The resulting aeration of the must increases the rate of fermentation.

The progress of fermentation is monitored by measuring the specific gravity. At a value of about 1.000, at which point most of the fermentable sugar will have been removed and the ethanol content will have reached 10–12% the pulp and skins will be separated from the fermented juice. The free liquid is run off but much of the liquid remains associated with the solid material, known as "pomace", and is removed by pressing the latter in a mechanical or hydraulic press. Several pressings of the pomace are usual: the liquid from the earlier ones is mixed with that already separated but the later pressings will be of increasingly poor quality and will be used for low quality wines or for distillation for industrial alcohol. A maximum of about 0.6 l juice can be obtained from 1 kg grapes. Great care is necessary to avoid introducing air as the wine is now very sensitive to oxidation. At this stage the wine will still contain 5–20 g/l sugar and a further slow fermentation, using the remaining fermentable sugars, occurs over a period of months, often interrupted by winter.

For the production of white wines it is necessary to avoid the extraction of tannins and pigments from the grapes. If white grapes are used, fermentation may be carried out by the same process as used for red wines: this is done in parts of Portugal. If the juice is separated from the skins before fermentation begins white wine may be produced from either white or black grapes and this is the more usual procedure. After crushing and addition of sulphur dioxide the must is pressed; the process may be repeated as many as eight times to extract all the juice, with a steady deterioration in quality. The avoidance of oxidation is even more critical than with red wine. The fermentation temperature is rather lower than for red wines and close temperature control is most important: the maximum permissible is about 25°C but modern practice tends towards much lower values, 10–12°C being common. For the fermentation of white wine the traditional use of small casks, which will lose heat more readily than large vessels, may reflect the need to keep fermentation temperatures lower.

For the production of sweet white wine, fermentation may be allowed to go to completion, with sugar or unfermented juice added afterwards, but a better flavour is achieved by halting fermentation with the correct amount of sugar remaining. This is done by decanting (racking) the wine to separate it from the yeast, most of which will have dropped out of suspension and formed a layer at the bottom of the fermenting vessel. Due to the large amounts of colloidal material remaining in suspension at this stage complete removal of the yeast is difficult. Instead the wine is chilled and sulphur dioxide may be added to prevent further fermentation. For the production of *rosé* wine the extraction of pigments is permitted for a shorter period than for red wine.

Fungal attack is a factor which may limit the time for which grapes can be left to ripen but in some districts, if the autumn weather is warm and damp, bunches of grapes may be deliberately be left on the vines to be attacked by so-called "noble rot", *Botrytis cinerea*. As it rots the grapes the fungus removes more water than sugar: the sugar content of the affected grapes thus rises. These grapes if carefully selected, can produce very sweet, white wines (known in Germany as *Trockenbeerenauslese*) which are highly prized for their aromatic character, derived partly from the fungus itself. Since the grapes are not all affected simultaneously, gathering them is highly labour-intensive and the resulting wines very expensive. This process is traditional in the Sauternes district in France, in Germany and in Hungary and has recently been practised in one Australian vineyard.

Malolactic Fermentation

The principle acids in grape juice are D-tartrate and L-malate. Yeast forms smaller quantities of succinate during the fermentation. Lactic acid bacteria present as contaminants can decarboxylate the malate to lactate, thus reducing the acidity of the wine.

$$HOOC.CH_2.CHOH.COOH \rightarrow CH_3.CHOH.COOH + CO_2$$

This process, known as the malolactic fermentation, is desirable in the production of red wines in cooler regions such as Burgundy in France where, due to the relatively cool climate, the grapes contain excessive acid. The malolactic fermentation normally occurs during the winter following the onset of fermentation although sometimes its onset is delayed until spring. Failure of the malolactic fermentation to occur can be serious: apart from the extra acidity remaining it is not unknown for the fermentation, having failed earlier, to start after bottling resulting in haze, fizzy wine and a serious deterioration of flavour. To prevent this happening it is usual to encourage the fermentation by avoiding very low cellar temperatures and by ensuring that the pH is above 3.0. If necessary, acidity can be reduced by the addition of chalk to encourage the onset of malolactic fermentation but this is likely to have undesirable effects on flavour. Where wine acidity levels are lower the fermentation is undesirable and steps are taken to prevent it. It is also undesirable, and does not normally occur, in white wines which lack essential nutrients for the growth of lactic acid bacteria and which are normally made with higher levels of sulphur dioxide.

It is surprisingly difficult to control the malolactic fermentation and it is important, whilst encouraging *Leuconostoc oenos*, the favoured organism, not to permit the growth of other lactic acid bacteria (especially *Lactobacillus brevis*, *Lact. plantarum* and *Pediococcus cerevisiae*). These produce a variety of undesirable flavours and are believed to be responsible for the formation of the biogenic amines histamine, tyramine and phenylethylamine, which are sometimes detected in red wines and which are blamed for symptoms such as severe headaches and vomiting experienced by sensitive individuals after drinking only small quantities. Growth of these bacteria is encouraged by excessive sulphur dioxide to which *L. oenos* is very sensitive, low levels of acidity and temperatures above 28°C towards the end of fermentation which kill off yeast cells leaving fermentable sugars for bacterial growth. It is common practice in California to start the malolactic fermentation, where required, by inoculating the wine with a pure culture of *L. oenos* at about 10^6 cells/ml but this is not permitted in the E.E.C.

Maturation

When fermentation is complete most wines are aged for a period to improve flavour. The period of maturation varies from weeks to years during which proteins and pigments settle out, potassium hydrogen tartrate and calcium tartrate are precipitated and condensation reactions involving pigments and tannins occur. Ester formation from ethanol and other alcohols occurs, the major esters being ethyl acetate, lactate, tartrate and malate. Many other trace volatiles are produced at this stage: a very slow reaction with oxygen diffusing in through the pores in the wood seems to be involved. Many attempts have been made to accelerate maturation using elevated temperatures and other means but none has been widely adopted. At intervals during maturation the wine is decanted off into a fresh vessel leaving the precipitate behind. It is essential that vessels are filled completely since acetic acid bacteria are usually present in immature wine and will quickly grow and spoil the wine if an air space is left.

Better quality wines are often matured in oak casks to extract flavouring components into the wine to give the characteristic vanilla-like flavours, the time of contact and surface to volume ratios being adjusted to achieve the required degree of flavour enhancement. Experiments conducted at the Robert Mondavi winery in California, in which a single batch of wine was matured in different barrels, produced wines differing substantially in character according to whether the barrel was made of American oak or French Nevers or Limousin oak, the latter being preferred. There were also substantial differences between Limousin oak barrels manufactured in France and those manufactured in the U.S., resulting from different degrees of charring of the wood. This comes about because American coopers normally bend the staves to shape by softening them with steam whereas the normal practice in France is to bend them by lighting a fire inside the barrel.

Finishing Processes

After maturation, the wine is subjected to one or more finishing processes designed to remove unwanted components. Proteinaceous materials such as gelatine, casein, egg albumin or isinglass can be added to react with excess tannins and form precipitates which settle out within days or weeks to leave a clear supernatant. Excessive protein may be removed by fining with bentonite and citrate or ferric ferrocyanide may be added to remove excess iron. Sodium hydrogen tartrate and calcium tartrate, which have very low solubilities, gradually precipitate and form unsightly deposits in the bottles. These may be encouraged to precipitate before bottling by flash cooling. Centrifugation and filtration are also used to improve clarity and eliminate bacteria and yeasts. Bottles and corks may be sterilized before filling. In the eighteenth century cork, known to the ancient world but forgotten for hundreds of years, was reintroduced to wine making. This, together with the use of cylindrical rather than conical bottles permitted wine to be kept for periods of many years: by storing cylindrical bottles on their sides the cork is wetted with wine and prevented from shrinking so remaining tight in the neck and keeping out air.

Cheap wines are intended to be consumed soon after bottling but some sweet white wines, and many high-quality red wines containing high levels of tannins, undergo slow and complex flavour changes in bottle, resulting in highly individual products surrounded by great mystique and commanding very high prices. Whereas cheap red wine can be purchased in the U.K. for around £1.50 per bottle, bottles of 1961 vintage Chateau Petrus, a prestigious red wine from the Bordeaux region of France, has recently been changing hands at London wine auctions for the equivalent of about £775. Unfortunately, there is at present no purely technological route to producing a wine of this quality and price.

Sparkling Wines

Sparkling wines, those containing carbon dioxide in solution under pressure, account for a small proportion of world wine production. The best known by far is champagne, produced under strictly regulated conditions in a delimited area of 35,000 hectares near Rheims in France. One white grape cultivar (Chardonnay) and two black (Pinot Noir and Pinot Meunier) are used. The grapes are pressed in vertical presses which are considered to produce a greater clarification than the more common horizontal variety, virtually none of the skin pigment being extracted unless the intention is to produce pink champagne. Legally, champagne can only be made from the first three pressings, a maximum of 2,666 l of juice from a 4,000 kg pressing of grapes. The most prestigious producers will use only the first pressing, amounting to about 2,000 l.

Fermentation, traditionally conducted in small oak casks, is now normally carried out in stainless steel vessels and takes three weeks at 20–25°C after which the wine is racked off and allowed to stand at a low temperature for about three months to precipitate sediment. From an initial selection of perhaps 150 wines from different vineyards, each produced from a single grape cultivar, the blender will mix about 30 in different proportions. In good years, vintage champagnes are produced by the leading manufacturers from grapes of the one year only. For non-vintage champagne, wine from earlier years will be added to improve consistency.

The blended wine is bottled, together with a small volume of sugar dissolved in wine, and an inoculum of a special yeast culture. The bottles are sealed with cork-lined metal caps and placed in cool cellars to permit a slow secondary fermentation to take place, generating enough carbon dioxide to produce a pressure of 5–6 atmospheres. Ethyl pyrocarbonate is formed in the bottle and, when the bottle is finally opened, slowly decomposes to produce bubbles over a period of time.

After a minimum of one year (three years for vintage champagnes) the yeast sediment will have settled and must be removed by a process known as *remuage*. The bottles are placed in racks, and each day a skilled operative gives each bottle a sharp twist. The racks are steadily adjusted so that the bottles are held at progressively steeper angles, and over a period of about ten weeks the sediment is progressively worked down to the cork. The bottle then is frozen at the neck end using brine at −25°C and the cap is removed. The ice plug is forced out by gas pressure, taking the sediment with it; extra wine is added to replace the lost volume, with varying concentrations of sugar according to the degree of sweetness required, and the special impermeable, multilayered cork is inserted. Some producers have installed computer-controlled machinery to carry out the process automatically. A more recent development appears likely to render both the manual process and the machines obsolete. If yeast cells are immobilised in alginate beads there is no production of free cells, and the beads and yeast can be sedimented to the cork in a matter of minutes. So far the indications are that the process works well with no difference from normal *remuage* detectable in blind taste trials.

Many other wines are made by the same process of secondary fermentation in bottle, the *methode champenoise*, but the process is expensive and cheaper sparkling wines are made using a secondary fermentation in closed tanks, or even by injecting carbon dioxide under pressure into still wines. Both methods are likely to produce wines of inferior flavour to the *methode champenoise* and, if less ethyl pyrocarbonate is formed, only a brief effervescence results. Some wines, e.g. the *vinho verde* wines of Portugal, owe their slight effervescence to being bottled immediately after the malolactic fermentation has taken place.

Spirits

Many different spirits are produced and the detailed methods used vary from one country to another. Two will be described as examples; whisky, with special reference to Scotch malt whisky, and London gin as an example of a compounded spirit.

Whisky

Whisky is a spirit made by distilling fermented worts derived from barley malt and other cereals. (The alternative spelling "whiskey" is used in some countries.) Whisky seems to have originated in Ireland, although the Scottish product, one of the most popular drinks in the world, is probably even better known. Whiskies from Canada and the U.S. are also well-known and widely exported.

Two types of Scotch whisky are defined according to the grain used in their production. Malt whisky is made only from malted barley which is dried with the smoke from peat fires, resulting in the characteristic peaty flavour of Scotch, and is always distilled in pot (batch) stills. Production is split between well over a hundred distilleries, generally small and often situated in rural areas. The product of each distillery is unique and experts are able to identify individual malt whiskies by taste. The prime requisite in production is to maintain the unique character in the face of changing conditions and variations in raw materials. The bulk of malt whisky is sold in the form of blends with the cheaper grain whiskies, each blend containing 20–30 individual whiskies, 30–40% of the total being malt. Smaller amounts are sold unblended as single malts. Grain whisky production is concentrated in about a dozen large distilleries. The main starch source is corn (maize), with a small proportion of malt to provide enzymes for hydrolysis, and distillation is carried out in a Coffey (continuous) still.

Most countries define the grain types to be used in whisky production, some ten different types being defined in the U.S. American bourbon employs corn (maize), rye and barley as, in different proportions, do American grain, Canadian rye and Canadian grain whiskies.

The malt for Scotch is mashed in a broadly similar fashion to that used for ale production, employing an infusion mash at 65°C, but using a mash tun with revolving knives to aid filtration, rather like a lauter tun. The wort has a mean specific gravity of around 1.055 (up to 1.080 for whiskies produced in some countries) to give an ethanol concentration of about 7% after fermentation. In contrast to beer production, no hops are used and the wort is not boiled. This has the important effect that malt enzymes are not destroyed and continue to act in the washback (fermenter), converting dextrins virtually completely to fermentable sugars and increasing the ethanol yield by about 15%. Many whiskies produced from non-malt grain involve a cooking stage to gelatinize starch before the mash. In North America the fermentation is conducted without separating the wort from the grains to ensure maximum extraction and conversion of starch and to inhibit foaming during the fermentation.

In Scotland it is usual to use a distilling yeast purchased from a supplier, most often mixed with spent brewer's yeast. The mixture is cheaper than pure culture yeast and, surprisingly, gives a higher ethanol yield than either yeast alone. A heavy inoculum ($5-20 \times 10^6$ cells/ml) is used. To reduce the cost of yeast, "bubbing" is frequently practised. This involves growing up yeast with a small portion of wort for a few hours prior to the main fermentation, permitting the amount of yeast purchased to be reduced.

A typical Scotch malt whisky fermentation takes 40–50 hours with most of the ethanol production during the first thirty. Cooling facilities are often absent and the temperature is allowed to rise, sometimes reaching 35°C, at which point there is a danger of the fermentation stopping due to death of the yeast. Because the wort is not boiled, bacteria derived from the malt are always present.

The yeast is another frequent source of infection and so is the plant itself in some old-fashioned distilleries. Most contaminating organisms die fairly quickly, unable to tolerate the ethanol, the absence of air, the high carbon dioxide concentration and the pH, which falls from about 5.2 to 4.2. Lactic acid bacteria, however, are able to grow under these conditions and can reach high populations; lactic acid concentrations of 30 mg/l have been reported in the wash (fermented wort). In small numbers bacteria probably do no harm but heavy infections of lactic acid bacteria can inhibit yeast growth by production of lactate and render the pH unfavorable for dextrin breakdown, resulting in small but economically significant losses of ethanol. The effects of bacterial infection on flavour are unclear. There is a belief that compounds secreted by bacteria have a favourable organoleptic effect on whisky, but some potentially unfavourable influences have been reported. Thus lactobacilli can metabolize glycerol secreted by yeast to form β-hydroxypropionaldehyde which breaks down during distillation to acrolein, producing a pungent aroma in the whisky.

Distillation

Pure ethanol boils 78°C so the dilute alcohol solutions produced by fermentation can be concentrated by distillation. The formation of non-ideal mixtures between water, ethanol and other fermentation products produces some unexpected results. Thus, pure ethanol cannot be obtained by simple distillation as a constant boiling point ethanol-water azeotrope is formed at 96.5% ethanol. Again, due to non-ideal behaviour, higher alcohols distil off more readily and methanol less readily than ethanol itself.

Scotch and Irish malt whiskies, along with rum and some brandies (cognac and armagnac), are distilled in pot stills. These are simple batch stills, roughly spherical at the base, with long conical necks. Vapour is carried off through a long horizontal arm, the "lyne arm" or "swan neck", and condensed by passage through a coiled tube immersed in water. Construction is always of copper. If polished this reduces radiant heat losses and it affects the flavour of the product by catalysing reactions such as ester formation and the reduction of aldehydes to alcohols. The still size varies from 0.9 m^3 for the smallest cognac still up to 135 m^3, and there are various differences in design and method of operation. Heating is achieved either by gas flame or by steam coils. The entire contents of the fermenting vessel are often distilled and provision is made for stirring to prevent solid materials sticking to the heated surfaces.

Scotch malt whisky is distilled using two pot stills in sequence. There is great reluctance to alter any detail of the distillation process because this is believed to be crucial in determining the individual character of each whisky. When new stills are ordered it is usual for the old pattern to be reproduced exactly. The distillate from the first, the "wash still", is known as "low wines". It contains about 21% ethanol and is transferred complete to the spirit still. The residue, the "pot ale", is combined with the spent grains from the mashing stage and dried to make cattle feed. The output from the spirit still is split into three fractions, the first ("foreshots") and last ("feints") are recycled back to the spirit still. The spirit fraction, containing about 60% ethanol, is collected in a receiver to be dispensed into casks for maturation.

Freshly distilled whisky has a fiery taste and in most countries there is a minimum period of maturation prescribed by law before sale is permitted. In the U.K. this is three years but most whisky is matured longer. Maturation is carried out in oak casks kept in unheated warehouses. New casks are used for bourbon, but in Scotland used casks which have previously been used for sherry or bourbon production are preferred. Some 2–3% of the whisky is lost each year by evaporation through the wood; since water penetrates most rapidly the whisky becomes more concentrated with time. The chemical changes during maturation are complex. They depend on the breakdown of lignin and hemicelluloses and extraction of components by the ethanol/water solution, oxidation reactions due to oxygen diffusing in through the wood and reactions between the fermentation products and substances extracted from the wood. Colour, and the levels of acids, esters, furfural and tannins all increase during maturation whilst aliphatic sulphur compounds such as dimethyl sulphide decrease rapidly. Vanillin, syringaldehyde and β-methyl-γ-octalactone have been identified as key flavour components extracted from the wood. The rates and extent of chemical change are dependent upon the type of oak, the degree of charring of the wood, the size of cask, the previous history and the mean temperature.

Caramel is used to achieve the required colour. Blended Scotch whisky is matured for a further six months or so after the individual components are mixed. Finally the whisky is bottled. Unlike wine, whisky undergoes no significant change in bottle.

One of the remarkable aspects of Scotch malt whisky production is the way in which the distilleries maintain the individual characteristics of their products over a period of time. This is of great commercial importance both for the sale of single malts in bottle and for the bulk product sold for blending but the reasons for the consistency of flavour are not clear. Thus the raw materials are not constant. Malt is not normally produced by the distiller but is bought in from as far afield as Australia. Yeast is not cultured in the distillery: distiller's yeast is bought from one of two main suppliers and brewer's yeast is a by-product from any one of numerous breweries. In emergency, baker's yeast has been used. Malt whisky distillers often attribute the character of their whisky to the water supply, usually extracted from a stream, but even this is likely to be highly variable in composition from season to season. The only obvious candidates which might determine individual characteristics are the pot stills. These do vary in shape and size from one distillery to another and great emphasis is laid on keeping the shape and size constant. By determining the refluxing of individual components each still design might determine the character of the resulting whisky. It is not likely that a definitive answer will be obtained to this problem: mystique is an essential part of the success of Scotch malt whisky and distillers are not likely to want this dispelled

EDITORIAL NOTE

There is a piquant story about the mystique of making whisky recounted by Professor Donald Glaser at a meeting in Asilomar in 1979. The story goes like this: Two former college friends had both done well. One was chairman of the board of a large chemical manufacturing corporation while the other was president of a distillery in Tennessee. The distillery was famous for its bourbon whiskey, matured in cask over wood chips for seven years, but the president was becoming fed up with the capital tied up in all that maturing whiskey. He was a modern man and felt that if only one could analyse the chemical differences between the raw and mature whiskeys it should be possible to add the missing chemicals to the raw spirit and turn it into the mature product.

He hired good scientists, provided a laboratory with all the instruments they needed and set them to find the answer. After six months or so the chief scientist came back. "We have found a compound which would do the trick", he said, "but at $100 a gram it is much too expensive for us because we would need 200 mg for each bottle." "Never mind" replied the president, "I will talk to my friend at the chemical company and see if they can make it for us more cheaply. After all, we would need lots and lots of it to mature all the whiskey we distil."

The president picked up the 'phone and called the chemical manufacturer. He explained the need, stressed the quantities he would want to buy and the long term contract to be signed, and asked for a substantial discount. The chemical manufacturer consulted his experts and argued with them for a good price because of the anticipated volume of sales. But they were unable to do very much to help and when he returned the call to the whiskey distiller he could go no lower than $95 a gram. The whiskey executive's advisers were aghast: technical success was within their grasp but the cost would kill the project. "You must get the price much, much lower" they insisted.

Another 'phone call to the chemical manufacturer and another discussion with his production experts. Back and forth, back and forth but all to no avail. The manufacturer was sad when he made the final call to his erstwhile friend in the distillery. "We really cannot go below $92.50", he said. "You see, the trouble is that the only way we can make the stuff is by steeping wood chips for seven years in raw whiskey . . . . ."

Alas, there is a lesson there for biotechnologists, the one about the good experiment not necessarily being a prescription for a good product.

Compounded Spirits

The manufacture of compounded spirits begins with the ethanol of fermentation. The character of the product does not depend mainly on the nature of the congenerics produced during fermentation so the distillation process is designed to produce ethanol solutions of high purity. In some cases compounded spirits have no flavour other than that of ethanol itself: minute amounts of tasteless permitted additives are introduced to bring the spirits within the legal definition of compounded spirits. In Britain this permits them to be sold without the minimum three year maturation period required for other spirits. The majority of compounded spirits are flavoured by components extracted from plant materials (botanicals). The manufacture of London dry gin will serve as an example.

London dry gin is the principal type of gin produced; its name refers to the method used, not the place of manufacture. Plymouth gin and Hollands are disinct products produced on a smaller scale. The spirit itself used may be produced by the gin manufacturer or may be purchased. Despite being highly purified it still contains traces of congenerics derived from the fermentation which will influence the character of the final product and which may make the spirit unsuitable for gin manufacture. Corn (maize) spirit is the most common starting material but spirit derived from molasses is also acceptable. Spirit derived from grape, date or rice carbohydrate is considered inferior. Batches of spirit are evaluated for suitability by taste panels and some information can be obtained by chemical assay.

The characteristic botanical of gin is the berry of *Juniperus communis*, the European juniper tree. Juniper berries for gin production are grown in Italy, Southern Germany and Yugoslavia. The other most important botanicals are the fruit of coriander (*Coriandrum sativum*), a herbacious annual, and the dried root of angelica (*Angelica officinalis*). Other botanicals such as the peel of the lemon (*Citrus limon*), bitter orange (*Citrus aurantium*), sweet orange (*Citrus sinensis*), cassia bark (*Cinnamomum cassia*), cinnamon bark (*Cinnamomum zeylanicum*), cardamom seeds (*Elettaria cardamomum*) liquorice root (*Glycirrhiza* spp.), nutmeg (*Myristica fragrans*) and orris root (*Iris pallida*) are used in smaller quantities. The particular minor components employed, as well as the proportions of the major components, are different for each distiller and are not disclosed. The three major botanicals are assayed by extracting the essential oils by steam distillation and subjecting them to chemical and organoleptic evaluation. Different batches can be mixed and the amounts used adjusted to produce a uniform product.

Gin is distilled in pot stills, rather similar in shape to those used in malt whisky manufacture. They are constructed of copper and consist of a spherical lower portion, designed to contain volumes ranging from a few hundreds to several thousands of gallons, and a head shaped like an inverted cone. The still head may be equipped with a water jacket or early distilling fractions may be returned to the still to increase refluxing. The exact shape, size and operation of the stills are important factors in determining the reflux ratios and hence the flavour of the final product. Heating is by steam, heat being transferred through internal coils or an external jacket. Botanicals, mixed in the correct proportions, are loaded into the still together with spirit diluted to about 50% ethanol. The middle portion of the distillate is collected in holding tanks for blending with other batches to improve uniformity. The early and late fractions are combined and redistilled in a rectifying still. The main ethanol-containing fractions are blended with fresh spirit for subsequent distillations. In an alternative procedure, botanicals are placed in a tray above the still and extraction occurs by the hot refluxing spirit.

Before bottling, the gin is diluted with water, normally to 40% ethanol in the United Kingdom, and filtered to improve the clarity. Since the flavour is derived from the botanicals, no maturation is required.

Industrial Ethanol

The production of ethanol in useful quantities for industrial purposes followed the development in 1830 of a multistage continuous still for the production of 95% ethanol by Aeneas Coffey, a former Inspector-General of Excise in Ireland. Ethanol was used in the 19th century as an industrial solvent and as a fuel for cooking, lighting and heating.

Before World War II several governments subsidised the production of industrial ethanol from crops such as corn, potatoes and sugar beet. Apart from some production from cane molasses, at that time an almost worthless waste product, and a scheme based on the use of sub-standard potatoes which soon drove up prices to uneconomical levels, production was always dependent on some form of government subsidy. These subsidies were intended to reduce dependence on oil imports in the event of war and to encourage home industry and agriculture and reduce trade deficits during the depression. During World War II, most motor vehicles in Germany ran on potato-based ethanol. From 1945 onwards the decline in subsidies, substantial increases in the price of molasses due to its use in cattle feed and the availability of cheap ethanol based on petrochemical ethylene led to a rapid decline in production by fermentation. The sharp rises in the price of crude oil in the early 1970s led to a renewed interest in the production of ethanol by fermentation for fuel and for other industrial uses and substantial amounts are now produced, principally in Brazil and the U.S.

Ethanol as a Fuel

Gasoline-engined cars will run without major modification on mixtures containing up to 20% anhydrous ethanol with gasoline (gasohol). To avoid the separation of an aqueous layer in cold weather, the ethanol has to be anhydrous. The heat of combustion of the mixture is lower than that of gasoline, leading to some reduction in performance and a 15–25% increase in consumption on a volume basis. Problems are experienced with cold starting, vapour blocks, increased engine wear and corrosion, and phase separation due to contamination with water. On the other hand the mixture has an enhanced octane rating, so ethanol can be used to replace tetraethyl lead. Many of the problems can be overcome using engines designed to run on pure ethanol; these will accept ethanol containing 5% water, reducing the cost of purification.

Substrate Sources

To be useful for production of industrial ethanol on a large scale, substrates must be available in sufficient quantity, at the right cost and for a large part of the year and commercial processes for their utilization must exist. The principal substrate sources currently in use are sugar cane, which is used predominantly in Brazil, and corn, which is used in the U.S. Other potential or actual sources are cassava (manioc) and waste products such as whey, and lignocellulose wastes.

Crude oil consumption is of the order of $2.5-3 \times 10^9$ tonnes per annum, and since the total production of starch and sugar are 10^9 and 10^8 tonnes per annum, respectively, only small proportions of which are likely to be devoted to ethanol production, the ultimate contribution to world fuel requirements from these sources is limited. The annual production of wood is about 10^{10} tonnes per annum so this is the only source of substrate which might conceivably provide amounts of ethanol to rival the use of oil as a fuel.

Sugar cane is currently the main source of fermentation ethanol. It offers a potential yield of over 4,000 litres of ethanol per hectare per annum, the highest for any crop, and the energy balance for ethanol production is more favourable than with other crops due to the contribution obtainable by burning the bagasse, the residue remaining after extracting the sugar. Because of the low price of sugar on the world market the opportunity cost of using it for ethanol is low. On the other hand, sugar cane requires good quality land in the tropics and in most countries only a single crop is obtained. Since the cane cannot be stored without extraction and concentration of the juice, ethanol production is possible only for a brief period during the harvest season unless molasses from sugar refining is available.

Corn yields only 1150 litres of ethanol per hectare per annum but can be grown successfully in a temperate climate. It can be stored indefinitely, so fermentation plant can be used throughout the year. The economics of ethanol production from corn are highly dependent on the value of by-products. Cassava yields up to 1,600 litres of ethanol per hectare per annum. Its attraction is that it can be grown successfully on marginal land and can be stored after drying.

Substantial quantities of cellulose and lignocellulose wastes are available, especially paper, sawdust, straw and municipal and industrial wastes. Most contain cellulose, hemicellulose and lignin in roughly equal proportions. Either chemical or enzymatic pretreatment is necessary; the lignin component hinders both enzymatic and chemical breakdown of the other components (see Chapter 28). With present technology, enzymic breakdown is so slow that conversion plant would be prohibitively large. Chemical treatment, which includes mechanical milling followed by acid or alkaline hydrolysis, is expensive and achieves only 60% conversion of cellulose to fermentable sugars. Pentoses from hemicelluloses can be fermented but present conversion yields are low. Although the materials are cheap, collection costs may be substantial. The only attractive substrate in this group is sulphite waste liquor from the delignification of wood pulp. This is used for production of about 120,000 tonnes of ethanol per annum. It has a negative cost since its high biochemical oxygen demand normally dictates a waste treatment operation before it can be discharged into a river. Despite substantial research efforts, no other commercial scale lignocellulose based ethanol production is now in operation except in the Soviet Union.

Brazilian Gasohol Programme

Brazil is a net food exporter with a very large land area, only about 4% of which is used for arable farming. In 1975 oil accounted for 25% by value of total imports, a proportion which had risen from only 9% in five years and the country had a large foreign exchange deficit. The Brazilian government instigated a massive program to encourage the production of industrial ethanol from crops, especially sugar cane, sweet potatoes and cassava (manioc). The intention was to produce 10^9 litres of ethanol per annum by 1985 to supplement, and eventually replace, imported oil as a fuel and chemical feedstock. Brazil has a rapidly rising population and another intention was to provide jobs to reduce unemployment and to support the sugar industry at a time of world sugar surplus.

The production cost of ethanol is equivalent to $40 per barrel, substantially higher than the cost of imported petroleum before tax. To encourage the production and use of ethanol the price of petroleum is raised by taxation and that of ethanol lowered by subsidy. Subsidised loans are available for the construction of distilleries while the sale of cars to run on 95% ethanol is encouraged by lower taxation and the provision of loan finance for purchase. Feedstock ethanol is priced at 35% the cost of ethylene on a weight basis.

The program has achieved many of its aims. Brazil is the world's leading producer of ethanol: production in the year 1982/3 was 5.8 billion litres, with a saving of $1.3 billion in foreign exchange. Most cars now run on ethanol or gasohol. Ethanol production currently employs some 300,000 people in farming, and 90,000 in sugar factories and distilleries, and has helped to minimize the drift of population into the towns. The number of jobs indirectly dependent upon ethanol production may be nearly a million. Almost all Brazilian gasohol is produced from sugar cane juice or molasses; of the 380 distilleries operating only one is utilizing cassava.

Unlike the U.S. (see below), Brazil has adopted a low technology approach relying on small plants (mean output 11,000 tonnes per annum), drawing supplies of sugar cane from the surrounding area to minimize the high cost of transport and often associated with sugar processing plants to utilize molasses.

Fermentation is conducted in open top vats of 100–200 m^3 capacity. These are usually made locally of low-carbon steel, coated with epoxy resin and have no mechanical agitation. Distillation is based on beverage ethanol techniques and is energetically inefficient. Heat and electrical energy are generated by burning the bagasse and, since this provides more than enough energy, the inefficient utilization is unimportant.

Stillage and the ash from burning bagasse are used as fertilisers where appropriate. Disposal of waste is a major problem: 12–14 litres of high B.O.D. waste are produced for each liter of ethanol; the Brazilian ethanol programme generates waste equivalent to one and a half times the sewage produced by the entire Brazilian population. For further comments see Chapter 28.

Gasohol in the U.S.

A programme to encourage gasohol production in the U.S. was set up in 1977 with three aims:

(i) To reduce dependence on imported oil for strategic reasons.
(ii) To reduce the adverse effects of oil imports on the balance of payments. (In 1985 the import cost of fuel was of the order of $10 million dollars per hour).
(iii) As a way of disposing of surplus corn stocks.

Corn production has risen steadily for many years, increasing from 123 million tonnes in 1967 to 165 million tonnes in 1977 despite subsidies to farmers to take land out of production. Much grain remains unsold and has to be stored from year to year, the total carried over at the end of 1982 being 71 million tonnes. The total cost to the goverment of storing this surplus for one year was estimated at about $2.4 billion.

Wholesale prices of anhydrous ethanol (35–42 cents per gallon) have been higher than wholesale gasoline prices (20–25 cents per gallon) over a number of years, making substitution uneconomic without government incentives. From 1977 the sale of gasohol (defined as containing 10% ethanol by volume) was encouraged by exemption from the Federal excise tax of four cents per gallon (later increased), amounting to a subsidy of nearly 11 cents per litre of ethanol. Tax credits were also offered to encourage investment in production facilities. Some 32 individual states offered tax incentives ranging from one to 16 cents per gallon of gasohol in addition to the federal incentives. The Surplus Agricultural Commodities Disposal Act, 1982 provided for excessive government stocks of grain to be converted to ethanol for use in government vehicles and industrial boilers by arrangement with distillers having spare capacity. One unintentional effect of subsidies was to encourage the import of ethanol from Brazil and other countries. An import duty of 60 cents per gallon was imposed to eliminate the Federal subsidy for foreign producers but individual states were unable to impose import duties or to prevent imports. Attempts are being made to disqualify imported ethanol for state subsidies by rewording the appropriate laws.

Unlike Brazil, the U.S. has relied mainly on corn for alcohol production although small amounts are produced from barley, milo, potato wastes, spent sulphite liquor, cane molasses, citrus molasses, cheese whey and wastes from breweries and soft drink production. The original plan envisaged major contributions from both large and small producers. In practice, although plants range in capacity from 0.5 to 150 million gallons per year, U.S. production has become dominated by the large scale producers and in 1982 six plants accounted for 80% of U.S. capacity. One reason is that the economics of large scale production seem inherently more attractive, due to lower capital costs per unit of output and the higher value of by-products. The other reason appears to be due to inexperience. Small producers often had no previous experience of fermentation, they were undercapitalised and often purchased plant unsuitable for the purpose. Difficulties were experienced in purifying the ethanol to the required water content of less than 1% and in some cases the system of Federal and state subsidies was not understood.

Small scale producers ferment the crushed grain without fractionation, yielding only spent grains as a by-product, whereas large scale production is often linked to the wet milling of corn which provides oil, gluten and other fractions as by-products, only the starch fraction being fermented. This difference results in a net raw material cost of about 60% of total production costs in the case of whole grains fermentations compared with only 40% in the case of a process linked to wet milling. Substantial economies in capital costs are associated with large scale production, and one analysis[5] suggests that ethanol can be produced economically only in plant with a capacity of at least 100 million gallons per year.

Before fermentation, cooking is necessary to gelatinize the starch, followed by hydrolysis by enzymes or acid. Acid treatment is less favoured because it tends to produce a lower yield of fermentable sugars. After milling in roller or hammer mills to obtain a fine meal, or wet milling and separation of the starch fraction, the substrate is cooked. Large plants employ a continuous process in which substrate is heated to 150–160°C for 2–10 minutes rather than batch cooking at 100°C for an hour. Before heating, water, α-amylase from *Bacillus licheniformis* and calcium hydroxide to improve enzyme stability are added. The enzyme is unstable at the cooking temperature but starts to break down the starch, preventing a return to the original insoluble structure on cooling. The mash is cooled to about 90°C and, after adding a further portion of α-amylase, incubated for 30–60 minutes to complete conversion of starch to dextrins.

Conversion of dextrins to fermentable sugars, mediated by amyloglucosidase from *Aspergillus niger*, takes place after cooling to about 60°C and adjusting the pH to 4.5–5.0. Finally, the mash is cooled to about 30°C and transferred to the fermenter. Alternatively, the conversion at 60°C can be omitted and amyloglucosidase from *Rhizopus niveus* added at the start of the fermentation period to act during the fermentation.

The three principal requirements of an economically sound fermentation are rapidity, favourable substrate conversion stoichiometry and high final ethanol concentration. Much more emphasis has been placed on these considerations in the U.S. than in Brazil where a more low technology approach has been adopted. Poor conversion may be due to a number of factors e.g. incomplete liquefaction of starch or conversion to fermentable sugars, excessive yeast growth, excessive formation of by-products or competition from bacteria. In extreme cases losses due to these causes may amount to as much as 20% of potential ethanol. Three types of fermentation systems are in use:

(i) batch
(ii) single-vessel continuous
(iii) multi-vessel continuous vessels in cascade.

Batch systems are simpler than continuous ones but suffer from the usual disadvantages of slow fermentation in the early stages before the yeast population has built up. The vessel has to be emptied at the end of each cycle, cleaned, sterilized and refilled: these processes can account for up to 20% of the cycle time. Most U.S. distillers do not grow their own yeast but buy in a dried preparation of a distilling strain of *S. cerevisiae*. Suppliers thus have some incentive to improve their strains and strains have been produced with higher than normal ethanol tolerance which will produce beers containing 12–13% ethanol without extended fermentation times. The use of *S. diastaticus*, which produces its own amylase, has been proposed but not yet adopted. As an alternative to purchasing yeast can be recovered after fermentation by centrifugal separation, washed with acid to remove bacterial contamination, aerated to permit synthesis of membrane lipids and used for a subsequent fermentation. This involves extra capital and handling costs but saves the expense of purchasing yeast and of pre-treating dried yeast to activate it. Since the yeast is obtained cheaply, a high level of inoculum can be used giving a rapid fermentation and reduced yeast growth as well as supressing the growth of bacteria. Yeast re-use is only possible if the medium contains little suspended solids and a proportion must always be discarded to prevent the build up of detritus.

During fermentation, temperature is prevented from rising much above 30°C; this may require substantial cooling with a large fermentation vessel. With batch systems, fermentation is complete in 48–72 hours and a final ethanol concentration of 8–12% is produced. The energy required to distil a given quantity of ethanol drops sharply as the ethanol content of the fermentation beer rises up to about 7.3% after which it is constant. The volume of stillage per unit of ethanol is inversely proportional to ethanol concentration, minimising disposal problems. It is thus advantageous to ferment concentrated mashes. However yeast growth and fermentation are inhibited by high ethanol concentrations and, to a lesser extent, high sugar concentrations so if the initial sugar content is too high, fermentation will take an excessive time or may even stop before all the sugar is converted.

Continuous systems offer the advantage of improved volumetric efficiency due to operating at a constant rapid fermentation rate and thus lower capital costs. Yeast costs are greatly reduced since inoculation has to be performed only once for each extended fermentation cycle. Control over the fermentation is improved due to steady state operations leading to a consistent product and improved operating efficiency of distillation. Peak loading on ancillary equipment is eliminated allowing reduced capacity. It is claimed that single-vessel continuous systems are more resistant to bacterial contamination than batch or cascade systems because they operate at high ethanol concentrations.

Most of the continuous systems in operation are of the multi-vessel type, usually employing four to seven vessels. The first vessel is aerated to promote yeast growth, the others have carbon dioxide mixing. Antifoam is added to the first vessel. Cooling is by external heat exchanger when the flow from tank to tank is pumped, or by external coils on the tank where transfer is by gravity. The substrate is fermented progressively as it passes from tank to tank, the first tank having an ethanol concentration of about 4%. Yeast growth can thus take place at a relatively low ethanol concentration and in the last vessels, where ethanol concentration may be high enough to inhibit growth, conversion of the remaining sugar can occur without growth. Residence times of 22–30 hours have been reported but if yeast is collected from the last vessel and recycled to the first, a higher yeast concentration can be attained, reducing the residence time to 10–14 hours. By maintaining a very high yeast concentration in the system, growth is minimised and ethanol yield enhanced.

Single vessel stirred tank reactors are analogous to laboratory chemostats. Several types are commercially available. Since they are homogeneous, yeast growth and metabolism take place at the highest ethanol concentration. Again, an increased throughput is obtained if yeast is collected from the output and recycled. To avoid the inhibitory effect of high ethanol concentration, one design continually removes ethanol by pumping off beer from the fermenter, removing yeast by centrifugation, distilling off ethanol and returning the stillage to the fermenter. Several advantages would accrue from the use of immobilized yeast cells since yeast could be removed from the fermentation easily and efficiently. Extensive laboratory study of this possibility has taken place but its use on a commercial scale has not yet been reported.

Some attention has been given to the possibilities of using organisms other than yeast to produce ethanol. The advantages sought are increased conversion yields of ethanol, faster fermentation rates, higher operating temperatures to reduce expenditure on cooling and the ability to grow on substrates such as starch and cellulose without an external source of enzymes. Much laboratory experimentation has been carried out with *Zymomonas mobilis*, the organism which is used for producing palm and cactus wine. This organism converts sugars to ethanol more effectively than yeast and strains have been reported to produce ethanol at rates up to 120 grams per litre per hour, more than three times as fast as yeast. However, optimum growth occurs at pH 5, at which pH fermentations are more susceptible to bacterial contamination and some 2–5% of acetic acid is produced which cannot be removed by conventional distillation procedures. Several strains of ethanol-producing thermophiles have been investigated including *Thermoanaerobacter ethanolicus*, which can grow on a range of sugars and on starch, and *Clostridium thermocellum* which grows on cellulose and its derivatives. So far, all the bacteria examined have drawbacks such as a high pH optimum, production of acetic acid, or poor yields of ethanol.

Distillation

This involves two or more stages. Operation is continuous. The fermentation beer is passed to a stripping column and heated by steam injection. The ethanol is removed as a vapour, equivalent to 50–70% concentration, which passes to a rectifying column where ethanol is recovered at about 95%. If the product is to be used for admixture with gasoline, the water content is reduced to about 1%, usually by azeotropic distillation. Benzene is the most common entrainer; other possibilities are cyclohexane, pentane, diethyl ether, diisopropyl ether and gasoline. The distillation techniques employed originally were inefficient in their use of energy having been derived from the beverage industry where profit margins were high and volumes low. They involved a series of condensations and redistillations. Substantial energy savings were obtained by improving the design of the distillation plant. New plant was based on principles derived from the oil industry involving the elimination of condensation between columns and operating successive columns at lower pressures, permitting the reuse of heat. In this way the steam requirement for distillation to produce 95% ethanol can be reduced from 6 kg/l to 1–1.9 kg/l.

More recently, some producers have eliminated the final azeotropic distillation, dehydrating the 95% ethanol with a potassium aluminosilicate molecular sieve. This process requires less operating expertise than azeotropic distillation and consumes less energy.

VINEGAR

Vinegar is a solution of acetic acid usually with a complex

mixture of congenerics. Apart from its use as a condiment, it is used in cooking and in some parts of the world plays an important role in food preservation. It is produced by the fermentation of carbohydrates to produce ethanol which is then oxidized by bacteria. Grain, molasses, oranges, peaches, pears, pineapples and whey can all be used as starting materials but the most common are grapes (or inferior-grade or spoiled wine as in France), rice (China and Japan), apples (U.S.) or malt (U.K.). Sometimes distilled ethanol, produced by fermentation, is used. The legal definition of vinegar frequently specifies a minimum acetic acid concentration of 40 g/l, the usual range being 40–50 g/l. Some countries permit diluted synthetic acetic acid to be sold as vinegar or to be used to increase the strength of fermentation vinegar; in others this is specifically forbidden. Spices and herbs, including tarragon, ruta, absynth, lavender, mint, celery, pontulaca and saffron are often added for flavouring.

Acetic acid is an important bulk chemical. World production is about 2.5 million tonnes per annum but the fermentation route is not competitive for non-food use and, since 1950, the bulk of world production has been supplied by chemical synthesis. In Brazil the biomass ethanol program has provided an opportunity to produce acetic acid by fermentation and production increased fivefold between 1975 and 1980. Official figures for world production do not seem to be available but Greenshields[6] in 1978 estimated world production at $6-10 \times 10^9$ liters per annum.

Fermentation

Details of the fermentation process vary with the carbohydrate source. The aim is to achieve virtually complete conversion of carbohydrate to ethanol. In the U.K. malt is the usual starting material. To comply with the definition of malt vinegar only malt enzyme can be used for starch breakdown, ruling out the use of fungal enzyme or acid conversion. Barley, maize or wheat may be used as adjunct to produce a wort of specific gravity up to 1.040. To achieve full carbohydrate conversion, the wort is not boiled: the process thus resembles the fermentation of whisky rather than that of beer. Lauter-tun mashing is used to improve filtration of the mash. For production of malt vinegar pressed brewer's yeast is preferred: by the end of the fermentation it is moribund and a new batch must be used for each fermentation. Sometimes *S. diastaticus* is also added to complete the fermentation which takes 48–72 hours at 21–30°C. For wine vinegar *S. ellipsoidues* is used at 24–32°C.

Care must be taken to avoid the build up of lactate due to contamination with lactic acid bacteria: the last few degrees of attenuation from S.G. 1.000 to 0.994 are critical if good yields are to be obtained. A continuous fermentation process using a tower fermenter has been described and the build-up of contaminating organisms must be avoided. After fermentation it was once customary to store the fermentation beer for up to twelve weeks in large wooden vats where clarification due to precipitation of proteins occurred and growth of acetic and lactic acid bacteria removed any remaining sugars. This is now known to be unnecessary and centrifugal clarification and acetification follow immediately after the alcoholic fermentation.

Acetification Processes

Pasteur made the first systematic studies of the bacteria involved in acetification, the oxidation stage of vinegar manufacture, and demonstrated their role in acetate production. The taxonomy of the genus *Acetobacter* is somewhat confused but De Ley demonstrated that there were no abrupt changes in the sequence of strains and proposed that specific names should be abolished.

The earliest method of acetification on an industrial scale was the field process in which wine or beer was placed in casks in the open air and left to oxidize. In an improved version, the Orleans Process dating from 1670, the barrels were kept in heated wooden cellars to speed up oxidation. A headspace was always left to improve contact with the air and extra holes were bored in the barrels to encourage air circulation. To start the process the barrels were partly filled with wine and vinegar was added to provide an inoculum. Further portions of wine were added each week. From the fifth week on portions of vinegar were withdrawn equivalent in volume to the wine to be added. A mat of *Acetobacter* cells, known as "mother of vinegar", formed on the surface of the liquid. A later modification, due to Pasteur, used a floating wooden grating on which the cells grew to prevent the surface mat becoming broken up and submerged during the weekly exchange of fluid. The Orleans process was an early example of continuous culture using immobilised cells.

Quick Vinegar Process

In the early nineteenth century factories began to adopt the German quick vinegar process. Large vats (acetifiers) were packed with porous support material, such as birch twigs or beechwood shavings, supported on a false floor. Wine or beer was distributed on to the top of the support material by a rotating spray arm, trickled down to the bottom of the vat and pumped back to be sprayed over the support again. Air was admitted through ports at the side and the bacteria grew on the surface of the support material. Later improvements included the introduction of forced aeration and the control of temperature to within the range 25–30°C. A 12% ethanol solution was converted to acetic acid in about five days. Production was much faster and the requirement for labour was reduced. The drawback of the system was that continued growth produced masses of slime which steadily blocked the channels through the porous support and, after a period of months, required the entire acetifier to be emptied and repacked. During the period of operation the efficiency of conversion of ethanol to acetic acid fell from 75–80% down to as low as 60% due to increasingly poor penetration of air. The use of two acetifiers in series has been described with claimed improvements in conversion efficiency up to 95%.

Deep Culture

The introduction about 30 years ago of deep culture techniques represented a major advance in vinegar production. Previous methods has used *Acetobacter* growing in surface films and some difficulties were experienced in obtaining controlled growth in deep culture. In particular, growth was extremely sensitive to oxygen tension and bacterial growth stopped if aeration was interrupted, even for brief periods. Several design variants have been described. The broth and cells are pumped out and mixed intimately with air before returning the resulting emulsion to the bottom of the acetifier. Temperature control, which is more critical than with the trickling process, is achieved by cooling coils within the vessel. Semi-automatic process control is possible. Once the problems of growth in deep liquid has been overcome some factories introduced continuous culture. Feed liquid is accumulated in a holding vessel prior to the fermenter where it is regularly analysed so that adjustments to the process can be made to allow for inevitable variations in ethanol content. The flow rate is then adjusted to keep the input of ethanol just equal to the rate of oxidation. Greenshields[6] described a commercial-scale system operating at 40°C using specially selected strains of *Acetobacter*.

In return for the greater complexities of operation, deep culture offers some advantages over the trickling generator. Ethanol oxidation is about thirty times faster on a volume basis so the capital investment is lower for the same throughout. Because of greater conversion efficiencies (90–98% of theory) it is claimed that raw material costs are cut by up to 40% compared with trickling acetifiers.

The crude vinegar is stored for several weeks to permit settling of protein precipitates as well as yeast and bacterial cells, and may then be matured by passing it over beechwood shavings. Before bottling it will usually be filtered and pasteurized. In the absence of pasteurisation or sterile filtration, vinegar may be spoiled by the growth of lactic acid bacteria or wild yeast. Also common in the past was "mothering", the formation of a surface film of *Acetobacter*; this can be combated by the addition of 1% sodium chloride which also enhances the flavour.

BAKER'S YEAST

The practice of leavening bread by yeast was known to the Egyptians as far back as 4000 B.C. and is mentioned in the Bible. The yeast was maintained in a flour and water dough. Fresh dough was inoculated by mixing with a portion of dough retained from the previous fermentation. Later, surplus yeast from brewing fermentations was used but this was unsatisfactory for large-scale bread production due to its inconsistent quality and poor keeping qualities. From the middle of the nineteenth century this started to be replaced by baker's yeast produced specially for the purpose. Most bread produced in industrialized countries now uses yeast produced specially for the purpose: its world-wide value in 1981 was estimated at £540 million ($865 million).

The main function of yeast in bread making is to produce carbon dioxide by fermentation of sugars: the bubbles of gas expand and lighten the structure. The expansion of the dough due to gas formation, together with the effects of reducing substances produced by the yeast, can also play a role in the conditioning of gluten resulting in an increase in dough elasticity which helps to retain the maximum amount of gas in the dough. By reducing the content of phytic acid, which is present in high content in wholemeal flour and which binds essential trace metals, yeast increases the nutritional value of the bread.

In use, yeast is mixed with flour and water to make a dough, sucrose is normally added along with ammonium salts to stimulate yeast growth and various salts are added to improve dough characteristics. Small amounts only of fermentable sugars are present in flour: sugars are produced during the fermentation by the action of amylases on starch and by breakdown of oligosaccharides by yeast invertase. Wheat flour contains β-amylase but little or no α-amylase; the addition of amylase preparations derived from *Aspergillus* is common. Fungal amylases, by increasing sugar production in the dough, increase dough volume and improve the aroma and taste of the bread; the production of dextrins from the starch improves the keeping qualities. Proteases, also present in the enzyme preparations, help modify the gluten. The yeast multiplies, fermenting the sugars and producing carbon dioxide which causes the dough to expand. Older processes used long periods of fermentation at 25°C: more recent modifications use larger amounts of yeast and much shorter fermentation periods at about 35°C. Vigorous mechanical mixing is employed to condition the dough instead of relying on prolonged periods of swelling caused by fermentation. Leavening can be brought about by carbon dioxide derived from sources other than yeast, but the product cannot normally be sold as bread.

In industrialised countries breadmaking is performed on a very large scale and the widespread adoption of methods which reduce the time allowed for fermentation impose very severe requirements on the yeast used. The most important qualities are the ability to ferment rapidly in dough, resistance to the salts added to the dough and to the high osmotic concentrations which occur in sweet doughs used for cakes and buns, good stability on storage and uniformity. The ability to ferment rapidly is a complex property and depends on rapid growth, high glycolytic activity, high invertase activity and the ability to ferment maltose rapidly without a lag phase once other sugars have been consumed.

Although dough fermentation is anaerobic, baker's yeast is usually grown under highly aerobic conditions to maximise yields and to obtain a product with improved keeping qualities. To avoid inefficient use of sugar by aerobic fermentation, the concentration of sugar must be kept low and, in order to obtain high yeast concentrations, a fed batch system is employed in which medium is added to the culture at regular intervals to maintain growth.

A typical process has been described by Burrows[7]. Starting with a pure culture on an agar slant, two successive aerobic cultures on liquid medium are made in the laboratory to produce a few hundred grams of yeast. At this stage stringent measures are taken to avoid contamination with bacteria. This yeast is used as inoculum for a preculture vessel. After 24 hours, (apostrophe) growth the yeast is concentrated by centrifugation and used to inoculate a single full-sized vessel of 50–200 m^3. After a further 20 hours, enough yeast is produced to seed five full-sized vessels, each of which is in turn used to seed another five, so the final stage involves 25 vessels. In 10–12 days 100–500 tonnes harvested moist yeast are produced and 3500–7000 tonnes of air will have been used.

The two most common starting materials are blackstrap molasses and beet molasses, both of which contain the residual sugars after the crystallisation of sucrose. The two materials are broadly similar in composition but vary considerably with the country of origin, with the particular source and with date of production. As supplied, both contain 50–60% by weight fermentable sugars, mostly sucrose in beet molasses but including substantial amounts of glucose and fructose in the case of blackstrap molasses. Numerous minor but often important components have been identified, including proteins, amino acids, organic acids, vitamins, nitrogenous bases, minor sugars, alcohols, aldehydes and salts. Various inhibitory substances, identified and unidentified, also occur. Their effects are avoided by using molasses from sources known to be satisfactory and by incremental feeding to keep their initial concentrations low.

The preferred medium is based on a mixture of beet and blackstrap molasses: beet is deficient in biotin, but too high a proportion of blackstrap causes problems with foaming. The mixture may require clarification before use by chemical precipitation of colloidal and particulate matter. The molasses is supplemented with phosphorus, nitrogen, magnesium and sulphur using combinations of ammonium phosphate, phosphoric acid, ammonium sulphate, ammonium chloride, ammonia solution and magnesium sulphate and, if necessary, with biotin and thiamin. Complete medium sterility is not essential for yeast production but the process is less resistant to contamination than alcoholic fermentations. Molasses contains numerous bacteria and yeasts but these cannot grow until it is diluted for use. Pasteurization by heating to 100–110°C for 1–2 hours or high-temperature short-time sterilisation using heat exchangers or steam injection is satisfactory.

Air must sterilized either by absolute filtration through a proprietary cartridge filter or by deep bed filtration through fibrous materials such as glass fibre or mineral wool. Air can be introduced at the bottom of the fermenter through radially-arranged perforated pipes; the addition of mechanical stirring increases the efficiency of oxygen transfer but increases plant costs and energy requirements. Air supply can be controlled using measurements of oxygen tension in the medium or by measuring ethanol in the exhaust gas.

In the early production stages, medium addition and aeration are adjusted to give the highest growth rates: medium addition is likely to be exponential to correspond with the increasing yeast concentration. Temperature is maintained at about 30°C and, since heat production is high (about 3500 kjoules/kg molasses), efficient cooling is necessary. To minimize bacterial growth, the pH is kept low (3.5–4.5) by balancing the ratio of ammonia to ammonium sulphate in the medium feed or by the addition of sulphuric acid.

Since quality is of greater importance than yield, the conditions are modified during the final stage of production to ensure that the final crop of yeast cells possesses the required properties. The pH may be allowed to rise to 5.0–6.0 to minimize the adsorption of coloured substances from the medium and the nutrient feed rate will be adjusted. The maximum cell yield is obtained by continuing the exponential medium feed to the end of the fermentation but the resulting yeast is still in exponential growth phase and has poor keeping qualities. Improved keeping is achieved by lowering the medium feed rate during the last few hours of growth; the yeast enters the stationary phase and its keeping qualities are greatly improved. Growth temperature may also be adjusted to improve yeast properties.

The final yeast concentration will be up to 80 g yeast dry weight per litre. The yeast is washed and concentrated to about 200 g/l by centrifugation, and further water is removed by rotary vacuum filtration or filter presses before the yeast is cut into blocks and wrapped in waxed paper. If necessary, the cake may be made firmer by removing more of the intercellular water. This is done by suspending the yeast in sodium chloride solution to cause osmotic shrinkage. Water is then added to lower the external osmotic concentration and the yeast immediately subjected to rotary vacuum filtration. The yeast cells continue to absorb water by osmosis after filtration, thus producing a firmer cake with lower intercellular water content and containing 28–30% dry matter. The yeast is cooled rapidly and kept below 5°C for storage and distribution to slow the rate of metabolism and to minimise decreases in enzyme activity.

Dried Yeast

As an alternative to pressed yeast, the use of dried yeast in the form of pellets or granules with a water content of about 8% is gaining popularity. This material has much greater stability than pressed yeast at the expense of some reduction in activity. Special yeast strains are used, chosen for their resistance to drying, and changes are made in fermentation conditions. A temperature of 36°C is used in the final stage of growth, and the supply of nitrogen in the feed is reduced, resulting in lower cell nitrogen content, increased content of lipid in the cell wall and elevated levels of trehalose which appear to improve stability during drying. Filter presses are used to obtain yeast containing 30–38% dry matter; this is extruded through a screen to give continuous threads which are chopped finely before being dried by hot air in rotary drums, on wire trays or in continuous tunnel dryers. Air temperature is carefully regulated so that evaporative cooling prevents the yeast temperature from rising. Drying takes up to 24 hours. Dried yeast has about two-thirds of the activity of fresh yeast on a dry-weight basis; because of its lower water content only 40–50% of the normal weight has to be added. It is stable at room temperature so transport and storage costs are reduced.

CHEESE

The manufacture of cheese is another process with very ancient origins: records exist of cheese production in the region between the Rivers Tigris and Euphrates (now Iraq) from as long ago as 6000 B.C. The process can be very simple. Milk is held in a warm place for a few hours to encourage the growth of bacteria which cause clotting: the resulting curds are pressed in cloths to expel moisture.

Originally practised in homes and farms, manufacture moved to factories from the 1850s onwards and most cheese is now made on an industrial scale. A large factory can use 5×10^5 litres of milk per day: most are much smaller, collecting milk from a restricted region to minimize transport costs.

World cheese production is about eight million tonnes annually and rising, especially in the U.S. (5% p.a.) and France (4% p.a.). In 1980 world sales were estimated at £14 billion ($22 billion), accounting for about 27% of the value of all biotechnological products and ranking second only to alcoholic beverages. Nearly 50% of the world's cheese is produced in Europe, with North and Central America (21%) and the USSR (14%) being major producers.

The purpose of making cheese is to convert the protein and fat of milk, a product susceptible to rapid spoilage, to a stable form. This is achieved by encouraging the growth of lactic acid bacteria which convert lactose to lactic acid, lowering the pH to inhibit the growth of pathogens and putrefying bacteria. A highly specific protease, "chymosin" (formerly known as "rennin"), is added which disrupts the micellar structure of casein, the major milk protein. The individual polypeptides released are insoluble at the low pH created by metabolism of the bacteria and precipitate to form a curd which can be easily separated from the fluid portion of the milk, known as "whey". After heating (in some cases), cutting and pressing to promote the expulsion of fluid, salt is added if required, and the curds are matured to permit the development of flavour prior to packaging for sale. Many cheeses depend on the development of a secondary bacterial and or fungal flora for their individual aroma and appearance.

Several hundred named varieties of cheese are known: many are simply local names for essentially the same product, perhaps packaged in a different shape, so the number of truly different varieties is much smaller. They can be classified into three main categories according to moisture content: soft (50–80% moisture), semi-hard and semi-soft (40–50%) and hard (<40%). Cheeses can be either ripened, i.e. dependent on a secondary microbial flora for their maturation, or unripened.

Milk

Cow's milk is the usual starting material, though good cheese with distinctive properties can be made from the milk of goats, sheep and buffalo. Whole milk is usually used but skim milk is used to produce cheese with a lower fat content. Milk quality is a vital factor in determining the properties of the finished cheese. It must have no off-flavours, which can arise from feed plants (such as leeks or turnips), or from other sources. A high bacterial count, which may arise from poor hygiene during milking, from inappropriate storage or from the inclusion of milk from cows infected with mastitis, is unacceptable. Milk containing antibiotics such as penicillins and tetracyclines, which are used to treat infected cows, must not be used as the starter cultures as bacteria are particularly sensitive to their action. Routine tests used in large cheese factories include organoleptic evaluation, plate counts for bacterial numbers, tests for inhibitory substances and fermentation and curd formation tests.

The principal protein in milk is casein which varies in concentration from 2.5–3.2%. Casein is a complex of five main types of phosphorylated subunits, forming micelles 50–600 nm in diameter at a concentration of about 10^{13}–10^{14}/ml. Other major components are fat globules (about 3.8%) and lactose, the predominant sugar (about 5%). In addition to differences arising from different herds, the milk composition (especially the contents of fat, protein and lactose) changes during the course of lactation and with the season. Much cheese is made from unpasteurized milk: pasteurisation reduces the natural flora, inactivates milk enzymes and can have a major effect on flavour development.

Milk Treatment

Milk produced by vacuum milking systems is chilled rapidly to 5°C; the growth of mesophilic bacteria is inhibited and it can be stored for a few days before the growth of psychrophiles becomes excessive. Standardisation, the adjustment of composition to maintain the desired fat:protein ratio, may involve either removing fat using a centrifugal separator or the addition of skim milk. In some cases, particulate material may be removed by centrifugation at 6000 rpm and higher speed centrifugation may be used to remove bacterial cells, particularly heat-resistant spores. Centrifugation is often avoided because it disrupts the fat globules and requires milk to be pasteurized immediately to inactivate lipases which would otherwise release fatty acids and produce unwanted rancidity.

Starter Cultures

Bacterial starter cultures are added to milk at the start of cheesemaking to avoid the uncertainties of relying on the bacterial flora of the milk and to speed up bacterial action. Commonly employed species include strains of *Streptococcus lactis*, *Strep. cremoris*, *Strep. thermophilus*, *Lactobacillus acidophilus*, *L. bulgaricus*, *L. casei*, *L. helveticus*, *L. lactis* and *L. plantarum*. Their function is to ferment lactose rapidly and produce lactic acid, thereby lowering the pH to about 4.6. This promotes curd formation because the individual casein subunits are insoluble at that pH. The growth of pathogens and spoilage organisms is inhibited but desirable organisms are able to grow slowly. Most of the cheese enzymes are below their pH optimum so flavour develops gradually and the cheese remains edible for long periods. Starters also affect the maturation process by maintaining a low redox potential thus keeping volatile sulphur aroma compounds such as hydrogen sulphide and methanethiol in the reduced state; they also produce compounds such as acetic acid, acetaldehyde, diacetyl and ethanol which may affect the final flavour profile.

Various other organisms are added to individual cheeses at different stages; these have the function of producing flavours, colours, textures or other effects specific to particular cheese varieties. *Propionibacterium freundrichii* ssp. *shermanii* is used in the ripening of Swiss cheese to produce propionic acid, an essential part of the characteristic flavour, and carbon dioxide which forms bubbles in the curd and thus produces the holes. *Penicillium roquefortii* is inoculated into the curd during the manufacture of Roquefort cheese. When the curd reaches the right consistency needles are pushed through to form channels to permit the entry of air: the blue-green veining is due to fungal growth and the formation of coloured conidiospores, whilst part of the characteristic flavour results from the formation by the fungus of methyl ethyl ketone, a metabolic product of the breakdown of milk lipids. In the production of Camembert cheese fungi, including *Penicillium camembertii*, *P. candidum* and *P. caseiocolum*, are encouraged to grow on the outside of the whole cheese where they secrete proteases which diffuse into the bulk of the cheese itself.

Fermentation

Successful fermentation on a large scale requires rapid and reliable bacterial growth: to achieve this an inoculum of 10^6-10^7 cells/ml milk is needed. The production of reliable starter cultures is not wholly straightforward. One author in 1978 commented that 99% of the problems experienced in cheesemaking were associated with the production of reliable bulk starter. The lactic acid bacteria are susceptible to attack by phages which may be introduced by dust or may be carried in a lysogenic bacterial host. Once introduced, phage can build up rapidly leading to a sudden failure of fermentation. In a large factory this can cause serious problems because of the rapid accumulation of labile raw material which cannot be processed. Usually phage-resistant variants will be present which will continue to grow and ferment in due course. Often these are slower growing than the original strain and in any case the delay is usually unacceptable. There are large numbers of different phage strains and a bacterial strain which acquires resistance to one will not be resistant to others so resistant strains do not appear to offer a simple solution. The answer lies in good microbiological practice to avoid introducing infection, in growing up starter cultures in medium low in calcium which does not support phage multiplication and in the rotation of starter culture strains. Phage strains are highly host specific so a build up of one phage strain can be overcome by switching to a different culture: rotations involving as many as ten strains are sometimes advocated.

Rather than producing their own starters, many cheese manufacturers prefer to use the commercially prepared cultures which have been available for some years. Freeze-dried cultures suffer from low viabilities and need to be subcultured on sterile skim milk two or three times to produce sufficiently active material for addition to the fermenting vat. Concentrated cell suspensions containing up to 10^{11} cells/ml, neutralised to ph 6.0 and rapidly frozen to −196°C, are a more recent development. They can be stored for months at −46°C without loss of viability and, because of the very high viable counts, they can be used for addition direct to the fermentation vat. Depending upon the viable count and the time allowed for fermentation, a starter culture equivalent to 0.5−1.0% of the milk is added.

Enzymes

As the milk pH drops, calcium and phosphate are leached from the casein micelles and precipitation of casein begins below about pH 5.2. When the acidity of the milk has developed to the required degree, chymosin is added. Chymosin is an acidic aspartyl protease which attacks casein micelles in a highly-specific manner, predominately at the bond between phe_{105} and met_{106} of the κ-subunit. This releases a small soluble peptide and destabilises the casein micelles. The individual casein subunits are insoluble and precipitation, already started by the drop in pH, is completed very rapidly. Stirring, cutting and heating, which are normal parts of the cheesemaking process, are needed to complete the aggregation of casein and expulsion of the whey.

Despite its very rapid action on one specific peptide bond, chymosin is able to attack the remainder of the casein structure only at a very low rate so the curd structure is not degraded. Chymosin is obtained only from the lining of the fourth stomach of the unweaned (bovine) calf and may be used in varying degrees of purity. Lipases present in impure preparations can contribute to flavour development. Due to increased yields of milk per cow, the number of calves slaughtered has decreased: between 1960 and 1980 the number killed in the U.S. fell from 8 million to 4 million per annum while cheese production increased by 47%.

The resulting shortage of chymosin has led to a search for alternative sources of enzyme. Other proteases are less suitable because of their lower specificity. This can conveniently be expressed in terms of the ratio of activity in a coagulation assay to that in a proteolytic assay. Chymosin has a value of 1.4; that for bovine pepsin is 0.04. A high non-specific protease activity weakens the curd structure and produces undesirable flavour changes due to increased levels of amino acids some of which, notably aspartic acid, histidine and tryptophan, have bitter tastes. Proteases with clotting activity from bacterial sources (*Bacillus subtilis*, *B. mesentericus*, *B. polymyxa*), have proved to be unsuitable for most purposes because of their high non-specific proteolytic activity, causing body defects and bitter tastes.

More success has been obtained with fungal enzymes. Preparations from *Mucor miehei* and *M. pusillus* have fairly high clotting to protease activity ratios (about 0.5); the former is generally preferred because its calcium requirements for activity are similar to those of chymosin, whereas the latter enzyme requires higher levels. Both enzymes are heat stable and persist in the whey, limiting its usefulness for other purposes. Recently heat-labile *Mucor* rennins have become available and are being used successfully. Another fungal enzyme, from *Endothia parasitica*, has a rather lower clotting to protease activity ratio (0.15) but can be used for cheese making with a 50°C heat treatment step which inactivates it and prevents excessive general proteolysis. Bovine calf chymosin has been produced on a small scale by cloning into *Escherichia coli* but has not been used for cheese production presumably due to the difficulties of gaining public acceptance for a cloned product as well as the expense of convincing regulatory authorities of its safety.

Bovine chymosin still commands a substantial price advantage over the substitutes. Burgess and Shaw[8] quoted the price of chymosin as £4.05 ($6.50)/litre, whereas rennins from other mammals sold for prices between $2.85 ($4.56) and £3.35 ($5.36)/litre. Microbial rennets sold for the equivalent of £2.50 ($4.00)–£2.70 (4.32)/litre. However, since 2.5 litres of enzyme is sufficient to convert 10 m^3 of milk to one tonne of cheese, the price of the enzyme amounts only to 0.75% about that of the milk so there is little cost advantage in using a cheap enzyme preparation.

Additives

Other additives are used. Calcium chloride may be added to adjust the level of calcium ion which is important for chymosin activity. In the preparation of some cheeses, e.g. Edam and Gouda, sodium or potassium nitrate may be added at about 200 p.p.m. to inhibit the growth of *Clostridium butyricum* or *C. tyrobutyricum*. Some worries have been expressed about this practice in view of the known reactions of nitrate with amines and amino acids to form nitrosamines. The dangers do not appear to be great, however, because nitrosamine levels in the cheeses concerned are low or undetectable. Colour in cheese is an impórtant factor determining consumer acceptance and, since the levels of milk pigments are variable, pigments such as b-carotene may be added. Lipases may also be added at this stage.

Maturation

Some proteolysis is essential during maturation to bring about the required change in texture from the springy curd to the inelastic cheese. A major part of this effect is due to the breakdown of the α_{s1} subunit of casein which, by forming strong interactions with other casein subunits, is responsible for much of the elasticity of the curd. Generalised casein breakdown causes the development of increased brittleness as maturation proceeds. In the later stages of proteolysis, the release of amino acids and peptides brings about flavour changes and assists the nutrition of the secondary bacterial and/or fungal flora which is in turn responsible for further changes in flavour and texture. More than 200 potential flavour components have been identified in cheeses. Chymosin, initially very specific in its effect, contributes to the generalised proteolysis during maturation. Low concentrations of free fatty acids also play a part in the flavour development occurring during maturation; Italian hard cheeses (Romana, Parmesan) depend on the formation of very high levels of free fatty acids for their characteristic flavours. These are achieved either by using crude chymosin preparations containing lipase or by adding lipase preparations. Blue cheeses achieve high fatty acid levels by the action of lipases produced by the lipolytic fungi inoculated into the milk.

Process Operations

After any necessary pretreatment which may include warming, cooling standing and aeration, the milk is brought to the require temperature (20–35°C) and the starter culture is added. A holding period of perhaps two hours to permit acid formation is followed by the addition of chymosin solution; coagulation normally occurs within 10–15 minutes. The curds are then cut into cubes (3–12 mm) by horizontal and vertical wire knives to aid the expulsion of whey and stirred to increase the rate of moisture expulsion and to prevent the cubes sticking together. Cooking to expel more of the whey is achieved by heating the vat via a steam jacket. The temperature will depend upon the final moisture content required and may be 38°C for hard cheese and up to 52°C for Swiss cheese; soft cheese may be uncooked. Whey is removed by pumping it off or by removing the curds to special draining vats. Pressing to expel more whey may be omitted for soft cheeses: pressures up to 170 kPa are applied to hard cheeses such as Cheddar. If required, salt is added either by applying it to the surface or by dipping the cheese in brine until sufficient penetration has taken place. Finally, the cheese is matured at 4–15°C for periods ranging from weeks to years. The development of flavour and texture continues right up to the point of consumption.

Final Products

The final cheese will contain 32–80% water, 0.8–2.1% lactic acid and 0.5–6.0% salt, and will range in pH from 4.7 to 5.1. Ten litres of milk produce 1 kg cheese and nine litres of whey which contain about 96% of the milk lactose, 22% of the protein, 14% of the fat and 74% of the minerals. Around four million tonnes of whey are produced annually. As a waste product it is a substantial nuisance because its high biochemical oxygen demand will normally preclude discharge in an untreated form. It can be used to produce lactose, whey proteins, single-cell-protein, ethanol and, in the Soviet Union, is used for the production of "Bodrost", a type of beer.

Ultrafiltration

An alternative to the traditional process for separating curds and whey is to use one based on ultrafiltration as in the French MMV process. Whole or skim milk is applied under a pressure of 3.4 kg/cm^2 to a supported cellulose acetate or polysulphone membrane with a molecular weight cut-off at around 20,000 daltons. The permeate contains most of the lactose, non-protein nitrogen, salts and water: the retentate is a plastic fluid containing the fat and protein at about five times the concentration in milk. Starter culture, together with chymosin, salt, pigment and fungal spores is injected into the fluid and curd formation occurs within five minutes. The advantages claimed for this process are: greater yields due to the incorporation of non-casein proteins which would otherwise be lost in the whey, a reduced requirement for chymosin and waste product with a neutral pH. The potential for continuous operation is also much higher. This process is used in Europe for the production of soft acid cheeses such as Camembert, Feta and St Paulin.

Variations in the Product

The considerable variety of cheeses produced is due mainly to differences in the following:

(i) Type, quality and treatment of milk.
(ii) Type and quantity of starter.
(iii) Type and amount of enzyme.
(iv) Secondary microbial flora.
(v) Timing and extent of whey expulsion.
(vi) Degree of heat treatment.
(vii) Maturation conditions: temperature, humidity, time.
(viii) Salt content.

YOGHURT

Yoghurt is an acidified food produced by heating milk and fermenting it with lactic acid bacteria. It is believed to have originated amongst nomadic people in the Middle East where, due to the subtropical climate, milk turns sour and coagulates within a few hours of milking. Using simple empirical techniques it is possible to prevent putrefaction and to encourage bacterial action to produce a product with a pleasant acid taste which will last for a few days. On storage of yoghurt in animal skins water evaporates, leading to the production of concentrated yoghurts with increased concentration of solids (12–13% to 25%) and of lactic acid (1.5% to 2.0%) and a life of about two weeks. Further improvements in stability can be achieved by techniques which include drying in the sun, smoking over a fire, pressing to expel moisture, addition of salt and storage in olive oil. A food known as "khishk" is produced by adding wheat flour, semolina or parboiled wheat to yoghurt, shaping it into rolls and drying in the sun. A variety of products is produced in this way in Iran, Iraq, The Lebanon, Syria and Turkey, some of which keep almost indefinitely.

It has been claimed that yoghurt has remarkable health-giving properties and these claims gave it a small initial market in Western countries. With the manufacture of fluit-flavoured yoghurts from 1960 onwards, and the widespread availability of domestic refrigeration which enabled ordinary yoghurt to be kept for about three weeks, yoghurt became a popular snack food with steadily increasing sales. According to figures compiled by Tamine and Robinson[9], consumption is rising steadily in all the Western countries for which data are available. In 1982 sales in the United Kingdom amounted to £120 million ($192 million), over 90% of which was ascribed to fruit-flavoured varieties.

Traditional Production Method

The traditional process for manufacture involved boiling the milk to reduce its volume by about a third. This served to sterilize the milk and increased the solids content to the point where the final product would have an acceptable consistency. After cooling, the milk was inoculated by mixing with a portion of yoghurt from a previous batch and incubated to allow bacterial growth, lactic acid production and coagulation. At the appropriate point, bacterial action was terminated by cooling.

Improved Production Methods

Current large-scale production methods incorporate a number of improvements on the traditional scheme. Preliminary treatments include filtration, standardisation and, if desired, addition of materials such as stabilizers. Milk is filtered to remove foreign particles, usually through a cloth filter. Since a pasteurisation or sterilisation stage is always included, special steps to remove bacteria are not necessary. As with cheese manufacture, milk is standardized before use to bring the content of fats and other solids within the range needed for an acceptable product and to eliminate variations in properties. Some countries specify minimum contents of total solids. In the United Kingdom, for instance, yoghurt should contain at least 8.5% non-fat solids. In practice most commercial yoghurts contain 14–15% non-fat solids because this is the range required to achieve an acceptable consistency. The concentration of non-fat solids is raised either by adding milk powder, whey powder or casein powder, by vacuum evaporation or by concentrating the milk by reverse osmosis or ultrafiltration.

The fat content of milk is likely to be in the range 3.7–4.2%, but commercial yoghurt contains about 1.5% fat (medium fat) or 0.5% fat (low fat). Adjustment may be performed by removing some fat by skimming or by adding skim milk. Stabilizers and emulsifiers may also be added at this stage, as permitted by local regulations. Their function is to enhance texture, viscosity and mouthfeel. Examples of the materials used are plant gums, cellulose derivatives, seaweed extracts, cereal starches and gelatin.

In the next step, milk is homogenized at 50–70°C. This reduces fat globule size and denatures why proteins. As a result casein micelles interact with the oil globules and the whey proteins, and milk viscosity increases.

The heat treatment is not intended to increase the solids concentration but to eliminate unwanted bacteria and to promote protein aggregation. Heating can result in either inhibitory or stimulatory effects on the growth of the starter culture, so the exact conditions are crucial. Common treatment regimes range from 30 minutes at 85°C, sufficient to kill all vegetative cells, to 16 seconds at 135°C, enough for total sterilisation.

The milk is rapidly cooled to incubation temperature and inoculated with starter culture at about 2% by volume. Incubation is at 42–45°C for about 2.5 hours or at 30°C for about 18 hours. Growth of the bacteria results in the production of lactate from milk lactose. The acid destabilizes the casein micelles and, as the isoelectric point of the casein approaches, gelling takes place due to casein aggregation. Bacterial metabolism is terminated by cooling when the product reaches the desired pH value.

Yoghurt has a natural flavour due principally to lactate and carbonyl compounds such as acetaldehyde and diacetyl but most yoghurt sold in western countries is flavoured after fermentation by the addition of fruit, often supplemented with specific flavouring and colouring agents.

Starter Cultures

The starter culture consists of a mixture of *Lactobacillus bulgaricus* and *Streptococcus thermophilus* which need to be present in equal numbers. The mixed culture is used because of a symbiotic relationship between the two organisms. As a result, acid production by a mixed culture is 50% faster than by *Strep. thermophilus* alone and 100% faster than by *L. bulgaricus* alone. It is clear that *L. bulgaricus* stimulates the growth of *Strep. thermophilus* by secreting amino acids. Reports differ as to exactly which amino acids are important, probably because of differences in the amino acid composition of milk samples used by different investigators. *Strep. thermophilus* also produces a growth stimulator for *L. bulgaricus*: formic acid is responsible for all or part of this effect. The possibility is under consideration of using *Strep. thermophilus* in pure culture and supplementing the milk with a source of amino acids such as casein hydrolyzate.

Starting with a laboratory culture several stages are necessary to obtain enough volume of active bulk starter to inoculate the production vessels. A 2% inoculum volume is normal at each stage so the use of four cultures of increasing volumes is common. *Strep. thermophilus* is more acid-sensitive than *L. bulgaricus* and care must be taken to prevent imbalance due to excessive acid formation at any stage.

Cultures can be maintained for about three months in litmus milk medium under refrigeration provided that the lactate concentration is below 0.85%. Freeze-dried cultures can now retain viability for long periods but show a long lag phase on regeneration and require at least two subcultures before use. However, concentrated freeze-dried cultures are now available which can be used directly for inoculation of bulk starter cultures. These may eliminate the need for trained microbiologists. Some success has been reported with culture preservation by spray drying but this technique has not been widely adopted. Perhaps the most successful preservation technique is freezing and storage at −196°C. Again the present usage is for inoculating the bulk starter culture, but the ultimate aim is to be able to inoculate the yoghurt directly with frozen culture.

FOODS FERMENTED WITH SALT

Many food materials other than milk have traditionally been preserved by microbial fermentation. Some examples are given in Table 2. Fermentation of these foods usually involves representatives of the lactic acid bacteria which lower the pH by production of lactic acid, often together with yeasts. Salt is added before the fermentation. This inhibits the development of toxin-producers such as *Clostridium botulinum* and *Staphylococcus aureus* and selects for harmless fermenting organisms. With soybean-based foods, the growth of fungi is often encouraged before the fermentation in order to produce amylases and proteases to degrade the food reserves of the bean, to soften the structure and to improve the flavour.

Soy Sauce

Soy sauce is a dark-brown, salty tasting liquid with a pleasant aroma. It is used as a seasoning agent in food preparation and

Table 2
Examples of Fermented Foods

	Raw Material	Principle Microorganisms
Soy Sauce	Soybeans, wheat	*Aspergillus oryzae* *Pediococcus soyae* *Saccharomyces rouxii* *Torulopsis* spp.
Tempeh	Soybeans	*Rhizopus* spp.
Miso	Soybean paste, rice	*A. oryzae* *A. soyae* *P. halophilus* *Saccharomyces rouxii* *Torulopsis* spp. *Streptococcus faecalis*
Natto	Boiled soybeans	*Bacillus subtilis*
Sufu (Chinese cheese)	Soybean cubes	*Actinomucor elegans*
Ang Khak (Chinese red rice)	Rice	*Monascus purpureus*
Gari (Nigeria)	Cassava	*Candida* spp. *Leuconostoc* spp.
Idli (India)	Rice, black gumbeans	*L. mesenteroides* *Streptococcus faecalis* *P. cerevisiae*
Kenkey (Ghana)	Corn	*Saccharomyces* spp. *Leuconostoc* spp.
Fermented fish	Cooked fish strips	*Aspergillus* spp.
Olives	Olives	*Pediococcus* spp. *Streptococcus* spp.
Pickles	Cucumbers	*Lactobacillus* spp.
Sauerkraut	Cabbage	*Lactobacillus* spp. *Leuconostoc* spp.

as a condiment. Originating in China, its use is now widespread in Oriental countries and in the West. Japan is the largest producer and manufactured about 1 billion litres in 1974.

The main starting materials are soybeans and roast wheat. Traditionally, whole soybeans were used but the sauce is now usually made from defatted flakes or meal. The material is washed, soaked for several hours with frequent changes of water, and steamed for several hours at 10 p.s.i. steam pressure or for shorter periods at higher pressure. The other main raw material is wheat. This is roasted to improve the flavour and colour, and coarsely crushed. The grain is cultured with fungus to produce an enzyme rich intermediate known as "koji".

The fungal starter culture is grown on rice or on soybeans, wheat and wheat bran. Polished rice is soaked overnight, steamed, mixed with wood ash as a source of nutrients and inoculated with spores of *Aspergillus oryzae* or a portion of a previous koji culture. The inoculated rice is spread on trays in layers about 1.5 cm deep, covered with damp cloths to maintain humidity and incubated at 30°C for five days. Lactic acid bacteria and bacilli also grow and the pH drops. The starter may be used at once, or dried intact and stored, or fungal spores and bacterial cells may be separated from the mass and dried.

Fungal inoculum is first blended with the wheat and the soybean is then added. Usually approximately equal weights of each of the two starting materials are taken. The water content of the mix is about 45%. As in the preparation of the inoculum, the mixture is incubated in shallow layers at 25–30°C covered with damp cloths. Stirring and turning is necessary at intervals to prevent the internal temperature from rising, to permit air to enter, and to prevent uneven distribution of moisture. After about 72 hours the koji turns dark green, indicating that it is mature. Recently automated processes have been developed for inoculating and mixing koji in large shallow vats in enclosed rooms with supplies of filtered air. The koji is rich in enzymes, especially amylases and proteases, which will continue to act during the fermentation stage.

When mature, the koji is transferred to deep wooden vats or concrete tanks and mixed with 1.1–1.2 volumes of brine to bring the salt concentration to 17–19%. Yeasts and bacteria are usually present, but mixtures of pure cultures are often added to speed the process and ensure the production of desirable flavours. Lactic acid bacteria such as *Pediococcus soyae* and *Lactobacillus delbrueckii* produce acid, yeasts such as *S. rouxii*, *Hansenula* spp. and *Torulopsis* spp. produce ethanol while *Bacillus subtilis* and other bacteria reduce turbidity and improve flavour. Fermentation is allowed to proceed for 6–12 months or even longer; at intervals the mash is aerated to discourage the growth of anaerobes.

When the brine fermentation is complete, the mash is pressed to separate the liquid, the raw soy sauce, from the cake which is used as animal feed. In the traditional process using tne entire soybean, the liquid separates into two layers. The lower layer is the soy sauce proper; the upper layer, a waste product known as "soy sauce oil", consisting mainly of esterified long chain fatty acids, is removed and discarded. The raw soy sauce is pasteurized at 70–80°C, filtered and bottled. Where permitted, preservatives such as benzoic acid or its derivatives are added.

The final product contains about 180 g/l sodium chloride, 15 g/l ethanol and 12 g/l glutamic acid. Sugars, sugar alcohols, nucleic acid bases and various organic acids are present in lower concentrations. The specific gravity is about 1.18 and the pH is in the range 4.6–4.8. About one tonne of defatted soybean, one tonne of wheat and one tonne of salt are required to produce 5,000 litres of soy sauce.

CITRIC ACID

Citric acid was originally crystallised from lemons in 1784 and this remained the source for some time, with Italy supplying the bulk of the fruit. In 1923 Pfizer started production in the U.S. using *Aspergillus niger* growing in surface culture on a sucrose-salts medium. Several processes for synthetic production have been described but none is able to compete with the fermentation product which now accounts for about 99% of production, the remainder being derived from lemons and pineapple wastes. The reduction in price after the near-monopoly of the Italian government was broken was followed by substantial increases in production which rose from 5,000 tonnes in 1929 to its current level of 300,000–400,000 tonnes per annum. In the West, production is dominated by a few companies and there is a substantial excess capacity. New producers are unlikely to enter the market except in countries where substantial quantities of very cheap feedstock are available locally.

Citric acid is used mainly as a flavouring agent in the production of food, especially jams and confectionery, and in soft drinks. It is an efficient metal chelator and this property leads to a wide variety of industrial, pharmaceutical and food uses. It is used as a cleaning and pickling agent for metals, to keep metals in solution for electroplating and in agriculture, to control the density of clay suspensions by regulating swelling and as a replacement for polyphosphates in the detergent industry. It acts as a blood anticoagulant and is used as an antioxidant in foods. Food, confectionery and beverages account for 75% of consumption, industrial uses for 15% and the remainder is used in the pharmaceutical industry.

The competitive market situation has led to secrecy amongst manufacturers and reliable details of the processes used are somewhat sparse. There is also a lack of agreement on the details of the underlying biochemistry. Part of this is due to some workers failing to appreciate the need to control exactly the levels of metal ions in the media. Others have worked with low-yielding strains and their conclusions may not apply to the highly selected industrial strains.

Biochemistry

The biochemical mechanism of citric acid production is based on the use of *Aspergillus niger*, an aerobic organism. Sugars are oxidized via glycolysis and the tricarboxylic acid cycle. Citrate, formed as an early intermediate in the cycle by condensation of acetyl coenzyme A and oxaloacetate, is normally oxidized by the later steps in the cycle. To induce the accumulation of useful amounts of citrate, its oxidation must be minimized without affecting its formation. During citrate accumulation, the activity of condensing enzyme rises whilst that of aconitase, responsible for the first stage of citrate metabolism in the tricarboxylic acid cycle, disappears. Addition of manganese reduces citrate yield and results in the production of aconitase.

One high-yielding mutant was found to lack the normal regulatory mechanism by which citrate inhibits phophofructokinase, thus controlling its own synthesis. Oxaloacetate is normally regenerated from citrate so during citrate accumulation it must be formed from pyruvate by an anaplerotic reaction catalysed by pyruvate carboxylase (Figure 8). Side reactions of citrate, leading to the formation of oxalate or itaconate must be minimized. Low levels of phosphate, control of pH and strain selection all help to prevent this.

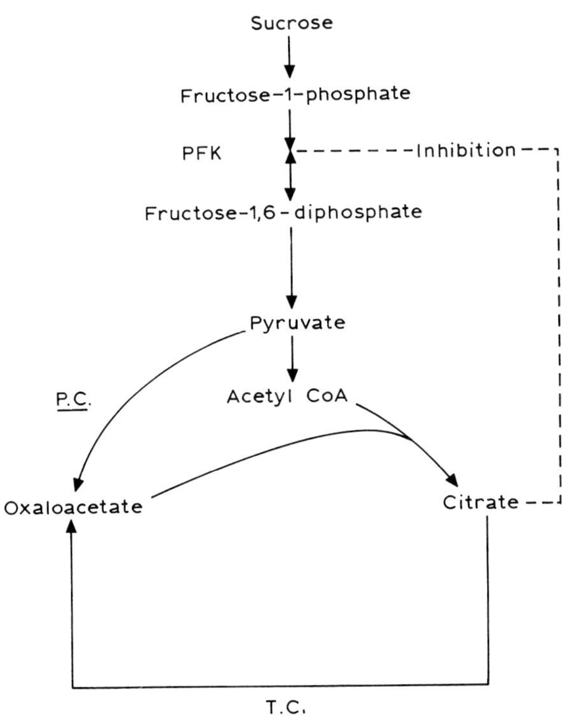

Figure 8. Key reactions in the accumulation of citric acid.
P.C. = Pyruvate carboxylase.
P.F.C. = Phosphofructokinase.
T.C. = Tricarboxylic acid cycle.

It has been widely reported that citrate does not accumulate in quantity unless the levels of several metal ions (copper, iron, magnesium, manganese, molybdenum and zinc) are kept below certain levels. In one experiment the addition of 1 ppb manganese to purified molasses reduced the yield of citrate by 10%. Media are purified by precipitating metals with ferrocyanide or calcium hexacyanoferrate, or by ion exchange. Preculture media must also have controlled levels of ions as sufficient manganese to affect yield can be carried over in a spore inoculum. The corrosive nature of citric acid, and the sensitivity of the fermentation to metals, dictate the use of resistant materials such as high-grade stainless steel or linings of glass, rubber or resin for the construction of fermentation plant. To obtain good yields, growth and sporulation must be restricted: limitation by either phosphate or nitrogen can be used.

More recently, the production of citric acid by yeasts has been reported, using either sugars or n-alkanes as substrates. In the latter case oxalocetate is regenerated from acetyl coenzyme A by the glyoxylate bypass. Yields of 700–900 g citric acid monohydrate per kilogram of carbohydrate used have been claimed. The theoretical yield on a weight basis is 118% from glucose or 124% from sucrose, so these figures correspond to the conversion of up to about 75% of the sugar into product.

Surface Mat Culture

The original culture method, growing *A. niger* in surface culture on liquid medium, is still in use and, in 1981, was estimated to account for 20% of world production of citric acid. The medium, based on beet molasses because low yields are obtained with cane molasses, contains 150–200 g/l sugar and is supplemented with ammonium nitrate and other salts. It is adjusted to pH 5–7 as spores will not germinate on a more acid molasses medium, probably due to the presence of acetic acid. Trays of high purity aluminium or stainless steel, held on racks in a ventilated chamber at 30°C, are filled with medium and sterile air is blown over the surface to supply oxygen and to dissipate heat. Spores are inoculated over the surface and germinate within 24 hours to form a convuluted mat of hyphal growth. Little sporulation occurs in the absence of heavy metals. The pH falls to about 3.0 as ammonium ion is absorbed: a low pH is essential to prevent excessive formation of oxalate. Citrate accumulates mainly after the phase of rapid growth. After 7–15 days the mycelium is separated and citrate recovered from the liquor. Oxalate and gluconate are formed as by-products: their formation is minimised by strain selection.

Deep Liquid Culture

The medium for deep liquid culture may be based on either cane or beet molasses. The initial pH is 5–7 with molasses-based medium but, if the carbohydrate source is glucose or fructose, the pH can be lower to help inhibit contaminants. The initial growth phase is critical: suitable hyphal morphology has been described as short and stubby, forked and bulbous, with aggregation into small pellets (0.2–0.5 mm). Inoculum may be grown in the presence of cyanide to help ensure that the morphology is correct. One volume of inoculum is added to ten volumes of medium.

During production the pH drops rapidly and is controlled between 1.5 and 2.8. Below this range growth is slow, above it less citrate and more oxalate are formed. Temperature is kept above 28°C to speed metabolism but below 33°C to minimise oxalate formation. Oxygen demand is high and the oxygen tension must not be allowed to fall below 20% saturation: air is supplied at 0.2 vol/vol of liquid/min. Substantial amounts of foam are formed and may occupy 30% of the vessel despite the addition of antifoam. Fermenters are either stirred and aerated tanks fitted with baffles or tower fermenters relying on air bubbles to achieve mixing, with volumes up to 220 m^3. Fermentation temperature is 30°C. As with surface culture, citrate formation occurs during a slow growth phase (idiophase) following rapid growth, the fermentation taking about eight days.

Yeast

A series of patents from 1968 onwards described the use of yeast strains for the production of citric acid. Eight genera were mentioned but *Candida* spp. were preferred, principally *C. guilliermondi*, *C. oleophila* and *C. lipolytica*. The last of these species is able to grow and produce citrate at the expense of low molecular weight alkanes. The main advantages claimed for the use of yeast rather than *Aspergillus* were tolerance of high initial sugar concentrations (a Pfizer patent dated 1974 describes the use of an osmophilic yeast which could grow and produce citrate on sugar concentrations up to 280 g/l), faster fermentation rates and insensitivity to heavy metals in the medium. Tower fermenters were suitable for the fermentation which took 4–5 days at 25–37°C. It was important not to ler the pH drop too low; calcium carbonate was added for pH control. A plant built by Pfizer in the U.S. was designed to use either type of substrate; after a brief period operating on n-alkane it switched to carbohydrate.

The operation of an Italian plant owned by Liquichimica was described in 1977. The medium was based on n-alkanes and a mutant strain of *C. lipolytica* was used with a low level of aconitase to minimize further metabolism of citrate. A 72 hour batch cycle was employed in 400 m^3 stirred and aerated tanks. Three phases were distinguished: rapid yeast growth occurred in the first, the bulk of the citrate formation in the the second slow citrate production until substrate was exhausted in the third. A yield of over 130% by weight was claimed. Removal of the yeast by centrifugation left an almost clear broth. The plant with a capacity of 50,000 tonnes per annum operated for a short time and then closed. Fears that oil-derived carcinogens might contaminate the product led to the abandonment of the B.P. plant to make single cell protein from n-alkanes in Sicily and similar considerations, together with the increasing cost of n-alkane substrates, were presumably responsible for the closure of the Liquichimica citric acid plant.

Product Recovery

The classical method of recovering citric acid is by precipitation as the calcium salt after removing the mycelium by filtration. The broth is heated and, if necessary, treated with calcium hydroxide at low pH to remove any oxalate; after neutralization, the addition of more calcium hydroxide precipitates calcium citrate. This is filtered hot to minimize the solubility of calcium citrate, washed and decomposed by addition of sulphuric acid. Many of the impurities are removed by this stage and further purification is achieved by filtration, treatment with active charcoal and passage through ion exchange columns. After concentration under vacuum, citric acid is crystallized. The monohydrate is obtained below 36°C; above this temperature the anhydrous product is formed. The major waste products are calcium sulphate and the broth supernatant which, if molasses-based medium is used, has a high biochemical oxygen demand.

As an alternative citric acid may be removed from the culture broth by solvent extraction with butan-2-ol, or with tributyl phosphate containing kerosene, and stripping the solvent with hot water. This is not suitable if the medium contains molasses as impurities are extracted.

ACETONE AND BUTANOL

Acetone and butanol are both important bulk chemicals with a variety of industrial uses. Acetone is used as a solvent and a starting point for chemical syntheses. Butanol is used as a paint solvent, in hydraulic fluids, plasticizers and for the extraction of antibiotics from culture broths.
Clostridium acetobutylicum and some related organisms can ferment glucose with the production of acetone and butanol as major end products. The production of butanol by bacteria was discovered by Pasteur and that of acetone by Fernbach. A German patent for industrial production was taken out in 1913 by Bayer & Co. Chaim Weizmann, working at the University of Manchester, developed the fermentation to the point where industrial production was possible and it was

used in Britain during World War I for the production of acetone for the manufacture of cordite. Acetone produced by the pyrolysis of wood had previously been imported into Britain from Austria or the U.S. War against Germany and Austria, and the resulting submarine blockade of transatlantic shipping, generated pressure for an alternative source of supply. During the war butanol was largely a waste product. Afterwards, as the demand for acetone decreased, butanol became the principal product due to its usefulness as a solvent for the nitrocellulose paints used in the motor industry and plants were built in many countries especially the U.S. The development of cheaper petrochemical-based manufacture, first from ethylene and later from propylene, together with a rise in the cost of molasses, rendered fermentation economically non-viable and it is now practised only by National Chemical Products (NCP) in South Africa where its survival depends both on political restrictions on the supply of crude oil to that country and on the ready availability of molasses as substrate. The process has been described by Spivey.[10]

Culture Development

Cl. acetobutylicum ferments starch to give butanol, acetone and ethanol (6:3:1 by weight), together with carbon dioxide and hydrogen, as the major end products (Figure 9). The strains used by NCP are direct descendants of Weizmann's original strain. Initially developed to use corn (maize) as substrate, they have invertase activity and can grow on molasses without pretreatment unlike many of the early commercial strains. Corn is now too expensive for use in the fermentation and the medium is based on cane molasses.

Weizmann observed that solvent production is related to sporulating ability and was able to isolate highly productive strains by repeated cycles of heat-shocking, germination and sporulation, a method which is still used. A culture grown on potato/glucose medium is grown at 34°C for 48 hours, heat shocked for 90 seconds at 70°C and inoculated into fresh medium. After 3–4 days incubation to allow growth and sporulation, portions are transferred to sterile sand or soil and allowed to dry. In this state they remain viable for many years. The inoculum is grown up in four stages. The first stage is inoculated using spores which have been heat-shocked to stimulate germination and allowed to stand for a few hours to permit outgrowth. These are grown for 12 hours in 150 ml of potato/glucose medium. The next three stages are grown on molasses and produce culture volumes of 500 ml (6 hours), 3,500 ml (6 hours) and 27 litres (9 hours), respectively. The entire volume of each culture is transferred to the succeding stage. The morphology (cell length, cell width, chain formation and motility) changes at each stage of inoculum development and during the main fermentation; the changes are sufficiently reproducible to serve as a valuable guide to the progress of the fermentation. For reasons which are not understood the development of vigorous motility at the first stage is a particularly important sign and if this fails solvent yields will be poor.

Production

Twelve fermenters are used, each of 90,000 litres capacity. They are unstirred cylinders with hemispherical ends to withstand pressure differences. Fermentations are started at three hour intervals, fermentation proper takes about 36 hours and emptying, cleaning, sterilizing and filling extend the complete cycle time to 48 hours. Sterilisation of vessels and pipework is by steam: after sterilisation, the vessel is flushed with carbon dioxide. This is used to maintain a positive pressure at all stages of the fermentation to help exclude air and contaminants and to flush the medium before inoculation to remove traces of oxygen. The medium is based on molasses

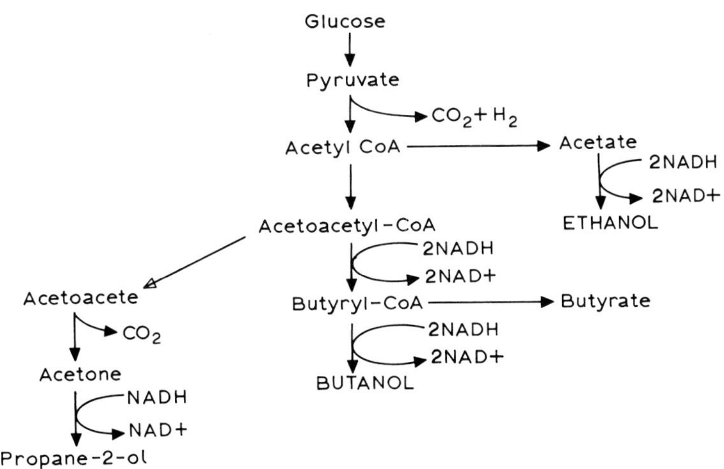

Figure 9. Outline Scheme of Reactions in Solvent Fermentations by Clostridium spp.

adjusted in concentration to give 60–65 g/l fermentable sugars, the highest concentration which can be fermented, with additions of corn steep liquor to supply nitrogen and growth stimulants, and calcium carbonate to help regulate pH. Sterilisation is performed by raising the temperature to 128°C for four minutes using steam injection in conjunction with a heat exchanger and holding vessel.

The medium is cooled to 34°C before transfer to a fermenter. Liquid ammonia is introduced to adjust the pH and as an additional source of nitrogen. Three distinct phases are evident in the fermentation. Up to about 18 hours there is a slow fall in pH down to about 5.0 as organic acids are produced; this fall in pH appears to be necessary to trigger off the second stage. The pH then rises gradually as acids are converted to solvents. In the final phase, from about 27–36 hours, the pH remains steady at about 5.8.

Gas (hydrogen and carbon dioxide in equal proportions) and solvents are produced at an increasing rate throughout most of the first two phases; production peaks at about 27 hours and declines rapidly in the last phase. The final solvent consists of n-butanol: acetone: ethanol in 6:3:1 ratio by weight, at a total concentration of 20 g/l. The maximum concentration is set by butanol toxicity. Solvent accounts for 30% of the sugar fermented, carbon dioxide for 50% and hydrogen for 2%.

Solvents are recovered by a five-stage distillation process. Carbon dioxide is separated from hydrogen by absorption in potassium carbonate solution and, after purification, is sold as bulk gas or as dry ice; the hydrogen, together with some carbon dioxide, is vented to the atmosphere. The stillage, which contains high concentrations of vitamins, is combined with stillage from ethanol fermentations conducted on the same site and dried before incorporating into various animal feed products. It is estimated that 97% by weight of the fermentation waste is sold in this form.

GLYCEROL

Glycerol has a wide variety of industrial uses but is not now produced by fermentation. Current methods involve chemical synthesis from propane or propanol, or the saponification of fats. During World War I the German explosives industry was short of glycerol because of the British naval blockade so for a brief period production by microbiological means was important.

It had been observed earlier that, if yeast fermentations were buffered to above pH 7.0 by addition of sodium carbonate, a Cannizaro reaction (dismutation) resulted, yielding one molecule of ethanol and one of acetic acid from two acetaldehyde molecules. The balanced production of reduced and oxidized products required no NADH. Each glucose molecule passing through the glycolytic sequence produced two molecules of reduced NADH so the latter was available for the reduction of dihydroxyacetone phosphate to glycerol phosphate; glycerol was formed from this by hydrolysis (Figure 1).

Alkaline yeast fermentations proved very prone to contamination so sodium sulphate, a well-known inhibitor of bacterial growth, was used instead of sodium carbonate. In the presence of carbon dioxide this gave rise to sodium bicarbonate and sodium bisulphate; the latter forms an addition compound with acetaldehyde making it unavailable for reduction to ethanol and so forcing the production of glycerol. The theoretical yield of this process is one glycerol molecule per glucose utilized; in practice, due to incomplete inhibition of the normal fermentation and to poor recovery of glycerol from the fermentation broth, yields were only about half this quantity.

PURIFICATION OF SEWAGE AND ORGANIC WASTES FROM AGRICULTURE AND INDUSTRY

It has been claimed that public health in the industrialized nations is more dependent upon the efforts of the water purification engineer than on those of the medical profession. In terms of volume, sewage purification is the largest industry involving the application of microorganisms. World wide figures are not available but Dunnhill (1981) estimated that, in the United Kingdom, 6×10^9 tonnes of water are purified per annum, amounting to over 100 tonnes per head of the population. In 1982 it was estimated that the capital cost of providing purification in plant in the United Kingdom was £100–200 ($160–320) per head of population served. Expenditure on sewage purification continues to rise due to population growth and especially because of increased standards of environmental quality. In the U.S. total spending on pollution control between 1976 and 1986 was estimated at $\$4 \times 10^{11}$. From any point of view the industry is one of substantial importance.

Reasons for Purification

Most sewage is discharged into rivers or the sea where adverse effects can be caused by four types of component:

(i) readily oxidizable organic compounds
(ii) solids in suspension
(iii) toxic materials like ammonia, and in the case of industrial effluents, heavy metals and toxic organic compounds such as phenol.
(iv) pathogenic bacteria and viruses.

Microbiological methods of water treatment can reduce the concentration of all four components.

If an organic waste is discharged into water, oxidation by aerobic bacteria causes rapid depletion of dissolved oxygen leading to the death of fish and other aerobic organisms. Suspended solids can be deposited in a layer over a river bed and change the ecology. Treatment of sewage is designed principally to lower the content of organic materials, and of suspended solids, to levels which can be dealt with by normal biological processes without adverse side effects. Many industrial wastes have high concentrations of organic compounds e.g. those from dairies, slaughterhouses, breweries, wineries and distilleries. They are usually much more concentrated than domestic sewage and may present special problems for handling.

Treatment to remove organic compounds also leads to a substantial decrease in the numbers of pathogenic organisms and to the removal of ammonia by conversion to nitrate or gaseous nitrogen. If the water is to be recycled for domestic purposes nitrate itself is undesirable in high concentrations because it reacts with haemoglobin and is especially toxic to young children. Some removal of heavy metals and toxic organic components also takes place but substantial concentrations of these components will require specialized treatment.

Measurement of Waste Concentration

The strength of organic wastes is defined in terms of biochemical oxygen demand (BOD_5). This is measured by preparing a series of dilutions of the waste with aerated water is stoppered bottles with the addition, if necessary, of suitable bacteria. The bottles are incubated for five days in the dark at 20°C. Oxygen concentration is measured at the beginning and end of the period. In bottles still containing oxygen at the end of the incubation the quantity used is a measure of the strength of the waste. The oxidation of organic compounds is usually a first order process and is incomplete after five days. If required, the ultimate oxygen demand can be calculated from the BOD_5. Oxidation of ammonia to nitrate can cause deviations from first order kinetics: this usually occurs after the five day measurement but the effect can be detected earlier if nitrifying bacteria are present in high concentrations. Allyl thiourea may be added to suppress nitrification and permit a determination due to carbon compounds alone.

BOD_5 measurements are intended to provide a guide to the effect of discharging a waste into a river but they take too long to be useful for immediate monitoring. Thus, for rapid results two other measurements of organic content are available: chemical oxygen demand (COD) and total organic carbon (TOC). COD measurements are made by refluxing the sample for two hours with excess acidified potassium dichromate and titrating with ferrous ammonium sulphate to determine the amount of dichromate used. TOC measurements involve the use of a dedicated instrument in which organic material is oxidized catalytically to carbon dioxide which is determined by infra-red analysis. These measurements take only a few minutes. Neither provides information on how much of the organic material is biodegradable and the values obtained normally differ substantially from BOD_5 values. For a given waste a linear relationship will apply between BOD_5 and COD or TOC, but this will differ from one waste to another. Ammonia is measured because of its toxicity to fish and because it, too, will exert an oxygen demand.

Outline of Treatment Processes

Many different ways of treating sewage are in use and this description covers only the more common. A typical scheme for purification is shown in Figure 10. On arrival at the sewage purification works, pieces of wood, rags and other foreign objects are removed by screens to prevent damage to machinery. Grit in suspension is then sedimented by lowering the linear flow rate to 0.3 m/sec. To accommodate excessive flow during wet weather, provision is made for diverting part of the flow to storm tanks whence it may be returned later for treatment or may be discharged to the river after allowing suspended solids to settle.

The sewage is next passed to primary sedimentation tanks, circular in plan. Sewage enters at the centre and liquid leaves

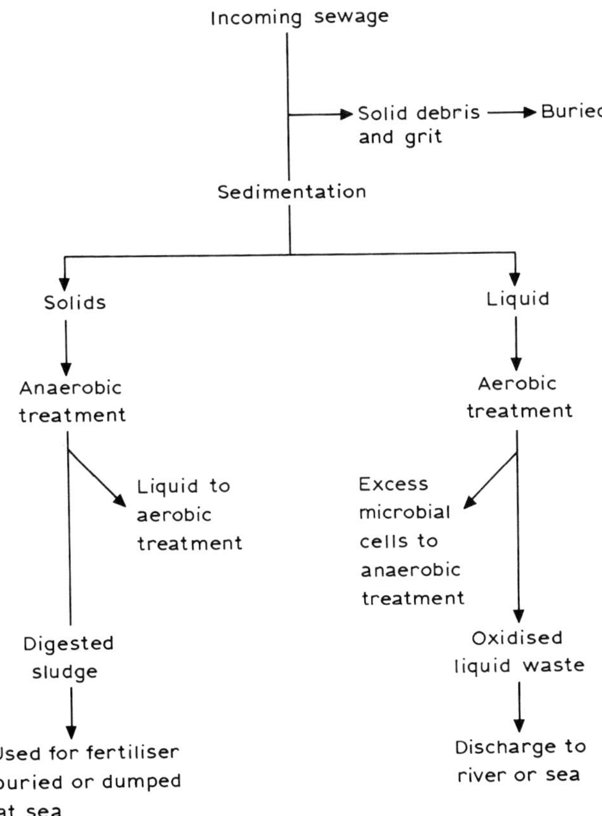

Figure 10. Outline of Typical Sewage Treatment Process.

by passing over a weir at the periphery. The very slow linear flow rates result in the sedimentation of suspended solid material which collects at the bottom and is pumped away. Up to 70% of suspended solids and 40% of BOD_5 is removed in the sludge. The supernatant liquid is treated by aerobic oxidation and the sludge by anaerobic digestion.

Secondary treatment follows, comprising aerobic or anaerobic treatment or a combination of the two. Anaerobic digestion produces a refractory sludge which is relatively harmless and unobjectionable. This is disposed of by burial or by dumping at sea or, provided its heavy metal content is not excessive, by use as a fertilizer. If necessary, a tertiary treatment, consisting of detention in a lagoon for up to 50 hours or passage through a sand or gravel filter, may be used to bring about the final purification.

Biological Filtration

This process, also known as percolating filtration, was first used in Salford, England in 1890 and was the earliest aerobic treatment process. It is widely used today with only minor changes and is found in the majority of treatment plants in Europe and the US. In operation it is a packed bed plug flow reactor: the term "filtration" is a misnomer. Treatment is performed in circular filter beds up to 40 metres in diameter, rectangular beds being less common. A retaining wall contains the packing material which consists of pieces of stone, clinker or wood, 40–150 mm in diameter packed to a depth of 1.5–2.5 metres. Liquid waste is sprayed evenly over the surface and percolates down to be collected by drains at the bottom. Oxidation of waste is brought about by microbes which grow in a film over the surface of the support material. Most of the organic material is oxidized in the top 0.5 m layer of the filter. Further down, ammonia is oxidised to nitrate. The liquid is aerated as it is sprayed onto the surface of the filter bed and air is able to penetrate readily into the voids between the support material.

No special inoculation procedure is used. With a new filter, liquid is sprayed onto the filter bed and a population of organisms, mostly originating from the incoming waste, is built up on the surface of the support material. The population is a complex mixture of bacteria, protozoa, fungi and invertebrate animals. The bacteria are responsible for most of the oxidation. Efficient oxidation requires the penetration of air and liquid to all active parts of the system. Below the oxidation layer is a zone where little organic carbon is removed but much autotrophic nitrification occurs.

The rate at which waste can be treated is limited by the need to avoid excessive film growth which can lead to blockage of the voids. Long term operation is dependent on a rough balance between the increase in the amount of film due to growth, its removal by the gazing activities of invertebrate animals and by sloughing off of thick layers of film due to autolysis. Excessive film growth is likely to be most serious in cold weather when the grazing by invertebrates is at a minimum. It occurs at the top of the bed where nutrient concentrations are highest and leads to the accumulation of liquid on the surface. Fragments of film which break away from the support are separated by sedimentation and are usually treated in an anaerobic digester.

Excessive growth at the top of the bed can be minimized by increasing the interval between succesive applications of liquid to the filter. Normally this is sprayed onto any given position every 0.25–2 minutes. Increasing this interval to once every 5–10 minutes, and applying a correspondingly larger volume, allows nutrients to penetrate more deeply into the filter and increases the zone in which organic material is being oxidized. Very strong wastes can be dealt with by recycling the effluent to dilute the incoming waste. Another approach is to use alternating double filtration in which two filters are used in series, the order being changed at intervals of about a week. Heavy film growth occurs in the first filter which experiences nutrient rich conditions but the second filter is starved of nutrients and the amount of film decreasses due to autolysis.

Biological filters have many attractions. They are cheap and easy to maintain and operate. Plant life is very long at 30–50 years and the quantities of surplus sludge produced are small.

As an alternative to the traditional stone support, specially fabricated plastic packing has been used consisting either of randomly packed shapes or of modular sheet material. In each case the intention is to increase the surface-to-volume ratio and to provide increased voidage to assist penetration of liquid and air. Such systems permit the removal of more BOD_5 at higher rates and because of the lower density, towers up to 10 m high can be built without special structural provisions. Biological filters based on plastic support material have been widely used for the purification of high-BOD_5 industrial wastes.

Rotary Biological Contactor

The rotary biological contactor was first reported in 1929 and became commercially available in 1965. It is an attempt to increase the efficiency of biological filtration by providing a greatly increased surface area for film attachment with adequate access of both liquid and air. The apparatus consists of a series of discs, 2–3 metres in diameter, with honeycomb surfaces, mounted on a shaft. The lower part of each disc, amounting to 40% of the surface area, is immersed in a trough containing the liquid waste which flows at right angles to the disc surfaces. The discs are rotated at up to 10 revolutions per minute so that the microbial film growing on the surface is alternately in contact with air and with nutrients. Several thousands of these units are in operation.

Activated Sludge Process

The activated sludge process was first used in 1914. It differs in principle from the biological filter and similar systems in that the biomass is not attached to a surface but exists as flocs suspended in the liquid. Liquid wastes are treated by vigorous aeration in a rectangular tank with plug flow, with a transit period of 4–8 hours. The aeration tank is about 4 m deep and at least three times as long as it is broad. Aeration is by means of compressed air introduced by diffusers. As an alternative, the tank may be divided into a series of connected pockets, each of which is aerated by mechanical surface agitation.

Incoming waste is mixed with activated sludge, a complex system of bacteria and protozoa aggregated together into flocs. As it passes through the tank, organic material is oxidized by the bacteria in the sludge. The aeration tank is followed by a sedimentation tank in which the flocs of sludge settle out. Most of the sludge is returned to the aeration tank as inoculum; excess is treated by anaerobic digestion. Frequently the sludge is aerated before return to the main tank, so that food reserves are depleted and incoming waste is oxidized more vigorously. This variant is known as the "contact stabilisation process". No pure culture is used for the activated sludge process: the microbial population is selected by the composition of the incoming waste and the operating regime. The return of sediment to the oxidation tank as an inoculum applies a strong selective pressure in favour of floc-forming organisms.

An activated sludge plant can treat waste about ten times as fast as a biological filter of the same volume; capital costs and land requirements are therefore lower. On the other hand, running costs are much higher, the plant is more difficult to operate and is more sensitive to changes in the composition of incoming waste, and greater amounts of waste sludge are produced.

A variant on the conventional activated sludge process is the oxidation ditch. This originated as a simple design for rural populations but has been developed into a sophisticated system capable of achieving a good effluent quality on a large scale. The main difference from the conventional activated sludge plant is that waste is treated for a longer period (more than 15 hours). Primary sedimentation is not practised as solid waste can be effectively oxidized. The oxidation ditch consists of a long continuous channel up to 4 metres in depth. To achieve the required period of treatment, waste is circulated round the ditch and is aerated by mechanical agitation at one or more points. A minimum velocity of about 0.15 metres per second is required to keep solids in suspension. Fresh waste is continuously added at one point and treated waste removed at another. Outgoing waste is passed through a sedimentation tank to remove activated sludge, most of which is then returned to the ditch. Oxidation ditches are simple, reliable systems to operate and produce only small amounts of waste sludge.

Activated Sludge Systems Using Pure Oxygen

Activated sludge systems using pure oxygen for aeration were introduced in 1972. They employ a closed tank divided into several compartments each of which is mechanically agitated. Gaseous oxygen is introduced above the liquid, sensors being used to control the addition of further gas as required. High concentrations of active biomass can be maintained permitting short residence times and the process seems to be able to deal with high-BOD_5 wastes which can cause problems with conventional activated sludge plants.

Deep Shaft Process

The ICI deep shaft process is a development of the activated sludge process designed for high intensity treatment. Several full-scale plants are in operation. The plant (Figure 11) consists of a shaft 50–150 metres deep and up to 10 metres in diameter. An inner concentric tube acts as the downcomer and a vigorous liquid circulation is induced with a downward velocity of about 1–2 metres per second.

Liquid circulation is started by introducing compressed air into the outer (riser) tube about one third of the way down

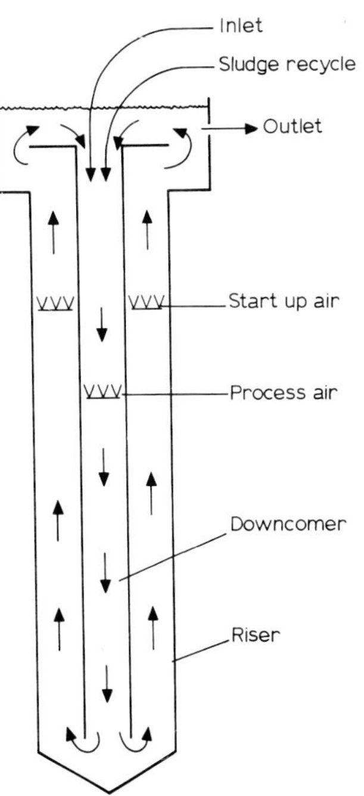

Figure 11. Deep Shaft Process for Sewage Purification.

from the top. Due to the reduced density of fluid above this point liquid rises in the outer tube and returns in the downcomer. At this stage, aeration is not efficient since air is introduced into the riser and bubbles tend to escape at the surface. Once liquid circulation is established, most of the air injection is transferred to the downcomer at a point below the injection into the riser. Because the downward liquid velocity is greater than the rate at which bubbles rise, the air is carried down and returns up the riser. Air injection takes place part way dawn the downcomer so the mean air content of the downcomer is less than that of the riser and liquid circulation is maintained by the density difference between the two columns of fluid. Little coalescence of bubbles takes place and the large bubble surface area, high turbulence and the high pressure in the lower part of the shaft result in high rates of oxygen transfer. Very high concentrations of active biomass are supported and rapid oxidation of organic material takes place, resulting in low residence times. Running costs are claimed to be low.

The main drawback of the system is that persistent microbubbles of gas remain in the liquid leaving the shaft, preventing the separation of sludge by sedimentation. The solution is to use a deep shaft plant of reduced size which removes only part of the BOD_5 load, followed by a plug flow aeration tank for the remainder of the treatment and for degassing the liquid. Sedimentation tanks can then be used to separate the sludge which may be returned to the deep shaft or sent to waste.

Fluidized Bed Processes

Fluidized bed processes can be regarded as combining the principles of biological filtration and of activated sludge processes. Biomass is grown on a support surface but this, instead of being fixed, is kept in circulation in the vessel by the injection of air or oxygen. The biomass concentrations are about five times those in a conventional activated sludge plant, reducing the size of plant required to treat a given amount of waste and, because biomass becomes firmly attached to the support material, no sedimentation stage is necessary before discharging the treated effluent.

The *Oxitron* system uses sand as the support phase and oxygen as gas phase. A proportion of the sand is allowed to leave the reactor and biomass is removed in an agitator before the sand is returned. The *Captor* system uses compressed air for aeration and plastic foam pads as the support phase. The pads are passed through a roller system to remove excess sludge. Both fluidized bed systems suffer from the disadvantage of producing large amounts of waste sludge.

Microbiology of Aerobic Processes

The microbiology of aerobic waste treatment processes is complex and is not fully understood. Most of the heterotrophic oxidation is due to bacteria and fungi, of which a number of genera are regularly present (Table 3). Species of *Zoogloea* are especially important since they secrete a polysaccharide slime which binds the microorganisms together and promotes the formation of flocs or film. The balance of organisms present is dependent upon the waste concentration and composition. Filamentous bacteria and fungi tend to be more resistant than cellular bacteria to adverse conditions. These include low dissolved oxygen concentration, major deviations from the optimum ratio between carbon, nitrogen and phosphorus, and deviations from neutral pH; they can lead to an increase in the proportions of the former groups. This causes an effect on the activated sludge process known as "sludge bulking" where, due to the failure of filamentous organisms to form dense compact flocs, the sludge fails to sediment normally, resulting in reduced biomass in the oxidation tank and a poor quality effluent.

The autotrophic genera *Nitrosomonas* and *Nitrobacter* are responsible for the oxidation of ammonia to nitrite and nitrite to nitrate. These organisms are slow-growing and are unable to compete with the heterotrophs for oxygen so, if nitrifi-

Table 3
Microorganisms in Aerobic Sewage Treatment Processes

HETEROTROPHIC BACTERIA & FUNGI	
Non-filamentous bacteria	Filamentous bacteria
Achromobacter	*Beggiatoa*
Arthrobacter	*Leptothrix*
Chromobacter	*Nocardia*
Flavobacterium	*Rhodococcus*
Zoogloea	*Sphaerotilus*
Filamentous fungi	
Ascoidea	
Fusarium	
Geotrichum	
Saprolegnia	
Subbaromyces	
AUTOTROPHIC BACTERIA	
Nitrosomonas	*Nitrobacter*
ALGAE	PROTOZOA
Cyanophyceae	*Amoeba*
Phormidium	*Aspidisca*
Oscillatoria	*Chilodonella*
Chlorophyceae	*Colpidium*
Chlorella	*Hemiophrys*
Stigeoclonium	*Opercularia*
Ulothrix	*Paramoecium*
	Stylonichia
	Trachelophylum
	Vorticella

cation is required, aeration of the waste must be continued after most of the organic carbon has been removed and sludge must be allowed to attain a mean age of at least 10 days in activated sludge processes.

Protozoans also play an important part in aerobic treatment mainly by scavenging organic detritus and bacteria; if the numbers of protozoa are reduced below normal levels, a more turbid effluent is produced with a higher BOD_5 value. Numerous invertebrate animals occur as part of the normal population of biological filters. They feed on the biological film and prevent blockage of the voids.

Although waste management concentrates on reduction of BOD_5, suspended solids and ammonia to acceptable levels an important reduction in pathogenic microorganisms is also brought about by waste treatment processes. Thus Pike and Carrington[11] examined the fate of *Salmonella, Shigella, Escherichia coli, Vibrio cholera* and enteric viruses during integrated sewage treatment procedures. In each case the number of viable organisms was substantially reduced, the reduction ranging between 90 and 99%. The content of heavy metals can also be reduced by aerobic treatment. Metals are removed principally by binding to extracellular slime[12].

Anaerobic Processes

The principal use of anaerobic digesters has been to digest sludge obtained by primary sedimentation and the waste biomass originating from aerobic treatment processes. The traditional process involves incubation of the sludge with stirring in a closed tank at 35°C. Anaerobic conditions inside the tank permit the growth of a mixed microbial population which breaks down about 50% of the organic matter, producing mainly carbon dioxide and hydrogen together with a recalcitrant sludge which is relatively inoffensive and has a reduced pathogen count. At intervals part of the digested sludge is drawn off and replaced by raw sludge.

The traditional process is unsatisfactory in two respects: it is slow (mean residence time 10–30 days), so plant costs and the requirement for space are high, and its operation is easily upset by changes in the composition of incoming waste.

Microbiology of Anaerobic Digesters

As with aerobic treatment processes, the microbial community involved in anaerobic digesters is complex. Three interdependent phases of microbial activity are recognised (Figure 12). In the first phase, involving fermentative bacteria (e.g. *Bacteroides, Clostridium, Eubacterium, Peptococcus* and *Propionibacterium*), polymers such as polysaccharides are hydrolyzed to monomers and the monomers are fermented to a variety of short chain organic acids, alcohols and esters, together with carbon dioxide and hydrogen. In the second phase acetogenic bacteria (*Peptococcus, Propionibacterium,*

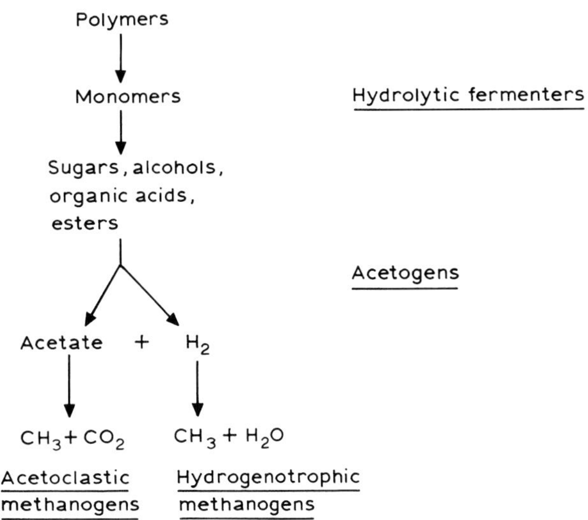

Figure 12. Phases of bacterial activity in anaerobic digestion of sewage.

Syntrophobacter and *Syntrophomonas*) convert the products of the first phase into acetic acid, hydrogen and carbon dioxide. *Desulphovibrio* changes lactate and hydrogen to acetate and sulphide. In the third phase, two distinct groups of bacteria are involved. The acetoclastic methanogens (*Methanosarcina, Methanospirillum* and *Methanothrix*) produce methane and carbon dioxide from acetate and the hydrogenotrophic methanogens (*Methanobacterium* and *Methanobrevibacterium*) produce methane from hydrogen and carbon dioxide.

The interactions between the groups of bacteria are only partially understood but the information available is useful in operating anaerobic digesters to their best advantage. The ability of the acetogens to release hydrogen requires a very low partial pressure of hydrogen (~1 Pa, 10^{-6} atm) in the medium. This is dependent on the removal of hydrogen by the hydrogenotrophic methanogens and by *Desulfovibrio*. The hydrolytic fermenters and acetogens can grow much faster (doubling times about 30 minutes and 1–4 hours respectively than the hydrogenotrophic methanogens (doubling times about 8–10 hours). Thus sudden changes in the medium composition can cause surges of hydrogen production, exceeding the capacity of the methanogens to remove it. The partial pressure of hydrogen rises, leading to a change in the metabolic pattern of the acetogens which produce lactate, propionate, butyrate, valerate and caproate instead of acetate. the amount of hydrogen produced falls, but the products cannot be utilized by the methanogens. This shows that sudden changes in load must be avoided and that fermenter function can usefully be monitored by measuring hydrogen concentration, pH and the types of organic acid present.

In recent years there have been some attempts to apply anaerobic digestion to the treatment of liquid industrial wastes, particularly those from food processing and beverage production. The acetoclastic methanogens, which are responsible for about 70% of methane production, are the slowest-growing group of organisms (doubling times 2–3 days) and in simple stirred fermenters this limits the maximum throughput. Modified digester designs, by preventing the free escape of biomass with digested waste, increase biomass concentration and reduce mean residence times to the point where plant costs are competitive with other methods. Four systems have been used. The anaerobic contact proces employs a stirred vessel, biomass escapes with the treated waste which is sedimented and returned to the digester. Fluidized bed reactors employ sand as a support phase and sediment this after it leaves the digester. Upflow sludge blanket reactors rely on the sedimentation of flocculent biomass within the unstirred digester to retain biomass whilst in anaerobic filters biomass is retained by the packed support phase.

Methane Generation

The methane generated by anaerobic waste digestion ("biogas") can be used for cooking, heating, generation of steam or electricity or compressed for use as a vehicle fuel. If it is to be transported through pipelines hydrogen sulphide, which is corrosive, must be removed. If it is to be compressed it is usually necessary to remove carbon dioxide and water. The low liquefaction temperature (−70°C) means that liquefaction is usually uneconomic on a small scale.

In some less-developed countries considerable use is made of small scale anaerobic digesters acting on human and animal faeces and on vegetable waste to produce methane as a fuel. In China there are over seven million such plants along with some hundreds of larger plants for electricity generation; rather smaller numbers of plants are in use in Africa, India and the Far East. Their major attraction is the provision of an alternative to wood for cooking and heating, a rapidly diminishing resource. In industrialized countries, wood is less important as a domestic fuel. Here, conventional economic calculations are of rather more importance and the few cost analyses available suggest that methane generation is at best of marginal cost benefit.

Serious consideration has been given to the possibility of using other feedstocks for methane generation and the potential contribution to energy needs is significant. Thus, in the U.S. it is estimated that the digestion of all crop and animal residues could provide between 1% and 10% of total U.S. energy reguirements and in the EEC 3% of energy requirements (1980 levels) are expected to be provided in this way by the year 2000. In many countries substantial quantities of straw are available as a waste product; other possibilities are the stems of cassava, rape, sisal, potato and sugar beet. Satisfactory technology is not yet available for the utilization of these materials, especially the first four which are difficult to digest because of low moisture content and high fibre, and the extended holding times necessary for decomposition require large plant volumes and high holding costs.

CONCLUSIONS

The industries considered in this chapter are described as "established" or "traditional". Many have evolved over thousands of years and, perhaps for this reason, it is difficult to foresee many startling new developments.

Substantial efforts have been devoted to the exploration and introduction of new technology, particularly in the areas of process engineering, strain improvement and analytical quality control. The main results have been reduced capital and labour costs, more efficient use of raw materials, the substitution of cheaper alternatives and greater product consistency.

The industries producing foods and beverages using microbial technology are largely protected from competing chemical processes by statutes defining the means of production, by the complex nature of the products themselves and by consumer prejudice against "artificial" products. To a great extent, the same forces act as constraints on the introduction of radical new products or production methods. The adoption of new technology is always limited by the need to avoid changes in product character which may endanger consumer acceptance. In particular, the use of gene manipulation, already commonplace in research laboratories, is unlikely to be extended to production strains until it is completely acceptable to the general public who may in the end prove more conservative than the regulatory agencies.

Even where it *is* entirely acceptable to the consumer, it is difficult to escape the conclusion that improved technology has only a small part to play in competition. Unlike the bulk chemical industry, in which profit margins are generally small and product quality can be satisfactorily defined in terms of a few objective analytical parameters, food and beverage producers generally enjoy rather larger margins and product quality is largely a matter of consumer preference. To a substantial extent competition between manufacturers operates via advertising to promote brand image and by the control of distribution and sales networks: marginal price differences are thus likely to be of minor importance in determining success.

The microbiological industries producing bulk products are subject to fewer constraints on the use of new technology. Here there is one obvious area where substantial developments might occur. In the discussion on industrial ethanol reference was made to the large quantities of lignocellulose wastes available and the lack of an adequate technology to utilise them. The problem is to produce a useful end product, which can be used either as a fuel or as a feedstock, at a rate sufficiently rapid to achieve economic viability. The potential rewards are great, but although substantial efforts are being made, success is by no means assured. Chapter 14 addresses these matters further.

REFERENCES

1. Fors, S.M. & Nordler, H. (1987) *Lager-type Beer Made from Extruded Malt, Sensory and Chemical Analyses.* Journal of the Institute of Brewing **93**, 496–500.
2. Williams, A.A. (1982) *Recent Developments in the Field of Wine Flavour Research.* Journal of the Institute of Brewing **88**, 43–53.
3. Clapperton, J.F., Dalgliesh, C.E. & Meilgaard, M.C. (1979) *Progress Towards an International System of Beer Flavour Terminology.* Journal of the Institute of Brewing **82**, 7–13.
4. Verzele, M. (1986) *100 Years of Hop Chemistry and its Relevance to Brewing.* Journal of the Institute of Brewing **92**, 32–48.
5. Keim, C.R. (1983) *Technology and Economics of Fermentation Ethanol.* Enzyme and Microbial Technology **5**, 103–114.
6. Greenshields, R.N. (1978) *Vinegar.* In Economic Microbiology Vol. 2, Primary Products of Metabolism, 121–186 (Editor Rose, A.H.). Academic Press, London.
7. Burrows, S. (1979) *Baker's Yeast.* In Economic Microbiology Vol. 4, Microbial Biomass, 32–64 (Editor Rose, A.H.). Academic Press, London.
8. Burgess, K. & Shaw, M. (1983) *Enzymes in Cheese Production.* In Industrial Enzymology, 260–283 (Editors Godfrey, T. & Reichert, J.). MacMillan, London.
9. Tamine, A.Y. & Robinson, R.K. (1985) *Yoghurt Science and Technology.* Pergamon Press, Oxford.
10. Spivey, M.J. (1978) *The Acetone/Butanol/Ethanol Fermentation.* Process Biochemistry **13**, 2,3,4, & 25.
11. Pike, E.B. & Carrington, E.G. (1979) *The Fate of Enteric Bacteria and Pathogens During Sewage Treatment.* In Biological Indicators of Water Quality, a Symposium at the University of Newcastle upon Tyne, 12–15 September 1978 **20**, 1–32 (Editors James, A. & Evison, L.M.). John Wiley, Chichester.
12. Brown, M.J. & Lester, J.N. (1979) *Metal Removal in Activated Sludge: the Role of Bacterial Extracellular Polymers.* Water Research **13**, 817–37.

FURTHER READING

Berry, D.J. (1984) *Physiology and Microbiology of Scotch Malt Whisky Production.* In Progress in Industrial Microbiology **19**, 199–245 (Editor Bushell, M.E.). Elsevier, Amsterdam.

Berry D.R., Russell, I. & Stewart, G.G. (1987) *Yeast Biotechnology.* Allen & Unwin, London.

Bu'lock, J.D. & Kristiansen, B. (1987) *Basic Biotechnology.* Academic Press, London.

Enari, T.M. (1987) *Prospects of Biotecbology for Brewers.* Journal of the Institute of Brewing **93**, 501–505.

Ennis, B.M., Gutierrez, N.A. & Maddox, I.S. (1986) *The Acetone-Butanol-Ethanol Fermentation: A Current Assessment.* Process Biochemistry **21**, 131–147.

Essien, D. & Pyle, D.L. (1983) *Energy Conservation in Ethanol Production by Fermentation.* Process Biochemistry **18**, 31–37.

Faust, U., Prave, P. & Schlingmann, M. (1983) *An Integral Approach to Power Alcohol.* Process Biochemistry **18**, 31–37.

Forster, C.F. (1985) *Biotechnology and Wastewater Treatment.* Cambridge University Press, Cambridge.

Guidoboni, G.E. (1984) *Continuous Fermentation Systems for Ethanol.* Enzyme and Microbial Technology **6**, 194–200.

Hacking, A.J. (1986) *Economic Aspects of Microbiology.* Cambridge University Press, Cambridge.

Hastings, J.J.H. (1978) *Acetone and Butanol.* In Economic Microbiology Vol. 2. Primary Products of Metabolism 31–72. (Editor Rose, A.H.). Academic Press, London.

Higgins, I.J., Best, D.J. & Jones, J. (1985) *Biotechnology: Principles and Applications.* Blackwell Scientific Publications, Oxford.

Higgins, I.J., & Burns, R.G. (1975) *The Chemistry and Microbiology of Pollution.* Academic Press, London.

Holmberg, S. (1984) *Genetic Improvement of Brewer's Yeast.* Trends in Biotechnology **2**, 98–102.

Hough, J.S. (1985) *The Biotechnology of Malting and Brewing.* Cambridge University Press, Cambridge.

Lafon-Lafourcade, S. & Ribereau-Gayon, P. (1984) *Developments in the Microbiology of Wine Production.* In Progress in Industrial Microbiology **19**, 1–46 (Editor Bushell, M.E.). Elsevier, Amsterdam.

Law, B.A. (1984) *Microorganisms and their Enzymes in the Maturation of Cheeses.* In Progress in Industrial Microbiology **19**, 245–285 (Editor Bushell, M.E.)

MacDonald, J., Reeve, P.T.V., Ruddlestone, J.D. & White, F.H. (1984) *Current Approaches to Brewery Fermentations.* In Progress in Industrial Microbiology **19**, 47–198 (Editor Bushell, M.E.). Elsevier, Amsterdam.

Maule, D.R. (1986) *Fermenter Design.* Journal of the Institute of Brewing **92**, 137–145.

Moo-Young, M. (Editor 1985) *Comprehensive Biotechnology.* Pergamon Press, Oxford.

Murtagh, J.E. (1986) *Fuel Ethanol Production — The U.S. Experience.* Process Biochemistry **21**, 61–65.

Rose, A.H. (1977) *Economic Microbiology Vol. 1, Alcoholic Beverages.* Academic Press, London.

Serra, A. & Poch, M. (1987) *A Survey of separation systems for Fermentation Ethanol Recovery.* Process Biochemistry **22**, 154–158.

Sodeck, G., Modl, J., Kominek, J. & Salzbrunn, W.(1981) *Production of Citric Acid According to the Submerged Process.* Process Biochemistry **16**, 9–11.

Stanbury, P.F. & Whitaker, A. (1984) *Principles of Fermentation Technology.* Pergamon Press, Oxford.

Stewart, G.G. & Russell, I. (1986) *One Hundred Years of Yeast Research and Development in the Brewing Industry.* Journal of the Institute of Brewing **92**, 537–558.

Wheatley, A.D. (1984) *Biotechnology and Effluent Treatment.* In Biotechnology and Genetic engineering Reviews **1**, 261–309 (Editor Russell, G.E.)

Watson, D.C. (1985) *Current Developments in the Potable Distilling Industry.* Critical Reviews In Biotechnology **2**, 147–192.

Wood, B.J.B.W. (1985) *Microbiology of Fermentated Foods.* Elsevier, Amsterdam.

Chapter 17

Industrial Chemicals: Fermentation and Immobilized Cells

Saul L. Neidleman

INTRODUCTION AND OVERVIEW

Versatility of performance and ease of handling have favored the use of microorganisms for the production of industrial chemicals for a long time. Some early examples of industrial fermentation processes for the production of chemicals include: lactic acid by *Lactobacillus* sp. (1881), acetone and butyl alcohol by *Clostridium acetobutylicum* (1916), gallic acid by *Aspergillus wentii* (1916) and citric acid by *Aspergillus* niger (1923). The versatility is recognized by noting that microorganisms synthesize a vast array of chemical compounds including the simple amino acids, monosaccharides, and fatty acids and the very complex alkaloids, polysaccharides, nucleic acids and proteins. Further, microbial systems, as a result of their broad complement of enzymes, are capable of a wide variety of chemical reactions some of which are listed in Table 1.

The chemical diversity of microbial products anticipates their functional diversity. Among the commercially significant applications of microbial metabolites are their use as flavors and fragrances, flavor enhancers, pesticides, pigments, surfactants, polymers for the oil industry, nutritional supplements such as vitamins and amino acids, enzymes for use in the food, chemical and pharmaceutical industries, drugs such as antibiotics and steroid derivatives, and foreign proteins for therapeutic use such as human interferons, interleukins and growth hormone. These last components introduce the concept that microorganisms are no longer exploited exclusively for chemicals produced as a result of their natural endowment of genetic information but that now, with the advent of genetic engineering and recombinant DNA technology, microorganisms have an expanded versatility to produce peptides and proteins native to higher forms, including the human.

It should be emphasized that the impact of genetic manipulation, whether referred to as genetic engineering, recombinant DNA technology, protein engineering or directed or random mutagenesis, is much broader than merely allowing the biosynthesis of foreign molecules in microorganisms. For example, yields of many microbial products, notably antibiotics such as the penicillins, tetracyclines and erythromycin, organic acids such as citric acid, and vitamins such as B-12, have been increased many-fold by random mutagenesis with x-ray, ultraviolet radiation and chemical mutagens. The original strain of *Penicillium notatum* produced about two units of penicillin per milliliter in 1939. By 1960, mutation had resulted in strains yielding 10,000 units per milliliter and the levels have continued to increase since then.

The purpose of this chapter is to present a overview of the applications, actual and potential, of microorganisms for the production of a broad latitude of industrial chemicals. Many of the areas touched upon in this presentation will be developed in greater detail in other chapters of this book, but it is important to see the forest as well as the trees.

The estimates presented in Table 2 give some perspective as to the considerable commercial value and the market size for selected chemicals dependent upon microbial processes.

Why Use Microbial Cells?

Microbial cells are used for the production of industrial chemicals because of the catalytic activities of the enzymes they contain. More than 2,200 enzymes have been identified and it has been estimated that this represents about 10% of the total enzymes that occur in nature.

Enzymes isolated from microorganisms have impressive credentials as catalysts for the synthesis of industrial chemicals,

Table 1
Representative Enzymatic Reactions

Acylation	Depolymerization	Methylation
Amidation	Epimerization	Nucleotidation
Amination	Epoxidation	Oxidation
C-C bond cleavage	Esterification	Phosphorylation
Condensation	Halogenation	Polymerization
Deamination	Hydration	Reduction
Decarboxylation	Hydrolysis	Transglycosylation
Deesterification	Hydroxylation	
Dehydration	Isomerization	
Demethylation		

Table 2
Market Size of Selected Fermentation Derived Chemicals

Chemical	World Market *Use*	*Year*	*Estimate ($M)*
Bacterial proteases	Detergents	1985	140
Total enzymes	Diverse	1985	400
Citric acid	Foods and other	1982	360
High fructose syrup	Sweetner	1982	1,400
Antibiotics	Pharmaceutical	1981	1,400
Riboflavin	Pharmaceutical	1981	70

but they are not without their problems. Their protein structure may result in stability deficiencies detrimental, for example, to their long term use at elevated temperatures. In addition, most enzyme reactions are carried out in water and the enzymes must be separated from the product stream. The latter is often very dilute, presenting problems of product concentration and recovery. Many advances are being made to overcome such difficulties through enzyme immobilization, genetic and chemical enzyme modifications and enzymatic reactions in organic solvents. These approaches are increasing the actual use and potential of enzymes in the production of industrial chemicals. Another approach is to use the microbial cells containing the desired catalytic activity without isolation of the responsible enzymes.

Microbial cells may be used for the synthesis of industrial chemicals in a number of ways including: 1) fermentations with living cells; 2) immobilized growing cells; 3) immobilized living; and 4) immobilized dead cells. The cells may be used in reactions requiring only a single catalytic event or in a process requiring multicatalytic activities.

Among the advantages derived from using microbial cells are: 1) potential for reduced catalyst cost; 2) increased enzyme stability; 3) ease of running multicatalytic processes; and 4) decreased time for catalyst production. Among the disadvantages are: 1) product contamination by cell products; 2) product degradation by cellular enzymes; 3) cell structures acting as diffusion barriers; and 4) reduced catalytic specific activity.

The decision as to which approach, enzymatic, fermentation, or immobilized cells is most economical for production of a particular product is best carried out on a case-by-case basis. The analysis of the various factors involved is a critical part of the decision-making process and involves input from scientists, engineers and marketing personnel.

Industrial Chemicals by Fermentation

In this chapter, fermentation generally refers to a batch process in which a microorganism is grown in a fermentor using a medium containing a carbon source such as glucose, starch hydrolysate or molasses; a nitrogen source like soybean meal, corn steep liquor or cotton seed meal; a source of vitamins, perhaps as yeast extract; and minerals and other grown factors. The chemical products may be extra — or intracellular, each requiring unique, optimized recovery and purification steps.

The material presented in the various tables that follow is highly selective rather than all-inclusive. It is to serve as an indicator of microbial diversity and versatility, not as an encyclopedic compendium.

It has already been noted that enzymes are critical to the synthesis of industrial chemicals by microorganisms. Enzymes are also among the most important industrial chemicals since they have many commercial applications in the food, chemical and pharmaceutical industries. Table 3 lists representative enzymes produced in microbial fermentations. Included among them are enzymes used to degrade starch, cellulose, lipids and proteins: the amylases, cellulases, lipases and proteinases, respectively. These are but a few of the enzymes that can be produced by fermentation and, in many cases, as illustrated by the lipases, a variety of microorganisms may produce the same or closely related enzymes.

The enzymes of Table 3 are proteins and as such are polymers of amino acids. Other polymeric substances are produced by microorganisms and some of these are presented in Table 4. All the compounds included are polysaccharides, polymers of various carbohydrate monomers, with the exception of poly-β-hydroxybutyrate, which is synthesized from the monomer β-hydroxybutyrate. Some of these polysaccharides find use as bulking and texturizing agents in the

Table 3
Production of Enzymes by Microbial Fermentation

Enzymes	*Microorganisms*
α-Amylase	*Bacillus amyloliquifaciens*
β-Amylase	*Bacillus polymyxa*
Amyloglucosidase	*Aspergillus niger*
Cellulases	*Trichoderma reesei*
Glucose isomerase	*Streptomyces olivochromogenes*
Glucose-1-oxidase	*Aspergillus niger*
α-D-glucosidase	*Aspergillus niger*
Lipases	*Aspergillus niger*
	Candida cylindracae
	Geotrichum candidum
	Rhizopus arrhizus
Pectin esterase	*Aspergillus oryzae*
Proteinase, alkaline serine	*Aspergillus oryzae*
Proteinase, acid	*Aspergillus saitoi*
Proteinase, neutral	*Bacillus stearothermophilus*
Pullulanase	*Aerobacter aerogenes*

Table 4
Production of Polymers by Microbial Fermentation

Polymers	*Microorganisms*
Alginate	*Azotobacter vinelandii*
Cellulose	*Acetobacter* sp.
Curdlan	*Agrobacterium* sp.
Dextran	*Acetobacter* sp.
Levan	*Leuconostoc mesenteroides*
Phosphomannan	*Hansenula capsulata*
Poly-β-hydroxybutyrate	*Alcaligenes eutrophus*
Scleroglucan	*Sclerotium glucanicum*
Xanthan	*Xanthomonas campestris*

food industry and as supports for enzyme immobilization.

It was mentioned that enzymes are polymers built from amino acids. Microorganisms can produce the amino acids as well as the catalytic proteins in quantity. Not all of the amino acids are incorporated into proteins; citrulline and ornithine are examples of some which are not. Table 5 lists many of the amino acids produced by fermentation together with the responsible microorganisms. The amino acids are used as precursors for commercial products such as the artificial sweetener, aspartame, and as food supplements for man and animals.

One of the hallmarks of microbial fermentation has been the production of antibiotics. More than 2,000 microbial metabolites have been isolated, characterized and shown to possess antibiotic activity. A few of these substances are listed in Table 6 in conjunction with their producing microorganisms. Aside from being a source of profit for pharmaceutical houses and a boon for the health of mankind, antibiotics have served a number of other useful purposes. The long and varied experiences associated with antibiotic production have made invaluable contributions to the development of fermentation hardware and improved processes for the production, isolation and purification of microbial products. The majority of antibiotics that have been characterized are produced by the *Streptomyces*. In developing genetic approaches to increase antibiotic yields and generate new antibiotic structures, an intense body of research has been realized that has contributed to our understanding of gene structure and regulation, gene cloning and recombination, and the nature and construction of cloning vectors employing plasmids and bacteriophages. Furthermore, the diverse chemistry of the antibiotics has stimulated many advances in techniques of chemical analyses. The compounds in the abbreviated listing of antibiotics include aminoglycosides, such as kanamycin, neomycin and streptomycin; β-lactams, such as the penicillins; polypeptides, such as the gramicidins; polyenes, such as amphotericin B and nystatin; tetracenes, such as tetracycline, chlortetracycline and hydroxytetracycline; and macrolides, such as erythromycin and oleandomycin.

In addition to chemical diversity, metabolites produced by microorganisms illustrate a broad spectrum of other biological activities. To a considerable degree, it is true to say that when

Table 5
Production of Amino Acids by Microbial Fermentation

Amino Acids	*Microorganisms*
DL-alanine	*Brevibacterium flavum*
L-arginine	*Brevibacterium flavum*
L-citrulline	*Bacillus subtilis*
L-glutamic acid	*Brevibacterium flavum*
L-histidine	*Corynebacterium glutamicum*
L-isoleucine	*Brevibacterium flavum*
L-leucine	*Brevibacterium lactofermentum*
L-lysine	*Corynebacterium glutamicum*
L-methionine	*Brevibacterium flavum*
L-ornithine	*Microbacterium ammoniaphilum*
L-phenylalanine	*Brevibacterium lactofermentum*
L-proline	*Corynebacterium glutamicum*
L-serine	*Corynebacterium hydrocarboclastus*
L-threonine	*Corynebacterium glutamicum*
L-tryptophan	*Brevibacterium flavum*
L-tyrosine	*Corynebacterium glutamicum*
L-valine	*Brevibacterium lactofermentum*

Table 6
Production of Antibiotics by Microbial Fermentation

Antibiotics	*Microorganisms*
Amphotericin B	*Streptomyces nodusus*
Cephalosporin C	*Cephalosporium acremonium*
Chloramphenicol	*Streptomyces venezuelae*
Chlortetracycline	*Streptomyces aureofaciens*
Demeclocycline	*Streptomyces aureofaciens*
Erythromycin	*Streptomyces erythreus*
Gentamicin C	*Micromonospora purpurea*
Gramicidins	*Bacillus brevis*
Griseofulvin	*Penicillium griseofulvum*
Hydroxytetracycline	*Streptomyces rimosus*
Kanamycin A	*Streptomyces kanamyceticus*
Lincomycin	*Streptomyces lincolnensis*
Neomycins	*Streptomyces fradiae*
Nystatin	*Streptomyces noursei*
Oleandomycin	*Streptomyces antibioticus*
Penicillins	*Penicillium chrysogenum*
Rifamycins	*Nocardia mediterranei*
Streptomycin	*Streptomyces griseus*
Tetracycline	*Streptomyces aureofaciens*

an assay is developed to detect a particular type of biological activity in chemical compounds, microbial metabolites will be found exhibiting the activity sought. Table 7 presents a few examples of compounds giving biological activities in mammalian species not normally associated with microbial responses. Where logic might make sense of the production of antibiotics, the production of such pharmacologically active agents is more obscure. Whatever the reason, microbial fermentations are still an untapped source of compounds with unexpected activity and promise for therapeutic applications.

An area of considerable interest at this time is the replacement of synthetic, expensive and rare fragrance and aroma compounds by similar or identical products produced by microorganisms. The aim is to develop more economical sources of natural substances. Table 8 illustrates some of the substances synthesized by microorganisms that fall into this general category. That microorganisms can smell like a rose, a gardenia, wintergreen, peaches and butter somehow seems somewhat incongruous but potentially profitable. Chapter 26 develops this theme further.

Table 9 is a nonspecific repository for miscellaneous microbial metabolites with a wide diversity of useful characteristics. The purposes for presenting this listing include the further demonstration of the versatility of microbial cells as synthetic machines and the wildly diverse types of activities that are associated with these synthetic achievements. Any list that includes pigments, ergot alkaloids, plant hormones, surfactants, insecticides, a vitamin and enzyme inhibitors must be impressive.

The microbial synthesis of indigo by *Escherichia coli* represents an exciting example of the application of recombinant DNA technology to the field of chemical synthesis. Indigo is a dye known for centuries and was originally obtained from extracts of plants of the genus *Indigofera*. In 1883, the structure of the dye was determined and a chemical synthesis was derived. Recently, using genetic engineering techniques, genes from *Pseudomonas putida* responsible for coding enzymes responsible for naphthalene oxidation were cloned and expressed in *E. coli*. The resultant construct was capable of the synthesis of indigo. Whether this microbial method will successfully compete with the chemical process remains to be seen, but it serves to illustrate the broadening effect of recombinant DNA technology on the biosynthetic capabilities of microorganisms.

At the height of the popularity of blue jeans in 1983, it was estimated that a worldwide market in excess of $100 million existed for indigo. This dye was and is produced as an emulsion paste in the U.S. and as a dry powder in Japan. The market was shared at the time principally by four producers and the selling price was $10–12 per pound. There seemed to be a good opportunity to produce indigo using genetic engineering techniques at a cost which would permit entering the world market, and both Amgen and Eastman Kodak undertook a program to do just that. The details of indigo production were known to the existing producers but not to the new entrants. At the time of writing (early 1989), it is not clear what the cost to the new entrants would be. They would have to include the cost of new plant and equipment in their calculations, a cost the existing producers could ignore (their equipment already having been written off). Another mystery to the new entrants is whether existing producers are willing to reduce selling prices without regard to cost in order to preserve market share. In other words, the economics of the existing production processes undoubtedly included depreciated equipment and direct costs of manufacture sufficiently low to allow for significant price reductions in the

Table 7
Microbiological Production of Biologically Active Compounds

Compounds	*Pharmacological Activities*	*Microorganisms*
Ascofuranone	Antilipidemic	*Ascophyta viciae*
Bestatin	Immunomodulator	*Streptomyces olivoreticuli*
1,3-Diphenethylurea	Antidepressant	*Streptomyces* sp.
Dopastin	Hypotensive	*Pseudomonas* sp.
Griseofulvin	Anti-inflammatory	*Streptomyces griseofulvum*
Naematolin	Coronary vasodilator	*Naematoloma fasciculare*
Phialocin	Anticoagulant	*Phialocephala repens*
Slaframine	Salivation inducer	*Rhizoctonia leguminicola*
Zearalenone	Estrogenic	*Gibberella zeae*

Table 8
Production of Fragrance Chemicals by Microbial Fermentation

Compounds	*Fragrance*	*Microorganisms*
Anisaldehyde	Anise-like	*Trametes sauvolens*
Benzaldehyde	Almond-like	*Trametes sauvolens*
Benzyl alcohol	Fruity	*Phellinus igniarius*
Citronellol	Rose-like	*Ceratocystis varispora*
J-decalactone	Peach	*Sporobolomyces odorus*
Diacetyl	Buttery	*Streptococcus diacetylactis*
p-α-Dimethylphenyl alcohol	Grassy	*Mycoacia uda*
Linalool	Floral	*Ceratocystis variospora*
p-Methylbenzyl alcohol	Hyacinth, gardenia	*Mycoacia uda*
Methyl-*p*-methoxyphenyl-acetate	Anise-like	*Trametes odorata*
Methylphenylacetate	Honey-like	*Trametes odorata*
Methyl salicylate	Wintergreen	*Phellinus igniarius*
6-Pentyl-α-pyrone	Coconut-like	*Trichoderma viride*
Tetramethylpyrazines	Nutty	*Corynebacterium glutamicum*

Table 9
Production of Miscellaneous Compounds by Microbial Fermentation

Compounds	*Characteristics*	*Microorganisms*
Antipain	Protease inhibitor	Various *Streptomyces*
Avermectin	Anthelminthic	*Streptomyces avermitilis*
Carotenoids	Pigments	*Dunaliella bardarwil* (Alga)
Dopastin	Dopamine-β-hydroxylase inhibitor	*Pseudomonas* sp.
Elastatinal	Elastase inhibitor	Various *Streptomyces*
Emulsan	Surfactant	*Acinetobacter calcoaceticus*
Gibberellins	Plant hormones	*Gibberella fujikuroi*
Herbicidin	Herbicide	*Streptomyces saganonensis*
Indigo	Pigment	*Escherichia coli*
Inosine	Flavor enhancer precursor	*Bacillus subtilis*
Lysergicacid	Ergot alkaloids derivatives	*Clariceps paspali*
Oudenone	Tyrosine hydroxylase inhibitor	*Oudemansiella radicata*
Piericidin	Insecticide	*Streptomyces mobaraensis*
Tetranactin	Miticide	*Streptomyces aureus*
Vitamin B12	Vitamin	*Propionobacterium shermanii*

face of new entrants to the market. Thus, it is not clear whether a new process whose target cost is $3–5 a pound can realistically expect a decent market share. To complicate matters further, blue jeans are not as popular as they were in the early 1980s, and thus the demand for indigo and the price at which it can be sold are probably soft. Such is the real world.

Production of Chemicals by Immobilized Microorganisms

To this point, this review has considered the biosynthesis of chemicals by microbiological fermentation. In addition to this method of microbial production of chemicals, there is a vast literature on the use of immobilized microbial cells for the synthesis of chemicals. Basically, cell immobilization involves attaching the microorganism to an insoluble matrix that may be noncellular or cellular, that is may be a synthetic polymer or biopolymer or the microorganisms itself. There are six general methods for immobilization of microorganisms. These include: entrapment in a matrix, absorption on a matrix, encapsulation in a matrix, covalent binding to a matrix, chemical cross-linking of cells and flocculation. The most commonly used technique is that of entrapment.

In selecting the matrix, a number of factors must be considered, including: 1) stability; 2) compatibility with the microbial activity desired; and 3) compatibility with the substrates and products of the process. It is important that enzyme not leach from the support nor should the support itself leach into the product.

The use of immobilized microbial cells for the production of chemicals has involved three distinct types of cells: dead cells, living cells and growing cells. In early work, most of the processes studied involved a single enzyme step and for this purpose dead cells with active enzyme sufficed. However, in many cases, several enzyme steps are involved in the biosynthesis of the desired end product. In addition, regeneration of cofactors may be necessary for efficient enzyme utilization. In these cases, both immobilized living or growing cells are best suited to the process.

Some of the advantages the immobilized cell processes may offer as compared with immobilized enzymes and fermentation procedures are as follows:

1. Higher enzyme operational stability than immobilized enzyme systems.
2. Endogenous cofactor regeneration.
3. Possible multistep enzyme reactions.
4. Higher volumetric productivity and less plant pollution than traditional fermentation.
5. Possibility of continuous operation.
6. Eliminates need and cost of enzyme extraction and purification.
7. May reduce enzyme cost.
8. Possible higher cell density as compared to traditional fermentation.

It would be misleading, however, to suggest that the use of immobilized microorganisms does not have a list of potential disadvantages. A number of these are:

1. Bacterial contamination may occur.
2. Side reactions may occur due to multiplicity of enzymes in microbial cells.
3. High molecular weight products may encounter diffusion problems with certain matrices and microbial cells.
4. Gas transport may be impeded by matrices and microbial cells.
5. Oxygen levels may be limited by low solubility in matrices.
6. Products such as acids or bases may cause a detrimental pH environment if diffusion in the matrix is limiting.
7. Specific catalytic activity may be lower than with immobilized, purified enzymes.

In the final analysis, the biological approach needs to be carefully considered on a case-by-case basis. For example, some of the factors that determine the cost of using an immobilized cell process include:

1. Enzyme cost for preparation.
2. Enzyme specific activity.
3. Enzyme stability.
4. Enzyme and support reuse.
5. Cost of immobilization.
6. Performance of the system.
7. Capital investment requirements.
8. Clean-up and pollution control.

For immobilized enzyme and fermentation-based process, similar factors exist and must be analyzed. There is no universal solution best for all problems in the microbiological production of chemicals.

Amino acids synthesized with immobilized microorganisms are illustrated in Table 10 while organic acid production is indicated in Table 11. The synthesis of antibiotics and related compounds is shown in Table 12. It should be noted that there are three different types of processes included in Table 12: 1) total synthesis of an antibiotic as with bacitracin, penicillin G, or streptomycin; 2) production of precursor substances such as 6-APA and 7-ACA; and 3) the preparation

Table 10
Production of Amino Acids by Immobilized Microorganisms

Amino Acids	*Microorganisms*
L-alanine	*Corynebacterium dismutans*
L-arginine	*Serratia marcescens*
L-aspartic acid	*Bacterium cadaveris*
L-citrulline	*Pseudomonas putida*
L-glutamic acid	*Brevibacterium flavum*
L-isoleucine	*Serratia marcescens*
L-lysine	*Microbacterium ammoniaphilum*
L-methionine	*Aspergillus ochraceus*
L-phenylalanine	*Escherichia coli*
L-serine	*Klebsiella aerogenes*
L-threonine	*Escherichia coli*
L-tryptophan	*Escherichia coli*
L-tyrosine	*Citrobacter freundii*

Table 11
Production of Organic Acids by Immobolized Microorganisms

Organic Acids	*Microorganisms*
Acetic acid	*Acetobacter* sp.
D-araboascorbic acid	*Penicillium notatum*
Citric acid	*Aspergillus niger*
α, μ-Dodecanedioic acid	*Candida tropicalis*
Erythorbic acid	*Penicillium cyaneofulvum*
Fumaric acid	*Rhizopus delemar*
Gluconic acid	*Aspergillus niger*
Itaconic acid	*Aspergillus terreus*
2-Ketogluconic acid	*Serratia marcescens*
α-Ketoglutaric acid	*Candida hydrocarbofumarica*
2-Keto-L-gulonic acid	*Gluconobacter melanogenus*
Kojic acid	*Aspergillus oryzae*
Lactic acid	*Lactobacillus lactis*
L-malic acid	*Brevibacterium ammoniagenes*
Urocanic acid	*Achromobacter liquidium*

of antibiotic analogues from a precursor molecule such as 6-APA or 7-ADCA in the presence of an unnatural side chain precursor such as D-phenylglycine methyl ester. This variety of reaction types gives further illustration of the broad possibilities inherent in the use of immobilized microorganisms for the biosynthesis of chemicals.

In Table 13 are listed a number of miscellaneous chemicals produced by immobilized microorganisms. They range from polymer precursors (acrylamide and alkene oxides), enzyme cofactors (coenzyme A, NADP, and NADH), to a plant hormone (gibberellic acid).

Table 14 presents some commercially significant reactions involving carbohydrate modifications employing immobilized cells. The list is headed by the production of high fructose syrup using immobilized cells containing the requisite enzyme activity, that of glucose isomerase.

Foreign Protein Synthesis by Microorganisms

The impact of genetic engineering, in particular recombinant DNA technology, on the utility of microbial synthesis of chemicals is already formidable and will become increasingly

Table 12
Production of Antibiotics, Antibiotic Precursors and Derivatives by Immobilized Microorganisms

Compounds	*Microorganisms*
Adenine arabinoside	*Enterobacter aerogenes*
7-Aminocephalosporanic acid (7-ACA) from cephalosporin C	*Bacillus subtilis*
6-Aminopenicillanic acid (6-APA) from penicillin G	*Escherichia coli*
Ampicillin from 6-APA and D-phenylglycine methyl ester	*Bacillus megatherium*
Bacitracin	*Bacillus* sp.
Candicidin	*Streptomyces griseus*
Cephalexin from 7-Aminodesacetocy-cephalosporanic acid, (7-ADCA) and D-phenylglycine methyl ester	*Bacillus megatherium*
Cephalosporin C	*Streptomyces clavuligerus*
Colistin	*Bacillus polymyxa*
Nikkomycin	*Streptomyces tendae*
Nisin	*Streptococcus ylactis*
Patulin	*Penicillium urticae*
Penicillin G	*Penicillium chrysogenum*
Streptomycin	*Streptomyces griseus*
Tylosin	*Streptomyces* sp.

Table 13
Production of Miscellaneous Chemicals by Immobilized Microorganisms

Compounds	*Microorganisms*
Acrylamide	*Brevibacterium* sp.
Adenosine triphosphate (ATP)	*Saccharomyces cerevisiae*
Ethylene oxide	*Corynebacterium* sp.
Coenzyme A	*Brevibacterium ammoniagenes*
Cytidinediphosphate-choline	*Hansenula jardinii*
Gibberellic acid	*Fusarium moniliforme*
Glucose-l- and -6-phosphates	*Escherichia freundii*
Nicotinamide adenine dinucleotide phosphate (NADP)	*Achromobacter aceris*
Nicotinamide adenine dinucleotide, reduced (NADH)	*Brevibacterium ammoniogenes*
Panthothenic acid	*Escherichia coli*

Table 14
Carbohydrate Modification with Immobilized Microorganisms

Carbohydrates	*Products*	*Microorganisms*
D-Glucose	High fructose syrup	*Actinoplanes missouriensis*
Inulin	High fructose syrup	*Kluyveromyces marxianus*
D-Lactose	D-glucose + D-galactose	*Bacillus stearothermophilus*
D-Raffinose	D-sucrose + D-galactose	*Absidia lignierii*
D-Sucrose	Invert sugar	*Aspergillus niger*

so as time passes. One example has been cited above: the biosynthesis of indigo. However, the most intense and most successful application of this technology has been in relation to the production of foreign and, most especially, of human proteins and peptides in microorganisms. Table 15 illustrates this fact.

While the imagination is, of course, particularly stimulated by the reality of producing human proteins in microorganisms, one is led to wonder what effects such substances as human growth hormone, proinsulin, interferons, interleukins, and tumor necrosis factor have on the cell physiology of the producing microorganism. A study of such effects may yield some basic insights into the strategy of evolution and the universality of certain aspects of biological systems.

The use of genetically engineered microorganisms in processes to produce chemicals results in advantages and disadvantages peculiar to such processes. Among the positive driving forces favoring the application of genetic engineering, especially recombinant DNA techniques, to the microbiological production of chemicals are the following: 1) increased availability and yields of rare and useful compounds; 2) new sources of biological products in more readily controlled bioprocesses; 3) increased ability to use new feedstocks for which organisms have been optimized; and 4) cost reductions due to these preceding factors. On the other side, there a number of problems that will require solution. Among them are: 1) many foreign proteins produced in microorganisms are fragile molecules and since they are, in many cases, to be used for human therapy, their integrity and purity must be tested and assured; 2) this imperative need for quality control puts more demands on bioprocesses yielding such products; 3) the fact that there are genetic instabilities in many recombinant DNA constructs requires continuous monitoring and, often, curative surgery; 4) the genetics of many potentially valuable microorganisms is too poorly understood for present applications; and 5) the additional burdens of governmental regulations, especially designed for recombinant DNA-related products, are a constant companion. Despite all of this, the ultimate marvels of biosynthesis using microorganisms modified by genetic engineering are yet to astound us. It must be remembered that the use of genetic and chemical methods to accomplish protein engineering means that we are not limited to producing the proteins that nature designed. We can construct our own variants, based on the hope that some of them will have improved properties — and indeed they do as, for example, in the cases of subtilisin and β-interferon. It follows,

Table 15
Microbial Production of Foreign Proteins

Foreign Proteins	*Host Microorganisms*
Aspergillus glucoamylase	*Saccharomyces cerevisiae*
Bacillus subtilis penicillinase	*Escherichia coli*
Bovine growth hormone	*Escherichia coli*
Calf prochymosin	*Escherichia coli*
β-endorphin	*Saccharomyces cerevisiae*
Erwinia chysanthemi pectinases	*Escherichia coli*
Human growth hormone	*Escherichia coli*
Human α-interferon	*Bacillus subtilis*
Human β-interferon	*Escherichia coli*
Human j-interferon	*Escherichia coli*
Human interleukin-2	*Escherichia coli*
Human proinsulin	*Bacillus subtilis*
Human tumor necrosis factor	*Escherichia coli*
Streptococcus equisimilis streptokinase	*Escherichia coli*
Thermomonospora cellulase	*Escherichia coli*
Wheat α-amylase	*Saccharomyces cerevisiae*

then, that modern techniques of recombinant DNA technology are vastly superior to more traditional methods for the large scale production of rare human peptides and proteins and superior variants of these molecules.

Steroid Transformations by Microorganisms

Many microorganisms, immobilized and not, are used to modify the structure of a broad range of chemicals including antibiotics, alkaloids, cyclic and linear hydrocarbons, pesticides, terpenes and steroids. Steroid transformation, in particular, has been a most fruitful area in which microorganisms have been used to alter the structure of chemicals foreign to the microorganism. This application of microorganisms differs conceptually from most of the other microbial processes so far described in that the previous examples, with the exception of the foreign proteins involved chemicals normally produced by microorganisms. Many microorganisms contain enzymes that recognize steroids as substrates even though they are, in general, novel to the organism. These microbial enzymes recognize particular domains within unfamiliar chemicals, presumably because these domains bear a resemblance to related domains within familiar molecules.

In the early 1950s chemical methods for the conversion of plant steroids such as diosgenin and stigmasterol to progesterone had been well developed. However, chemical processes for the introduction of an α-hydroxyl group at C-11 of progesterone were not suitable. This reaction is necessary to convert progesterone to corticosteroids. In 1952, it was shown that a *Rhizopus* sp. could, in fact, perform this hydroxylation with commercially useful efficiency. Since then many additional microbial hydroxylations and dehydrogenations have been developed and some have achieved industrial utility. Table 16 illustrates, at some length, a variety of these reactions. The ability of microbiological cells specifically to incorporate hydroxyl groups at so many positions in the steroid nucleus is truly amazing and remains one of the best examples wherein the superior selectivity of biological catalysis over chemical catalysis is readily evident. If one adds to this display of chemical versatility the additional oxidative and reductive reactions that can be performed microbiologically, the exquisite subtleties embodied in microbial catalysis are even more breath-taking: neither nook nor cranny in the steroid molecule can escape the rapier of biocatalysis.

Effects of Substrate and Environment on the Structure of Chemicals Produced by Microorganisms

In some cases the chemical structure of compounds produced by microorganisms can be altered by substrate composition and environmental variables such as temperature. In other words, the normal chemicals formed can be modified by applying conditions that deviate from those usually confronting the microorganism.

Table 17 shows that the number of carbon atoms occurring in the wax esters of *Acinetobacter* sp. H01-N can be varied depending upon the number of carbon atoms in the substrate. Since wax esters consist of long chain acids and alcohols

Table 16
Steroid Transformations by Microorganisms

CH_3 CH CH_2 CH_2 CH_2 CH_2 CH

CH_3 CH_3

Reaction	*Substrate*	*Product*	*Microorganism*
1α-Hydroxylation	Androst-4-ene-3,17-dione	1α-Hydroxyandrost-4-ene-3,17-dione	*Penicillium* sp.
1β-Hydroxylation	Androst-4-ene-3,17-dione	1β-Hydroxyandrost-4-ene-3,17-dione	*Xylaria* sp.
2α-Hydroxylation	Androstane-7,17-dione	2α-Hydroxyandrostane-7,17-dione	*Wojnowicia graminis*
2β-Hydroxylation	Adrost-4-ene-3,17-dione	2β-Hydroxyandrost-4-ene-3,17-dione	*Penicillium* sp.
3α-Hydroxylation	Androstane-7,17-dione	3α-Hydroxyandrostrane-7,17-dione	*Diaporthe celastrinia*
3β-Hydroixylation	17β-Hydrooxyandrostan-11-one	3β,17β-Dihydroxy-androstan-11-one	*Wojnowicia graminis*
4β-Hydroxylation	17α-Methylestra-1,3,5(10)-triene-3,17β-diol	17α-Methylestra-1,3,5(10)-triene-3,4,17β-triol	*Aspergillus flavus*
5α-Hydroxylation	A-Nor-5α-Pregnane-2,20-dione	5α-Hydroxy-A-nor-pregnane-2,20-dione	*Cokeromyces recurvatus*
5β-Hydroxylation	3β,14-Dihydroxy-5β,14β-card-20(22)-enolide	3β,5,14-Trihydroxy-5β,14β-card-20(22)-enolide	*Absidia orchidis*
6α-Hydroxylation	Androstane-1,17-dione	6α-Hydroxyandrostane-1,17-dione	*Calonectria decora*
6β-Hydroxylation	17β-Hydroxyestr-4-ene-3-one	6β,17β-Dihydroxyestr-4-ene-3-one	*Helminthosporium rasonoi*
7α-Hydroxylation	Androst-4-ene-3,17-dione	7α-Hydroxyandrost-4-ene-3,17-dione	*Mucor griseocyanus*
7β-Hydroxylation	Androst-4-ene-3,17-dione	7β-Hydroxyandrost-4-ene-3,17-dione	*Xylaria* sp.
8β-Hydroxylation	17,21-Dihydroxypregn-4-ene-3,20-dione	8β,17,21-Trihydroxypregn-4-ene-3,20-dione	*Cercospora melonis*
9α-Hydroxylation	Androst-4-ene-3,17-dione	9α-Hydroxyandrost-4-ene-3,17-dione	*Nocardia corollina*
9β-Hydroxylation	9β,10α-Pregn-4-ene-3,20-dione	9β-Hydroxy-9β,10α-pregn-4-ene-3,20-dione	*Cephalothecium roseum*
10β-Hydroxylation	17β-Hydroxyestr-4-ene-3-one	10β,17β-Dihydroxyestr-4-ene-3-one	*Botrytis paeoniae*

11α-Hydroxylation	Progesterone	11α-Hydroxyprogesterone	*Rhizopus*
11β-Hydroxylation	11-Deoxycortisone	Hydrocortisone	*Curvularia lunata*
12β-Hydroxylation	17β-Hydroxyestr-4-ene-3-one	12β,17β-Dihydroxyestr-4-ene-3-one	*Collectotrichum derridis*
14α-Hydroxylation	Androst-4-ene-3,17-dione	14α-Hydroxyandrost-4-ene-3,17-dione	*Dematiaceae* Strain M202
15α-Hydroxylation	11α-Hydroxy-5α-pregnane-3,20-dione	11α,15α-Dihydroxy-5α-pregnane-3,20-dione	*Calonectria decora*
15β-Hydroxylation	Androst-4-ene-3,17-diore	15β-Hydroxyandrost-4-ene-3,17-dione	Xylaria sp.
16α-Hydroxylation	Androst-4-ene-3,17-dione	16α-Hydroxyandrost-4-ene-3,17-dione	*Staurophoma* sp.
16β-Hydroxylation	17β-Hydroxyestr-4-ene-3-one	16β,17β-Dihydroxyestr-4-ene-3-one	*Mycosphaerella latebrosa*
17α-Hydroxylation	Pregn-4-ene-3,20-dione	17α-Hydroxypregn-4-ene 3,20-dione	*Cephalothecium roseum*
17β-Hydroxylation	Androstane-3,11-dione	17β-Hydroxyandrostane-3,11-dione	*Wojnowicia graminis*
18β-Hydroxylation	11β,21-Dihydroxypregn-4-ene-3,20-dione	11β,18,20-Trihydroxypregn-4-ene-3,20-dione	*Corynespora cassiicola*
19-Hydroxylation	6α-Hydroxyandrostane-3,17-dione	6α,19-Dihydroxyandrostane-3,17-dione	*Calonectria decora*
21-Hydroxylation	A-Nor-pregn-3-ene-2,20-dione	21-Hydroxy-A-nor-pregn-3-ene-2,20-dione	*Aspergillus niger*
-Dehydrogenation	10β,17β-Dihydroxyestra-4-ene-3-one	10β,17β-Dihydroxyestra-1,4-diene-3-one	*Corynebacterium simplex*
4-Dehydrogenation	5α-Androst-1-ene-3,17-dione	Androsta-1,4-diene-3,17-dione	*Pseudomonas testosteron*
1,4-Dehydrogenation	5α-Androstane-3,17-dione	Androsta-1,4-diene-3,17-dione	*Calonectria decora*
7-Dehydrogenation	Cholest-5-ene-3β-ol	Cholesta-5,7-diene-3β-ol	*Azotobacter oxydans*
9(11)-Dehydrogenation	3-Hydroxyestra-1,3,5(10)-triene-one	3Hydroxy-14β-estra-1,3,5(10),9(11)-tetraene-17-one	*Glomerella fusaroides*
Ring A aromatization	Estra-4,7-dione-3,17-dione	3-Hydroxyestra-1,3,5(10)-7-tetraene-	*Corynebacterium simplex*
Double bond reduction	Estra-1-ene-3,17-dione	Estrane-3,17-dione	*Aspergillus flavus*
Ketone reduction	Androsta-1,4,9(11)-triene-3,17-dione	17β-Hydroxyandrosta-1,4,9(11)-triene-3-one	*Saccharomyces cerevisiae*

Table 17
Effect of Substrates on Number of Carbon Atoms in Wax Esters Produced by *Acinetobacter* sp. HO1-N

Substrate	*Number of Carbon Atoms in Major Wax Ester*
n-Hexadecane	32
n-Octadecane	36
n-Eicosane	38
n-Docosane	42
Acetic acid	34
Propionic acid	34
Ethanol	34
Propanol	34

joined by an ester linkage, the basic effect is to alter the chain length of these two building blocks.

In Table 18 is a second and more subtle example of altering the carbon chain length of wax esters by substrate chemistry. When acetic acid is the carbon source for *Acinetobacter* sp. H01-N, the wax esters are primarily even in carbon number, while with propionic acid, the esters are both even and odd. The mixture of acetic and propionic acid also yields even and odd carbon number wax esters, but in larger amounts than with propionic acid alone. The metabolism of propionic acid by the bacteria opens the world of odd numbered carbon chains.

Another device for altering the chemical structure of the wax esters of *Acinetobacter* sp. H01-N is by varying the temperature. The capacity of the microorganism dramatically to vary the level of ester unsaturation can be enhanced by such temperature stresses. In nature, there exists a common and inverse relationship between lipid unsaturation and temperature: high temperature leads to low unsaturation; low temperature leads to high unsaturation. The primary function of this relationship is to preserve membrane function and fluidity over a range of temperatures. Table 19 shows that the wax esters produced by *Acinetobacter* sp. H01-N at 17°C are much more unsaturated than those at 30°C. By combining the aspects of side-chain size and unsaturation, a process has been designed for the microbial production of a wax ester mixture similar in composition to that of jojoba oil, a product obtained from the beans of the jojoba plant. This plant material is widely used in cosmetic formulations.

Table 18
Synthesis of Odd Carbon Number Wax Esters by *Acinetobacter* sp. HO1-N in the Presence of Propionic Acid

Substrate	*Carbon Number of Wax Esters Synthesized*
Acetic acid	32, 34, 36
Propionic acid	31, 32, 33, 34, 35, 36
Acetic acid + propionic acid	31, 32, 33, 34, 35, 36

These examples, when combined with the concept of producing foreign proteins in microorganisms, clearly illustrate that microorganisms can be manipulated in the laboratory to allow the production of new and desirable chemicals.

THE FUTURE

The production of chemicals by microorganisms has a future. A Japanese view of some of the hopes for this future as seen in Table 20. Therein are listed a number of commercial reactions presently carried out by chemical means. The wish is to replace these by bioreactions. Many of the examples of amino acids, organic acids and other chemicals cited in preceding tables will also require process improvement. They have shown their promise, but they need to be better.

The future will be concerned with making improvements at all stages of bioprocesses, beginning with improved microorganisms and immobilizing procedures through improved scale-up and downstream handling to facilitate the discovery and exploitation of new and commercially significant products.

A brief outline of some of the steps in a typical bioprocess will serve as an indicator of the diversity of process elements that will be the objects of optimization research:

1. Growth and improvement of cells for catalytic use.
2. Immobilization of biocatalyst.
3. Preparation of chemical feedstocks to be modified.
4. Bioreactors to allow contact of immobilized biocatalyst and feedstock.
5. Reaction conditions in bioreactor.
6. Separation of product from byproducts and waste products.
7. Recycling or disposal of byproducts and waste products.
8. Product isolation from dilute aqueous solutions.
9. Product purification and formulation.

Detailed consideration of these various bioprocessing steps is beyond the scope of this discussion. They are introduced to supply some perspective as to where the immobilized catalyst fits into the integrated process. A few parting comments will, however, be appropriate.

As far as the microorganisms are concerned, knowledge of the genetics of species other than those presently used in genetic engineering and recombinant DNA-dependent processes will have to be developed in order to bring more flexibility into the choice of organism to be used. In addition,

Table 19
Effect of Temperature on Unsaturation of Wax Esters Synthesized by *Acinetobacter* sp. HO1-N from Ethanol

Temperature (C)	*Diene Fractions (32:2, 34:2, 36:2) Total (%)*	*Monoene Fractions (32:1, 34:1, 36:1) Total (%)*	*Saturated Fractions (32:0, 34:0, 36:0) Total (%)*
17	72	18	10
24	29	40	31
30	9	25	66

Table 20
Chemical Reactions Desired to be Replaced by Bioreactions in Japan

Reaction Types	*Example*
Addition reactions	Olefins → alcohols → alkyl amines → fatty acids
Condensation reactions	Carbon monoxide/H_2 → alkanes → olefins → glycols
Oxidation reactions	Alkenes → epoxides → glycols Aliphatic hydrocarbons → fatty acids Benzene → phenols Butadiene → tetrahydrofuran Cyclohexanol → adipic acid
Miscellaneous	Aryl chloride → aryl alcohol Biomass → olefins → fatty acids → monosaccharides Industrial wastes → useful substances

thermostable, high activity microorganisms with resistance to environmental stresses such as solvents, extremes of pH, and high salt concentrations, and with improved genetic stability will have to be developed. These better microorganisms will then be used in bioprocesses improved with respect to scale-up problems and separation and purification steps. Greater efficiency in dealing with the dilute nature of most bioprocesses as well as the fragile nature of many of the products will be required.

Scale-up of a bioprocess requires design, construction and operation of a laboratory scale process on a new and larger scale. The process may be more or less traditional in its characteristics and demands, or it may be a radical departure from the usual, requiring complex inventiveness in its biological, chemical, and engineering aspects. All of this futuristic discussion for the displacement of traditional chemical processes by new biotechnological methods has an overwhelming barrier: the demand that, in real terms, these new processes will be commercially viable.

The development of new and improved bioprocesses depends, or course, on the realities of the commercial world: there must be a profit in the production of a particular product; the bioprocess must have a significant advantage over existing or potential chemical processes; and the technical difficulties involved in bringing the new process to commercial production must be solvable within the framework of existent or newly emerging technology. One other reality, which is, perhaps, the most stringent is the willingness of the chemical (and other industries) to replace a traditional, operating, capital-equipment-in-place technology with one that requires new substantial capital expenditure. One example, that of the microbial production of indigo in competition with the well-established chemical process, has already been cited to emphasize the point that it is one thing to invent an alternative; it is another to get it into the marketplace.

Another illustration of this reality is the work on the microbial or enzymatic production of alkene oxides, such as ethylene or propylene oxide. During development over the last 10 years the biological production of alkene oxides has run into all of these problems with the result that no commercial process has, as yet, been developed. This example is an international one with work having been pursued in the United States, Holland, Great Britain, Japan and elsewhere.

The two major, established chemical processes for propylene oxide synthesis were a chlorohydrin and a peroxidation route. Similarly, the biocatalytic approach had two primary methods: a chlorohydrin and an oxidative procedure. In certain of the chemical and biocatalytic processes, a co-product was also synthesized which both improved the economics and complicated processing steps. In one manifestation of the biocatalytic approach involving an enzymatically-synthesized chlorohydrin intermediate (propylene chlorohydrin) en route to propylene oxide, the co-product was crystalline D-fructose. This method was able to produce propylene oxide in serious competition with the chemical processes. In 1982, the list price for propylene oxide was 46.5¢/pound with an estimated annual consumption of 4×10^9 pounds, an impressive target for biocatalysis. The biocatalytic system never materialized into a replacement process because of the commercial realities noted above, particularly the struggle with traditional methods. Work, however, is still proceeding in this area and a viable process may yet result.

A final example of the difficulties in achieving technology replacement is that of the "microbial jojoba oil" discussed above. While the production economics favors the microbial process, the material obtained from plants has a "natural" attribute so popular today, not offered by the microorganism. The plant growing in the field is easier to sell as a component in cosmetics than the microbe in the fermenter. The fact is, however, that microorganisms have produced chemicals for industry for many years. Their potential to produce chemicals for industry in the years to come is enormous. It remains for the biotechnologists to reduce this dream to reality by demonstrating that in some cases biotechnology is the alternative of choice as judged by the criteria cited throughout this discussion.

One of the most exciting, yet often frustrating, aspects of the use of microorganisms for production of industrial chemicals is that in contrast to classical chemical catalysts, we are dealing with "living catalysts." As such, they offer tremendous malleability, but they can be unpredictable. They, as their employers, strive for survival and retain some independence in decision-making. The survival drive of the two, the microorganism and industry, is occasionally in conflict. Usually a compromise is worked out to mutual advantage; namely a good relationship. If it does, a successful process emerges; if not, it is back to the drawing board or laboratory for another look at the problem.

FURTHER READING

1. Anonymous (May 24, 1981). 1981 *Market for fermentation products.* Scrip, No. 695, p. 14.
2. Anonymous (March 31, 1986). *Enzyme demand growth shows signs of slowing down.* Eur. Chem. News, pp. 11–12.
3. Best, D.J. (1985). *Applications of biotechnology to chemical production.* In: Molecular Biology and Biotechnology (J.M. Walker and E.B. Gingold, eds.), 228–267, The Royal Society of Chemistry, Special Publication No. 54, Dorchester: Dorset Press.
4. Hopwood, D.A., Bibb, M.J., Bruton, C.J., Chater, K.F., Feitelson, J.S. and Gil, J.A. (1983). *Cloning Streptomyces genes for antibiotic production.* Trends in Biotechnology, **Vol. 1**, pp. 42–48.
5. Linko, P. (1985). *Fuels and industrial chemicals through biotechnology.* Biotechnology Advances, **Vol. 3**, pp. 39–63.
6. Linko, P. and Linko, Y-Y. (1983). *Applications of immobilized microbial cells.* Applied Biochemistry and Bioengineering, **Vol. 4**, pp. 53–151.
7. Neidleman, S.L. (1984). *Applications of biocatalysis to biotechnology.* Biotechnology and Genetic Engineering, **Vol. 1**, pp. 1–38.
8. Yamada, H. and Shimizu, S. (1988). *Microbial and enzymatic processes for the production of biologically and chemically useful compounds.* Angew. Chem. Int. Ed. Engl., **Vol. 27**, pp. 622–462.

Chapter 18

Industrial Enzymes

Donald A. Cowan

INTRODUCTION

The enzymic modification of raw materials has been an important component of industrial processing for centuries. However, only in the past half century has our increasing understanding of molecular structure and function enabled us to design processes which can start to utilize the enormous capacity provided by those naturally-evolved catalytic systems, the enzymes. Despite the fact that the industrial and commercial application of *biocatalysis* is responsible for products worth billions of dollars, there is good reason to think that we have barely scratched the surface of the range of enzyme capabilities. In this chapter it is hoped to provide an overview of the diversity of current enzyme-based or related industrial processes and to indicate some of the areas into which enzyme technology may expand in the coming years.

It proves to be extremely difficult to assess the exact extent of national consumption of any particular enzyme, let alone that of the total global enzyme utilization. Figures from 1981 suggest that the total world sales of commercial enzymes was of the order of $900 million. The accelerating trend of enzyme usage (about 15% per year since 1975) has certainly continued for those enzymes where data are available. We can thus estimate that the 1990 figures for global enzyme sales will be something like $2 billion.

Industrial applications are by no means equally distributed over the various classes of enzymes. As demonstrated in Figure 1, the emphasis is strongly biased towards the hydrolytic enzymes, and more specifically toward the peptide hydrolases (the proteinases). Of course, this unequal division is no coincidence. Historically, many of the most important industrial processes relied, sometimes unwittingly, on the action of intrinsic or exogenous hydrolytic activities. The bating (hair removal) of hides in leather production using the endogenous protease activity of dog faeces and the natural saccharification of starch in alcoholic fermentations are two

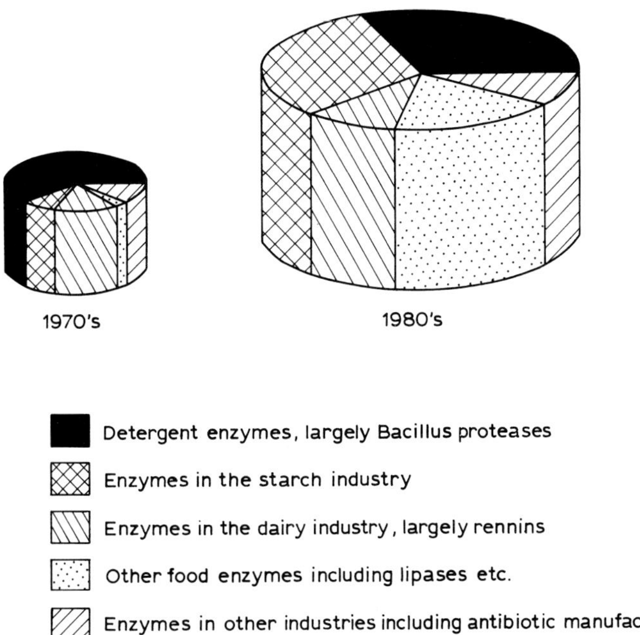

Figure 1. Current sales distribution of industrial enzymes.

obvious examples. The logical step, of identifying and then supplementing the critical enzymes, has led directly to many of the major industrial enzyme applications.

Of the many tens of thousands of different enzymes potentially available for commercial use, only a small faction are of any commercial significance. This is partly the result of industrial conservatism but is also closely linked to market economics. For example, where an industry uses a substantial enzyme component in processing (say tonnes per year), it is unlikely that any new enzyme of the same function, even if significantly more efficient, will be considered seriously unless it is available in the same form, at the same (or lower) price, and with a similar guaranteed supply. The new enzyme will be an industrially feasible proposition only if it can replace an existing enzyme with little or no modification of process or plant and if its improved properties translate into a significant commercial benefit.

There are, however, some groups of enzymes where a high proportion of those known have some (relatively small scale) commercial applications. The best examples are the restriction enzymes. While any newly isolated restriction enzyme has a significant chance (maybe 1-in-10) of finding a place in the rapidly expanding list of DNA-manipulating enzymes, in most cases the annual sales will not exceed a few tens of thousands of dollars.

Breaking into the industrial enzyme market is a more difficult task than it might appear. The two approaches, identifying a process where the existing enzyme might be improved, or finding an "interesting" enzyme and then searching for a suitable application, are equally fraught with dangers. The former will involve considerable expense of time and money either in searching for an enzyme with appropriate properties or in attempting to modify the existing enzyme by either chemical or genetic techniques. None of these alternatives hold any guarantee of rapid success. The second alternative is even less certain, although this route does provide a stimulant for the development of novel enzyme-based processes.

In a discussion of industrial enzyme applications it is necessary to define our area of interest. Exactly what constitutes *industrial* as opposed to *commercial* is rarely defined (the implication is that the separation relates to the size of the application) and making a definitive separation is rather artificial. This chapter deals with all the major enzyme-based processes (both industrial and commercial) and some of the smaller examples. Space does not allow a detailed review of all of the minor "commercial" enzyme applications.

INDUSTRIAL ENZYME APPLICATIONS

In a cursory assessment of the relative advantages and disadvantages of using enzymes in industrial processes (Table 1), it seems somewhat surprising that they are used at all. Nevertheless, as demonstrated in this chapter, both widespread and profitable applications exist.

The advantages of using enzymes are primarily derived from two intrinsic properties: catalytic rate enhancement and specificity. The ability of enzymes to enhance reaction rates by many orders of magnitude may seem obvious but is particularly significant when we appreciate that these rates are achieved under very mild conditions. For most enzymes, this can be translated as an aqueous environment at atmospheric pressure, a temperature between 15°C and 50°C, and a pH of 2 to 10. In comparison with the conditions used in chemical processing, they are mild indeed. The consequences of these environmental conditions are that firstly, reactor

Table 1
Advantages and Disadvantages of the Industrial Use of Enzymes

Advantages	Potential Problems
Enzymes of high or low specificity can be selected to suit the desired function.	The cost of enzyme preparations is often high.
Little (or no) by-product formation is observed.	Enzymes are intrinsically unstable.
Optimum activity occurs under very mild reaction conditions.	Enzymes are easily inhibited.
	Substrates or products with a low solubility in aqueous solution can pose difficulties.

technology need not be so sophisticated and secondly, the opportunity for the formation of chemically-induced by-products is vastly reduced. For example, in starch processing, traditional chemical degradation methods yielded a product containing some 6% of residual polysaccharide as well as coloured degradation products, the removal of which required a further purification step. The most recent enzymic process produces a clean product containing at most 0.1% oligosaccharide.

The ability to obtain very rapid reaction rates under very mild conditions facilitates the processing of relatively sensitive substrates (particularly foodstuffs) where extremes of temperature, pH or pressure would be undesirable.

Enzyme specificity is the other great advantage. The necessity for the substrate to possess the conformationally correct structure endows enzymes with a degree of selectivity unattainable in chemical processing. Different enzymes possess different levels of specificity and, indeed, it is possible to select an enzyme for a given process to suit the desired level of specificity. In practical terms, specificity not only reduces interference by undesirable substrates but minimizes the problems of unwanted by-products.

By-product formation can be a costly inconvenience in industrial processing. The addition of another process step is always economically undesirable. Even where by-product removal is not required, any product other than that desired reduces the overall efficiency of the conversion.

The molecular characteristics which are responsible for the useful properties of enzymes may also have certain disadvantages. Enzymes are proteins, complex three-dimensional macromolecules whose function relies on strict maintenance of that structure. This in turn requires the presence of a suitable environment. In consequence, considerable expenditure on temperature and pH control is usually necessary. Much deviation from either results in irreversible inactivation of the catalyst. Even under optimum conditions, enzymes are subject to the deleterious effects of denaturation, irreversible inhibition and enzymic degradation. The product of these influences is observed as the enzyme "half-life", the time taken for the loss of 50% of the initial enzyme activity under the particular set of conditions imposed.

Enzymes are particularly prone to inhibition, both reversible and irreversible. Reversible inhibition by substrate, product or an analogue of either is good justification for either seeking an alternative enzyme with improved inhibition characteristics, or for introducing some prior processing of the feedstock. Inhibition is often a property of the particular class of enzyme (e.g. heavy metals strongly inhibit sulphydryl enzymes but effect serine enzymes to a lesser extent).

The conditions under which enzymes operate optimally are generally quite suitable for the growth of microorganisms. For processes which either utilize continuous reaction systems or long reaction times, bacterial or yeast contamination can sometimes be a problem.

Table 2
Typical Costs for Some Industrial and Speciality Enzymes

Industrial Enzyme Preparations:	
Proteases	\$3–\$10/kg
Carbohydrases	\$10–\$30/kg
Lipases	\$30–\$200/kg
Speciality Enzymes:*	
Thermolysin	\$100,000/kg
Alcohol dehydrogenase	\$100,000–\$300,000/kg

* These values have been estimated directly from 1988 catalogue prices (actually quoted on a "per mg" basis). These are highly purified enzymes designed for research use. For an economic large-scale application, prices might be reduced by as much as one-to-two orders of magnitude.

All of these factors relate to the ultimate cost of using enzymes for any commercial process. This cost is determined by the "dose" of enzyme required for the bioconversion of a particular tonnage of substrate. As biological products, enzymes are produced in relatively small quantities and are expensive (Table 2). Optimizing the yield of the enzyme is thus of great importance. Moreover, the expectation that the enzyme cost should contribute no more than 0.1%–1% of the value of the product places a severe limitation on the range of possible conversions. For example, the maximum enzyme cost for processing a product worth \$200 per tonne is \$2. For the specialist enzymes of high cost, it is obvious that only those processes producing very high value products are worth considering in economic terms.

Ultimately, the forces that dictate the use of enzymes in industry and commerce are supply and demand. Where a need arises which cannot be filled by other means but can be met by biocatalysis, a process will develop. Other factors such as the discovery of new enzymes or new reaction conditions may influence the rate of development.

Sources of Enzymes

Where a decision is taken to introduce an enzymic conversion into an industrial process, one of the first decisions will be related to the source of the enzyme required. Relatively few enzymes are available in bulk from commercial suppliers. Most are hydrolases (proteases, amylases, lipases) and, for a process requiring an enzyme other than these, "in house" isolation and production may be the only feasible alternative.

Any organism, whether plant, animal or microorganism, is a potential source of enzymes. However, the nature of the source dictates the availability, the cost of source material,

Table 3
Various Sources of Enzymes

General Source	Specific Source	Advantages/Disadvantages	Example
Animals	Human blood.	No longer a viable source.	–
	Bovine, porcine, and ovine tissues.	Available in vast quantity. Enzymes often of low stability, some of the more "exotic" enzymes not found. Purification often complex.	Pancreatic lipase, Rennin Trypsin
Plants	Leaves, fruit.	Purification can be a problem.	Papain
Microorganisms	Bacterial, algal, fungal and yeast.	Large-scale production technology advanced, purification often simple sophisticated methods for enhancing yield. A wide variety of unusual enzyme activities available. Only limited range of microorganisms approved for use in the food industry.	Proteases, amylases, lipases, etc.

Table 4
Source of Major Industrial Enzymes

Enzyme	Process	Source
Proteases-alkaline	Detergents	Bacterial
Proteases-acid	Cheese-making	Animal, fungal
Proteases-neutral	Various	Bacterial
Amylases	Starch industry	Bacterial, fungal
Isomerases	High-fructose syrups	Fungal
Pectinases	Wine, beer, condiments	Fungal
Lipases	Various	Bacterial, fungal, animal

the ease of recovery and many other factors. Table 3 is a brief summation of factors which may be relevant to a choice of enzyme source.

Of those enzymes used on an industrial scale, the majority are derived from microbial sources (Table 4). The one major exception is that of rennin, the protease derived from calf stomach which is used in cheese-making. Even here, a microbial substitute, *Mucor* rennin or chymosin, is now being used in a significant proportion of the world-wide dairy industry.

The method of application of an enzyme may significantly influence the preparation procedures. Where crude preparations are satisfactory, it may be necessary to do no more than concentrate the primary extract by ultrafiltration or precipitation or to immobilize the whole cells. If it is necessary to remove contaminating proteins and other enzymic activities (e.g. as often required in the food industry), then more sophisticated purification protocols must be developed. High capacity purification methods such as ion exchange chromatography are generally preferred for industrial enzyme processing.

Enzyme Preparations

There are a number of ways in which an enzyme preparation can be presented to the market: as an amorphous or microcrystalline powder, in solution, or in some absorbed or covalently linked (immobilized) form. The nature of this preparation will be determined largely by the requirements of the industry. In most cases, large-scale users of enzymes

Table 5
A Typical Composition of an Industrial Enzyme Preparation

	Approximate content (% dry solids)	Function
Proteins and amino acids	10–15	
Enzyme protein	2–5	
Polysaccharides (e.g. starch)	5–12	Bulking
Sugars or polyols	2–40	Stabilizing, bulking
Inorganic salts	3–40	Stabilizing, bulking, buffering
Preservatives	0–0.3	Antimicrobial, antioxidant

require a minimum of purification and in the case of microbial extracellular enzymes (the bacterial proteases, for example) a lyophilized cell-free supernatant treated to remove the coloured components is quite acceptable.

Whether in liquid or powdered form, industrial enzyme preparations are usually bulked out with various additives. In powdered form, a typical enzyme preparation would consist of less than 5% enzyme protein (Table 5). Other additives are included as buffers, as stabilizers, antimicrobial agents and simply to increase the volume. Justification for bulking out enzyme preparation comes from the fact that it is usually simpler to add 5 kg of enzyme to a process tank than 5 g. Bulking also provides an easy mechanism for standardizing enzyme preparations.

Liquid preparations are often preferred. Although enzymes are inherently less stable in solution, liquid preparations have significantly advantages. Volume measurement is simple and the need to accurately weigh small amounts of material (possibly performed by relatively unskilled workers) is avoided. More importantly, solutions do not suffer from the very real problems of dust formation.

In the early 1960s, finely powdered preparations of bacterial protease were used in detergent preparations. Widespread reports of allergic reactions in process workers were linked with the appearance of skin reactions in housewives (these reactions were later shown not to be caused by the proteases). This led to a massive swing in public opinion resulting in the withdrawal of "enzyme"-based washing powders from the U.S. market (and others) for almost a decade. Even in the United Kingdom, where detergent preparations containing enzymes are again common, the term "enzyme" is nowhere in evidence and has been substituted by the term "biological".

One of the immediate results of this rather harsh lesson on the devastating effects of adverse public opinion was a development in the presentation of dry enzyme preparations. Techniques for the encapsulation and granulation of enzyme preparations have effectively removed the problems of enzyme dusts. Early improvements involved "prilling". An enzyme concentrate was mixed with surfactants, pigments and a low melting point non-ionic detergent such as fatty alcohol ethoxylate. The molten mixture was poured onto a rotating disk which generated and dispersed "droplets" from the rim. The droplets solidified after leaving the disk, were collected and dried. This method was successful in embedding the protease in an inert but soluble carrier, although active enzyme was still present on the particle surface.

A more recent development is the process of mixed granulation. A plastic mixture of enzyme and other constituents is forced through a 0.5 to 2 mm sieve. The extruded product is sliced into short sections and these are abraded to spherical beads by a rapidly rotating disk. After drying the beads are coated with wax to form a soluble powder of regular particles having no surface protease activity.

Enzyme immobilization, a technique which also reduces the potential problems of enzyme toxicity, is used only in specific instances and will be discussed in more detail below.

Legislation

Legislative attitudes on the use of enzymes are clearly separated on the basis of end-usage. There are no controls on the use of enzymes for research purposes (although controls on the production and shipment in the form of required safety practices do exist).

Intended use of microbial enzymes in the food or drug industry incurs strict controls, the exact nature depending on the country. In the United States, the U.S. code of Federal Regulations (1981) and the Food and Drug Administration (FDA) GRAS (Generally Recognized As Safe) guidelines operate. In the U.K., legislative control is provided by the Government via recommendations from the Food Additives and Contaminants Committee (FACC) under advice from the Committee on Toxicity of Chemicals in Food and the Environment (COT).

FDA guidelines for safety evaluations of food additives are based on a three-tiered structure relating to the expected human exposure to the additive:

(i) Where the structure of the additive is unrelated to any known toxic substance and the expected daily diet is less than 0.05 ppm (parts per million), tests should include a 28 day continuous feeding study and a genetic toxicity screen, using a single rodent species.

(ii) Where the structure of the additive is unrelated to any known toxic substance and the expected daily diet is between 0.05 ppm and 1.0 ppm, tests should include a 90 day subchronic feeding study in each of a rodent and a non-rodent species, a reproduction study with a teratology phase and a genetic toxicity screen.

(iii) Where the structure of the additive is unrelated to any known toxic substance and the expected daily diet is greater than 1.0 ppm, tests should include a lifetime feeding study for carcinogenicity in two rodent and non-rodent species, a reproduction study with a teratology phase and a genetic toxicity screen.

In recent times, requirements for FDA approval have apparently stiffened and now may include: demonstration that the microorganism is non-pathogenic in man and other animals and that it does not produce exo- or endotoxins or antibiotics, multigeneration feeding studies at 1.24, 2.4 and 5% of diet in a rodent species, and a reproductive study with *in utero* exposure and with teratological analysis.

Details of these data, together with those on manufacturing practice, enzyme properties and end-usage are submitted to the FDA in support of an application for approval as "Generally Recognized As Safe".

The stringent requirements of the GRAS regulations provide a major stumbling block to the addition of new enzymes (and particularly enzymes from new sources) into the food and beverage industry.

Enzymes from animal and plant sources are not included under these requirements. However, no new enzymes from either of these sources were used in the American food industry between 1958 and 1982.

For those enzymes not intended for use in the food and beverage industries, controls are relatively limited. Legislative requirements include an accurate description of the state of purity, the presence of contaminants and the composition and the characteristics of the enzyme.

In all cases, there are quite distinct requirements for good manufacturing practice in order to safeguard both the manufacturing operators and the end-users.

Bioreactors (see also Chapter 13)

There are many different types of reactors used on an industrial scale. They are broadly divided into batch and continuous configurations (e.g. Figure 2). The most efficient type of reactor to use with a given process will depend on the characteristics of that process (Table 6). For example, where very high viscosity or insoluble substrates must be used, soluble enzyme preparations must be used. Plug-flow reactors (where insoluble enzyme particles are packed in a column down which the substrate flow passes) are particularly susceptible to blocking and compression. In a fluidized-bed configuration, some of these problems are avoided by passage of the substrate stream in an upward direction. Despite the apparent advantages of continuous reactor configurations, most bioconversions in the food and beverage industries utilize batch reactors.

There is a considerable degree of standardization in the construction of biochemical reaction vessels. For example, they are almost always of stainless steel construction. Only where catalytic processes require a combination of high temperature (70°–110°C), high salt concentration and low pH would some internal coating of greater chemical resistance such as Teflon^R or enamel be required. Although the author is not aware of any biocatalytic processes currently utilizing this combination of conditions, such precautions are necessary in the construction of fermentation vessels for the thermoacidophilic archaebacteria.

Reactor size is variable, depending on the process. Generally, vessels for batch reactions need to be much larger than

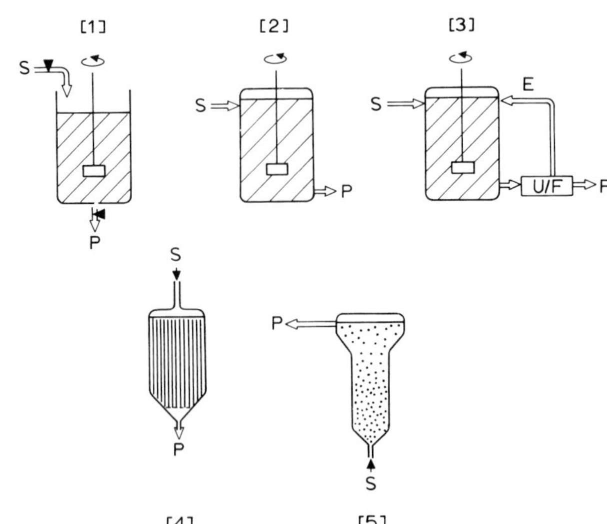

Figure 2. Diagrammatic representations of enzyme reactor configurations.
[1] Batch reactor; [2] Continuous stirred tank reactor (CSTR); [3] CSTR with ultrafiltration (U/F) enzyme recycling; [4] Plug flow reactor (PFR); [6] Fluidized bed reactor.

Table 6
Properties of Some Different Reactor Types

Reactor Type	Used with Free or Immobilized Enzymes	Properties
Batch	Free	High viscosity or insoluble substrates can be used. New enzyme required for each batch. Substrate inhibition can be a problem.
Continuous-flow stirred tank	Free or immobilized	pH control simple. Enzyme addition/replacement simple. Colloidal or insoluble substrates can be used. Less problem with substrate inhibition.
Continuous-flow stirred tank with ultrafiltration	Free or immobilized	Colloidal or insoluble substrates can be used. Poor enzyme stability over long-term operation. Enzyme denatured or adsorbed at membrane surface.
Plug-flow	Immobilized	High conversion efficiency. Less problem with product inhibition. Cannot be used with insoluble or high viscosity substrates.
Fluidized-bed	Immobilized	Better heat and mass transfer. Insoluble and high viscosity substrates can be used. Low pressure drop. Energy input to maintain a fluidized bed is large.

those for continuous processes. On an industrial scale, they vary in capacity from a few to hundreds of cubic metres.

Reactors will incorporate a variety of additional components depending on the nature of the reaction. The capacity for steam sterilization influences construction to the extent that the design must be capable of withstanding internal pressures of at least 2 atmospheres and must be built to stringent industrial specifications.

Ports for feed-stock addition and product recovery are necessary, together with secondary ports for the addition of other chemicals (acid, alkali, enzyme, etc.). The vessel may be baffled, stirred and may incorporate heating elements, steam pipes or direct steam injection.

Control may be extensive or minimal. Sensors for pH and temperature may be included and connected via feed-back control facilities to appropriate inputs. Overall control may range from strictly manual to total control by computer programming.

In batch reactors, no attempt is usually made to recover the enzyme. In many cases, the enzyme is deliberately inactivated by a subsequent heating step. Where immobilized enzymes are used, the enzymes can be either recovered (e.g. by filtration) or retained within the reactor (in the plug-flow or fluidized bed reactor). The efficiency of enzyme utilization in immobilized enzyme biocatalysis is thus much greater than in batch reaction.

Despite this fact, the vast majority of industrial biocatalytic processes currently use "throw-away" enzymes. The reasons for this are complex but derive partly from the fact that the enzyme catalysis step often constitutes a small part of the overall process and the cost of the enzyme is usually less than 0.1% of the product cost. In addition, the technology associated with immobilized enzyme reactors is considerably more complex than that for a simple batch reactor.

The Technology of Enzyme Immobilization

Enzyme immobilization involves the presentation of an enzyme in an insoluble form as a macromolecular matrix. In 1970, when industrial enzymology was still in the early stages of development, it was predicted that immobilized enzyme technology would revolutionize the industry. It was apparent that many advantages could be achieved (Table 7), not the least being that enzyme costs could be substantially reduced.

Despite these apparent advantages, relatively little of the world's current enzyme-based industry utilizes immobilized enzyme technology. Only one process, the conversion of glucose to fructose by glucose isomerase in the production of high fructose syrups, uses immobilized enzymes at a rate of more than 50 tons per annum.

Several other immobilized enzymes are used at a rate of 5–50 tons per annum: aminoacylase in the preparation of L-amino acids from racemic mixtures of α-*N*-acetyl-DL-amino acids; penicillin G acylase in the production of acylated penicillins; and β-galactosidase in the hydrolysis of milk lactose. Other immobilized enzymes which are used on an industrial scale but at less than 5 tons per annum are glucoamylase, thermolysin, hydantoinase, invertase, nitrilase, RNase, and penicillin V acylase. As an indication of the relative importance of immobilized versus soluble enzymes, it is significant that nearly 99% of the world's production of glucose is generated by soluble glucoamylase.

In anticipation of a major role in industrial processing, an enormous amount of research has been targeted at new immobilization matrices, techniques and chemistries.

Table 7
Perceived Advantages of Using Immobilized Enzymes

Resistance	Immobilized enzymes are more resistant to denaturation and proteolysis.
Recovery	Immobilized enzyme preparations can be recovered and recycled in CSTR* systems, or used over long periods in plug-flow reactors.
Cost	Despite the expense of manufacturing immobilized enzyme preparations, the factors listed above yield a net positive cost-benefit.
Technology	Immobilized enzyme preparations allow new and potentially more efficient reactor technology to be developed.

* Continuous stirred tank reactor

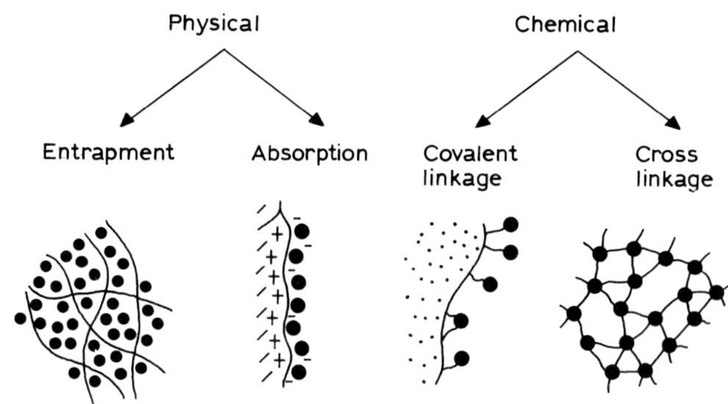

Figure 3. Common modes of immobilization.

Immobilization techniques can be divided into physical and chemical methods (Figure 3). Physical methods include absorption and entrapment. Chemical methods include covalent attachment to a matrix and the formation of a macromolecular matrix by cross-linking the enzyme (with or without a second polymer present). A enormous number of different types of matrices have been used in laboratory immobilization studies (a selection is listed in Table 8).

Some of the relevant factors to be considered in selecting a suitable matrix are shown in Table 9. The exact nature of the process design, the physical properties of the feedstock and the product, the reaction conditions and many other factors will place constraints on the type of matrix which will be most suitable. In an industrial operation, maximized enzyme-matrix life-span is a vital component. For this reason, covalently coupled conjugates, which are less prone to enzyme leakage than adsorbed or entrapped preparations, have played a major role.

The chemistry of covalent enzyme immobilization is highly complex and cannot be reviewed in detail here. Table 10 lists those matrix groups which are commonly used for immobilization, together with the reagents employed. The successful preparation of an immobilized product requires an understanding of the nature of the reactive groups both on the matrix and the enzyme. For example, it is most important that the immobilization chemistry is selected to minimize the covalent modification of active site amino acid side chains.

The reaction most frequently employed for the activation of polysaccharide hydroxyl groups (e.g. in dextrans such as Sephadex^R and Sepharose^R, or cellulose) is the generation of reactive imidocarbonate moieties using cyanogen bromide (Figure 4). The activation process takes place readily at high pH but the unstable cyanate intermediates are slowly converted into inert carbamates in aqueous solution, resulting in a gradual loss of reactivity. In the subsequent coupling step at moderately alkaline pHs, protein amino groups react with the imidocarbonate moieties to form, among other things, N-substituted isourea linkages (Figure 4). These linkages are quite stable and there is little evidence of enzyme leakage.

Table 8
Experimental Enzyme Immobilization Matrices

Matrix	Immobilization Chemistry
Carbon (or phospholipid coated C)	Adsorption
Cellulose	Adsorption
CM- and DEAE-cellulose, Sephadex, etc.	Adsorption
Cellulose acetate	Adsorption
Glass-controlled pore	Adsorption
Hydroxylapatite	Adsorption
Silica gel	Adsorption
Stainless steel (coated with TiO_2)	Adsorption
Polyacrylamide gels and beads	Entrapment
Nylon microcapsules	Entrapment
Liposomes	Entrapment
Cellulose	Covalent attachment
Agarose (e.g. Sepharose)	Covalent attachment
Bacterial or fungal cells (non-growing)	Covalent attachment
Ceramics (TiO_2/MgO; SiO_2/Al_2O_3; SiO_2/ZeO_2, etc.)	Covalent attachment
Polyacrylamide	Covalent attachment
Polystyrene	Covalent attachment
Polyamides (e.g. nylon)	Covalent attachment
Porous glass	Covalent attachment
Metal oxides (Fe,Ni)	Covalent attachment

Table 9
Factors to be Considered in the Selection of an Immobilization Matrix

Factor under Consideration	Examples
Cost of matrix	Beaded dextrans and controlled-pore glass are expensive compared with ceramics and celluloses.
Chemical resistance of the matrix	Silica-based matrices are significantly soluble at pH values above 8.0. Cellulose and dextran-based matrices can be degraded enzymically. Some organic polymers change shape in organic solvents.
Physical properties of the matrix	Ceramic matrices have a high resistance to pressure compared with beaded dextrans.
Complexity of the immobilization chemistry	Ion exchange and adsorption interactions can be generated rapidly and minimize the inactivation of unstable enzymes. Covalent attachment can be laborious, expensive and destructive.
Stability of the enzyme-matrix association	Enzymes immobilized by physical means undergo slow leakage compared with covalently attached enzymes.
Special requirements of the process	Pressure sensitive matrices (e.g. agarose) are unsuitable for plug-flow reactors. Magnetic matrices are useful for the recovery of enzyme in CSTR* systems.

* Continuous stirred tank reactor

Table 10
A Summary of Some Common Immobilization Chemistries

Matrix group	Examples of matrix	Coupling reagent	Reactive group on protein
Hydroxyl	Dextrans, celluloses	Cyanogen bromide	Amino
Carboxylate	Acrylic acid/acrylamide copolymers	Carbodiimides	Amino
Amino	Modified ceramics	Glutaraldehyde	Amino
	Modified ceramics	p-Nitrobenzyl chloride/dithionite/ sodium nitrite, acid	Tyr-hydroxyl
Aldehyde	Polymeric aldehydes	React directly via Schiff's base	Amino and others
Imidoesters	O-alkylated nylon	React directly	Amino
Aryldiazonium	Modified ceramics and polysaccharides	React directly	Tyr-hydroxyl His-imidizole Amino
Thiol	Modified polysaccharides	React directly	Cys-thiol

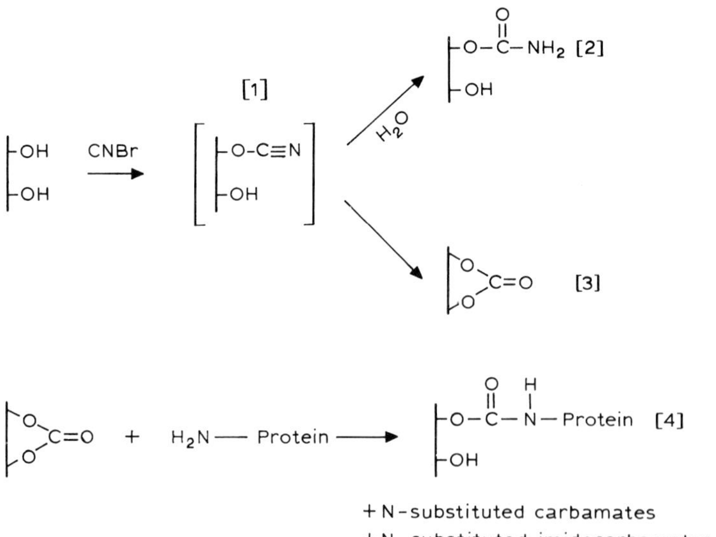

Figure 4. Covalent attachment of protein to polysaccharide using cyanogen bromide.
[1] Cyanate intermediate; [2] inert carbamate; [3] reactive imidocarbonate; [4] N-substituted isourea.

Hydroxyl groups on ceramic matrices are not usually accessible for direct activation. The insertion of reactive groups involves reaction with substituted silanes such as γ-aminopropyl triethoxysilane. The alkylamine derivative is suitable for direct coupling using a bifunctional reagent such as glutaraldehyde or a carbodiimide (Figure 5a–5b) or for further derivitization to an arylamine, to a carboxylate, or to a thiocyanate (Figure 5c–5f). Each of these groups is suitable for subsequent coupling, either directly (as in the thiocyanate and the aldehyde), or indirectly using a bifunctional reagent. The extreme toxicity of the thiophosgene used in the generation of the thiocyanate reduces the popularity of this reaction.

Beaded polyacrylamide gels (Eupergit[R], Biogel[R], Enzacryl[R], etc.) can be activated by a variety of reactions, each requiring the preliminary modification of the polymer (Figure 6). Where acrylamide copolymers are formed (e.g. with acrylic acid, methacrylic acid, *p*-aminoacrylanilide, or acroyl hydrazide), many other coupling options are introduced by

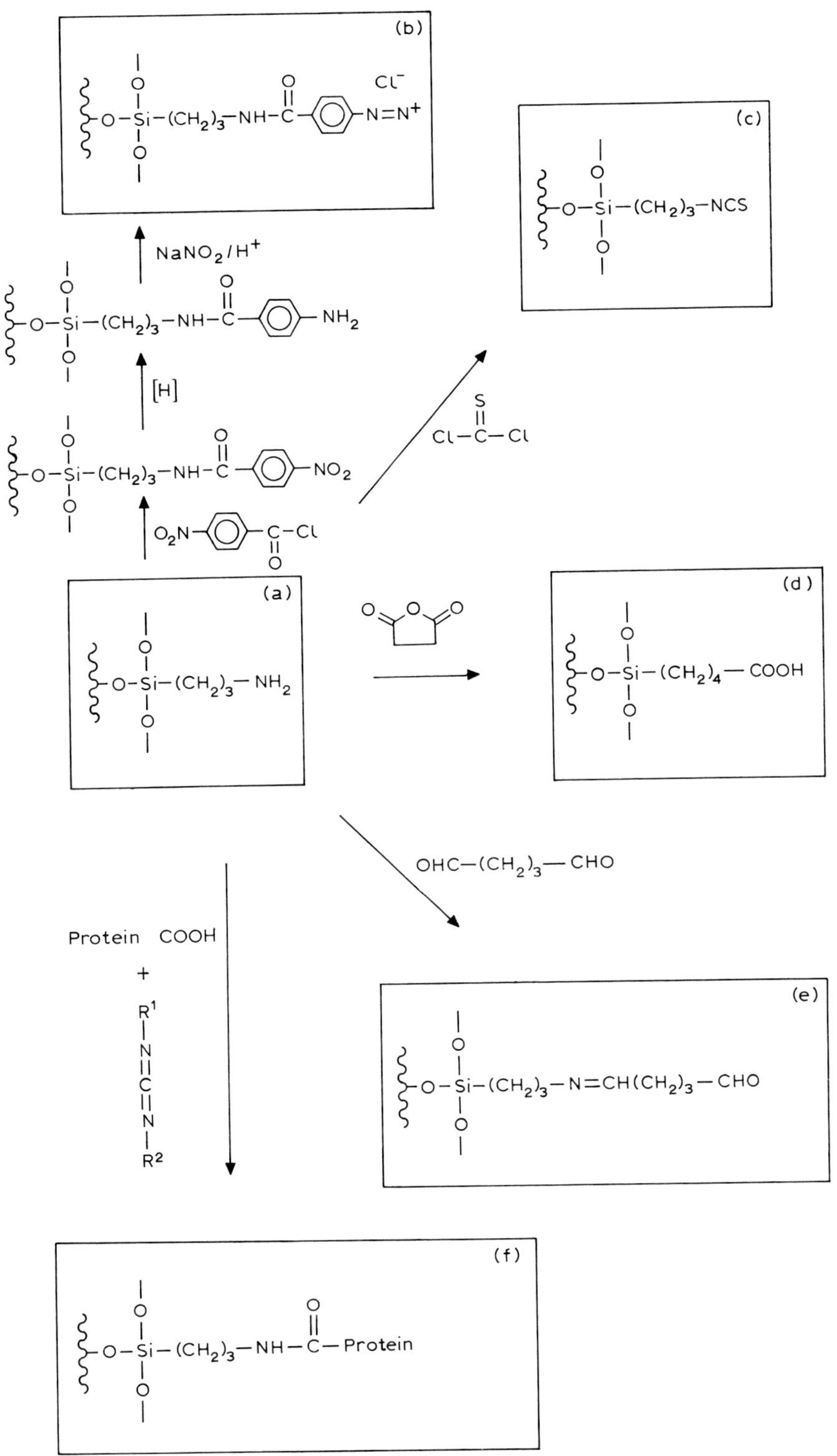

Figure 5. Pathways for immobilizing proteins to silane-modified ceramics: [a] Ceramic modified with γ-aminopropyl triethoxysilane; [b] diazo adduct; [c] thiocyanate; [d] carboxylate; [e] aldehyde; [f] direct linkage using carbodiimide.

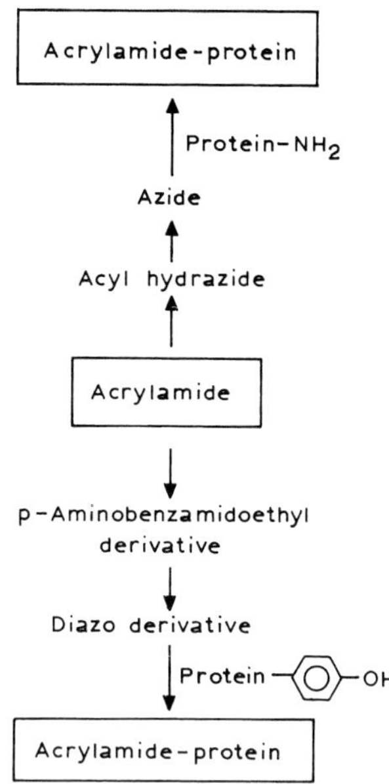

Figure 6. Immobilizing protein to acrylamide.

the presence of the carboxylate, arylamino or azide groups.

Future commercial developments in this field are difficult to predict because economics play a greater part than science. However, recent scientific advances include the synthesis of better ceramic matrices, the co-immobilization of enzymes to enhance reactant recycling or generate multistep synthetic pathways and the steady development of whole cell immobilization/entrapment techniques.

INDUSTRIAL ENZYMES

Introduction

Some 80% of the total industrial enzyme consumption comes from low specificity enzymes, largely hydrolases degrading high molecular weight natural polymers such as proteins and carbohydrates. This is a reflection of the historical development of the enzyme industry and an indication of favourable economic factors inherent in processing high volume, low cost products. In all cases, the enzyme is a minor cost component of the process. There is little apparent incentive to improve the functional characteristics of the enzyme in many of these applications (e.g. in the detergent industry). In others, the expenditure in plant and technology is so high as to preclude the introduction of new technology such as immobilized enzymes or functionally superior enzymes which require different reaction conditions.

The past decade has seen substantial changes in the market share of different enzymes and, most significantly, a rise in the application of high specificity enzymes. The detergent industry, for the past 30 years the major user of enzymes (all

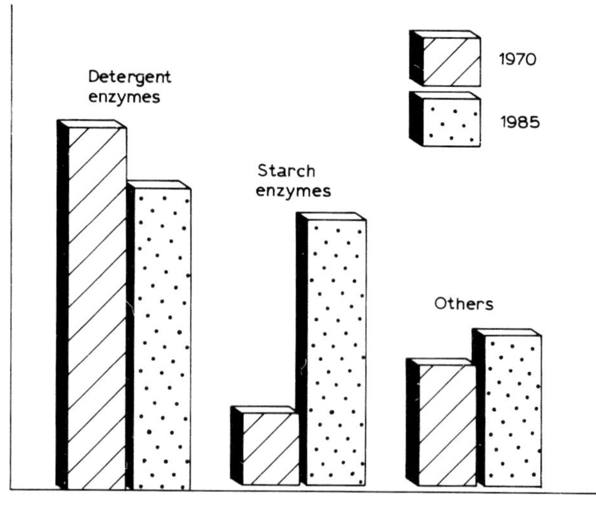

Figure 7. Changing patterns in the industrial use of enzymes.

of low specificity), has grown rather more slowly than other industries such as starch processing. The requirement for quantities of high specificity enzymes such as glucose isomerase has engendered a significant shift in the relative importance of the two groups of enzymes (Figure 7).

In this chapter, industrial enzymes have been separated into those of high specificity and those of low specificity. Although this is an artificial distinction, there is a close correlation with the separation of modern and traditional enzyme applications, respectively. It is likely that this correlation is also indicative of future trends in the development of industrial enzymology.

Amylases and the Starch Industry

The starch industry accounts for between 20 and 28% of the total annual industrial consumption of enzymes, a market share which is conservatively estimated to be worth more than $200 million. The bulk of this market is comprised of α-amylase, amyloglucosidase (also referred to as glucoamylase) and glucose isomerase, the three enzymes used primarily in the conversion of starch to a variety of sweetening agents. The first two are low specificity enzymes capable of hydrolysing a variety of substrates to a limited range of products. The latter is a high specificity enzyme and will be discussed more fully in the next section.

α-Amylases (α-1, 4-D-glucan glucanohydrolase, EC 3.2.1.1) are endoglycosidases specific for the α-1,4 glycosidic linkages in glucose polymers such as starch (amylose and amylopectin) and glycogen (Figure 8). They will not attack the α-1,6 linkages of branched polysaccharides. Hydrolysis products are primarily maltose and maltotriose (from linear substrates) and these plus limit dextrins (from branched substrates). The

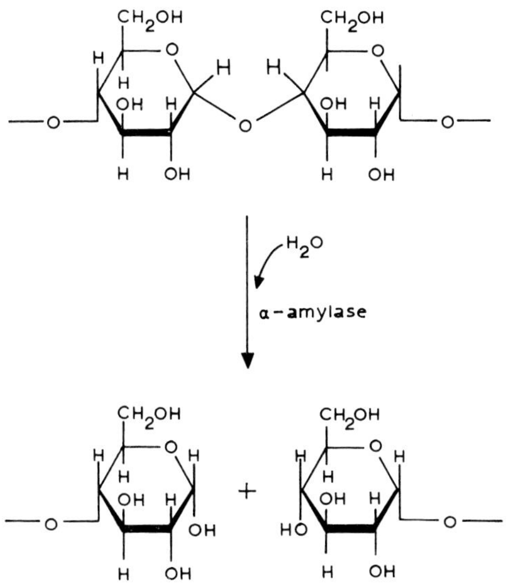

Figure 8. Endo-hydrolysis of α-1, 4-glucose polymers.

limit dextrin structures vary with different enzymes but all contain α-1,6 branching points.

α-Amylases are produced by a wide variety of organisms. They are monomeric proteins with molecular weights ranging from 20,000 to 100,000 (average about 50,000). Many but not all require calcium to retain stability at higher temperatures and some are calcium-activated. They are enzymes of generally high thermal stability and many have the so-called "temperature optimum" in the range of 70°–90°C.

Numerous chemical manufacturers and supply companies offer α-amylase preparations for industrial applications.

Amyloglucosidases (α-1,4-D-glucan glucohydrolase, glucoamylase, EC 3.2.1.3) are exoglucosidases hydrolysing terminal 1,4-linked α-D-glucose residues from the non-reducing ends of glucose polysaccharide chains. The sole product is β-D-glucose. Some hydrolysis of α-1,6 glycosidic linkages also occurs although the size of the substrate and the position of the linkage influences the rate of hydrolysis. In sufficient excess and over a prolonged period of time, they will totally degrade starch to monosaccharides.

Amyloglucosidases are monomeric proteins with molecular weights ranging from around 20,000 to over 100,000. Most have pH/activity optima between 4.5 and 5.0. These enzymes are less thermostable than the α-amylases and most are rapidly denatured at temperatures above 70°C. *Aspergillus niger* strains provide most industrial amyloglucosidase. The other enzymes used in starch technology are fungal α-amylase and plant β-amylase (Table 12). β-Amylases (α-1,4-D-glucan maltohydrolase, EC 3.2.1.2) are exo-glycosidases hydrolysing alternate glucosidic linkages to yield maltose (with some maltotriose). α-1,6 linkages are not hydrolysed and complete maltogenic saccharification of starch can take place only if an enzyme with debranching (α-1,6) activity such as pullulanase is present. At present, it has proved more economical in the production of high maltose syrups to use fungal α-amylase, a broad specificity enzyme which cleaves both α-1,4 and α-1,6 linkages to yield maltose as the major product.

Conventional technology for the conversion of starch into glucose involves three processes: gelatinization, thinning and dextrinization (liquefaction), and saccharification (Figure 9). The products of these processes are used in numerous food products (Table 11) although high maltose syrups have greater demands in Japan than in the United States.

In the first step, the raw starch is heated to above 60°C to disrupt the starch granules and expose the polymer to enzymic action, while denaturing and precipitating associated protein. The very high viscosity product is thinned before further treatment.

There have been significant developments in the technology of subsequent starch conversion over the past two decades (Figure 10). In the traditional process, dextrinization was achieved by the use of acid. The pH was adjusted to 1.5–2 before heating to 140–155°C for 5–10 minutes. Although this process gave a product of good rheological properties, coloured byproducts and reversion products (e.g. in the chemical isomerization of maltose to maltulose) were generated and purification was a significant problem. Replacement of the acid step with a high temperature enzymic hydrolysis step has improved both the quality and the yield of the dextrinized product. The first development was the use of the Novo BAN[R] α-amylase capable of operating at 85°C. In a later development, the introduction of the more thermostable *B. licheniformis* α-amylase (e.g. Novo Termamyl[R]) enabled

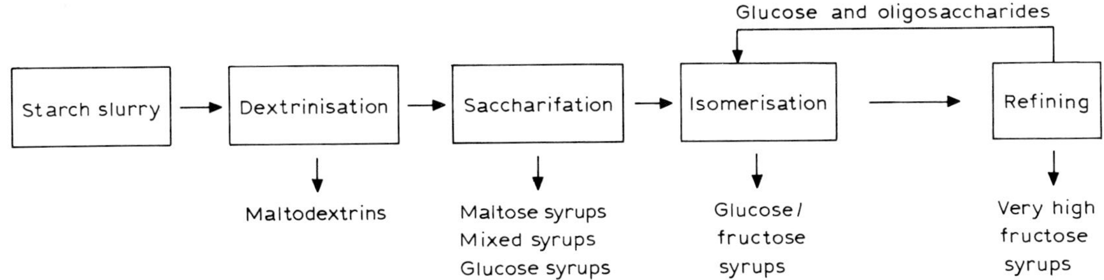

Figure 9. Schematic summary of starch processing.

Table 11
Uses of Starch Hydrolysis Products

Maltodextrins	Fillers, stabilizers, glues, pastes, thickeners
Mixed syrups	Confectionary, soft drinks, brewing and fermentation, jams, conserves, sauces, ice cream, baby food
Maltose syrups	Hard confectionary
Glucose syrups	Soft drinks, caramel, wine and juice fermentations
High fructose syrups	Soft drinks, conserves, sauces, yoghurts, canned fruits, low calorie products, topical application (after crystallization)

the use of continuous jet cooking for short periods at 105°C followed by more prolonged dextrinization at 95–100°C without the necessity for further enzyme addition.

Generally, subsequent purification involves filtration followed by treatment with activated carbon and an ion exchange resin (to remove the enzymes). The purified dextrose product is either marketed as a syrup, crystallized, or further processed by isomerization to a glucose/fructose mixture.

The production of maltose and mixed syrups from starch slurries ("maltogenic saccharification") utilizes fungal α-

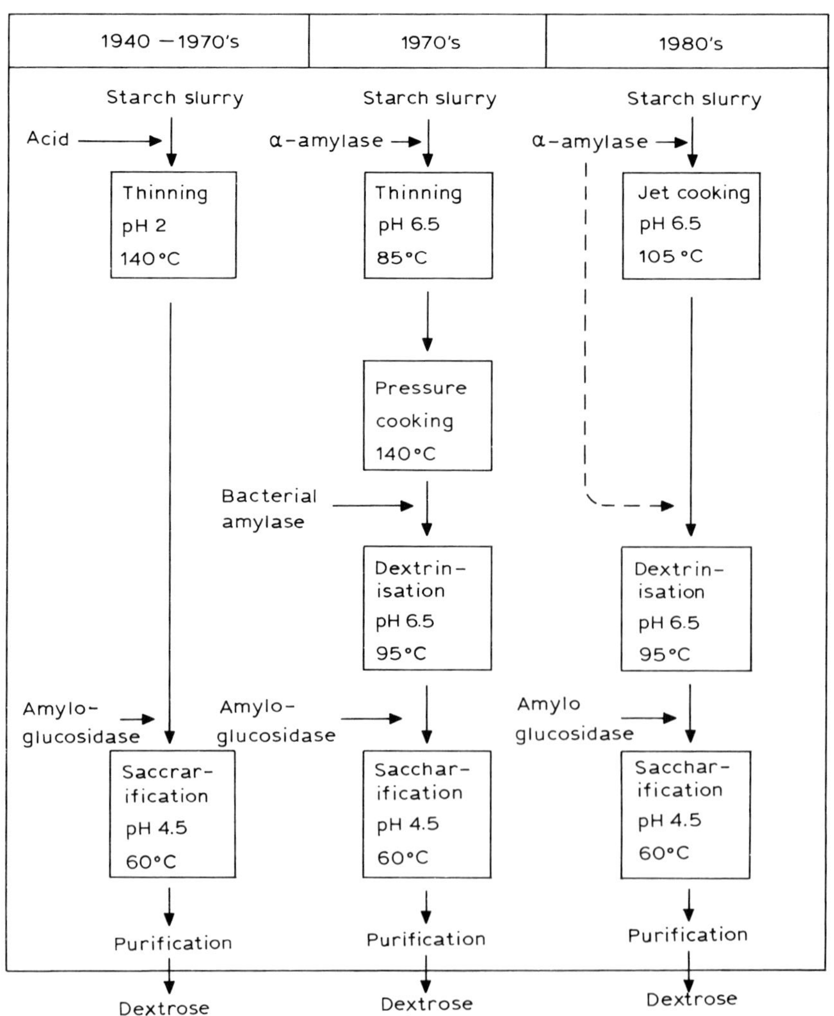

Figure 10. Developments in starch liquefaction and saccharification technology.

Table 12
Product Profiles from Starch Hydrolysis Methods

	D.E.*	Glucose	Maltose	Isomaltose	Maltotriose	Oligos
Acid	95	91.5	2.5		6.0	
Acid/enzyme	97	93	2.5		3.5	
Enzyme	98	96	1–2	1.3	–	0.1
Maltose/dextrose	42	18	43	?	?	?
High maltose	53	5	52	?	15	?

* Dextrose equivalents

amylase although bacterial β-amylases are now known. A combination of fungal α-amylase and bacterial amyloglucosidase yields a mixed glucose/maltose syrup.

Composition profiles from the various starch hydrolysis procedures indicate the advances resulting from the development of the all-enzyme technology (Table ?). Furthermore, it is clear that the variety of enzymes available provides the flexibility to vary product characteristics in response to the needs of the market.

Other Industrial Uses of Glycohydrolases

The non-specific α-amylases have been used for many years in other areas of industry. These include the sizing and desizing of textiles, in paper manufacture, in starch degradation for potable alcohol production, in baking and flour treatment and in detergent preparations. To the author's knowledge, amylases are still used routinely in all these industries although it is almost impossible to determine the current national or international usage. Certainly, there has been a tendency for these more traditional applications to vary in relation to changes in industrialization. For example, the decline in the natural fibre textile industry has led to a significant drop in the use of enzymes.

Textiles

Natural fibres are placed under considerable stress during weaving and in order to minimize breakages are usually pretreated with a "size". Sizes are adhesive polymers, most of which are starch-based and are pretreated by partial enzymic hydrolysis. Once the fabric has been woven, it is often necessary to remove the starch in order to dye, bleach or treat with other chemicals. Most modern textile factories use amylase preparations for this purpose. Enzymic treatment has the advantage of causing much less damage to the cloth than the alternative chemical and physical methods. Earlier application of pancreatic and malt amylases has now largely been replaced with bacterial enzymes. The availability of the thermostable *B. licheniformis* α-amylase has allowed the development of modern high-temperature continuous processing, where overall process time is reduced to no more than 5 minutes and the starch hydrolysis occurs in a steam chamber at 100–110°C for 20–120 seconds. This compares most favourably with earlier lower temperature semi-continuous processes, where a holding period of 2–4 hours at 70–75°C (or overnight at 50°C) would be necessary.

Paper Manufacture

The addition of starch to paper, either as a size to coat cellulose fibres or as a surface coating, improves a number of physical properties such as strength, erasibility and stiffness. In order to reduce the viscosity of natural starch before application, the polymeric structure is partially hydrolysed (dextrinized) either by thermochemical treatment with heat and acid followed by sodium hypochlorite, or by partial enzymic hydrolysis. Enzymic treatment was first introduced in the '60s, only to be superseded by thermochemical methods. In the past decade (in line with the availability of better enzymes and greater understanding of the process involved), enzymic starch technology has been steadily increasing. Currently, more than 30% of starch used in the paper industry is enzyme-treated.

Baking

The use of wheat and other cereals as a source of flour for baking (particularly in the production of bread, probably the major staple food item in the western world) provides a demonstration of a natural enzymic process which can be modified artificially to optimize product quality. Amylases are a natural constituent of flour. The levels of amylase activity in flour are strongly influenced by the climatic conditions in which the grain was grown. A high amylase content, the result of a moist climate, results in high dextrin production during baking. The resulting dough has a low water retention and tends to "stickness", while the loaf is crumbly and dry. A dry environment yields flour with a low amylase content. In consequence, the dextrin yield is low, fermentative gas production is poor and loaf size is small.

Since the early 1960s, amylase levels in flour have been monitored and supplemented (or diluted) where necessary. Traditionally, malt (containing plant β-amylase) was used as an enzyme supplement. More recently, this has been replaced by fungal α-amylase. The more thermostable bacterial amylases are of little use since they are not inactivated during baking and result in excessive dextrinization.

Modern developments in the baking industry are tending towards continuous processing with shorter holding and baking times. This requires higher levels of amylase supplementation in order to generate the required levels of dextrinization and fermentable sugar production. The future expectation is for increased levels of enzyme utilization in the baking industry.

Potable Alcohol

The processes involved in the fermentation of starch-containing substrates (barley, wheat, rye, sorghum, rice, potatoes, etc.) to yield potable alcohols are highly variable, depending on the nature of the substrate and the intended properties of the product. In all cases however, supplementation of the natural levels of saccharifying (and other) enzymes is now routine practice.

Supplementation can occur at various stages during the process. During the initial steps of decoction and mash formation in which probably 80% of the original starch is converted into fermentable sugars (glucose, maltose, maltotriose), bacterial and fungal α-amylases are often added, together with bacterial and fungal glucanases. The latter are important in the removal of β-glucans, β-1,3 and β-1,4-linked polymers which are viscous gum-like substances. Failure to hydrolyse the glucans introduces problems in the efficiency of wort filtration and in the later production of hazes. Further amylase and glucanase additions may occur during the filtration of the wort. During subsequent fermentation, particularly for low calorie beers where soluble polysaccharide levels need to be minimized, fungal α-amylases and amyloglucosidases are added.

Where the hemicellulose content of the substrate either inhibits complete starch extraction or results in hazes in the fermented product (e.g. in wheat and sorghum), pentosanases (very broad specificity enzymes or enzyme mixtures capable of hydrolysing arabans, galactans, mannans, and xylans) are added to the fermentation broth or to the maturation tank.

For economic reasons, unmalted sources of starch are a regular addition to mash in most breweries. These "adjuncts" require processing via gelatinization, liquefaction, dextrinization and saccharification (see above) in order to present the carbohydrate content in a fermentable form. As described above, these processes rely on addition of enzymes. The addition of bacterial amylases is a substantial improvement over the traditional malt amylases, but the efficiency of the process, as determined by the extent of gelatinization and the maintenance of a low viscosity, has been even further improved by the use of thermostable *B. licheniformis* α-amylases.

Minor Applications

Amylases and other glycohydrolases are used in many minor applications. For example, thermostable amylases are added to some detergent preparations (e.g. dish-washing detergents). Amylases and amyloglucosidases are used in the removal of starch hazes in the preparation of fruit juices. Amyloglucosidases are used in many bakery products and in the preparation of "instant" cereals. Cellulases are used to enhance oil extraction, and have been added as a supplement to animal feeds.

Proteinases

The proteinases (proteolytic enzymes, endopeptidases, peptidyl-peptide hydrolases; EC 3.4.21–3.4.24 and 3.4.99) are a very broad group of enzymes carrying out essentially the same function: the hydrolysis of a peptide bond. Within this group there is a huge variation of specificity for the amino acids on either side of the cleavage site and in the nature of the enzymes themselves. The proteinases are categorized on the basis of their catalytic mechanism, as indicated by active site studies or by the effect of pH. The four major categories are:

(i) Serine proteinases (EC 3.4.21): These have active centre histidine and serine residues, the inhibition by covalent modification of the serine with organophosphates being particularly diagnostic. Many of the bacterial serine proteinases chelate one or more calcium ions in surface binding sites, the presence of which enhances structural stability.

(ii) Sulfhydryl proteinases (EC 3.4.22): The SH-proteinases have a cysteine residue in the active site. Inhibition by heavy metals, mercury compounds (e.g. p-chloromercuribenzoate) and iodoacetate is taken as being indicative of such enzymes.

(iii) Acid proteinases (EC 3.4.23): The acid or carboxyl proteinases have a pH optimum below 5 due to the involvement of an active site carboxylate residue in the catalytic mechanisms.

(iv) Metalloproteinases (EC 3.4.24): These enzymes are categorized by the presence of a catalytic zinc atom. The rapid and complete loss of activity in the presence of chelating agents (EDTA, *o*-phenanthroline) is diagnostic.

Proteinases have traditionally held the predominant share of the industrial enzyme market (estimated at about 60% in 1981). However, the rise in industrial application of the glycohydrolases has seen the market share of proteinases reduced somewhat in recent years. The major applications of proteinases, with the exception of the use of rennin in cheese-making (discussed below), all involve the non-specific hydrolysis of "natural" high-molecular-weight protein substrates, often as a means of removing a potential contaminant or interference to subsequent processing (Table 13). For such purposes, the cost component of the enzyme is necessarily very low, a constraint reflected in the range of proteinases employed on an industrial scale (Table 16).

The use of proteinases in detergents is a good example of the factors controlling enzyme application. The total detergent enzyme market (conservatively estimated at around $100 million in 1987) is derived almost exclusively from the bacterial alkaline proteinases, largely from strains of *B. subtilis* and *B. licheniformis*. These enzymes have broad substrate specificities and will function to some extent under the rather extreme conditions encountered in domestic washing; temperatures of 20 to 70°C, a pH up to 11 and high concentrations of detergents, polyphosphates, chelating agents such as EDTA and oxidizing agents such as sodium perborate. Despite the fact that these enzymes are clearly not ideally suited to function under such extreme conditions, there have been only limited indications that better alternative enzymes will replace them. Proteinases from the alkalophilic bacilli (which have pH optima much closer to that found in domestic washes) have found increasing application in the past decade. However, those from extreme thermophiles such as *Thermus* (which are much more thermostable and resistant to other denaturants) are unlikely to be employed as replacements since much lower production levels are reflected in unacceptably high enzyme costs. The cloning and super-production of these enzymes provide a means of overcoming this barrier although current trends towards low temperature fabric washing (in the interests of energy conservation) require enzymes with high catalytic activity between 20 and 40°C.

One of the traditional industrial applications of proteinases, the production of leather, has benefitted from the increasing range of proteinase specifications available. Replacing the traditional dehairing processes (using lime and sulphides) with enzymic processing has increased the quality of the end-product while reducing both the processing time and problems of disposal of the toxic liquor. During bating, where the hide is softened by partial degradation of the interfibrillar matrix proteins (elastin and keratin), enzyme preparations with low levels of elastase and keratinase activity but no collagenase activity have been particularly useful.

The brewing industry is a major user of proteinases. In the production of brewery wort, *B. subtilis* proteinases are used to solubilize protein from barley adjuncts, thereby improving the available nitrogen supply. The proteolytic action also activates β-amylase. In the final stages of beer-making, papain is used in chill-proofing, a treatment designed to prevent the formation of precipitates during cold storage. Beer "hazes" are complex co-precipitates of polyphenols and oligosaccharides. Hydrolysis of the protein component prevents aggregation of the insoluble complex.

In the baking industry, proteolytic action on the gluten component is vital to the quality of the product. Partial hydrolysis of the gluten reduces the dough viscosity and improves the grain and texture of the baked bread. Since cereals usually have low proteinase levels, supplementation with fungal (*A. oryzae*) proteinase is routine. The more thermostable bacterial proteinases are generally used only in biscuit and pizza dough where the higher cooking temperature rapidly inactivates the enzymes and prevent over-proteolysis and "stickness".

The use of proteinases in the production of condiments, especially in meat extracts and concentrates, is particularly

Table 13
Major and Minor Industrial Applications of Proteinases

Application	Proteinase source
Detergents and cleaning products	*B. lichiniformis*, *B. subtilis*, *S. griseus*
Leather	*B. lichiniformis*, *B. subtilis*, Pancreas
Baking	*Aspergillus*
Flavouring/condiments	*Aspergillus*, *B. subtilis*, papaya
Alcoholic beverages (beer)	*Aspergillus*, *B. subtilis*, papaya
Meat tenderizing	Papain, ficin, bromelain
Gelatin production	Various
Photographic industry	Various

important in Japan, though less significant in Western industry. A number of Oriental foods (e.g. soy sauce, tamari sauce and miso) have traditionally employed *Aspergillus* fermentations as a means of generating a crude enzyme preparation (Koji), the proteolytic action of which is a major contributing factor to the final product.

Several other minor applications of proteinases involve the recovery of protein by hydrolysis. These include the "scavenging" of waste protein from animal carcasses in abattoirs and from fish in processing plants. The product can be used for the manufacture of soups and other canned meat products or spray-dried and used as an animal feed supplement. There is particular interest in carrying out such hydrolyses at elevated temperatures (55 to 65°C) where problems of microbial contamination are reduced. Even at these temperatures, the risk of contamination limits the hydrolysis period to 30 to 60 minutes. Proteinases which were stable at 70 to 80°C would permit reaction temperatures where contamination problems would be almost totally eliminated. Other advantages would be the faster reaction rates induced by the partial denaturation of the substrate proteins and a broader substrate specificity (e.g. collagen is hydrolysed non-specifically at elevated temperatures).

Other minor commercial and industrial applications of proteinases include gelatin production, the recovery of silver from photographic emulsions by enzymic hydrolysis, the production of partially hydrolysed gelatin for dietetic use, specifically formulated enzyme preparations for cleaning (e.g. the Genex drain cleaning preparations, purified enzyme preparations for cleaning delicate instrumentation and ultrafiltration membranes) and the preparation of culture media (peptones).

Pectinases

Pectin is a complex polysaccharide composed of polygalacturonides with additional non-uronides bound to the unbranched chain of the α-1,4-D-galacturonide units. A variety of other sugars are also present in the polysaccharide, including L-rhamnose, L-arabinose, D-galactose, D-xylose and L-fucose. The carboxylate groups of the galacturonic acid groups are partially methoxylated. This complex and insoluble polymer is present in many fruits and, while being most advantageous in the preparation of jams and jellies, can interfere during the production of wine and juices by the formation of "hazes".

It is therefore not surprising that the industrial application of pectin-hydrolysing enzymes (pectinases, pectic enzymes) is of considerable importance (the market share in 1980 was $3.7 million). A variety of pectinase preparations are available commercially. These preparations are generally crude extracts of fungal cultures and contain a variety of pectinolytic activities (Figure 11) including:

(i) Pectinesterase (EC 1.1.11): de-esterifies pectin to pectic acid by removal of methoxyl residues.
(ii) Endo- and exopolymethylgalacturonase: hydrolytic cleavage of α-1,4 linkages.
(iii) Endo- and exopolymethylgalacturonate lyase: random and sequential cleavage of pectin by transelimination.
(iv) Endo-, exopolygalacturonase and exodigalacturonase: random, sequential and digalacturonate cleavage of pectic acid by hydrolysis of α-1,4 linkages,
(v) Endo- and exopolygalacturonate lyase: random and sequential cleavage of pectic acid by transelimination.

Enzymes capable of acting on oligo-D-galactosiduronates may also be present.

Commercial pectinage preparations are widely used in the preparation of fruit and vegetable purees, in the extraction and clarification of fruit juices (particularly those from apple, pear and grape) in the clarification of wine, and as an aid in the extraction of olive oil. In extraction processes, pectin hydrolysis reduces the pulp viscosity and increases the liquid product yield. For juice and wine production, pectinase action results in greatly enhanced filtration rates.

Other Enzymes

Lipases are used to a limited extent in industry for a variety of purposes, both of broad and limited specificity. The latter will be discussed in the chapter below. The worldwide lipase market is currently about 3% of the total and is increasing rapidly in the face of a growing number of commercial applications.

Lipases (glycerol ester hydrolases; EC 3.1.1.3) cleave the ester linkages of triglycerides, yielding free fatty acids, partial glycerides and glycerol. These enzymes are produced by a wide variety of microorganisms. Individual enzymes differ on the basis of their regiospecificity (preferential cleavage of the C1 and/or C2 ester linkages) or their fatty acyl chain specificity. Enzymes capable of cleaving only ester linkages where the aliphatic chain is less than four carbons in length should more correctly be entitled "esterases". The ability to catalyse the hydrolysis of insoluble long-chain fatty acid esters thus distinguishes lipases from other esterases. Although lipases are produced by a wide variety of different organisms, the most common sources for industrial use are either yeast (*Candida cylindracea*), fungal (*A. niger*, *Mucor miehei*, *Penicillium roqueforti* and *Rhizopus*) or animal (bovine pancreas) sources.

The largest commercial use of lipases is in flavour development. Butter oil partly hydrolysed with lipases has an enhanced creamy flavour and is added to a wide variety of foodstuffs including popcorn, cooking oils, fats, cereals, candies, snacks and baked goods. Lipase-modified creams are added as dairy flavour enhancers to coffee whiteners, candies, doughs, soups

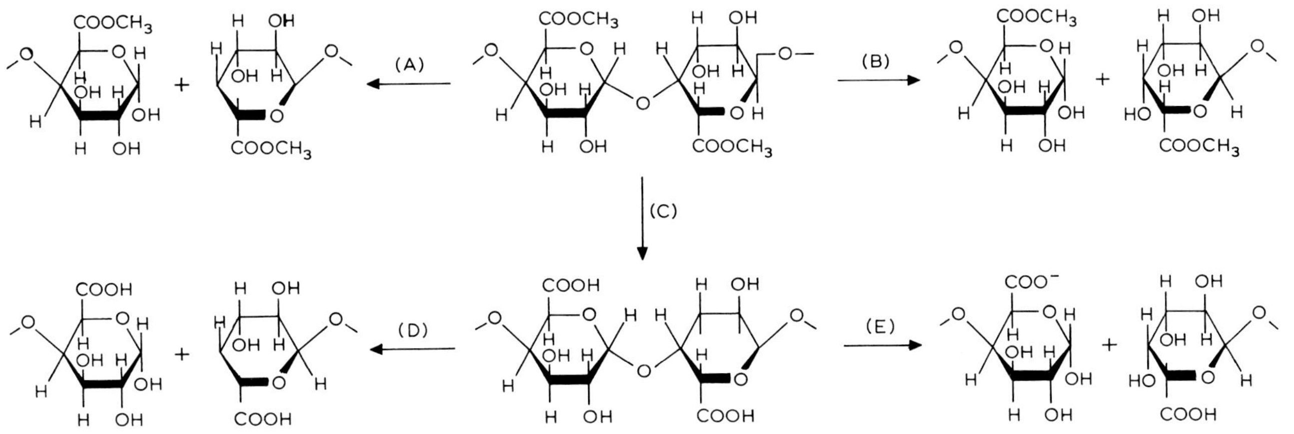

Figure 11. Principal enzymes of the pectinase complex. [A] Polymethylgalacturonate lyase; [B] polymethylgalacturonase; [C] pectinesterase; [D] polygalacturonate lyase; [E] polygalacturonase.

and baked products. Lipases are also used in the flavour development and accelerated ripening in cheeses. The free fatty acids released from milk fat act as substrates for subsequent conversion to methyl ketones and secondary alcohols, typical flavour substances in blue cheeses. Although used to some extent in the U.S. and Europe, this process is not permitted in the U.K. The pregastric esterases (isolated from the forestomachs of calves, lambs and kids) are also used widely in similar processes for the development of flavours in dairy products.

Recently, crude lipase preparations have been used successfully in effluent treatment, although the relatively high cost of the enzyme ($30–$200 per kg) is likely to limit such usage to situations where alternative methods of disposal are not economic.

Over the past decade, there has been a great expansion in research on the enzyme components of the cellulase complex. The ready availability of cheap cellulosic feedstock as a potential source of carbohydrate for conversion to other organic compounds of economic value (glucose, ethanol, butanol, etc.) has proved to be a tempting subject for investigation. However, despite these efforts there are to date no large-scale industrial uses of cellulases either in culture or in purified form. In part this is due to more favourable economics in the use of alternative sources; i.e. production from fossil fuels or by fermentation of cheap simple sugars from beet and cane.

Cellulases are used commercially on a small scale as digestive aids, particularly as supplements in cattle feedstocks.

INDUSTRIAL APPLICATIONS OF ENZYMES: HIGH SPECIFICITY FUNCTIONS

Glucose Isomerase

The big success story of the 1970s and '80s in enzyme technology has been the application of glucose isomerase in the production of high fructose syrups from enzymically derived glucose (corn) syrups. The application of this enzyme has yielded a completely new commercial product, high-fructose syrup, produced in excess of 5 million tonnes per annum worldwide. Fructose has a higher perceived sweetness than sucrose but a lower calorific value and as a replacement for sugar in soft-drinks, foods etc, provides a lower calorie product.

The enzyme commonly referred to as glucose isomerase (GI) is almost certainly a xylose isomerase (EC 5.3.1.5). The reaction catalysed is an aldose-ketose isomerization and involves and alkaline enediol mechanism (Figure 12).

Xylose isomerases are produced by many microorganisms although there is much variation in yield and in the characteristics of the individual enzymes. Most of the enzymes are induced by xylose. They frequently require magnesium (and in some cases cobalt) for optimum activity. Many are strongly inhibited by calcium. Some polyols are powerful competitive inhibitors. This is attributed to the fact that the rate limiting step for glucose binding to the active site is the opening of the pyranose ring while the polyols are acyclic.

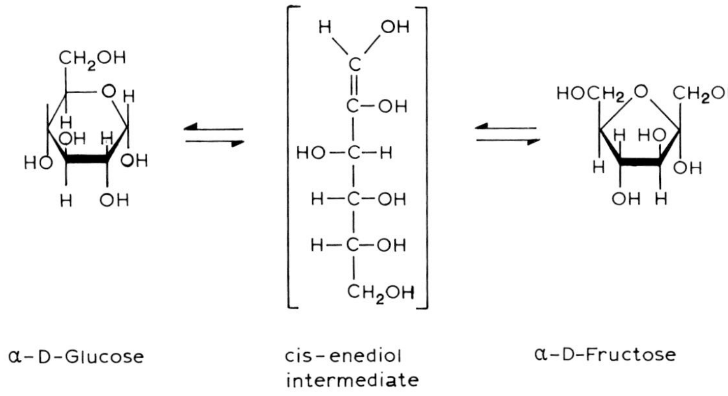

α-D-Glucose ⇌ cis-enediol intermediate ⇌ α-D-Fructose

Figure 12. Isomerization of glucose by xylose isomerase.

The source used for the industrial production of the enzyme include *Actinomyces missouriensis*, *B. coagulans*, and various *Streptomyces* species. The majority of commercial plants use immobilized glucose isomerase, largely in the form of cross-linked or entrapped cells with matrix properties suitable for use in column or fluidized bed reactors. Since such preparations do not require extraction and purification procedures, costs are minimized. In addition, the intracellular glucose isomerase is protected during chemical cross-linking of the matrix and little activity is lost during preparation.

The form of the immobilized complex is manipulated to suit the reactor system. Immobilized cell preparations may be in the form of fibres, filaments, beads, cylinders, plates, etc.

Commercial users of glucose isomerase require that the preparations be chemically and functionally stable at the optimum operating temperature (60 to 65°C), and not subject to inhibition. The enzymes currently in use are highly stable, although more thermostable examples with even longer operating lifetimes would be desirable providing that current levels of activity were retained. It is unlikely that the reactor temperatures will be increased since undesirable colour production from fructose degradation would become significant.

The product of glucose isomerase activity, high-fructose syrup, has a typical composition of 42% fructose, 51% glucose and 7% oligosaccharide (derived from incomplete hydrolysis of the corn starch) and is isosweet with sucrose. This is enriched chromatographically to 55% fructose, a product which has major applications in the beverage industry, particularly in such products as Coca-Cola and Pepsi-Cola. Recent success in the production of a crystalline product has generated a further expansion of the high-fructose syrup market as the product competes as a low-calorie alternative to accepted sweeteners such as sucrose.

Recent work has aimed at removing the expensive chromatographic enrichment of fructose. A 55% fructose syrup product was obtained by carrying out the reaction in 85% ethanol in which the glucose-fructose equilibrium was shifted to the right. The recovery of the ethanol by distillation does, however, impose a cost which must be balanced against the saving incurred on removal of the chromatographic step.

Rennin

One of the most traditional uses of enzymes in food production (dating back more than 6,000 years) is the addition of extracts of calf stomach to milk to induce clotting in the production of cheese and similar products. The active component of this extract, rennet, most usually derived from the fourth stomach or abomasum, is the acid proteinase rennin (chymosin, EC 3.4.23.4). This enzyme (together with the microbial rennets) comprises some 10–15% of the total world enzyme sales, although the relative share of chymosin has been diminishing over the past decade in the face of microbially-derived alternatives (see below). In the United States in particular, a general reduction in the number of calves available for slaughter has reduced the supply of rennet, increased the price and stimulated interest in alternative enzymes.

The success of chymosin in the production of milk protein curd suitable for cheese-making relies on the specificity of the proteolytic function. In the first steps of curd formation, chymosin removes a glycopeptide from χ-casein by cleavage at a single phenylalanine-methionine peptide bond, destabilizing the casein micelles. The resulting para-χ-caseins aggregate in the presence of calcium ions to form insoluble complexes (curds). Limited non-specific proteolysis during the cheese maturation phase assists with flavour development.

While many other proteases cleave phe-met bonds, most will equally well cleave a variety of other peptide bonds. Non-specific proteolysis results in a loss of curd volume and in the production of unpleasant flavours caused by proteolytic peptides. The pepsins have a higher level of non-specific proteolysis than chymosin and coagulate milk more slowly but have been used with some success.

Microbial Rennets

As the result of extensive programmes of screening for microorganisms with milk-clotting activity, a limited number of fungal acid proteases have been found to be suitable for cheese-making (Table 17). The *Mucor miehei* and *M. pusillus* enzymes can be used in place of rennet without any significant alteration in cheese-making practice and produce a product which is usually organoleptically indistinguishable from that made with rennet. The *Endothia parasitica* enzyme can produce good quality cheese in some circumstances, particularly where high temperatures are used for the coagulation step. Their ability to replace rennet is a result of similar peptide bond specificities; e.g. both *M. miehei* acid protease and chymosin preferentially cleave oxidized β-insulin at the glu_{13}-ala_{14}, leu_{11}-val_{12} and leu_{17}-val_{18} peptide linkages.

Most bacterial proteases possess undesirably high levels of proteolysis. However, *B. mesentericus* protease has yielded some positive results in trials and other bacterial enzymes might be suitable with alterations in the production technology and/or in conjunction with rennet. The presence of contaminating lipases and broad-specificity proteases in microbial rennet preparations is also undesirable and both must be removed or inactivated before industrial use.

Lipases

There is currently a considerable amount of industrial interest in lipases, particularly in regiospecific lipases capable of cleaving specifically at the 1,3 or 2 position on the triglyceride. Regiospecificity, in conjunction with reaction conditions which promote interesterification rather than lipolysis, provide a mechanism for the synthesis of fats of desirable qualities. For example, industrial plants have recently come into operation utilizing fungal lipase to catalyse the interesterfication of readily available cheap oils (e.g. 1,3-dipalmitoyl-2-oleoyl, a palm oil fraction) with stearic acid in the production of high value cocoa-butter substitutes (1,3-distearoyl-2-oleoyl glycerol, the major component of cocoa butter).

Other aspects of lipase function are also of considerable interest although not currently applied on an industrial scale. For example, it is possible to synthesize sugar esters by forcing the transesterification reaction between a fatty acid and a monosaccharide against the normal equilibrium in an environment of low water activity (Figure 13). Sugar esters are potentially valuable emulsifiers.

Stereospecific lipases could also be valuable in the synthesis of specific optical isomers. The lipase-catalysed transesterification of (+/−)-*sec*-butanol with tributyrin produces almost quantitative yields of the two optical isomers (Figure 14). One isomer is unreactive and is recovered from the reaction mixture by distillation. The other is released by alkaline hydrolysis of the reaction product.

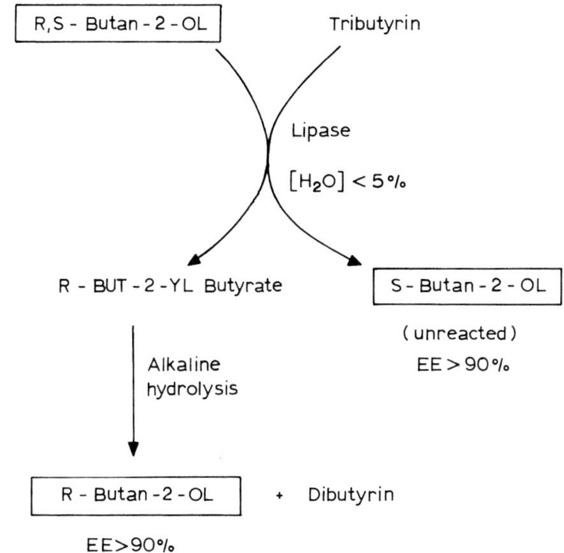

Figure 14. Lipase-catalysed synthesis of optically pure secbutanol.
(EE = Enantiomeric excess).

β-Galactosidases

The disaccharide lactose (4-0-(β-D-galactopyranosyl)-D-glucopyranose) is present in bovine milk at a concentration of about 4.5%. Its presence in milk concentrates (whole milk or skim milk powder) and their products poses both medical and technical problems. Infants deficient in intestinal β-galactosidase can suffer severe clinical effects from high intestinal lactose levels, including tissue dehydration, low calcium adsorption and diarrhoea. This problem is particularly severe in under-developed countries where diet supplementation with milk powder is common but it has also been established that only the Northern European population and two nomadic tribes in Africa are truly lactose-tolerant.

In unfermented milk products such as ice-cream and condensed milk, lactose crystallization can yield an unpleasant gritty texture. The low sweetness rating of lactose precludes the use of lactose-containing residues such as whey as sweetening agents and the traditional dumping of whey into sewerage systems was unsatisfactory both on the grounds of resource management and the resulting waste treatment burden. Enzymic hydrolysis of lactose using β-galactosidase offered a potential solution to all these problems, both in the removal of the causitive agent and in the production of a marketable product.

Columns of immobilized β-galactosidase (available commercially from *Saccharomyces lactis*, *Klebsiella fragilis* and *A. oryzae*) are now used in various countries for the hydrolysis of whey lactose. The hydrolysed product has a much higher sweetness and after concentration is suitable for use as a sweetening agent in various foodstuffs.

Naringinase

Naringin (4′,5,7-trihydroxyflavanone-7-rhamnoglucoside) is the main bitter component in certain citrus fruits (e.g. grapefruit). The removal of this bitter compounds yields a more

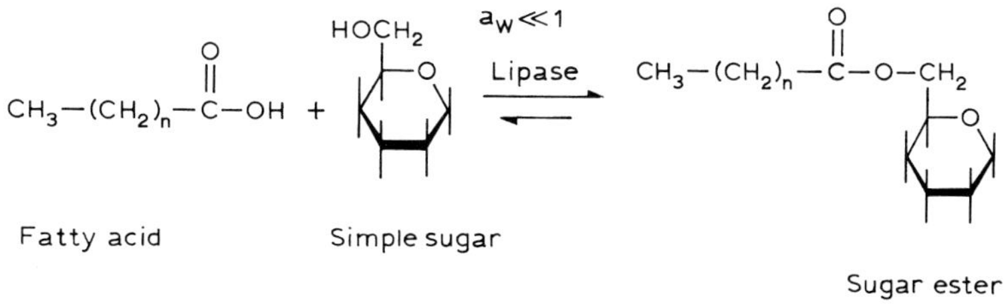

$CH_3-(CH_2)_n-C(=O)-OH$ + HOCH$_2$ (simple sugar) $\underset{\text{Lipase}}{\overset{a_w \ll 1}{\rightleftharpoons}}$ $CH_3-(CH_2)_n-C(=O)-O-CH_2$ (sugar ester)

Fatty acid — Simple sugar — Sugar ester

Figure 13. Enzymic synthesis of sugar esters.

palatable and marketable fruit juice. The enzyme is obtained from various *Penicillium* species and possesses both α-rhamnosidase and β-glucosidase activities (Figure 15). Prunin has less than 30% of the bitterness of naringin so that only the rhamnosidase activity is critical.

Treatment of filtered citrus juices with immobilized naringinase has been used on a pilot scale. It is necessary to remove the juice solids prior to hydrolysis to avoid plugging of the immobilized enzyme reactor.

Thermolysin

Thermolysin is a thermostable extracellular zinc metalloproteinase produced by *B. thermoproteolyticus*, a Japanese industrial strain of *B. stearothermophilus*. This enzyme is currently employed by the Toyo-Soda Company in Japan in the synthesis of the disaccharide sweetening agent aspartame. One method of synthesis employs immobilized thermolysin in a single phase aqueous-organic solvent containing water-saturated ethyl acetate at a reaction temperature of 50°C (Figure 16). A major advantage of the enzymic method over the chemical synthesis is that none of the bitter β-peptide linked-aspartame is produced.

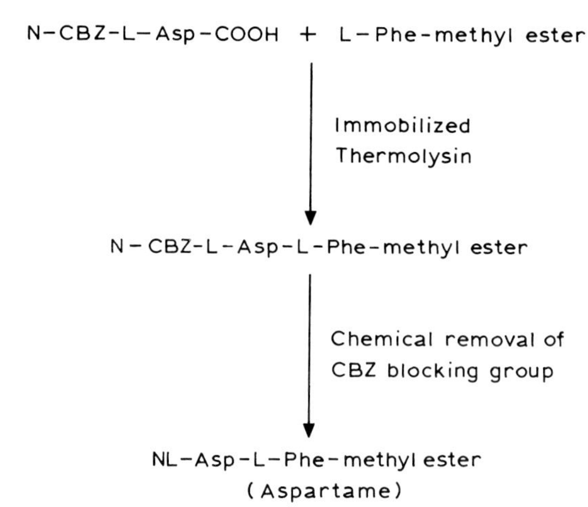

Figure 16. Synthesis of aspartame precursor with immobilized thermolysin.

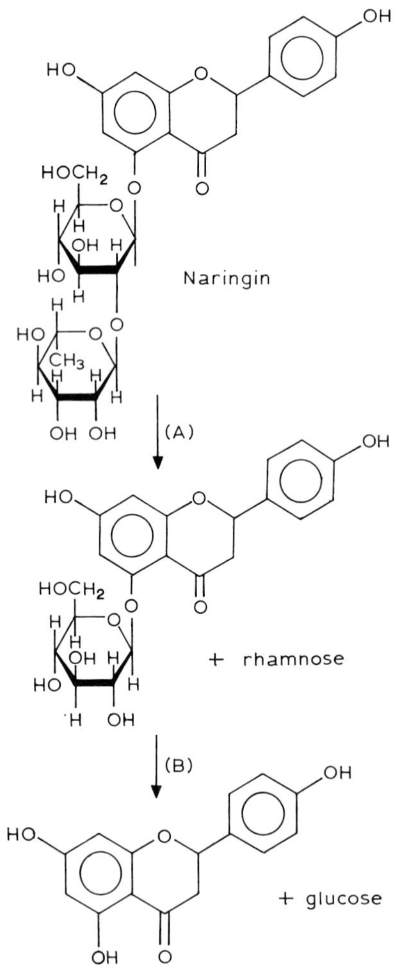

Figure 15. Enzymic hydrolysis of naringin. [A] Rhamnosidase; [B] β-glucosidase.

Glucose Oxidase

Glucose oxidase (EC 1.1.3.4) catalyses the oxidative conversion of glucose to gluconic acid utilizing molecular oxygen and producing hydrogen peroxide. The industrial applications of this enzyme are dependent on its action as an antioxidant (since oxygen is removed in the reaction), for glucose scavenging and to a minor extent, as an antibacterial agent (by the production of H_2O_2). The major analytical applications of glucose oxidase will be discussed elsewhere.

Many foodstuffs and drinks are subject to oxidative deterioration. Addition of glucose oxidase to fruit juices, soft drinks, beer and white wine, mayonnaises and salad dressings and dried foods such as instant coffee, cake mixes, and dried soups is effective in preventing product browning and changes in flavour and odour.

The removal of trace levels of glucose in certain foodstuffs, particularly dried eggs, can avoid browning (via the Mallaird reaction) and the production of off-flavours.

Penicillin Acylase

Immobilized penicillin acylase is used on a limited industrial scale for the deacylation of penicillin to 6-aminopenicilloic acid, a precursor in the manufacture of semisynthetic antibiotics (Figure 17). Although the annual utilization of the enzyme is low, the reaction produces a very high value product.

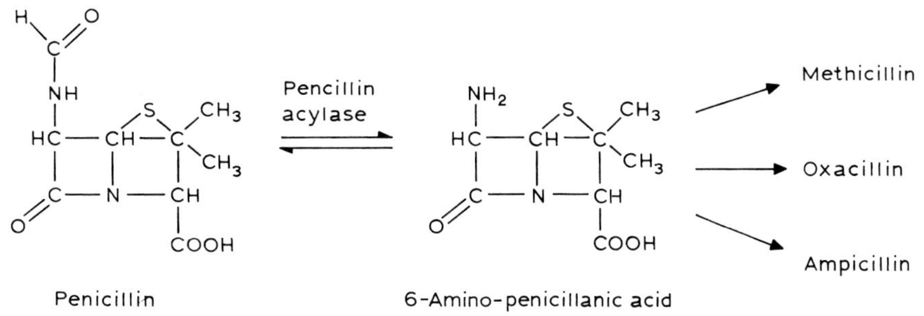

Pencillin acylase

Methicillin

Oxacillin

Ampicillin

Penicillin

6-Amino-penicillanic acid

Figure 17. Deacylation of penicillin with penicillin acylase in the manufacture of semi-synthetic antibiotics.

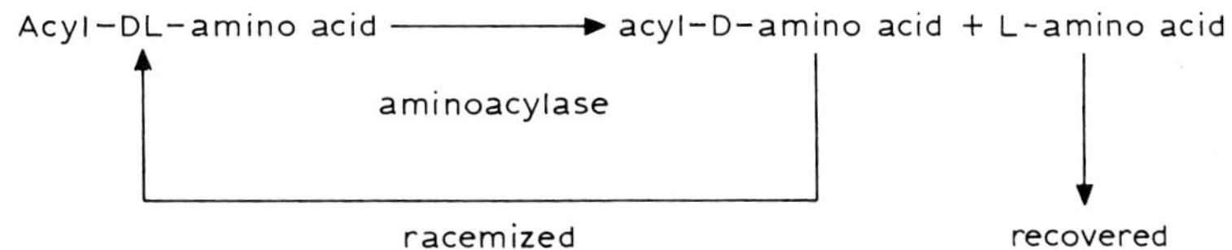

Figure 18. Production of L-amino acids by stereospecific deacylation of racemic acyl-amino acids.

L-aminoacylase

L-aminoacylase (EC 3.5.1.14) catalyses the acylation/deacylation of various L-amino acids. Its high level of stereospecificity has been used commercially in Japan since 1969 in the production of optically pure amino acids (Figure 18). After incubation of a racemic mixture of the acyl-amino acids with the enzyme, the unhydrolysed acyl-D-amino acid is separated by virtue of its lower solubility and is recycled after racemization. L-aminoacylase from *A. oryzae* is generally used in an immobilized form.

Aspartase

Aspartase (EC 4.3.1.1) will asymmetrically add ammonia across the double bond of fumarate to yield L-aspartate (Figure 19). This process is carried out on an industrial scale using immobilized *E. coli* cells as the enzyme source.

Cyclodextrin Glucosyltransferase

The production from starch of β-cyclodextrin (a circular oligosaccharide composed of 7 glucose units) is a small-scale industrial process utilizing cyclodextrin glucosyltransferase isolated from various *Bacillus* species (*B. macerans*, *B. megaterium* or *B. stearothermophilus*). Commercial production of the 7-membered β ring is favoured over the 6- and 8-membered α and γ-cyclodextrins.

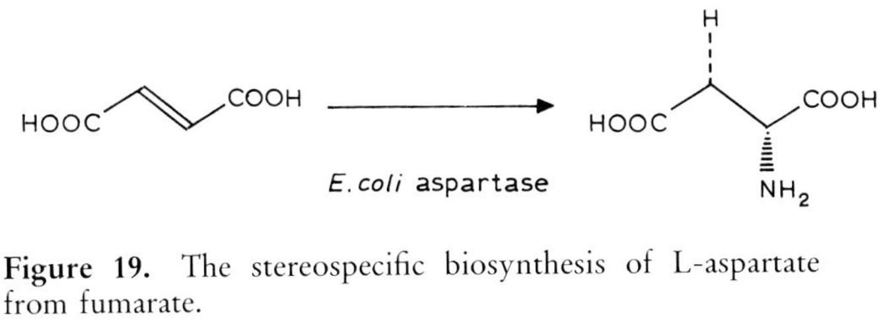

E. coli aspartase

Figure 19. The stereospecific biosynthesis of L-aspartate from fumarate.

L-α-Aminolactam Hydrolase

Cryptococcus laurentii cells containing the enzyme L-α-aminolactam hydrolase are used in a commercial process converting L-α-amino-ϵ-caprolactam to L-lysine (Figure 20). Using a racemic substrate mixture and the enzyme D-α-aminolactam racemase to racemize the residual D-form, yields of close to 100% conversion can be obtained.

Phenylalanine Ammonia Lyase

The high value of L-phenylalanine has prompted the development by the Genex Corporation of a production process using the enzyme phenylalanine ammonia lyase isolated from the yeast *Rhodococcus rubra* (Figure 21). The starting material, t-cinnamic acid, is produced by chemical synthesis.

Other High Specificity Enzymes

A large number of other enzymes can potentially be used in the production of optically pure amino acids (Table 14). While few of these are likely to be economically viable on an industrial scale in the near future, the stimulus required will

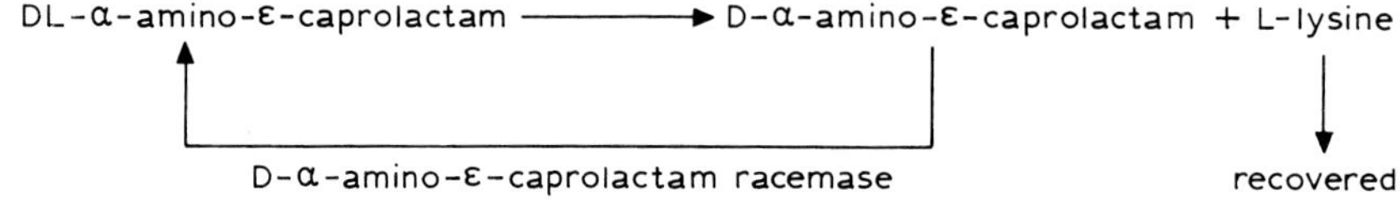

Figure 20. Enzymic synthesis of L-lysine.

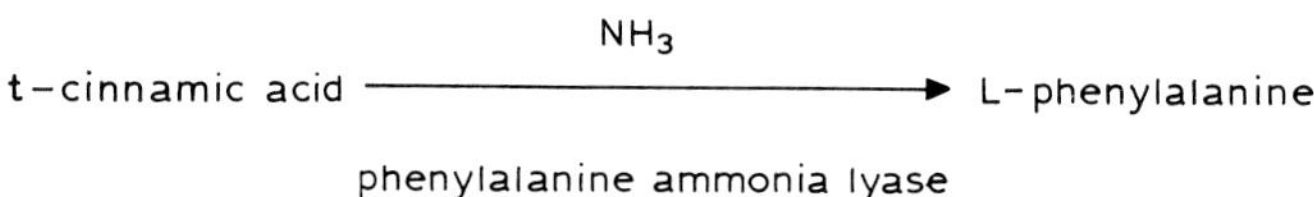

Figure 21. Enzymic synthesis of L-phenylalanine.

be a change in the product markets. This has been vividly demonstrated by the increase in the market for L-aspartate and L-phenylalanine generated by the growing manufacture and consumption of aspartame.

A number of other enzymes are used to a limited extent in industry. For example, invertase is incorporated in certain condiments (e.g. soft-centered chocolates) where the enzymic action is cleaving sucrose to glucose and fructose generates the liquid characteristics of such products. Other minor applications will not be discussed here and the reader is directed to the review by Prave *et al.* (1987).

FUTURE TRENDS

Introduction

Two features are clear from the developments of industrial enzymology over the past two decades. First, the predicted revolution in industrial enzymic processes has definitely not appeared and appears very unlikely to do so. Second (and more optimistically), it is highly probable that the gradual but steady expansion in new enzyme applications over the past decade will continue in the future. The two processes which will fuel this growth will be the discovery or "synthesis" of new enzymes and specificities and the appearance of new processes to which existing or new enzymes can be tailored.

New Enzymes

The increase in the discovery of new enzymes far exceeds the development in new enzyme applications. Almost every issue of any of the major biochemical journals will carry on one or more reports of newly characterized enzymes. Such enzymes may be derived from novel sources or may have wholly new specificities. Bacteria, because of their ability to evolve metabolic systems to utilize new substrates, are excellent sources of novel enzymes. The antibiotic synthesis enzymes of the *Streptomyces* and the aromatic degradation enzymes of the *Pseudomonas* species are particularly good examples of "useful" activities.

Thermostable Enzymes

A good number of industrial processes require conditions which involve relatively extreme environments. For example, the enzymic saccharification of starch is greatly improved if temperatures approaching 100°C can be used. In this case, the *Bacillus* amylases possess sufficient thermostability to

Table 14
Some Examples of the Enzymic Synthesis of Amino Acids

Reaction	Enzyme
Phenol + pyruvate + NH_3 ⟶ *L-tyrosine* + H_2O	Tyrosinase
Indole + pyruvate + NH_3 ⟶ *L-tryptophan* + H_2O	Tryptophanase
L-aspartic acid ⟶ *L-alanine* + $C?_2$	Aspartate-β-decarboxylase
L-arginine ⟶ *L-citrulline*	Arginine deiminase
Pyrocatechol + DL-serine ⟶ *L-DOPA* + H_2O	Tyrosinase
Glycine + formaldehyde ⟶ *L-tryptophan* + H_2O	Serine hydroxymethyltransferase
L-serine + acetic anhydride + NaHS ⟶ *L-cysteine*	O-acetylserine sulphatase

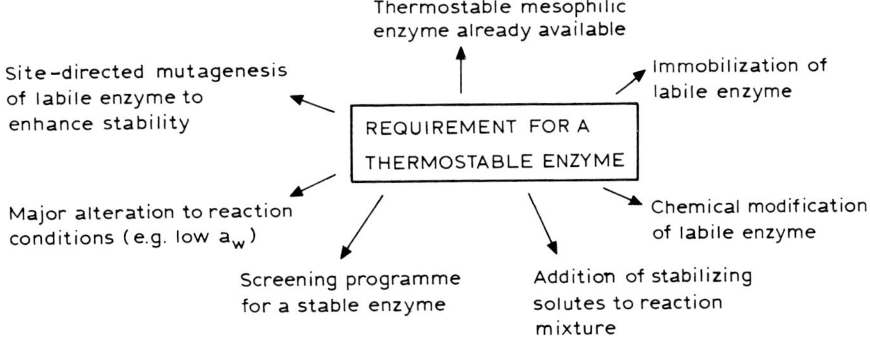

Figure 22. Practical options for the acquisition of a thermostable enzyme.

enable their use at these temperatures for considerable periods. Generally, however, enzymes do not possess particularly high levels of thermostability and most are inactivated at temperatures much above 70°C. This is an inevitable consequence of the source of most enzymes: mesophilic organisms, growing optimally at temperatures from 20 to 37°C.

There are a number of options available to the industrialist in selecting an enzyme capable of withstanding harsh reaction conditions (Figure 22): (a) a mesophilic enzyme possessing suitable properties and sufficient stability may already be commercially available; (b) immobilization of a less stable enzyme may result in enhanced thermostability; (c) covalent chemical modification (including cross-linking with glutaraldehyde, guanidation, succinylation, and attachment to polyethylene glycol) can enhance stability; (d) stabilization by the addition of agents such as substrates, cofactors, metal ions, salts (e.g. ammonium sulphate), simple hydroxylated reagents (sugars, polyols) and polymeric compounds (polyethylene glycol); (e) modification of the reaction environment such as reduction of water activity and increasing the solute concentration by substituting the aqueous phase for an organic phase; (f) finding an enzyme of greater thermostability; and (g) engineering an existing enzyme by site-directed mutagenesis to enhance the intrinsic molecular stability.

Any or all of these options may be inappropriate for many reasons. The nature of the process may prevent some alternatives; for example, immobilization will be inappropriate if a fully soluble enzyme preparation is required. Others may not be considered opportune because of the technical difficulties (e.g. site-directed mutagenesis of the gene encoding a particular enzyme is an expensive and time-consuming scientific objective or because of financial constraints.

One of the more feasible long-term options for achieving thermostability is to utilize resources where evolution has already overcome the problems of finding practical answers to protein thermolability.

Thermophilic microorganisms, growing optimally at 45 to 55°C and maximally at below 70°C, have been known for many centuries. In 1967, the first organisms capable of growing optimally at much higher temperatures were isolated. The extreme thermophiles (optimum temperature from 70 to 105°C, maximum temperature from 80 to 110°C) are a diverse group of bacteria including members of the archaebacteria which are now recognized as a separate primary kingdom. The most thermophilic organism currently known is the archaebacterium *Pyrodictium*. It was originally isolated from undersea volcanic vents in the Bay of Naples and has an optimum growth temperature of 105°C and a maximum of 110°C.

Macromolecules from organisms growing at elevated temperatures must either be intrinsically thermostable or must be replaced at a very rapid rate to compensate for accelerated breakdown. Since there is no evidence for rapid resynthesis in thermophilic organisms, it follows that macromolecular structures have evolved to a sufficient level of thermostability. This contention is now supported by a considerable volume of experimental evidence. Comparisons of functionally similar enzymes from mesophiles, thermophiles and extreme thermophiles have demonstrated a general correlation between growth temperature and enzyme thermostability. As a general rule then, quests for enzymes of higher thermostability should best be directed at organisms growing at higher temperatures.

Another correlation of great potential significance for industrial enzymology is the positive relationship between protein thermostability and resistance to denaturation (e.g. by organic solvents, detergents and chaotropic agents) and degradation (by proteolytic attack). With the increasing industrial interest in biocatalytic processes using non-aqueous or mixed-phase solvent systems, these observations should indicate an optimistic industrial future for thermophilic enzymes. There are several attractive advantages in the use of thermostable enzymes: losses during purification and preparation are lower, losses during storage and transportation are reduced. Both these factors may favourably effect the economics of production and application.

The number of thermophilic enzymes currently used on a large scale is limited. Thermolysin, the thermostable protease from a strain of *B. stearothermophilus*, is used in the synthesis of the sweetening agent aspartame [see above]. An increasing number of thermophilic enzymes are available commercially and used in substantial amounts for analytical purposes [e.g. restriction enzymes, *T. aquaticus* DNA polymerase]. The currently limited large-scale application of thermophilic enzymes is a reflection of several factors: the relative novelty of the group, the time required between screening and application and, to some extent, the conservatism of the industry. The potential application of thermophilic enzymes is also currently hindered by low enzyme yields and by a poor understanding of the genetics of many of the novel extremely thermophilic eubacteria and archaebacteria.

Recent reports from several laboratories of the cloning and expression of a number of thermophilic enzymes are an optimistic indication that problems of low production levels will be successfully overcome.

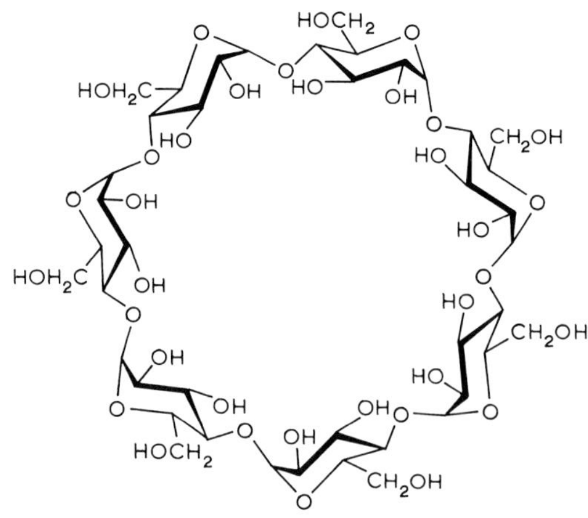

Figure 23a. The structure of β-cyclodextrin.

Artificial Enzymes

The possibility of carrying out reactions without the disadvantages of relatively delicate macromolecules while yet retaining the catalytic rate enhancement and specificity characteristics of an enzyme has stimulated interest in the production of artificial enzymes. Major design objectives are to duplicate the properties of the enzyme active site while deleting the requirement for a globular polypeptide supporting structure.

In duplicating active site characteristics, the artificial enzyme must present a correct special arrangement of ligands to bind a potential substrate (i.e. the enzyme must display substrate selectivity) and must generate a suitable activated complex in order to provide a satisfactory enhancement of reaction velocity. Higher levels of selectivity (e.g. regioselectivity and stereoselectivity) may also be desirable.

Several types of molecules have attracted particular attention as model systems for artificial enzyme design. Probably the most important are the (α- and β-) cyclodextrins (Figure 23a). The ring-shaped structure provides a potential substrate-binding cavity liberally endowed with hydroxyl groups capable of participating in H-bonding interactions. The hydroxyl groups are also suitable for chemical modification (e.g. acylation) while the C6 carbons can be modified in

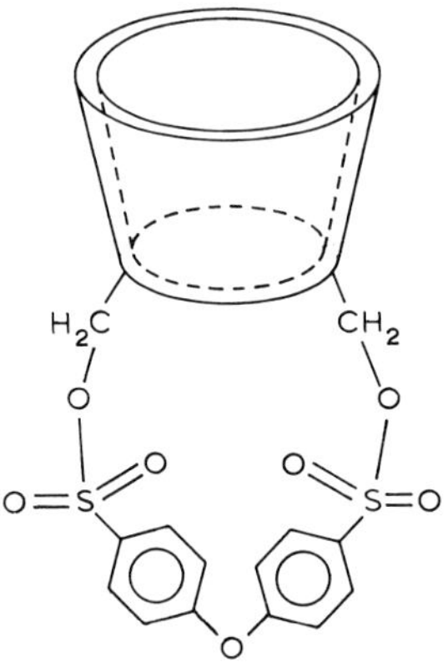

Figure 23b. Schematic horizontal view of cyclodextrin demonstrating the binding cavity. One face of the molecule is capped to minimise non-productive binding.

many ways. For example, substitutes which 'cap' the cyclodextrin structure (Figure 23b) prevent substrate access to the lower surface and reduce non-productive binding.

Some spectacular rate enhancements have been observed. Cyclodextrin enhances the hydrolysis of E-[3]-carboxymethylene-1,2-ferrocenocyclohexene *p*-nitro ester (Figure 24) by a factor of 3,200,000. Furthermore, a reaction rate ratio of 20 for the two enantiomers indicated a strong enantioselectivity. Rate enhancements for simpler less rigid structures are usually much lower. The deacylation of *m*-tert-butylphenyl

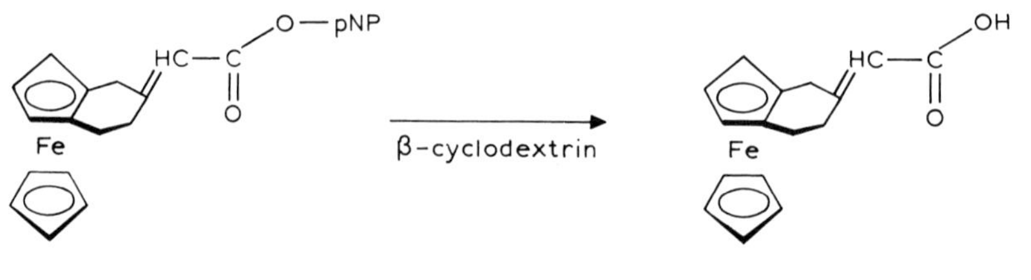

O—pNP
HC—C
Fe
β-cyclodextrin
OH
HC—C
Fe

Figure 24. The hydrolysis of E-(3)-carboxylene-1,2-ferrecenocyclohexane *p*-nitrophenyl ester by cyclodextrin.

acetate by β-cyclodextrin is only 250 times faster than deacylation by water.

Recent work has involved the addition of thiamine and pyridoxal ligands to the cavity structure. These adducts will duplicate to some extent the catalytic action of enzyme-coenzyme complexes.

Other macrocyclic structures can also be used as synthetic catalysts. Cyclotetramine-phenyl complexes yield rate enhancements of a similar order to cyclodextrins.

While considerable advances have been made in duplicating enzyme function, synthetic enzymes are not likely to facilitate progress in industrial biocatalysis in the short term. The reactions currently being carried out are relatively simple and the rate enhancements are still far short of those generated by true enzymes.

NEW PROCESSES

Non-aqueous Reaction Systems

One of the most exciting new developments in enzyme technology has been the discovery that enzymes can function successfully in non-aqueous and mixed-phase solvents. This technology opens a diverse range of new reaction possibilities, particularly those using substrates and/or products with low aqueous solubility.

There are several options available in the presentation of enzyme and substrate in organic solvent biocatalysis (Figure 25). The simplest system is a mixed phase macroheterogeneous system (e.g. hexane:water) in which contact between the enzyme (in the aqueous phase) and a hydrophobic substrate (in the organic phase) is largely dependent on the efficiency with which the organic phase is distributed in the aqueous phase; it is thus a product of stirring rate and fermentor configuration. In such a system the enzyme is exposed to a high liquid-liquid interfacial area which in turn can cause substantial enzyme denaturation.

An alternative biphasic microheterogeneous system utilizes the ability of certain amphipathic molecules to interact with the organic and aqueous phases in the formation of micelles and reversed micelles. The most popular detergent for reversed micelle formation has been AOT (Aerosol OT, diisooctyl sulphosuccinate; Figure 26). Reversed micelles provide a mechanism for suspending a low volume of aqueous phase in a large volume of organic phase. A correctly proportioned mixture of buffered enzyme solution, immiscible organic solvent and detergent will spontaneously transform into a microheterogeneous system in which uniformly sized "droplets" of aqueous phase surrounded by a monolayer of detergent are dispersed in the bulk organic phase. Reversed

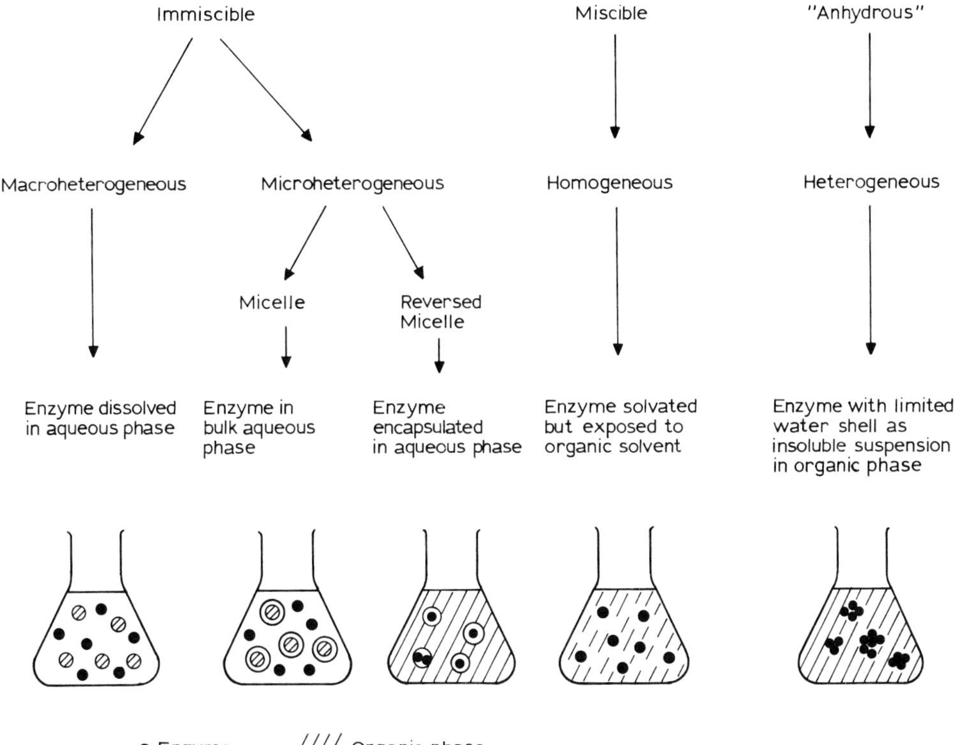

Figure 25. Schematic representation of the alternative miscible and immiscible organic: aqueous solvent systems.

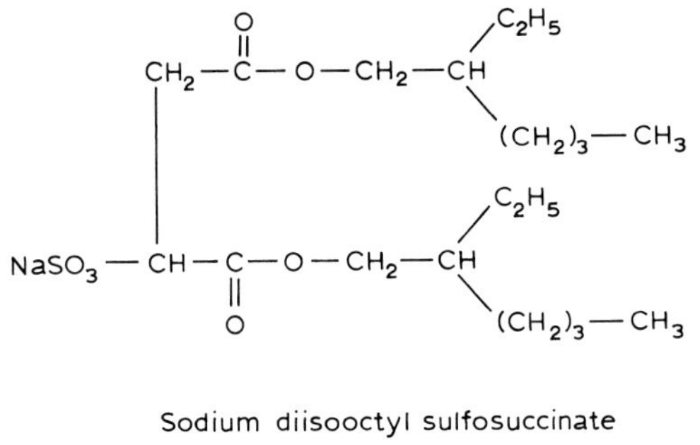

Sodium diisooctyl sulfosuccinate

Figure 26. The structure of AOT.

micelles have a number of advantages as an experimental system. They are very easy to generate reproducibly, they are stable and uniform, the mixture is optically transparent and the enzyme is protected from the organic phase. Furthermore, by adjusting the ratios of organic and aqueous constituents, it is possible to generate micelles of a particular diameter suitable for encapsulating a single enzyme molecule or a number of proteins in a multi-enzyme complex. Micelle-encapsulated enzymes will readily catalyse the transformation of hydrophobic substrates. It is evident that a finite concentration of substrate is dissolved in the detergent monolayer in a configuration accessible to the solvated enzyme.

Miscible organic-aqueous solvent systems are potentially more denaturing than immiscible solvents systems and therefore probably of less industrial interest. The extent to which proteins are denatured by organic solvents is partly related to the ability of the organic solvent to perturb the shell of bound water associated with the surface of the protein molecule. This bound water participates in intramolecular interactions which contribute to the stability of the protein structure. Its removal changes the solvation state of surface residues and influences the energetics of protein stabilization. In a miscible organic-aqueous solvent system, the protein is exposed directly to high concentrations of relatively polar organic molecules, resulting in considerable perturbation of the bound water layer and a decrease in protein stability. In immiscible solvent mixtures, protein in the aqueous phase is exposed to a very low organic solvent concentration (equivalent to the solubility of the organic in the aqueous phase) and denaturation occurs largely at the liquid-liquid interfaces as a function of the interfacial tension.

A guide to the selection of solvents for biphasic biocatalysis can be obtained from the log P value of the organic phase. [The log P value is determined from the partitioning of the organic "reagent" between octan and water. Higher log P values are thus associated with greater hydrophobicity (Table 15).] It has been suggested that as a general rule, solvents with log P values below 2.0 are inappropriate for organic solvent biocatalysis, solvents at between 2.0 and 4.0 may be useful in some circumstances but not in others, while those above 4.0 should be suitable. This assessment is based on as yet limited experience of enzymes in organic solvents and some interesting exceptions are already known. For example, subtilisin can catalyse transesterification reactions in dimethylformamide.

Table 15
Log P Values for Some Common Organic Solvents

Solvent	Log P
N,N-dimethylformamide	−1.0
Ethanol	−0.24
Acetone	−0.23
Propanol	0.28
Ethyl acetate	0.68
Butanol	0.80
Diethyl ether	0.85
Cyclohexanol	1.5
Chloroform	2.0
Benzene	2.0
Toluene	2.5
Octanol	2.9
Xylene	3.1
Hexane	3.5
Heptane	4.0
Octane	4.5

One of the most interesting developments in the field of organic solvent biocatalysis has been the demonstration that functional enzymes actually require very little liquid water and can operate efficiently in almost anhydrous conditions. The little water that is retained is probably in the form of a tightly bound solvation shell, associated with critical surface residues and active site components. The enzyme is present in the organic solvent in insoluble form but retains functionality and even demonstrates greatly enhanced thermostability. For example, porcine pancreatic lipase, which has a half-life of less than 5 minutes at 100°C in neutral buffer, is stable for hours in hexane at a water content of 0.0125%. Under conditions of low water activity, enzymes can show potentially useful changes in substrate specificity and stereospecificity. The other major advantage of low water activity systems is the ability to reverse the equilibria of hydrolytic reactions. It is very likely that enzymes in low water activity systems will ultimately prove to be very useful in industrial peptide and ester synthesis.

Gas-Phase Enzymology

A spectacular development in the known capabilities of enzymes has come from the demonstration of gas-phase enzymology. Immobilized *Methylosinus* methane monooxygenase in a gas phase of propylene/oxygen is capable of synthesizing propylene oxide, an important product in the chemical industry. Reduced nucleotide $NADH_2$ is regenerated by periodically flushing with methanol.

The ability of enzymes to operate in an essentially dry state such as a low relative humidity gas flow is consistent with our current understanding of the ability of enzymes to operate in low water activity organic solvent environments.

Enzyme Engineering

One of the traditional approaches to the selection of a suitable enzyme for industrial use has been a sequence of screening, selection and production optimization, and is sometimes associated with random mutation experiments in the hope of modifying some property in a desirable manner.

The development over the past decade of the techniques of protein engineering (see Chapter 12) offers a completely different approach to the selection of industrial enzymes with suitable properties. Moreover, site-specific mutagenesis enables the biochemist to induce structural modifications on the basis of rational design factors. Theoretically, no enzyme function or property is inaccessible to modification by this technology. Enzyme specific activity, substrate binding affinity, thermostability, pH/activity responses, pH stability, cofactor-binding sites, stability with respect to oxidation or denaturation by chaotropic agents, allosteric control and inhibition characteristics: all these properties are potential targets for modification by site-specific modification.

Despite its potential, this new technology is still in a state of infancy and currently has a number of severe limitations, both conceptual and practical. It is currently not possible to predict the long-distance consequences of most single amino acid replacements (or addition/deletions). This is largely the consequence of the subtlety of protein structure and function and our limited understanding of the interaction between the two. A number of studies have shown that even well-considered and conservative modifications to protein structure at points spacially distant to the active site have resulted in unexpected and undesirable side effects on catalytic function.

In practical terms, there are even more severe limitations. It is possible to replace any amino acid with only 19 alternatives, most of which will be quite inappropriate for structural reasons. The range of structural options is really limited to no more than three or four.

Before any intelligent decisions can be made on the nature and consequences of desirable modifications, it is necessary to have access to high quality three-dimensional structure data. Similar data for any modified protein are also necessary for the detailed analysis of the consequences of the changes induced. This places a strong emphasis on protein crystallization and X-ray diffraction analysis technologies which are inevitably rate-limiting. Since only about 50% of enzymes can be successfully crystallized, and not all of those are suitable for X-ray diffraction, this places a severe limitation on the capacity of site-specific mutagenesis. Expectation of future developments in protein crystallization (currently more of an art than a science), in X-ray diffraction analysis and in alternative methods of detailed structural analysis such as two-dimensional nuclear magnetic resonance (NMR) offer some hope for protein engineers.

In the meantime, enzyme engineering of industrial enzymes is feasible only where the enzyme holds a major market position, where considerable financial resources (and time) are available and where the targets are relatively simple. Current attempts to improve the stability of glucose isomerase and of subtilisin fulfil these criteria, yet both are proving to be difficult objectives.

CONCLUSIONS

Many overoptimistic predictions on the future of biotechnology have been immortalized in print. This warning notwithstanding, a note of cautious optimism on the future of enzymes in industry seems quite appropriate.

There is no doubt that industrial enzymology is not going to solve any of the world's major problems. The success of enzymes will primarily be in circumstances in which alternative technology (e.g. chemical technology) has failed and where their special properties, particularly specificity, can provide a viable process.

Over the past two decades, we have seen a steady (rather than a meteoric) rise in small-scale industrial enzyme applications but comparatively little change in the patterns of enzyme usage in larger industries. This is a probable clue to the future of enzymes over the next decade: relatively few new major industrial applications but a large number of relatively minor uses. However, the products of some of these minor applications (e.g. in the pharmaceutical industry) may be of disproportionate benefit to mankind.

Two of the major problems encountered in the industrial use of enzymes are production capacity and low biocatalyst stability. Predictable advances in current technologies such as genetic manipulation will undoubtedly increase the supply and reduce the cost of industrial enzymes. Manipulation of protein structure (by genetic or chemical methods) and/or the reaction environment should reduce the problems encountered in enzyme applications. Not all the developments will be derived from these new technologies; the discovery of new or better enzymes using old and familiar techniques is still a valid approach to future developments.

FURTHER READING

Industrial Enzymology

Godfrey, T. and Reichelt, J. (1983) *Industrial Enzymology*, Macmillan Publishers Ltd, London, 582pp.

Cheetham, P.S.J. (1985) The Applications of Enzymes in Industry. Chapter 3 in *Handbook of Enzyme Technology* (Wiseman, A., ed.) 2nd Ed., Ellis Horwood Publ., Chichester, pp. 275–279.
Leuenberger, H.G.W. and Kieslich, K. (1987) Biotransformations. Chapter 14 in *Fundamentals of Biotechnology* (Prave, P., Faust, U., Sittig, W. and Sukatsch, D.A., eds) VCH Verlagsgesellschaft mbH, pp. 564–601.
Anderson, D.M. (1987) Enzymatic Production of L-amino acids, in *Biotec 1: Microbial Genetic Engineering and Enzyme Technology* (Hollenberg, C.P. and Sahm, H., eds.) Gustav Fischer, Stuttgart and New York, pp. 41–59.

Immobilized Enzymes and Cells

Chibata, I. (1978) *Immobilized Enzymes: Research and Developments*, John Wiley & Sons, New York.
Mosbach, K. (1976) Immobilised Enzymes, Ch. 44 in *Methods in Enzymology*
Kennedy, J.F. and White, C.A. (1985) Principles of immobilization of enzymes. Chapter 4 in *Handbook of Enzyme Biotechnology* (Wiseman, A., ed.) 2nd edition, Ellis Horwood Ltd, Chichester, pp. 147–245.
Scott, C.D. (1987) Immobilized cells: a review of recent literature. *Enzyme and Microbial Technology*, vol. 9, pp. 66–73.

Fermentation Technology

Schugerl, K. and Sittig, W. (1987) Chapter 6 in *Fundamentals of Biotechnology* (Prave, P., Faust, U., Sittig, W. and Sukatsch, D.A., eds) VCH Verlagsgesellschaft mbH, pp. 179–224.

Organic Solvent Biocatalysis

Hahn-Hagerdahl, B. (1986) Water activity: a possible external regulator in biotechnological processes. *Enzyme and Microbial Technology*, **vol. 8**, pp. 322–327.
Laane, C. (1987) Medium-engineering for bio-organic synthesis. *Biocatalysis*, **vol. 1**, pp. 17–22.
Brink, L.E.S., Tramper, J., Luyben, K.Ch.A.M. and Van't Riet, K. (1988) Biocatalysis in organic media. *Enzyme and Microbial Technology*, vol. 10, pp. 736–743.
Khmelnitsky, Yu.L., Levashov, A.V., Klyachko, N.L. and Martinek, K. (1988) Engineering biocatalytic systems in organic media with low water content. *Enzyme and Microbial Technology*, vol. 10, pp. 710–724.
Laane, C., Tramper, J. and Lilly, M.D. (1987) Biocatalysis in Organic Media, *Studies in Organic Chemistry*, **vol. 29**, Elsevier, Amsterdam, 426pp.

Thermophiles and Thermostable Enzymes

Brock, T.D. and Zeikus, J.G. (1986) *Thermophiles: General, Molecular and Applied Microbiology*, John Wiley & Sons, Inc., New York.
Kandler, O. and Zillig, W. (1986) *Archaebacteria 85*, Gustav Fisher Verlag, Stuttgart and New York.
Sonnleitner, B. (1984) Biotechnology of thermophilic bacteria-growth, products and application. *Advances in Biochemical Engineering*, vol. 28, pp. 69–138.
Bergquist, P.L., Love, D.R., Croft, J.E., Streiff, M.B., Daniel, R.M. and Morgan, H.W. (1987) Genetics and potential biotechnological applications of thermophilic and extremely thermophilic micro-organisms. *Biotechnology and Genetic Engineering Reviews*, vol. 5, pp. 199–244.

Artificial Enzymes

Breslow, R. (1986) Artificial enzymes and enzyme models. *Advances in Enzymology*, vol. 58, pp. 1–60.

Protein Engineering

Querol, E. and Parilla, A. (1987) Tentative rules for increasing the thermostability of enzymes by protein engineering. *Enzyme and Microbial Technology*, vol. 9, pp. 238–244.

Chapter 19

New Materials

David Brown

LEARNING FROM NATURE

Nature is extremely good at materials science. Although natural materials must be synthesised at low temperatures and often have to serve in hostile environments, they are well-matched to their particular functions and achieve high efficiency in their usage of energy and of the substances from which they are built up.

The materials encountered in biological systems are often themselves well-designed composites, frequently anisotropic and usually subject to changes over time as the requirements of the living organism change. The distinction between a material and a structure thus becomes rather blurred. Moreover, the performance requirements imposed upon such a material may be just as demanding in certain respects as those appropriate to more conventional engineering materials, High extensibility, toughness and strength-to-weight ratio are frequently important, while resistance to corrosive environments and good fatigue performance (resistance to cyclic loading) are critical. A human heart valve, for instance, is quite capable of reliable operation for several billion cycles.

Not surprisingly, this use of materials by nature provides a wealth of lessons for the designer, the engineer and the materials scientist (table 1). The principles involved can be and are applied, consciously or unconsciously, to the design of 'conventional' engineering structures based on inorganic or synthetic organic materials. However, biotechnology allows us to go further: by enabling large quantities of natural materials to be manufactured reproducibly, it makes possible the use of these materials in conjunction with or in place of conventional materials, especially polymers. In doing so, we derive benefit in areas ranging from medical technology to the protection of the environment.

TRADITIONAL BIOMATERIALS

Many of the earliest polymers and composite materials used by man were of biological origin. Silk is a protein fibre whose mechanical and aesthetic properties were valued by the textile industry long before the amide bond was used by polymer scientists in the creation of nylon. Wool is another protein fibre, this time composed essentially of keratin. Cellulosic materials are undoubtedly the most significant of all: cellulose in the form of cotton constitutes one of the world's half-dozen major cash crops, while cellulose derivatives such as cellulose nitrate and cellulose acetate figured strongly in the beginnings of the polymer industry. Perhaps the major structural material of mankind, timber, comprises cellulose fibres assembled in a matrix consisting of a phenolic macromolecule (lignin) together with hemicellulosic polysaccharides to form an anisotropic composite with a degree of porosity appropriate to its function.

For biomaterials to be of technological importance, however, they must be available in large quantities in an easily accessible form. This is true of most of the materials mentioned above: cellulose really does grow on trees, and wool at least grows on sheep. Silk is the exception, and its low yields are reflected in its high cost which in turn imposes limitations on its use.

Furthermore, the final product must be reproducible in its chemistry and properties, a requirement which is difficult to satisfy in some plant-derived materials. Fortunately, large scale fermentation provides a means of polymer production which fulfils the requirements both of accessibility and of reproducibility.

MATERIALS FROM MICROORGANISMS?

To develop technologically useful polymeric materials derived from microorganisms is an attractive and an exciting goal, particularly if in doing so we emulate the highly optimised use of materials in biological structures themselves. Nevertheless, our scope must be restricted and our enthusiasm checked by practical and economic considerations. We can identify a series of "needs" which must be fulfilled.

Table 1
Some Comparisons Between the Design of Biological and Artificial Materials and Composites

DESCRIPTION	NATURAL	ARTIFICIAL
Strong, tough fibres in stiff but brittle matrix	Bone	Reinforced concrete
Use of porosity to improve toughness and raise stiffness/weight ratio	Wood, cancellous bone	Cellular polymers, honeycomb structures
Enhanced toughness by deflection of fracture along interfaces (crack-stopping")	Bone, wood, teeth	Fibre reinforced Composites
Encapsulation of brittle crystalline phase by tough interfacial polymer layers	Tooth enamel, shells cuttlebone	High-toughness cements and ceramics
Subdivision of tension members to avoid catastrophic failure	Tendons	Suspension cables, sailing ships
Liquid crystalline order in polymers to achieve anisotropic properties	Silks	Aramid fibres ("Kevlar")
Prestressing by fluid pressure	Plant stems, fungal hyphae	Hydraulic systems
Strong, oriented fibres in a polymer network matrix	Skin, connective tissues	Reinforced rubbers (motor tyres)
Water immobilisation to impart rigidity to swollen network	cartilage (proteoglycan gel)	Hydrogels (soft contact lenses)

Access To Production and Extraction Technology

However good the material, we still have to manufacture it: a first and fundamental demand is for large-scale fermentation and downstream processing technology, with the usual requirements as to sterile or hygenic engineering. Since microbial polymers will frequently be nearer to the "bulk" than to the "speciality" end of the manufacturing spectrum (at least in comparison to many fermentation products), it will be necessary to operate on a tonnage scale before commercial viability can be expected, whether on a continuous or on a batch basis. At the same time a high degree of control must be exercised with respect, for instance, to the control of molecular weight distribution during both the fermentation and the extraction and purification processes.

High Yield

Economics again dictate that we concentrate on materials which form a substantial component of the biomass. We can consider, perhaps rather arbitrarily, three categories of material (figure 1). The first comprises the major structural materials produced by the organism, whether as a cellular component (e.g. chitin in fungal cell walls) or to fulful some extracellular structural role (e.g. the cellulose network synthesised by some strains of *Acetobacter xylinum*). The second category

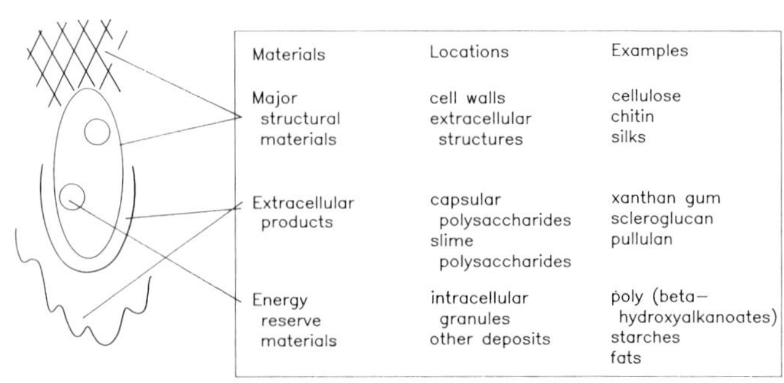

Figure 1. Candidates for exploitation: categories of biological materials.

covers those extracellular products which do not strictly play a structural role at a higher level than the molecular, their functions being typically those of adhesion or protection. Here we include the wide range of microbial polysaccharides which find applications related to, for instance, the control and stabilisation of gel structures. Finally, our third category is that of energy reserve materials, analogous to fats in mammals and to starch in plants, and exemplified by energy storage polyesters to which we return in detail below.

Potential for Further Increase in Yield

Rarely will the microorganism in its natural state provide a sufficient yield of the required material. Just as with large domestic animals, our organism can be improved by selective breeding! In principle, the methods of genetic manipulation using recombinant DNA technology could be applied to improve polymer yields, but in practice more mundane techniques of strain selection and nutrient limitation are more likely to be of use in the short to medium term.

Customers!

Like any new product, microbial polymers will first become available in modest quantities at relatively high cost. They can thus be expected to follow a pattern of first finding uses in high value applications, perhaps exploiting any unusual properties, and then moving gradually into larger scale applications as costs fall and quantities available increase. Such a pattern is typical of synthetic polymers (and indeed of commercial materials in general): a classic example is the progression of polyethylene from a specialised insulator in radar equipment to a cheap and common commodity polymer. In addition, any novel polymer will have a substantial advantage if it can be processed using similar methods to established materials and on the same equipment. The net result of meeting these four needs will be an economically and technologically acceptable balance of cost and properties: a balance as essential to the commercial success of a fermentation product as to that of any conventional material.

POLYMER PRECURSORS

Microbial technology need not necessarily provide the "finished" polymeric material: it may instead supply a chemical intermediate or low molecular weight prepolymer which can then be used as a precursor for polymer manufacture by conventional means. This biologically synthesised compound may have advantages such as purity or stereospecificity over its conventionally synthesised counterpart in addition to the benefits offered by a more efficient or a more environmentally acceptable method of production.

Lignin

One potentially valuable source of precursors for polymer manufacture is lignin, which as a major constituent (some 30%) of timber is a large scale by-product of the pulp and paper industry. Lignins have complex and variable macromolecular structures, but may be regarded as rigid networks built up from three closely-related cinnamyl alcohol monomers: p-coumaryl, coniferyl, and sinapyl alcohols (figure 2). These monomers are linked together by oxidative polymerisation to form a structure of which a portion is shown schematically in figure 3. Despite the unusual complexity of the lignin structure, depolymerisation can be achieved by a range of microorganisms as well as by conventional chemical procedures such as acid hydrolysis. Such microorganisms

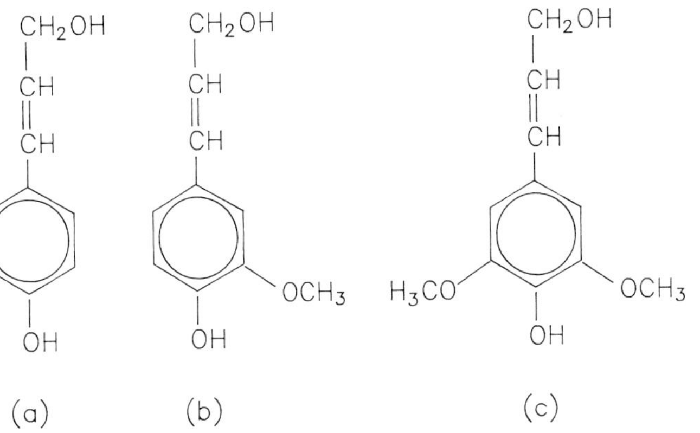

Figure 2. The building blocks of lignin:

(a) *p*-coumaryl alcohol
(b) coniferyl alcohol
(c) sinapyl alcohol

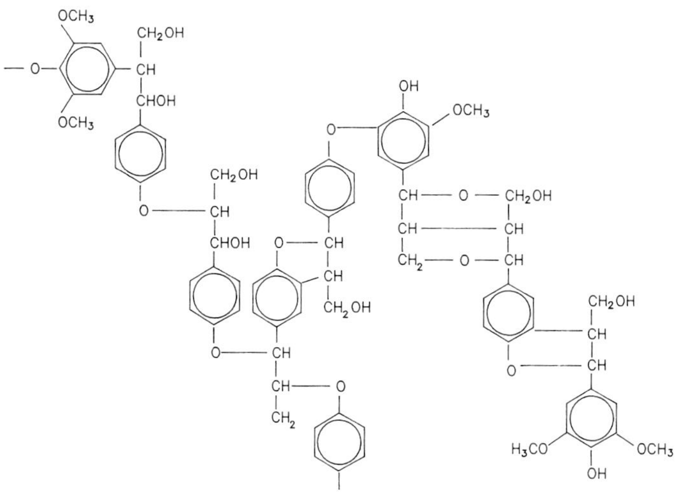

Figure 3. A schematic picture of part of a lignin macromolecule, showing some typical linkages between the basic units.

include those responsible for the rotting of timber. In wood, degradation is primarily by fungal action, although bacteria play a significant role in the degradation of lignin in plant tissues (e.g. grasses) having a lower lignin content. Some progress has been made in clarifying the mechanism of lignin depolymerisation by wood-rotting organisms, particularly by the white-rot species *Phanerochaete chrysosporium*. There are obvious difficulties in arriving at an enzyme mechanism for lignin degradation: the structural irregularity of the lignin rules out the highly stereospecific modes of action normally associated with enzyme operation. Studies on lignin itself and on low molecular weight model compounds have indicated that reduced oxygen species such as O_2-, H_2O_2, .OH, and $^1O_2$ (singlet oxygen) are produced by the microorganisms involved in degradation; enzymes which destroy such species inhibit the lignin breakdown. In 1983 Tien and Kirk reported the discovery of an extracellular ligninase, dependent on H_2O_2 for its activity, acting as the catalyst for one type of lignin cleavage. The method of action of this enzyme, a protein of molecular weight 42,000, has since been shown to involve haem, the iron-porphyrin complex essential to the action of a wide range of proteins. Spectroscopic studies indicate that in the ligninase, as in other peroxidases, the iron is oxidised from Fe (III) to Fe (IV) by H_2O_2, forming an oxo-ferryl (Fe(IV)−O.) complex which is then able to act as a one-electron transfer agent. Radical cations created by this one-electron transfer can then be involved in a variety of reactions resulting in degradation of the lignin structure — including regions remote from the original enzyme.

Further work is necessary before the potential of enzymes such as this peroxidase can be harnessed in the production of useful monomers, but wide-ranging studies on the products of lignin degradation by conventional chemical means have already shown the value of lignin products as precursors for phenol-formaldehyde resins and polyurethanes, two important categories of engineering plastics. Another potentially valuable precursor is p-hydroxybenzoic acid, which has been extensively studied as a component of liquid crystal polymers. It is closely related in structure to vanillic acid, the most widely reported small-molecule aromatic product of lignin degradation (figure 4).

The structural heterogeneity of lignin means that degradation procedures will in general produce a mixture of compounds; the yields of the desired species within this mixture will be somewhat variable from one lignin source to another and from batch to batch. We may therefore need to resort to (potentially costly) separation processes, or to tolerate a reduced measure of control over the properties of the final polymeric material into which the precursor is incorporated.

The yield of useful product from enzymatic degradation may be rather low in aqueous solution and the use of organic solvents has been shown to allow an increase in efficiency in the case of lignin degradation by horseradish peroxidase. A small amount of water surrounds the enzyme, while the organic solvent makes up the bulk of the system: similar methods have been shown to increase yields from a wide range of enzymatic processes. To aid further in the manufacture of lignin products, the transfer of activity to a more convenient organism is desirable and the gene coding for the ligninase discussed above in *P. chrysosporium* has successfully been cloned into a bacteriophage and into yeast. Progress in lignin exploitation continues, therefore, and there are excellent prospects for the fuller use of a material which in tonnage terms (perhaps 20,000,000,000 tons per year!) is one of nature's major structural materials.

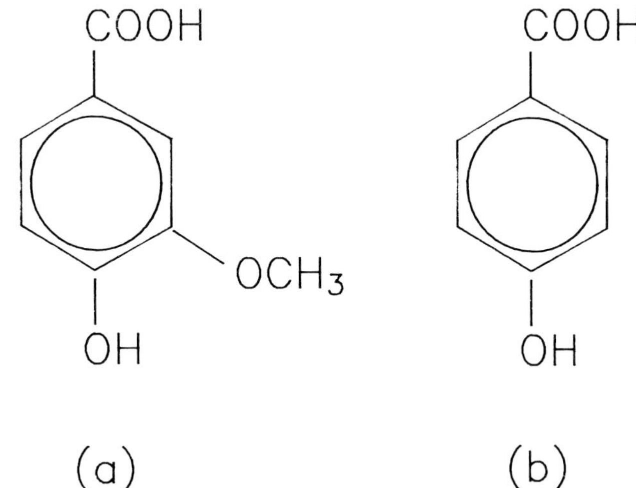

Figure 4. Small-molecule aromatics derived from lignin:
(a) vanillic acid
(b) *p*-hydroxybenzoic acid

Cyclohexadiene Synthesis

A contrasting example of precursor manufacture starting not from a complex macromolecule but from simple benzene, is the synthesis of 1,2-dihydroxy cyclohexa-3,5-diene (more manageably known as benzene-cis-glycol or BCG) by *Pseudomonas putida*. A dioxygenase enzyme is responsible for the reaction of interest (figure 5). In the industrial process the whole organism is used since the enzyme itself is unstable in its isolated form.

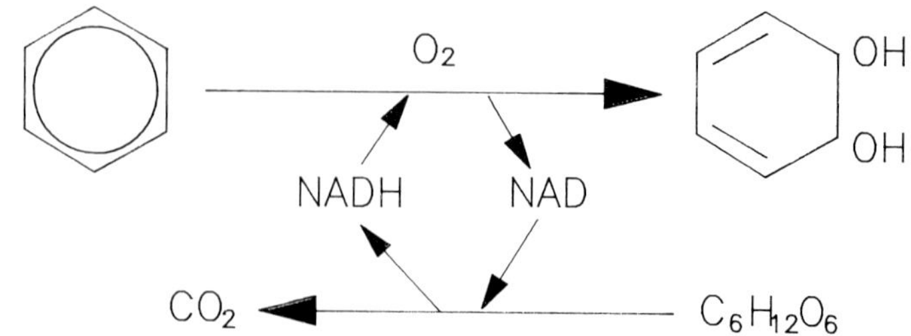

Figure 5. Synthesis of 1,2-dihydroxy cyclohexa-3,5-diene ("BCG").

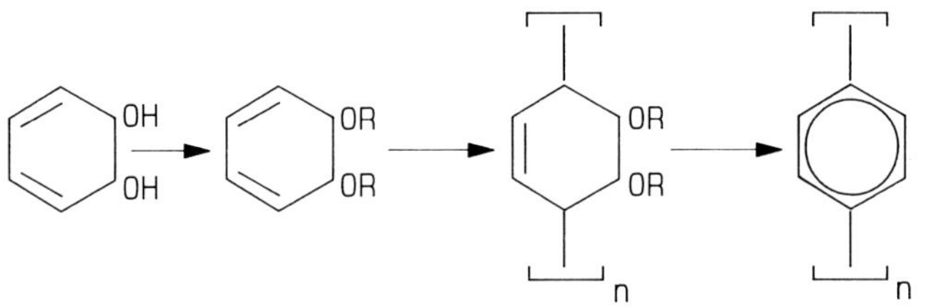

Figure 6. Synthesis of poly-*p*-phenylene from BCG: in this case, R-$COCH_3$.

The yields of BCG via the microbial route are superior to any obtainable by conventional chemistry and the product serves as an intermediate in the manufacture of poly-p-phenylene (figure 6), a polymer with valuable and unique properties.

MICROBIAL PLASTICS: THE CASE OF POLY(3-HYDROXYBUTYRATE)

The manufacture by microbial means of commercial polymers, rather than just their precursors, is well-established. Xanthan gum, for instance, the extracellular polysaccharide produced by the bacterium *Xanthomonas campestris* (see Chapters 17 and 25) is a successful alternative to plant polysaccharides in a range of applications such as those involving control of the rheology of foodstuffs, and indeed has some unique and useful properties of its own. We concentrate in this chapter, however, on structural polymers — materials analogous to the common plastics such as polyethylene, polypropylene and poly(vinyl chloride). In one instance, a bacterial product has been exploited as a structural plastic and its development provides an instructive case study.

PHB: The Polymer and its Structure

Poly(3-hydroxybutyrate), or PHB, is an energy storage medium present in a wide variety of bacteria. At the primary level of structure, it is an aliphatic polyester with the repeat unit shown in figure 7. The molecule adopts a 2_1 helical conformation (i.e. two repeat units per complete twist of the helix) and crystallises in the orthorhombic system with two antiparallel helices and a total of four repeat units in the crystallographic unit cell. The space group, describing the crystal symmetry, is $P2_1\ 2_1\ 2_1$.

Within the bacterial cell, the PHB is accumulated as discrete granules which can attain a size of order 200 nm and are readily revealed by transmission electron microscopy following embedding and sectioning or freeze-fracture and replication (figure 8). Each granule is encapsulated in a membrane, which accommodates the enzymes responsible for polymerisation and depolymerisation.

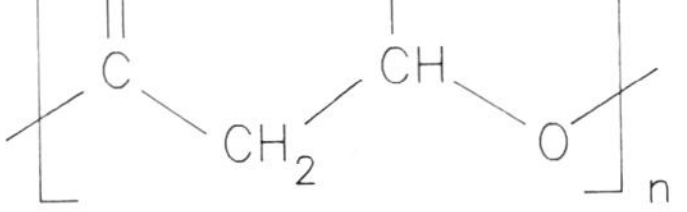

Figure 7. Chemical structure of poly(3-hydroxybutyrate).

Biosynthesis

PHB synthesis takes place by a relatively simple biochemical pathway commencing with the conversion of any of a wide range of carbon sources to acetate and thence to acetyl coenzyme A. Condensation of two acetyl coA molecules produces acetoacetyl coA and, by subsequent reduction, 3-hydroxybutyryl coA. The linking of the 3-hydroxybutyryl units by a polymerase regenerates the coenzyme and generates the PHB macromolecule (figure 9).

Polymers of other 3-hydroxyalkanoates can be synthesised by analogous mechanisms, some alternative alkyl group replacing the methyl side group of HB. Although less common in nature than PHB, several other poly(3-hydroxyalkanoates) have been reported, with side groups as large as pentyl, and both homopolymers and copolymers have been detected.

Fermentation

PHB production is carried out in a two stage batch fermentation. The first stage is one of cell growth, typically with glucose as the carbon source. In the second, an essential nutrient such as oxygen, nitrogen or phosphorous is denied to the cells while the supply of the carbon source continues. Unable to grow and multiply, the bacteria convert the carbon source into PHB until, at PHB contents of some 80% of total dry mass, they are literally crammed so full of polymer granules that the taut cell membranes are unable to hold more. The fermentation takes several days in all and can reach total solids concentrations in the broth of over 100 grams per litre.

Product Recovery

The extraction of the polymer can be accomplished by several methods. Cell breakage is an important step, improving the accessibility of the cell contents to subsequent stages in the extraction procedure. It can conveniently be achieved by subjecting the fermenter broth to high pressure and temperature: sudden release of pressure causes rupture of the cell walls. Once the cell contents are liberated, the PHB can be recovered by solvent extraction into chloroform or methylene

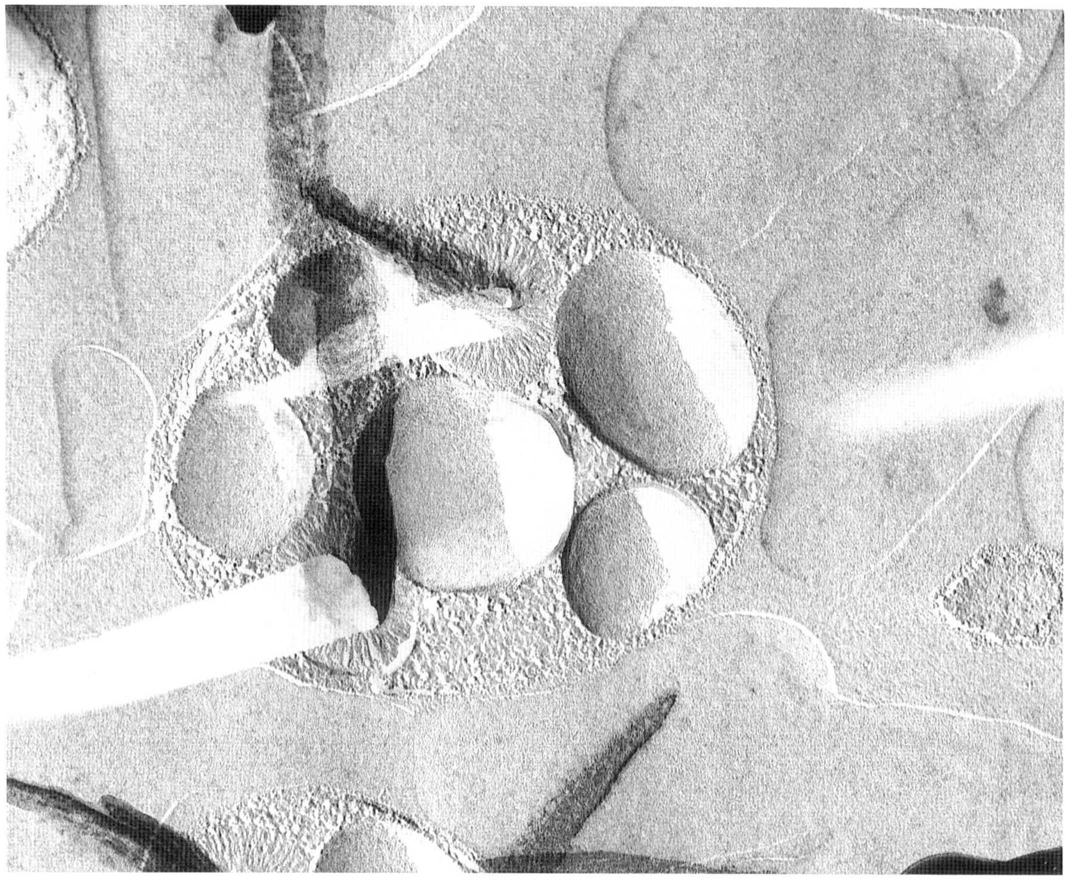

Figure 8. Granules of PHB within a cell of *A. eutrophus*. Freeze-fracture replica, scale bar 0.5 μm.

chloride; alternatively, the remaining cellular material can be digested using protease and lipase enzymes (somewhat similar to those incorporated in "biological" washing powders) and the PHB recovered as a powder after flocculation.

The choice of extraction method is important, since, in conjunction with the choice of organism and growth conditions, it influences the molecular weight of the recovered product.

The final product form is also important if the polymer is to be readily processable by the user and for most applications the PHB powder is dried, extruded and granulated to the usual "chip" form appropriate to standard plastics processing equipment. Any additives, such as pigments or plasticisers, are incorporated prior to the extrusion/granulation step.

Polymer Properties

The properties of PHB follow in part from its bacterial origin. Impurities such as catalyst residues typical of conventionally synthesised polymers are absent from the microbial material. The repeat unit contains a chiral centre, and the enzymatic synthesis dictates that this is always in the D(−) (or R absolute) configuration. Most significantly, microorganisms in the environment are able to degrade PHB: this takes place more slowly than the breakdown in nature by PHB-synthesising organisms of their own internal polymer granules, but nonetheless means that items made from PHB will "biodegrade" in the presence of suitable organisms (for instance following soil burial, or disposal in sewage systems) by enzymatic depolymerisation following microbial colonisation of the surface.

Other properties are consequences of structure, both at the primary chemical level and at higher levels of structure ranging from the molecular conformation and symmetry to the crystallinity and microstructure of the particular solid sample in question. The latter two factors are strongly dependent — as for most materials — on the thermal and mechanical history of the sample, so that precise property data are to be treated with caution. Some typical data are given in Table 2, where a comparison is made with a common conventional plastic, polypropylene (PP). The two materials are similar in many respects though PHB has lower gas permeability while PP is substantially tougher.

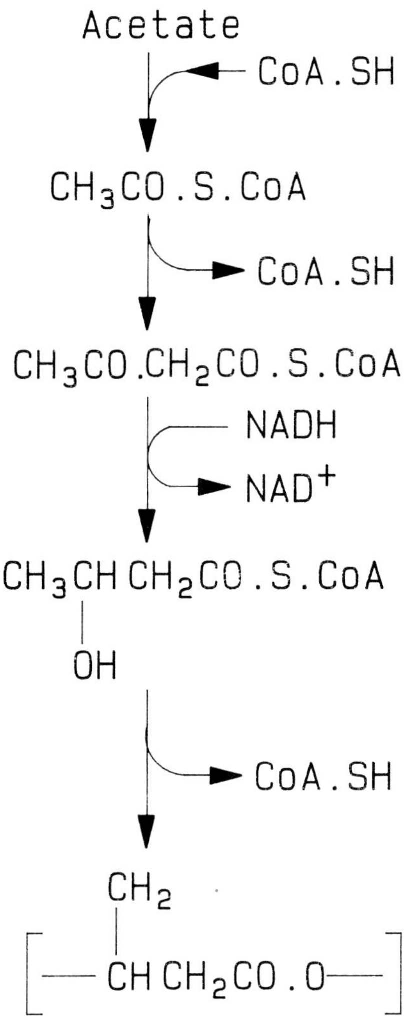

Figure 9. Biosynthetic pathway for PHB manufacture.

Table 2
Comparison: PHB — Polypropylene (PP)

	PHB	*PP*
T_{melt} (°C)	180	180
T_g (°C)	15	−10
Crystallinity (%)	80	70
$\overline{M}_w$	500,000	200,000
Density	1.25	0.9
Tensile Strength (MPa)	40	38
Flexural Modulus (GPa)	4.0	1.7
Extension to Break (%)	8	400
UV Resistance	good	poor
Solvent Resistance	poor	good
O_2 Permeability, 25 μ film ($cm^3/m^2/atm/day$)	45	1,700

As a thermoplastic, PHB can be melt-processed (provided care is taken to minimise melt degradation) and hence used in injection moulding, blow moulding, and the production of films and fibres, as well as being incorporated into polymer blends and composite materials. A wide range of plasticisers, fillers and other additives can be incorporated if required, though these are by no means always necessary. The most commonly required additive is a *nucleating agent*, for the following reason. In conventional polymers, catalyst residues and other impurities provide a plentiful supply of sites for the heterogenous nucleation of polymer crystals during cooling from the melt. The high nucleation density determines (in conjunction with crystal growth rates) the overall rate of crystallisation and thus influences the cycle time in moulding and other processes. It also ensures the creation of the fine scale microstructure which is desirable if the final material is to have acceptable mechanical properties. Since PHB is substantially free from such impurities, an extraneous nucleating agent may have to be added. Small additions of talc or boron nitride are suitable. On the other hand, if the nucleation density is allowed to remain low, the very large scale spherulitic microstructures so formed (figure 10) are both attractive and ideal for scientific studies of crystallisation behaviour!

Applications: A Changing Perception

Although PHB has been known since its isolation and identification by Lemoigne in 1925, its successful exploitation is a recent development. Studies in the early 1960s by the American company W. R. Grace appear to have been discontinued owing to production and extraction difficulties, though some examination of possible medical applications was reported in the patent literature.

The crucial incentive for the development of PHB was provided in 1973 by the dramatic increases in oil prices, and the uncertainties as to continued oil supply, brought about by the Middle East war in October of that year. An urgent need was perceived for materials able to replace commodity polymers derived from petrochemicals and the similarity of PHB to some conventional plastics made it an obvious candidate. Extensive development and characterisation work took place.

Politics is an unpredictable business, however, and subsequent trends in oil prices were quite different from those anticipated. It became clear that PHB was unlikely, in the foreseeable future, to become available at prices as low as those of existing common commodity polymers.

The story might then have come to an end had two significant developments not intervened. The first was the realisation that, although not a potentially "cheap" commodity polymer except in the very long term, PHB possessed certain speciality properties of particular value. One was its exceptionally high degree of toleration by mammalian tissue,

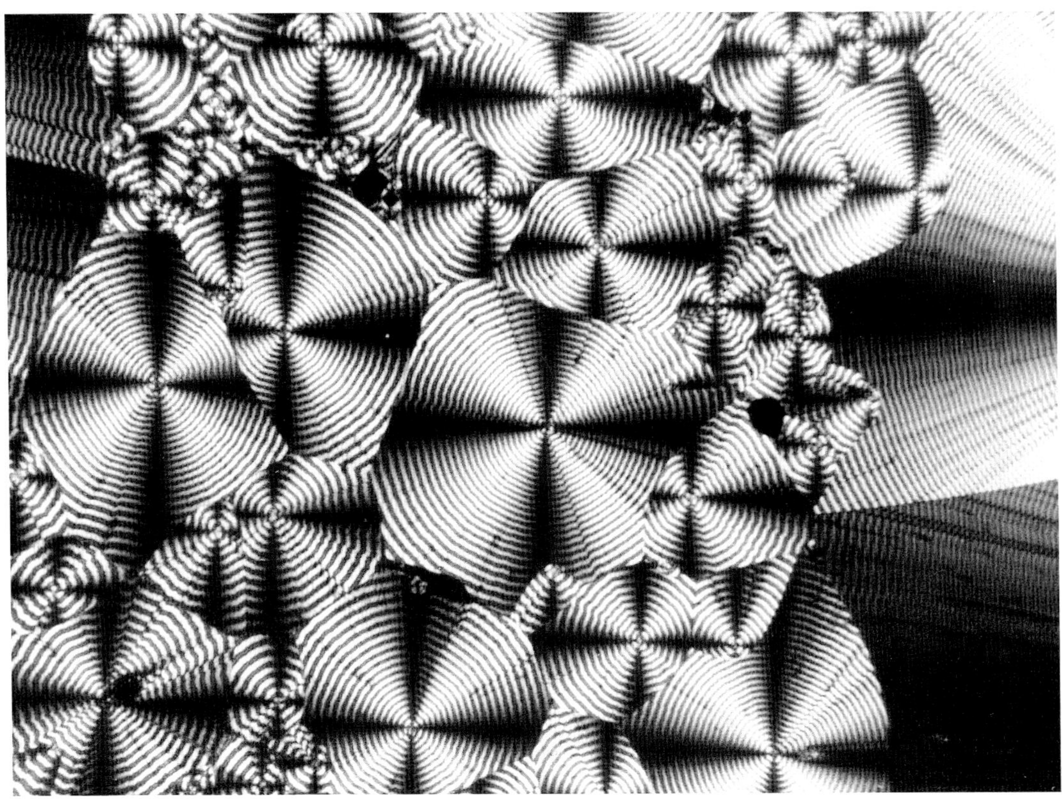

Figure 10. Large spherulites in a thin film of PHB; scale bar 200 μm. Spherulitic microstructures are in some respects analogous to the granular structure of a polycrystalline metal but each spherulite is itself an assemblage of many crystals interspersed with regions of non-crystalline polymer.

with a minimal inflammatory reaction (i.e. the polymer was unusually "biocompatible"), leading to potential medical and health care applications of high added value. Another speciality property was its ability to be fabricated into environmentally biodegradable items for use in disposable products and as packaging materials.

The second key development was the discovery that, by suitable changes in the carbon source during the polymer accumulation stage of fermentation, *Alcaligenes eutrophus* could be induced to synthesize not only PHB homopolymer but also copolymers of 3-hydroxybutyrate with controlled amounts of 3-hydroxyvalerate (HV) (figure 11). The inclusion of HV units brings about substantially improved toughness and thus helps to overcome the principal deficiency of the homopolymer.

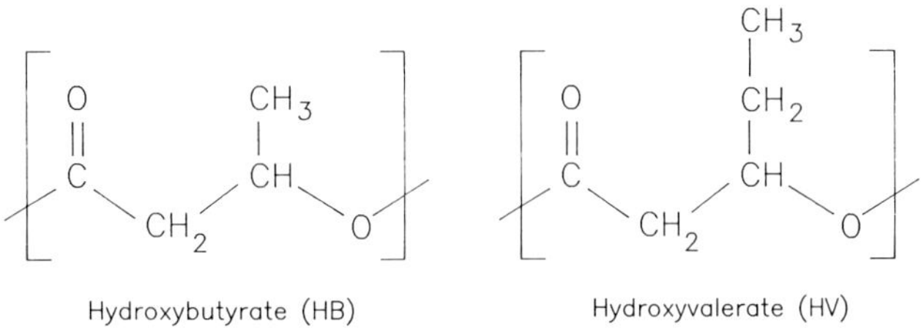

$$\left[-\overset{\overset{\displaystyle O}{\|}}{C} - CH_2 - \overset{\overset{\displaystyle CH_3}{|}}{CH} - O - \right] \qquad \left[-\overset{\overset{\displaystyle O}{\|}}{C} - CH_2 - \overset{\overset{\displaystyle CH_3}{|}}{\overset{\displaystyle CH_2}{\overset{|}{CH}}} - O - \right]$$

Hydroxybutyrate (HB) Hydroxyvalerate (HV)

Figure 11. Poly(3-hydroxybutyrate/3-hydroxyvalerate) copolymers.

Aided by these two factors, the exploitation of the bacterial polymers continued. Development of potential applications was pursued in parallel with the improvement and scaling-up of the fermentation and extraction processes. With polymer available in limited quantities and at high cost in the early stages, low-volume, high added value applications were the first to receive serious attention. A "speciality" business of this kind is often best handled by a small, responsive organisation rather than directly by a large multinational, although skills and resources provided by the latter are essential to success. The opportunities presented by PHB and its copolymers were developed by Marlborough Biopolymers Limited, a subsidiary of ICI PLC and MTM PLC based in the North East of England — a region which has become a focus of expertise in biotechnology. Marketed outside the U.S. under the trade name "BIOPOL", the polymers are now produced in tonnage quantities.

By the mid 1980s, the emphasis in the evaluation and use of PHB/HV had begun to shift towards environmentally acceptable plastics. The trend has been driven by pressure of public opinion backed up by present and proposed legislation in major industrial countries including Italy and the Federal Republic of Germany: an increasing scale of production and falling costs have so far enabled the PHB/HV materials to keep up with the increased "market pull" from this environmental trend.

Nevertheless, speciality uses remain potentially significant. "Biocompatibility" combined with controllable mechanical properties has created widespread interest in surgical uses of PHB/HV, for instance in orthopaedic devices, wound care, and controlled-release implants. The chiral purity of the HB repeat unit has led to the use of the monomer, obtained by the hydrolysis of PHB, as a valuable intermediate in the synthesis of fine chemicals where a single optical isomer is required.

Polymer Composition and its Consequences

The proportion and distribution of dissimilar repeat units in a copolymer are important factors affecting mechanical and other properties. In PHB/HV, the HV units appear from NMR evidence to be incorporated in a random sequence, although some crystallisation studies suggest deviations from randomness. The effect of HV inclusion is to lower the melting point and to reduce both the rate of crystallisation and the final crystallinity resulting from a standard thermal history. Lower levels of crystallinity in turn lead to somewhat lower stiffness, higher gas permeabilities and considerably improved toughness as judged for example by standard impact tests (e.g. the Izod test) or by percentage extension to break (breaking strain). Some of the effects of copolymerisation are illustrated in figures 12–14.

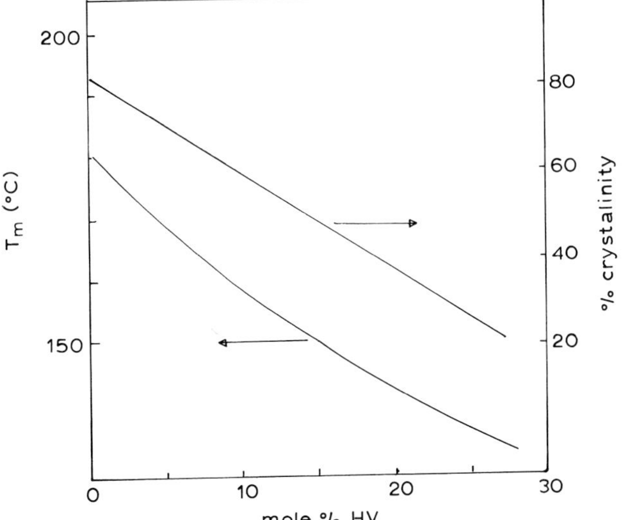

Figure 12. The effect of HV comonomer content on melting point Tm (°C) and percentage crystallinity. These data refer to samples with a particular thermal history (cooling from the melt at 20°C/min).

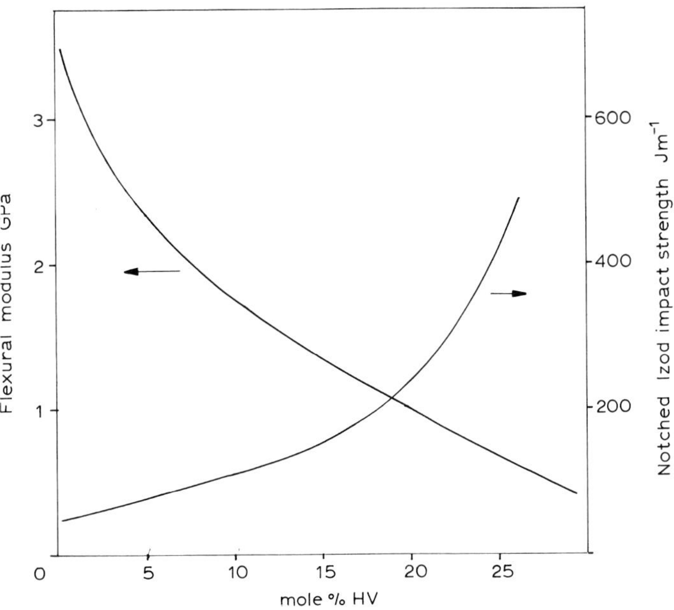

Figure 13. The effect of HV comonomer content on flexural modulus and notched Izod impact strength (a comparative measure of toughness).

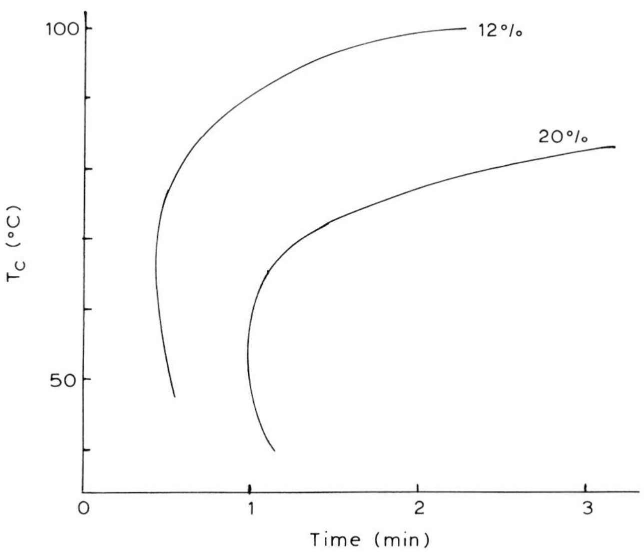

Figure 14. Isothermal crystallisation time for PHB/HV copolymers of two different HV contents. Samples were rapidly cooled from the melt to a temperature Tc and allowed to crystallise isothermally: points on the curve represent the time taken to reach the peak in a DSC crystallisation endotherm (i.e. maximum rate of crystallisation).

The influence of HV content on crystallisation rate is considerable (figure 14) and means that, if realistic cycle times are to be achieved, the addition of a nucleating agent is much more likely to be necessary in high HV copolymers than in PHB itself. This illustrates the importance of controlling polymer behaviour if a new material is to be processed successfully on existing equipment. Minor changes to normal practice are likely to be acceptable — for instance controlling mould temperature at perhaps 60°C to exploit the peak crystallisation rate revealed by figure 14 — but formulations which drastically curtail output through poor solidification rates are not. Further control is possible by subjecting the material to a prescribed thermal and mechanical history: stiffness can be reduced and toughness enhanced by deforming the polymer, e.g. by cold-rolling. The changes induced can be interpreted in terms of spherulite breakdown and the healing of microstructural cracks which, if allowed to remain, could initiate and help to propagate brittle fracture. Achieving substantial molecular orientation, whether uniaxially as in a fibre or biaxially as in a drawn film, is often desirable in order to improve tensile strength, clarity, or gas barrier performance. Figure 15 summarises the "PHB story".

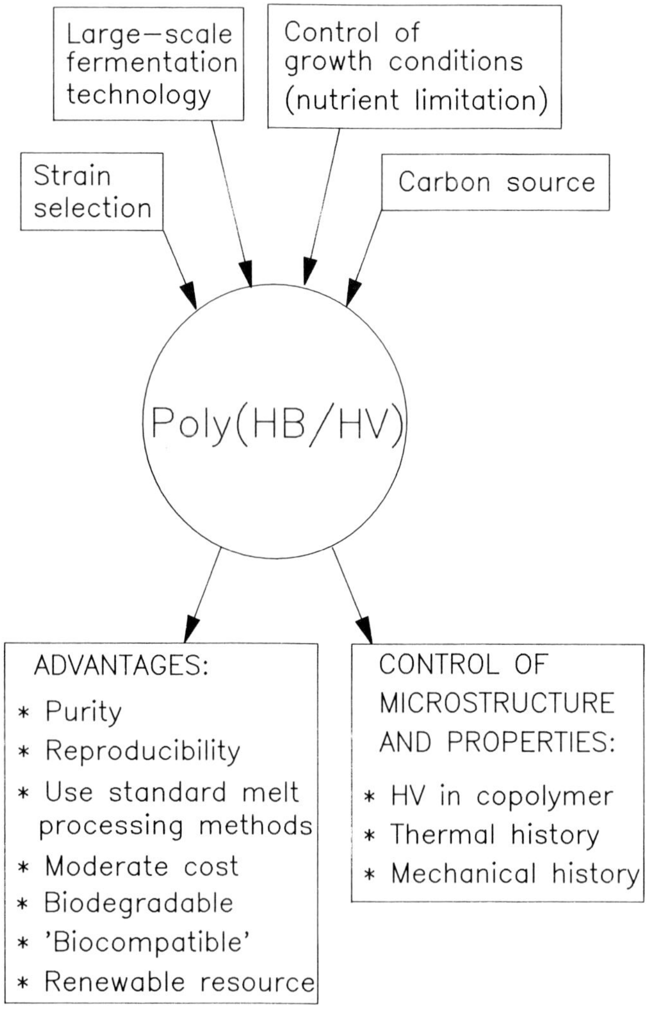

Figure 15. Summary of factors controlling PHB/HV fermentation and product properties.

Some Potential Uses

The wide range of applications, current and proposed, for polymers based on 3-hydroxybutyrate is illustrated by figure 16. Cost factors will be critical in determining whether, in the long term, such polymers remain "speciality materials" or enter into widespread use in fields previously dominated by conventional commodity plastics. Advances in carbon conversion efficiencies, scale of fermentation and the economics of production and extraction have made it likely that the larger-scale uses will predominate. Much depends however on the price premium to be attached to biodegradability and this will vary from country to country as well as from one market type to another. A careful analysis of all factors is essential in developing a strategy for the successful exploitation of any new material, including those derived from biotechnology.

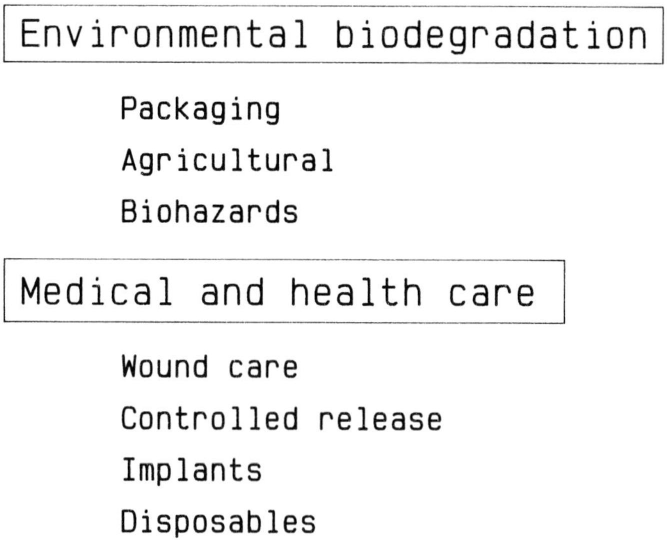

Environmental biodegradation

Packaging
Agricultural
Biohazards

Medical and health care

Wound care
Controlled release
Implants
Disposables

Figure 16. Examples of the potential applications of PHB/HV copolymers.

POLYSACCHARIDES

Microbial polysaccharides are already widely known and used. Applications — which include food additives, emulsifiers, fluids for enhanced oil recovery, adhesives and blood plasma substitutes — often involve the polysaccharide (or a combination of polysaccharides) in combination with water as a gel or solution, where the particular rheological performance of the polymer is of value. In other areas, however, the polysaccharides is used either as a dry solid or as a component (e.g. a coating) in a more complex structure.

The archetype among polysaccharides is of course cellulose (poly 1,4,-β-D-glucopyranose). The bacterium *Acetobacter xylinum* synthesizes a highly-swollen mesh of fine cellulose

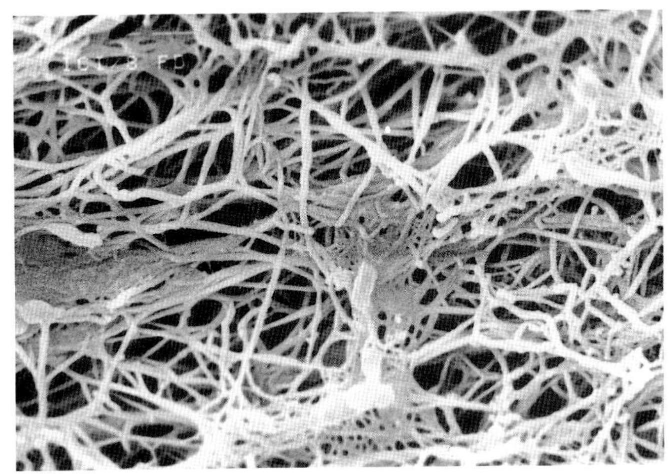

Figure 17. A network of cellulose fibres synthesised by *A. xylinum*. These form a sheet on the surface of a fermentation medium. Scale bar 2 μm.

fibres which forms a tough sheet or *pellicle* on the surface of a fermentation medium (Figure 17). The strength and resilience of the pellicle are remarkable given that the ratio of cellulose to absorbed water is typically 1 to 100. The properties of the material are a reflection of the high molecular weight and crystallinity of the cellulose, the branched and entangled network nature of the fibrous mass and the very high surface area-to-mass ratio of the fibres themselves: each fibre is a "twisted ribbon" perhaps 50 nm broad and 5 nm in thickness, and is itself an assembly of fibrillar sub-units at several levels. Possible uses for such a material include artificial skin grafts, surgical dressings, separation membranes and leather substitutes. However, costs are likely to be high.

Somewhat similar applications are among those proposed for chitin which can be produced in a fibrous form from fungal hyphae. There is evidence that healing is promoted by chitin used as a component in wound dressings while in broader textile applications use can be made of the fine scale of the hyphal fibres: though their diameters are of micron order rather than the nanometre scale typical of the cellulose discussed above, they are nevertheless finer than conventional melt-spun textile filaments. Food applications may be significant: chitin is a source of dietary fibre for humans and as an animal feed additive can assist in the digestion of lactose and hence in the utilisation of lactose-containing whey from the dairy industry.

Alkali treatment of chitin yields chitosan which itself has a range of uses as a film-forming polymer and as a biodegradable component in medical dressings in addition to applications as a food additive and in the purification of drinking water by removal of particulate contaminants.

Several microbial polysaccharides, including chitin derivatives, have uses as film-forming polymers, encapsulants, or tabletting media. Non-toxic, bioerodible materials are required for drug delivery in environments as diverse as the human bloodstream and the animal gut. Controlled delivery is seen as a key to future developments in more efficient and safer drug usage and demands both a range of timescales and a high degree of tissue compatibility on the part of the materials concerned.

Related uses, somewhat less sophisticated but nonetheless important, occur in the coating, pelletisation and preservation of foods. A recently developed example is the production of edible films based on pullulan, a polyglucose related to starch and synthesised from starch hydrolysates using the black yeast *Aureobasidium pullulans*. Polysaccharides such as this benefit from the "natural" image which is now an important commercial advantage in the food industry.

Polysaccharides cannot normally be processed as readily as thermoplastics but it may in future be possible to overcome this problem. Successful extrusion of starch has been demonstrated, the key being the maintenance of a small but finite level of moisture in the material.

MICROBIAL POLYAMIDES

Polyamides, or nylons, are an extremely successful family of synthetic polymers whose excellent mechanical properties make them suitable for high tensile strength fibres and for light, wear-resistant engineering components such as gear wheels. Consisting essentially of short hydrocarbon chains linked by the -CONH- amide or peptide bond, they exhibit an obvious similarity to proteins in their primary chemical structure and admit some comparison of function with the structural proteins such as silks, collagens, keratins, and the "protein rubbers" — elastin, resilin and abductin.

Not surprisingly, attempts have been made to develop microbial processes for the synthesis of industrially useful fibre-forming proteins. Silk as formed by the larva of *Bombyx mori*, the silk moth, is perhaps the best model. Its crystalline fraction, fibroin, has a regular structure dominated by the amino acids glycine, alanine and serine and a polymer very similar to this has reportedly been synthesised by an American company, Syntro Corporation, using an artificial gene introduced into a suitable bacterium. An alternative approach, using the natural gene from the silkworm inserted into a vector and used for the transformation of *Escherichia coli* or *Saccharomyces cerevisiae*, has also been reported.

Many other organisms use silks and spiders will often produce several types for different purposes. One type of particular interest is the dragline silk used for web frameworks and as a "safety rope" when the spider is climbing. The dragline silks of the species *Araneus diadematus* and *A. sericatus* are characterised by very high tensile strengths together with high extensibilities — some 1,400 MPa and 30%, respectively. For comparison, values for *B. mori* silk would be about 700 MPa and 20%, while those for high strength synthetic fibre — Du Pont's polyaramid "Kevlar"

— are 2,760 MPa and 2.5–4%. The combination of high strength with high extensibility means that the energy required to break the fibre (corresponding to the energy under the force-extension curve) is very high indeed: the breaking energy of *A. sericatus* dragline silk has been estimated at 158 MJ m^{-3}. The isolation of the gene sequence for a dragline silk, and its transfer to a suitable bacterium for larger scale synthesis, has recently been reported: suggested applications in bullet-proof clothing and flak jackets would exploit the high breaking energy of the material.

Similar progress has been made in relation to adhesive proteins based on mussel glue which has the unusual property among adhesives of applicability to a wide variety of substrates under wet conditions. Although mussel glue protein is already available commercially on a small scale, and is likely to find significant medical uses (for instance in ophthalmic surgery), larger-scale engineering uses would require more efficient production methods combined with sequence modifications to "tailor" the properties of the adhesive for specific applications. Microbial synthesis offers the possibility of achieving both objectives. A clone of the natural gene, and a related synthetic gene, have been introduced into both yeast and *E. coli*: development is at an early stage but applications first in high-value medical areas and then in other demanding environments can be anticipated.

An important feature of structural proteins in nature is their highly ordered state at secondary and tertiary levels. *B. mori* silk fibroin has the pleated β-sheet structure and the silk fibre is a composite consisting of the crystalline fibroin fibrils in a non-crystalline matrix. The structural arrangement of collagen is based upon a triple helix, while keratin occurs in both α-helical and β-sheet forms. The crystallinity of such a protein and the typical crystallite size, two parameters which influence mechanical and physical properties, are controlled by the particular amino acids present (e.g. "helix breakers" and "helix formers") and by their distribution (the degree of "blockiness" — a term used in polymer science to describe a preference for sequences of the same repeat unit within a copolymer rather than a random distribution of the different repeat units present). Further influence on properties is afforded by covalent crosslinking via disulphide bridges and by suitable choice of molecular weight. All these factors make it clear that the design of "engineering proteins" to exhibit particular properties is a complex task. Although genetic manipulation makes possible the synthesis of such proteins once they have been specified, major efforts in basic polymer science research will be essential if we are to understand how to arrive at the optimum amino acid sequences.

THE FUTURE?

The long term outlook for the availability and cost of some of the industrial world's basic resources, including oil, remains a cause for concern. In contrast, sources of carbon suitable as fermentation substrates are plentiful — witness the embarrassing agricultural surpluses, such as the "grain mountain", of the European Community. Over the next few decades the relative costs of materials or their precursors derived from fermentation, and those based on petrochemicals, will inevitably change.

Industries for the Developing World

Already many Third World countries find it economically impossible to import sufficient petrochemicals to support their home demand. Some, however, do have readily available and comparatively cheap supplies of fermentable material, such as molasses, which could form the basis of a local polymer industry using indigenous resources thereby making a contribution to the balance of payments of a developing nation.

Newer Materials?

The ability of microorganisms to produce technologically valuable materials has barely begun to be harnessed. Polysaccharides such as cellulose and chitin can be synthesised, often in a highly ordered form; protein synthesis via genetic manipulation allows the polymer scientist greater scope than in the design of nylon polymers, while the development of poly(3-hydroxybutyrate) has pioneered techniques for the recovery of a polymer from large scale fermentation and for its conversion into an industrially acceptable plastic processable by straightforward methods.

Looking ahead, the degree of structural order in biological materials might perhaps be exploited to obtain polymers (as well as low molecular weight compounds) exhibiting liquid crystalline behaviour. Naturally occurring composites, often highly optimised, might be copied using the microbial synthesis of their components — collagen in bone, perhaps, or the proteins which although present only in very small quantities (total organic content about 2%) make tooth enamel suitable for its demanding role. The gene coding for one of the latter, amalogenin, has reportedly already been cloned into a bacterium. A final benefit of the "learning from nature" philosophy is that it reminds us not to forget onë f the most ubiquitous of all structural components — water! Highly hydrated polymer systems, notably the glycosaminoglycans (such as the chondroitin sulphates and hyaluronic acid) in association with proteins, play a vital structural role in cartilage and other soft tissues as well as acting as sophisticated lubricants. The understanding, let alone the exploitation, of such systems will be a formidable goal.

Much remains to be done in all of these areas but the potential benefits encourage both the biologist and the materials scientist to take up the challenge.

FURTHER READING

Materials Science and Biology:

The New Science of Strong Materials (or Why You Don't Fall Through the Floor), JE Gordon, Penguin, 1968

Structures (or Why Things Don't Fall Down), JE Gordon, Penguin, 1978

Mechanical Design in Organisms, SA Wainwright, WD Biggs, JD Currey and JM Gosline, Princeton, NJ, 1982; or Edward Arnold, London, 1976

Structural Biomaterials, JFV Vincent, Macmillan, 1982

Lignin Degradation:

Lignin-Degrading Enzyme from the Hymenomycete Phanerochaete chrysosporium Birds, M. Tien and T.K. Kirk, Science vol. **221** (1983) p. 661–3.

PHB:

Application of PHB — a Microbially Produced Biodegradable Thermoplastic, PA Holmes (1985) Phys. Technol. **vol 16**, p 32–36

Biologically Produced (R)–3-Hydroxyalkoanate Polymers and Copolymers, PA Holmes, in "Developments in Crystalline Polymers — 2' (ed DC Bassett) Appl. Sci. Publ. London, 1988

Cyclohexadiene:

Synthesis of Polyphenylene from a cis-Dihydrocatechol, a Biologically Produced Monomer, D.G.H. Ballard *et al.* (1988), Macromolecules **vol. 21**, p. 294–304.

Chapter 20

Biosensors — "A Marriage of Biochemistry and Microelectronics"

Michael Gronow

INTRODUCTION

Until recently the prospect of sophisticated but simple and user-friendly diagnostic instrumentation seemed remote. In medicine, for example, tests near to the patient were limited to very simple equipment like a stethoscope or thermometer, any novel biochemical tests had to be done in advanced laboratory surroundings, often using expensive and time-consuming systems; nowadays, however, the market is demanding simple and accurate on-the-spot testing and current technology is rapidly permitting this demand to be met. This chapter is concerned with how it is possible to meet this challenge and revolutionize the face of rapid testing and analysis in all walks of human activities.

Biochemical reactions occur and can be induced in every living organism, whether human, animal, vegetable or bacterial; the nature and extent of these reactions are indications of the condition of the organism. It is now possible to develop biosensors to utilize and measure such biochemical changes. Biosensors are synergistic combinations of biochemistry, membrane technology and microelectronics which enable the signals produced by specific biochemical reactions to be registered, quantified and recorded. They have been described as "Today's Technology, Tomorrow's Products" in a recent market research publication. At the time of writing they are still very largely in the research mode but commercial examples are starting to appear on the market.

Although some of the underlying technology of biosensor construction has been available for about twenty years and working prototype sensors have been designed for several applications, generally they have not been exploited outside the laboratories in which they originated.

However, the sensitivity, accuracy, speed and safety with which biosensors will be able to detect and measure biochemical analytes offers a wide range of potential applications in human and animal diagnostics, industrial process control, pollution monitoring and detection of bacterial contamination and the presence of toxic gases. The commercial use of biosensors is expected to change rapidly in the next ten years or so, not only because of the increased R & D activity on biosensors arising from the biotechnology boom of the early 80s but also because new, cheaper and more rapidly available biological materials for biosensor construction have recently become available. In this short chapter one can only hope to give a flavor of this promise to come rather than a comprehensive coverage of this very rapidly evolving area of biotechnology. For further information the reader is referred to some of the reviews, books, monographs and other reading matter available some of which are quoted in the Appendix.

WHAT IS A BIOSENSOR?

To begin with it is necessary to define what is a biosensor as opposed to a straightforward biological probe. Thus a "bioprobe" as such is clearly any sensor probe placed in a medium (e.g. an enzyme/substrate mixture) which can measure a biochemical or biological reaction; an example is a pH electrode. A biosensor is more refined in that the sensor itself contains an integral biochemical component. Various definitions have emerged to cover this arrangement, perhaps the most simple being:

> "A biosensor is an analytical tool or system consisting of an immobilized biological material in intimate contact with a suitable transducer device which can convert a biochemical signal into a quantifiable electrical signal".

The concept behind the above definition is illustrated in Figure 1. The substrate to be analysed (S) and any coreactants diffuse through the outer protective membrane which may also perform the function of selectively eliminating interfering species (e.g. proteins and/or cells in biological samples). Reaction then takes place with the biological material (e.g. enzyme, antibody or cell) producing the product (P) to be detected. This in some cases passes through a second, selectively permeable membrane, and is detected at the transducer. The signal-processing equipment then coverts the transducer signal into a suitable (e.g. digital) display.

The biologically sensitive component can be an enzyme, multienzyme system, antibody, antigen, whole cell or organelle (from any origin) suitably immobilized to the transducer required. The biological component of a biosensor, while

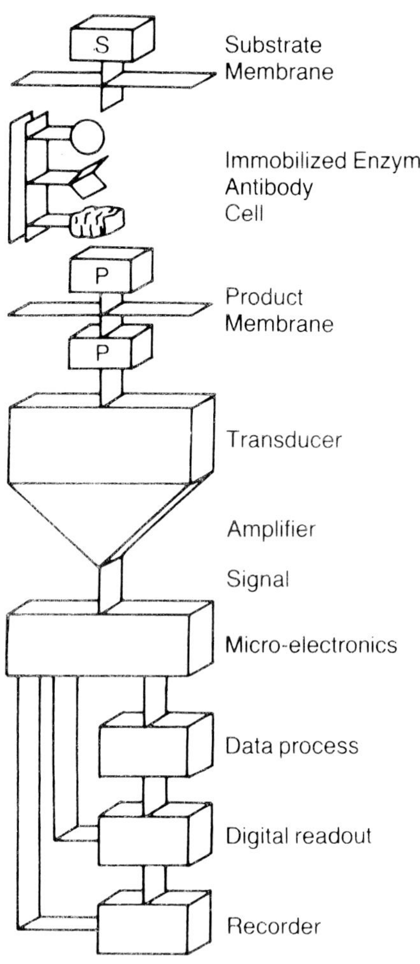

Figure 1. Schematic of a biosensor.

allowing exquisite specificity and sensitivity, is often unstable and subject to interference from unexpected quarters. However, various design combinations, particularly those using novel membrane formulations, are leading to increasingly sophisticated analytical possibilities even in the presence of interfering materials. The result is the evolution of self-contained analytical systems distinct from standard instrument combinations such as spectrophotometers fluorimeters, etc. Biosensors differ from standard analytical equipment in that they are designed for a specific purpose (which can be the measurement of a single substance or a group of substances) and the fact that they are miniaturized, utilizing the benefits of modern electronics to interpret the chemical signal generated. Ideally, the end result is a definitive reading as opposed to data readout which requires further processing.

IMMOBILIZATION AND MEMBRANES – THE KEY TO BIOSENSOR CONSTRUCTION

Immobilization

The last two decades have seen great advances in the technology of immobilizing biological molecules to various natural and man-made materials. The preparation of highly active and stable materials for use in large-scale biotechnology has often established the groundwork for the successful use of immobilized biologicals in analytical devices. These methods and the materials used with them have been discussed in many reviews particularly with regard to enzyme immobilization, whole cells and organelles.

The techniques used for immobilization in biotechnology are fairly well known and covalent attachment and physical entrapment have so far had the greatest impact on biosensor construction. Cross-linking is of limited use because of the attendant loss of activity and microencapsulation has not yet come into its own, perhaps because of the expense involved.

Covalent attachment is commonly used in the research forms of biosensor. In this technique chemical groups on the active biological material which are not essential for activity (e.g. non-essential amino acids of enzymes) are attached to chemically activated supports in a wide variety of materials such as synthetic and natural polymers, glass, metals and ceramics. The linking molecule may form a bridge (e.g. when using cyanuric chloride) or be expelled after coupling (e.g. carbodiimides).

Physical entrapment has proven to be one of the most popular techniques which, because of its simplicity, results in highly active materials. Gels or polymers can be used: materials such as polyacrylamides, silica gel and starch are cross-linked in the presence of the enzyme or other biological material which is thereby trapped or captured. The pores of the matrix are large enough to allow substrate and product diffision but small enough to prevent loss of the active high molecular weight biological material. One method of particular relevance to biosensors is entrapment within the pores of asymmetric membranes, giving thin, highly active layers of biomaterial.

Membranes

Membrane technology has been evolving rapidly in recent years. Extensive use of membranes in diverse large scale aspects of commercial activity has provided some of the basic materials which can be utilized in biosensors. One of the earliest commercial examples relevant to biosensor construction was the entrapment of glucose oxidase in cellulose acetate films.

It can be seen from Figure 1 that membranes in one form or another are a key element in biosensor construction. Ideally one would like to mimic the supreme biosensors — the membranes of the sensory cells of living organisms. However, from what little we know of living membranes it is clear that the complexities of their construction are not easy to reproduce artificially. Being able to exclude interfering molecules while allowing selective passage of the substance of interest will remain the *art* of the membrane biotechnologist for some time to come.

Many sorts of membranes being used in current biosensor research and development come from diverse sources including commercial materials developed for microfiltration, ultrafiltration and haemodialysis, membranes derived from biological sources and completely new polymer research materials. In addition various polymer meshes, gels and coatings can be formed *in situ* over the sensing element, often in conjunction with standard membrane materials.

Membranes can have various functions in the successful operation of biosensors. They can be involved in the screening out of interferents, in filtering out cells or debris from the sample (such as blood) and in excluding other substances from contact with the transducer in order to avoid modifying its response by poisoning or clogging. Uses of membranes which separate on the basis of size, charge or solubility are now commonplace in biosensor technology and many forms are available commercially.

Membranes with molecular weight cut-offs ranging from 190 to 1,000 kilodaltons are available from companies such as Amicon, Millipore, etc. One current disadvantage of them is their slow rate of diffusion, necessitating the application of pressure for successful filtration; this limits their direct use in simple biosensors.

Another function of a discrete membrane, which is not immediately obvious, is to limit the rate of diffusion of an analyte to the biological element of a biosensor. This avoids a "swamping" effect of a high analyte concentration and allows the achievement of a linear response to concentration. This is important when the sensor may have to measure analytes over a wide range of unknown concentrations. When *in vivo* or implanted biosensors are developed for use in living systems biocompatible membranes will need to be employed with the function of keeping the pathway from the biological fluid to the sensor clear for prolonged periods.

Examples of membrane types for biosensor applications are shown in Table 1. Currently the only successful commercial product in this area are produced by the Yellow Springs Instruments Co. (USA). They market the widest variety of *enzyme*-containing membranes for the determination of glucose, ethanol, lactic acid, etc. A number of Japanese companies are also active, among them TOA Electric Co., Fuji Electric and Toyojyozo Co. (making similar membranes) as well as Tateishi Electric Co. and Mikkiso Fujisawa. Recently Denki Kagaku and Keiki Nisshin Electric have brought out bacterial membranes to measure ethanol, acetic and BOD (see section on microbial biosensors).

One potentially exciting area for biosensor construction involves the extensive work being directed towards the synthesis of Langmuir-Blodgett films. This is an elegant technique to produce ultrathin layers, often only several molecules thick; they are constructed by laying down selected monolayers on a suitable surface. Generally they start with a unimolecular layer of a hydrophobic substance (such as a lipid) to which can be added a larger, more complex molecule, part of which possesses hydrophobic areas to bind to the initial layer. Specific substances such as membrane transport and electroactive proteins could be bound in this way. Chiral surfaces can be constructed by the deposition of end-chain functionalized alkanoic acid derivatives. The construction of Langmuir-Blodgett films using natural phospholipid molecules should be possible in the near future.

Although the original technique was pioneered in the 1930s it is only in the last six years that there has been renewed interest in Langmuir-Blodgett films, particularly in the electronics industry for field effect transistor construction (see later). However techniques for producing the films require expensive equipment and are still labour intensive which may be the reason for the slow progress in this area. This is surely going to be a key technology in future biosensor constructions.

The art of membrane construction is a relatively new technology which is rapidly evolving commercially to meet the needs of biosensor construction. It is highly specialized, involving techniques from simple solution casting (and its variants) to spin and spray coating (casting membranes on membranes) and interfacial polymerization together with electropolymerization at a surface (e.g. polypyrrole deposition). The development of biosensors may well stimulate commercialization of a greater variety of membrane types. The Japanese Ministry of International Trade and Industry (MITI) has recognised this as a critical area in its drive to support commercial biosensor development. It has set up a Biomembrane Project at Ibaraki to develop membranes for biosensors.

TRANSDUCER COMBINATIONS

In general engineering terms a transducer describes any device which converts one form of energy to another. In biosensors a transducer provides a means of converting chemical into electrical energy; sometimes intermediate substances or materials are involved. From the earliest electrochemical types of transducer the evolution of a large number of possibilities has taken place in recent years, often from rather unexpected quarters. Modern physics and sensor technologies are constantly bringing up new variations. Some current examples used in biosensor combinations are given in Table 2.

Table 1
Types of Membranes Utilized in Biosensor Construction

Type	*Composition and Properties*	*Commercial Availability*
Heterogeneous multilayer	Composites of multilayered structures each section having a different function, often contain entrapped biological material	Difficult to produce commercially (and guarantee quality). (Yellow Springs membranes containing immobilized oxidase enzymes)
Microfiltration	Developed for accurate and rapid filtration of aqueous — careful control of pore size. Can have straight, cylindrical pores or tortuous infrastructure	Polycarbonate membranes (Nucleopore); Polyamides or nylons (e.g. Pall biodyne); novel ceramics being developed
Materials of biological origin	E.g. collagen, cellulose and gelatin — Good porosity and properties for immobilizing biological materials	Used for blood filtration (Haemodialysis) in medicine, (Haemophane Haemophane)
Hydrogels and hydrophilic structures	Synthetic polymers with high water regain and entrapment	Some already utilized for analytical purposes (such as polyacrylamide). Others used in various clinical analysers
Hydrophobic	Not generally permeable to larger mol. wt. water soluble substances but allow passage of ions or gases	PTFE membranes, polyvinyl chloride membranes used in ion selective electrodes
Miscellaneous active transport films	Polymer films which are able to enhance or impede transport of molecules. Examples are conducting polymers (electrochemical transport)	Semi-conducting polymers, with conductivities in range 10^5-10^{-9} S/cm such as "doped" polyacetylenes
Biocompatible	Needed for implanted or *in vivo* sensors to prevent premature rejection	A number of "natural" materials available but new artificial polymers appearing such as acrylonitrile sodium methyl allyl sulphonate

BIOSENSOR DEVELOPMENT

The earliest biosensors, constructed in the 1960s, consisted of immobilized enzymes in conjunction with pH or oxygen electrodes. In its simplest form the enzyme was trapped in a dialysis membrane wrapped around the electrode. The reaction of the analyte (the species to be measured) with the enzyme was followed by monitoring the consumption of a co-substrate, or the appearance of a product. The oxygen electrode was useful as this allowed the monitoring of the reactions of oxidase enzymes such as glucose oxidase (amperometric type). As changes pH are associated with many enzyme reactions it follows that pH measurement should be highly applicable to biosensor configurations (potentiometric type); however, dependence on the sample buffer capacity, and hysteresis in use, has limited this approach.

The evolution of these electrochemical types of biosensors has been extensively reviewed by many authors; a brief summary is shown in Figure 2 illustrating some early assemblies of electrochemical types of biosensor combinations. Table 3 lists some of the published data and properties of such systems which arose from electrochemical concepts in the 1970s.

Over 600 papers have been published on these electrochemical types of biosensors, many of them concerned with glucose or urea measurement (using the cheap and readily available glucose oxidase and urease enzymes). In general,

Table 2
Transducer Combinations Used in Biosensor Construction

Transducer	*Interactive Response-Output*
Conductimetric, electrochemical electrodes	Differences in conductivity and potential compared using a variety of electrode combinations
FETs (Field Effect Transistors)	Modified miniature semi-conductor devices normally used for microelectronics (potentiometric change at gate)
Gas sensing electrodes	Gases such as CO_2 and NH_3 detected — potentiometric response
Ion selective electrodes	Common ions found in biological fluids
Hall devices	Change in magnetic field strengths detected
Fibre optic devices/Optothermal (photoacoustic sensors)	Generation of absorption and reflection changes; changes in wavelength of light also measured
Oxygen electrode, amperometric electrode	Consumption of oxygen, evolution of hydrogen peroxide
Photodiodes, light sensitive films	Electrochemical-light absorption combination; luminescence measured
Piezoelectric crystals, surface acoustic wave sensors (SAW)	Change in mass on surface of crystals gives variation in vibrational frequency
Semiconductor surfaces	"Electron acceptor" materials; redox changes monitored
Thermistor devices	Very small changes in temperature measured

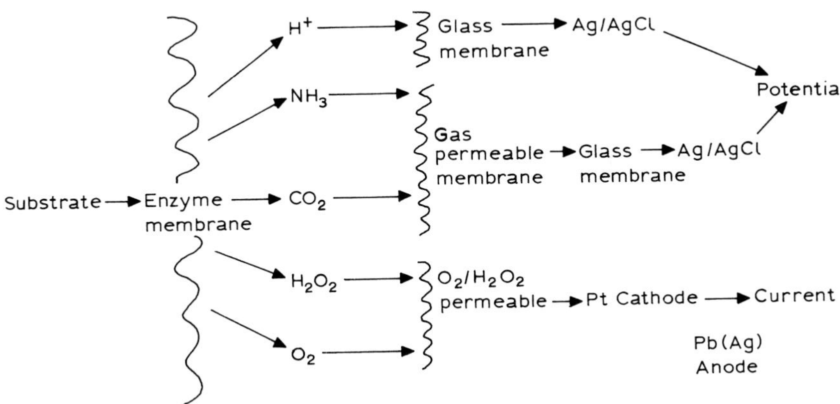

Figure 2. Early assemblies of electrochemical type biosensors.

most simple enzyme electrode biosensors exhibit a linear response in the range of 10^{-2} to 10^{-4}M of substrate while some electrodes respond to concentrations as low as 5×10^{-7}M or as high as 10^{-1}M. Depending on the enzymes and immobilisation protocols used, lifetimes of such sensors may range from a few days to weeks or months, with response times in the range 10 seconds to 3 minutes.

BIOSENSOR DIVERSIFICATION

The last ten years have seen considerable diversification from the traditional electrochemically-based biosensors described above. Some have shown promise in the laboratory but, because of fabrication problems, have not been commericialized. Others have presented insurmountable difficulties

Table 3
Typical Enzyme Biosensors (Electrochemical)

Substrate	*Immobilized Enzymes*	*Stability (Days)*	*Ranges Possible mol. litre^{-1}*
Alcohol	Alcohol oxidase	120	10^{-1} to 1.6
Amino acids (general)	L-amino acid oxidase	120–180	10^{-2} to 10^{-5}
Cholesterol	Cholesterol esterase + oxidase	30	10^{-2} to 3×10^{-5}
Glucose	Glucose oxidase	20–420	10^{-1} to 10^{-5}
Sucrose	Invertase	14	10^{-1} to 2×10^{-3}
Urea	Urease	20–112	10^{-2} to 5×10^{-5}

when faced with measuring a "natural" sample due to the presence of interfering moieties. Examples of these attempts at biosensor construction are described below. Some of these may now be only of historical interest but it should be borne in mind that as a result of future advances in the technology (for instance in the construction of sophisticated membrane construction and the increasing availability of microelectronic devices such as "transputers") we may well see a revival of some of the previously discarded types of biosensor construction.

Conductimetric Biosensors

The conductimeter showed early promise as a transducer capable of detecting a wide range of enzyme reactions. In a typical prototype two sets of electrodes were used in planar configuration with the enzyme immobilised across one set; the other set acted as a blank for background conductance. Theoretically, any reaction producing charged species could be detected by this method. In practice, the high and variable background conductivity of biological solutions made this technique too insensitive for most analytical applications.

Field Effect Transistors (FETs)

In recent years strenuous efforts have been made to produce a miniatured electrochemical type of biosensor using conventional electronic devices called "field effect transistors". Suitably modified, these very small devices have the ability to measure charge accumulation at their surface, e.g. they can be modified to be pH-sensitive. FETs can be made to measure ions by using selective materials over the sensitive gate of the FET, thus giving ion-selective FETs (ISFETS) similar in use to a miniature ion-selective electrode. By adding enzymes (enFETS) or antibodies (immunoFETs) a range of true biosensors may be contemplated, very small and cheap enough in construction to be disposable. However, the fundamental problems of construction and selectivity of these devices, and the difficulty in miniaturisation of a suitable reference electrode, has resulted only in limited practical use for ion and gas measurements. The early promise of cheap, mass fabricated FET-based biosensors has not yet materialized but in Japan the Mitsubishi Electric and the NEC corporations continue to report good progress using this technology to produce a glucose enFET.

A recent interest variant on this technology has been described by a California company (Molecular Devices Corp.). They use a light emitting diode to create a photoresponse in a silica-based chip, this being recorded as an AC current. As the potential across the device is varied by an external power supply the capacitance is changed and thus the magnitude of the AC current; a biochemical reaction at the surface can induce a measurable effect on the current. While still at an early development stage this represents an interesting combination of electrochemical and optical based biosensing techniques (described later). This company has recently exploited the technology to produce the first commercially available DNA probes-based sensor.

Redox-Mediated and Other Direct Electron Transfer Biosensor Systems

It is in this area that the most progress has occurred. The redox-mediated enzyme electrode arose from work being carried out on bio-fuel cells. The main aim in constructing this type of biosensor is to facilitate the transfer of electrons generated by an oxido-reductase enzyme to the electrode surface. Natural mediators such as the cytochromes have been shown to promote passage of electrons but redox-active dyes and other artificial mediator compounds have proven more useful: one of the most extensively studied of these is ferrocene and its derivatives. In the case of an oxidase the mediator is able to replace the requirement of the enzyme for oxygen, thus eliminating dependence on the oxygen content of the sample. Mediators may also be used with certain NAD-independent dehydrogenases such as lactate dehydrogenase (cytochrome b2) and the quinoproteins. By varying the structure of the compound used it is possible to tailor a mediator to meet specific requirements. For instance, to give low solubility to aid retention at the electrode surface, or change the half-wave potential of the mediator in order to reduce the required operating potential and minimise interference. This sort of flexibility has made the use of mediators the method of choice of many configurations. However, to construct a stable system some clever chemistry must be employed to ensure that the mediator is properly immobilized, remains active and stays in place. A problem for commercialisation of such devices is that the fabrication of such systems for large scale production is likely to be an expensive business.

To avoid the use of soluble mediators and their attendant problems, some systems have been developed for direct electron transfer using chemically modified electrodes. A system described by a London University group shows great promise. A carbon-platinum-polymer complex containing chemically bound glucose oxidase has given excellent results in the measurement of glucose as shown in Figure 3a. The response time of this system is very short — a reading is obtained in seconds and the stability is remarkable; good current is generated even after a year's use at room temperature. This platinized activated carbon electrode (PACE) biosensor in various forms is at present under commercial development at Cambridge Life Sciences plc. It gives excellent results with whole blood glucose, correlating well with standard laboratory methods such as the Yellow Springs 23AM analyser (Figure 3b).

The PACE system works well with other oxidase enzymes such as those for lactate, ethanol, etc. Recent modifications have allowed the system to utilize NADH/NAD reactions thus considerably expanding the range of dehydrogenase enzymes that can be utilized in this type of biosensor.

Such developments clearly indicate that modified metal or semi-conductor electrodes are going to play a key role in future biosensor constructions and represent a significant advance in commercial biosensor construction.

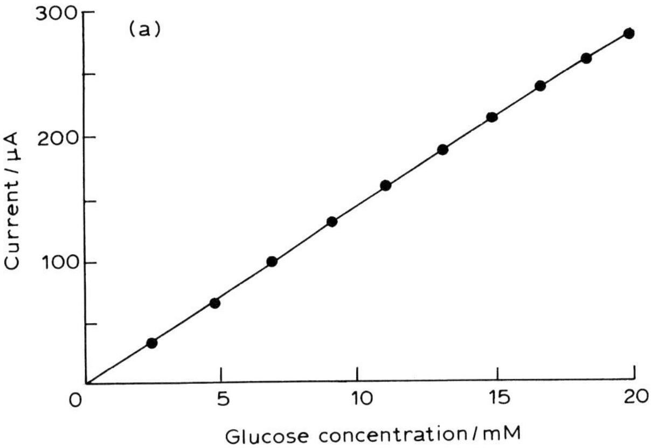

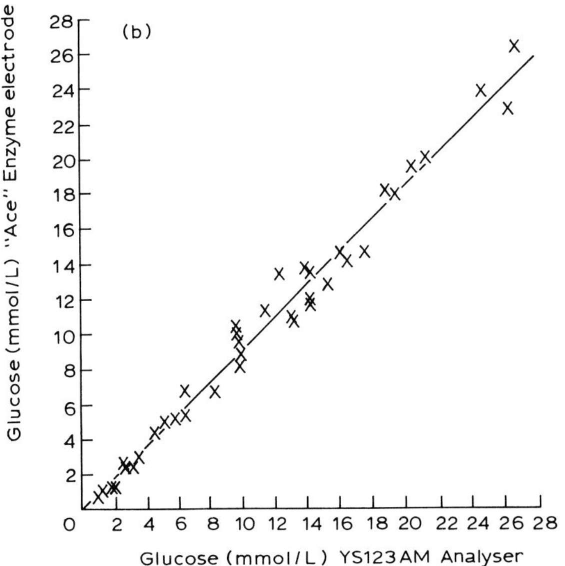

Figure 3. (a) Measurement of glucose with the ACE biosensor. (b) Whole blood glucose correlation with standard laboratory instrument.

Piezoelectric Crystals

The piezoelectric crystal has been put forward as a very sensitive transducer for biosensor applications. Binding of a molecular species to the crystal surface causes a mass change that is sensitively monitored as a change in oscillating frequency. Due to the damping effect of immersion of the crystal into liquids, useful sensitivity can be achieved only for analytes in the gas phase. Organophosphorus compounds have been detected in air by immobilising the enzyme acetylcholinesterase onto a crystal, a device which could be used to detect nerve gas. By using selective membrane coatings, gases such as carbon monoxide and ammonia can be measured. By immobilising antibodies or special "receptor molecules" to these crystals, there exists the possibility of making selective "electronic noses" for applications such as detecting illegal drugs.

Thermistor Type

One interesting development from the 1970s utilizes a thermistor to monitor the small temperature differences generated in many biochemical reactions. A linear response to substrate involving temperature changes in the range 0.01 to 0.001°C can be obtained. Early versions based on the measurement of heat generated from an immobilised enzyme column have been described by Swedish groups. The use of a column upstream from the thermistor means these are not true "biosensors" in the strict sense. The need for effective thermal screening of such devices makes miniaturization into a biosensor format very difficult but there is hope that new microelectronics techniques will evolve in the future to filter out the "noise" in the system. Substances such as cholesterol ($50-150 \times 10^{-6}$M), ascorbic acid ($50-100 \times 10^{-6}$M) and sucrose ($50-100{,}000 \times 10^{-6}$M) have been assayed using this technique.

Optic/Optoelectronic Biosensors

The use of light instead of electrical potential or current to measure a biochemical reaction has been accelerated since the development of cheap light-emitting and photosensitive diodes together with fibre optic systems which can be used as transducers.

One of the initial attempts to construct a biosensor around such devices was called an "optoelectronic sensor". The device consisted simply of a membrane-dye combination to which was co-immobilised a suitable enzyme. Addition of the substrate to this complex generated a pH shift resulting in a change of colour of the dye (e.g. penicillinase generate H^+, urease NH_4^+). The colour change was detected using a light-emitting diode of appropriate wavelength on one side of the membrane and a photodiode on the other. The components were inexpensive, a good signal was generated and the stability was reasonable. Unfortunately, the chemistry of linking the components together was too variable and unreliable to permit mass production of such devices.

In recent years some extremely sophisticated approaches have evolved using fibre optic systems. The measurement of light absorption and reflectance, surface plasmon resonance, fluorescence, bio- and chemi-luminescence may be used giving the fibre optic approach wide verstility. Figure 4 gives some examples of possible biosensor constructions using fibre optics. These possibilities will be discussed later in the section on immunosensing.

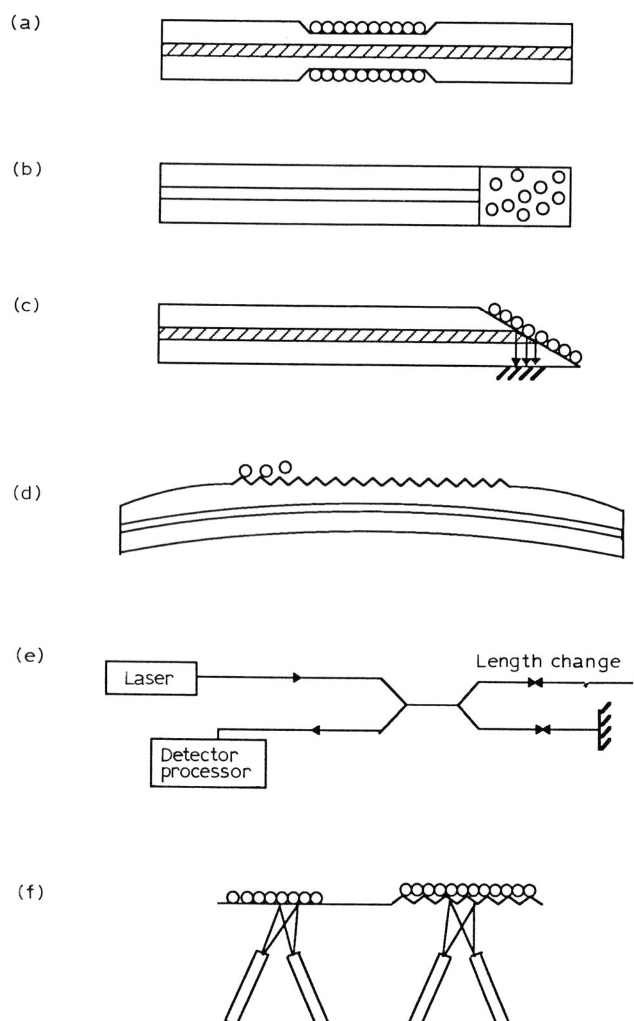

Figure 4. Optical-fibre sensors. The sensing position is indicated by 'oooooo'. (a) polarization or evanescent field modification; (b) porous glass tip; (fibre polished and configured to detect refractive-index change (light in the core is incident on the interface at an angle close to the critical angle), '//////' = mirror coating; (d) grating feedback; (e) Michelson interferometer; and (f) remote detection of changes occurring near plasmon-generating surfaces.

VARIATIONS ON THE BIOLOGICAL/BIOCHEMICAL COMPONENT — BIOAFFINITY PRINCIPLES

In addition to the classical form of enzyme biosensors described previously a new form has arisen termed the "bioaffinity sensor". An example of this in its broadest form is the weak binding of a labelled receptor to a determinant analogue immobilised onto a transducer surface. Adding free determinant (the sample) displaces this receptor to form a tightly bound complex. Increasing determinant concentrations can therefore be measured by a reduction in signal coming from the labelled receptor. An interesting form of this type biosensor mode uses the biotin-avidin system in conjunction with an oxygen electrode. Biotin concentrations (corresponding to ligand concentrations) of 10^{-5} to 10^{-8}g mL^{-1} could be measured in one minute. Other possibilities for biosensor construction using biosubstances capable of molecular recognition are:

Antibodies — for antigens such as drugs and proteins
Antigens — for antibodies, such as auto-antibodies and AIDS antibody
Lectins — for saccharides
Hormone receptors — for hormones
Drug receptors — for drugs and active drug metabolites
Nucleic acids (DNA, RNA) — as gene probes for inherited diseases, lineage fingerprinting, etc.

This makes them less sensitive to local concentration changes in the micro-environment. Biosensors based on bioaffinity principles can offer a high degrees of selectivity when appropriate receptors are employed. Measurement is based on equilibrium binding, not rate measurement.

These features are illustrated by a classical and exciting development by two U.S. researchers which is a form of miniature affinity biosensor for glucose measurement (Figure 5). The sensing element consists of a short length of hollow dialysis fibre remotely connected to a fluorimeter via a single optical fibre. Onto the inner surface of this fibre is immobilised the lectin Concanavalin A (Con A), which binds carbohydrates, and a high molecular weight fluorescein-labelled dextran is added as a competing ligand. Glucose in the external medium diffuses through the dialysis fibre into the sensing element and competes with dextran for binding to Con A. At equilibrium, the level of free fluorescein in the hollow fibre lumen is measured via the optical fibre and is correlated with the concentration of glucose. Blood glucose was measured in 5 to 7 minutes and the response of the biosensor was linear from 50–400 milligrams percent. With recent advances in computer-aided molecular modelling and the production of genetically engineered proteins one can predict that simple low cost receptor synthesis may soon be feasible which will greatly expand this type of biosensor construction.

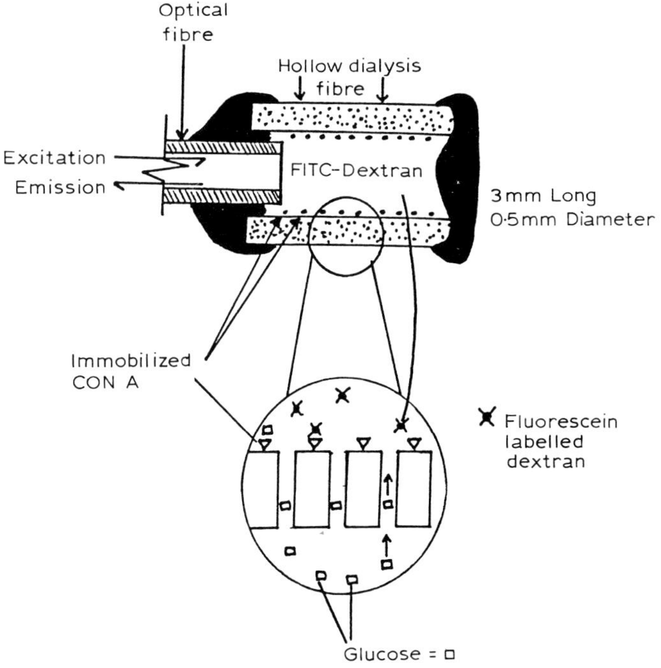

Figure 5. Novel optic fibre biosensor for glucose.

Immunosensing

The most widely studied form of bioaffinity sensor is the immunosensor, of which several types exist. They rely on various methods of measuring the antibody: antigen interaction. The newer methods are extremely diverse as the growth of the commercial immunoassay market in clinical biochemistry from products containing radio-isotope labels to chemiluminescence markers testifies.

The earliest attempts at monitoring immunology reactions by biosensor technology were very simple. One way was to simply measure the change in potential or conductivity across a membrane containing either an immobilized antibody or antigen when it was put into contact with a solution containing its complementary partner. Using this electrochemical approach a sensor was devised for detection of syphilis using cardiolipin on an acetylcellulose membrane. Similarly blood types were monitored by determinants on this type of membrane. Human chorionic gonadotrophin (hCG) was measured by immobilized antibody on a titanum oxide wire surface. Naturally the strength of the signal generated in these systems depends on several factors, one of the main ones being the amount of protein that can be coupled to the surface to give a high density layer. This is not easy to accomplish in practice with the result that such sensors lack the desired sensitivity.

Strenuous attempts have recently been made to measure such direct antibody — antigen interaction using optical techniques. A number of exciting new variations using optic fibre technologies are currently under study in academic and industrial laboratories (see Figure 4). These methods have a common thread — the direct measurement of binding events at surfaces. If, for instance, an antibody is first immobilised onto a surface, interaction with an antigen in a sample may be measured by the altered reflectance or absorption qualities of that surface. In the method known as total internal reflectance spectroscopy, a beam of light is passed down a waveguide such as a fibre optic or a pair of parallel plates. At each of the multiple reflections of the beam a component of the light known as the "evanescent wave" penetrates a short distance into the medium on the other side of the waveguide. Absorption of this evanescent wave by an antibody immobilised on the outer waveguide surface is measured as an attenuation of the light signal; this is altered when an antibody-antigen complex is formed. Sensitivity of this method has been reported to be as low as 30 nmol/L. Im Clone Systems Inc. (NY) and ORD Inc. (Cambridge, MA) have recently reported a new 4 minute test to detect AIDS using a fibre optic wave biosensor.

Another widely studied technique involves monitoring changes in surface plasmon resonance. This uses a silver-coated glass slide onto which antibody or antigen is bound. By shining light at a certain angle onto the slide a surface plasmon — a change in the electron plasma of the metal film — is excited. When the angle of incidence of the light is plotted against the intensity of light reflected from the film a sharp drop can be seen at the critical angle for surface plasmon formation; this angle is highly dependent on the presence of the responding species at the film surface. Antibody/antigen binding is observed as a change in the angle at which this drop occurs. Optical techniques under study involve ellipsometry and Brewster angle measurements. Other combinations of techniques have also been used, such as internal reflection spectroscopy using fluorescently-labelled species and surface plasmon resonance using an optical fibre.

One of the most heavily researched areas (both academically and commercially) of measuring direct the antibody-antigen interaction mentioned earlier involves the use of FETs. Commonly the antigen was immobilized over the "gate" of the FET and, on interaction with an antibody, produced a change in potential. While showing enormous promise in their early stages of development it has been disappointing that reliable and analyte-selective immuno FET sensors have not yet been constructed. The major hurdle is the need to construct a very thin but fully insulating layer or membrane between the antigen (or antibody) coating and the semiconductor surface which is thin enough to allow a small charge redistribution, induced by formation of the immune complex, to exert a detectable change in electrical field. It must also provide adequate insulation to prevent dissipation of the field by leakage of ions or by electron tunnelling effects. The solution to these and other problems in this type of device requires the development of new technology before the immuno FET can become a reality. This particular research and development story illustrates clearly the risks and frustrations inherent in biosensor commercial development.

By far the bulk of publications on immunosensors have been based on indirect methods of measuring the formation of the immune complex. They are based on a wide variety of techniques which are now available to synthesise antibody or antigen conjugates with labels such as enzymes or light-emitting molecules permitting the detection of antibody-antigen complex formation at very low levels indeed.

Labelled antibodies or antigens may be used in biosensor configurations based on enzyme — linked immunoassay or enzyme — linked immunosorbent assay (EIA or ELISA) principles; two forms are illustrated in Figure 6. The antigen ligand (L) to be measured may be mixed with an enzyme-labelled ligand derivative (E-L), with competition between these two species for immobilised antibody (A). Alternatively, free ligand may be used to displace enzyme-labelled ligand from its complex with the immobilised antibody. This "displacement" technique probably has the best potential from a practical point of view as there are no additions before interaction. In both cases the remaining enzyme label is measured by adding the enzyme substrate and monitoring the product (P) by a suitable method, e.g. at an electrode. The signal is then processed and a result calculated. EIA has the advantage of high sensitivity due to the signal amplification that can be achieved by suitable enzyme combinations. Examples of some

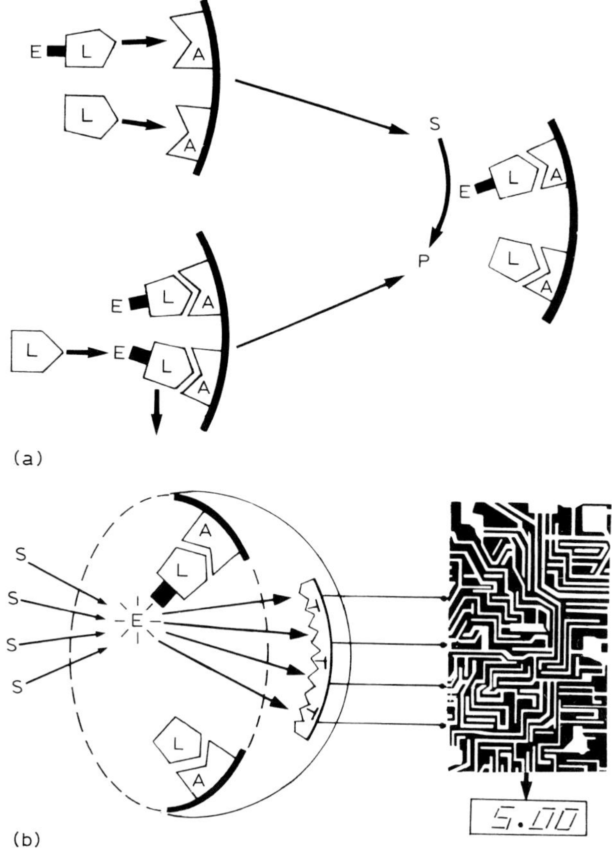

Figure 6. Schematic of an immuno-biosensor based on an enzyme-labelled competitive immunoassay. (a) Labelling the active surface of a biosensor. (b) Measurement by biosensor. A = antibody; E = enzyme; S = substrate; P = product; L = ligand or hapten; — — — = selective membrane; T = transducer.

biosensors that have been constructed using EIA principles are given in Table 4.

Although compared to the now flourishing micro-titre plate mode of immunoassay much of the earlier work on electrochemically based immunoassay has had limited practical applications, there have been some notable advances in recent years. Both homo-and heterogeneous enzyme immunoassays have been monitored using electrochemical detection and, in some cases, they have been developed into biosensors. Particularly promising are those systems utilizing the amperometric detection of NADH. For example, the drug phenytoin (antiepileptic) and digoxin (heart drug) have been labelled with glucose-6-phosphate dehydrogenase which catalyses the reduction of NAD^+ to NADH. These have been used for displacement-type electrochemical immunoassays to give sensitive, clinically useful analyses. Quantities in the range 10–20 μg/mL phenytoin and 0.5–2.5 ng/mL digoxin were detected in patients' serum samples. A number of other similar electrochemical techniques not involving enzymes have been explored by U.S. researchers.

Table 4
Examples of Enzyme — Immunoassay Biosensor

Analyte	*Enzyme Label in Conjugate*	*Transducer*	*Sensitivity*
HORMONES			
Human chorionic gonadotrophin (hCG)	a) Catalase	Amperometric (O_2)	0.02 to 100 IU ml^{-1}
	b) Glucose oxidase	Amperometric — Redox (Ferrocene)	0.15 IU ml^{-1}
Oestradiol — 17β	Horse radish peroxidase	Electrochemical (I^-)	5.7×10^{-13} to 9×10^{-9} mol. $litre^{-1}$
DRUGS			
Digoxin	Alkaline phosphatase	Electrochemical (phenol)	from 50×10^{-12}g ml^{-1}
Theophylline	Catalase	Oxygen electrode	5×10^{-8} to 5×10^{-7} mol $litre^{-1}$
IMMUNOLOGY			
IgG	Catalase	Amperometric	10^{-3} to 10^{-6}g ml^{-1}
IgG	Alkaline phosphatase	Electrochemical	10^{-11} to 5×10^{-9}g ml^{-1}
CANCER DIAGNOSIS			
α — Fetoprotein	Catalase	Amperometric	10^{-11} to 10^{-8}g ml^{-1}

The enzyme thermistor device described earlier has also been used for antibody-antigen study: a Thermometric Enzyme Linked Immunoabsorbant Assay (TELISA) sensitive to 10^{-13} moles per litre has been demonstrated. Recently a piezoelectric immunosensor has been demonstrated for the detection of *Candida albicans* yeast cells. Using piezoelectric quartz surface acoustic wave (SAW) devices, IgG has been measured in serum.

Lastly, optic systems can be utilized employing bio- and chemi-luminescent-labelled antibodies and antigens. These methods allow high sensitivity, rivalling that achieved by radioimmunoassay. The principle of the bioluminescence sensor has been demonstrated using the enzyme luciferase on an optic fibre to monitor ATP in the range of 10^{-6} to 10^{-7}M. Workers in Japan have described a solid phase luminescent immunoassay (using catalase) for human serum albumin with a 1 ng/mL detection limit.

WHOLE CELL BIOSENSORS

This type of biosensor construction utilizes immobilized whole cells or organelles instead of discrete enzymes; examples for in different commercial areas have been developed by a number of groups (Table 5). These sensors are potentiometric or amperometric in design but characteristically have a slow response and often react to a broad spectrum of substrates. The latter property has proved useful in the construction of a microbial biosensor which performs the Ames mutagenesis test in a fraction of the normal assay time. Immobilized *Salmonella typhimurium* revertants or *Bacillus subtilis* Rec were used in conjunction with an oxygen electrode to measure the mutagenicity and potential carcinogenicity of various chemicals. Another area where whole organisms can be used to great advantage is for measurement of biological oxygen demand (BOD) and such a biosensor is probably one of the first to be commercialized in Japan.

Whole cell biosensors may come into their own when tailor-made, genetically engineered cells become available to supply particular specified enzyme sequences or to regenerate complex co-factors. When these factors are taken into consideration one can see the possibility of them being more cost-effective than other forms of biosensor.

Table 5
Examples of Microbial Biosensors

Substances Measured (Class & Examples)	*Micro-organism Employed*	*Detected Substance**	*Useful Concentration Measured*
ALCOHOLS			
E.g. Ethanol	*Trichosporon brassicae* (or *Acetobacter xylinium*)	O_2	Below 22 mg litre^{-1}
AMINO ACIDS			
L arginine	*Streptococcus fæcium*	NH_3	10^{-5} to 5×10^{-5} mol litre^{-1}
L-glutamate	*Escherichia coli*	CO_2	10^{-3} to 10^{-5} mol litre^{-1}
ANTIBIOTICS			
Nystatin	Yeast cells	O_2	0.5 to 80 units ml^{-1}
Cephalosporin	*Citrobacter freundi*	H^+	Below 22 mg litre^{-1}
CO-FACTORS			
NAD^+	*Escherichia coli*/NADase	NH_3	8×10^{-4} to 5×10^{-5} mol litre^{-1}
GASES			
Methane	*Methylomonas flagellata*	O_2	Up to 6.6×10^{-3} mol litre^{-1}
ORGANIC ACIDS			
Formate	*Clostridium butyricum*	FUEL CELL	Up to 1.0 g litre^{-1}
SALTS			
Nitrate & nitrite	*Azobacteria vinelandii*	NH_3	8×10^{-4} to 10^{-5} mol litre^{-1}
SUGARS			
General	Bacteria from human dental plaque	H^+	10^{-4} to 10^{-5} mol litre^{-1}
VITAMINS			
Nicotinic acid	*Lactobacillis arabinosus*	H^+	5×10^{-8} to 5×10^{-6} gm ml^{-1}

* Usually detected by potentiometric or amperometric methods

PRACTICAL FORMS OF BIOSENSORS

Practically, Four Forms of Biosensor are Emerging for Medical and Industrial Applications

Small, hand-held devices

These are designed for consumer use, the main market being for the monitoring of blood glucose levels in diabetics. The sensor configuration may be a dipstick pen-shaped device (ExacTech^{TM} system originally developed by Genetics International in the U.S.) or a device the size of a large hand-held calculator (Cambridge Life Sciences, U.K. — see Fig. 7). Each of these devices has its own particular merits and in the case of the precalibrated system quality control is critical and delicate yet must be very reliable. The Cambridge Life Sciences device has relied on precalibration by the user to instil the necessary confidence in its accuracy.

Devices for the measurement of other clinical parameters in the home and the doctor's office are also under development. The major requirements for such devices are robustness, ease of operation by unskilled persons, small size, fast speed of measurement and an easily read display.

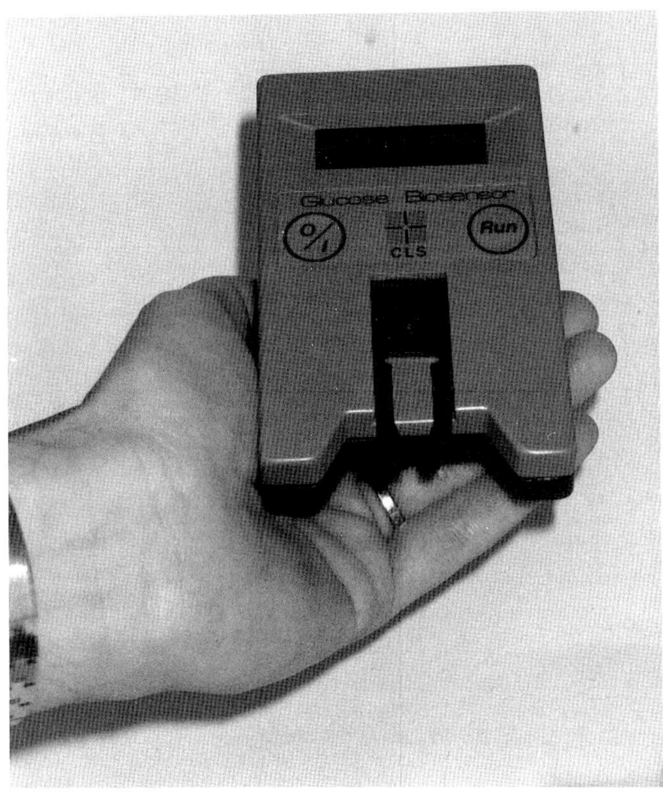

Figure 7. Advanced prototype of hand-held blood glucose biosensor for diabetic monitoring (Cambridge Life Sciences – ACE Technology).

The Laboratory Analyser

The use of biosensors in laboratory clinical chemistry potentially confers several advantages over currently-employed methods of analysis. The use of undiluted blood measurement allows for:

(a) faster analysis since no separation step is required
(b) avoidance of errors in pipetting and dilution
(c) the manufacture of a completely self-contained unit requiring no external resources other than a power supply
(d) measurements which approximate more closely to the *in vivo* situation than when using serum or plasma

Currently, clinical laboratory testing is mainly carried out on multi-channel analysers. These are capable of measuring many parameters in parallel or in series and can quickly analyse large numbers of samples. Adaptations of these systems include a nylon tube-based immobilized glucose oxidase system employed in the Techicon auto-analysers already in use in large numbers of laboratories. Many biosensor configurations are constructed in-house: as a recently-made nylon coil device for an automated analyser constructed by an Italian group, for example, had a useful life-time of 6 months. Complementary to the multi-channel systems are the "stat" clinical laboratory analysers, designed for the rapid measurement of single or small numbers of samples. These are usually small, discrete instruments, often transportable between laboratories and clinics, the main demand being for glucose measurement in diabetic clinics. One of the few commercially successful bench-top instruments is the Yellow Springs YSI 23A glucose analyser which uses glucose oxidase immobilised between two polymer membranes; the instrument has the disadvantage of incorporating a dilution step to bring values within the measurement range.

Flow Devices

These are needed for "on line" monitoring of continuous processes, e.g. large volume production in food processing, fermentation control, pollution monitoring and environmental control. An example of this type of biosensor is a portable pesticide monitor, one cubic foot (27 L) in volume and weighing approximately 30 lb (14 kg), constructed some years ago by a U.S. company. This compact device employs immobilized cholinesterase on special porous pads through which suspect water is pumped. If various pesticides, such as organophosphates or carbamates, are present in parts per million the enzyme is inhibited, the level of inhibition being measured by injection of a specific substrate. After such a reaction has taken place, a new pad is then inserted into the sampling flow cell for the next measurement.

The most commercially relevant area for online monitoring is that of fermentation control. Although the best arrangement would be to have sensors within the fermentation vessel, this approach has many of the restrictions associated with implanted sensors, i.e. the absolute need for sterility, the difficulty in calibration and the required stability. As a result, interest has concentrated on use of nonsterile sensors in "offline" configurations where a small continuous flow of fermentation broth leaves the vessel and passes over the active biosensor surface before discharging to waste. Another approach is to mount a membrane window in the side of the vessel on which a non-sterile head can be held allowing access to a dialysate of the fermentation broth. The sensor is withdrawn for periodic recalibration.

In Vivo Continuous or Implanted Monitor

Miniaturized implanted devices, some incorporated in catheters, have been constructed and tested but the major difficulties of biocompatibility and sensor stability have not successfully been resolved. The sensor must be capable of surviving long term implantation in a hostile environment and not exhibit pronounced drift, resulting in a need for frequent calibration. In addition it must be sufficiently biocompatible not to present a hazard to the patient: this is a major difficulty. Sterility of the biosensor is also problematic, since any enzyme it contains is easily denatured by conventional sterilisation methods.

The main thrust in this area is to construct a system for diabetes which uses a glucose sensor to control the rate of insulin infusion from a miniature pump (closed loop insulin pump). The overall size of such a device would allow it to be worn on a belt by ambulatory patients, or even to be completely implanted, the insulin reservoir being replenished via injection through a septum. The current technology is based on the principles of an on-line monitor with a venous cannula taking blood from the patient to be read by a "portable" instrument on a trolley. These systems already use biosensor technology for blood glucose measurement but are limited in size by the pumps, anticoagulation reservoirs and other equipment needed to remove the blood sample.

APPLICATIONS AND USES OF BIOSENSORS

Biosensors have many attractions for use in clinical analysis, general health care monitoring, veterinary and agricultural applications, industrial processing and monitoring and environmental and pollution control. Their advantages are expected to include low cost, small size, rapid and easy use and greater sensitivity and selectivity than current instruments.

Clinical Chemistry, Medicine and Healthcare

Benchtop biosensors of the electrochemical variety are in current use in clinical biochemistry laboratories for measuring glucose and lactic acid; the Yellow Springs glucose analyser has already been mentioned in this context. Several variants of this technology are already in existence but a key feature needed is direct measurement on blood without dilution.

Another area of clinical medicine and healthcare which commercial biosensors will impact is consumer self-testing, especially self-monitoring of blood components.

Current methods are based on colorimetric dry-reagent chemistries, often in conjunction with a portable refelectance meter, but they have frequently been shown to be unreliable and misleading unless used by skilled personnel. Biosensors offer the potential of reusable systems and other advantages by employing electrochemistry rather than colour changes whereby the problems of poorly-sighted people some diabetics are alleviated. Reusable sensors also allow for calibration and quality control unlike the present disposable sticks where only one measurement can be carried out.

Such testing will improve the efficiency of patient care, replacing the often slow and labour-intensive present tests. It will bring clinical medicine closer to the bedside, facilitating rapid clinical decision making. A wide variety of analytes need to be monitored in these situations, including antigens, antibodies, cholesterol, neurochemicals, drugs and many others. Examples of potential biosensor forms and uses in diagnostic medicine are:

(a) Single test with a small portable instrument such as glucose for diabetic monitoring, cholesterol for cardiovascular care and specific drug tests for compliance and abusë etection. Besides uses in Outpatients, Casualty and Homecare, such instruments will find uses in specialized clinics, drug centres, etc.

(b) Multi-test-Benchtop instrument, e.g. glucose and specific ions (such as potassium) for general health care; creatinine and urea determination on urine (renal functions); progesterone, oestrone sulphate, oestriol, etc., for fertility monitoring. Many clinics, health cen tres and specialist centres will use such instruments in addition to the standard clinical chemistry laboratories.

(c) Critical care, invasive monitoring with miniature sensor probes. There will be many opportunities when the problem of probe biocompatibility can be solved: e.g. glucose for insulin pump coupling, specific toxic drugs in therapeutic drug monitoring and glucose, together with creatinine, urea and lactic acid levels in short-term critical care situations.

The advent of cheap, user-friendly biosensors will no doubt revolutionise the practice of healthcare monitoring, enabling more in depth diagnoses to be made on a metabolic basis.

Veterinary, Agriculture and Food

Here there are many areas where even conventional analysis systems are not available. The introduction of suitable biosensors would have considerable impact in the following areas among others:

Small and large animal care	—	fertility and infectious disease monitoring
Dairy industry	—	milk (protein, fats, antibodies, hormones, vitamins)
Fruit and vegetables	—	viral and funal diagnosis
Foodstuffs	—	contamination and toxins, e.g. salmonella
Beverages	—	wine, spirits and beer — improvements in production and quality control

Fermentation Industries, Pharmaceutical Production

In addition to conventional industrial fementation producing materials like alcohol and antibiotics, an increasing number and variety of new products are being produced by large-scale bacterial and eukaryote cell culture. The monitoring of these delicate and expensive processes is essential for minimising the costs of production; specific biosensors can be designed to measure the generation of a fermentation product.

The construction of low cost biosensors for use in industrial processes can benefit the manufacturer in many ways, such as: a) biosensors may be made compatible with both on-line assay and discrete sampling; b) rapid responses allow improved feedback control; c) no interference with the process stream; d) a biosensor has a long lifetime which releases technical staff for other duties; e) rapid sampling and rejection of below standard raw materials on delivery is facilitated and low-cost monitoring of stored products and raw materials can be expected; f) access to remote environments.

Environmental Control and Pollution Monitoring

Because they can be miniaturized and automated, biosensors have many roles to play in these areas. A successful system for pesticide monitoring has already been described. One area in which whole cell biosensors may have substantial advantages is in environmental water monitoring to combat the increasing number of pollutants finding their way into the groundwater systems and hence into drinking water. Many undesirable materials now appear in groundwater making single analyte measurements insufficient and a broad spectrum biosensor will have many advantages. This area of biosensor development is becoming increasingly of interest to the military and, one company has already produced an enzyme biosensor to detect and measure nerve gas (the NAIAD device by Thorn-EMI-Simtec, U.K.). With recent trends towards developing sophisticated biological and chemical weapons this aspect of biosensor development must receive increasing priority.

MARKET PREDICTIONS

Market predictions of biosensor sales potential have demanded not inconsiderable guesswork on the part of the market researchers. It is difficult to forecast the impact of this new technology on existing markets where low technology and price beats high technology and speed! Biosensor market penetration will be almost totally dependent on price and ease-of-use.

It has been estimated that the 1988 global biosensor market was \$46 million; this has been predicted both by Frost & Sullivan in 1985 and by Ambion Associates in 1989 to rise steadily to reach \$1–2 billion by the year 2000. It is interesting that although much of the early technology has been developed in Europe, and the U.S. currently dominates manufacture, by 1993 the main manufacturers will be Japanese who, it is predicted, will flood the markets of Western Europe and North America in the late 1990s with simple, easy to use, inexpensive biosensor devices, most of them for medical use.

CONCLUSIONS

Research into biosensor design and application is still at a primary stage. Despite intensive commercial and non-commercial activity in Japan, Europe and the U.S., serious problems remain to be solved. Factors which will be important in the construction of future biosensors will include:

- unique combinations of miniaturized tranducers with specific biological materials
- the use of "arrays" of biosensors
- low cost considerations (e.g. adaptation of semi-conductor fabrication techniques)
- the ability to produce sterile probes which, if necessary, can be disposable
- multiple, coordinated rapid assays need to be achieved
- the ability to perform simultaneous replicate assays increasing confidence in the accuracy of the assay
- intimate involvement of real time computation — use of microprocessors to perform data reduction.

The evolution of such devices may provide virtually unlimited scope for the research worker, but it will be some time before ultimate commercial development is a reality.

We are faced with the exciting prospect that such work on the interfacing of biological materials with transducers, particularly those which are based on semiconductor materials or fibre optic systems, will increase our knowledge of biological molecules and their interaction with electronics to such an extent that ultimately we can contemplate the construction of molecular switching devices as "biochips" for the computers of the future (see Chapter 21). When this happens a leap forward will have occurred comparable to the current advances in superconductor technologies.

FURTHER READING

Biosensor articles are published in many types of books and journals.
The main journal is simply called "Biosensors" and is published bimonthly by Elsevier Applied Science (eds Heinman W.R., Higgins I.J., Potter W.G., Turner A.P.F. and Wingard L.B. Jr.). This journal also publishes a very useful current literature search and bibliography on biosensors at the end of each edition.
A recent comprehensive book is: A.P.F. Turner, I. Karube & G.S. Wilson (eds.) (1987): "*Biosensors: Fundamentals and Applications*".

Oxford University Press
Another useful monograph was published in 1985 by the U.S. Association for the Advancement of Medical Instrumentation (Arlington Virginia) **19** No. 4.
In membrane technology a useful review is:
Supersieves Hit the Market by Carl Rainin High Technology Nov 1983, 69–75.
Another useful publication which presents a regular update is:
Membrane and Separation Technology News – a Monthly Newsletter from BBC Inc. Publication PO Box 207OC Stamford CT USA.
Some interesting reviews are as follows:
Suzuki S., Satoh I. and Karube I. (1982) in *Recent Trends of Biosensors in Japan* Appl. Biochem & Biotechnol 7, 147.
Guilbault G.G. (1980) *Enzyme Electrode Probes*, Enz. Microb. Technol. **2** 258–264.
Ikariyama Y., Furuki M. and Aizawa M. (1983) *Proc of an International Meeting on Chemical Sensors*. Kodansha.
Gronow M. (1984) *Biosensors* Trends in Biochemical Sciences, **9**, 336–340.
Aston W.J. and Turner A.P.F. (1984) *Biosensors and Biofuel Cells* Biotechnol and Genetic Eng. Rev., **1**, 89.
Neujahr H.Y. (1984) *Biosensors for Environmental Control, Biotechnology and Genetic Engineering Reviews* **1**, 167
Place J.F., Sutherland R.M. and Dahne C. (1985) *Opto-Electronic Immunosensors a Review of Optical Immunoassay at Continuous Surfaces* Biosensors, **1**, 321–353.
Clarke D.J. et al (1985) *The Development and Application of Biosensing Devices for Bioreactor Monitoring and Control* Biosensors, **1**, 213–320.
Scheller F.W. et al (1985) *Biosensors: Trends and Commercialization*, Biosensors, **1** 135–160.
North J.R. (1985) *Immunosensors: Antibody – Based Biosensors* Trends in Biotechnology, **3(7)** 180–186.
Cororan C.A. and Rechnitz G.A. (1985) *Cell-based Biosensors* Trends in Biotechnology, **3**, 92.
Brunt J.V. (1985) *News Review* Biotechnology, **3**, 209.
Mascini M. and Guilbault G.G. (1986) *Clinical Uses of Enzyme Electrode Probes* Biosensors, **2**, 147–172.
Mullen W.H. and Vadgama P.M. (1986) *Microbial Enzymes in Biosensors* J. Appl. Bact., **61**, 181.
Kulys J.J. (1986) *Enzyme Electrodes Based on Organic Metals* Biosensors, **2**, 3–13 (also Transient Response of Bienzyme Electrodes ibid, 135–146).
Suzuki S. and Karube I. (1987) *Biochemical Sensors Based on Immobilized Enzymes, Whole Cells and Proteins* Appl. Biochem and Bioeng., **3**, 145–174.
Wolfbeis O.S. (1987) *Fibre-optic Sensors in Biochemical Sciences.* Pure and Appl. Chem., **59(5)** 663–672.
Important earlier works relevant to biosensor construction are:
Campbell J. and Hornby W.E. (1977) in *Biochemical Applications of Immobilized Enzymes and Proteins* (TMS Chang, ed), Plenum Press.
K. Venkatsubramanian (ed.) (1979) *Immobilized Microbial Cells* ACS Symposium Series, 196, American Chemical Society.
Carr P.W. and Bowers L.D. (eds.) (1980) *Immobilized Enzymes in Analytical and Clinical Chemistry*. John Wiley, New York.
Kennedy J.F. and White C.A. (1985) in *Handbook of Enzyme Biotechnology*, 2nd ed. (A. Wiseman, ed), Ellis Horwood, Chichester, U.K.

Commercial and Patent Publications

On the commercial side some rather expensive speculative market research reports have been published such as:
Biosensors (1984) by Innovation 128–24 (Paris, France).
Also:
Todd Jarvis M. (1985) Biosensors: *Today's Technology, Tomorrow's Products*, Technical insights Inc NJ. ISBN 0914993–22–4.
This publication has an important section on patent activity from 1980–85. For a thorough review of the 1985 Patent literature see Graham Davies (1986), *Biosensors* 2, 101–124.

Good updates on a monthly basis are given in The International Patent Gazette section published in *Biodetector News* (Ambion Associates, Bedford, U.K.)

Chapter 21

Bioelectronics: "Biochips"

Vivian Moses

INTRODUCTION

This chapter is not about bioenergetics nor does it concern itself with Nature's own information storage and retrieval system, DNA and the genetic code. Instead, it discusses one of the most intriguing concepts in biotechnology, but also one of the most speculative: that of building computers out of biological components. Why bother? Are conventional computers using silicon chips not good enough? It seems not. Future computers are expected to be severely limited by their fundamental hardware technology. One difficulty is that the smaller one attempts to make conventional chips, the greater the manufacturing problems not only of miniaturisation but also of "cross-talk", the leakage of electricity between neighbouring circuits because of the increasing thinness of the bands of insulating material. The minimum size of a single chip, the more chips which will be required as computer elaboration grows, the increase in the number of operations as processing becomes more complex, the length of wiring needed to make the connections: all these limit the speed of computer operation because of the time it takes electricity to flow along those wires, even with modern chips the small size they are and electric signals flowing at 186,000 miles (300,000 km) a second! And current flowing in wires generates heat so, the more tightly packed the chips (thus reducing the distance the current has to flow), the greater the cooling problems.

Computer designers and manufacturers are thinking of new ways to overcome such problems. Superconducting wires might be one technique for minimizing heat production but they will not reduce the overall distance to be travelled. Computers designed around "chips" as small as individual molecules would have enormous benefits of miniaturisation although their manufacture would pose equally enormous problems of assembly and interconnection. That is where biological systems might come in with their existing powers of self-assembly spontaneously to generate the right structure without each unit having individually to be placed by an external agency. If means of intercommunication between units could be developed other than by electric currents flowing in wires, "biochips" might in time offer very attractive answers to some of these problems. Such solutions would, of necessity, do no more than postpone the time when the rate of signal propagation again became limiting but, for the moment at least, that postponement would be very useful. There might also be new limitations if the speed of signal propagation in biochips were much less than that in silicon chips; but those are matters for experimental resolution.

MOLECULAR ELECTRONICS

Computers are based on a pattern of integrated and intercommunicating switches, each one at any instant either in the "on" or in the "off" position. Not, of course, restricted to biological molecules, *molecular electronics* is about the deployment of molecular arrays as memory stores controlled and connected by molecular switches and conduction paths for address, interrogation and information processing.

The development of molecular wires and switches represents the first stage in constructing a molecular electronic device. Conducting polymers, such as polyacetylene and polysulphurnitride, have been proposed as candidates for organic molecular wires, although they are poor conductors of electricity. Carter at the U.S. Naval Research Laboratory thinks that the conductivity of these polymers may be due to the movement of wavelike particles (solitons) along the polymers, moving at the speed of sound. His view is that solitons change the electronic configuration of the polymer while simultaneously releasing electrons. Workers at the I.B.M. Laboratories in New York have looked at the potential for certain hemiquinones (substances used for electron transport in photosynthesis) to act as molecular switching devices. These molecules can exist in two distinct electrical states which, as the result of a shift of two protons, differ slightly in the distribution of electrical charges. That charge distribution can be altered by applying an electric current. Back to Carter: he has suggested the use of chromophores, embedded within conducting polymers, as molecular switches. The response of the chromophores to light could be changed by propagating a single soliton along the chain to rearrange the bonding pattern. Hence, bistable "on" and "off" states could be produced. To be useful these on/off changes would need to be very rapid so that chemical changes within or between molecules are unlikely to be candidates. Rather they would depend on intramolecular electronic transitions.

Carter listed a number of possible memory storage devices[1]:

- a dynamic storage element composed of a soliton generator and a soliton-controlled electronic tunnel switch (reader) separated by two long chains of $(CH)_x$;
- bridged transition metal atoms simultaneously in a ring of low and high valence states, the location of these states being stabilised by the dipole field of the Driver moiety. A metal atom in the ring acts as a control group for the electron tunnel switch reader. Reversal of the charges in the Driver moiety (e.g. by two pairs of charged solitons) would result in a disturbance propagated round the ring, changing both the control group and the configuration round the switch;
- an arrangement of valves attached to several input $(CH)_x$ chains feeding a single output chain. The valve arrangement ensures that a soliton on any input chain must exit on the exit chain; the resulting configuration in turn ensures that a soliton now input on that exit chain remembers which was the prior input chain and exits on that one, simultaneously restoring the memory element to its original condition.

What seems to be lacking in these (non-biological) models is a means of organising the individual elements into a coherent integrated and intercommunicating structure. Biology and biotechnology may be able to offer ways of doing so.

POTENTIAL ADVANTAGES OF BIOMOLECULAR COMPUTERS

The need for biochips stems from the limits foreseen for current silicon chip technology. New lithographic techniques may allow the reduction of spacing between the elements down to 0.2 μm. However, beyond this point significant heating problems arise. Packing densities for elements of molecular size may be increased by orders of magnitude compared with existing practice and this will allow the storage of much more information in a much smaller space. According to some views a single biochip could hold a billion times more information than a current silicon wafer. Heat production in biomolecular computers would be minimal; manufacturing and operating costs (inasmuch as they can presently be identified) are expected to be low. It has been suggested that biochips may be capable of parallel information processing in a network rather than working in a linear mode. Furthermore, the miniaturisation and biological nature of biochips might allow their deployment in medicine for implants in the body to circumvent damage in the brain, to regulate heartbeat or drug delivery and to control artificial limbs[2].

One of the crucial biochemical features of cellular organisation is the ability of collections of protein molecules spontaneously to aggregate in specific ways to form complexes with certain defined functions. They do so with extraordinary specificity and without an external template: each protein molecule participating in such an aggregate must bear as part of its structure a region on the surface precisely tailored to interact with its neighbour(s), all those regions being determined genetically. A growing number of multi-protein complexes have been identified, the pyruvate dehydrogenase complex of *Escherichia coli*, for example, being composed of 60 subunits with a molecular weight of about 4 million, while the mammalian complex is about twice as large. Biomolecular elements constructed of proteins might be designed with a similar capacity for self-assembly and, depending on how such elements intercommunicated, they might be more reliable than those based on silicon chips as a consequence of reduction in cross-talk. The mechanism of intercommunication is indeed one of the major factors: one option might be to do so with light rays rather than by electricity. Durham[3] has even suggested how useful that might be to the military since light may be resistant to the destructive electromagnetic pulse generated by nuclear explosions!

DEVELOPMENTS TOWARDS A BIOMOLECULAR COMPUTER

A number of ideas have been put forward for the potential use of biological molecules in the construction of biochips. Few if any have reached the experimental stage in the laboratory. However, many workers are involved in research into protein engineering (see Chapter 12): those studies may become highly relevant at some future date for the construction and operation of biomolecular devices although most are not being pursued primarily for that purpose. Robert Haddon of A.T. & T. Laboratories (quoted by van Brunt[4]) explained why laboratory experimentation to construct biochips has not yet commenced: "...biochip development is so far away that it's hard to know what to do." Ideas for employing biological molecules in electronics, however, have been floated in a number of areas.

Thin Film Electronics

Kevin Ulmer (then of the Genex Corporation) has proposed a model for the construction of a substrate in which a two-dimensional crystal would be formed on a solid base using large proteins to form a lithographic mask. These proteins would consist of subunits engineered to have strong edge effects and photolysable bonds. The areas not covered by the proteins could be coated with conducting or insulating materials, followed by removal of the proteins to leave a regular grid-like pattern on the surface of the substrate. Other laboratories are also working on film deposition techniques based on the notion of organising molecules on non-biological surfaces.

Biomolecular Wires and Switches

Another idea is to use conventional electron beam lithography to expose a pattern on polylysine after covering it with a layer of polymethyl methacrylate. The exposed pattern can be developed in absolute ethanol to reveal the free terminal amino groups of the lysine side chains on which ammoniacal silver stain is deposited. This is subsequently reduced to metallic silver to produce a series of conducting lines about 10 μm wide. This system is not a true molecular electronic device since it uses macroscopic bulk properties rather than molecular phenomena. At least two types of biological molecules have been proposed as potential molecular switches: hemiquinones and chromophores. Although the existence of two different electronic states in these molecules has been demonstrated they have not yet been linked with conducting wires.

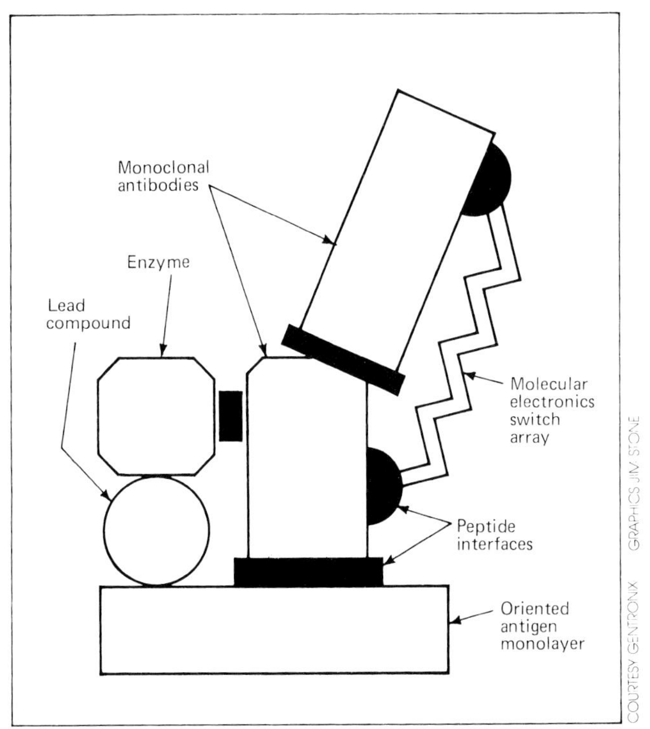

Figure 1. A conception of a molecular self-assembly ("Moleton") to produce an organic "biochip". By permission of *Bio/Technology*.

Mechanisms of Unit Assembly

While conventional chemistry appears for the moment to offer no way of assembling a structure as complex as a molecular electronic device, biological systems do offer distinct advantages in this regard because of their widespread dependence on specific macromolecular recognition and interaction. One sub-assembly routine proposed by McAlear and Wehrung[5] is illustrated in Figure 1. The model, the so-called "Moleton", is not itself a device but rather a means for organisation. It seeks to demonstrate possible ways in which complex structures of defined configuration might be assembled, using in this example the very precise interactions between antigens and their homologous antibodies. These highly specific subassembly units might be used to achieve a three-dimensional array. Molecular electronic switches would connect one antibody with another, thus allowing for the transfer of information within the structure. The lead compound is the designated entry or exit point for information. Alternatively, subunits might assemble in solution by their specific binding sites randomly contacting each other, the structure growing in three dimensions just like a crystal. The precision of the fit of enzyme- or antibody-binding sites would result in a self-correcting assembly.

Speculation has advanced to the point of contemplating the genetic information which, perhaps using conventional biochemical routes for protein synthesis, could produce molecular circuitry directly. Thus Ulmer (quoted by Yanchinski[6]) observed that "The ultimate scenario is to develop a genome for the computer that would function in a manner quite similar to that of a host and its virus." In Ulmer's proposition the relevant portion of the genome, instead of supporting viral propagation, would specify the biological assembly of a fully-operational computer inside the cell. The genes would encode structural protein molecules as well as enzymes for producing other, perhaps non-protein, components to form the bio-electronic circuitry. Although it might by some be regarded as prodigious in its audacity, the idea is patently not absurd. After all, animals do indeed spontaneously "wire" themselves up on the basis of inherited genetic information. They develop an extremely complicated and correctly aligned set of electrical connections both in the brain and throughout the nervous system. Erroneous connections appear to be comparatively rare. This form of organisation may have relevance for future generations of computers but it would be wise neither to underestimate the complexity of existing biochemical organisation within a cell nor to minimise the problems of constructing an artificial genome coding for the synthesis and assembly of a highly elaborate bioelectronic structure.

Although it is at present not clear what molecular structures might be used to build a molecular electronic (or non-electronic) device and computer, certain consequences of using such small active elements are to be expected. Haddon and Lamola[7] have observed that thermodynamic considerations dictate a minimal error rate in the construction of complex molecular structures. Furthermore, side reactions, both thermal- and radiation-induced, will lead at some constant rate to defective elements. Errors in the synthesis of the unit assemblies will inevitably occur to some extent, though their frequency could probably be kept low and defective elements possibly destroyed at an early stage. No doubt protection against and thermal- and radiation-induced degradation of assembled structures could also be offered in the completed instrument. Nevertheless, the decay rate is certain to be faster for complex organic and biochemical substances than for the inorganic materials of contemporary solid-state devices. Living systems do indeed devote a substantial fraction of their available free energy and employ a large number of enzyme systems and complex energy-intensive processes to detect, repair and eliminate faulty structures and correct errors.

Design for a Biomolecular Photonic Computer

Clearly one of the major problems of molecular bioelectronics resides in signal transmission and the intercommunication and interrogation of a molecular memory store with the onward transmission of the response. How can wires be attached to molecules? Perhaps they cannot but it may not be necessary; optical address systems (photonics) may be used instead. For optical systems the limiting spatial resolution (minimum size of an addressable region) is of the order of the wavelength of the incident light; near ultraviolet light might represent a reasonable lower limit. The spatial resolution would then be of the order of 0.25 μm, far greater, of course, than the dimensions of most organic molecules.

Perhaps in time improvements in photonic technology will permit the spatial resolution to be improved. Lawrence at Hughes Aircraft (quoted by Durham[3]) has proposed a biochip system using light radiation rather than electricity; the biochip would communicate optically with other components. Light would be converted into excitons and these could be conducted along columns of stacked molecules. In Britain, an experimental computer has been built in which tiny pulses of light, generated by miniature lasers, can replace micro-electronic circuits. Alan Miller at the Royal Signals and Radar Establishment takes the view that it will be possible to make the optical equivalent of electronic components and he envisages an optical microchip consisting of a thin glass plate the size of a postage stamp carrying the equivalent of 100,000 of today's electronic switches. The pulses of light are said to be several hundred times faster than electronic switches and less susceptible to accidental interference and deliberate jamming.

A photonic biomolecular memory store

Although probably none has yet been made, it is possible to conceive of a memory store being formed by a series of domains, each comprising repeating units of a chomophoric protein such as one bearing a porphyrin or other light-absorbing pigment. Such a model would be based on a chromophore which, in its protein-bound configuration, could undergo photochemical excitation by absorption of a light quantum of the requisite frequency to produce a long-lived excited state. A very low ambient temperature for the memory store might be necessary to ensure stability of such excited molecules. The memory store would thus consist of an array of local domains of identical molecules, each either in the excited or in the ground state; the minimum size of each domain would be determined by the limits of spatial resolution prescribed by the optical address system. The domains would be built up of substances which would generate conduction bands between adjacent molecules such that the excitation would be randomly distributed throughout the local domain. (Randomisation of this sort takes place in the antenna array system of chlorophyll molecules in photosynthesis: energy absorbed from light by the antenna molecules migrates rapidly from molecule to molecule by resonance energy transfer until it is eventually channelled into a photochemical reaction centre.) Imprinting in the memory store would hence be achieved optically and addressed presumably on the basis of geometrical or spatial coordinates.

Interrogation might be accomplished by light of a different frequency chosen so that domains of molecules already in the excited state, but not those in the ground state, would be energised into a "super-excited" and very short-lived state from which they would decay by fluorescence. The emitted light, different in frequency from either of the exciting beams, would constitute a response from a previously excited domain and thus form a positive memory trace. Molecules in the ground state would not fluoresce, representing a negative memory trace. Depending on the electronic properties of the sensitive molecules, the super-excited state might decay either to the original excited state (in which case the memory trace would remain) or to the ground state (resulting automatically in a further pulse of the original exciting radiation to restore the memory imprint). The deployment of molecules possessing one or other of these decay modes would determine the operating procedure.

Many biological chromophores are known, some associated with proteins. A notable group are the porphyrins, tetrapyrroles arranged in a macrocyclic ring ligated to iron or magnesium. The functional properties of a particular prosthetic group vary according to the nature of its interactions with a surrounding polypeptide chain in a molecular complex. Thus, in principle at least, deliberate chemical modification of the prosthetic groups might be used systematically to alter their properties: Figure 2 shows the spectral variation in different cytochrome enzymes, all containing versions of hæm, while Figure 3 compares various types of chlorophyll. Developments in protein engineering, coupled with a judicious choice of chromophore and perhaps also with chemical modification, might enable molecules to be constructed with suitable exci-

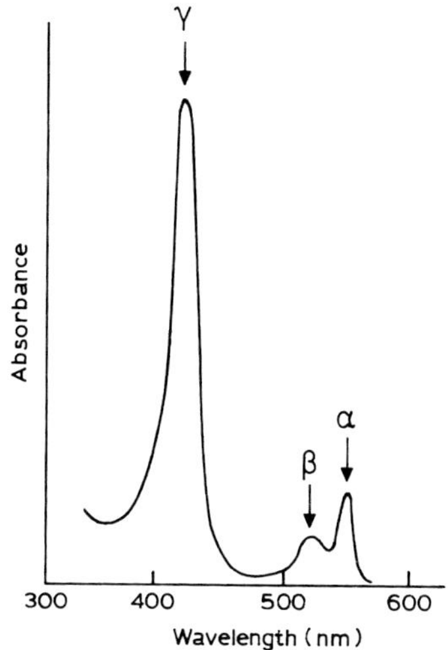

Figure 2. Absorption spectra of cytochromes.

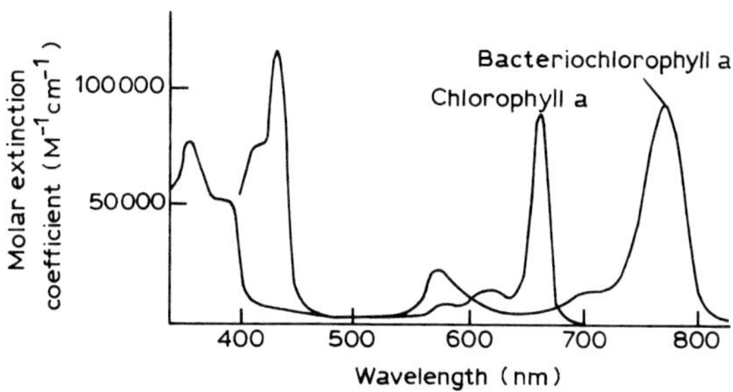

Figure 3. Absorption spectra of chlorophyll *a* and bacteriochlorophyll *a*.

tation and emission spectra for the optical hardware as well as excited state lifetimes commensurate with a rôle as a memory store.

Assembly of a photonic biomolecular memory store

The photoresponsive domains of the two-dimensional arrays would have to be made of self-assembling protein units of two types (Figure 4): those recognising only one another and those recognising also a category of interdomain proteins, devoid of prosthetic groups, with the function of separating and insulating the photoresponsive domains from one another. The size of each domain will be determined by including in the self-assembly system such a proportion of the various protein components that, at equilibrium, spontaneous assembly will produce discrete domains of a specified size, separated by insulation zones. For example, in Figure 5 the proportions of the four constituent proteins are different from those shown in Figure 4 and the domain size is correspondingly larger. The whole of such a structure might be supported on a solid surface to form, in this model, an array of two-dimensional memory trace domains, isolated from one another and addressable at specific locations in the array.

Information processing in a photonic biomolecular computer

Such a biomolecular model might, with modification, itself serve as a processor. One way of doing so would be to use a chromophore receptive to light of the frequency emitted from the memory store upon interrogation. Excitation by a single memory domain responding to interrogation would result in a lower level excited state, with rapid decay of fluorescence of a defined frequency. Excitation by two memory domains responding simultaneously would shift the chromophore to an upper level excited state, with decay by fluorescence of a different frequency. The sensor would be designed to respond only to light of the frequency corresponding to the second fluorescence.

There are mechanisms in biochemistry which might serve as different models for processors. Chloroplasts have two photosystems linked in series. The efficiency of that system in converting light energy into chemical energy is greater if it is illuminated with light of two wavelengths (say, green at 562 nm and red at 650 nm) than if illuminated solely with light of one wavelength at a similar energy input. The photosynthetic two-light system is probably too complex and too slow to be itself useful as a processor in a molecular computer but it serves nevertheless as a well-studied example of a biochemical phenomenon in which two inputs are required in order to generate an output. It might be possible to find ways of simplifying the structure and accelerating the response time of biomolecular processing of this type.

Such a system might be based on bacteriorhodopsin, possibly from the halophile *Halobacterium halobium*, a resident of the Dead Sea. At ambient temperatures the molecule undergoes a rapid conformational change when illuminated by green light, relaxing with the transfer of energy to biochemical receptors. But at liquid nitrogen temperature relaxation does not take place until the molecule absorbs a photon of red light. Thus, alternate illumination with light of these two colours will cause it to flip between the two configurations. Thin films of bacteriorhodopsin have already been made in a psuedo-biological membrane and the molecules irradiated with green or red light from a helium-neon laser source moved over the array by a scanner, leaving a memory trace in the form of bacteriorhodopsin molecules in one or other of the two conformations depending on whether or not they were photonically illuminated. Reading the memory is achieved by scanning with green laser light: the colour of the reflected light indicates whether a molecule is in the "red" or "green" configuration. However, the act of reading converts the "green" to the "red" configuration so that any molecules

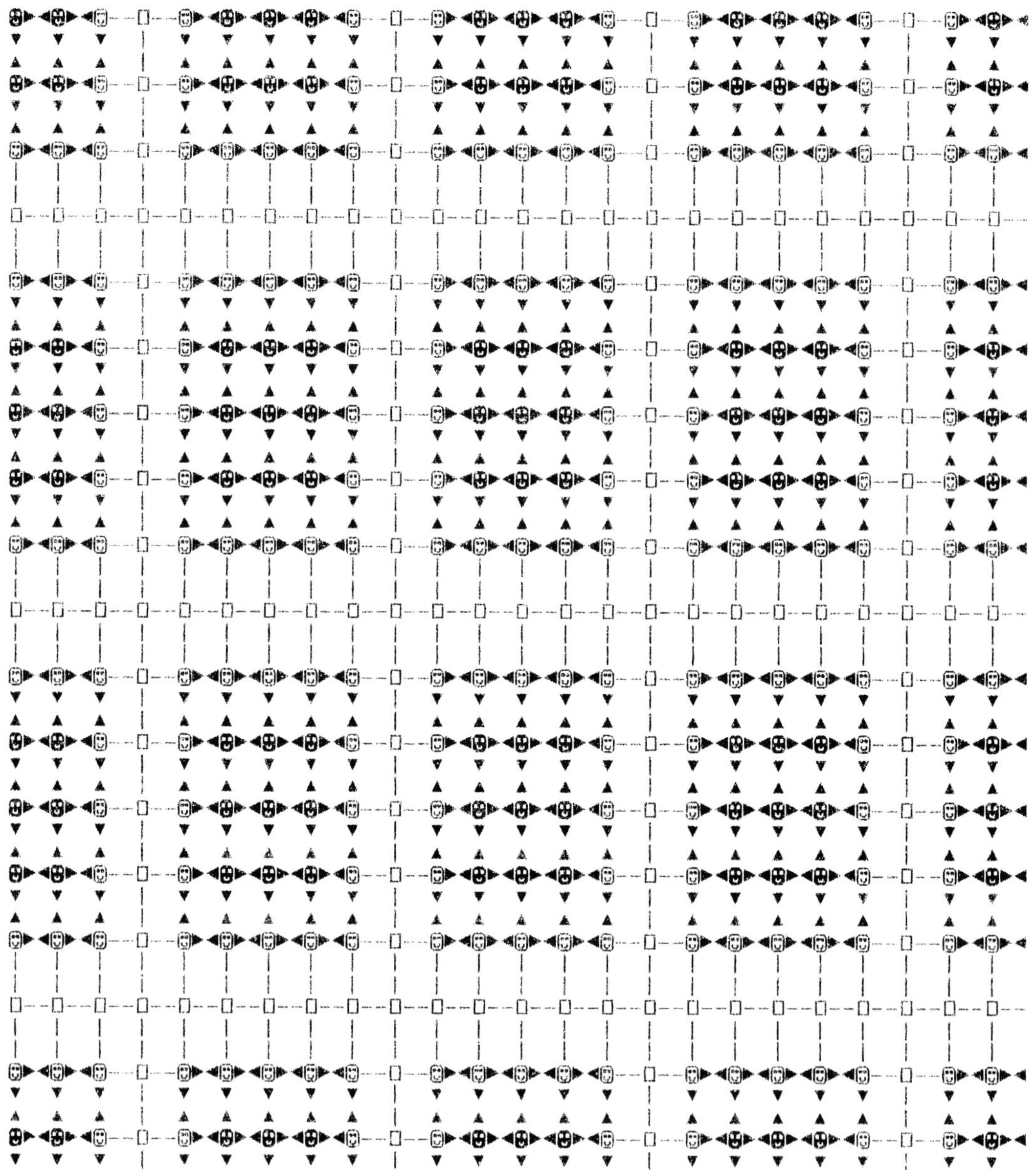

Figure 4. A model for a molecular memory store.

This conceptual model for a self-assembling two-dimensional memory store involves four categories of protein:

= central chromphoric proteins of memory store domains

and peripehral chromophoric proteins of memory storage domains

= interdomain proteins

The four types of protein are present in the proportion 2.25:3:1:3 (compare Fig. 5).

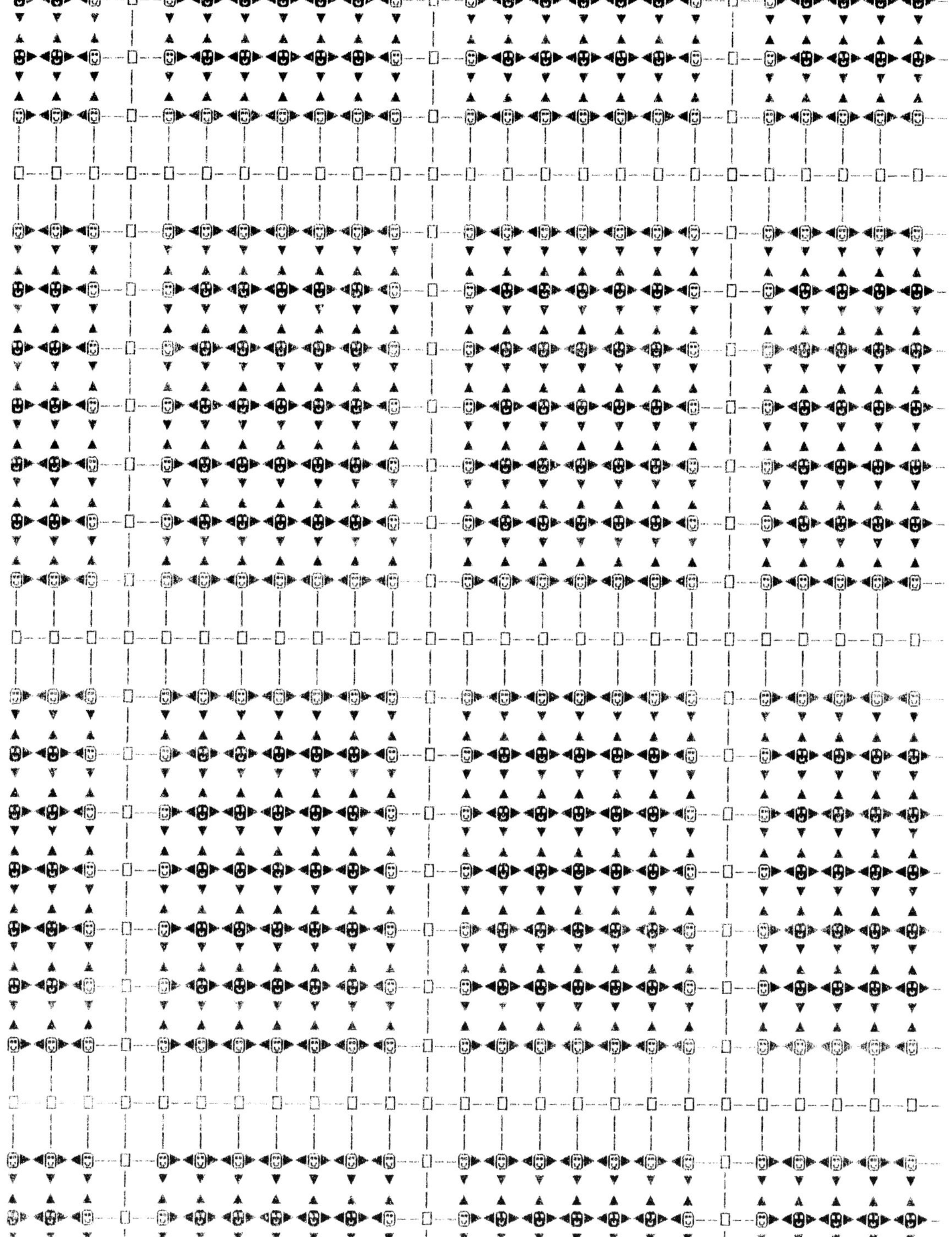

Figure 5. A molecular memory store with larger domains.

In this model each domain comprises 49 proteins, compared with 25 in Fig. 4, and the proportions of the four categories of protein are accordingly different:

: : : in the proportion 6.25:5:1:4

responding green must be reactivated as part of the reading process. A thin film of these memory molecules only 2.5 cm wide is reported to store 200 million bits; the time to read each bit is about 20 nsec, most of the reading time being taken up with moving the scanner. It is expected that the reading time will fall to around 2 nsec when the scanning mechanism is improved. It is perhaps too early to predict costs with accuracy but preliminary estimates suggest that a molecular memory store with laser interrogation may be 10–20 times cheaper than an equivalent random-access memory made from silicon.

COMMERCIAL PROSPECTS FOR BIOMOLECULAR COMPUTING SYSTEMS

It is clear that attractive though some of these ideas may be they are probably a long way from surfacing as working systems. But in the last couple of decades electronic computing and biotechnology have probably been the most rapidly advancing of all the new technologies and a combination of the two of them is likely sooner or later to produce something interesting in practical and commercial terms. An assessment of the size of a future bioelectronics market must take account of the rate and cost of development, performance, reliability and difficulty of manufacturing biochips compared with non-biological devices. Government agencies in more than one country are showing an interest in this field and significant investment by them may be an important factor influencing development rates and times to the market.

Several estimates have been made by various workers about a plausible timescale for biochip development. Some people during the 1980s have spoken of five years work for about 40 people to develop a model of an organic computer, or five years with an expenditure of $60 million, foreseeing biochip-driven systems by the mid-1990s allowing home computers to tap satellites, receive news and prices and conduct business. Not surprisingly, others have thought these estimates optimistic.

There seems little doubt that some organisations are putting considerable resources into biochip development. Gentronix was said to have budgeted $654 million in 1984–7 for research and development in this area. The U.S. Naval Air Systems Command was reported to be proceeding with a five-year $12–15 million programme to study biomolecular research and biochips. A few years ago MITI, the Japanese Ministry of International Trade and Industry, started a 10-year "biochip project" through its Exploratory Research for Advanced Technology Programme for an outlay of ¥8–10 billion. The project aims to involve industry, the universities and government in researching information-processing mechanisms in the nervous systems of lower animals, examining biochemical reactions in biological organic materials and establishing production and processing technology for organised molecular complexes and membranes. A projection made by Creative Strategies International of San Jose, CA suggested that the market size for biosensors and bioelectronics will exceed $1 million in 1989 and reach $1.3 million in 1990, with an annual compounded growth rate thereafter of 21%. Curtis Industries of Washington has estimated that if biochip costs could be reduced to $1,000 each it could sell 40 million.

These are guesses and projections. Most are likely to be wrong in detail but, however optimistic or pessimistic the forecaster, all seem agreed that before too long bioelectronics will be here to stay.

REFERENCES

1. Carter, F.L. (1984). *Molecular electronic devices; today's dream — tomorrow's reality.* World Biotech Report 1984, **vol. 2**, pp. 127–138. Pinner, Middlesex: Online Publications Ltd.
2. Office of Technology Assessment (1984). *Commercial biotechnology: an international analysis.* New York, Oxford, Sydney, Paris and Frankfurt: Pergamon Press Ltd.
3. Durham, T. (1984). *Four steps to realizing the sugar cube biochip.* Computing Magazine October 26th, 1984, p. 26.
4. van Brunt, J. (1985). *Biochips, the ultimate computer.* Bio/Technology, **vol. 3**, pp. 209–215.
5. McAlear, J.H. and Wehrung, J.M. (1982). In *Molecular Electronic Devices*, ed. by F.L. Carter, pp. 175–180. New York: Dekker.
6. Yanchinski, S. (1985). *Setting genes to work: the industrial area of biotechnology.* p. 66. Harmondsworth, Middlesex: Viking/Penguin.
7. Haddon, R.C. and Lamola, A.A. (1985). *The molecular electronic device and the biochip computer: present status.* Proceedings of the National Academy of Sciences of the United States, **vol. 82**, pp. 1974–1978.

Chapter 22

Healthcare

Douglas McCormick

Lepidus: *What manner o' thing is your crocodile?*
Antony: *It is shap'd sir, like itself, and it is as broad as it hath breadth. It is just so high as it is, and moves with it own organs. It lives by that which nourisheth it, and the elements once out of it, it transmigrates.*
Lepidus: *What color is it of?*
Antony: *Of it own color, too.*
Lepidus: *'Tis a strange serpent.*
Antony: *'Tis so. And the tears of it are wet.*

There is, indeed, no single thing called "biotechnology," just as there is no biotechnology industry. There are, however, a handful of supremely powerful biotechnologies and these are the wellsprings of research in a surprisingly wide spectrum of established industries.

The tools of biotechnology are so powerful, and their targets so varied, that any attempt at a synthetic definition is doomed to ludicrous failure. One can emphasize the tools (with sections on recombinant proteins, monoclonal antibodies, gene probes and so on) only to find that many of the applications are identical except for the provenance of the applied molecule. One can emphasize the product categories (with sections on interleukins, thrombolytics, adjuvants or neurotransmitters) and by focusing on a small number of molecules lose the breadth of biotech. Or one can focus on the conditions to be treated (with sections on heart attack, cancer and kibes) and find oneself repeating in each section "This is the recombinant-protein approach; this is the monoclonal-antibody approach; and here is a novel application of gene probes and super glue."

And in each case, one leaves out vital concepts and market areas.

Thus, given the task of describing the impact of biotechnology, even initiates tend to fall back not on fact but on fable: The Blind Man and the Elephant or "I can't define it, but I know it when I see it" or, as above, a drunken soldier's description of what seemed to him a near-mythical beast.

Thus, biotechnology in the pharmaceutical industry is best approached by way of a few views of the beast itself. It may not be complete but it shows the essential color and character of the dim shape beneath the waves.

Even if it eludes clear definition, though, biotechnology will be *the* driving force in pharmaceutical development through the coming century. Biotechnology is simply the way the work has to be done. Whether or not the blockbuster products of the next decade are proteins produced via rDNA techniques, it is quite clear that biotechnology must be the fountainhead of all pharmaceutical development from here on. It has become an ancient litany in molecular biology: increasing understanding of the structure of physiological proteins, and the relationship of structure to function, we will have greater and greater freedom in choosing points and avenues of intervention.

Traditional pharmacology is based on small organic molecules (at least, they are small compared to the long chains of amino acids and nucleic acids that are the molecular biologist's tools). The focus has shifted to proteins because we have begun to harness the machinery needed to make the complex keys and locks that hold the body's chemistry together. But several forces are driving a slow return to the smaller, more stable drugs of the past: digestion does not break them down; they are cheaper and easier to manufacture; they offer alternative building blocks from which to construct bioactive structures (giving us an option when the protein chemistry stumps us).

We should also remember, however, that biotechnology has lead us into a much more complex world, opening up the interlocking feedback networks of physiological regulation. As biotechnologists seek to develop new drugs, vaccines and diagnostics, we are also seeking to understand and balance systems that shift subtly with every intervention. This may mean that we will be doing more and more research to produce drugs for narrower molecularly defined indications — all this while watching the whole system for remote perturbations. And while watching the bottom line, knowing that the economics of the industry are increasing the demand for broad, wide-indication, "blockbuster" drugs even as the technology is pushing us toward more precise, "hand-tailored" therapies.

MONOCLONAL ANTIBODIES[1]

To meet the challenges of a dazzling array of antigens, the B cells of the immune system have developed mechanisms for producing antibodies from more than 10^{12} different genetic combinations. Biotechnologists have exploited antibodies' selectivity and specificity — to detect and purify various ligands and to diagnose and treat a wide range of diseases. Antibodies' versatility has resulted in molecules with diverse biological functions, from receptor binding to catalysis. And anti-idiotypic antibodies' ability to preserve internal images of antigenic epitopes permits vaccination with tailored immunoglobulin instead of antigen.

Diagnosis

The diagnostic use of antibodies dates back four decades to the introduction of precipitin-based methods[2]. The introduction of radioimmunoassay (RIA) by Yalow and Berson[3] revealed the extreme sensitivity possible with high-affinity antibodies. Since then, fast, sensitive immunoassays — RIAs, enzyme immunoassays (EIAs or ELISAs) and fluorescence immunoassays (FIA) — have been applied to a wide variety of molecules.

The literature teems with diagnostics improved — or made possible — by monoclonal antibodies (MAbs). Monoclonals against unique microbial epitopes have made it possible to discriminate between closely related organisms — and even among subtypes. They can distinguish between closely related molecules: between morphine and heroin; between testosterone and related steroids; and even between enantiomers of the same molecule. Furthermore, pharmacokinetic studies may use MAbs to monitor levels of drugs and their metabolites or to study the difference in the clearance of two enantiomers. Such selectivity is impossible with conventional polyclonal antisera.

Monoclonals do have some disadvantages, however. Cross-reactivity is one, a direct consequence of the reagent's monoclonality. For the same reasons, a monoclonal antibody may sometimes be *too* selective. Small changes in antigen structure — due to genetic polymorphism, heterogeneous glycosylation, or slight denaturation — may so change the epitope that the antibody cannot bind.

The growing understanding of monoclonal antibodies' distinctive features has obviously made it possible to design new types of high-performance assays. The two-site immunoassay, for example, uses a pair of antibodies, each recognizing a different epitope: one antibody binds the analyte to a matrix; the other, linked to a marker, reveals the analyte's presence[4]. This assay performs well in comparison with standard RIA and EIA and has a definite advantage when one must use cross-reacting antibodies. Cross-reacting substances are unlikely to carry both antigenic determinants specifying the monoclonal pair.

So far, murine monoclonals have accounted for most applications. In general, the antibody's origin has no impact on the assay. Some human antigens (such as the Rh antigens), however, have stymied efforts to produce murine monoclonal antibodies with the desired specificities. In this case, human monoclonal antibodies have solved the problem. Human MAbs are now also available against other bloodgroup antigens — including A, A1, Rh(G), Rh(c), Rh(E) and Kell. In the future, human monoclonals will likely replace polyclonal antisera for blood typing.

Therapy

Antibody-mediated immunotherapy was first used over sixty years ago: hematopoietic tumors were treated with hyperimmune sera from rabbits. It was not, however, until the introduction of monoclonals[5] that antibody-based therapy of different diseases could be systematically investigated. As analytical tools, monoclonals have helped researchers identify a number of tumor-associated antigens, virus and lymphokine neutralizing epitopes, endotoxins and other important structures. The repertoire of cell-surface antigens has also been investigated on a number of human tumors, using murine monoclonal antibodies. No real tumor-specific antigens have yet been identified — except for the idiotypic T- and B-cell receptors in lymphoproliferative diseases.

This is not entirely surprising. The mouse immune system identifies foreign cells mainly by transplantation and blood group antigens. It might therefore overlook small antigenic changes specific for a human tumor cell. For example, mouse monoclonals exhibit none of the human antibody's fine-tuned specificity against the polymorphic structures of human histocompatibility antigens. Thus, the mouse immune system might ignore the small structural changes specific to human tumor-cell surfaces — conformations readily recognized by immunocompetent human cells.

Human MAbs might thus be advantageous for treating human neoplasms. And, *in vivo*, human monoclonals might not elicit as strong an anti-immunoglobulin response as mouse immunoglobulin. Murine monoclonals have made it possible to detect a large variety of tumor-associated antigens expressed little — or not at all — by normal cells. Many experimental and clinical therapeutic systems have applied such antibodies (directed against melanomas, carcinomas, or sarcomas, for example) in different modalities and administration schedules, with varying degrees of success. Thus, unconjugated, complement-fixing, or antibody-dependent cellular cytotoxicity-mediating antibodies have been tested. Their main advantage is their relatively low systemic toxicity. Antibodies conjugated to toxins or radioactive isotopes have also been used but unspecific uptake in normal tissue remains a problem.

Patients sensitized to mouse proteins have suffered a number of side effects such as fever, rashes, vomiting, urticaria, bronchospasm, tachycardia, and dyspnoea. These side effects are normally transient and disappear as soon as the infusion of mouse antibodies stops.

Much more serious is the reduction of therapeutic effect as the patient mounts an anti-mouse response. The patient's immune response first targets the therapeutic monoclonal's constant region but it focuses on an idiotypic response after only a few injections. These reactions can produce secondary allergic reactions due to immune complex deposition in various tissues: the kidneys, liver and lung. Therapeutic antibody dosage, the target antigen's tissue distribution and the antibody's reactivity all affect the anti-mouse immunoglobulin response. Human monoclonals should solve most of these problems though it remains to be seen just how these will be used.

At present, human monoclonals have been used only as native unconjugated molecules or as radiolabelled imaging agents. Current developments in immunoconjugates — especially those using small, highly toxic compounds — should be of utmost importance when applied to human antibodies[6].

Today, a few human monoclonals can be used to treat tumors, infectious diseases, autoimmune conditions and drug overdoses. Clinical studies are very scarce (Table 1), mostly because of the technical barriers to routine production. This is changing. Recent progress in *in vitro* immunizations and immortalizing human B cells by Epstein Barr Virus (EBV) infection have made it possible to obtain antigen-specific human hybridomas at significantly higher frequencies.

Antibodies as Vaccines

In 1981, two groups[7,8] first proposed using antibodies as vaccines, a logical consequence of Jerne's idiotype-anti-idiotype network theory[9]. Antibodies obviously bind to antigen epitopes. They can also serve as antigens themselves, to be recognized by still other antibodies which bind to their variable regions (idiotypes). Some of these anti-idiotypic antibodies carry the internal image of the original antigen: they can therefore act as antigenic stand-ins, eliciting an antibody response.

Clearly, not all idiotypes can serve as vaccines: some will produce a protective immunity; some will not. There are at least two reasons for this:

First, only a few anti-idiotypes mimic the antigen and bind to the primary antibody's (Ab1) antigen-binding area (paratope). The other antibodies target parts of the Ab1 variable region that do not participate in antigen recognition and binding. (Note, however, that anti-idiotypes binding outside the paratope can sometimes elicit production of antibodies against the nominal antigen. Such anti-idiotypic antibodies may not make proper vaccines. They probably will not generate a relevant T-cell immunity.)

Second, some anti-idiotypes seem to induce suppressive rather than protective immunity in the vaccinated animal even though they elicit both B- and T-cell responses against the antigen.

Anti-idiotype vaccines could replace microbes and microbial toxins, both hazardous to the patient. Anti-idiotypes also offer peptide alternatives to some microbes' primarily glycan epitopes — particularly important for vaccinating infants against bacterial polysaccharides. And modern hybridoma processes can produce these in almost limitless supply, a particularly significant consideration where carbohydrates make up the antigen's most important structures, putting them, at least for now, beyond the reach of recombinant DNA technology.

Anti-idiotypic antibodies have reportedly produced vaccines against microbial antigens such as parasites, bacteria and viruses (Table 2).

Anti-idiotypic cancer therapy is obviously another area of great interest. Although Hollinshead[10] has demonstrated the benefits of vaccinating lung tumor patients with autologous tumor extracts, immunization with tumor-associated antigens has generally been rather disappointing.

There are many reasons for this. Tumor-associated antigens are often unidentified, hard to purify, and "self." Anti-idiotypic antibodies have been tried in several experimental systems for vaccination against tumors (Table 2). Such idiotype-based antigens could potentially outperform conven-

Table 1
Clinical Effects of Human Monoclonals Against Solid Tumors

Tumor	No. of Patients	Clinical Effects	Comments
Malignant melanoma	8	2 complete remission 2 partial remission 2 objective response	Anti-GD2 (IgM) antibody No side effects
Glioma	1	Not available	Antibodies administered in a subcutaneously implanted culture chamber
Breast carcinoma	6	Localization	^{111}In-labeled IgM antibodies for tumor localization

tional tumor-associated antigens especially since they are easy to mass-produce and are free of the tumor viruses that may be present in conventional tumor-extracted antigens. Furthermore, by putting the epitope in a new molecular environment, such as an anti-idiotypic antibody coupled to keyhole limpet hemocyanin (KLH) or tetanus toxoid, it may mobilize T-cell clones that would not otherwise participate in the anti-tumor-antigen response.

Several laboratories have demonstrated immunity to tumor-associated antigens after vaccination with anti-idiotypic antibodies: melanoma, virally induced sarcomas, bladder tumor, B- and T-cell lymphomas, and colon carcinoma (see Table 2). The 17−1A murine monoclonal has had therapeutic effects in patients suffering from colorectal cancer. This may not be a direct effect; rather, the 17−1A may induce anti-idiotypic antibodies, immunizing the patient[11]. More recently, others have obtained a set of human monoclonal anti-idiotypic antibodies following EBV transformation of B cells from patients treated with 17−1A.

H. Kohler and his group have developed and characterized several anti-idiotypic antibodies which induce T- and B-cell immune responses. Although these antibodies bind to the same paratope, some induce protective immunity, and some do not. The anti-idiotypic antibody that failed to induce protective immunity elicited suppression rather than protection. The reason is unclear: it may depend on the anti-idiotypic antibody's ability to activate T-effector cells via direct idiotype binding. Protective antibodies induced by vaccination with irradiated tumor cells reacted with the anti-idiotype giving protective immunity. On the other hand, serum antibodies (from individuals with growing tumors) bound to the anti-idiotype inducing suppression. This suggests an organic relationship between tumor development and the type of antibody response evoked. The results also caution us: Anti-idiotypic vaccination can have complex effects on the immune system.

We can now produce enormous numbers of different antibody specificities as internal images, with a corresponding variety of biological functions. Thus, research has produced anti-idiotypic antibodies containing internal images of such molecules as insulin, angiotensin II, and adenosine, and to adrenergic, nicotinic and opiate compounds (see Table 3). Such antibodies can bind to their respective receptors and some of them have demonstrated an agonistic effect.

Antibodies as Enzymes

Recent inquiries have focused on still other exciting possibilities: antibodies new-found ability to form structures that complement enzyme substrates. Antibody-antigen interactions obviously resemble enzyme-substrate interactions in their affinity and binding specificity. There is, however, one important difference between the two groups of molecules. Antibodies interact with their ligands in stable, low-energy configurations; catalytic enzymes bind to unstable, high-energy transition forms of their substrates. The enzyme's binding energy then helps break a chemical bond in the

Table 2
Infective and Other Diseases Treated with Anti-Idiotype Vaccines

Antigen source	Anti-idiotype source	Species vaccinated
Streptococcus penumoniae	mouse monoclonal	mouse
E. coli K13	mouse monoclonal	mouse
Trypanosoma cruzi	rabbit serum	mouse, rabbit, guinea pig
Hepatitis B surface antigen	rabbit serum	chimpanzee
Polio virus type II	mouse monoclonal	mouse
Rabies virus	rabbit serum	mouse
Reovirus	mouse monoclonal	mouse
Cytomegalovirus	mouse monoclonal	mouse
Human immunodeficiency virus	rabbit serum	mouse
Murine sarcoma	mouse monoclonal	mouse
Murine bladder tumor	mouse monoclonal	mouse
Murine lymphoma	mouse monoclonal	mouse
Murine B-cell lymphoma	mouse idiotypic IgM	mouse
Human B-cell lymphoma	mouse monoclonal	human
Human melanoma	rabbit serum	mouse
Human T-cell lymphoma	mouse monoclonal	mouse
Human colon carcinoma	goat serum	human
Human colon carcinoma	human monoclonal	— —

Table 3
Anti-idiotypic Antibodies with Receptor-Binding Ability

Antigen	Source of Anti-Idiotype	Activity	Receptor
Insulin	Rabbit serum	Agonist	Insulin
Angiotensin II	Rabbit serum	--	Angiotensin II
Adenosine	Mouse monoclonal	Agonist	Adenosin I
Alprenolol	Rabbit serum	Agonist	Beta adrenalin
Nicotine	Mouse monoclonal	--	Rat brain nicotine
Morphine	Guinea pig serum	Agonist	Opiate

substrate molecule[12]. By analogy, an enzymatic antibody's structure should complement the substrate's transition state which usually exists for an inconveniently short time. So investigators have produced stable, low-energy analogs of transition states for a variety of compounds. Using these, they have produced several "abzymes" (Table 4).

Antibodies with catabolic activity against complex substances, such as proteins and nucleic acids, could be of great importance. Such antibodies could possibly cleave protease-resistant amide bonds and might display greater substrate specificity than common proteolytic enzymes. A dependence on surrounding structures could be built into the antibody's catalytic site, allowing it, rather than proteases, to cleave only specific proteins.

Producing Optimal Antibodies

Different applications require different antibody qualities: high-affinity for diagnosis, switch or low-affinity for affinity chromatography, various affinities and isotypes for therapeutic antibodies of human origin. Human monoclonals may be preferable for affinity-purifying human therapeutics. To match these requirements, we must be able to design and produce MAbs with pre-defined properties. The immunotechnologist's obvious goal will be to prepare antibodies of the desired xenotype, isotype, specificity and affinity.

Reshaping Monoclonals by Molecular Biology

We can now manipulate these parameters using the techniques of molecular biology — the same techniques have been used to construct chimeric antibodies, i.e. antibodies with mouse variable domains and human constant domains[13]. These "humanized" antibodies may eliminate some problems associated with the anti-mouse-immunoglobulin immune response. Also, the effector functions can be tailored as required. Thus IgG1 and IgG3 human isotypes have been shown to be the most effective in complement and cell-mediated lysis. They would therefore be selected for destroying tumor cells.

Sequence comparisons of variable heavy (V_H) and variable light (V_L) chain domains have shown that each domain has three hypervariable regions (CDR1–3), flanked by four conserved framework regions (FR1–4). Antibodies with different specificities show greatest variability in the CD regions, and

Table 4
Antibodies with Enzymatic Activity

Enzymatic Activity of Antibody	Substrate of Reaction	Acceleration
Chorismate mutase	Chorismate	10^2
Esterase	Hydroxyester	1.7×10^2
Esterase	Carboxyl ester	9.6×10^2
		2.1×10^2
Esterase	Carbonate ester	7.7×10^3
Esterase	Coumarin ester	1.5×10^3
Esterase	Carbonate ester	8.1×10^2
Esterase	Carbonate ester	6.3×10^6
		1.2×10^5

these regions evidently form the principal determinant of the antigen combining site. Thus, both V_H and V_L domains are implicated in antigen binding, although their relative contributions are unknown. Chimeric antibodies have been taken a step further: each of the CDR1–3 regions of the heavy and light variable regions has been transplanted into a human framework.

Reichmann, *et al.*[14] reported the elegant modification of a human IgG1 antibody by transplanting just the antigen-binding sites of a rat anti-human lymphocyte antibody (CAMPATH-1). Grafting of CDRs into human FRs did not turn out to be simply a matter of replacing the six human complement-determining regions of the human antibody with those from the rodent immunoglobulin. The resulting human antibody reacted poorly with the CAMPATH-1. This suggested an error packing the reshaped domain in the human FRs, reducing antigen reactivity by a factor of about 40. Only after site-directed mutagenesis did researchers obtain a V_H exhibiting restored antigen binding. This illustrates that hypervariable regions are not isolated within the antigen binding site. Rather, they make a number of contacts with residues of the framework. This might prevent "humanizing" from becoming the general approach unless antibody engineers can foresee interactions between the hypervariable and framework regions[15].

Monoclonals derived from human B cells recognize epitopes not detected by xenogenetically derived antibodies. This poses another, more serious, problem for mouse/human chimeric antibodies — implying that only today's few mouse MAbs with acceptable specificities are worth turning into chimeric antibodies for eventual clinical application. Human/human chimeric antibodies could overcome all of these difficulties if the human V_H and V_L domains produced by *in vitro* immunization were cloned into a vector containing the desired human constant gene segments. This would yield a human/human chimeric monoclonal antibody exhibiting a "true" human specificity in a totally human framework.

Human V_H and V_L regions could be enzymatically amplified via polymerase chain reaction with a set of degenerate primers. These variable regions could then be modified by site-directed mutagenesis to obtain higher affinities or specificities. They could then be cloned directly into a sequencing vector or joined together with (for example) an IgG1 constant region domain, resulting in a human/human chimeric monoclonal antibody.

Shaping Monoclonals by Cell Biology

Using cell biological techniques, the researcher may influence antibody affinity and isotype at two levels: during *in vitro* immunization and in existing hybridomas. Hybridoma cells spontaneously switch isotype at a frequency of 10^{-5} to 10^{-6}/cell/generation. These switched cells can be identified and isolated using a number of techniques, including fluorescence-activated cell-sorting and sequential sublining. Some workers have also used large-scale sequential sublining to select for hybridomas producing higher-affinity antibodies. Other investigators have exploited the antigen-specific membrane Ig expressed on most hybridomas. These cells were repeatedly allowed to bind to surfaces coated with bound antigen. The cells that bound most firmly and resisted extensive washings were found, quite naturally, to produce high-affinity antibodies. By one estimate, the procedure was sensitive to affinity-increasing mutations occurring about ten times in 10^8 cells[16]. Several mutations in the antibody variable region might be necessary to increase still higher affinities: the probability is extremely low.

One must have recourse to other methods: reshaping the existing antibody, or concentrating on the immunization step — guiding B-cell development towards production of high-affinity antibody *before* immortalization.

The latter approach has become a distinct possibility with the advent of *in vitro* immunization techniques. Although still in its infancy, this method has shown great potential. It will allow production of both murine and human antibodies to a variety of antigens, including self antigens[17]. *In vitro* immunization procedures often yield IgM antibodies exhibiting affinity comparable to a primary *in vivo* response. In the murine system, at least, the isotype can be switched from IgM to IgG or IgG2a by adding IL-4 or IFN-gamma, respectively. Co-cultivating B-cells with cloned T-cells of the TH1 or TH2 subtype, producing either IL-4 or IFN-gamma, can also influence isotype. In addition, the affinity of antibodies produced after *in vitro* immunization depends on the amount of antigen added to the cultures; low levels of antigens favor development of cells producing higher-affinity antibodies. A combination of *in vivo* and *in vitro* immunizations produces antigen-specific hybridomas, mostly of the IgG isotype. Development of a secondary response depended on the presence of antigen during the *in vitro* stimulation. Generating IgG required at least a two-week interval between the primary *in vivo* immunization and the secondary *in vitro* stimulation. Furthermore, the IgM distribution pattern shifted towards higher affinities and the IgG affinities appeared higher than obtained after immunization *in vivo* only.

In vitro immunization typically takes 5 to 8 days. This period may conceivably be too short to allow proper Ig switching and affinity maturation. Culturing normal B-cells over longer periods has met with great difficulties. Treating B-cell-containing mononuclear blood cell preparations with the lysosomotropic agent L-leucyl-L-leucine methyl ester (which quantitatively eliminates lysosome-rich large granular lymphocytes, cytolytic $CD8^+$ T-cells and monocytes) prolongs the survival time of cultured B cells to at least 40 days. In the future, it might thus be possible to cultivate normal B-cells over still longer periods, either by removing inhibitory cells or by the controlled addition of cells delivering the required signals. To produce high-affinity antibodies, it would be desirable to selectively activate those B cells that recognize specific antigens. One could control proliferation and differentiation by limiting amounts of the antigen. Such an activation would mimic the *in vivo* situation and favor development of high-affinity antibodies. It should be recognized, however, that we still know too little about the molecular and cellular demands of B-cell activation and maturation.

BIOLOGICAL RESPONSE MODIFIERS – INTERLEUKINS[18]

Though exquisitely orchestrated and designed to protect us from harm, the body's immune system can often revolt — with quite opposite results. Interfering with this response, by suppressing it or enhancing it, has long been a therapeutic dream. And now that the hormones of the immune system — interleukins, lymphokines, cytokines — are yielding their secrets, such approaches to immunotherapy seem feasible.

The new immunotherapies ultimately rely on the principle of antigen-specific triggering of the appropriate cells, i.e. on the clonal selection theory proposed by Sir MacFarlane Burnet. Antigens interact with specific receptors expressed on the surface of both T and B lymphocytes; thereafter the cells express a specific set of genes that program the immune response. In T cells, these genes encode the interleukins and their receptors, the molecules that direct the cells to proliferate, differentiate and eliminate antigen. Thus, while antigen recognition initiates this response, it is the interleukins and their receptors that actually direct it. Accordingly, there are two potential targets for therapeutic intervention: the antigen-recognition event and interleukin-receptor interactions.

Given that only a few clinical trials have commenced, and patient data are yet scarce, it is hard to predict the difficulties that may lie ahead in developing any new immunotherapy. However, in the laboratory, the technical hurdles at least seem manageable. What follows is a best-case forecast for the future.

Ligands and Analogs

Interfering with ligand-receptor interactions has already proven a fruitful approach for developing drugs for the central nervous, neuromuscular and endocrine systems. The ligand-receptor reactions that govern these systems all convert the molecular energy of ligand binding into chemical signals that function inside the cells. The initial ligand-receptor binding interaction obeys the law of mass action, which dicatates the proportion of receptors occupied. In turn, this depends on the affinity of the two molecules for each other. Therefore, the concentrations of both the ligand and receptor molecules ultimately become the determinants of receptor occupancy. Given this principle, it is straightforward to imagine the development of interleukin analogs that might have a higher affinity for the receptor, thereby behaving as "superleukins."

Authentic receptors do more than bind specific ligands, however: they also have the capacity to signal the cells. As such, it should be possible to separate these two functions. In fact, researchers have already done this in other experimental systems — particularly for neurotransmitters. They have identified ligand analogs that can bind to the receptor, but are incapable (or poorly capable) of triggering it. If the two defining aspects of genuine receptors (i.e. binding and signaling) can be separated, in principle they can also be exploited in drug development.

There are three basic kinds of ligands: small molecules like the neurotransmitters (Mr about 1,000); small peptide hormones (Mr=1,000–2,000) that have no known rigid secondary and tertiary structure; and larger protein hormones (Mr=5,000–20,000), such as insulin and the interleukins, that have intrachain disulfide bonds and a definite secondary and tertiary structure in solution. At first, it was impossible to make analogs of the larger proteins. More recently, we have learned to use molecular-genetic and protein-engineering approaches to create altered interleukins. Structure prediction methods, as well as the availability of actual three-dimensional structures of some proteins, now make it possible to analyze the interleukin structure-activity relationships (SAR). Their relatively large size, the stable core of secondary structure and the packing arrangement of each of the amino acid side chains can all be used advantageously to develop analogs.

Take for example interleukin-2 (IL-2), the T-cell growth factor. The peptide backbone of IL-2 is known from X-ray crystallographic analysis and the molecule's hydrophobic core is comprised of four tightly packed anti-parallel amphipathic α-helices. Using peptide synthesis in combination with recombinant DNA (rDNA) methods, researchers made multiple changes in the most C-terminal α-helix, carefully correlating changes in molecule conformation with detectable differences in binding activity or signal-transduction capacity. Analogs created in this way appeared to bind to the receptor but were deficient in T-cell growth stimulation, indicating that it may be possible to engineer IL-2 analogs that will behave as antagonists. That is, the molecules will "crowd out" the natural molecule, blocking its effects.

It appears that most of the interleukins themselves share a common genetic ancestor: they have a similar genomic organization of 4–5 exons distributed over approximately 5,000 nucleotides; most have a signal peptide; they are about the same size (10–20 Kd); and most are α-helical proteins, containing no β secondary structure. Therefore, the principles discovered from studies of IL-2 and its receptor are likely to apply to many of the other interleukins.

Vaccines and Antimicrobials

Since the interleukins are responsible for stimulating the proliferation and differentiation of antigen-activated T and B cells, they are ripe for development as the first truly effective immune stimulants. Steven Rosenberg and his colleagues

(National Cancer Institute, Bethesda, MD) first championed IL-2 as an immunostimulant in cancer therapy.

In addition, the interleukins are sure to find a place as safe, relatively nontoxic adjuvants for vaccines. This will likely grow even more important as recombinant proteins and synthetic peptides — rather than live attenuated organisms — are developed and used as vaccines. Moreover, accumulating experimental data indicate that interleukins can be used as immunostimulants to treat a variety of infectious diseases. These include diseases, such as in lepromatous leprosy, in which the host response is relatively deficient or those for which effective antimicrobial agents are unavailable. Even when effective drugs are available, it is exciting to imagine that physicians will be able to boost the immune response using interleukins while simultaneously administering antimicrobial drugs. Such an approach could also be used to augment immune responsiveness in hospitalized patients whose host defense mechanisms are often compromised by severe underlying diseases, multiple trauma or extensive surgical procedures.

Toxins, Antibodies, Receptors

Interleukins and their receptors are already being exploited as immunosuppressives. For example, Murphy and coworkers[19] and Pastan and coworkers[20] engineered bacterial toxin-IL-2 conjugates that bind to high-affinity IL-2 receptors on recently activated T cells without affecting the vast majority of circulating T cells which remain quiescent and do not express IL-2 receptors.

If such conjugates can kill all T cells activated by a graft or transplant, then the transplant recipients should retain their overall immunocompetence while tolerating the graft's alloantigens. It follows that if IL-2-toxin conjugates are effective alloantigen-specific immunosuppressants, then they should also work for autoimmune diseases, such as type I diabetes. This approach (deleting activated autoreactive T cells via IL-2-toxin conjugates) is particularly attractive because it obviates the laborious process of identifying the autoantigen but still produces antigen-specific immunosuppression.

Similarly, antibodies to interleukin receptors should also inhibit receptor-ligand interactions. Like the interleukin-toxin conjugates, monoclonal antibodies conjugated with toxins could delete cells "programmed" to react with specific antigens. Alternatively, anti-receptors and genetically engineered soluble interleukin receptors themselves should be able to block interleukin-receptor interactions competitively, controlling the responsiveness of activated cells without actually killing them. For interleukin receptors expressed on resting cells (such as for IL-4 and IL-5) it could be advantageous to block the receptor only temporarily — during acute allergic reactions or allograft rejection episodes, for example.

Probing the Unknown

We still do not know which biochemical pathways the interleukins activate. Once they are known, however, it will be possible to develop traditional pharmaceuticals to interrupt signaling. Ultimately, genetic intervention will be feasible as well. All available data indicate that the interleukins affect cellular responses by stimulating expression of distinct sets of genes. For example, detailed studies have shown that IL-2 binding to high-affinity receptors on B cells stimulates specific transcriptional activation of the immunoglobulin J-chain gene. Once the principles governing J-chain expression become clear, it should be possible to develop antagonists of J-chain transcription which would markedly suppress IgM production. The same approaches can be envisioned for interleukin-promoted Ig isotype switching; for example, it could well be quite advantageous to prevent Ig heavy chain isotype switching to IgE, thereby dampening allergic states.

The total number of cytokines released during inflammation still remains unclear. Thus far, we have identified about a dozen such molecules but the identification techniques are self-limiting. The traditional approach is first to develop a defining bioassay and then use the assay to identify and isolate the molecules responsible. Bioassay development is still an art, dependent on the ingenuity of the investigator. But gene cloning offers a way around this problem: it is now possible to identify new interleukins by virtue of their characteristic primary structures. Some researchers[21] have already demonstrated the power of this disciplined approach. They identified approximately 60 novel genes expressed within four hours of T-cell receptor activation. At least two of these genes appear to be members of the cytokine family: they have a signal peptide and code for proteins of 10–20 Kd. By definition, then, these molecules are cytokines.

Experimental problems will now focus on how to define the biological activities of the new molecules. One might argue that we have traded one conundrum for another but at least we know enough about the functions of the "original" interleukins to use them as guidelines for understanding those of the "new" ones. Since we already know that interleukins trigger biological responses by interacting with cell-surface receptors, any new candidates can be surveyed automatically for specific, saturable binding to a variety of cells and tissues. Once we know the receptor distribution, we can assay known functions of different cell types in the presence of the putative cytokine. For example, if B cells bind the new cytokine, it is obvious that one can study their proliferation and differentiation (Ig secretion) as appropriate functions carried out by normal B cells. By comparison, polymorphonuclear leukocytes cannot proliferate but they do respond to chemotactic stimuli by directional migration; they are also phagocytic. Thus, the key to analyzing the function of a new cytokine is to find where its receptors appear — and when.

Conclusions

For the first time we have a detailed understanding of, and appreciation for, the fundamental role of interleukins in regulating the immune system. Moreover, we are now on the verge of actually creating new immunoactive agents based upon this knowledge. Consequently, we can anticipate new immuno-stimulatory interleukins and their analogs for use as vaccine adjuvants, for treating chronic intractable infectious diseases and perhaps even for treating cancer. Simultaneously, interleukin antagonists, interleukin-toxin conjugates, soluble interleukin receptors and monoclonal antibodies reactive with both the interleukins and their receptors offer promising new immunosuppressive approaches to allograft rejection, autoimmune diseases and allergic disease states. Thus, the interleukins provide the first rational means for therapeutic manipulation of the immune system.

BIOLOGICAL RESPONSE MODIFIERS — LYMPHOKINE RECEPTORS[22]

Immunology is just beginning to understand the complexities of the cytokine/lymphokine network: the hormones, their cell-surface receptors, and the cellular responses they invoke (Fig. 1). Although it has now been quite some time since scientists isolated, characterized and cloned the first interleukin gene, getting at interleukin receptors has proven a thornier problem. Some cells of the immune system do not express any cell-surface receptors when they are in a resting (unstimulated) state. And even when they do, the number of receptors can be very small — from 200 to 5,000 receptors per cell depending on type. This makes isolation all the more difficult. But, creative as ever, molecular biologists have devised new tricks to fish out these receptors, clone their genes, analyze their sequences and predict their structures. Once it becomes possible to produce these receptors at will, and in quantity, the door to using them as therapeutic agents opens wide.

Though most lymphokine-receptor interactions are part of and necessary to a normal functioning immune system, they can also have their dark side — leading, for instance, to autoimmune disorders, tumorigenesis and diabetes. If circulating interleukins could be bound before they found their receptors, the theory goes, it should be possible to prevent or treat such disease states. Already, considerable effort has gone into producing monoclonal antibodies as binding agents. A newer approach is to develop soluble receptors to mop up circulating lymphokines.

The Interleukin-1 Receptor

In order to do that one must, of course, first have a working knowledge of its natural, membrane-bound counterpart (Fig. 2). And the receptor with the fewest secrets left to discover seems to be that for interleukin-1 (IL-1).

Interleukin-1 actually comes in two varieties: α and β. They are distinct glycosylated polypeptide molecules with only 26-percent amino acid homology but both interact with the same receptor and have identical biological activities. In general, the IL-1s play a central role in regulating the immune system, including inflammatory responses. Human IL-1 is produced by a variety of cells, including activated macrophages. It also acts on many types of cells, regulating their proliferation, maturation and functional activity. Yet the precise way in which this all occurs is still largely a matter of conjecture, especially because most of these cells have very few IL-1 receptors, ranging from a few hundred receptors on lymphocytes to a few thousand on fibroblasts.

Despite this paucity, there is now a wealth of information on both the murine and human IL-1 receptors. The former is a single polypeptide chain with an approximate molecular weight of 80,000 Daltons. Moreover, the extracted receptor has the same IL-1 binding specificity as its membrane-bound counterpart. Interestingly, although the receptor binds both forms of IL-1, it does discriminate: it will bind the IL-1 α-precursor molecule, but IL-1 β must be processed first to its mature form. One can speculate as to what this might mean: IL-1 α can bind to T-cell receptors; if it is also the particular molecule that binds to macrophages, it could bridge the two and transmit signals.

One group[23] has succeeded in cloning the gene for the murine IL-1 receptor protein as well. The extracellular IL-1-binding portion of this protein consists of 319 amino acids, comprising three immunoglobulin-like domains. The cytoplasmic portion is 217 amino acids in length. How it functions in signal transduction is unclear: it does not contain the sequences that usually point to some kind of tyrosine kinase activity.

With this information in hand, researchers have gone on to create soluble versions of both mouse and human IL-1 cloned receptors by removing their trans-membrane and cytoplasmic domains.

Early *in vivo* experiments showed that soluble IL-1 receptor suppressed lymphoproliferative response to allogeneic cells in mouse model systems and prolonged the survival time of cardiac allografts.

Interleukins 2 and 4

The IL-4 receptor might be used for treating graft-versus-host disease and transplant rejections as well as counteracting

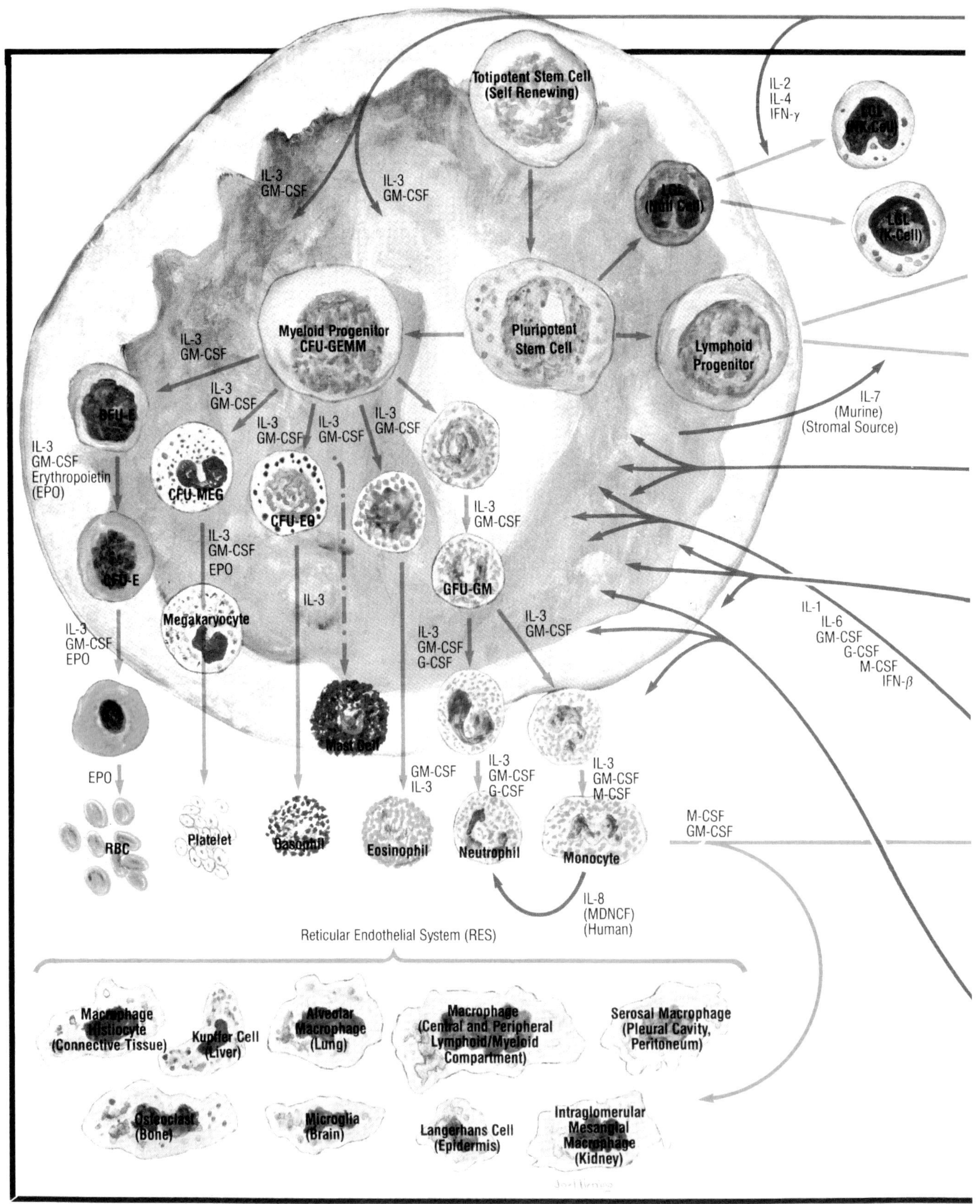

Figure 1. The lymphokine network.

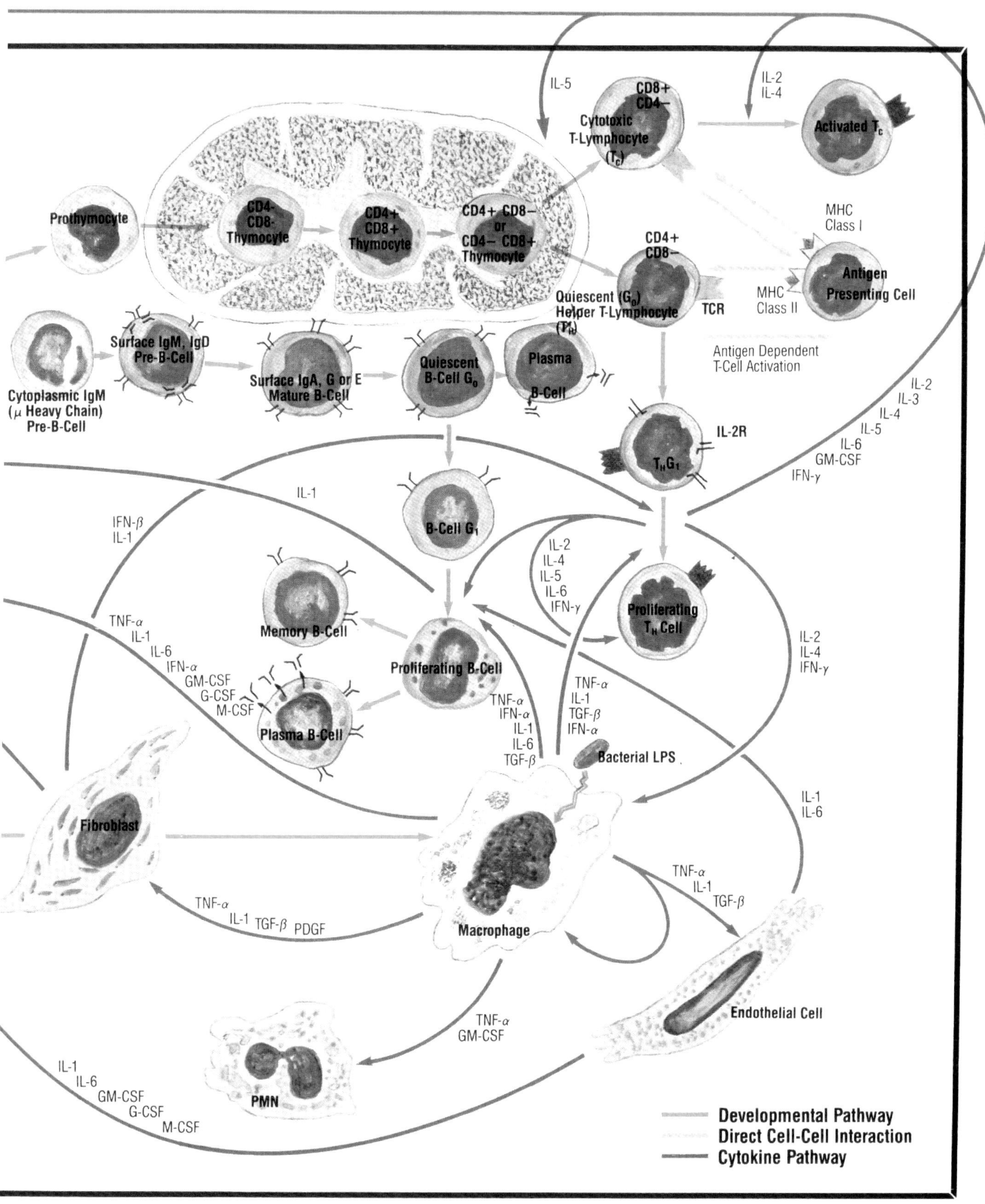

IL-5
CD8+
CD4−
Cytotoxic
T-Lymphocyte
(Tc)
IL-2
IL-4
Activated Tc
Prothymocyte
CD4-
CD8-
Thymocyte
CD4+
CD8+
Thymocyte
CD4+ CD8−
or
CD4− CD8+
Thymocyte
MHC
Class I
CD4+
CD8−
Antigen
Presenting Cell
MHC
Class II
Quiescent (G0)
Helper T-Lymphocyte
(TH)
TCR
Surface IgM, IgD
Pre-B-Cell
Surface IgA, G or E
Mature B-Cell
Quiescent
B-Cell G0
Plasma
B-Cell
Antigen Dependent
T-Cell Activation
Cytoplasmic IgM
(μ Heavy Chain)
Pre-B-Cell
IL-2
IL-3
IL-4
IL-5
IL-6
GM-CSF
IFN-γ
IL-2R
THG1
IL-1
IFN-β
IL-1
B-Cell G1
IL-2
IL-4
IL-5
IL-6
IFN-γ
Memory B-Cell
Proliferating
TH Cell
TNF-α
IL-1
IL-6
IFN-α
GM-CSF
G-CSF
M-CSF
Proliferating B-Cell
IL-2
IL-4
IFN-γ
TNF-α
IL-1
TGF-β
IFN-α
TNF-α
IFN-α
IL-1
IL-6
TGF-β
Plasma B-Cell
Bacterial LPS
IL-1
IL-6
Fibroblast
TNF-α
IL-1
TGF-β
TNF-α
IL-1 TGF-β PDGF
Macrophage
TNF-α
GM-CSF
Endothelial Cell
IL-1
IL-6
GM-CSF
G-CSF
M-CSF
PMN
Developmental Pathway
Direct Cell-Cell Interaction
Cytokine Pathway

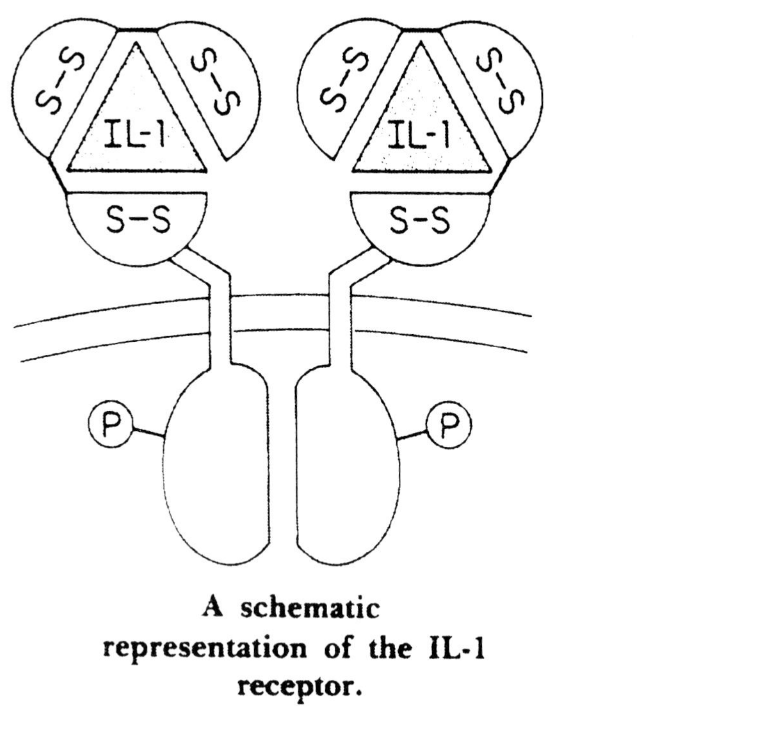

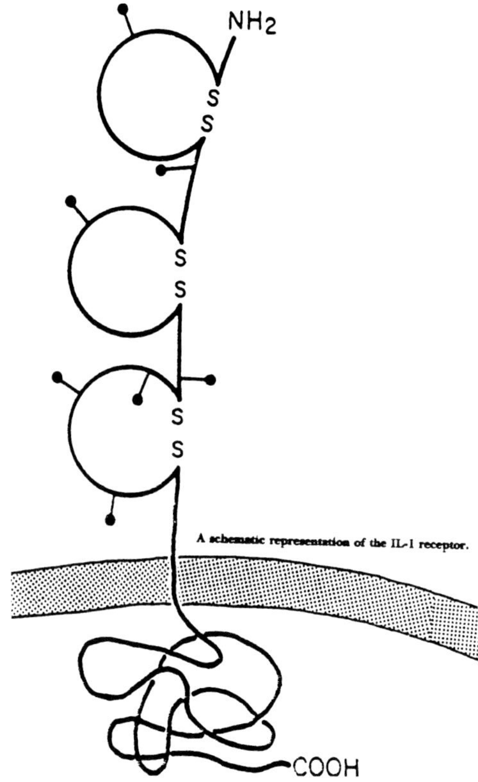

Figure 2. A schematic representation of the IL-1 receptor. (Reproduced by courtesy of S. Gillis, Immunex.)

IL-4's ability to induce allergic reactions by stimulating IgE production.

And, since malignant cells seem to express IL-2 receptors, devising means to block them may well hold promise. Interleukin-2 regulates the expression of its own receptors. Resting T cells do not normally express either IL-2 or its receptor: this requires antigen-specific induction. Resting cells express as few as 200 receptors each, whereas stimulated cells can express between 4,000 and 11,000. Normal, activated T cells proliferate only transiently but HTLV-1-infected adult T-cell leukemia cells express IL-2 receptors constitutively although in both cases the receptors' protein sequence is the same: a 251-amino-acid glycoprotein weighing 47,000 to 58,000 Daltons.

That receptor-based therapy might indeed work is still questionable given the limited clinical trial data. In one of the earliest attempts, Thomas Waldmann (National Cancer Institute, Bethesda, MD) tested the efficacy of an antibody to the IL-2 receptor in clinical trials on patients with adult T-cell leukemia. Of the five patients who received intravenous injections of the antibody, three had an insignificant response and two went into remission[24].

GM-CSF and Beyond

Although cloning the interleukin receptors has not been easy, obtaining receptors for other factors — granulocyte macrophage colony stimulating factor (GM-CSF), for example — has been harder still.

GM-CSF stimulates precursor cells to proliferate and differentiate; it can also modulate the function of mature cells of each type. When it goes awry, however, this lymphokine (and its receptor) may contribute to the pathology of malignancy: in fact, there is now evidence that many myeloid leukemias express GM-CSF receptors. And myeloid leukemia cells cannot proliferate *in vitro* unless exogenous colony-stimulating factors are present.

GM-CSF receptors are present only in small numbers, estimated at 100–500 per cell. These receptors, like those for the interleukins, seem to belong to a single class with very high binding affinity. And again, soluble GM-CSF receptors may have therapeutic value.

Will this approach hold for the other colony stimulating factors, interleukins and associated lymphokines?

CANCER TREATMENT[25]

The biomedical community has spent the last 40 years searching for new and effective ways to treat cancer. During that time, research scientists have made great strides in understanding the nature of neoplastic cell transformation and the body's reaction to it. From this, new ways to treat cancer are emerging — revolutionary methods that harness patients' own defenses to fight the disease within them.

Cancer Therapy in Perspective

Surgery is still the mainstay of current cancer therapy: 80 percent of cancer cures are due, at least in part, to surgery. It can be completely curative if performed on an accessible tumor that has not yet metastasized. For those patients with widely infiltrating, metastatic, or disseminated disease (e.g. leukemias), however, surgery offers little benefit.

Radiation therapy, used since the early part of this century, has been applied against disseminated or inaccessible tumors either by external beam therapy or by implanting radioactive "seeds." As with surgery, improvements over the years in the type and energy level of the radiation used have resulted in more effective treatment regimens *per se*, or combined with surgery or chemotherapy.

The first chemotherapeutic agent was developed in the early 1940s. Since then, 800,000 compounds have been screened for potential anti-cancer activity; of these, a mere 40 have proven effective and safe enough for clinical use.[26]

Both radio- and chemotherapy target dividing cells and their therapeutic benefits depend on large differences between normal and neoplastic cells' division frequencies. But these therapies also affect those tissues with naturally high turnover rates — the skin, mucus membranes, and bone marrow — and are limited by the resulting toxicity. Chemotherapy-induced bone marrow suppression is particularly dangerous: a cessation in the production of erythrocytes, platelets and granulocytes leads to anemia, uncontrolled bleeding and susceptibility to infection.

To add to the problem, many tumors become resistant to any given chemotherapeutic agent after a few treatment cycles. Although tumors appear to be clonally derived, they become quite heterogeneous during progressive growth, containing subpopulations with different growth rates, surface phenotypes and drug-resistance properties. While it may be possible to overcome this drug resistance by using combination therapy, such treatments are more toxic to normal tissue as well.

Today, most cancer treatment protocols use all three "traditional" methods, in combination or in sequence. For instance, surgical resection of a primary tumor can be followed by radiation of local lymph nodes to eliminate occult metastases; alternatively, an invasive tumor may be shrunk with radio- or chemotherapy prior to surgical excision. For certain tumors (childhood acute lymphatic leukemia, for instance) combinations of multiple-agent chemotherapy and prophylactic central nervous system radiotherapy have resulted in cures or dramatically increased long-term survival rates. On the other hand, the prognosis for patients with many common tumors, including lung, breast, and colon, has hardly changed.

Biotherapy

And now there is a fourth weapon in the anti-cancer arsenal. Biotherapy involves the therapeutic use of any substance of biological origin — biological response modifiers can be derived from viruses, bacteria, plants or mammals. Immunotherapy activates the host immune system to recognize a tumor as foreign and destroy it. Parallel advances in immunology and molecular biology have allowed the identification, cloning and expression of several key molecules involved in immune regulation. Research has identified a number of factors that can slow the growth of neoplastic cells and force them to differentiate.

First-Generation Immunomodulators

Immunotherapy *per se* is not a new concept. It stems from century-old observations that malignant tumors may regress in patients who have contracted severe bacterial infections[27]. These observations were repeated and expanded by William Coley, an American physician who proceeded to develop anti-cancer "vaccines" consisting of bacteria, including the Gram-negative *Serratia marcescens*[28]. Although Coley's bacterial preparations were clearly successful, radiotherapy eclipsed his pioneering efforts. Only in the late '60s and early '70s did immunotherapy re-emerge.

At that time, it was already well-known that certain bacteria, notably *Bacille Calmette-Guerin* (BCG) and *Corynebacterium parvum*, acted as adjuvants by enhancing antibody production and cell-mediated immune responses. These microorganisms stimulate the immune system in an intense but non-specific manner, presumably because mammals have evolved powerful defenses against these long-standing pathogens. In animal tumor models, BCG and *C. parvum* effectively caused the host to reject several types of tumors, with optimal effects when the tumor burden was small. Microbially derived immunomodulators can be effective in humans, too (Table 5).

All of these non-specific immunomodulators activate cells of the monocyte/macrophage series. These cells are produced in the bone marrow and most organs, particularly skin, liver and lung; they also circulate in the blood. Macrophages play a vital role in initiating and coordinating specific immune responses (though they retain their primitive phagocytic function). Macrophages cause the release of cytokines, molecules that modify the behavior, growth and differentiation of other effector cells: T- and B-lymphocytes and natural killer (NK) cells. This cascade of effector mechanisms, triggered in this case by a microbially derived immunomodulator, is depicted in Figure 3.

The early immunomodulators such as BCG, *C. parvum*, and OK432 consisted of whole microorganisms which often caused toxic side effects such as intense local inflammation and granuloma formation. Research scientists have since isolated active subfractions. For instance, the minimal subcellular fraction from BCG that is nontoxic but retains most of the microbe's immunomodulatory activity (muramyl dipeptide or MDP) and its synthetic analogs turn out to be powerful adjuvants. If encapculated in liposomes and administered systemically in animal models, they cause metastatic tumors to regress.

BCG made its way into humans in the 1970s: there was a spate of trials, many of which had small patient populations, were poorly controlled and were designed without a clear understanding of the immunomodulator's probable mechanism of action. Unlike many chemotherapeutics, immunomodulators do not show a linear dose/effect relationship; more is not necessarily better, and may be considerably worse. Apparently trivial differences in dosing and schedule between similar trials can therefore lead to very different outcomes. Despite all this, certain tumors, notably bladder cancer, respond well to BCG: complete and partial response rates of up to 70 percent have been reported. Other bacterially derived immunomodulators that have shown clinical benefit include OK432, a whole-cell preparation from *Streptomyces pyogenes* and a ribosome/membrane preparation from *Serratia marcescens*.

The Interferons

The search for immunomodulators of defined composition and more clearly delineated modes of action has turned to the components of the immune system itself — in particular, to the cytokines (Table 6).

The cytokines that have received the widest clinical attention to date are the interferons: α (macrophage-derived), β (fibroblast-derived) and γ (lymphoblastoid or "immune"). The interferons were originally described as proteins produced by virally infected cells; they prevent infection by a second

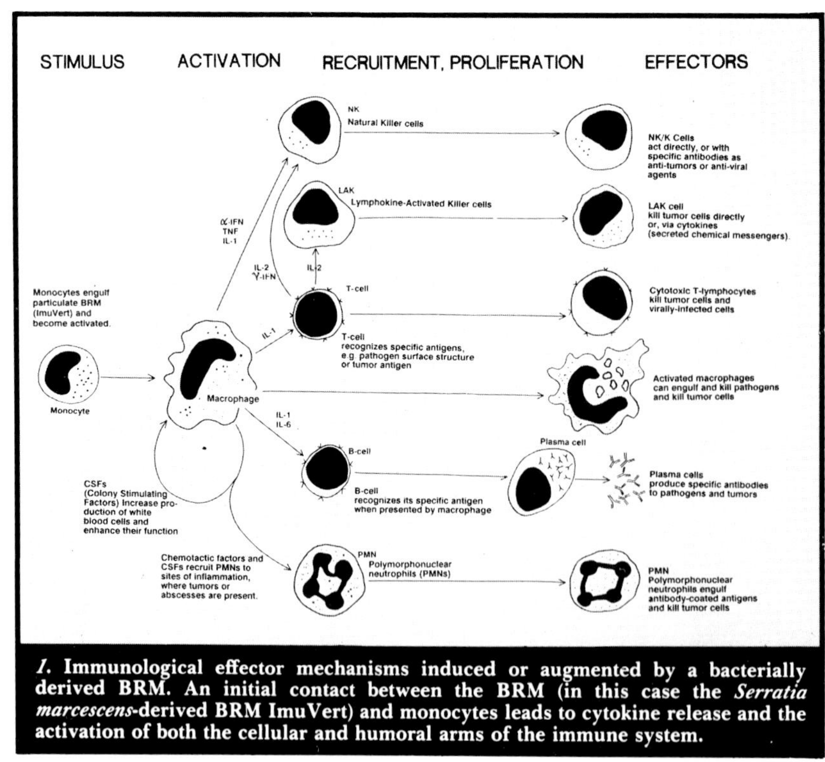

***1.* Immunological effector mechanisms induced or augmented by a bacterially derived BRM. An initial contact between the BRM (in this case the *Serratia marcescens*-derived BRM ImuVert) and monocytes leads to cytokine release and the activation of both the cellular and humoral arms of the immune system.**

Figure 3. Immunological effector mechanisms induced or augmented by a bacterially-derived biological response modifier (BRM). An initial contact between the BRM, (in this case the *Serratia marcescens*- derived BRM ImuVert) and monocytes leads to cytokine release and the activation of both cellular and humoral arms of the immune system. Copyright *Bio/Technology*

Some Biological Response Modifiers Derived from Micro-Organisms

Immunomodulator	Source	Preparaticn	Biological Effects
B.C.G.	*Bacillus Calmette-Guerin*	Whole bacterium	Activates macrophages with resulting cytokine release and augmentation of cellular cytotoxicity. Enhances survival or remission length in some tumors (e.g., leukemia). Direct intravascular application in bladder cancer gives 70% response rate.
Bestatin	*Streptomyces oliroreticuli*	Dipeptide	Activates macrophage and T lymphocytes.
Picibanil (OK432)	*Streptomyces pyogenes*	Lyophilized whole bacterium	Activates macrophages and NK cells. Increased IL-2, IFN, TNF release by macrophages. Increased survival in lung and stomach cancer patients.
Biostim (RV41.740)	*Klebsiella pneumonia*	Purified glycoprotein	Activates macrophages. Increases NK activity. Restores delayed-type hypersensitivity in cancer patients, reducing number of infections.
Corynebacterium parvum (propionibacterium acnes)		Whole bacterium	Activates macrophages. Increases NK activity. Early clinical trials inconclusive. Recent promising results in ovarian cancer.
Lentinan	*Lentinus edodes*	Purified polysaccharide	Activates macrophages. Induces release of IL-1, IL-3 and CSF. Effective against stomach and colorectal cancer when given with chemotherapy.
Krestin (PSK)	*Basidiomycetes*	Protein bound polysaccharide	Restores immune function in tumor bearing mice. Preliminary clinical studies indicate some efficacy in leukemia.
Monophoshoryl Lipid A (MPLA)	*Salmonella typhmuruim endotoxin*	Purified monophosphorylated Lipid A	Activates macrophages. Preliminary results show that given with *P. acnes* extract stabilizes disease in ovarian cancer.
ImuVert	*Serratia marcescens*	Membrane/ribosome preparation	Activates macrophages, induces IL-1, IL-2, GM-CSF, TNF and IFN production. Enhanced NK and T lymphocyte activity. Preliminary results show responses in primary brain tumors.

Table 5.

virus. Additionally, these proteins exhibit anti-proliferative, maturation-inducing and immunoregulatory traits. For instance, interferons cause several types of cells to increase their expression of histocompatibility antigens (which may render tumor cells more susceptible to cytotoxic effector cells). And macrophages exposed to γ-interferon show an increased ability to engulf and kill bacteria; they also kill tumors. Interferon treatment consistently renders NK cells more active *in vitro* (less consistently *in vivo*).

These and other properties of interferons make them strong candidates for biotherapy: by 1989 there had already been a large number of clinical trials in various tumor types. Overall, the clinical data demonstrate that interferons, administered as single agents, do not have widespread efficacy as anti-tumor compounds, but they do work in a few instances. The most impressive case is in hairy cell leukemia; 70–90 percent of patients treated with α-interferon achieve complete or partial remission. Because high doses are necessary to induce remission, it is probable that the compound is exerting a direct anti-proliferative effect.

Interferons are also successful in treating other forms of leukemia. In patients with chronic myeloid leukemia, they can produce "cytogenic" remissions in which leukemic cells bearing the characteristic chromosomal disease marker become undetectable in the bone marrow. In contrast, chemotherapy does not completely eliminate leukemic blast cells, even in patients with otherwise complete remission.

Interleukin-2

Of all the cytokines, interleukin-2 (IL-2) has received the most early attention in clinical trials. IL-2 is produced mainly by T cells after they have been exposed to antigen presented on an appropriate accessory cell (usually a macrophage) and interleukin-1 (also elaborated by the macrophage). T lymphocytes exposed to IL-2 transiently up-regulate a high-affinity IL-2 receptor and begin to proliferate: thus, IL-2 acts as an autocrine (self-produced) growth factor.

In addition to its mitogenic effects, IL-2 also stimulates the cytotoxic activity of T cells and NK cells in a dose-dependent fashion. Incubating human peripheral blood mononuclear cell preparations (which contain T, B, and NK cells) with IL-2 for several days generates cytotoxic lymphocytes that can kill a variety of tumors. These lymphokine-activated killer cells (LAK) appear to derive from two main precursor populations — NK cells and specific cytotoxic T lymphocytes (CTL). CTLs normally kill only those target cells bearing the

Clinically Relevant Cytokines

Cytokine	Characteristics	Producer Cells	Biological Properties	Clinical Applications
IL-1 alpha IL-1 beta	glycoproteins MW 17,500	Monocyte/macrophage fibroblasts Endothelial and smooth muscle cells	Activation factor for T cells. Fibroblast proliferation. Induces fever, promotes bone resorption, initiates acute phase protein synthesis. Radioprotective.	Promotes wound healing. Protection against radiation induced bone marrow failure.
IL-2	glycoprotein MW 17,200	Activated T Cells NK cells	T cell growth factor. Augmentation of cytotoxicity of T cells, NK, LAK.	Used alone or with *in vivo* activated LAK or TIL. Good response rates seen in melanoma (20-50%) and renal cell carcinoma (50%).
IL-3	glycoprotein MW 17,200	Activated T Cells	Multi-CSF—stimulates division of early hemopoietic precursors and macrophage, granulocyte and mast cells. Enhances activity of mature granulocytes and macrophages.	May increase resistance to infection by stimulating both precursors and mature cells. Early clinical trials underway.
GM-CSF	glycoprotein MW 19,600	Activated T Cells Endothelial cells Fibroblasts	Promotes differentiation, growth and functions of granulocytes and macrophages.	Prevention and mitigation of radio- and chemotherapy—induced cytopenias. Speeds bone marrow engraftment. Early clinical trials very promising.
TNF	glycoprotein MW 17,000	Macrophages, endothelial cells, smooth muscle cells	Mediates endotoxic shock/cachexia. Enhances cytotoxic activity of NK and macrophages. Induces necrosis in some tumors.	Anti-cancer as single agent or with other biologicals, e.g., gamma IFN. Early clinical trials show some efficacy, significant toxic side effects.
Interferon-alpha	glycoprotein MW 20,000	Macrophages	Direct anti-proliferative effects. Activates macrophages, NK cells. Upregulates HLA antigen expression.	Directly anti-cancer via anti-proliferative and immuno-modulatory effects. Extensive clinical testing
Interferon-gamma	glycoprotein MW 20-25,000	Activated T Cells NK cells	Induces differentiation in some tumor types (e.g. HL-60 leukemia).	shows clear efficacy in defined tumor types—notably leukemia.

Table 6.

specific antigen recognized by the T cell in association with the appropriate matching histocompatibility antigen. T-cell-derived LAK cells appear to have lost this specificity and can kill many different tumor targets. Steven Rosenberg and his associates were the first to demonstrate that extracorporeally generated LAK cells produced by co-culturing a patient's white blood cells with IL-2 could, on reinfusion with a high dose of IL-2 into the same patient, induce impressive tumor regressions[29].

Alternate treatment protocols, modified as to dose and schedule, have shown that certain tumors, notably melanoma and renal cell carcinoma, are particularly susceptible to LAK therapy. If the cell population used for generating LAK cells is drawn from those lymphocytes that have actually infiltrated the tumor and can be separated from excised tumor tissue (tumor infiltrating lymphocytes or TIL), the treatment's efficacy is enhanced[30]. A similar "auto-adoptive" immunotherapy, using specific CTL or monocytes activated with γ-interferon, is now in preliminary clinical trials.

Tumor Necrosis Factor

Another cytokine is tumor necrosis factor (TNF). Monocytes produce TNF in response to a variety of stimuli, most notably bacterial endotoxin. In fact, TNF is identical to cachectin, a mediator (produced by endotoxin-stimulated macrophages) that causes the wasting syndrome (cachexia) exhibited by cancer patients and parasitically infected individuals.

In animal models, TNF affects a tumor's vascularization, leading to central necrosis and regression. In addition, TNF can augment the cytotoxic capacities of macrophages and NK cells. In early human clinical studies, however, TNF has displayed limited efficacy.

The Limits of Cytokines

Although the cytokines appear to be effective against certain types of tumors, they are also toxic, a property not anticipated in natural molecules. High-dose interferon treatment can cause fever, fatigue, hypotension, confusion and depression. High-dose IL-2 therapy has severe side effects as well; the most prominent is "capillary leak syndrome," with potentially life-threatening pulmonary edema.

These toxic effects are probably a result of the nonphysiological doses being administered: suddenly there are high systemic levels of a single agent that normally is present at low levels in concert with other mediators. In a normal immune response, cytokines are released in defined amounts, sequence and combinations. In most cases their activities are spatially and temporally limited, high concentrations being found only at sites of inflammation.

Practical cytokine therapy awaits a better understanding of how the immune system's molecular and cellular components interact. Then it will be possible to design combination therapies of cytokine "cocktails" plus other immunomodulators such as non-specific BRMs, monoclonal antibodies, or purified effector cells, tailored to each tumor type or even to an individual patient's tumor.

Cell-Surface Antigens and Immunotoxins

Tumors induced artificially — by chemicals or viruses — often display distinct new cell-surface antigens, called "tumor-associated transplantation" antigens (TATAs). Animals can be rendered immune to these tumors by injecting them with inactivated tumor cells. The immunized animals are then able to reject a subsequent challenge with liver tumor cells. It has been found that these animals generate both specific antibodies and cytotoxic T lymphocytes that specifically recognize TATAs. The search to identify TATAs on spontaneous tumors (both human and animal) was less successful. Instead, many of the tumors expressed the same antigens (usually embryonic) as normal adult tissues but at much higher levels. Antibodies raised against these antigens, such as the carcinoembryonic antigen associated with colorectal cancers, should, therefore, be relatively specific for the tumor.

There are a number of strategies for using monoclonal antibodies in cancer therapy. Of these, the one with the nearest-term clinical utility involves employing immunotoxins: antibodies raised against particular tumor antigens are coupled to a toxin such as Ricin A chain and infused into the patient. Such immunotoxins may be particularly useful in treating B cell lymphomas where each tumor expresses a unique antibody molecule that itself can be a target for an appropriate monoclonal. In such cases the therapy can be truly tailor-made to the patient.

Monoclonal therapy may prove useful for bone marrow transplants as well. Patients with bone-marrow tumors could first be treated with ablative chemotherapy and reconstituted either with autologous bone marrow (treated with anti-tumor monoclonals) or partially histocompatible donor marrow from which potentially host-reactive cells have been removed by antibodies to normal lymphoid subsets.

Attacking Tumor-cell Behavior Directly

The therapeutic strategies discussed so far have all involved aspects of the immune system. In the future, however, biotherapy may encompass approaches that seek to modify tumor growth and spread. For instance, basic research on the mechanisms by which tumors induce their own blood supply has uncovered a constellation of angiogenic and anti-angiogenic factors, signals that trigger or halt development of blood vessels feeding the tumor. These might be manipulated to deprive the growing tumor of its vascular support. Similarly, basic studies on how tumors invade local tissues and metastasize to distant sites may suggest new strategies to prevent tumor dissemination, perhaps by blocking tumor cell motility or by neutralizing the enzymes that break down connective tissue barriers. And it may be feasible to induce maturation in tumor cells, pushing them towards a terminally differentiated state incapable of division. Tumors of hematopoietic origin are particularly attractive candidates for this approach. A complementary strategy would be to treat the tumor with an antibody to block the binding of growth factors. (This approach, using anti-epidermal growth factor receptor antibodies, has had some success in animal models.)

Biotherapy Futures

Clinical experience with biologicals such as recombinant interferon and IL-2 shows that these agents are at least as effective as the best chemotherapy for some tumors. It is reasonable to expect that combination therapy using biologicals with complementary or synergistic activities will extend these positive effects to other tumor types.

Biotherapy will also be used in many different ways to augment or complement surgery, chemotherapy and radiation regimens. For example, the hematopoietic growth factor granulocyte macrophage-colony stimulating factor (GM-CSF) can be used to mitigate the bone marow suppression caused by chemo- or radiotherapy and speed the take of bone marrow grafts. Similarly, an active immune response to a tumor may disrupt the tumor vasculature, allowing the more efficient penetration of chemotherapeutics into the tumor bed. This approach could greatly increase the drug's efficacy while sparing normal tissues.

In the near future the oncologist will have access to an arsenal of biologicals that act very differently from standard chemotherapeutic drugs. Perhaps the major challenge will then be how best to use this powerful anti-cancer armamentarium.

VACCINE DEVELOPMENT[31]

In the years since the dramatic global eradication of smallpox, vaccination has also been remarkably successful in reducing morbidity and mortality due to yellow fever virus infections in Africa and Central America. In the United States, vaccination programs have nearly eliminated deaths due to diphtheria, measles, mumps, pertussis, paralytic poliomyelitis and rubella; the incidence of tetanus, moreover, has declined by about 90 percent.

But vaccination programs are still needed in certain regions of the world and the need for new and improved vaccines remains as great as ever: AIDS, malaria (with drug-resistant strains of parasites spreading) and malignant diseases, such as virus-induced and certain other tumors.

Mechanisms of Protective Immunity

The immune system uses several different effector mechanisms to protect against infectious agents. In some cases, antibodies of any isotype can protect provided that they have sufficient affinity for the antigen. This is true, for example, of antibodies against diphtheria and tetanus toxoids. In other cases, antibodies of isotypes that can activate complement and act synergistically with antibody-dependent effector cells (IgG2a if the mouse and rat and IgG1 and IgG3 in the human) confer better protection than antibodies of other isotypes. Using murine monoclonal antibodies in which class switching has occurred, it is possible to compare the protective efficacy of antibodies with the same antigen-binding (Fab) site but with different isotype-determining (Fc) moieties. Such studies show that antibodies of the IgG2a isotype are superior to those of the IgG1 isotype in anti-tumor immunity. IgG2a antibodies are also more effective in providing immunity against infectious agents. Although IgE antibodies may contribute to protection against some helminth parasites, there is no evidence that they are effective against other organisms and, since they produce acute allergic reactions, their elicitation by vaccines is in general undesirable.

Cell-mediated immunity plays a major role in host defense against some bacterial, viral and parasitic infections. In fact, to vaccinate effectively against herpes viruses, retroviruses or tumors, it is necessary to elicit cell-mediated immunity as well as antibodies of protective isotypes. Sensitized T-lymphocytes can lyse autologous virus-infected cells or virus-transformed cells. Immune T-lymphocytes stimulated by antigen produce γ-interferon and granulocyte monocyte-colony stimulating factor which activate natural killer cells and macrophages.

Vaccines from Live, Attenuated Organisms

Live, attenuated viruses and bacteria elicit both cell-mediated and humoral immune responses. Their efficacy is established in several important vaccines (vaccinia virus, yellow fever virus, oral poliomyelitis virus, measles virus, rubella virus and *Mycobacterium bovis* BCG). However, persons with congenital or acquired immunodeficiency risk severe infections from this type of vaccine. Inherited immunodeficiency can be general (children with defective T-lymphocyte function suffer from severe vaccinia or BCG infections) or specific (responses to some antigens but not others). Children in developing countries are often immunodeficient because of malnutrition as well as from infections with parasites and viruses, including the human immunodeficiency virus (HIV) which is now known to be widely prevalent in Central Africa.

Vaccinia Virus as a Vector

The possible applications of live viruses for immunization have been extended by the discovery that genes encoding antigens of unrelated viruses, for example influenza, hepatitis B and HIV, can be introduced into vaccinia virus and then expressed in infected cells[32]. Experimental animals infected with such vaccinia virus vectors can develop immunity not only to challenge with vaccinia virus but also to the organisms from which the unrelated genes originated.

This provides a valuable experimental technique. For example, either the hemagglutinin (HA) or the nucleoprotein (NP) antigen of influenza virus can be expressed on the surface of target cells through the use of vaccinia vectors. Such cells can then be used to show that, in previously infected humans, cytotoxic T-lymphocytes usually recognize NP rather than HA. Moreover, individual epitopes of NP are recognized in association with particular major histocompatibility complex (MHC) glycoproteins. Vacinnia vectors have also been used to show that, in humans infected with HIV type 1, cytotoxic T-lymphocytes can recognize envelope and, in some individuals, core (*gag* gene product) antigens.

In principle, vaccinia vectors could be used to immunize humans against a wide range of antigens, including those for HIV, hepatitis B virus and malaria. However, this may not be the best available strategy. Vaccinia strains have been known occasionally to produce severe infections including, though rarely, fatal encephalitis. Complications are likely to be more frequent in developing countries where immunodeficiencies are common.

It may be possible to attenuate vaccinia virus vectors without reducing their capacity to immunize but, since adequate virus replication is required for immunogenicity, this remains to be demonstrated. If the use of vaccinia vectors is the only way to prevent a disaster such as an epidemic of AIDS, the benefit may outweigh the risk. However, developing other classes of efficacious vaccines may even eliminate the risks.

Inactivated Virus Vaccines

Inactivated polio virus and influenza virus vaccines have been used successfully for several years. However, responses to influenza virus vaccine vary. Low responses are more frequent in persons over the age of 65, in whom influenza infections are more severe than in younger persons. In such cases, improving antibody responses may be possible by developing appropriate adjuvants — agents that increase antibody or cell-mediated immune responses to antigens — for these vaccines.

Antigens Produced by Peptide Synthesis

Inactivated viruses contain nucleic acids, even fragments of which could have possible biological effects. Two methods for producing vaccines completely or virtually free of mammalian virus nucleic acids have been developed: peptide synthesis and production of viral subunit antigens by recombinant DNA (rDNA) technology. The synthetic peptide antigens and the antibodies they elicit are valuable research tools but there are reasons for doubting whether peptide vaccines will always be efficacious. The three-dimensional structures of some antigens, such as influenza virus HA and poliovirus capsid proteins, as well as their major epitopes, have been defined[33,34]. Epitopes that elicit protective antibodies usually have conformations which depend on the particular folding of the polypeptide chains. Configuration can be a critical requirement for antigenicity: the hepatitis B virus core antigen, when treated with the detergent sodium dodecyl sulfate, is converted into the "e" antigen which elicits antibody responses that are useful in monitoring the course of virus replication. Except in special circumstances, it is difficult to use synthetic peptides to reproduce the conformational epitopes that are present in intact proteins.

Co-operative binding of antibodies to several epitopes on a protein may be required for optimal protection. There are often genetically controlled differences in immune responses to peptides, in humans as well as in experimental animals. For these reasons, vaccines that elicit protective immune responses should incorporate as wide a repertoire of epitopes as possible rather than just one or a few peptides.

Antigens Produced by rDNA Technology

Vaccines using recombinant DNA-produced viral subunits have demonstrated efficacy and one is now licensed for use in humans in the United States. Expression systems can vary according to the individual antigen: *Escherichia coli*, yeast, mammalian cells or baculoviruses. The prototype is hepatitis B virus surface antigen (HBsAg), cloned and expressed in yeast in a form physically and antigenically resembling the 22 nm particles found in serum[35,36]. Recombinant HBsAg effectively immunized chimpanzees against infection with hepatitis B virus; following trials in humans, a recombinant HBsAg-based vaccine was approved in the United States. The core antigen (HBcAg) can be expressed in *E. coli* in a form physically and antigenically resembling the natural protein.

In some cases, proteolytic cleavage, glycosylation or myristilation may be necessary for recombinant proteins to attain configurations comparable to those in intact virions and on infected cells. Expressing these proteins in mammalian cells ensures the correct type of post-translational modification. For example, Berman et al.[37] have demonstrated that herpes simplex virus glycoprotein D, expressed in Chinese hamster ovary (CHO) cells, can protect guinea pigs against genital infection with the virus.

Conclusions

There is no doubt that vaccines produced using live attenuated viruses and bacteria have been efficacious in eliminating or substantially reducing morbidity and mortality for a wide variety of diseases. The risk of these vaccines is that they can elicit severe infections in recipients whose immune responses are deficient. The same is likely to be true if vaccinia virus is applied on a wide scale as a vector for antigens from other organisms. A safer strategy would be to use inactivated viruses or bacteria in vaccines. Perhaps the safest vaccines of all, however, will be those that contain no DNA. While peptide vaccines have their limitations (difficulty in reproducing conformational determinants and overcoming genetically controlled low responsiveness), vaccines composed of major viral or bacterial antigens produced by recombinant DNA technology do not.

ADJUVANTS[38]

Vaccination programs have wiped out or controlled some of this planet's most pernicious diseases. Yet despite this success, technical limitations have so far restricted the total number of commercialized human vaccines to about 20. Biotechnology, through its high-tech subunit, anti-idiotype and synthetic rDNA approaches, could double the number of marketable prophylactics within the next decade or two. But even though these recombinant products will probably be safer — due to their increased purity and absence of potentially infective pathogens — they may not elicit as strong an immune response as their first-generation predecessors.

Enter the adjuvants, substances that "wake up the immune system." Hailing from a staggering array of sources, including bacteria, plants and the human immune system itself, these "helper" chemicals can be administered along with vaccines to elicit an increased immune response.

But there remains a serious hurdle: although scientists clearly understand the general mechanism of vaccine action, they know much less about adjuvants and how they stimulate the body's defense mechanisms (Fig. 4).

Nevertheless, with aluminum hydroxide and aluminum phosphate as the only widely approved adjuvants, the field is certainly wide open not to mention highly competitive. Adjuvants are just beginning to attract high-powered commercial attention.

Detoxifying Bacterial Products

The first-discovered and best-known adjuvants come from bacterial sources. These kinds of products cause profound human immune responses which have evolved over millenia to mount an early and intense response to the first indications of bacterial invasion.

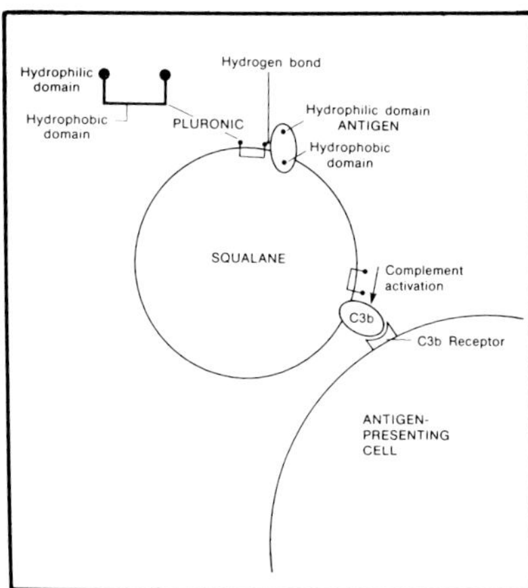

Figure 4. Diagram of the putative structure of a microsphere in the adjuvant formulation, showing the antigen held at the interface partly because of its amphipathic character and partly because acceptor groups in the antigen form hydrogen bonds with the pluronic polymer. The latter also activates complement by the alternative pathway and C3b formed is retained at the surface of the microspheres, facilitating their binding to C3b receptors on antigen-presenting cells. Copyright *Bio/Technology*.

Most bacteria-derived products, however, deliver a toxic effect along with their adjuvancy. Researchers are countering with two strategies: detoxify the toxic preparations or find new, non-toxic bacterial sources.

One approach[39] emphasizes chemically purified and detoxified products extracted from the cell walls of bacteria like *Mycobacteria bovis, Salmonella typhimurium* and *Propionibacterium acnes*. The resulting compounds include monophosphoryl lipid A,[40] trehalose dimycolate, mycobacterial cell wall skeleton and *Propionibacterium acnes*-pyridine extract. The company combines these products into proprietary preparations.

Various combinations of such materials, formulated in various delivery systems, have been used to intensify responses to vaccines against melanoma, malaria, ovarian cancer, colorectal and bladder cancer, hepatitis and tetanus.

Synthesizing Bacterial Analogs

The feat of chemically synthesizing an adjuvant has already been achieved by several groups for muramyl dipeptide (MDP) (Fig. 5), one of the active ingredients in Freund's complete adjuvant, a highly potent but toxic formulation consisting of killed mycobacteria in mineral oil. MDP contains just a single sugar group and two amino acids, making it one of nature's smallest bioactive structures. One of these compounds, a fatty-acid-substituted MDP called "Murabutide," is now being tried along with tetanus toxoid in human clinical trials. And MDP seems to work better when encapsulated in liposomes.

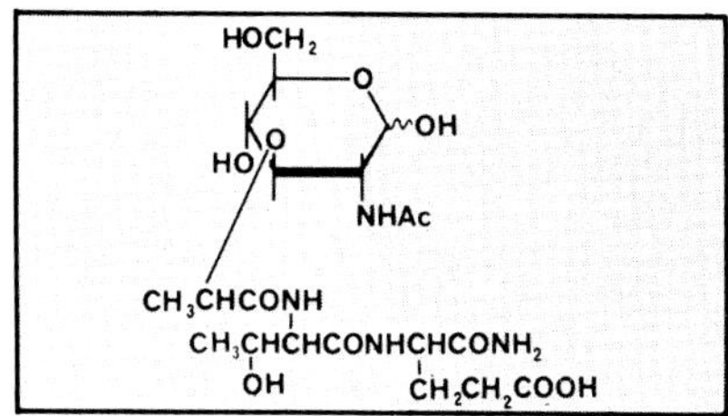

Figure 5. Structure of N-acetylmuramyl-L-threonyl-D-isoglutamine, the threonyl analog of muramyl dipeptide. Copyright *Bio/Technology*.

MDP-derivatives have shown effectiveness in animal vaccine trials against feline leukemia, simian AIDS, influenza, hepatitis B, Epstein-Barr and herpes simplex viruses.

Another Approach to Bacterial Adjuvants

Other developers believe, however, that detoxification may yield sufficiently non-toxic substances but it is also bound to decrease adjuvant potency. They decided to search for organisms that already have adjuvant properties without deleterious side effects. Some researchers, for example, are working on purifying a preparation derived from bacteria of the genus *Amycolata*[41] for use against hepatitis and influenza.

Other researchers collect aggregated ribosomes from a basically non-toxic Gram-positive bacterial strain,[42] bodies which elicit a strong immune response and then break up quickly within the body.

Don't Forget Plants

Bacteria are not the only natural source of adjuvants — certain plant extracts can also boost vaccine activity. Best studied is a saponin extract called "Quil A" that is derived from the bark of the South American tree *Quillaja saponaria*. Several groups are working with these semi-purified glycosides. One U.S. commercial group says that, fully purified and characterized, the extract proves to contain some 17 major components,[43] many of which have extremely high adjuvant activity while others are toxic.

Of these, perhaps the most promising is a complex molecule that consists of a polysaccharide plus a triterpenoid and fatty acid group. The molecule is water-soluble rather than an oil emulsion; it can be used in small, microgram quantities; it does not seem to generate an autoimmunological response; and it has been effective at eliciting neutralizing antibodies in cats without producing side effects. The compound has been demonstrated to be safe and effective when used along with recombinant antigens in animal trials of a feline leukemia vaccine.

Harnessing the Body's *Own* Adjuvants

Adjuvants work by tweaking the body's immune system, so another promising approach is to administer recombinant biological response modifiers along with vaccine antigens. Candidates include interleukin-2[44] (which enhances the differentiation and proliferation of activated T cells and seems to play a role in B-cell differentiation) and, perhaps most important, interleukin-1[45] (which stimulates antigen presentation to T cells, encouraging immune response). In animals, IL-1 has stimulated production of antibodies to soluble and membrane-associated antigens, and also to recombinant proteins, a more direct immune stimulation than bacterial compounds afford, some say.

Still another potentially important immune stimulator is a fraction from human leukocytes,[46] Imreg-1.

Endless Possibilities

Although the goal of many companies is eventually to synthesize their naturally derived adjuvants, a wide variety of *already* synthetic compounds also have immunostimulatory effects: some of these chemicals include surfactants,[47] polynucleotides and carbohydrates.[48]

Add to this wide array of adjuvant choices the possibility of *combining* these products for additive or even synergistic effects and the permutations are staggering. In addition, the various colony-stimulating factors could prove "adjuvants to adjuvants" via their general ability to stimulate the human immune system.

Adjuvant compounds are not just adjuncts to vaccines. Some may be administered without any antigen at all, strictly for their therapeutic, immunostimulatory properties. Others are being applied to animals along with sex hormones to elicit an antigenic response and thereby render "immunological sterilization."

There are other possibilities as well. It may be necessary, as some executives have pointed out, to re-think the definition of a vaccine. Conceptually, it is a therapeutic but (in most cases) it is solely a preventive measure. Vaccines are not usually considered for post-occurrence therapy. With the ability to arouse and target the body's own immune defenses, it may become practical to develop vaccines against even non-infectious diseases already manifested.

NUCLEIC ACID PROBES[49]

Nucleic acid probes are commonplace in today's research labs — even taken for granted. Nonetheless, they have played an instrumental role in much of the molecular biological research that has occurred in the three frantic decades following the revelation of DNA's structure. Indeed, scientists have employed labeled, single-stranded DNA to uncover virtually all of what is now known about how, when and where organisms translate genetic sequences into proteins. Probes have been (and undoubtedly will continue to be) integral tools in the advancement of both basic science and commercial biotechnology from the original cloning of the gene for human insulin to the proposed effort completely to map and sequence the human genome.

The affinity of one strand of DNA for its complementary sequence is, in fact, one of the strongest and most exquisitely specific interactions found in nature. Ambitious scientist/entrepreneurs have long dreamed of harnessing this specificity to detect and diagnose infectious diseases, genetic disorders and cancer. As yet, however, the clinical laboratory has adopted only a handful of probe-based tests; immunological and culture-based screening and diagnostic methods continue to dominate in these laboratories.

For the most part, specific shortcomings of DNA probes reflect the difficulties associated with adapting basic research techniques to the clinical laboratory. For example, current nucleic acid-based tests are difficult to automate and tend to be relatively complicated to run. The assays frequently require tedious sample preparation, numerous wash steps and long incubation times. Under typical research lab configurations, they lack the sensitivity required for some clinical diagnostic applications. Finally, many tests employ expensive, inconvenient and potentially dangerous radioisotopes.

When all these hurdles are overcome, DNA probes will likely play a major role in future diagnostics. The availability of nucleic acid hybridization-based systems will create unique niches, such as in testing for genetic disorders, that they alone are qualified to fill. In other markets, nucleic acid probes and immunoassays will compete relatively evenly. This is already true, for example, in *Salmonella* diagnostics, where the food processing industry can choose between probe- and antibody-based tests.

In perhaps the most interesting case, the two types of assays can provide *complementary* information. A notable example occurs in AIDS testing, where an ELISA (enzyme-linked immunosorbent assay) can provide data on a patient's immune state, while a nucleic acid probe that binds to human immunodeficiency virus (HIV) DNA can specifically determine whether and to what extent the viral genome is present. Similarly, immunoassays are quite effective in screening blood or detecting exposure to hepatitis B virus (HBV). But only a DNA probe-based test can quantify the *amount* of infectious HBV present or accurately monitor the course of an HBV infection.

The Amplification Issue

Although DNA probes have the advantage of directly recognizing genetic material — as opposed to antibody-based tests which detect gene products — in certain instances they are nonetheless less powerful than immunoassays. By detecting a protein coded for by a portion of the probe assay's target sequence, immunoassays benefit from what amounts to two levels of *in vivo* analyte amplification: (1) transcription of the target DNA to yield many molecules of messenger RNA; and (2) translation of the messengers to yield many copies of the particular protein. The challenge, then, is to develop probe assays that are at least as sensitive as immunoassays.

The majority of today's commercially available nucleic acid probes consist of single DNA sequences complementary to a target sequence, just like the probes first developed and used in research laboratories. In response to demands of the marketplace, however, the original radioactive labels are now giving way to non-radioactive detection schemes. Because these labeling techniques tend to reduce probe sensitivity, a great deal of creative thought has been directed toward the selection of optimum target sequences. Some companies[50] have developed probes for the ribosomal RNA (rRNA) of specific bacteria. Because rRNA is present at much a higher copy number than the genomic DNA from which it was transcribed, the target sequence is effectively amplified. The rRNA strategy does not apply, however, when analyzing other targets, such as viral genes, genetic disease markers or oncogenes, that generally occur in just a single copy per haploid genome or virus particle.

An elegant alternative concept has come to dominate thinking about probes. Polymerase chain reaction, or PCR[51] (see Chapter 11), amplifies target DNA *in vitro* using a thermostable polymerase to generate hundreds of thousands of copies (or more) of a target DNA sequence which can then be detected by standard methods. Since its introduction in 1985, PCR has drawn increasing attention from clinical laboratories and the technique seems destined to find important application where very large amplifications are needed. PCR may, however, multiply some background DNA along with the target; the enzyme used may even introduce new errors. Further, because PCR *does* identify such small amounts of target DNA, the clinician must weigh the diagnostic relevance of tiny quantities of pathogens likely to be present even in healthy individuals.

An alternative means of increasing a probe assay's sensitivity is to amplify the signal-generating capacity of the system. This can be accomplished either by concentrating more label at the site of the target molecule or designing each label to produce a stronger signal (e.g. by attaching multiple enzyme molecules to each DNA probe[52] or using multiple probes targeted for different portions of the target DNA.)[35] Some probe developers have combined these approaches — attaching multiple enzyme reporter molecules to multiple probes[54] or developing multiple secondary probes, each of which carries one or more enzyme molecules, that hybridize to multiple target-specific primary probes[55].

A more recent approach[56] uses bacteriophage Q-β RNA polymerase (replicase) exponentially to amplify *probe* sequences rather than *target* sequences as in the polymerase chain reaction.

RNA synthesis by the replicase is autocatalytic: highly specific single-stranded RNAs serve as templates for synthesizing complementary single-stranded products. When product-strand synthesis is complete, both strands can therefore serve as templates in the next round of synthesis. So, as long as there is an excess of replicase, the number of RNA strands increases exponentially. As little as one molecule of template can initiate replication.

HUMAN GENE THERAPY[57]

Today, "human gene therapy" means somatic cell therapy: replacing defective genes in individuals already born with non-functioning physiological systems. For the most part, researchers have tabled the wider, more troubling issue of introducing heritable traits. Such are the body's defenses against foreign genes, defenses evolved to protect against viruses, that, for now at least, researchers are having a difficult time getting sufficient expression even in somatic cells to make the intervention medically useful.

Early target systems included Lesch-Nyhan syndrome, an X-linked hypoxanthine guanine phosphoribosyltransferase (HPRT) deficiency that produces gouty arthritis and cerebral palsy in 200 newborn Americans each year (its victims also suffer a compulsion to mutilate themselves and often bite off their own lips, tongues and fingers); adenosine deaminase deficiency (40–50 newborns/year), which disables the victim's immune system and produces severe combined immune deficiency (SCID); purine nucleoside phosphorylase deficiency (about 10 recorded cases), which also causes an immune deficiency; arginosuccinate synthetase deficiency (53 cases); and ornithine carbamoyl transferase deficiency (110 cases).

At this writing (1989), no true gene therapy experiments have taken place in humans, though a team headed by Steven Rosenberg and W. French Anderson has begun experiments using the techniques of gene therapy to label immune cells. These cells will be used to evaluate manipulations of the human immune system that might help it fight cancer more effectively.

Despite the diversity of target diseases, all researchers are concentrating on a single tissue: the bone marrow. Techniques for bone-marrow transplant are established and are notably successful where a suitable donor exists (Fig. 6). Bone-marrow and skin are the only normal human tissues that may be routinely cultured outside the body. This external manipulation is vital in the early stages of gene therapy: because of concerns about safety, and because transformation is so tricky, researchers will not expose subjects directly to the viral vectors used to transfer genes into human cells.

To be successful, gene-therapy must pass five technical hurdles: a high-titer vector; highly efficient infection of target

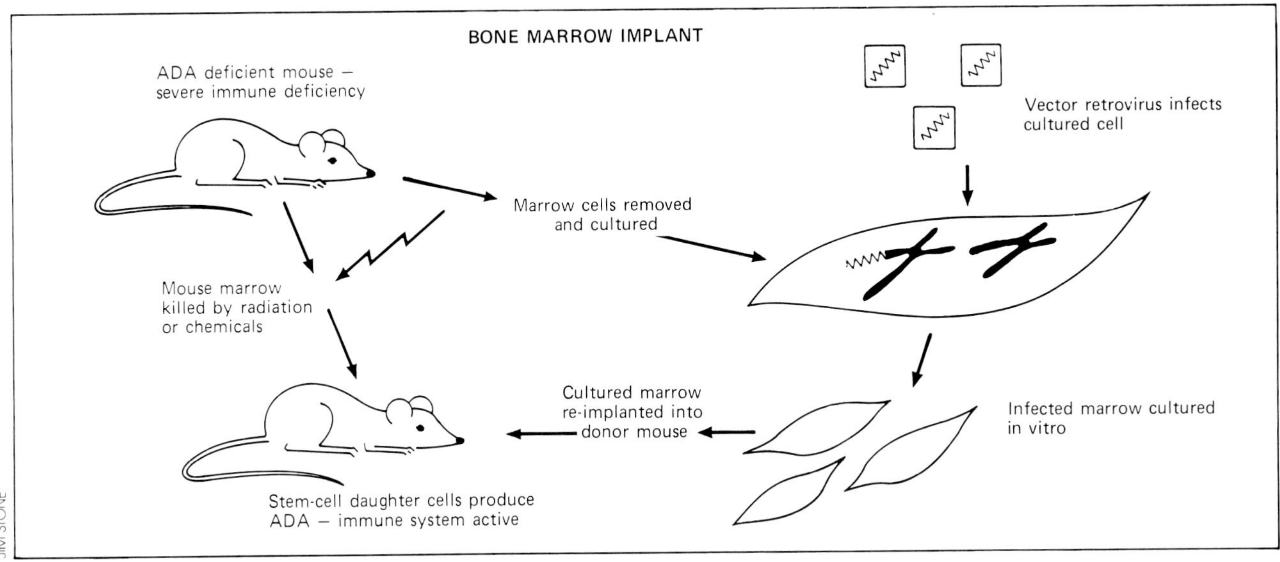
BONE MARROW IMPLANT
ADA deficient mouse – severe immune deficiency
Vector retrovirus infects cultured cell
Marrow cells removed and cultured
Mouse marrow killed by radiation or chemicals
Cultured marrow re-implanted into donor mouse
Infected marrow cultured in vitro
Stem-cell daughter cells produce ADA – immune system active
JIM STONE

Figure 6. Diagram of bone marrow transplantation in mice. Copyright *Bio/Technology*.

cells; stable integration into the target cell's genome; adequate expression of the desired protein; and safety, to the patient and others.

The retroviral vector is the basic tool of the gene-therapist's trade (Fig. 7). The vector, used to move new genetic material into the host cell, is usually one of two closely related mouse viruses: Moloney murine leukemia virus (MoMLV) or Moloney murine sarcoma virus. One of the early objectives of gene therapy research was to make these vectors as innocuous as possible.

The retrovirus itself consists of a chain of RNA: a cap (R) at the 5′ end, followed by an introductory sequence (U5), a packaging sequence (psi), genes coding for retroviral proteins, a downstream sequence (U3) and a repeated capping sequence (r). The retroviral RNA must contain a copy of the psi sequence if it is to be packaged in the viral capsid. There are three genes for structural proteins: gag (group-specific antigens) coding for the retroviral core; pol (DNA polymerase) coding for reverse transcriptase, the enzyme which constructs a DNA copy of the virus's native RNA; and env, coding for the viral envelope or capsid which buds off from the wall of an infected cell.

The env gene is the key to the vector's specificity. Wild-type MoMLV env genes produce a capsid the binds only to mouse cells. When the vector system is applied to humans or other primates, the envelope's receptor binding regions will have to be replaced either by structures that bind specifically to cells of the new target species or by wide host-range (amphotrophic) binding regions. Finally, the 3′ end of the retrovirus carries signals that mark the end of transcription. The U3 region includes enhancer and promoter sequences.

Domesticating the virus takes a lot of work. First, the researcher needs a proviral copy of the retrovirus, a strand of DNA copied from the virus's RNA. This provirus is then closed into a convenient plasmid for further manipulation. When the retrovirus is copied into proviral form, elements of the U5, U3 and R sequences are shuffled about, switching end-for-end to form the characteristic proviral long terminal repeat (LTR). This puts the U3 enhancers and promoters upstream of the structural genes.

Work now proceeds in two directions: first, a helper virus or a packaging cell line is developed, deleting the psi packaging site from the provirus. This altered provirus, in command of the cell's machinery, produces core proteins, reverse transcriptase and capsids but it cannot pack viral RNA into the capsids to produce viable virus.

The vector itself is another matter: the genes for all of the virus's structural proteins are excised, leaving only the controlling LTR and packaging psi sequences; this produces, in effect, a virus with no viral genes. The new genes of interest are then inserted. These often include a selectable marker (such as the gene for dihydrofolate reductase [DHFR] or hypoxanthine phosphoribosyltransferase [HPRT]), followed by the gene for some desired product such as adenosine deaminase [ADA], purine nucleoside phosphorylase [PNP], human growth hormone [hGH] or β-globin). The modified gene may also carry a promoter (the metallothionein promoter, for example) just upstream of the gene for the target product. In theory, these promoters could provide tissue-specific expression of the target gene. The alternative is to let the viral enhancer sequences take charge of the whole process.

In the final step of the vector-production process, the investigator inserts the "psi-plus" vector provirus (which cannot produce any natural viral proteins) into the packaging

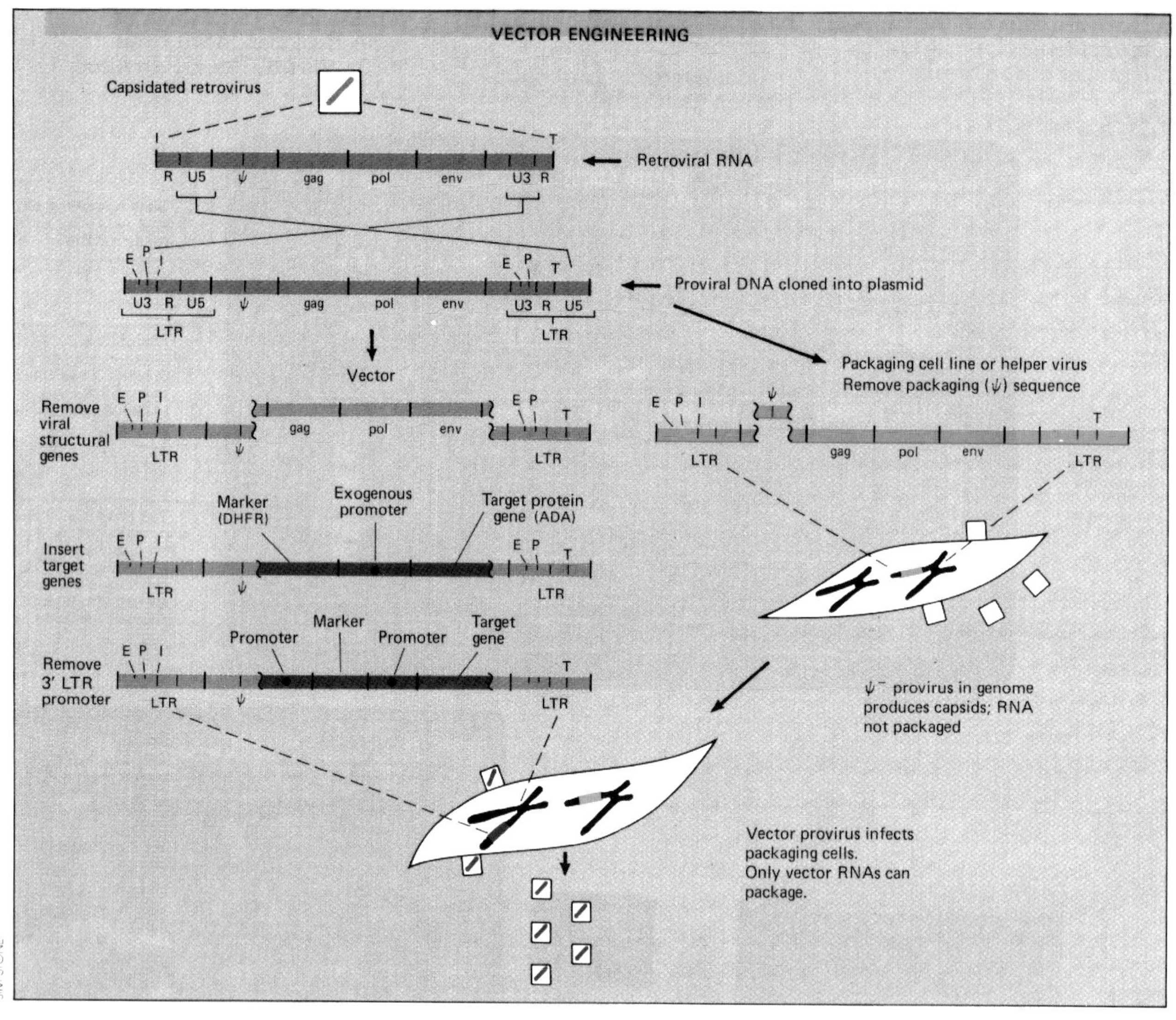

Figure 7. Constructing a gene-therapy vector from a retrovirus (such as Moloney murine leukemia virus). LTR = long terminal repeat; E = enhancer in U3 portion of LTR; P = promoter in U3 portion of LTR; I = initiation site for viral RNA synthesis; [psi] = packaging sequence; T = termination site for viral RNA synthesis; *gag* = viral core protein gene; *pol* = reverse transcriptase gene; *env* = capsid protein gene. Copyright *Bio/Technology*.

cell line. The vector integrates into the cell's DNA and starts producing RNA: this is the RNA that is packaged into the waiting capsids and released into the supernatant.

The gene therapist recovers these viruses (which totally lack the gag, pol, and env genes needed for further replication) and uses them to infect cells taken from the patient. The highly modified retrovirus infects the new host cell, integrates into the chromasomes and begins transcribing and translating the new genes — producing ADA, PNP, HPRT, hGH, or what have you.

So far, researchers cannot guide the provirus to integrate at a particular site — ideally, over the locus of the defective gene. There is a small probability that the virus will disrupt a vital gene by inserting itself into the middle of it. These insertional mutations will most likely die off. And there is an even smaller probability that the provirus's 3′ LTR (which contains copies of the virus's enhancer and promoter sequences) will activate harmful genes. There is a solution: delete enhancer and promoter sequences from the provirus's 3′ LTR. Since the retrovirus switches its LTRs end-for-end during replication, this flaw soon spreads to the 5′ end as well. By the time the vector has integrated into the target cell's genome, both the upstream and downstream LTRs are completely crippled, leaving almost none of the original viral sequences active. It is, researchers say, theoretically impossible for such a virus to spread (though some evidence suggests that subsequent infection with a healthy wild-type retrovirus can cause the cell to package some of the engineered viral material).

With the virus's natural promoters deactivated, however, the researcher *must* add promoters scrounged from other sources. There are other reasons for turning off the vector's natural promoter regions: left unmolested, the viral regulatory units tend to make the cells "read off" the viral transcript as a single unit, the protein equivalent of a run-on sentence.

A vector, however, is just a means to an end: appropriate expression of the inserted gene. And expression levels do remain a problem. Workers in this area repeatedly report high levels of ADA and HPRT in tissue culture but fail to obtain similar levels in transgenic animals. A variety of approaches have been tried:

- using very large numbers of vectors;
- stimulating the subject's marrow so that many more stem cells are in their active phase (the only phase in which they can be infected by a retrovirus); and
- engineering the viral vector to link the target gene to selectable marker (a dihydrofolate reductase gene makes the recipient cell resistant to the anti-cancer drug methotrexate, for example), giving transformed cells an advantage in the body.

Ultimately, retroviral vectors may be used therapeutically or investigatively. Indeed, the first "human gene therapy" protocol approved by the U.S. National Institutes of Health Recombinant DNA Advisory Committee used engineered genes to tag immune cells so they could be tracked to evaluate their roles in fighting cancerous tumors.

ADA deficiency will probably be the first condition to yield to gene therapy. Because of the way the blood-brain barrier insulates the brain from most of the body's biochemical changes, investigations of conditions like the HPRT deficiency that causes Lesch-Nyhan syndrome may be most useful in telling us how the immune system works and how engineered tissues react in the body.

Down the road, perhaps, diseases like phenylketonuria and familial hypercholesterolemia might become candidates for genetic intervention. Still later, when we learn more about constructing vectors specific for particular tissue, physicians might have access to healing viruses — viral cultures that could be injected directly into the patient to home in on an ailing pancreas or heart.

DRUG DELIVERY[58]

The vast majority of new-generation therapeutic drugs are peptides or proteins, molecules that the body will readily break down unless they are protected in some way. Thus new therapeutic technologies require new delivery technologies designed to deliver these powerful but delicate molecules to their sites of action and control their release to maximize their therapeutic benefit.

The 1950s saw the first boom in delivery technologies. Encapsulation made oral administration possible for many drugs. In the 1970s, transdermal patches appeared, allowing timed absorption of drugs through the skin. A third explosion in delivery technology followed, from minute infusion pumps, liposomes and nasal sprays to monoclonal antibodies and bioerodable polymers.

Liposomes

Because liposomes are readily absorbed by lipoprotein-coated cells, researchers have long striven to adapt them as drug delivery vehicles (though it can be difficult to direct these minuscule capsules to the target site). Liposomes consist of two layers of highly polar phospholipids, either natural or synthetic in origin. A coating of phospholipids on an aqueous droplet (containing a water-soluble drug, for example) quickly orient themselves with their hydrophilic portions toward the water and their hydrophobic portions "tucked in" to form a double membrane.

Liposomes are preferentially absorbed by the reticuloendothelial system. Because the droplets are too large to pass through capillary walls, injected liposomes accumulate in the liver and spleen where they can persist for days or weeks. They also accumulate at sites of inflammation.

Various workers have proposed using liposomes to deliver drugs via oral inhalation (for bronchodilators, for example), ocular droplets (for dry eye and glaucoma), injection (for metastatic carcinomas and systemic fungal infections) and topical administration (minoxidil for male pattern baldness).

Nasal Sprays and Transmembrane Carriers

A drug can carry a carrier molecule as a sort of passport, helping it penetrate some of the body's key barrier membranes such as the mucus membranes of the nasal passages. This latter is particularly attractive for delivering smaller peptide drugs (especially such hormones as insulin), far outstripping self-injection in convenience and, perhaps, safety.

Bioerodable Polymers

One approach to delivering drugs on target is to encase them in a polymer matrix that dissolves slowly in the body's aqueous environment. The precise kinetics of the dissolution are important. Water attacked many early candidate polymers throughout their volumes. This altered their permeability, causing them to "dump" their charge of protein rather than releasing it at a constant, controlled rate.

One solution was to develop polymers of highly hydrophilic molecules, such as anhydrides. Water binds tightly only to the exposed surfaces, lifting the material off in a monomolecular layer. This maintains the shape of the delivery matrix and delivers the embedded drug at a constant rate with zero-order kinetics. Polyanhydride matrices have been coupled with anticancer drugs such as BCNU, also known as "carmustine," used to treat brain tumors. Because the drug may be released directly into the target site, therapists may subject the tumor to much higher drug concentrations than the subject could tolerate through systemic introduction. Extended, controlled release also allows the physician to contemplate implanting the drug through operations too complex for therapeutics that must be delivered repeatedly.

Osmotics

The osmotic pump is another application of polymer technology to delivering peptide drugs. It is essentially a tablet coated with a permeable (but insoluble) polymer membrane. Water diffuses through the polymer, dissolving the drug at a controlled rate from the tablet's surface. The dissolved protein (too large to diffuse through the membrane) is then expelled under osmotic pressure through a minute, laser-drilled hole. Designers can control the delivery rate by varying the size of the laser hole and the thickness and composition of the membrane.

The two-chambered osmotic pump is a refinement. This consists of two compartments: one, totally enclosed in a permeable membrane, contains an osmotic agent. The other, bonded side-by-side with the first, contains the drug. As the osmotic compartment swells in an aqueous environment, it presses against the wall it shares with the drug-containing compartment. This pressure forces dissolved drug out through another laser-bored channel.

PHARMACEUTICAL IMPLICATIONS OF STRUCTURE

Protein Structure[59]

Our decade-old ability to isolate genes and express them in other species raises two dramatic possibilities: in principle, we can produce any rare protein in quantity in order to study its structure and function or for possible pharmaceutical use. And we can modify and ultimately design proteins to perform novel functions. But a paradox lurks in this potential. The very factors inherent in heterologous gene expression present significant obstacles to producing heterologous proteins: our fundamental ignorance of how proteins fold impedes efforts at design.

The Special Characteristics of Recombinant Proteins

Introducing a working mammalian gene into a heterologous host such as a bacterium alters several aspects of the complex protein biosynthetic apparatus. The codons used in the original gene may not be optimal for the new host or additional codons may be required for the gene to function in its new environment. The gene is likely to be overexpressed, so special genetic signals controlling transcription and translation may be present. The new host may inaccurately perform vital co- or post-translational modifications. The local environment in which the protein folds may not be appropriate.

Each has structural consequences, which in turn may affect the protein's function (Fig. 8), resulting in inactive protein, altered or unexpected activity or increased difficulties in purification. But remember that recombinant, and indeed "natural," protein activity is empirically defined according to the results of a *particular* assay or analytical technique. Sadly, these results may not always mean what they seem. It may be far from simple to determine if an observed structural difference (like altered glycosylation) actually affects the protein's function. γ-Interferon is naturally glycosylated but the recombinant product produced in bacteria is undecorated, without any apparent change in activity. Still, no-one really knows whether there are unsuspected effects like altered serum half-life or a loss of a specific receptor-mediated activity.

It is not even always straightforward to equate a well-defined altered structure with an observed functional difference. Human growth hormone can be produced in bacteria as both a 191-amino-acid "natural" protein and a 192-amino-acid variant with an additional methionine. Whether the natural product is less immunogenic than the methionyl derivative has been a question of intense dispute between manufacturers with substantial stakes in different forms of the molecule[60].

Finally, the very meaning of "authentic" as it applies to a recombinant-produced protein can be elusive. If the protein is rare enough, the only material available in sufficient quantity for careful analytical determinations may be recombinant-derived. The disulfide bridging and secondary structure of α-interferon, for example, are known only for the bacterial produced protein. From this, the native structure is inferred and, indeed, probably inferred correctly.

Some Structural Consequences

Although many researchers still use *Escherichia coli* as a host for their cloned genes, they are far from satisfied with the favorite organism of classical molecular genetics. Bacteria may be easy and inexpensive to work with, and offer considerable advantages because of the range of genetic manipulations to which they are amenable, but they can present

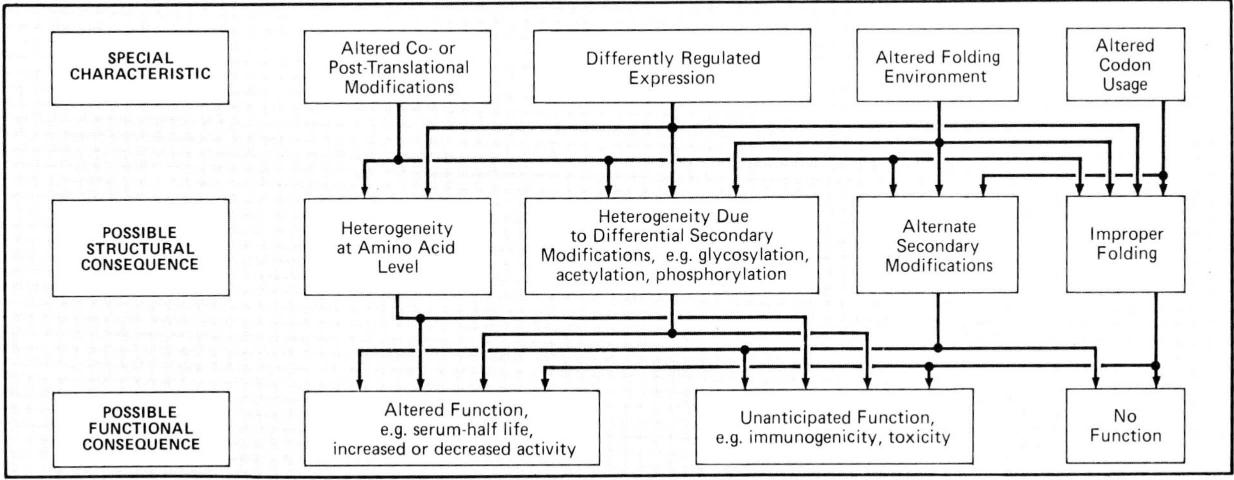

Figure 8. The structural and functional consequences of heterologous gene expression. Copyright *Bio/Technology*.

significant problems in modifying, overexpressing and folding foreign proteins.

Even a partial list of the reactions *E. coli* cannot carry out is formidable: it is unable to achieve N- or O-linked glycosylations, phosphorylations, acetylations or palmitations; it cannot form γ-glutamates, proteolytically process proteins or even completely remove initiating methionines. Moreover, because of its reducing internal environment, proteins that require intramolecular disulfide bridges cannot properly fold. For example, the inability to enzymatically process a protein and allow it to form correct disulfide linkages keep the bacterial production of insulin (which needs to be synthesized as separate chains that are disulfide bonded *in vitro*) much less efficient than it might be.

Yeast is the favored alternative host for the expression of some human proteins. It can translationally modify proteins and has been used to produce correctly N-terminal acetylated superoxide dismutase, N-glycosylated plasminogen activator and correctly processed HIV reverse transcriptase. Yeast also allows complex assembly processes to occur as shown by the formation of fully immunogenic hepatitis B surface antigen particles.

Yeast, however, is not without its drawbacks. The fidelity of the glycosylation patterns may not be high, an important consideration for proteins of pharmacological interest like antibodies, clotting factors, hormones and lymphokines. Further, the range of regulatable expression constructions is still quite limited (Table 7).

Although it might seem that mammalian cells serve to produce the most structurally accurate human proteins, this cannot be taken for granted. The ability to perform a particular post-transcriptional modification does not guarantee a faithful replica of the natural molecule. Moreover, for rare proteins, heterogeneity in the recombinant population would be very difficult to assess and various co-factor dependent modifications (like the vitamin K-dependent γ-carboxylation required for fully active clotting factor IX) have been notoriously difficult to achieve. Although reasonable yields of partially active molecules have been reported, only poor (1.5%) yields of fully active species have thus far been obtained.

The amplification of cloned genes in the foreign host generates other kinds of protein heterogeneity. Multiple copies can arise during or after transformation and alterations in these copies can lead to minor subsets of the desired protein.

Differential transcription of cloned genes may introduce still other structural inhomogeneities. If transcripts terminate or initiate at different points, heterogeneity at the termini can result. Transcripts terminated before the translational stop codon will differ from full-length transcripts at their carboxy-termini. And even transcripts containing the full-length coding sequence could produce different proteins due to unanticipated secondary RNA structures that affect translational fidelity. IN eucaryotic expression systems, differential initiation or termination might generate unwanted splice-junctions. Finally, overexpression of a protein past its solubility can lead to the formation of aggregates that need to be denatured and refolded *in vitro*.

As though structural differences due to modification, processing and transcription effects of the host were not enough, the very codon bias reflected in a heterologously expressed gene can itself alter the protein in a variety of ways. Codon bias may arise as part of normal genetic control mechanisms. The most efficiently translated genes frequently rely on codons corresponding to abundant tRNA species. The transplanted gene may therefore be either more or less well-translated depending on the various amounts of charged tRNAs in the new host. Using site-directed mutagenesis to change synonymous codons to those presumably favored by the new host can also have unpredictable results.

Take β-interferon, for example. A cDNA clone was synthesized that contained a theoretically optimized set of codons for translation in *E. coli* but the engineered gene was barely

A comparison of the biosynthetic capabilities of various expression systems.

Native and/or Desired Property	Ability of organism to mimic natural situation				
	E. coli	Yeast	Aspergillus	Insect	Mammalian Cell Culture
Glycosylation	No	Yes(a)	Yes(a)	Yes(a)	Yes(b)
Accurate Secretion	Yes/No	Yes	Yes	Yes	Yes
Amidation	No	No	Probably Not	?	?
Folding	Yes/No	Yes/No	Yes/No	Yes	Yes
Myristylation	Probably Not	Yes(b)	?	?	?
Acetylation	Yes	Yes	Probably	Probably	Yes
Phosphorylation	No	Yes(b)	?	Yes	Yes
Particle Assembly	No	Yes	?	Yes	Yes
Non-immunogenic	No	Yes/No	?	?	?
Homogenous with regard to:					
a) Methionine removal	Yes/No	Yes/No	?	?	Yes(c)
b) Proteolysis	?	Yes/No	?	?	?
c) Internal initiation and misincorporation	No	Probably Yes	Probably Yes	Probably Yes	Yes

(a) Probably not authentic. (b) Probably approximates authenticity. (c) All secreted.

Table 7.

transcribed, let alone efficiently translated. Unanticipated interferences, perhaps from mRNA secondary structures, may have blocked polymerization.

Intriguingly, clusters of rare codons may influence protein folding by selectively affecting the rate of polypeptide chain elongation. If this occurs even occasionally, it raises serious obstacles to translating such genes in hosts accustomed to different codon preferences.

Immunogenicity and Heterogeneity

Even with all of these real and potential difficulties in obtaining "authentic" proteins from a recombinant system, a fair number of proteins have been produced with impressive specific activities. For those intended as human pharmaceuticals, however, questions regarding their possible, immunogenicity will persist.

A recombinant-derived protein may provoke antibodies in patients in clinical trials for a number of reasons. The actual immunogen may be a heterologous host-derived contaminant that has not been completely removed in the purification. One or more metabolic detours may lead to a population of molecules which is free of any heterologous contaminants but is still heterogeneous with respect to attached carbohydrates, N- or C-termini, or tertiary structures. These variants, even in small amounts, are potentially immunogenic. It is also possible that a discrete structural alteration, a lack of acetylation, perhaps, or an additional methionine, may elicit an antibody response. Conceivably, a protein may be virtually authentic and still be antigenic. If self versus non-self discrimination depends on populations of suppressor cells, even a self-protein in sufficient amounts could overload the suppressing idiotypic network.

As relevant and troublesome as the problem of immunogenicity is for first generation recombinant proteins, it becomes that much more critical for the second generation products which, *by definition*, will differ from the native material.

If a recombinant protein preparation does provoke an immune reaction, it is important to examine the kind of antibodies formed. Are they neutralizing? Are they associated with hypersensitivity? Are they directed at epitopes specific to the recombinant molecule? These questions need to be addressed before the results of a positive ELISA test are used to predict the efficacy of a new protein therapeutic.

Clearly central to the sometimes contentious issue of immunogenicity is that of homogeneity. What criteria will ultimately be used to evaluate the extent to which molecular preparations contain sequence or conformational micro-variants (Figs 9 and 10). Genetic engineers are well aware that it is easier to produce a recombinant protein than to characterize it and it is only now that the most sophisticated anlytical techniques, such as mass spectroscopy, are being applied to determining protein structures.

Solving the Problems

There are three basic approaches to overcoming these difficulties.

Conventional

Focus on the compound. A range of straight-forward approaches, from finding or engineering a suitable new host to chemically treating the product after harvesting.

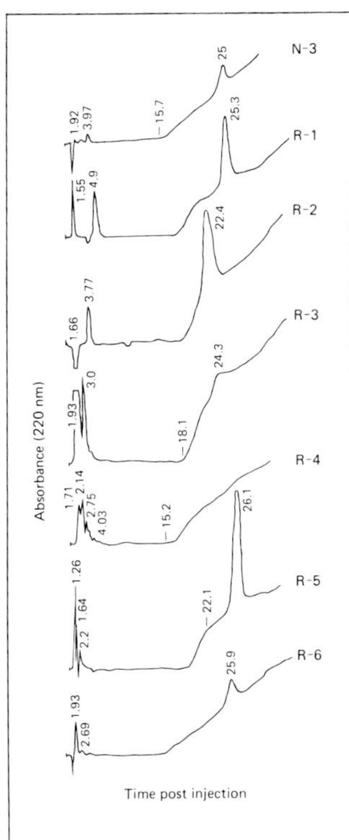

Figure 9. HPLC profiles of six recombinant interleukin-2 preparations from six different companies (R-1 to R-6) and a highly purified lymphoid preparation (N-3). (Redrawn from Thurman *et al.* 1986. *J. Biol. Response Mod.* 5: 99–105.)

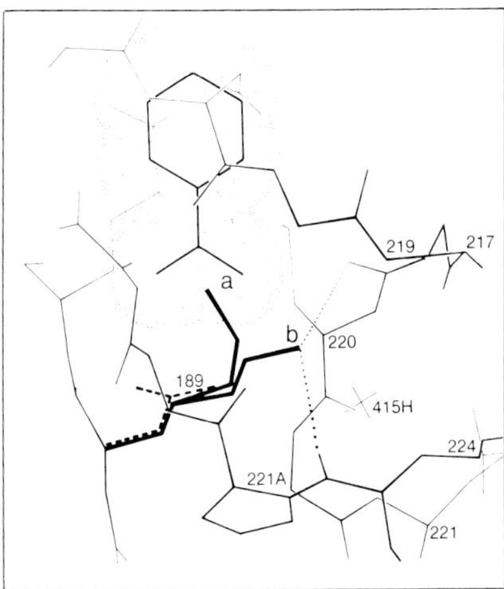

Figure 10. Computer graphics representation of part of the substrate-binding pocket of trypsin. The van der Waals surface of the inhibitor benzamidine is positioned to fill the interior of the specificity pocket. The recognition residue Asp-189 is shown in dashed lines. Two positions, a and b, are drawn for the modeled Lys-189. In position b, the side chain is extended into a hydrophilic environment where it would form two H-bonds (dotted lines) with the carbonyl oxygens of residues 219 and 244. In position a, the side chain extends into the pocket. (Redrawn from Graf *et al.* 1987. *Biochemistry* 26: 2616–2623.)

Natural

Focus on the cell. Begin with a cell that normally manufactures the compound in a natural form and engineer the cell for higher expression. The cell's normal protein "background" may make purification difficult. Some people have responded by deleting "nonessential" genes from the cell. Others have engineered whole animals to produce properly processed proteins in relatively familiar substances, such as milk.

Synthetic

Focus on the shape of the active site. Perhaps the most visionary approach gives recombinant DNA technology pride of place as developmental tool, but may employ other means for producing bioactive molecules themselves. These researchers would harness the machinery of biotechnology to obtain precise structural knowledge of the physiological proteins and their chemical interactions. Based on this information, they would then synthesize, "from the ground up," small organic molecules that mimic or inhibit the protein's natural activities.

Codon Bias, Translation, and Protein Folding

The analysis of disulfide bond formation has provided strong evidence that proteins begin to fold while they are still bound to ribosomes and before their synthesis is complete. In an intriguing "hypothesis" Ian Purvis et al.[61] argue that organisms may use sets of rare codons to influence the rate at which nascent polypeptide chains elongate. Positioning these codons at key junctures in the protein, thus introducing pauses in translation, may allow discrete functional domains to fold more efficiently. They suggest that some proteins may have evolved this mechanism as a means of avoiding secondary folding pathways leading to stable but aberrant conformations.

The pyruvate kinase gene of the yeast *Saccharomyces cerevisiae* provides their example. It has an unusual arrangement of five consecutive rare codons located about four-fifths through the coding region (Fig. 11). The polypeptide chain of pyruvate kinase consists of three distinct domains, the central domain (A) being flanked by two smaller domains (B and C). The string of rare codons is located near the beginning of domain C, where it separates the catalytic site on domain A from the allosteric ligand-binding site of domain C. The suggestion is made that a translational pause close to the A-C junction influences how the polypeptide chain folds to form an active enzyme. If this turns out to be a general mechanism, it has significant implications for the accurate folding of proteins in heterologous sytems since the codon

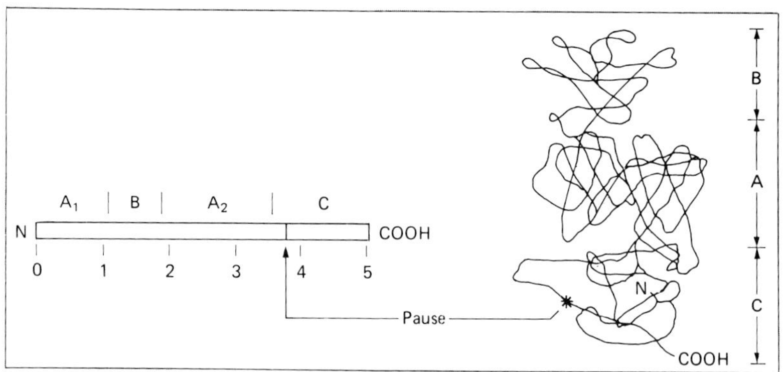

Figure 11. The location of the proposed translational pause within pyruvate kinase, *Left*: The contribution of the primary sequence to the three domains (A, B and C) in the folded polypeptide. *Right*: A representation of the folded polypeptide chain with the approximate position of the translational pause and the three domains. Copyright *Bio/Technology*.

bias of the original organism is unlikely to be reflected in the tRNA pools of the new host.

BEYOND PROTEIN STRUCTURE[62]

As impressive as the feats of genetic engineers have been, their success remains incomplete. Though they can coax organisms into producing useful peptides and proteins, scientists still cannot truly recreate Nature's molecules. Many of these molecules, including almost all protein and peptide drugs, exist in the body not as naked peptides but as conjugates, closely associated with carbohydrate side-chains that affect their ability to bind to other compounds. The structures of these complex glycoproteins are beginning to yield to probing and the first applications are already on the market. But some of the most exciting objectives, such as improving biopharmaceuticals and diagnosing disease, require extremely sophisticated molecular remodeling that is out of reach today.

Sugar residues on glycoproteins play such a pervasive biological role that some workers in the field see them as dwarfing the protein in importance. As one leading researcher[63] puts it: "Proteins are just a platform for presenting different sugars." Sometimes a substitute "platform" does just as well. The carbohydrates responsible for blood group specificity, for example, still evoke blood group antigenicity if attached to a synthetic polymer.

Arrays of oligosaccharides covalently bonded to the outer, interactive molecular surface may cover only a small portion of the protein or may, as in the case of the human immunodeficiency virus (HIV), form a three-dimensional network that covers the protein like a cloud, masking its structure and perhaps helping it escape the immune system's surveillance.

Because of their position and their inherent variability, oligosaccharides (defined as polymers of 2–25 monosaccharide residues) are well suited to their role as information carriers and recognition molecules. Besides determining the specificity of blood groups, they serve as receptors for binding toxins, viruses and hormones. They also alter drug pharmacokinetics and efficacy, control vital events in fertilization and early development and target aging cells for destruction.

The Glycoprotein Machine

For many years, our understanding of carbohydrate structures was limited by the need to use laborious techniques such as gas chromatography of derivitized samples and paper chromatography, often requiring paper as long as 10 meters to get good resolution. Later improvements in methodology — specialized columns for liquid chromatography, high-voltage electrophoresis and chemical synthesis of analogs as well as binding studies with lectins — aided progress but still demanded expert skills.

But the greatest progress in carbohydrate methodology has come during the 1980s. During this decade, it has become apparent that many protein-based therapeutics either do not function or cause immune reactions when not properly glycosylated. Erythropoetin (EPO), for example, loses all biological activity if deglycosylated. Another impetus for carbohydrate research is the establishment of companies and research centers focusing on selling carbohydrate analytical equipment and reagents. Current manufacturers[64] offer laboratory systems that detect oligosaccharides in amounts as low as 10^{-10} M without requiring derivitization. Others[65] are developing instrument for sequencing oligosaccharides of glycoproteins.

The two largest university carbohydrate research groups are the glycobiology unit at Oxford and the Complex Carbohydrates Center at the University of Georgia in Athens. One of the Georgia projects is to establish the CarbBank database. An international effort, CarbBank will eventually contain 5,000 carbohydrate structures, including synthetic structures.

Delving even deeper into carbohydrate structure by using techniques such as the construction of novel glycoconjugates, cloning of enzymes, fast-atom bombardment mass spectrometry, X-ray crystallography, nuclear magnetic resonance (NMR) and supercomputer graphics, scientists have now been able to construct models of some glycoproteins or portions of glycoproteins.

Impact on Biotech Drugs

If carbohydrates affect a drug's potency and determine its target tissue, glycosylation research will obviously have implications for biopharmaceutical development. Industry is already feeling some of this impact since lack of proper glycosylation by microorganisms is forcing it to favor mammalian cells as production vehicles rather than relying on simpler fermentation processes.

On the regulatory and legal horizon, carbohydrate profiles of novel glycoconjugates are becoming part of patent applications and defenses. And the Food and Drug Administration (FDA) is interested in carbohydrate verification as a means of increasing drug efficacy, reducing the chance of immune reactions to non-native carbohydrate and providing more precise quality control and assurance. According to the agency, proteins without the appropriate carbohydrate structure may have altered pharmacokinetics and tissue distribution; they may cause other unknown and possibly adverse effects.

This could present a substantial and unexpected problem for producers of biopharmaceuticals. Proteins are already expensive to produce; the cost of obtaining and verifying the oligosaccharide could become prohibitive.

On the other hand, changing or adding carbohydrates to second- and third-generation biotechnological drugs may unlock their full potential, improving efficacy, reducing dosage, increasing half-lives or solubilities and (perhaps) targeting specific tissues.

Wrestling a Cloud

The structure of carbohydrates is much more complex that of proteins. Sequencing a single carbohydrate is, say researchers, like simultaneously sequencing 40 or 50 proteins. Because carbohydrate structures are a branching series of linked rings, they can combine in many more ways than linear peptide chains can. Thus, three amino acids can combine in only six ways; three carbohydrate monomers can form over 1,000 different trisaccharide structures.

Glycoproteins are linked to a protein backbone through either N- or O-linkages. In mammalian cells N-linkages form when an N-acetylglucosamine residue attaches a carbohydrate chain to the protein backbone via an N-glycosidic linkage to asparagine. O-linked carbohydrates have an O-glycosidic link to serine, threonine, hydroxy-lysine, or hydroxy-proline.

N-linked oligosaccharides, more abundant in nature, have stable core structures consisting of two N-acetyl glucosamines. One is attached to asparagine and the other to a mannose residue from which two more mannoses branch. The three main types of oligosaccharide structures share this core structure but have different sugars extending out from the core. These are 1) "high-mannose," with 4–11 more mannose groups attached to the core; 2) "complex", with galactose and sialic acid residues; and 3) "hybrid", featuring a mix of complex and high-mannose sugars.

Glycosylation is species-, cell- and tissue-specific. Brain and thyroid tissue, for instance, both produce the glycoprotein thymosite-1 but they produce it with very different oligosaccharides despite having identical peptides coded for by a single gene. Mammalian cells produce a wide range of glycosylation, different for each species. For example, rat α_1-acid glycoprotein has complex oligosaccharides with a different degree of branching and fucosylation than human α_1-acid glycoprotein. Yeasts, on the other hand, glycosylate only with N-linked oligomannose-type structures and bacteria do not glycosylate at all.

In bioreactor cultures, still more factors affect glycosylation of the final product. They include the culture medium, level of product expression and the purification protocol. According to Joseph Olechno, senior applications chemist at Dionex, even such subtle differences as whether or not a culture is grown in a roller bottle or a spinner flask can alter glycosylation.

On top of this amazing diversity, Nature adds what glycobiologists call "microheterogeneity" in the form of discrete subsets (glycoforms) of a glycoprotein. These may have different physical and biochemical properties. Where there is only one glycosylation site, the number of glycoforms is simply the number of different oligosaccharide structures at that site. The number of possible glycoforms clearly increases dramatically as either the number of sites on the protein or the heterogeneity at each site increase.

Tissue plasminogen activator (t-PA), for example, with four possible glycosylation sites, exists in over 1,000 different glycoforms. The potential number of glycoforms for the gp120 coat fragment of HIV, with its 24 possible glycosylation sites, is at least several hundred.

The "demographics" of its glycoform population determine the composite activity of a glycosylated compound. According to Rademacher, Parekh, and Dwek,[66] "Any given glycoprotein that consists of different glycoforms will . . . have a composite activity, reflecting a weighted average of the activity and incidence of each glycoform."

Carbohydrates at Work

Oligosaccharides can up-regulate, down-regulate or turn off a compound's activity entirely. For human chorionic gonadotropin (hCG), deglycosylation increases receptor affinity but causes a near-total loss of bioactivity, apparently because deglycosylated hCG cannot activate adenyl cyclase. Deglycosylation of granulocyte macrophage-colony-stimulating factor (GM-CSF) has the opposite effect, giving the cytokine about sixfold-higher specific activity than normal human GM-CSF.

Studies of tissue plasminogen activator (t-PA) show how oligosaccharide composition can affect drug kinetics. The clot buster exists in two forms — Type 1 and Type 2 — differing in the number of attached sugars. In Type 1, oligosaccharides occupy three of four possible glycosylation sites while in Type 2 they occupy two sites. Type 2 t-PA appears to be 30% more active than Type 1. "Naked" t-PA, stripped of its glycosylation, cleaves plasminogen even in the absence of fibrin. Thus, the oligosaccharides attached to t-PA may downregulate the compound's activity so that it becomes active only in the presence of a clot.

Unique carbohydrates, present only at critical times in development, also play major roles in embryonic development. For example, neural cell adhesion molecule (NCAM), a binding protein essential in embryogenesis, expresses a unique polysialic acid that can be up to 200 residues long, ten times longer than the NCAM protein itself. It is specific to NCAM and occurs only during the early stages of development, never in the adult. This large carbohydrate may modulate NCAM's affinity to give looser cell-cell binding while cells are still migrating to the proper sites.

Carbohydrates play another essential developmental role in the kidney. During embryogenesis, cells express a unique glycolipid that marks the site of ureter development. Administering antibodies to these carbohydrates *in utero* totally blocks the development of the ureter.

Glycoproteins in Disease

Many infectious diseases, such as influenza, herpes and urinary tract infections occur only when the bacteria or virus responsible for them binds to the host target tissue which it recognizes by characteristic carbohydrates sequences. In addition to initiating disease states, carbohydrates also *reflect* a range of diseases and conditions. In some cases, the relative proportion of oligosaccharides changes; in others, such as cancer, oligosaccharides are detectable in novel glycoforms. Cancerous

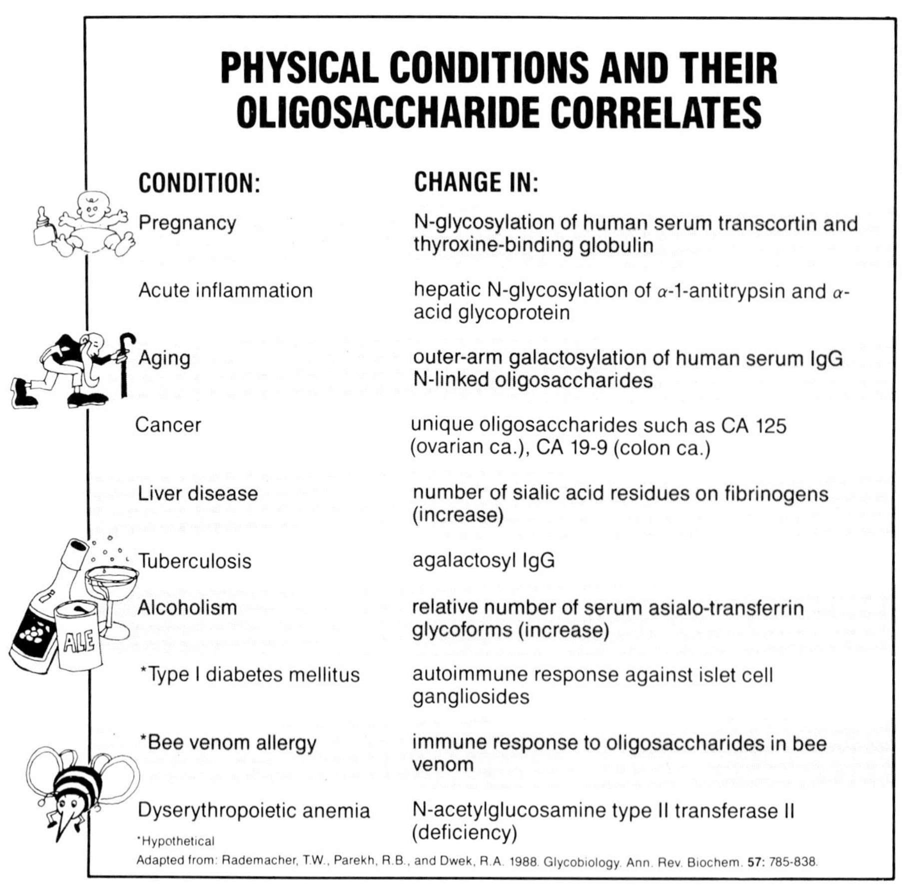

PHYSICAL CONDITIONS AND THEIR OLIGOSACCHARIDE CORRELATES

CONDITION:	CHANGE IN:
Pregnancy	N-glycosylation of human serum transcortin and thyroxine-binding globulin
Acute inflammation	hepatic N-glycosylation of α-1-antitrypsin and α-acid glycoprotein
Aging	outer-arm galactosylation of human serum IgG N-linked oligosaccharides
Cancer	unique oligosaccharides such as CA 125 (ovarian ca.), CA 19-9 (colon ca.)
Liver disease	number of sialic acid residues on fibrinogens (increase)
Tuberculosis	agalactosyl IgG
Alcoholism	relative number of serum asialo-transferrin glycoforms (increase)
*Type I diabetes mellitus	autoimmune response against islet cell gangliosides
*Bee venom allergy	immune response to oligosaccharides in bee venom
Dyserythropoietic anemia	N-acetylglucosamine type II transferase II (deficiency)

*Hypothetical

Adapted from: Rademacher, T.W., Parekh, R.B., and Dwek, R.A. 1988. Glycobiology. Ann. Rev. Biochem. **57:** 785-838.

Table 8.

changes involve abnormally high degrees of branching.

Alterations in oligosaccharides are associated with over 15 different types of conditions (Table 8), ranging from lysosomal enzyme storage diseases such as Gaucher's disease, to pregnancy, to alcoholism (Fig. 12).

One of the more promising near-term applications for oligosaccharide microheterogeneity, therefore, is in screening at-risk populations for incipient disease. Early entries[67] included a radioimmunoassay based on monoclonal antibodies, notably to the CA 125 antigen (produced in ovarian cancer) and the CA 19–9 antigen (associated with colon cancer).

Changes in carbohydrates relate not only to the presence of disease but also to disease status. Incipient disease, disease remission and response to therapy may announce themselves in oligosaccharide profiles.

For example, in rheumatoid arthritis characteristic changes in immuno-γ-globulin (IgG) galactosylation fluctuate with response to treatment and remission. These changes also signal disease onset which may one day help physicians to begin therapy early, when it is most effective.

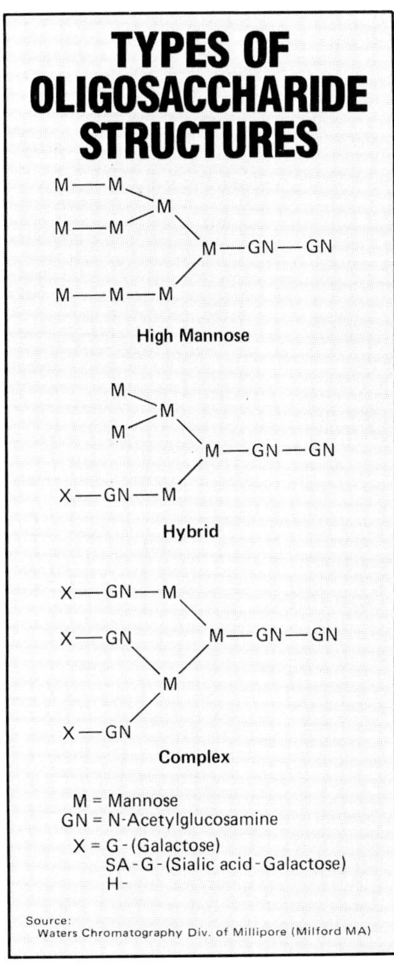

Figure 12. Types of oligosaccharide structure. Copyright *Bio/Technology*.

Another clinical area that may someday benefit from carbohydrate research is AIDS therapeutics. Half of the molecular weight of the HIV coat protein is carbohydrate. Its multitude of potential N-linked attachment sites, as mentioned above, give ample opportunities for variations. Not only do the oligosaccharides change whenever the amino acid sequence of the coat protein changes, they can also mask the epitopes of the polypeptide that neutralizing antibodies attack.

Can Carbohydrates Be Engineered?

Some researchers believe that engineering through choice of cell line will prove the best way to produce correctly glycosylated compounds. Others[68] are remodelling carbohydrate side-chains, using enzymes to remove and replace oligosaccharides to alter glycoprotein activity; for example, transferases and glycosidases are employed to add sialic acid residues and extend drug half-life. This approach has been applied to developing a treatment for Gaucher's disease, a rare genetic enzyme-insufficiency syndrome.

Another synthetic approach involves cloning the genes for transferase enzymes and transfecting cells. The recombinant cells then synthesize carbohydrates they would not normally produce. Recent research succeeded in generating non-typical glycosylation patterns by transfecting Chinese hamster ovary (CHO) cells with a full-length cDNA from rat liver for expression of a sialyltransferase. This group found evidence that the gene was expressed in the CHO cells' Golgi apparatus stack and was able to compete with native enzymes for binding to galactose.

REFERENCES

1. Adapted from *Monoclonal Antibodies into the '90s: The All-Purpose Tool*, by Roland Carllson and Cristina Glad, BioInvent International AB, 223 70 Lund, Sweden; and Carl A.K. Borrebaeck, Department of Biotechnology, University of Lund, P.O. Box 124, 221 00, Lund, Sweden, published in Bio/Technology 7: 567, June 1989.
2. Oudin, J. 1946. *Methode d'analyze imunochemique par precipitation specifique en mileiu gelifie*. C.R. Acad. Sci. **222**: 115–116.

   Schultze, H.E.; Schwick, G. 1959. *Quantitative Immunologische Betimmung von Plasmaproteinen*. Clin. Chim. Acta **4**: 15–25.

   Mancini, G.; Carbonara, A.D.; Heremans, J.F. 1965. *Immunochemical quantitation of antigens by single radial immunodiffusion*. Immunochem. **2**: 235–254.

   Laurell, C.-B. 1966. *Quantitative estimation of proteins by electrophoresis in agarose gel containing antibodies*. Anal. Biochem. **15**: 45–52.
3. Yalow, R.S.: Berson, S.A. 1959. *Assay of plasma insulin in human subjects by immunological methods*. Nature **184**: 1648–1649.

4. Uotila, M.; Ruoslahti, E.; Engvall, E. 1981. *Two-site sandwich enzyme immunoassay with monoclonal antibodies to human alpha-fetoprotein*. J. Immunol. Meth. **42**: 11–15.
5. Koehler, G.; Milstein, C. 1975. *Continuous culture of fused cells secreting antibodies of predefined specificity*. Nature **256**: 495–497.
6. Yang, H.M.; Reisfeld, R.A. 1987. *Doxorubicin conjugated with a monoclonal antibody directed to a human melanoma-associated proteoglycan suppresses the growth of established tumor xenografts in nude mice*. Proc. Nat. Acad. Sci. USA **85**: 1189–1193.
7. Nisonoff, A.; Lamoyi, E. 1981. *Implications of the presence of an internal image of the antigen in antiidiotypic antibodies: Possible application to vaccine production*. Clin. Immunol. Immunopathol. **21**: 397–406.
8. Roitt, I.M.; Male, D.K.; Guarnotta, D; de Carvalho, L.D.; Cooke, A.; Hay, F.C.; Lydyard, P.M.; Thanavala, Y.; Invanyi, J. 1981. *Idiotype networks and their possible exploitation for manipulation of the immune response*. Lancet **1**: 1041–1045.
9. Jerne, N.K. 1974. *Towards a network theory of the immune response*. Ann. Immunol. (Paris) 125C: 373–389.
10. Hollinshead, A.; Stewart, T.H.M.; Takita, H.; Dalbow, M.; Concannon, J. 1987. *Adjuvant specific active lung cancer immunotherapy trials: Tumor associated antigens*. Cancer **60**: 1249–1262.
11. Koprowski, H.; Herlyn, D.; Lubeck, M.; DeFreitas, E.; Sears, H.F. 1984. *Human anti-idiotypic antibodies in cancer patients: Is the modulation of the immune response beneficial for the patient*? Proc. Nat. Acad. Sci. USA **81**: 216–219.

    Herlyn, D.; Lubeck, M.; Sears, H.F.; Koprowski, H. 1985. *Specific detection of anti-idiotypic immune responses in cancer patients treated with murine monoclonal antibody*. J. Immunol. Meth. **85**: 27–38.
12. Jencks, W.P. 1969. *Catalysis in chemistry and enzymology*. McGraw-Hill, New York.
13. Jones, P.T.; Dear, P.H.; Foote, J.; Neuberger, M.S.; Winter, G. 1986. *Replacing the complementarity determining regions in a human antibody with those from a mouse*. Nature **321**: 522–525.
14. Reichman, L.; Clark, M.; Waldman, H.; Winter, G. 1988. *Reshaping human antibodies for therapy*. Nature **332**: 323–327.
15. Cheetham, J. 1988. *Reshaping the antibody combining site by CDR replacement — Tailoring or tinkering to fit*? Protein Engineering **2**: 170–172.
16. Martel, F.; Bazin, R.; Verrette, S.; Lemieux, R. 1988. *Characterization of higher avidity monoclonal antibodies produced by murine B-cell hybridoma variants selected for increased antigen binding of membrane Ig*. J. Immunol. **141**: 1624–1629.
17. Borrebaeck, C.A.K.; Moeller, S.A. 1986. *In vitro immunization: Effect of growth and differentiation factors on antigen-specific B-cell activation and production of monoclonal antibodies to autologous antigens and weak immunogens*. J. Immunol. **136**: 3710–3715.
18. Adapted from *Interleukin Futures* by Kendall A. Smith, M.D., professor of medicine at Dartmouth Medical School, Hanover, NH 03756, published in Bio/Technology **7**: 661–667, July 1989.
19. Bacha, P., Williams, D.P., Waters, C., Williams, J.M., Murphy, J.R., and Strom, T.B. 1988. *Interleukin 2 receptor-targeted cytotoxicity: Interleukin 2 receptor-mediated action of a diphtheria toxin-related interleukin 2 fusion protein*. J. Exp. Med. **167**: 612.
20. Lorberboum-Galski, H., FitzGerald, D., Chaudhary, V., Adhya, S., and Pastan, I. 1988. *Cytotoxic activity of an interleukin 2-Pseudomonas exotoxin chimeric protein produced in Escherichia coli*. Proc. Natl. Acad. Sci. U.S.A. **85**: 1922.
21. Matsui, K., Nakanishi, K., Cohen, D.I., Hada, T., Furuyama, J.-I., Hamaoka, T., and Higashino, K. 1989. *B cell response pathways regulated by IL-5 and IL-2: secretory mu-H chain-mRNA and J chain mRNA expression are separately controlled events*. J. Immunol. **142**: 2918.
22. Adapted from *Lymphokine Receptors as Therapeutics*? by Jennifer Van Brunt, Managing Editor, Bio/Technology **7**: 668–9, July 1989.
23. at Immunex (Seattle, WA).
24. Bio/Technology **4**: 256, Apr. '86.
25. Adapted from *Biotherapy: A New Dimension in Cancer Treatment*, by Catherine A. McCall, Director of Research, Lori Weimer, Research Associate, Susan Baldwin, Research Associate, and Frederick C. Pearson, Vice President Scientific Operations, Cell Technology, Inc., 1668 Valtec Lane, Boulder, CO 80301, published in Bio/Technology **7**: 231, Mar. 1989.
26. Oldham, R.K. 1987. *Biotherapy: general principles*, pp. 1–20 in *Principles of Cancer Biotherapy*. R.K. Oldham (ed.). Raven Press, New York.
27. Busch, W. 1868. *Niederrheinische Gesellschaft fur Natur- und Heilkunde in Bonn*. Aus der Sitzung der Medizinischen Sektion vom 13. November 1867. Berlin. Klin. Wschr. **5**: 137–139.
28. Coley, W.B. 1891. *Contribution to the knowledge of sarcoma*. Ann. Surg. **14**: 199–220.
29. Rosenberg, S.A., Lotze, M.T., Muul, L.M., Leitman, S., Chang, A.E., Ettinghausen, S.E., Matory, Y.L., Skibber, J.M., Shiloni, E., Vetto, J.T., Seipp, C.A., Simpson, C., and Reichert, C.M. 1985. *Observations on the systemic administration of autologous lymphokine activated killer cells and recombinant interleukin-2 to patients with metastatic cancer*. New Engl. J. Med. **313**: 1485–1492.
30. Ronsenberg, S.A., Speiss, P., and La Frenieve, R. 1986. *A new approach to the adoptive immunotherapy of cancer with tumor infiltrating lymphocytes*. Science **233**: 1318–1321.
31. Adapted from *Vaccine Technology: Developmental Strategies*, by Anthony C. Allison, vice president for research, and Noelene E. Byars, staff researcher, Department of Immunology, Syntex Research, 3401 Hillview Avenue, Palo Alto, CA 94304, published in Bio/Technology **5**: 1038, October 1987.
32. Moss, B., Smith, G.L., Gerin, J.L., and Purcell, R.H. 1984. *Live recombinant vaccinia virus protects chimpanzees against hepatitis B*. Nature **311**: 67.
33. Wiley, D.C., Wilson, I.A., and Skehel, J.J. 1981. *Structural identification of the antibody binding sites of Hong Kong influenza haemagglutinin and their involvement in antigenic variation*. Nature **289**: 373.
34. Hogle, J.M., Chow, M., and Filman, D.J. 1985. *Three-dimensional structure of poliovirus at 2.9 resolution*. Science **229**: 1358.
35. Valenzuela, P., Medina, A., Rutter, W.J., Ammerer, A., and Hall, B.D. 1983. *Synthesis and assembly of hepatitis B virus surface antigen particles in yeast*. Nature **291**: 503.
36. Murray, K., Bruce, S.A., Hinnen, A., Wingfield, P., van Erd, P.M., de Reus, A., and Schellekens, H. 1984. *Hepatitis B virus antigens made in microbial cells immunize against viral infection*. EMBO J. **3**: 645.
37. Berman, P.W., Gregory, T., Crase, P., and Lasky, L.A. 1985. *Protection from genital herpes simplex type 2 infection by vaccination with cloned glycoprotein D*. Science **227**: 1490.
38. Adapted from *Adjuvants: A Real Shot in the Arm for Recombinant Vaccines* by Arthur Klausner, Senior Editor, Bio/Technology **7**: 773, July 1988.

39. Pioneered by Ribi ImmunoChem (Hamilton, MT).
40. Preclinical studies indicate that monophosphyoryl lipid A decreases suppressor T-cell activity, rather than amplifying helper T cells. This suggests that the compound might be used against AIDS (where amplifying helper T cells could be dangerous) and in vaccine preparations for young children (who develop, suppressor T cells before helper T cells).
41. Otisville BioPharm (Otisville, NY).
42. Cell Technology Inc. (Boulder, CO).
43. Cambridge BioScience Corp. (Cambridge, MA).
44. Championed by companies like Cetus Corp. (Emeryville, CA) and Smith Kline & French (Philadelphia, PA).
45. The favorite of Immunex (Seattle, WA), a company specializing in lymphokines.
46. Being commercialized by Imreg Inc. (New Orleans, LA).
47. CytRx (Norcross, GA).
48. Alpha-Beta Technology (Worcester, MA).
49. Condensed and adapted from *Amplifying DNA Probe Signals: a Christmas Tree Approach*, by Paul D. Fahrlander, Ph.D., senior scientist, and Arthur Klausner, corporate planning intern, ImClone Systems Inc., 180 Varick St., New York, NY 10014, published in Bio/Technology **6**: 1165, October 1988, with additional material.
50. Gen-Probe (San Diego, CA) and Gene-Trak Systems (Framingham, MA).
51. Cetus Corp., Emeryville, CA.
52. Digene, College Park, MD.
53. Orion Corp., Helsinki, Finland.
54. Chiron Corp., Emeryville, CA.
55. ImClone Systems, New York, NY.
56. P. Lizardi, et al. 1988. *Exponential Amplification of Recombinant-RNA Hybridization Probes*, Bio/Technology **6**: 1197. Oct. '88.
57. Adapted from *Human Gene Therapy*, by Douglas McCormick, Editor, Bio/Technology **3**: 689, Aug. '85.
58. Adapted from *Novel Drug Delivery Systems*, by Jennifer Van Brunt, Managing Editor, Bio/Technology **7**: 127, Jan. '89.
59. Adapted from *Recombinant Proteins: Virtual Authenticity*, by Harvey Bialy, Research Editor, Bio/Technology **5**: 883, Sept. '87.
60. Genentech, South San Francisco, CA, and Eli Lilly, Indianapolis, IN.
61. Purvis et al. 1987. JMB **193**: 413–417.
62. This section is adapted from *The Carbohydrate Frontier*, by Pamella Knight, Associate Editor, Bio/Technology **7**: 35, January 1989.
63. Raymond Dwek, professor of glycobiology, Oxford University, Oxford, U.K., personal communication
64. such as Dionex (Sunnyvale, CA)
65. Oxford Glycosystems (Abingdon, U.K.)
66. Rademacher, T.W., Parekh, R.B., and Dwek, R.A. 1988. *Glycobiology*. Ann. Rev. Biochem. **57**: 785–838.
67. from Biomira (Edmonton, Alta., Canada) and Centocor (Malvern, PA).
68. notably Genzyme, now part of Integrated Genetics, Boston, MA.

Chapter 23

Seeds of Change: Applications of Biotechnology to Agriculture

Allen J. Dines

INTRODUCTION

Agricultural applications of biotechnology will eventually touch the lives of virtually everyone in some way. The agricultural sector, while only a subset of the entire universe of the industries biotechnology will influence, contains a full complement of the opportunities, issues and applications created by the technology.

For thousands of years farmers have sought to overcome the many uncertainties imposed by nature on crop and livestock production. More fundamentally, the search for improved plants and animals that produce more valuable products, that give higher yield and that are resistant to pests and environmental stress has been underway since the outset of agriculture.

The search has been extremely successful. The art and, more recently, the science of selective breeding has evolved into an extremely complex body of knowledge. If we think for a moment of genetic engineering broadly as the manipulation of genetic material for the purpose of attaining useful products, then traditional plant and animal breeding could be considered genetic engineering.

This form of traditional genetic engineering has clearly produced results. Breeders and farmers, through painstaking selection and crossing, have developed crop lines that produce larger yields of grains, vegetables and fruits; they have produced plants that survive in harsh environments; and plants that resist attack by disease and insect pests. Similarly, selective breeding of animals has produced livestock with the ability to withstand unfavorable environmental conditions while yielding substantially more meat, milk or fiber than their undomesticated predecessors.

But genetic engineering as we think of it today is different. The term is relatively new and, as generally used, it is not intended to include traditional plant and animal breeding. It refers to a variety of modern techniques of molecular biology ranging from recombinant DNA technology to cell fusion, somaclonal variation and monoclonal antibody technology. Thus, although selective or traditional breeding might be considered genetic engineering in a literal sense, it is in fact imprecise and crude relative to the techniques now emerging to improve agricultural production.

Given this history of accomplishment of "conventional" genetic engineering, "modern" genetic engineering, for all the dramatic novelty the new molecular biology affords, has some distance to go in generating substantial benefit before it matches the contributions to agriculture already made by its conventional predecessor.

The early applications of the new genetic engineering to agriculture seem at first glance merely to offer an extension of techniques which have already proven to be a vast success.

In this light the new technologies will contribute to further advances, many of which would never be possible using conventional technologies. These advances might generally be characterized as improved products for existing markets. They are not new products for new markets. They offer better solutions to problems that we have been working to solve for many years with conventional technology. For example, chemical pesticides now exist that afford control of most serious pests. Yet substantial improvements in control may be possible with genetically engineered plants that carry their own resistance internally. This would eliminate the adverse environmental effects of chemical pesticides while arguably giving the farmer better control because the threshold of application would not depend on the active participation of the farmer in deciding when to treat the fields.

But this is not the whole story. With the first commercially valuable agricultural products from this technology barely introduced to the marketplace, it would be shortsighted to cast the potential contributions of the technology in so limited a light. In this chapter we will examine the likely contributions of biotechnology to agriculture in the broadest terms possible.

First, we will consider the near term products that will come to the marketplace in the next several years. These products might be characterized as "incremental improvements". They are new and improved solutions to problems faced by farmers and ranchers for many, perhaps thousands, of years.

But biotechnology will also lead to whole new approaches for attaining useful products from agricultural commodities. These applications of biotechnology could be classified as new opportunities rather than new solutions to old problems. These opportunities may not even address what we think of today as current problems. We will therefore, in as credible a manner as is possible at this early stage of the development of the technology, examine the longer range opportunity presented by this dramatically new science to agriculture. Here, by definition, the actual products are still quite vaguely defined. They are only in the earliest phases of development or are perhaps only a concept in the minds of researchers.

These near-term and long-term developments comprise the "content" of agricultural biotechnology. Before we move to consider them, we must first review some underlying fundamentals that set the stage and characterize the environment in which the new applications of this technology will emerge. This is the "context" of biotechnology. We will consider how the technology will apply to crop and animal science, where it will fit in the larger scheme of food and fiber production and how the companies developing the technology will relate to agribusiness. Also to be considered is the way these emerging products and companies relate to the public policy arena.

Taken together the content and the content of agricultural applications of biotechnology comprise a dynamic and exciting arena that will see many changes over the next decades. This chapter will provide a brief overview of how that change may take shape and what the contributing components will be.

CONTEXT OF AGRICULTURAL BIOTECHNOLOGY

This section relates the science and business concepts described in earlier chapters of this book to applications of biotechnology to agriculture. At the research level, agriculture will challenge scientists substantially to further refine the techniques of genetic engineering. Products for agriculture will involve a broad spectrum of applications including genetically altered microbes, plants, and ultimately, animals.

Some agricultural biotechnology applications will include the use of genetic engineering technologies identical to those in use for production of products for human healthcare. These technologies have been discussed in other chapters. Their application to agriculture will include use of bacteria as living factories to produce new therapeutics for use in animal healthcare and new growth enhancement products to improve the efficiency of meat and milk production.

These production technologies, however, are relatively simple in comparison with the technologies required in applications involving the direct use of modified microbes in farm fields, the use of new varieties of plants developed through genetic engineering, and the use of new lines of improved animals in livestock agriculture.

In most cases the organisms developed for use in agriculture will not have the luxury of the optimized growing conditions of a fermenter in a contained production environment. Rather, in the case of crop agriculture, they will complete in farm fields for space and nutrients. And, if they are indeed to be successful in offering a better solution to the farmer's problems than conventional products, they will do so more vigorously than their conventional competitors. These technologies and their role in the agricultural sector are discussed in the first section of this part of the chapter called "The Biotechnologies of Agriculture."

"The Agricultural Sector" is the second part of this section. Agriculture as a component of the economy is immense. The ultimate unit of production is the farm. The farmer is increasingly more than a sole proprietor of a family land holding. More likely, today's farmer is a small or sometimes large businessman who manages assets worth, in some cases, many millions of dollars. The farm sector is thought by many economists to be the closest representation in today's economy to pure competition. This is a sector where many farmers produce largely undifferentiated commodity products for many buyers under a set of uncertain environmental conditions. By virtue of the collective value of production of a nation's farms, the agricultural sector is generally among the top industries in national rankings. Not infrequently, it is the leading industry.

Agribusiness is generally defined as the collection of companies that provides the inputs necessary for farm production. Non-farm inputs include such items as fertilizers, animal healthcare and nutrition products, chemicals, and farm machinery. A major farm origin input that is supplied in large part by a group of specialized agribusiness companies is seed. Included among the principal suppliers to the farm sector are the world's major corporations. The bulk of biotechnology applications to agriculture will reach the farmer through this agribusiness industry. For example, agribusiness will offer products of biotechnology in the form of improved seeds, new products for animal health or new biological pesticides. The companies that comprise this agribusiness sector as well as the agrochemical industry and the animal health products industry are discussed as the third part of this section, called "Companies in Agricultural Biotechnology."

Agribusiness depends substantially on the economic viability of the farmer for the sale of its products. The farmer is in turn subject to world economic conditions, food commodity prices, farm technology, farm management and, perhaps most significantly, government policy issues. In the fourth and final part of this section, "Constraints to Growth," we identify some of the regulatory and public policy issues relevant to agriculture and biotechnology as they contribute to the continually shifting balance of the farm economy.

The Biotechnologies of Agriculture

The agricultural benefits of the new technologies of genetic engineering are widely acknowledged to be enormous.

Scientists will develop products that will increase food production, reduce fertilizer use, and decrease the need for costly, and in some cases environmentally questionable pesticides. Fundamentally the new technologies are likely to be superior to conventional technologies because they are faster, more precise and they will afford greater flexibility in selection of genetic traits.

The task facing the scientist charged with development of new useful products for agriculture is different from that facing the scientist wishing to apply biotechnology to pharmaceutical production: Biotechnology products of agriculture must compete in the environment, attain high yields comparable to conventionally-produced products *and* deliver the extra desirable trait that was the basis for development of the product in the first place.

Broadly, the technologies differ for crop agriculture and for animal agriculture. In the area of crops, the technologies in development include recombinant DNA technology and plant tissue culture technology. A third technology, that of conventional plant breeding, is critical to this area but as it has already been in widespread use it is referenced here only for comparative purposes.

The area of animal agriculture partially parallels biotechnology applications in human healthcare. This area includes the application of genetic engineering techniques to the production of substances directed at protecting animal health or directed at improving animal performance. The technologies involved in development of these "animal pharmaceuticals" and "animal vaccines" are essentially identical to those described in Chapter 22 of this book.

Beyond this, however, additional technologies are emerging that entail the alteration of the animal genome to attain improved products. This technology is less developed than its parallel in plant genetic engineering and its dramatic potential has not yet been widely discussed or publicized.

Crop Agriculture-Recombinant DNA Technology

The applications of recombinant DNA technology to plants are not as well developed as similar techniques used to produce novel products based on incorporation of selected genes into bacteria and other single-celled organisms. A number of factors contribute to this.

First, plants are substantially more complex than bacteria. They are multicellular organisms with complex specialized functions capable of myriad responses to changing internal and external conditions.

Second, plants are poorly understood by scientists relative to the knowledge base applicable to bacteria and animals. Animal and bacterial systems have been the subject of extensive scientific study as part of the larger, decades-old effort directed at solving human disease problems.

Third, traits that influence key aspects of plant performance are complex at the molecular level and are controlled by many genes. While a specific protein coded by a single gene may provide a valuable component for a human drug, plant traits that offer a promising basis for yield improvement are often controlled by many, perhaps hundreds of genes. As researchers learn more about plant molecular biology, yield improvement is increasingly believed to be mediated by a complex series of primary and secondary plant metabolic interactions.

Fourth, the modified plants, even when they produce a particular new protein, still must function as effectively in the field environment as their unmodified counterparts. In other words, the new plant must do everything its best predecessors did as well as exhibit the new trait added through genetic engineering.

Fundamentally, the task of adding new genes to plants is the same as adding new genes to microbes: the scientist must insert the new DNA into the plant cell in such a way as to get the new gene to express (that is produce the protein for which it codes). In practice there are more obstacles that must be overcome as the techniques available for bacterial genetic engineering often require substantial modification to be usable in plant systems. In some cases, they simply have not yet been successfully adapted even after years of research effort.

Genes must be added to cells. In genetic engineering of microbes, the cells that are the basis for adding the novel genes are also the complete organisms. With plants this is not the case and this poses the first of several hurdles that the plant genetic engineer must overcome. Once a gene has been inserted into a plant cell it must be coaxed to develop into a whole plant capable of reproducing viable seed that can pass on the newly-inherited trait. In addition, the new gene must not disrupt the normal functioning of the cell. This is more critical for plant genetic engineering than for genetic engineering of single cells for production of new proteins in contained and highly controlled systems.

This limited tolerance for disruption is related to two factors:

> First, a plant is an extremely complex organism relative to single cell systems. The genetic makeup of the plant comprises a finely balanced system of specialized cells programmed to carry out complex functions in response to developmental as well as situational conditions. Addition of new genes can disrupt these higher functions even though the critical functions necessary for cell metabolism may remain intact. Discovery of such a potential malfunction may not be evident to the research team at the outset. Rather, it may take field growing conditions to bring out the difference and field testing is not likely to be carried out until much later in the process.

Second, the plant will be ultimately required to survive in the field and produce a yield comparable to the best available conventional seed. This means that the genetically engineered plant must not only have its full functional complement of capabilities, but the plant must also still be capable of performing well under the wide variety of circumstances that typically accompany the field environment.

The steps in successful genetic engineering of a plant have generally involved five distinct tasks using the most widely practiced method of plant gene insertion. Each of them must be accomplished properly though not necessarily in sequence after the first two steps:

Identification and characterization of the gene to be inserted.

Insertion of the new gene into the plant cell (this is an imperfect process and only a small percentage of the cells subjected to the insertion of the DNA actually take up the DNA in a functional manner, thus necessitating the next step).

Separation of the cells that have successfully incorporated the new gene from those that have not. This process, called selection, is intended to assure that only those cells that have taken up the new gene will reproduce to form the whole plant. This is essential if the seed ultimately attained is to exhibit the desired new genetic trait.

Expression of the intended trait by the new gene. Generally, genes code for proteins. When the new gene inserted into plant tissue results in production of the desired protein, the new gene is said to express in the plant. Expression must occur in such a way that the new DNA is integrated into the chromosome of the cell and is stably passed on to future generations. Once a foreign gene has been inserted and stably expressed in plant tissue, the tissue is considered "transformed." Plant transformation is the term used to refer to this process.

Regeneration of the cell into a whole plant that carries and expresses the new genetic trait.

An important and sometimes overlooked part of this process is the seed increase that must be carried out to attain a volume of seed sufficient first for testing and then for commercial use. This single regenerated whole plant becomes the basis for production of seed through the traditional techniques requiring a number of generations of field production. At some appropriate stage, field evaluation of the new plant must carried out. This typically requires two or more seasons to assure adequate experience under a number of field and weather conditions and to allow for the assessment of performance of the new variety in farmers' fields.

If the plant variety used to obtain tissue for the laboratory manipulations was not from a line that will be desirable ultimately for sale, the genetically engineered seed derived from the research must be crossed with appropriate breeding stock in order to attain a marketable product. This is, of course, an extra step adding further to the time-frame and to the complexity of developing a new seed product.

Unfortunately, the ability of scientists successfully to transform and regenerate plants is, at this time, for the most part limited to a few species within the plant kingdom. Among those species, transformation is further limited to a few amenable lines. Those lines are frequently not the ones used as commercial inbred lines in the seed industry and are poor performers in comparison to the lines farmers want for commercial crop production. For example, even in the case of tobacco, the plant that is the workhorse of the genetic engineer and the plant with which scientists have had the most success, the lines most commonly used in genetic engineering experiments are not desirable from the standpoint of commercial production. Similarly, the lines of maize used in the early successful regeneration experiments were not commercially popular lines. Their selection was based on the suitability of the line to respond to the regeneration protocol. The same holds true for scientists' current transformation capabilities in cotton.

Currently the technology in this area is rapidly expanding albeit from a very limited base. Dramatic achievements have been made in the model systems such as tobacco, petunia and tomato. In them, scientists have learned routinely to produce genetically engineered plants that express novel traits. The traits are limited but they nonetheless are representative of the breadth of the near-term products on which the agricultural biotechnology industry has focused. These include insect resistance, disease resistance and herbicide resistance and are described in more detail later in this chapter. The rest of this section will discuss the principal methods in use now to incorporate new genes into plants.

Agrobacterium-based Plant Transformation

The oldest and best understood system for transferring new genetic material into plants is Ti plasmid-mediated transformation based on the bacterium, *Agrobacterium tumefaciens*. *A. tumefaciens* is a naturally occurring soil-borne bacterium that is, in essence, nature's own genetic engineer. The bacterium is the causative agent for a plant disease known as "crown gall disease". The disease results from infection by the bacteria which gain entry to the plant through a wound or break in the plant's outer protective layer. The symptoms of infection are galls, or tumor-like growths on the infected plant. The unsightly galls are associated with an alteration of the plant's hormone balance which diverts the plant's metabolic function to produce substances the bacteria use as food. The metabolic imbalance is itself the result of an alteration of the genetic make-up of the plant by transfer of genes from the bacterium to the plant.

Scientists have learned that in the course of infection, the *Agrobacterium* transfers a plasmid called the Ti-plasmid from the cytoplasm of the bacterium to the cytoplasm of the plant's cells in the infected area. Once transferred, the new genes overproduce a plant hormone known as cytokinin. This overproduction distorts the plant's normal cellular metabolism and leads to the formation of the galls which support the proliferation of the bacteria in the infected plant. This natural form of plant genetic engineering provides an excellent model for gene transfer on a broad scale. The objective of scientists is to transfer traits into the plants that are useful to the farmer rather than traits that are useful to the bacteria.

As this disease became better understood, it was apparent that the key to transporting genes into plants via the *Agrobacterium* was the elimination of the disease-causing genes and replacement of them with other genes of the scientists' choosing. This has been accomplished and the system has proven versatile and reliable in transforming dicotylededous (broad leaf) plants such as tobacco, tomato, potato, petunia and sunflower. Tobacco is the most widely used model system and has proven to be an effective tool in the study of new genes and promoters. The Ti-plasmid mediated system has been used in most of the accomplishments in plant genetic engineering to this date. These include, for example, disease resistance to crown gall in tobacco, resistance to tobacco mosaic virus in tobacco and tomato, insect resistance in tobacco using the *Bacillus thuringiensis* crystal protein toxin gene and various herbicide tolerances.

The system is not universally effective in dicotyledonous plants as there remain many species where the transformation has not yet been successful. The Ti-plasmid system has also proven generally inapplicable to transformation of the other major group of plants called monocotyledonous plants or grasses. These include such plants as maize, cereal crops, and rice. Although limited successes using the Ti-plasmid vector in maize have been reported, as of mid-1989 routine maize transformation does not appear yet to be attained.

Other Plant Transformation Technologies

While the Ti-plasmid has proven to be a major tool of the genetic engineer to date, it is limited as to the range of host plants susceptible to transformation. In addition to this, there are other obstacles associated with the dependence of the technique on lengthy regeneration protocols requiring intensive management at every stage of the process. For example, cotton regeneration after transformation via *Agrobacterium* requires a year or more.

In a search for alternative transformation systems that could overcome these limitations, scientists have identified several techniques that offer some promise. To date only one of the alternative systems has been refined to the point where it shows promise for transformation directed at commercial production of improved seed. The following highlights the most significant of these new techniques:

Particle Acceleration

This technique, also called particle bombardment, involves coating DNA onto tiny particles and then accelerating them into plant tissue with the intent of promoting the integration of DNA into selected target plant cells. substantial promise of this technique is evidenced by report of the first genetic engineering of soybean in mid-1988. The method uses an electric discharge apparatus to propel DNA-coated gold particles at rapidly growing soybean tissue taken from immature seeds. Stable transformation was attained and foreign genes have been shown to express in progeny plants. A major advantage of this technique appears to be its applicability to a wide range of species and varieties because it is not dependent on the *Agrobacterium*-based system and it is not dependent on many of the most time- and labor-intensive parts of tissue culture regeneration.

Initial use of this concept was reported by scientists at Cornell University who described a machine adapted to use .22 calibre blanks as the propulsion source to accelerate DNA into onion tissue. The first paper on this technique reported that the particles had carried the DNA into the individual onion cells but evidence of transformation or expression was not attained. Subsequent papers reported progress in both transformation and expression working with improved versions of this same device with a variety of plant tissue targets.

Because the particle acceleration technique is so new, it is difficult to assess how valuable it will prove in the long run to the advancement of plant genetic engineering. Fine adjustment of the device used to accelerate the particles into the tissue appears to be critical to success. Enough DNA must enter the cells to allow uptake of the new genes, yet excessive damage to the cells due to the particle bombardment must be avoided.

There are several major advantages of this technique over the *Agrobacterium*-based method. For one, because it does not use the Ti-plasmid, it does not require transfer of DNA other than that which the experimenter requires to incorporate into the plant. Second, it does not have the host range limitations inherent with the *Agrobacterium* and thus should be widely applicable to any plant species. Third, because it can be directed at rapidly growing plant tissues, it does not require the time-consuming steps of tissue redifferentiation associated with tissue culture and it is not limited to the lines that are amenable to regeneration through the tissue culture process.

Electroporation

This technique involves use of an electric current to alter the cell membrane temporaily so as to allow DNA to cross into the cytoplasm and thereby become a part of the cell's genetic code. This direct DNA uptake method, like particle acceleration, has the advantage that only the DNA of specific interest to the investigator is needed in order to conduct the experiment.

Unlike particle acceleration, electroporation requires the use of plant protoplasts. A protoplast is a single plant cell with the cell wall removed through use of enzymes that dissolve the cellulose content of that normally rigid and relatively impervious structure. The electroporation technique was developed originally for use with bacterial and animal cell transformation experiments where no rigid cell walls complicated the process. Enzyme digestion of the cell wall requires carefully controlled conditions to ensure that the cells will be permeable to the DNA upon the passage of the current while at the same time providing sufficient numbers of viable cells to make it likely that the transformed protoplasts will survive regeneration. Because of its dependence on tissue culture regeneration protocols, this technique must be perfected anew for virtually every new plant variety tested as each has unique traits that affect viability and permeability.

Once the protoplasts have been prepared, hundreds of thousands of cells can be treated simultaneously. Cells that express the desired new gene can then be selected for further tissue culture or plant regeneration. Electroporation has been used to transfer genes into several cereal crops including rice, wheat, and maize. As noted above, these monocot plants have been the least responsive to use of the Ti-plasmid vectors in transformation experiments.

There are two principal limitations to the use of electroporation. First, because the technique requires use of protoplasts, lengthy tissue culture manipulations are required and many cells are lost in the subsequent regeneration steps. Some plant species do not lend themselves well to protoplast formation and do not recover subsequently due to initial low viability. Secondly, while the technique has been useful in transforming plant cells, in many cases the transformation has only been transient. Scientists have had considerable difficulty in routinely getting stable transformed plants out of the process at the end of the lengthy plant regeneration period. The method nonetheless shows promise and recent work indicates the problems of transient expression can be overcome in certain circumstances.

Microinjection

Microinjection is a technique where the DNA to be incorporated into the cell is physically injected directly into the cytoplasm or the nucleus of the target cell using a special micromanipulator and fine glass micropipettes. The process is an exacting one that must be carried out under a microscope. It demands considerable skill and is quite labor intensive as the DNA must be introduced individually into each cell. Figure 1 illustrates the microinjection of a single plant cell using a micro-pippette. To facilitate the procedure, protoplasts must be used. As noted above, this requires the enzymatic digestion of the cell walls and poses the challenge that adequate cell viability must be maintained until the DNA has been successfully transferred. Added time and care are also required in tissue culture to bring these cells back to health and to regenerate whole plants from them. Despite these limitations, the technique may prove to have utility. The transformation of thousands of cells at a time is not necessarily an advantage as only a single cell need be transformed provided that one cell survives and can be regenerated into a whole plant. Scientists have reported a higher frequency of uptake of the new DNA using microinjection than that attainable using mass transformation techniques such as electroporation.

Except for particle acceleration, common to all of the techniques designed to insert foreign genes into plant tissue is an extensive plant tissue culture process. Depending on the specific technique used, there may be more or less tissue culture effort required to produce whole plants. While tissue culture is thus an integral step in attaining genetically engineered plants using recombinant DNA methods, the tissue culture process may itself be used to develop novel plants without use of recombinant techniques.

Crop Agriculture-Tissue Culture Techniques

The recombinant approaches to altering the genetic make-up of plants described above represent the most elegant and potentially most powerful ways to attain novel variability in plants for use in agriculture. However, a group of techniques collectively known as "cell or tissue culture techniques" offer an alternative approach capable of delivering genetic variation without the complexities associated with use of recombinant methods to introduce foreign genes.

Tissue culture techniques offer advantages over the conventional methods of plant breeding principally because new plant traits can be selected at the cellular level in the laboratory instead of at the whole plant level in the field. This affords advantages of time in that cellular screening for traits requires weeks or months whereas screening of whole plants typically requires entire growing seasons. A related advantage is that the space required for cell screening is substantially less than that required for field screening of traits. More

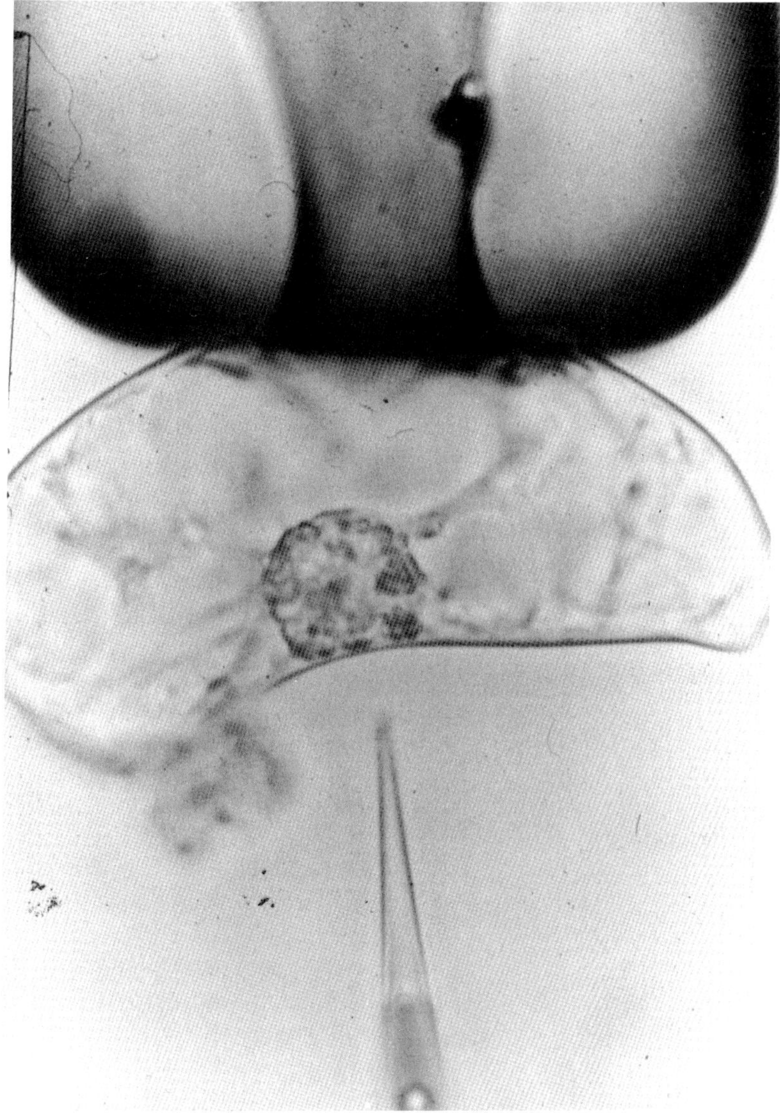

Figure 1. Microinjection allows the direct incorporation of DNA into the nucleus of a variety of plant protoplast cells. (*Photo courtesy of Calgene, Inc.*)

substantively, plants derived from these technologies are said to be capable of greater uniformity because they are derived from single cells in laboratory cultures rather than through sexual reproduction. On the negative side, unlike recombinant methods where the sources of new genetic material can include virtually any living entity, traits attainable using cell culture techniques must be drawn from those which are already a part of the plant's own genetic structure.

The common thread of these techniques is the production of new plants from a few selected plant cells. Several techniques comprise this area of development including protoplast fusion, clonal propagation, somaclonal variation and mutant selection.

Protoplast Fusion

This technique involves the creation of novel plants through fusion of the cells of two different species that would not otherwise cross in nature. By removing the cell walls of plant cells with digestive enzymes, two protoplasts may be joined or fused together in a tissue culture medium. If the fused cells can be regenerated into whole plants, the resultant plant product is called a somatic hybrid.

This hybrid exhibits some of the traits of each of its parent plants. Plants developed using this technique have not as yet proven to be commercially useful, although some interesting possibilities appear to exist. For example, a potato plant resistant to the herbicide triazine was produced by fusing a potato protoplast with a protoplast of the wild black nightshade. Nightshade is a relative of potato and is naturally resistant to triazine. A less useful, though more widely reported, example of protoplast fusion is the "pomato" plant, a cross of a tomato protoplast with a potato protoplast. While the pomato indeed had traits of each plant, and even produced both potatoes and tomatoes, the fruit was small and the seed quality was poor. At present, the technique is labor intensive and uncertain as to its outcome. It appears that the more closely related the species used in the protoplast fusion, the greater the likelihood of attaining a commercially useful plant. The fusion process typically yields a mixture of fused cells of the same species along with fused cells of the two different species. These must be separated and then the desired fusion products must be encouraged to develop into plants. Only a portion of the fused cells usually are capable of this and, once novel plants are attained, there is no assurance that the resultant mixture of traits expressed by the somatic hybrid will actually have commercial value.

Protoplast fusion's main advantage is that the space required for cell screening is substantially less than that required for field screening of traits. More substantively, plants derived from these technologies are said to be capable of greater uniformity because they are derived from single cells in laboratory cultures rather than through sexual reproduction. On the other hand, as we have observed earlier, the method is restricted to the transfer of genetic traits already contained with the plant's own genetic base.

Clonal Propagation

Clonal propagation is a method for production of uniform or disease-free plants. The technology involves culture of large numbers of protoplasts obtained from a single plant in a bioreactor. Because the cells are somatic, that is they contain both the male and female genetic components, the plants grown from the protoplasts are identical or clonal. The technique has been applied to high value crops where uniformity is commercially advantageous. Orchids, oil palm and potatoes derived from clonal propagation are already commercially available. The technique is also useful where seed or planting stocks are likely to carry plant disease. The bioreactor culturing process assures control over the disease-causing organisms. Commercially available disease-free species include potato, sugar cane, and strawberry.

Somaclonal Variation

While the clonal propagation technique emphasizes the production of uniform plants from somatic cells, somaclonal variation seeks to utilize what had been observed as a problem in clonal propagation. Scientists observed that in some cases, variants would develop from somaclonal cells, that is, cells that had identical genetic material. This genetic variation of a few cells relative to thousands is typically masked in the whole plant. However, when plants are derived from single cells which express a particular variation, all cells of the new plant contain the variant and the trait thus becomes manifest. Early work on this technology was done on tomato with the objective of attaining tomatoes with high solids content and tomatoes with improved harvesting traits. Work using this technique is now directed at several crops including maize, wheat, celery, carrot, bananas, potato and sugar cane.

Mutant Selection

By combining the cell culture techniques of somaclonal propagation with selection and screening methods, researchers are working to develop new plants that are resistant to herbicides, disease and stress. By exposing protoplasts or dividing cells in cell culture to an herbicide, for example, and then selecting only those cells that survive for regeneration, the resultant whole plants may themselves be resistant to the herbicide. A similar approach can be used to attain plants resistant to disease and plants resistant to environmental stresses. The first plant patent issued for an herbicide resistant maize plant derived from this technique. The maize line was developed by Molecular Genetics, Inc. in collaboration with American Cyanamid and is resistant to American Cyanamid's imidazolinone herbicide. The line has been licensed to Pioneer Hi-bred International and is expected to reach the market by the early 1990s. Pioneer is field testing these lines now (see figure 2) and making backcrosses to incorporate the trait into commercially valuable inbred stocks.

Animal Agriculture-Health Care Applications and Products to Improve Productive Performance

Just as conventional pharmaceuticals developed for human applications have found applications in animal health, biotechnology-based animal health applications in agriculture largely derive from development of recombinant products for human health care purposes. Products in development for sale in the animal health market in therapeutic applications as well as vaccine applications utilize the same technology as are the basis for human health care products discussed in Chapter 22. Indeed, some of these products are the identical proteins or, in some cases, the animal analogue of the same form produced for human consumption. Examples include use of interferons or interleukins to enhance the animal immune response as well as the use of a species-specific growth hormone to enhance milk or meat production.

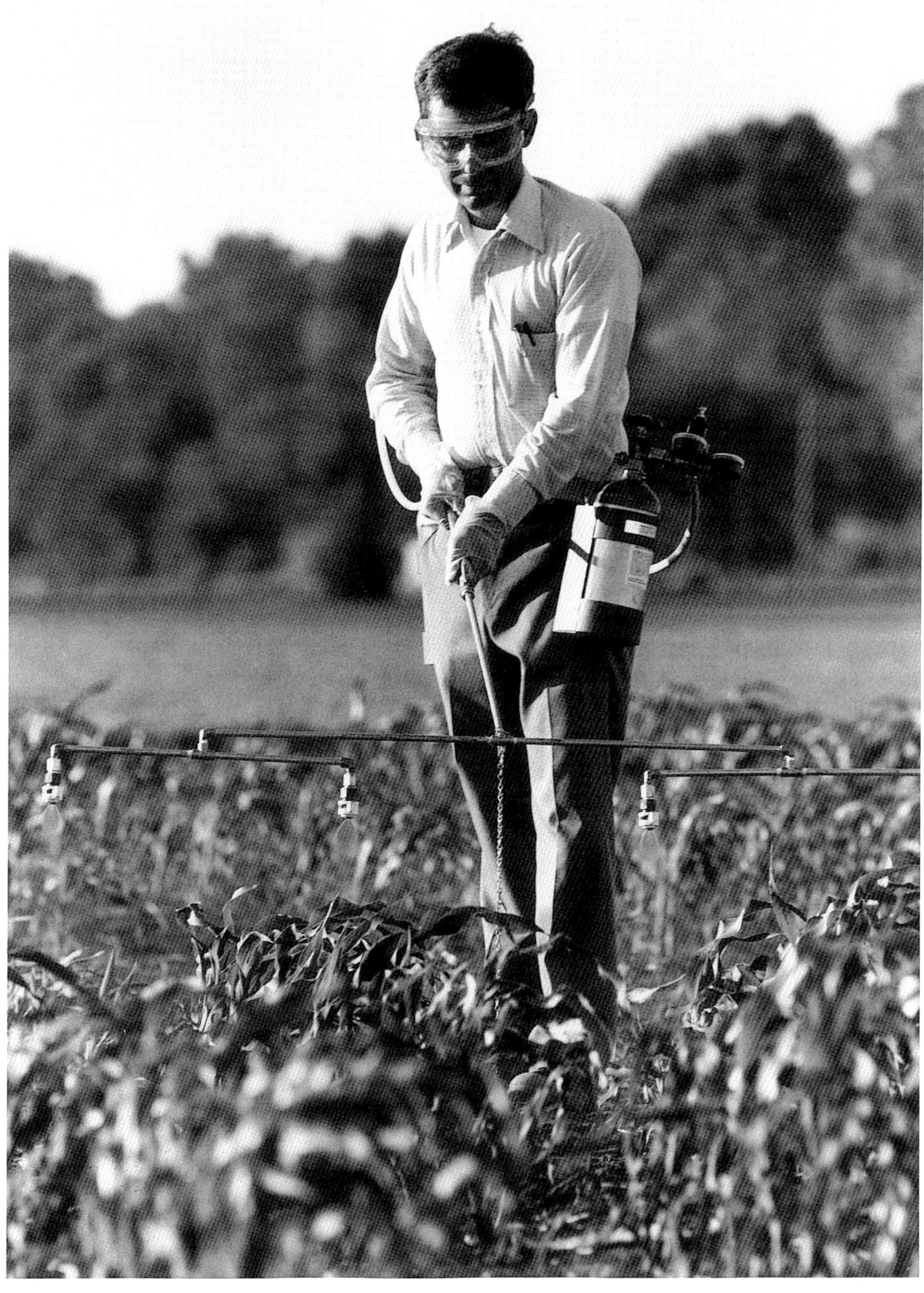

Figure 2. A scientist from the Biotechnology Research Department of Pioneer Hi-Bred International, Inc., applies herbicide to an experimental plot of corn. Pioneer is developing new hybrids resistant to the imidazolinone family of herbicides produced by American Cyanamid Company, under license from American Cyanamid. (*Photo courtesy of Pioneer Hi-Bred International, Inc.*)

Animal Agriculture-Transgenic Animals

Introduction of new genetic material into animals to produce transgenic animals may be applied in a number of areas ranging from applications to attain higher quality meats by virtue of alterations in the fat to lean content of the animals' muscle, to the production of useful proteins secreted into milk or eggs. The technologies to attain these results lag somewhat behind other areas of agricultural biotechnology. Transgenic mice, rabbits, pigs and sheep have been routinely produced by direct injection of DNA to the pronucleus of fertilized eggs.

The Agricultural Sector

Agriculture is said to be the only truly indispensable industry. As such, agriculture is the underpinning of developed as well as developing economies. In virtually every country of the world, agriculture is the largest single category of economic activity. In the U.S., agriculture touches nearly every sector of industry, even though the value of farm commodities is small relative to the value added downstream in the industrial processing sector.

The agricultural sector is comprised of the nation's physical production facilities, the farms and the people that operate them. In addition to the farms, the input industries that serve agriculture with input products such as agricultural chemicals, seeds, machinery or financing are also integral to the farm sector. The principal forces that affect the farm sector are public policy, exogenous variables and technology. Included in the public policy variables are price supports, direct payments, commodity loans and acreage diversion programs. Collectively, these public policy choices are called "the farm program" and as such are a topic of constant debate among legislators, farmers, input suppliers and consumers. The program, whatever the specific components, seems always to be under critical review for substantially failing to accomplish its intended objectives. Exogenous variables comprise a wide variety of factors including weather, disease, pest infestations, economic conditions and international trade factors. The consequences of these variables on the farm sector often provide incentive for further adjustment of public policy, thus leading to ever-changing dynamics of the farm sector. Technology defines the level of capability of the farm sector and, to an extent, the nature of the output of farms. Technology has had a major influence on the farm sector this century, accounting for a total transformation in the way food and fiber are produced.

Food and Fiber Consumption Trends

U.S. households spend more on products derived from agriculture than any other category of goods and services, including housing. This is true despite the U.S. being noted for low food costs in comparison to other countries. In 1984, consumer end use expenditures for farm origin foods was $332 billion. The value of the farm component of this expenditure was only 27% or $89.5 billion, while the balance amounting to $243 billion comprised the marketing bill. This $243 billion is made up of packaging, processing, transportation, wholesale and retail markups, advertising, taxes, interest, repairs and other factors. Labor, at the various stages in the food marketing chain, is the largest single component of the marketing bill, about 33%. In general, the value of the farm component of retail food expenditures is declining as a percent of the total.

In 1986, for the first time, the value of the processing component of food purchased at the checkout counters of foodstores in the U.S. exceeded the value of the food itself. The USDA Economic Research Service reports that about 30 cents of every dollar spent in foodstores in 1986 went to cover the cost of food production while about 31 cents paid for the processing (including processing labor) of the food after it left the farm. This trend toward declining farm share of food value as a percentage of consumer food expenditure is about a decade old. The farm value component of food expenditures had been relatively constant at between 30–40% of the consumer food dollar through the 1960s and 1970s. Since 1979, that share has been steadily declining. This suggests either that the processing sector is undertaking an increasing role in food preparation or that overproduction of farm commodities is depriving the farmer of a share of increasing consumer food spending. In fact, both of these trends are known to be occurring.

In 1984, 5.8 million people, about 2.4% of the U.S. total, lived on farms. This population comprises the workforce for direct production of U.S. crop and livestock products. Another 19% of the U.S. workforce is employed in manufacturing, processing, transportation and retail industries related to farm equipment supplies and services. When non-food uses of products from the agricultural sector are included, the market value generated by the farm sector measured at the end use level is about $575 billion. Of this, farm sector income amounts only to $174 billion. Other than food products, the components that make up the balance of the more than half trillion dollar value are exports, non-food goods such as clothing, shoes and industrial goods, tobacco and tobacco products and farm origin inputs for agriculture. Farm origin inputs include seed, animal feeds and livestock for breeding.

Size and Nature of Modern Agriculture

U.S. farming has changed dramatically in the last five decades. The most noticeable difference is in farm structure and organization. Many studies have analyzed and characterized these changes. The following factors are usually cited in most studies as principal indicators of the changes that have occurred:

- Fewer and larger farms
- Increasing concentration of production
- Increasing specialization
- Growth of multi-ownership farms
- Use of capital requirements with commensurately more complex financial structures

- Greater concentration of wealth and income among the larger farms
- Fewer young people entering farming than older operators leaving

Many factors aided in bringing about these changes. Some of the frequently cited influences include:

- Inflation
- Increased exports of farm products
- Availability of capital-intensive new technologies
- Non-farm employment opportunities
- Availability of institutional credit for land purchase and capital goods
- Commodity programs supporting prices for farm products
- Tax laws applicable to incomes and estates

Changes in the Farm Sector

The most significant and perhaps most obvious structural change of those mentioned above is the decline in the number of farms and the increase in average size of the farms remaining. The number of farms in the U.S. has decreased from 6.5. million in the 1930s to about 2.4 million in the 1980s. Total cropland use has declined slightly only recently. In 1979, the amount of land in crops in the U.S. was about the same as it was in the 1930s, about 370–380 million acres. In recent years, with the acreage reduction programs of the federal government in effect, land in crops has dropped to little more than 300 million acres. Thus, with the decline of the number of farms has come the consolidation of small farms to form more economically efficient entities. A good part of this consolidation occurred between 1930 and 1960. The rate of decline in the number of farms has slowed since that time. In the 1950s farm numbers dropped 30%. From 1949 to 1970 the rate of decline was substantially less at 1.1% per year. By the early 1980s, the decline had ceased but with the low prices and agricultural instability of the farm sector brought on by overproduction, the number once again began to drop.

Average farm size has doubled since the 1950s to 430 acres per farm in the 1980s. The number of farms greater than 500 acres in size doubled from 1960 to 1978 while the number of farms less than 100 acres in size declined twofold during the same period. In 1978, the number of farms having greater than 1,000 acres accounted for only 7% of the U.S. farms, the total acreage of these farms comprised 90% of the total U.S. cropland.

While the rate of change in the total number of farms has slowed in the 1980s, the rate of change is still significant within certain segments. Small farms, defined by the USDA as farms having annual sales of $2,500 or less, and large farms, those having sales of $100,000 or more, both increased in number while mid-size farms, those with sales between $20,000 and $40,000 declined. Thus, mid-size farms are under considerable pressure to become larger or to become smaller. If this trend continues, U.S. agriculture will be characterized by a concentration of very large farms on the one hand, providing most commercial output and occupying the vast majority of the land and, on the other hand, a large number of very small farms occupying a small percentage of the land collectively and producing very low output. USDA data indicates these small farms are owned increasingly by the so-called hobby farmer. These are part-time farmers who have regular, and perhaps significant, off-farm income sources and embrace an affection for the quality of life afforded by a rural environment. For these farmers, the farm serves primarily as a rural residence. Sale of farm commodities appears to be only a secondary activity and is only nominally pursued by farmers in this category.

A phenomenon that was first noted in the early 1980s, which has received considerable attention, is the so-called "superfarm". Superfarms are defined by USDA as farms having sales in excess of $500,000 annually. Table (1) provides a summary profile of the superfarm as described by USDA.

The Farmer as Customer

Because a significant portion of the applications of biotechnology to agriculture will take the form of products designed to improve the profitability and productivity of the farm, the purchaser of these products is generally going to be the farmer. As the ultimate buyer of seed, chemicals, implements and other farm services, those marketing biotechnology-based products will have to gain the farmer's attention sufficiently to convey the unique features these new products offer and why they afford benefits over currently available alternatives. An advantage held by many of the companies developing new products for agriculture is a long history of serving farmers and farm markets. Even with this customer familiarity, some companies will find marketing biotechnology products a new challenge as numerous products already populate the market. The sheer number of such products has heightened price competition as companies fight for market share in a current era of declining acreage due to over-production of farm commodities. In addition, the increasing sophistication of farm use products has created a skeptical buyer who carefully evaluates the probable pay-off of each prospective purchase before buying. Nonetheless, farmers have generally demonstrated a strong interest in the potential of biotechnology and its likely contribution to farm productivity. Farmers have proven themselves capable of widely and rapidly adopting new methods, practices and

Table 1
Superfarm Profile

* Although superfarms accounted for only 1% of total farms, product sales from these farms accounted for nearly 30% of total farm sales. This amounted to about $30 billion in 1978.
* Average size is 4,700 acres
* Total land in superfarms was 84.5 million acres or 7% of total farmland. Cropland accounted for 25% of superfarm land, pasture and rangeland accounted for 64% and other land uses for 11%.
* Superfarm crop sales totaled $10 billion, while livestock and other farm product sales totaled $20 billion in 1978.
* Net superfarm income amounted to $14.3 billion in 1982, accounting for 60% of U.S. net farm income.
* Corporations owned about 40% of superfarms and nearly half of superfarm land in 1978. Sole proprietorships accounted for 37% of superfarms and partnerships for 20%.
* Superfarms are concentrated in California (about 20% of total superfarms) Texas (7%); other states, including Florida, Iowa, Nebraska, Kansas, Illinois, Colorado, Washington, Arizona and North Carolina, comprise 33%. California and Texas together accounted for one third of the superfarm sales.
* Superfarms are most concentrated in specialty crops. Percentage figures indicate percent of total production in that crop category which originates on superfarms:

Vegetables	62%
Nursery and greenhouse products	55%
Fruits, nuts, and berries	44%
Grains	7%

* In livestock, superfarms are less concentrated.

Cattle and calves	44%
Poultry and poultry products	42%
Dairy	13%
Swine	9%

* Superfarms typically are more efficient than smaller farms relative to level of expenses as a percent of each dollar of gross income ($0.69 per dollar gross income for superfarms versus $0.84 per dollar gross income for farms having between $200,000.00 and $499,000.00 per year sales).

products once they are shown to be valuable. As noted above, these improvements have revolutionized farming over the last 40 years. In the U.S., for example, according to USDA the average farmer produced enough food for 14 people in 1947. In contrast, by 1986 the average farmer produced enough for 93 people. such change has not come without a strong sense of experimentation by farmers towards new technology.

While on the one hand farmers have generally proven themselves to be willing to try new products, the price they are willing to pay for them is typically only a fraction of the benefit they are likely to derive from their use. In the industry this is referred to as the "benefit cost ratio". For example, a 4:1 benefit cost ratio indicates that a farmer is willing to pay $1.00 for a product that will generate $4.00 of added value to his operation. In the U.S., farmer benefit cost ratios vary from less than 2:1 in the case of some highly effective and well accepted pesticides to greater than 10:1 for some implant products for animal growth enhancement. Typically, a benefit cost ratio of 3:1 or 4:1 is common for agricultural inputs such as pesticides and seed.

The principle factor that influences the benefit cost ratio is risk. Farmers usually purchase products early in the season and hope for returns on their use by the end of the season. Many uncertainties will intercede between product purchase decision and payoff. Most of these uncertainties are beyond the farmer's control. Weather and market price for his crop are the two principal categories for this uncertainty but other performance factors associated with the product itself, with the field conditions, with farm equipment interfaces and other factors also contribute to the discount the farmer applies to the value of a product.

The net effect of this for companies developing products, whether they be biotechnology-based or otherwise, is that the value of the benefits to farmers associated with use of a particular product is substantially greater than the available market for the product.

The Agricultural Input Industry

The point has already been made that, the agricultural input industry comprises the companies that provide the inputs necessary for the farmer to produce farm commodities. These range from crop inputs such as fertilizer, seed and pesticides, to animal inputs such as animal health products and breeding stock for animal production. Other inputs include farm machinery, financial services and, increasingly, information services and computer hardware and software dedicated to farm applications. The sectors of this industry most generally applicable to marketing of biotechnology-based products are companies engaged in production and marketing of seed, agricultural chemicals and animal health products. The following briefly highlights these three key sectors in terms of the participants and the nature of the businesses they operate:

Seed

The seed industry world-wide accounts for about $25 billion in sales annually. The commercial value of seed used by farmers globally has been variously estimated at between $45 and $60 billion. The difference in these values is due to the widespread farm practice known as plant-back. Farmers often plant seed saved from the prior year's harvest for the next year's production instead of purchasing certified seed from a seed company. This practice is particularly common in the major field crops such as wheat and soybean. To a lesser extent, it is common in some production regions for cotton. Because these crops are open pollinated, parent plants transfer traits uniformly through seed to progeny plants. The progeny will have the same genetic potential for yield and other traits associated with crop performance as the parent plants. Thus, for these crops, as long as the farmer is satisfied with the performance of his prior year's crop, there is limited incentive again to purchase seed. Generally, the price of open-pollinated seed is a small premium over the commodity value of the seed. The premium is based on the cost of cleaning and conditioning the seed plus a charge to offset breeding of improved varieties. Only in the hybrid crops, where progeny segregate into non-uniform populations with varying traits relative to their parent plants, is the practice of plant-back seldom found. The yield loss associated with these dissimilar field populations eliminates any economic incentive to plant with saved seed. Major hybrid crops include maize, milo, sunflower and tomato. Because of the limitations on plant-back, hybrid seed can be sold at a greater premium over the basic commodity price. Also, because of the hybrid vigor associated with hybrid seed, the crops are higher yielding and hence of greater value. Thus, the seed price per acre of hybrid seed in comparison to non-hybrid seed is usually substantially higher. As a result of this greater price flexibility, greater performance potential and inherent protection of the commercial value-added, companies spend considerably more in research to develop improved lines for the crops that can be hybridized than for the crops that are open pollinated. The seed industry may be segmented by crop and by geographic area: within the various segments, there are significant differences that limit the usefulness of any generalizations.

That notwithstanding, there are generally two broad types of companies in the seed business. On the one hand are small, typically family-owned seed companies that focus on serving a regional market with seed for crops grown in that area. These companies generally specialize in varieties particularly well adapted to their marketing regions. They have limited research capability and often rely on public germplasm or germplasm licensed from foundation seed companies. On the other hand, a group of large diversified, often multinational seed companies have emerged with significantly larger marketing power than the small regional family operations. Some of the growth of these companies has come as a result of and perhaps a reward for the development of superior lines often associated with hybrid technology. A number of the other large seed companies have grown through acquisitions of prominent small regional companies to gain broader market access. Many of the larger companies have been acquired by major agrochemical companies in the last few decades. At the present, it is not unusual for a major agrochemical producer to have a seed company subsidiary that holds a significant share of the seed market in one or another major world crop.

Agricultural Chemicals

The pesticide industry has been traditionally comprised of basic producers and formulators who often also act as wholesalers to the distribution system. The pesticide industry emerged as a major supplier to farmers after World War II largely as a result of the successful application of synthetic organic chemistry to the development of farm pest control products. The introduction of such new products contributed to major changes in the economics of farming by allowing farmers to farm more land and preserve a greater share of the crop for harvest. Pest control afforded by the new chemistry provided a major advantage to farmers and thus rapidly grew into a major industry. The estimated 1986 sales of the world-wide agrochemical industry were $17.4 billion. The vast majority of agrochemical sales are for farm use.

The basic producers who made early commitments to research efforts to develop new chemical pesticides generally became the most successful in the marketplace and typically dominate the industry today. The companies best positioned to undertake this research were already the major chemical producers who had access to the appropriate feedstocks, the production facilities and technical expertise necessary to bring the products to the market. Today, most of the principal agrochemical basic producers are also major chemical producers. As the industry was becoming established, regionally specialized companies purchased the active ingredients from the basic producers and prepared formulated material for sale into the farm distribution channels. Often the companies operated distributorships as well as formulation plants. As the industry matured, the control of the formulation function increasingly shifted to the basic producers. This shift was encouraged by the increasing competition within the industry as more products crowded the market. With the greater competition, formulation became an integral part of product market positioning. The basic producers began to integrate forward into formulation as a means of improving margins and gaining more control over the channels of distribution. Formulators increasingly turned to producing off-patent active ingredients as a means of maintaining sales of their formulated products. In some cases, they would market these products themselves through their own distribution system but they would also produce the chemicals under private label for sale by others.

As the biotechnology applications to agriculture emerge, the entry of new companies into the pest control marketplace will speed up. Chapter 24 of this section provides a more detailed discussion of the pesticide applications of biotechnology insofar as actual pest control materials such as biopesticides are concerned. There is likely to be an assured role for the agrochemical companies in the new biotechnology as most of the major players have already made commitments to seed company acquisitions, to biopesticide research and to development of plant genetic engineering skills.

Animal Health Products

In 1985, world animal health product sales were reported at $6 billion annually according to *Animal Pharm*, a major trade publication of the industry. The products that comprise these sales include animal therapeutics, animal vaccines and nutritionals. The provision of animal care products to veterinarians is dominated by companies who are already major participants in the human health care business. That is, a company already committed to the development of human pharmaceuticals is in a good position to create a division charged with finding applications of the developed technology for animal care markets whether that be marketing to producers of farm animals or to the veterinarians who provide animal care. Biotechnology applications to animal health appear at present to fit well within this industry structure. Many of the most significant efforts in the development of new biotechnology products in this sector are being pursued in small start-up companies who have special research capabilities in the new techniques; these companies are frequently allied through funding or marketing arrangements with the major animal health companies.

A number of studies have attempted to inventory the activity in this rapidly changing area. One recent one reports that there are more than 240 companies and 316 other organizations active in developing products for just the veterinary vaccine market.

Constraints to Growth: Regulatory and Public Relations Issues

This section highlights the major constraints to growth applicable to the use of biotechnology in agriculture. Many of the factors involved are the same as those discussed in earlier chapters of this book; thus they are not covered again here other than to note aspects of these issues specific to biotechnology in agriculture.

The success of the agricultural biotechnology industry, while clearly dependent on the progress of the research and the demand for new biotechnology products in the marketplace, is also critically dependent upon public policy and public perception. Agricultural applications of this technology will require widespread use in the environment on thousands, indeed more likely millions, of acres. To be effective, the products must survive and compete in the field environment whether they are seeds or microbial products applied to crops or improved vaccines for use in animal health applications. In the view of the regulatory agencies there is no clear line which distinguishes the degree of viability that a crop plant or an agricultural microbe must have to be effective in the field and the degree of viability that would be undesirable in a weed or an out-of-control microbe.

The history of the debate about the appropriate level of regulatory scrutiny to be applied to securing clearances to market, and indeed even to conduct small scale field tests of biotechnology products, has been characterized by a concern that unpredicted adverse effects may accompany their introduction. Proponents of a slow approach to approvals of biotechnology field tests have argued that past experience with chemical technology has demonstrated the value of proceeding with the utmost caution. The record of the regulatory debate contains many references to the dangers of introduced species. The suggestion is that our experience with such introductions should teach us that genetically engineered microbes or plants released to the open environment without appropriate containment may lead to unexpected environmental problems. The heritage of the environmental movement of the 1970s, the argument continues, dictates that the only rational way to proceed is to conduct a careful assessment of the likely environmental and ecological effects of each introduction before the introduction is actually carried out.

While arguments like these have an elementary appeal to the casual participant, there are several problems they pose for the encouragement of innovative research in the area of agricultural biotechnology. First, there is not yet the ability effectively to predict the behavior of even known organisms in the environment. This lack of so-called predictive ecology has been held up as reason for caution in proceeding quickly to introduce new products of biotechnology. On the other side of the issue is the conviction that predictive ecology is an illusive goal at best and more probably is never attainable (somewhat like the goal of predictive economics or predictive psychiatry). The argument is that no matter how much additional science is known and how much additional data can be assembled, there is little likelihood that accurate predictions about the behavior of complex organisms in even more complex environments will result.

Second, with or without predictive ecology, it is not clear that one can assess *a priori* the problems likely to derive from an environmental introduction. The most frequent analogies cited are to toxic chemicals and to hazardous pesticides. The more extreme analogy is that, of nuclear power. The argument is that had we known the downside effects of introducing these new technologies we would have proceeded more cautiously. The basis for the suggestion that these analogies are appropriate appears to be that, as events turned out, we learned things about these technologies later that we might have wished to have known earlier. This appears somewhat of a circular argument. While it may be reassuring to be able to say we know now all the downside risks and unexpected outcomes that are ever going to befall society as a result of the adoption of new biotechnologies, such an outcome is clearly never possible. Certainly nations will suffer problems from biotechnology as there have been problems from any new technology. Certainly we would prefer to avoid as many such problems as possible. But clarification of the problems themselves does not evolve from a theoretical debate before experience has been gained. We have to experience a problem in order to understand it so that we can solve it. To talk of solving problems before they emerge borders on the fanciful. We can take positive steps in programs of accident prevention as, for example, in the case of highway automobile safety by careful study of prior experience and making adjustments in highway construction, traffic laws, auto construction or driving practices to eliminate conditions that have been associated with accidents. This is appropriate because accidents are by nature unpredicted events with undesirable outcomes. What is being urged for an *ex ante* analysis of biotechnology now is, in effect, analogous to the process of attempting to define the complete traffic accident prevention program prior to the emergence of mass highway travel by motor car. In 1920, for instance, there was simply not enough experience with the automobile to establish any such program. Any effort to develop a complete one during that timeframe would have been a hopeless failure in the light of affairs now and in the future.

Third, it is not clear that the risks of products of agricultural biotechnology are comparable to the technologies with which biotechnology is being compared. As noted before toxic waste problems, synthetic organic chemicals and nuclear power are the "bad" experiences that have been cited by the critics of biotechnology. Because of problems with these technologies, they argue, we must proceed especially carefully in adopting biotechnology. But this argument by analogy fails to demonstrate what, in fact, the similarity is between biotechnology and the selected other early technologies that led to unforseen adverse results. The similarity asserted by the proponents of this argument appears to be simply that all were new at one time and that new technologies invariably have unpredicted, adverse consequences. When reduced to a syllogism, the flaw of this argument is more apparent. It rests on the premise that "all new technologies have unpredicted . . . etc. . . . consequences". Support for this premise is the citation of a few technologies that have indeed resulted in unanticipated problems. But there has been no exhaustive demonstration to show that all new technologies have such problems. Many, indeed, have become integral parts of our daily lives with never a thought to a heritage of adverse consequences. Consider, for example, technologies such as computers, telecommunications, the adoption of jet engines for commercial airlines, and the use of electric lighting. While one can certainly imagine negative outcomes associated with all of these advances, they are largely accepted by most as, at worst, benign to society and more likely as contributory to substantial benefit.

A review of the safety record of the biotechnology industry and research establishment reveals no suggestion of a troublesome technology. The decade-and-a-half of safe recombinant DNA research in the laboratory is augmented by several decades of safe experience with extensive and often random genetic manipulations in plant and animal breeding in the field for the purpose of improved agricultural productivity. Indeed, this conventional work has been carried out without notice by those concerned with environmental degradation. The most recent relevant experience, though it is the least extensive, is the favorable experience of the field tests that *have* been carried out on a handful of genetically engineered plants and microbes. In none of the tests conducted as of this writing has there been a reported problem.

Perhaps because of these intuitive factors, it will be merely a question of time before the extreme scrutiny to which recombinant DNA experimentation has been subjected in the press and at the state and federal regulatory agencies will subside to a level more commensurate with the risks associated with the experimentation. In fact, the regulatory climate appears to have improved to some extent in 1988. In

Figure 3. Agracetus scientists inspect the progress of young tobacco plants during the first outdoor test of a genetically engineered plant in 1986 near Madison, Wisconsin. The plants were genetically engineered to be resistant to crown gall disease, a bacterial infection. (*Photo courtesy of Agracetus.*)

1986, field tests of a bacterium genetically engineered to protect plants from frost damage proposed by researchers at the University of California, Berkeley, and by their colleagues at a small biotechnology company called Advanced Genetic Sciences of Oakland, California, were repeatedly deterred by regulatory delays, court challenges and tactical errors in testing. Opponents of biotechnology were largely responsible for the delay. Similarly, also in 1986, a proposed field test of a microbe genetically engineered by Monsanto was dropped. Monsanto scientists had engineered the microbe to produce an insecticide that has been in common use in agriculture (the gene inserted into the microbe coded for the crystal protein toxin gene from the bacterium *Bacillus thuringiensis*). The U.S. Environmental Protection Agency determined that Monsanto must obtain an Experimental Use Permit under provisions of an interim policy adopted by the agency to review small scale field tests of biopesticides developed using biotechnology. The agency declined to approve the permit in 1986 and Monsanto eventually dropped the project.

Three separate tests of genetically engineered plants were conducted in 1986 (Figure 3) and again in 1987 further testing went forward for plants. All the plant tests were carried out without incident. In the area of field testing of genetically engineered microbes, two tests of the bacteria designed to prevent frost damage were conducted in 1987, along with a third test of a microorganism carrying a marker gene. The latter test proved that the microbes did not spread in the environment as the opponents of the tests had feared. By 1988, additional field test activity proceeded with both plants and microbes without widespread attention or incident. In general, the novelty of these tests has worn off to the point where regulatory agencies and the media no longer dwell on them. As a result, the general public is largely taking the view that these tests are mundane and unlikely to lead to environmental disruption. In this more reasonable atmosphere of public opinion, opponents of the technology have turned to other areas in an effort to plumb the imagination of the general public to take issue with the progress of biotechnology. Issues on the horizon for the industry in this regard are the patenting of animals and the long-term social and economic effects of adoption of biotechnology on the small farmer.

THE CONTENT OF AGRICULTURAL BIOTECHNOLOGY

This section covers the substance of what is coming in developments for the agricultural sector. Applications of biotechnology to agriculture may be divided into two broad categories:

Near-term Developments

Products in development now that will comprise the initial

applications of agricultural biotechnology. This section is based on announced products in testing or development by various companies in the ag-biotech industry.

Long-term Potential

These are products that will follow the initial applications described under near-term developments. Second generation ag-biotech products will generally require development of additional scientific understanding or further refinement of current techniques before they become a commercial reality.

Near Term

Many of the products of agricultural biotechnology now in development address problems for which solutions already exist rather than problems for which solutions are yet to be found. This is in contrast to biotechnology applications in human healthcare where most new therapeutics are being developed to solve problems that have not been amenable to treatment using conventional pharmaceutical technology. For example, medical science has yet to find a cure for cancer, but the recent advances in medical research made possible through biotechnology has crystallized the prospect that new drugs will soon be available that will cure selected cancers and will alleviate the severity of the disease in other instances. Considerable work is underway in this area directed toward commercialization of new products which will substantially address this type of unmet need.

In the case of agriculture, the near-term products of biotechnology are largely new solutions to problems that already have remedies even though the remedy may have several disadvantages. The new solutions will be better because they allow the farmer more flexibility, because they afford more complete management control of the production environment or because they may cost less than conventional solutions. Nonetheless, they are likely to be incremental improvements in the view of the farmer and perhaps also in the view of the investment and business community.

While product sales for many of these near term applications of biotechnology may be in the multi-million dollar per year range, they are not likely to be grossly different from the size of markets for current conventional products. The value of each product will likely depend on the degree of improved efficiency afforded by that product over its conventional vival.

Herbicide Resistance Traits in Plants

One of the major improvements to agricultural production practices realized over the last 30 years has been the development of effective chemical herbicides for weed control in crop production. The net effect of these chemicals has been to free the farmer from reliance on mechanical cultivation or hoeing for weed control. While cultivation employing disks or chisel plows pulled behind a tractor is still used physically to eliminate weeds in conjunction with herbicide spraying, it is now largely regarded as a minor tool used to supplement an herbicide program. The problems with cultivation were that the pratice did not provide long-lasting control and it required a major investment of the farmer's time. Weeds could grow back within days and the amount of land a grower could farm was limited in part by the farmer's capability to cultivate mechanically.

Modern herbicides changed all that. Control was long-lasting and spraying was a simpler operation than cultivation. This change contributed to making large scale farming operationally more feasible, particularly in the large acreage field crops such as maize and soybean. Freed from these cultivation limitations, farmers expanded their acreage to take advantage of the economies afforded by the larger scale of operation.

As a result of the demand for weed control chemicals, herbicides became the major segment of the agricultural chemicals market, accounting for $8,600 million or 43% of world wide agrochemical sales in 1987. Today there are multiple herbicides available for virtually every crop grown. In response to the large market potential, many companies are active in development of new herbicide products and there is considerable competition on performance, price, product flexibility and convenience.

Despite the foregoing, herbicides are still far from perfect. Some weeds are not well-controlled in some important crops. Some herbicides, when applied in sufficient quantity to control weeds, lead to crop damage. There are many complex weed-crop interactions that often require a farmer to use several products over the course of the growing season to attain adequate weed control. Timing of application may be critical to successful weed control in many situations while carry-over effects of the herbicide on the following year's crop can become limiting factors in selection of a weed control chemical. By the time the ideal mix of products is applied, the cost may be so high that the crop is no longer profitable. In addition, adverse environmental effects have been associated with some herbicides ranging from human health problems to impact on non-target organisms. High rates of application of some of the older herbicides have led to concern about spray drift, worker exposure and ecological effects of the herbicide program. Some of the newer chemicals now entering the market require as little as .02 lbs per acre. In comparison, many of the older chemicals required typically 5–10 lbs per acre.

The ideal herbicide would be one that provides long-lasting effective control of all the plants in the field except the crop plants. Although considerable effort has been directed at this objective by the agrochemical companies, synthetic chemistry has yet to attain such a perfect herbicide. Rather, a wide variety of herbicides have been developed with different levels of activity against different weeds and different degrees of phytotoxicity to various crops. The lack of a perfect herbicide has led to developmental efforts using genetic engineering to improve the tolerance of the host crop to selected herbicides. This is, in effect, using biotechnology to improve the safety margin of herbicide use and thereby extend the markets for the herbicides for which resistant crops can be developed. The market for the sales of herbicide tolerant crop varieties in the U.S. has been estimated at $50 million to $200 million by 1995. Analysts predict that herbicide sales will increase for those products where crop seed resistant to that herbicide becomes available. Such sales increases are expected to be at the expense of other, less versatile, herbicides.

The incentive for development of herbicide resistant crops generally comes from the companies offering the herbicide products themselves. Many of the most widely sold herbicides are popular because of their broad spectrum of weed control. However, in some cases, the wide use of an herbicide on some crops is not possible because of crop phytotoxicity problems. Also, a continuing stream of new product introductions offers farmers new weed control choices, possibly resulting in lost sales of a highly successful established product. Availability of crop seed carrying resistance to a particular herbicide product provides the company with a defensive tool to prevent loss of market share to new competition. At the same time, herbicide resistance can provide a strong offensive weapon to expand the market for a particular herbicide into crops that had not been possible before due to the chemical's phytotoxicity to that crop.

The potential benefit of herbicide resistance for the farmer is simple and effective weed control available with fewer chemical applications and less risk of crop damage. In some situations, the farmer may also gain added flexibility in the choice of herbicide or in the use of a more desireable crop rotation strategy. This is because some herbicides have the potential to damage crops the following season due to residues left in the field over the winter. With herbicide resistant varieties, the farmer could avoid this problem by choosing a seed variety that would not be affected by herbicide residues. The benefit for the company marketing a broad spectrum chemical with an already established reputation is the prospect of strengthened sales to the extent that farmers choose to use seed varieties carrying resistance to the herbicide.

As result of these incentives, there has been strong interest in biotechnology products able to address this need. An added factor virtually assures products from this research will be among the earliest to reach the farm. In many cases, herbicide resistance is a single gene function. Traits for resistance to a particular herbicide can be engineered relatively easily once the mode of action of the herbicide is understood. Usually the herbicide is effective against plants because the active ingredient attacks an enzyme critical to the plant's metabolic activities. If a gene coding for an alternative to this enzyme is added to the crop plant, and if the gene expresses the enzyme at sufficiently high levels, the plants should be unaffected by field applications of that herbicide sufficient to eliminate weed pests. Alternatively, if to the plant a gene can be added that produces an enzyme to break down the herbicide itself before it caused damage, the plant should be able to tolerate herbicide applications.

Work is well along on several seed products that will offer resistance to a particular herbicide. This work often involves a joint venture that may include a seed company, a chemical company and a crop genetics company. The major announced research programs on herbicide resistant crops are:

Imidazolinones

In terms of nearness to market, the most advanced research in the development of an herbicide resistant plant was carried out as part of a venture between Molecular Genetics Inc. of Minnetonka, Minnesota and American Cyanamid of Wayne, New Jersey (the plant research program of Molecular Genetics has been purchased by Biotechnica International of Cambridge, Massachussetts). Cyanamid has developed a new family of pesticides called "imidazolinones" which are low dose, highly effective and environmentally safe herbicides. "Scepter™" is the trade name for one of this family of herbicides that has been recently introduced and is labeled for use on soybean. Cyanamid worked with Molecular Genetics to expand the use of this herbicide to maize by developing maize hybrids resistant to Scepter. Using tissue culture techniques, Molecular Genetics has been successful in developing such lines. Because the techniques did not rely on recombinant DNA methods the project has not been held up by the transformation technology and the need for regulatory approvals. Cyanamid has licensed the resistant lines to Pioneer Hibred International where field work is under way and the trait is being backcrossed into Pioneer's parent inbred lines for hybrid production, a process that requires several years. Pioneer estimates the tentative introduction of a commercial hybrid carrying the resistance in 1992. In other work also directed at the imidazolinones, Cyanamid has a venture with George J. Ball, a seed company specializing in vegetable crops.

Glyphosate

Glyphosate is considered a highly effective and environmentally safe herbicide. However, it is non-selective, meaning it kills virtually any type of plant, although the amount of chemical necessary to impart a lethal dose varies from one plant to another. Glyphosate's use, therefore, has been limited to situations where it can be kept out of direct contact with the crop. The herbicide has also been effective in industrial applications such as utility rights-of-way and roadside weed control where crop phytotoxicity is not a factor. Despite these limitations, glyphosate has become one of the largest selling herbicides worldwide. Monsanto, of St. Louis, Missouri, the manufacturer of this product, has announced that it has successfully produced glyphosate resistant plants using recombinant DNA technology. In 1987, the company field tested tomato plants having this trait and found that the plants were able to tolerate glyphosate applications substantially better than those plants not modified the carry the resistance gene. The company has conducted subsequent field tests in 1988 and 1989 on additional plants genetically engineered to be resistant to glyphosate including rape, potato and soybean.

Separately, also using recombinant DNA methods, Calgene, of Davis, California, has developed plants resistant to glyphosate. The Calgene approach uses a different gene from the one developed by the Monsanto researchers. Calgene has field tested tobacco plants as a model for the resistance. Figure 4 shows the resistance level attainable with these recombinant plants. The company has venture arrangements with several seed companies and appears to intend to profit from royalties on seed sales in this area. In contrast, Monsanto, which has proprietary rights to glyphosate, will profit primarily from increased glyphosate sales. The company also has the benefit of being able to control the filings for expanion of the glyphosate label to be compatible with the status of development of additional resistant crop varieties.

Figure 4. Glyphosate resistant tobacco plants: the three plants to the left have not been transformed. The three plants to the right are genetically engineered to be resistant to the broad spectrum, non-selective herbicide, Glyphosate. The front two plants have been sprayed heavily with the herbicide. The plants in the middle row were sprayed moderately, the two plants in the back row were not sprayed with any herbicide. (*Photo courtesy of Calgene, Inc.*)

Atrazine

Atrazine is an older, inexpensive, and off-patent product that has been used widely for broad-leaf weed control in maize. Ciba-Geigy of Basel, Switzerland, has developed tobacco plants that exhibit resistance to trace levels of atrazine in the soil. Ciba-Geigy has indicated its goal is to develop soybeans resistant to residual atrazine so that soybeans following maize in rotation will not be damaged by residual soil levels of atrazine. This can be viewed as a defensive measure for Ciba-Geigy in that the availability of the resistant soybean varieties will make the use of atrazine a more viable choice for maize growers who might otherwise select a different product. Allelix of Mississauga, Ontario, Canada, in conjunction with the University of Guelph has also announced a program to develop rapeseed resistant to atrazine.

Sulfonylureas

DuPont of Wilmington, Delaware, has introduced its own family of new low dose, environmentally safe pesticides in the class of sulfonylureas. Products on the market already include "Glean," "Assure", "Classic" and others. Using non-recombinant techniques, DuPont has announced it has attained successfully resistant plants. The company is now reported to be at work on recombinant methods to achieve the same end. Advanced Genetic Sciences, prior to its merger with DNA Plant Technology of Cinnaminson, New Jersey, in collaboration with DuPont, and Northrup King are also working on lines resistant to the sulfonylureas.

Insect Resistance Traits in Plants

Insect control has been a priority target of agricultural biotechnology for several reasons. First, control of insect pests is a major market. In 1985, the value of insecticide sales in the U.S. was $900 million. Worldwide, it was $3.9 billion. Even with these expenditures, farmers still report losses of 5–15% and more of their crops to insect pests depending on the crop, the location, the timing of the pesticide application and the degree of insect infestation.

A second factor that has led biotechnology companies to focus on insect control is that substitutes for pesticides are increasingly considered environmentally desirable. Thus, there is pressure from both the consumer and from regulatory agencies to find better solutions to pest problems. Plants with built-in pest resistance will not leave pesticide residues, will eliminate problems of spray drift during application, will not adversely affect beneficial organisms and will not have problems of limited worker re-entry and groundwater or stream contamination.

A third factor is that built-in pest control is perhaps the ultimate application strategy. For the farmer it is convenient and built-in insect resistance eliminates the task and cost of field scouting and the choices inherent with timing of application. Finally, though this is not proven as yet, there is a good chance that genetically engineered plants that carry their own built-in pest control will overcome much of the problem of onset of pest resistance. According to the World Resources Institute, there are more than 400 species of harmful insects resistant to chemical controls. The first insect resistant plants will probably incorporate the *B. t.* toxin gene into the plant (see below). In two decades of use as a conventional biopesticide, there have been no field reports of pest resistance to this toxin. While it is too early to predict accurately whether this will remain true later when use is more widespread, the low level presence of a toxin or antifeedant gene in a plant may have the effect of preventing the build-up of pest populations in the field in the first place. Absent the large populations exposed to repeated sprayings of pesticides, there is likely to be a slower selection pressure applied through this strategy of pest control when compared with that of chemical spraying after field pest populations have risen past the threshold of economic damage.

An additional practical matter: insect control is an early application of biotechnology simply because it can be done with genes available today and expression systems have already been developed capable of controlling insects through modified plants.

The gene that has received the most attention in the insect resistance area is the gene for the δ-endotoxin of the bacterium *Bacillus thuringiensis*. The gene, for convenience sake is often simply referred to as "*B. t.*" even though that is only the organism from which it is derived. This toxin is highly specific to certain classes of insects and has been used in the whole-organism form for two decades as a biopesticide. Scientists have cloned the gene from many varieties of *B. t.* and have found there are differences in selective toxicity of the various genes. Genes isolated from the majority of strains are toxic to lepidopteran insects in their larval stage. Commonly known as caterpillars, these worms are among the most significant agricultural pests on certain crops because they are chewing insects that can devour a plant in a relatively short time. Some species of caterpillars are known to consume as much as 10,000 times their own weight in two weeks. Pests in this category are the tobacco hornworm, the cotton bollworm, the beet armyworm and the gypsy moth.

Other varieties of *B. t.* have been found to be selectively toxic to coleoptera, or insects of the beetle family. Diptera, including mosquitoes and certain flies, are susceptible to other strains. Thus, in one species of bacterium, biotechnology researchers have found a rich lode of insect control potential. Their task remains to transfer that potential into the appropriate crops to attain useful products.

Early work in cloning and expressing the toxin gene was done at a number of laboratories in the early- to mid-1980s. By 1986, a field test of tobacco expressing the *B. t.* gene was carried out in the U.S. by Rohm & Haas Co. in collaboration with Plant Genetic Systems N.V. of Belgium, whose scientists were the first to report successful expression of the gene. In 1987 two more laboratories reported successful plant expression of the gene sufficient to control caterpillar pests in laboratory assays. Figure 5 illustrates the protection from insect attack afforded to tomato plants by incorporation of the *B. t.* gene. Although at present, tobacco and tomato are the only crops that have been reported to carry sufficient levels of the gene to control susceptible pests, work is underway on several other targets, including cotton and maize. Companies involved in this research estimate commercial products will be available by the early 1990s.

Although use of toxin genes isolated from various strains of *B. t.* has been the major focus of early research to develop plants resistant to insects, other approaches are emerging to demonstrate that development of insect resistance traits in plants will involve substantially more complex science than the simple incorporation of a particular *B. t.* gene.

Several laboratories have identified other genes active against selected species of insects. One such area of research has been in development of trypsin inhibitor genes from various plant

Figure 5. Tomato plants illustrate protection afforded by an insect resistance gene. The plant on the right is transgenic and contains an insect toxin gene from *Bacillus thuringiensis*. The plant on the left, stripped by caterpillars, is a control that was not genetically engineered. (*Photo courtesy of Monsanto Agricultural Company.*)

species. Genes of this class have been identified by several laboratories. A trypsin inhibitor from cow pea has been isolated and plants expressing the gene have been attained. The spectrum of insects thus controlled is expected to be broadened when these non-*B. t.* genes are used in combination with *B. t.* genes. For example, Monsanto has reported a synergistic effect on insect killing activity in plants that express both the trypsin inhibitor gene and the toxin gene from *B. t.*. Additional work is expected to enhance the expression of the combined gene strategy. A further benefit is that plants carrying two insect resistance genes of a different fundamental nature are believed to have a strong likelihood of delaying the onset of pest resistance.

Yet another area of recent research focus is modification of the *B. t.* insect toxin gene to enhance its expression in the plant. At least two laboratories have reported that modifications to the coding sequence of the gene can result in improved expression of the gene in plant tissue even though the protein sequence remains unaltered. An extension of this research is being undertaken towards the identification of promoters that are selectively active in specific parts of the plant or at specific times in the plant's developmental life cycle. For example, for the control of the budworm/bollworm complex of pests in cotton, a toxin gene active only in the boll could provide an efficient approach to control since those pests confine their attack to the cotton boll.

A final area worthy of mention on the subject of insect control is the attention to use of antifeedant genes rather than toxin genes for insect control. In theory, this strategy could lead to effective plant protection without the potential for development of insect resistance as there would be no selection pressure on insect reproduction favoring mutants that had unique survival advantages.

Disease Resistance

Most of the advantages noted before in the section on insect resistance are equally relevant to the provision of incentives for the development of biotechnological approaches for the control of plant disease. Diseases of plants have long been major problems for farmers, but controlling disease loss is much less straightforward than controlling insect damage. Today, disease control poses a vexing problem for the farmer as well as for the companies contemplating products to assist him in choosing ways to control plant pathogens. While the problem is substantial, the best strategy to achieve effective control is not always apparent.

The advantages of built-in disease resistance are in fact analogous to those of built-in insect control:

- Plant disease has been a contributor to yield loss in the production of virtually every crop. Estimates of the extent of loss attributable to plant disease range from almost negligible though chronic yield impairment to total crop loss in occasional dramatic situations. In the U.S., expenditures of farmers to control plant disease are less than the sums spent for the control of weeds or insect pests, but they are nevertheless substantial. In Europe, expenditures for chemical fungicides to control plant disease are proportionally higher than in the U.S. suggesting a higher priority for plant disease control there. Wood Mackenzie & Co. estimate that for 1987 fungicides for plant disease control accounted for 21% of world agrochemical sales or $4.1 billion. This is in contrast to expenditures of $8.6 and $6.1 billion, respectively, for herbicides and insecticides, accounting for 42% and 31% of world agrochemical sales. But these expenditures by farmers do not purchase complete control. Studies of the extent of disease loss in major field crops often cite yield losses on the order of 12–14% due to plant disease even with availability of chemical controls. It is clear that some level of disease infestation in a farmer's fields will be tolerated as long as the pathogen populations do not become large. However, in some situations effective chemical controls are not applied in time to prevent crop damage. In other cases, effective chemicals simply are not available.

- As in the case of insecticides, there is growing pressure from consumers, and hence from government agencies, to limit the use of some currently registered fungicides as a result of environmental and safety concerns. Use of several of the most inexpensive and widely used fungicides have been cancelled in the last five years and several others are under scrutiny for cancellation or for significant use limitations. Concerns of the regulatory agencies range from ecological effects to human safety problems associated with residues on foods or with worker exposure. Unlike herbicides and insecticides, where a few field crops comprise the major use category of those chemicals, fungicides are used primarily on fruits and vegetables. These crops tend by the very nature of their production requirements to be more likely to involve worker exposure risks because of the frequent use of field labor for harvesting. Similarly, in the case of some fresh fruit and vegetables direct exposure of humans to chemical residues is a greater risk due to the absence of processing steps that can assure a safety margin through minimum washing or preparation operations performed by the food processor.

- As in the case of built-in insect control, which offers the advantage of an application method where problems of timing spray operations and effectively delivering the control agent to the pest are eliminated, built-in disease control carries parallel advantages. The presence of the trait inherent in the plant, whether it be incorporated by recombinant DNA methods or methods of tissue culture, affords the assurance that the disease will be controlled without the farmer having to decide that pest levels have risen sufficiently to justify application.

While the above are all incentives that encourage the development of disease resistance traits, the extent to which these traits will equal herbicide resistance and insect resistance in market size remains unclear. Despite the large loss numbers and the imperfect control afforded by current preparations, the benefit of a specific disease control product is likely to be limited. Unlike herbicides and insecticides, for which a few major crops and a few major pests account for large expenditures for agrochemicals, plant disease problems are spread widely among many crops and over many disease pathogens in each crop. The significance, on average, of any one of them is minor in comparison to the significance of, say, an insect such as cotton bollworm to cotton or maize rootworm to maize. Moreover, the incidence of problems is highly variable from year to year and from region to region, and it depends also on weather, crop management practices and soils. Because of this combination of factors, losses accrue to the farmer typically in two ways:

- Major loss of the crop associated with an epidemic outbreak of disease that occurs before adequate chemical controls can be applied.
- Subtle yield loss which, while due to pathogens, are in fact invisible to the farmer and are likely to be attributed to normal field and weather-induced agronomic variability. These circumstance do not lend themselves to the creation of market potential and hence do not encourage product development by companies seeking commercial opportunities. Since farmers cannot anticipate the outbreak of disease problems leading to catastrophic loss, they are unlikely to pay more than an "insurance" value at the beginning of the growing season for the control of a particular disease during that year. Similarly, the farmer is unlikely to pay for the value of a subtle yield loss that he is unable to distinguish from a loss associated with normal agronomic variability.

Despite all these negative factors, disease resistance is in fact a near-term application of biotechnology to agriculture and several products are already well along in development. Even though the market sales of any one disease resistant seed product may never rival those of seed products with herbicide or insect resistance, collectively farmers are likely to benefit from their availability. Some companies will probably establish market positions based on niche opportunities afforded by offering effective disease control to growers of certain crops for which no reliable disease control was previously available.

Disease resistance has been an objective of plant breeders for decades and indeed farmer use of disease resistant varieties has been an effective substitute in some situations for the use of chemical controls. The principal advantage the new techniques of biotechnology bring to the development of disease resistant varieties is selectivity and, once the genes and plant transformation capability is in place, speed. The conventional plant breeder's task is painfully slow because the desired disease resistance traits are developed over many generations of plant crosses in a gradual process that relies on artificial selection and natural laws of hereditary segregation. Often the desired traits, when they can be indentified, reside in plants that are distant relatives of the commercial crop varieties that have the otherwise desirable yield and quality traits. Once the breeder has crossed the two, he is faced with the time-consuming and tedious task of selecting repeated generations of progeny of the initial cross to eliminate the undesirable traits that he was initially forced to incorporate with the desirable characteristics.

The new methods of biotechnology changed this: recombinant DNA techniques allow the transfer of only the desired trait into the otherwise commercially optimal line. Similarly, techniques of tissue culture, when used in combination with artificial selection at the cellular level, permit scientists to accomplish in weeks what previously took years.

In one example, research efforts at Plant Genetics of Davis, California before it merged into Calgene, were directed at developing lettuce resistant to corky root disease using cultures of lettuce cells and artificial selection at the cellular level. Scientists isolated the disease-causing toxin from the microorganism responsible for the disease and applied it to growing cultures of iceberg lettuce cells. While most cells exposed to this artificial selection pressure died, the few remaining cells were regenerated and tested for resistance to corky root disease. Using techniques of recombinant DNA, researchers at several company and university laboratories have attained plants resistant to viral plant diseases such as tobacco mosaic virus, potato leaf roll virus and tomato mosaic virus. These initial commercial products are typical of others that will follow, targeted toward specialty vegetable producers where the high value of the crop and the absence of alternative methods of reliable control create niche opportunities.

Animal Vaccines

Much of the current interest in veterinary vaccine research has been spurred by the promise that biotechnology holds for improvements in vaccine safety and efficacy. Several products using vaccinia vector, rDNA subunit and synthetic peptide vaccines, and intended for use against viral diseases hitherto difficult to control, are expected to be on the market by 1990.

But development of new biotechnology-based vaccines

which offer improved efficacy or safety over current products on the market, and which would provide protection against diseases not controlled by traditional vaccines, are not the only promises offered by applications of biotechnology to veterinary biologicals. Antigenic materials might be developed with or without modification so that the appropriate antibodies can be induced in the animal receiving the vaccination. In parallel, work is also under way to improve delivery systems and to develop better adjuvant technologies.

Vaccine delivery has always been a problem for veterinary vaccinations because of the difficulty and inconvenience of extra animal handling usually associated with their administration. The vaccination of entire herds or flocks is often impractical due to time and labor costs. In the absence of a specific disease threat to a herd there may not be sufficient economic incentive to encourage the livestock producer to vaccinate. Research is currently directed at developing new delivery systems which may offer savings in time and labor as well perhaps as providing safer and more effective inoculation. Some of the approaches which show promise include:

- A ballistic delivery system that would deliver a freeze-dried vaccine in a biodegradable bullet via an air-powered gun that can be fired at some distance from the animal.

- An intra-nasal delivery technology. A few products have already been approved for the market in this area. Side effects are reported to be lower on animals receiving vaccines administered via this route in contrast to conventional ones.

- Aerosol formulations have potential advantages for confined facilities such as those used in poultry rearing and increasingly in swine production. Field research in the poultry area has yielded promising results indicating that vaccine administration by aerosols can give effective immunity and produce minimum side effects.

- Embryo vaccination is being examined for applications in the poultry industry where chicks must be vaccinated within a few days of hatching. In this way, immunity could be conferred to the developing bird before it hatches.

Vaccine adjuvants have traditionally been used to enhance the antigenicity of the vaccine. Practically speaking, typical adjuvants can be characterized as formulation improvements or perhaps as a part of the formulation itself. For example, the vaccine antigens are sometimes adsorbed on minerals such as alum, phosphate or aluminum hydroxide. In other cases, the antigens are emulsified in mineral oil and sold in a water-oil emulsion. Current adjuvant research can be classified into two groups. One is directed at refinement of the current adjuvant technologies so that they are better adapted to the new vaccines being developed by biotechnology. The other employs a novel strategy of combining vaccine antigens with immune system enhancers to increase the efficacy of the vaccine.

Many current adjuvants have been developed for use with traditional whole-cell vaccines but these approaches may not be effective when used with new subunit antigens. Thus, some other work is directed to developing new adjuvant formulations that will improve the efficacy of the subunit vaccines. A separate area of research involves the use of entirely new types of adjuvant materials which themselves have been found to have immune system enhancement capability. For example, the interferons and interleukins have been shown in animal and human clinical studies to heighten the immune system response to disease challenge. Interleukin-2 improves the protection afforded by vaccines in mouse and swine animal models.

Bovine Somatotropin

Bovine somatotropin (BST), often less precisely referred to as "bovine growth hormone", is a naturally occurring protein produced in the pituitary glands of cows; it has been known to scientists for decades. During the 1950s, university researchers learned that administration of BST to lactating dairy cows produced an increase in the amount of milk given. In the 1960s Monsanto established a research program to apply BST technology to improve the efficiency of milk production. Although the performance of BST was promising, that research was eventually discontinued because of the high cost of producing the hormone in large volumes. The advent of recombinant DNA technology has dramatically changed the production economics and allowed the research to proceed far more widely. In 1980, scientists at Genentech and Monsanto succeeded in expressing the BST gene in *Escherichia coli*. This accomplishment allowed the production of sufficient quantities of the material to conduct more extensive studies of its efficacy, with the prospect of a cost-effective production process now at hand.

The ensuing years of research and testing have demonstrated that the recombinant product works. Its molecular structure is virtually identical to the naturally-occurring form of the growth hormone so that the genetically engineered version of the protein behaves in the animal just like the native product. When administered to mature lactating dairy cows, BST causes a 10–25% increase in milk production while the feed intake of the cows increases only by about 15%. This significant increase in feed efficiency is the principal factor that has company officials and research scientists excited about the value BST could have to the dairy farmer. In tests carried out to date BST has not been found to have any effect on humans or other primates; milk naturally contains trace amounts of BST and its levels in milk from cows treated with recombinant-BST are not substantially different from those in milk from untreated animals. The Food and Drug Administration has approved the sale of milk and meat from cows involved in BST research. As of late 1989, final FDA approval awaits both the outcome of further research to determine effective doses of BST and the collection of long term safety data derived from BST administration to several types of dairy cows in different geographical locations (see Figure 6).

In addition to Monsanto, other companies developing BST products for dairy farm use include American Cyanamid, Elanco (the agricultural products division of Ely Lilly), International Minerals & Chemicals and Upjohn. Assuming that most of these companies complete their research and introduce new products, there will obviously be considerable competition in this segment of the market.

Although BST offers a significant new product with a substantial market estimated variously at \$100–300 million per annum, there has been a considerable controversy unleashed by the prospect of its introduction. The arguments span the full gamut of issues from the economics of the small family farm to safety to farm policy. Critics of BST have vociferously asserted that it is a product that neither the farmer nor the consumer wants. Overproduction in the dairy industry, the association of milk with child and infant nutrition and consumer fears of food additives and "unnatural" products have all served to enhance the arguments of activist groups seeking to prevent the introduction of BST as a product.

The reporting of positive results of BST testing and the announcement of considerable research expansion occurred at about the same time that the U.S. Department of Agriculture was initiating a dairy herd buy-out program in 1987. The program was intended to reduce the milk surplus problem by the purchase of cows from active dairy farmers with payments conditional on the non-replacement of the cows once sold. The proximity of these events was not overlooked by those seeking to halt BST technology. A concerted effort was made

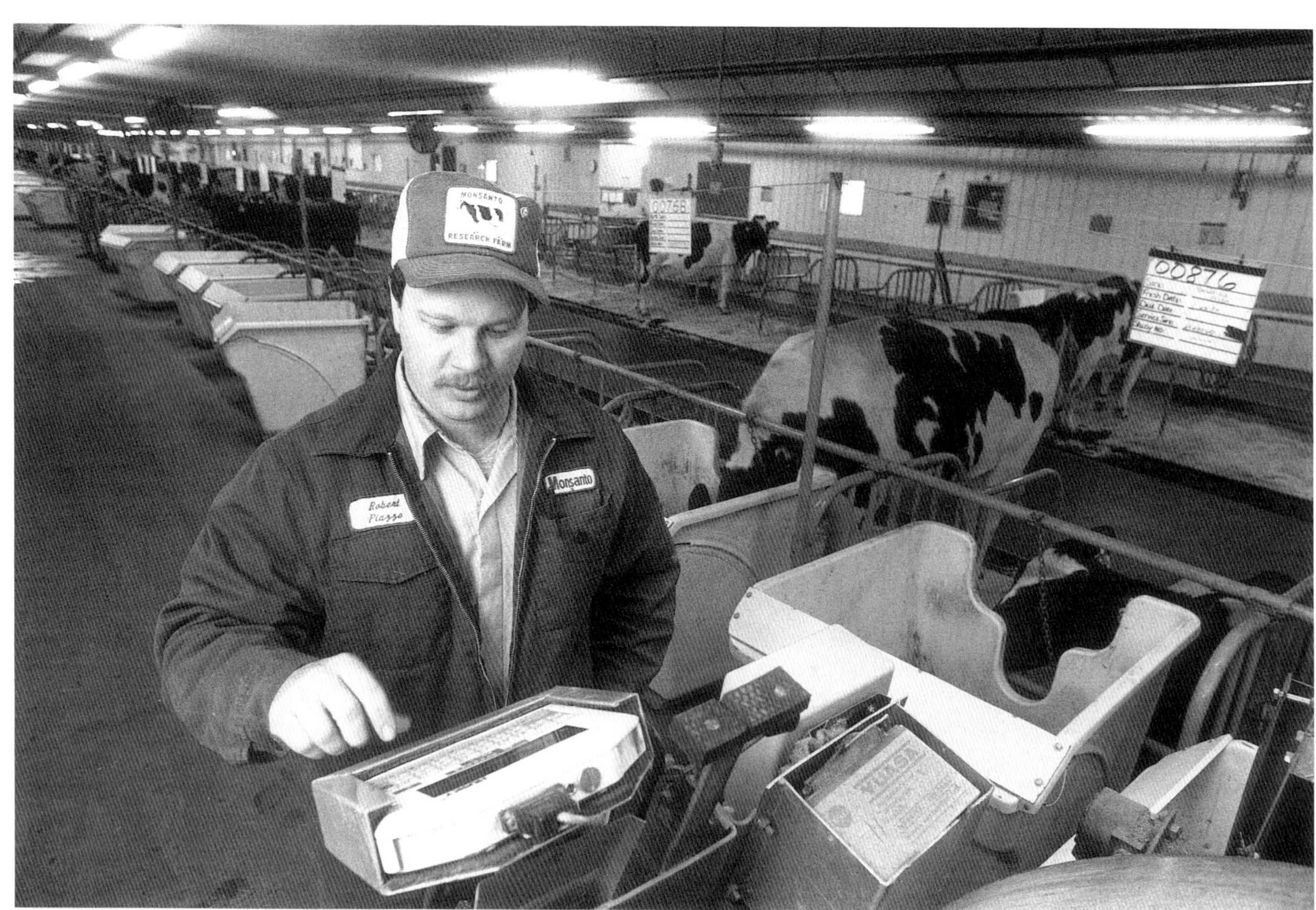

Figure 6. A research scientist uses a mini-computer to record feed consumption data on cows involved in bovine somatotropin research at Monsanto Company's research farm near St Louis, Missouri. (*Photo courtesy of Monsanto Agricultural Company.*)

by the activist groups bent on stopping the technology to label the effort to improve dairy productivity a misallocation of resources. A good part of the debate over BST has involved the relative advantage the new product may confer on the large dairy operation versus the small dairy farmer. Critics of the use of BST have alleged that it will strongly favor the large, sophisticated dairy operator at the expense of the small farmer, thus driving the latter out of farming altogether and forcing an undesirable concentration in the dairy industry. Ultimately, it is suggested, BST and similar biotechnologies will hasten the loss of the small family farm — an institution considered by many to have substantial intrinsic value to the nation.

Many company and university researchers maintain that BST is merely one additional input factor that dairymen will consider for use among the many already available: milking machines, dairy herd improvement rationing, improved antibiotics and other management practices. They point to government policy as the principal determinant of supply because the price support level establishes the guarantee that milk produced will have a market at a profitable price. Further, they argue that it is quite possible that dairymen will use BST to reduce the size of their herds by producing the same amount of milk with fewer cows at lower input costs.

Long Term

While the initial product applications of biotechnology to agriculture will largely offer improvements that modify existing agricultural practices, the longer term developments will open up entire new commercial ventures utilizing different processes to produce food and fiber and using existing food and fiber crops to generate brand new products.

As research with genetic manipulation progresses, and plant and animal systems become better understood, genetic engineering techniques will become obvious mechanisms to enhance the development of agricultural products to create new uses for old crops and permit new crops to become sources for old products.

Improved Quality and Processing Traits

Quality traits are a major factor in determining a crop's value as a food commodity. For grain crops, relative protein and fiber and oil content, all taken in conjunction with price, are key in the selection of one commodity over another. This is equally true whether the intended use is in animal feeds or for the production of oil, flour or meal for human consumption.

Several genes have already been identified that are associated with specific proteins or oils. Expressing these genes in selected crop plants has involved both recombinant methods and tissue culture techniques. For example, maize has very little of two important amino acids, lysine and tryptophan. These are essential for human and animal growth and their availability in maize would markedly change its value for use as a food or feed commodity. Similarly, soybean, which is high in overall protein content, is deficient in lysine and methionine, the latter another essential amino acid. Incorporation of these amino acids into soybean would provide a more balanced food source and increase the value of the meal.

Using conventional breeding, numerous attempts have been made to improve the protein content of maize and soybean. Maize which has significantly higher levels of lysine has indeed been developed this way but unfortunately the maize hybrids carrying the high levels of the otherwise deficient amino acids do not yield as well as the standard hybrids. Thus, absent the incentive of a higher price offered by grain elevators, farmers have not adopted use of these lines. Before its acquisition by Biotechnica International, the plant research group of Molecular Genetics Inc. of Minnetonka, Minnesota received a patent for a line of maize developed through a tissue culture process that has 50–100% greater levels of tryptophan. This line is in further development at this time and it is too early to say whether or not field tests will prove it to be competitive with other conventional maize hybrids. Yet clearly before us is the prospect of new techniques of biotechnology leading eventually to maize that has both high yield and improved levels of the critical amino acids.

Similar genes have been identified which improve the oil and protein content of soybean. Calgene has done considerable work on oil content and has announced the expression of a recombinant gene regulated by a seed-specific promoter in rapeseed. The promoter was isolated from a highly expressed seed storage protein and fused to a marker gene. The result was a genetic modification that was integrated into all the tissue throughout the plant but expressed only in the seed tissue. The company says it intends to use this promoter to control the expression of certain desirable fatty acid biosynthesis genes on which they are now working. Their goal is to develop new oils for the food and specialty industrial oil industry. For farmers, this would translate to new markets for growers who produce selected crops such as rapeseed (Figure 7).

Improvements in processing technology have already led to considerable attention to non-food uses for maize: they include the production of biodegradable plastic and environmentally safe road de-icing materials. Process improvements have also made possible the development of inks for newspaper printing based on the use of soybean oil. These inks have several advantages over petroleum-based varieties in giving better sharpness and depth of color, better adhesion properties and thus lessened susceptibility to being rubbed off. Because of their vegetable oil base, they are easier to clean up and disposal of wastes is environmentally more sound.

These process improvements are available today and their

Figure 7. Rapeseed, an important oil crop in Europe, Canada and Asia, is among the crops scientists are studying to improve oil quality traits for industrial and edible oil applications using recombinant DNA techniques. (*Photo courtesy of Calgene, Inc.*)

development is not associated with advances in genetic engineering. However, such process techniques are expensive given the cost of today's alternative feedstocks and, until the price of the conversion drops, are likely to be adopted only in specialized situations. The application of genetic engineering to plants will greatly enhance the opportunity to reduce the processing cost of these and similar products. As more is learned about the makeup of plants and their genetic control, scientists will find out how to manipulate the plant material so as to optimize the production process.

Similarly, the production economics of many crops will undergo vast change with improved understanding of the physiological and genetic basis of plant systems. As techniques of genetic engineering are applied to these plants, the food value of the commodities produced may be dwarfed by the value they hold as production systems for new materials. Whole new industries are likely to emerge and the farm as we know it today will likely experience substantial change as a new base of production for high value materials that had previously to be extracted or synthesized in industrial facilities. Such new industries might employ genetically modified plants as sources for pharmaceuticals, flavors, fragrances, coloring agents or other industrial products. Exploratory research along these lines is underway at the University of Wisconsin where pharmaceutical production of proteins such as insulin in alfalfa is being studied. Separately, Plant Genetic Systems has reported expression of pharmaceutical protein genes in transgenic tobacco. The inverse of this situation is a possibility that foods previously produced on the farm might one day be grown economically using cell culture technology without the need for reliance on the vagaries of nature and the extensive land commitment inherent to agricultural production. Escagenetics, Inc. reports its scientists are working to produce a natural vanillin using genetic engineering and tissue culture techniques. The new product would offer a high quality substitute for artificial vanillin and would be usable in some situations where presently only the high cost natural extract is possible. Other researchers have already developed a laboratory method for producing orange juice from cultured juice sacs obtained from orange cells. This approach may never compete with the naturally-produced orange juice either on the basis of taste or cost, yet specific applications may emerge where this way of getting orange juice is indeed a viable cost alternative.

Some university laboratories are seeking genes that will improve the drought and stress tolerance of crop plants. Given predictions of possible changing global weather patterns, the capabilities offered by genetic engineering may provide important tools in adapting agriculture to changing climatic conditions. Even aside from the prospect of change in climate, there are substantial benefits to be gained by the development of crops bearing improved tolerance to too little moisture, too much moisture or unfavorable soil conditions. Drought and flooding are frequent causes of crop losses today. If genetic improvements can be invented that would reduce the yield loss in the event of certain unfavorable weather conditions, farmers would have an important additional tool in dealing with these natural hazards.

Nitrogen Fixation

Improved plants that fix their own nitrogen, thus eliminating the need for application of some or all of the synthetic fertilizers typically applied today by farmers, has long been considered by many to be one of the primary ways that biotechnology will bring about improved crops for agriculture.

Based on current levels of the scientific understanding of plant systems, this is a long range goal at best and perhaps one that will remain no more than conceptual for many years to come. The genetic basis for nitrogen fixation involves many genes, only some of which are characterized today. The nitrogen fixation process itself is not completely understood and even, if it were, our ability to insert into a recipient plant the necessary genetic components in a fashion that would make their operation likely appears remote today. Unfortunately, as the scientific understanding of nitrogen fixation increases, so does the number of genes thought to be associated with it. This makes the task of the genetic engineer considerably more difficult. Beyond this, scientists continue to differ about whether the net effect of incorporated nitrogen fixation genes would ever result in plants with improved efficiency. It has been argued that the increased energy requirements of the nitrogen fixation process would detract from the plant's yield capability and hence offer no net benefit.

Depending on how these questions are resolved, initial nitrogen fixing plants, if they can be produced at all, are likely to have only a partial capability to fix nitrogen so that application of some synthetic fertilizers by the farmer would still be necessary. Some analysts have pointed out that because synthetic fertilizers are among the lowest cost inputs at current energy prices, the economic incentive to the farmer for such a partial reduction of fertilizer costs is likely to be marginal. In the absence of a clearly perceived strong market potential, commitment of funds to research in this area is going to lag behind relative to opportunities of more substantial potential.

Until research has clarified the technical issues and improved our understanding of plant energy utilization, the incorporation of an ability to fix nitrogen into important crops is likely to remain a long range prospect. However, fertilizer prices are subject to the cost vagaries of petroleum and natural gas feedstocks so the long run prospects for continued low price fertilizers are open to question. Furthermore, the availability of synthetic fertilizers in many of the less developed countries is limited and the existence of self-fertilizing crops would have considerable appeal to their goverments. It is increasing environmental concerns about fertilizer contamination of surface and ground water that may ultimately serve as the major incentive for commercialization of this technology.

The alternative to modifying plants to improve nitrogen fixation is to seek improvements in plant-microbe interactions which facilitate nitrogen uptake by the plant. Several companies have programs underway to develop improved strains of *Rhizobium* inoculants to increase yields of legume crops. *Rhizobium* bacteria have been known for decades to be associated with symbiotic nitrogen fixation of such crops as soybean, alfalfa, peanut and dry beans. The world market for such microbial inoculants in the mid-1980s was considered to be about $20–25 million with the U.S. accounting for 1/2 to 2/3 of the total. Research is underway to use recombinant techniques to enhance the nitrogen fixation abilities of these bacteria for legumes and, in the longer run, to find microorganisms that can be used to facilitate nitrogen fixation by non-legume crops. Several *Rhizobium* products have been on the market for many years but are used only infrequently by farmers because yield improvement results are seldom experienced and in any case are difficult to measure. It is widely thought that if *Rhizobium* products were available that demonstrably improved the yield performance of the crop, the market would increase by as much as tenfold. In 1988, Agracetus of Middleton, Wisconsin, announced that it had successfully developed a mutagenized form of *Rhizobium* inoculant for use by U.S. soybean farmers in the mid-south. The company indicates the product delivers reliable though modest yield improvements of 5–7% when used in soybean production where indigenous *Rhizobium* is already present. Separately, also in 1988, Biotechnica International of Cambridge, Massachusetts, field-tested in Wisconsin the first recombinant *Rhizobium* on alfalfa (see Figure 8). Biotechnica's *Rhizobium* has been genetically modified to increase expression of genes responsible for nitrogen fixation and the company estimates it will be ready to introduce the product in the early 1990s. Similar research is underway at Biotechnica to develop genetically engineered *Rhizobium* for use by soybean growers.

Genetically Improved Animals

Most research directed at improving the genetic make-up of animals has been focused on altering livestock, poultry or fish to give better reproductive performance and weight gain. As techniques are perfected, a wide variety of new genetic components may be incorporated into economic animals for production. For example, some research has been done in the area of livestock coat characteristics. This could have important benefits in animal health as well as in improving the value of wool produced by the animals. Improved aquaculture has also received some attention with reports of successful expression of growth hormone genes in commercial species such as trout and catfish. These genes have the effect of speeding the growth rate of the fish to improve production economics. Transfer of growth hormone genes has been accomplished by direct transfer of DNA using a heat shock treatment where fish embryos are exposed to abnormally high temperatures to change their chromosome number.

One non-recombinant DNA approach to animal genetic improvement which shows promise in preliminary testing is an approach to the embryonic cloning of animals. Figure 9 illustrates the results of two such cloning experiments. From a business standpoint this method is an extension of the

Figure 8. The first Midwest application of genetically engineered microorganisms was made by Biotechnica Agriculture, Inc., at the Chippewa Agricultural Station, located near Arkansaw, Wisconsin. The company is testing genetically engineered *Rhizobium meliloti* strains for increased nitrogen fixation in alfalfa.

techniques of artificial insemination: exceptionally fast growing or highly productive cows are selected and mated with similarly selected bulls. The embryo derived from such an *in vitro* fertilization is cultured until it reaches the 16 cell stage. At that time it is dissected into single cells and their nuclei removed and transplanted into the egg cells of a second group of cows from which the nuclei had been removed. These re-nucleated cells can be multiplied in the test tube to create whatever number of identical cells are desired. At an appropriate time the cultured cells can be transplanted to the uterus of a third group of cows and grown to full term calves. This third group need not carry any particularly valuable genetic feature. This technique has been shown to work but involves a lengthy and complex process in order to bring it to completion. As the method is refined it promises to yield virtually unlimited numbers of highly valued, genetically identical animals via the reproductive systems of ordinary cows.

Genetic engineering also holds promise for another activity of economic importance, the modification of insect pests for use in integrated pest management programs. In this application, biological as well as chemical control strategies are employed to prevent the economic loss of crops to the ravages of insects. By suitably changing the appropriate genes of the insects and then releasing large numbers of altered individuals to mate with wild pests, the natural population might effectively be wiped out by the genetic sterilization of the offspring of such matings.

CONCLUSION

This chapter has sought to convey a broad overview of how biotechnology will be applied to agriculture. The first part was devoted to a description of the context in which agricultural biotechnology will evolve. This includes the scientifically unique aspects of applying biotechnology to agriculture as well as an overview of the agriculture sector, agribusiness

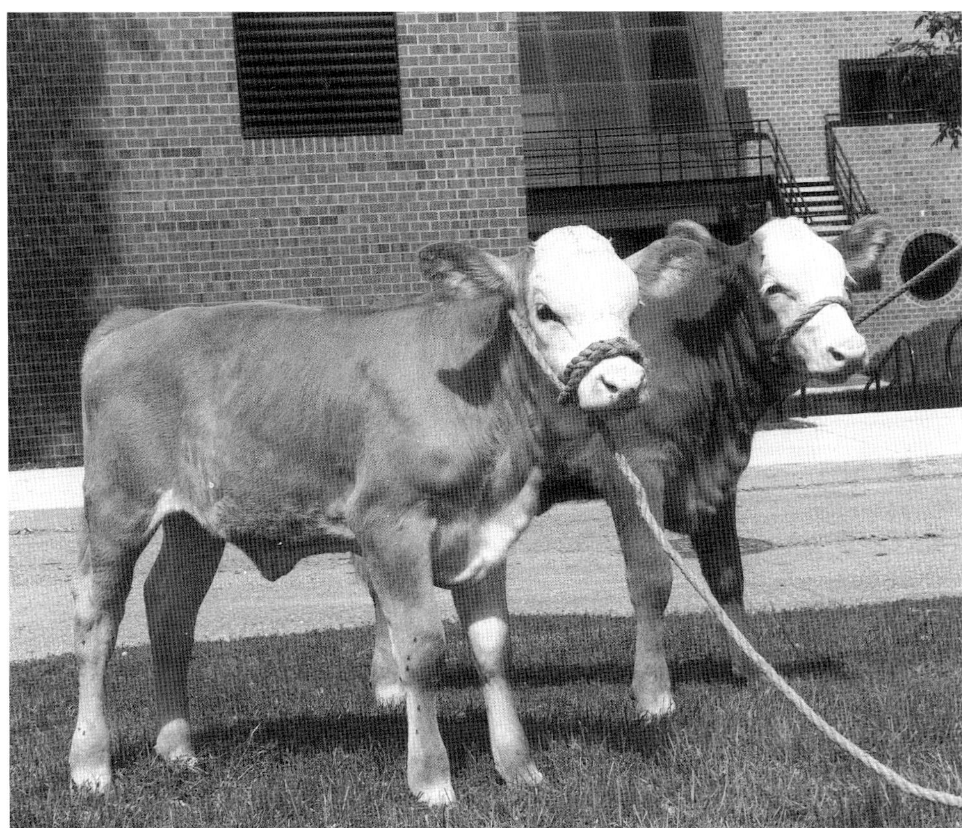

Figure 9. Two calves, "Fusion" (back) and "Copy" (front), which were the result of two independent experiments designed to demostrate the techniques of nuclear transplantation or "cloning". This research is being performed by Dr N. L. First and colleagues at the University of Wisconsin-Madison in association with American Breeders Service, a Division of W. R. Grace & Co. (*Photo courtesy of American Breeders Service, Inc.*)

and public policy issues as they affect the farmer and developer of biotechnological products. The section on the content of agricultural biotechnology then described the applications of the new technology to agriculture. Near term products encompass insect, disease and herbicide resistant plant varieties in crop agriculture while in animal agriculture, near term developments include new, more effective vaccines and growth or productivity-enhancing products such as bovine somatotropin. Longer term applications are considerably more diverse and range from crops with improved stress tolerance and new quality and processing traits to genetically engineered animals.

We certainly cannot today have an accurate view of the long term potential of this technology. Much of the development likely to be really significant will become evident to us only gradually in the next several years as scientific efforts progress and our understanding of plant and animal systems increases in tandem with our ability selectively to incorporate specific genes into plants and animals. The pace of the change is quickening as the seeds of change germinate.

FURTHER READING

Barton, K.A., Whiteley, H.R., Yang, N. (1987). *Bacillus thuringiensas — Endotoxin Expressed in Transgenic Nicotiana tabacum Provides Resistance to Lepidopteran Insects.* Plant Physiology, **vol. 85**, pp. 1103–1109.

Brill, W.J. (1988). *Why Engineered Organisms are Safe.* Issues in Science and Technology (National Academy of Science), **vol. IV**, No. 3, pp. 44–50.

Cocking, E.C., Davey, M.R. (1987). *Gene Transfer in Cereals.* Science, **vol. 236**, pp. 1259–1262.

Crossway, A., Hauptli, H., Houck, C.M. *et al.* (1986). *Micromanipulation Techniques in Plant Biotechnology.* Biotechniques, **vol. 4**, pp. 320–334.

Fischhoff, D.A., *et al.* (1987). *Insect Tolerant Transgenic Tomato Plants.* Bio/Technology, **vol. 5**, pp. 807–812.

Grimsley, N., Hohn, T., Davies, J.W., Hohn, B. (1987). Nature (London), **vol. 325**, p. 177.

Hardy, R.W.F. and Glass, D.J. (Spring 1985). *Our Investment: What Is at Stake*? Issues in Science and Technology, (National Academy of Science), pp. 69–82.

Hauptli, H., Newell, N. and Goodman, R.M. (May 1985). *Genetically Engineered Plants: Environmental Issues.* Bio/Technology, pp. 437–442.

Hinchee, M.A.W. *et al.* (August 1988). *Production of Transgenic Soybean Plants using Agrobacterium-mediated DNA Transfer.* Bio/Technology, **vol. 6**, #8, p. 915.

Klein, T.M., Wolf, E.D., Wu, R., *et al.* (1987). *High Velocity Microprojectiles for Delivering Nucleic Acids into Cells.* Nature, **vol. 327**, pp. 70–73.

Mabry, Tom J. (Editor). (April 6–7, 1987). *Plant Biotechnology: Research Bottlenecks for Commercialization and Beyond.* Conference proceedings.

McCabe, D.E. *et al.* (August 1988). *Stable Transformation of Soybean (Glycine max) by Particle Acceleration.* Bio/Technology **vol. 6**, #8, p. 923.

Miller, L.A. (June 11, 1986). *BST Research for Improved Dairy*

Operations. Testimony before the U.S. House of Representatives Livestock, Dairy and Poultry Subcommittee, Committee on Agriculture.

Pending and Potential Planned Introductions of Genetically Engineered Organisms. (1988). *New Developments in Biotechnology — Field Testing Engineered Organisms: Genetic and Ecological Issues*, (U.S. Government Printing Office, Washington, D.C.), U.S. Congress, Appendix A, OTA-BA-350.

Schertz, Lyle P. (1979). Farming in the United States. *Structure Issues of American Agriculture*, USDA Economic Research Service Agricultural Economic Report No. 438.

USDA Handbook of Agricultural Charts. (1984).

USDA. (April 1982). *Will Midsize Farms Fade as Small and Big Farms Multiply*? Farmline, pp. 4–6.

Chapter 24

Pesticides: Biological and Chemical Agents as Insecticides, Fungicides and Herbicides

James L. Garraway

INTRODUCTION

"Drought, pests and Civil War plague Ethiopia" was the headline of a 1985 issue of an Outlook and Situation Report of the United States Department of Agriculture; it also serves to illustrate a few of the factors affecting food production. Some parts of the world, with a favourable environment and methods on the use of high yielding cultivars, fertilisers and crop protection chemicals have a food surplus; others in harsher climates coupled with political incompetence and instability, inadequate education and specialist advisory services, or just inability to afford the advanced technology, are compelled to subsist on meagre, unreliable food supplies. Irrespective, the world population continues to grow and certain resources continue to shrink; while food surpluses accumulate in certain areas of the world, the developing nations find it even more difficult to market particular crops and support their fragile economies. World crop losses during production, due to diseases, pests and competition from weeds, have been estimated to be about 35% of potential yield — these losses being more severe in tropical than temperate regions; post-harvest losses due to the activities of insects, microorganisms and rodents during storage can be 10–20%. Pre-harvest losses in the U.S. have been estimated to be as high as 38%, with insects, plant pathogens and weeds accounting for 13, 12 and 12%, respectively. Thus in an industrialised country crop protection is important for high productivity and profitability — but in a developing country crop protection becomes essential for the prevention of disaster.

The use of chemicals in food production is not new. The writers of ancient Greece and Rome cite practices based on the use of house leek and wild cucumber extracts, olive oil lees, bitumen, soot and sulphur. Such materials continued to be used up to the 1800s when botanicals such as pyrethrum, derris, quassia and tobacco leaf infusate were introduced more widely. The same period also experienced some serious outbreaks of pests and diseases e.g. Colorado beetle and Gypsy moth in the United States, potato blight in Ireland, and vine powdery and downy mildews in Europe, leading to the introduction of inorganic pesticides like Bordeaux Mixture, Paris Green and lead arsenate. While some organic materials such as oils, tars and soaps were already in use, the application of specific synthetic organic compounds, apart from 4,6-dinitro-*o*-cresol (DNOC), did not really commence until the mid-1930s with the discovery of the fungicidal properties of the dithiocarbamates. The period 1939–45 saw the introduction of the organochlorine insecticides 1,1,1-trichloro-2,2-di-[4-chlorophenyl]ethane (DDT) and γ-hexachlorocyclohexane together with the selective herbicides 2,4-dichlorophenoxyacetic acid (2,4-D) and 2-methyl-4-chlorophenoxyacetic acid (MCPA), followed closely by the organophosphorus insecticides. Systematic research based on chemical structure versus biological studies has since ensured a steady stream of new compounds with various degrees of selectivity and potency, and a considerable expansion of research on the biochemical mode of action, metabolism and fate of such compounds in the environment. A further milestone in crop protection was passed in the 1960s with the discovery of commercial systemic fungicides. However, the publication of "Silent Spring" by Rachel Carson in 1962 was to spearhead a fresh look and reappraisal of the use of chemicals in food production. Environmental pressure groups and public concern about pesticide residues in food and reported effects of pesticides on wildlife were beginning to have some impact on the pesticide industry causing it to have second thoughts about some of the chemicals in use. Particular pest control problems including the greater incidence of resistant strains of fungi and insect, the persistence of the organochlorine pesticides and effects on beneficial organisms all served to accelerate the need for a new pest control strategy. Since the 1960s the value of non-chemical methods of pest control has become more widely appreciated and these, combined with pest monitoring and prudent use of chemicals, have formed the basis of *integrated pest management*. Research on natural products has been intensified together with the discovery of new pesticides based on microbial products. Stricter controls and conditions for pesticide clearance have been introduced while certain chemicals with persistent properties or high mammalian toxicity have been steadily withdrawn.

Development of Chemicals as Pesticides

Inevitably during the earlier stages of the development of chemicals as pesticides many discoveries were entirely empirical. However, the application of chemical synthesis and the production of analogues increased further the range of chemicals with useful properties. Commercial screening of natural products and many chemicals synthesised as drugs have also led to the discovery of new pesticides. However, discovery by chance is both limited and inefficient; recent approaches have tended to be based more on theoretical concepts embracing information about the likely mode of action, chemical reactivity and the desired physical properties of the potential pesticide. The ultimate effect of a chemical on a living organism is determined by a series of interactions, i.e. penetration of outer protective tissues and cell membranes, transportation in a vascular system and, finally, gaining access to a biochemical site with which it interacts. Penetration of membranes and transportation demands a favourable hydrophilic-lipophilic balance, while interactions at the site of action may require some intrinsic chemical reactivity and a particular stereochemical configuration. This somewhat oversimplified picture of pesticide action has been embodied in a multiparameter approach to pesticide and drug design developed by Hansch and coworkers and is expressed formally by the equation;

$$\log \frac{1}{C} = K_1(\log P)^2 + K_2(\log P) + \rho\sigma + K_3 E_S + K_4$$

where C is molar concentration for a standard biological response,

P octanol-water partition coefficient,

σ a factor derived from the Hammett equation and corresponds to the substituent constant.

E_s steric factor,

and K_1, K_2, K_3 and K_4 and ρ are constants for the particular system. The subsequent concentration and toxicity of a chemical in the tissue of an organism is also complicated by various metabolic processes such as detoxification, incorporation into biological materials and excretion. While resistance to degradation is important for persistence and effectiveness in relation to pest control, degradability is also important for ensuring safety to non-target organisms and achieving low levels of pesticide residues in essential foodstuffs. Alternatively, if often proves advantageous to use the chemical in a non-active form, i.e. propesticide, to be selectively activated by the pest species. The use of propesticides can also offer other advantages: improved effectiveness and ease of formulation, as well as environmental safety.

While the Hansch equation has provided a semi-theoretical basis for pursuing many structure-activity studies in fields of drugs and pesticides, other considerations are important for the commercial success of a chemical to be used on field crops. With the growing emphasis on operator safety and environmental awareness, registration authorities concerned with the clearance of a chemical as a pesticide will require extensive information on that chemical (Table 1).

Table 1
Information Required on a Chemical to Be Used as a Pesticide

Physical and chemical properties of the active ingredient
Stability to air, light and moisture
Biochemical mode of action
Metabolism, breakdown and behaviour in living organisms, soil and water
Likely residues and their toxicity
Acute and short-term toxicity to animals
Activity in tests for mutagenicity and carcinogenicity
Formulation
Intended use; timing of application and subsequent harvesting of a crop
Environmental and wildlife hazards
Appreciation of possible long-term effects/problems.

Possibly the most exciting stage in pesticide research is the discovery of a chemical with unique biological properties; less glamorous, yet essential, are the more mundane toxicological and formulation investigations to ensure effectiveness and safety in the field. Few chemicals survive the stringent standards required these days, while development and production costs together with a poor potential market may serve to eliminate an interesting chemical at a very early stage.

The formulation of a chemical and its method of application are essential for its success in the field, formulations fall generally into a number of basic types (Table 2).

Few chemicals used as pesticides are soluble in water; those that are can be marketed as aqueous concentrates or watersoluble granules. However, the chemical must be rapidly absorbed by the plant leaf to ensure rainfastness; a surfactant, functioning as a wetting agent, is frequently added to ensure good coverage and contact between the spray and waxy plant surface. The majority of chemicals used as pesticides must be formulated with a suitable solvent of low volatility and phytotoxicity or sorbed onto an inert solid material of mineral or biological origin; such formulations will also include a surfactant to ensure rapid dispersion on addition to water for

Table 2
Summary of Important Pesticide Formulation Types

Formulation type	*Mode of application*
Aqueous concentrates Water soluble granules	Spray, as solution in water
Emulsion concentrates Self-emulsyfying concentrates	Spray, as emulsion in water
Suspension concentrates Wettable powders	Spray, as suspension in water
Dusts Granules	Dry, sorbed onto inert carrier
Miscellaneous, e.g. smokes, baits, etc.	Various

subsequent application to the crop. Dusts are applied directly and are useful in areas where the terrain is difficult or the water supply is limited, while granules are particularly useful for applying highly toxic chemicals directly to the soil.

Droplet and particle size of the applied pesticide is important in determining biological efficacy, coverage, tenacity, uniformity of distribution, minimisation of drift and economy in use of the chemical. Older application techniques, based on relatively large volumes of water to dilute the formulation and generating droplets with hydraulic nozzles and airblowers, produce droplets with broad droplet distribution; more recently developed controlled droplet applicators, based on spinning disc and electrostatic atomisation, produce a much narrower spectrum of droplet, whose size can be tailored to suit the nature of the intended target. Besides greater precision with droplet size control and distribution, controlled droplet applicators eliminate the need for water as a medium for conveying the pesticide to its target as well as using smaller quantities of pesticide; at the same time, this provides new challenges for the formulations expert to meet such requirements as low solvent phytotoxicity and volatility while at the same time retaining sufficient solvent power to ensure high solubility of the active ingredient.

FATE OF PESTICIDE RESIDUES IN THE ENVIRONMENT

Field pests are controlled by applying chemicals to foliage or the soil; crop seed can be dressed with pesticides before sowing, protecting it from subsequent fungal and insect attack. Foliar applied chemicals and seed dressings can have local protectant action or be translocated throughout the growing plant, affording protection to new and developing tissue. Many soil applied chemicals depend on absorption and translocation by the plant for effectiveness but their action is complicated by interactions with various soil constituents. Irrespective of the way in which a pesticide is used residues can be present for some time on foliage, in the plant and in the soil.

Pesticide residues in the soil interact with such constituents as clays and organic matter. Adsorption of a pesticide onto a clay surface and interactions with organic matter can result in partial or even complete inactivation. Soil moisture associated with a clay surface coupled with a moderately high pH, can lead to hydrolysis of organophosphorus insecticides. The nature of soil-pesticide interactions can in turn determine the extent to which a pesticide is leached in the soil. Microorganisms in the soil play an important part in the degradation of pesticide rsidues; on the other hand some microbial species can be adversely affected by the presence of pesticides. Certain persistent pesticides, such as DDT and the associated breakdown product 1,1-dichloro-2,2-di-[4-chlorophenyl]ethene (DDE), can remain in the soil for considerable periods of time and accumulate in soil fauna which form part of the food chain for higher animals.

Residues on a leaf surface are invariably present as a thin film which is susceptible to photodecomposition, oxidation and hydrolysis as well as losses due to volatilisation. While certain pesticides persist and are active at the leaf surface, others are absorbed and translocated throughout the plant, becoming susceptible to enzyme modification leading to products which can become incorporated into plant constituents such as lignin. Persistence of a pesticide residue in an active form is welcomed to the extent that protection from a pest in assured throughout the growing life of the plant; on the other hand, degradability is important for ensuring low levels for pesticide in the harvested crop, particularly if it is destined as food for animal and human consumption.

Pesticide approval in the U.K. ensures that treated crops are safe by requiring a suitable interval to elapse between the final spray application and harvesting. However, a small residue is inevitable especially if insecticides and fungicides are subsequently used during storage of the harvested crop. Tolerances or Maximum Residue Limits and Guideline Levels are recommended by the Joint FAO/WHO Meetings on Pesticide Residues and these are adopted by individual countries according to their circumstances. Such recommendations are based on extensive studies of the behaviour and toxicology of the pesticide and its breakdown products. Workers in the pesticide industry, operators of spray equipment and animals treated with pesticides used as veterinary products are inevitably exposed to higher concentrations than consumers of treated crops and are of particular interest when seeking information about the long-term effects and fate of particular substances. Casual contact with a pesticide can lead to absorption through the skin, inhalation as vapour and absorption from the gastrointestinal tract especially if contaminated food and drink have been ingested. While most tissues of the animal body have some ability to metabolise foreign chemicals, the liver is probably unique in its ability to handle and metabolise a wide range of substances comprising drugs, food additives, natural products, and air and water pollutants as well as pesticide residues. Excretion of the breakdown products follows in exhaled air, urine, bile and faeces although a few materials may be less readily excreted and become incorporated with constituents of particular tissues.

Not unexpectedly pesticides are also metabolised by pest organisms and studies on their fate are of importance for understanding their mode of action and selectivity as well as providing information for designing more efficient chemicals. The interactions of pesticides with plants have already been referred to above and differences in uptake and metabolism are important for achieving selectivity between crop and weed. As with higher animals, absorption of pesticides by insects can take place by various routes insofar that pesticides can enter the insect body through contact with the cuticle, as vapour through the tracheoles or by ingestion of sprayed plant material; inevitably redistribution via the haemolymph follows, accompanied by metabolism and excretion. Differences in the rate and route of metabolism of pesticides between insects and higher animals are particularly important for ensuring safety in the use of pesticides, especially those affecting similar biochemical processes. The simplicity of bacteria and fungi means that uptake and transfer of pesticide to the cytoplasm is relatively uncomplicated; even so considerable differences in toxicity exist between various species, the basis of which remains of considerable interest.

METABOLISM OF PESTICIDES

Metabolism of a pesticide, or any foreign molecule, by living organisms can be considered as taking place in two well defined stages. Phase I reactions, such as oxidation, reduction and hydrolysis, involve small changes to the structure and polarity of the molecule; such reactions can lead to either greater toxicity or detoxification. Most important of the Phase I reactions is a variety of oxidation reactions brought about by the enzyme monooxygenase in conjunction with cytochrome P-450. The monooxygenase of mammalian liver has been studied most but the enzyme occurs widely in all organisms. Phase II reactions are those which entail conjugation with groupings such as sulphate, glucose, glucuronide and amino acids; such reactions lead to a marked decrease in toxicity and a considerable increase in polarity which facilitates either storage or excretion. The nature of the conjugates formed varies from species to species; however, distinct differences exist between animals, plants, insects and microorganisms. For example, plants and insects tend to conjugate phenols with glucose, while animals form conjugates with glucuronide and sulphate; microorganisms, on the other hand, show little tendency to form conjugates with polar molecules and Phase II reactions are limited to methylation and acetylation. Most foreign molecules after modification and conjugation are sufficiently polar to be readily excreted by animals and insects; plants, on the other hand, are restricted to storing the products of metabolism in their cells or incorporating fragments into tissue components. Depending on the availability of alternative carbon sources and other nutrients, microorganisms, in contrast to plants and animals, can degrade many compounds completely.

Various aspects of the metabolism and fate of pesticide can be illustrated by reference to a few examples, DDT is a well known organochlorine insecticide which has now been replaced by less persistent compounds. One of its best known biological conversions by organisms is dehydrochlorination to DDE; Both substances are lipophilic and relatively stable resulting in their accumulation in the lipids of living organisms and food chains.

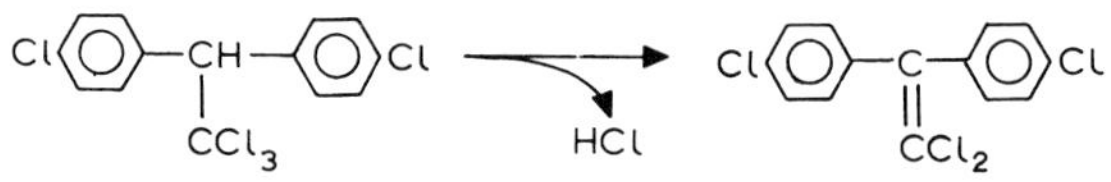

DDT → DDE (− HCl)

Fenitrothion is an organophosphorus insecticide; the $>P<^{S}$ group confers chemical stability and other desirable physical characteristics. Fenitrothion shows little reactivity towards cholinesterases but in insects and animals it is converted by monooxygenases to the oxygen analogue which in turn reacts rapidly with cholinesterases leading to toxicity.

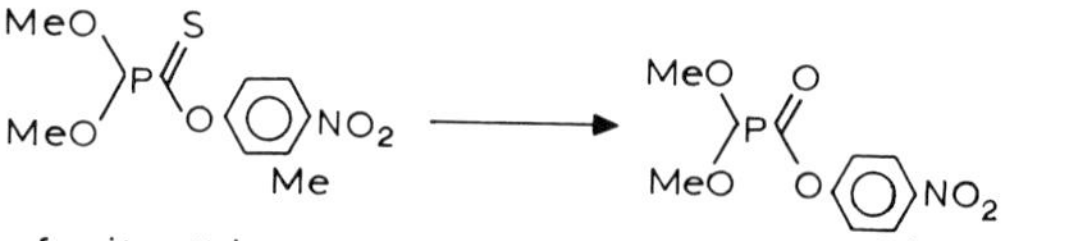

fenitrothion →

The systemic fungicide thiabendazole was originally introduced as an anthelminthic and is still used to control intestinal parasites of farm animals. It is readily converted to 6-hydroxythiabendazole by animals and excreted as conjugates with sulphate and glucuronide.

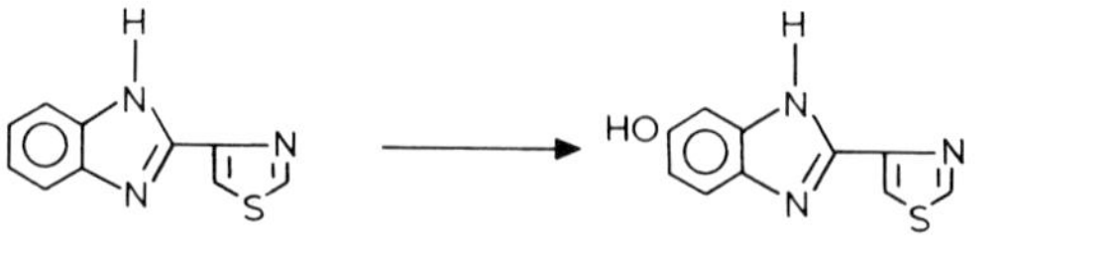

thiabendazole → 6-hydroxythiabendazole

2,4-D is a well known selective herbicide used to control broadleaved weeds in grasses and cereals. It is often formulated as an ester which after application undergoes hydrolysis by esterases in the plant to the physiologically active acid. 2,4-D can undergo a variety of transformations in plants; only hydroxylation followed by glycoside formation represents real detoxification as glucose ester and amino acid conjugates

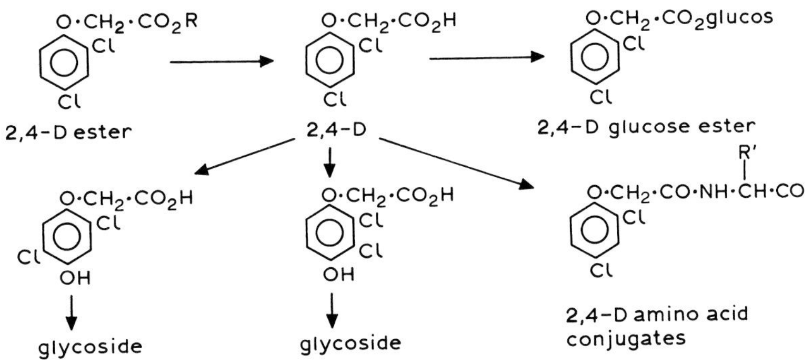

2,4-D ester → 2,4-D → 2,4-D glucose ester; 2,4-D → glycoside; 2,4-D → glycoside; 2,4-D → 2,4-D amino acid conjugates

possess latent activity through hydrolysis to 2,4-D. Residues of 2,4-D associated with food are normally excreted unchanged by animals.

MODE OF ACTION AND SELECTIVITY OF PESTICIDES

In view of the fundamental biochemical and physiological differences between insects, fungi and plants, it is not surprising that chemical pesticides fall into well-defined groups according to use and toxicity. Insects are dependent on acetylcholine and cholinesterases for nerve transmission which, coupled with the complex nature of their activities, makes them extremely sensitive to chemicals able to disrupt the function of the central and peripheral nervous system. Animals, like insects, are equally dependent on cholinergic nerve transmission and can also be seriously affected by the same groups of insecticides. On the other hand, chitin is important to the insect only as a constituent of the cuticle; thus an opportunity for improved selectivity exists as, for example, with the chemical diflubenzuron which disrupts chitin biosynthesis in moulting insect larvae.

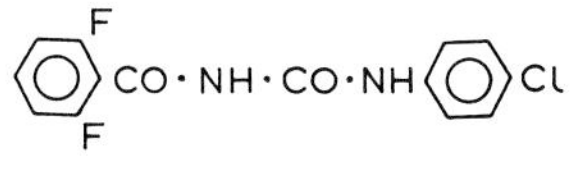

diflubenzuron

Fungi are relatively simple organisms which are probably sensitive to a greater range of chemicals than animals or plants due to the accessibility of sensitive biochemical systems. Energy production is readily disrupted and systems dependent on biological thiols are particularly vulnerable. Elemental sulphur diverts reducing power from the electron transport chain while a number of fungicides, e.g. thiram, react with glutatione (GSSG) and other thiols.

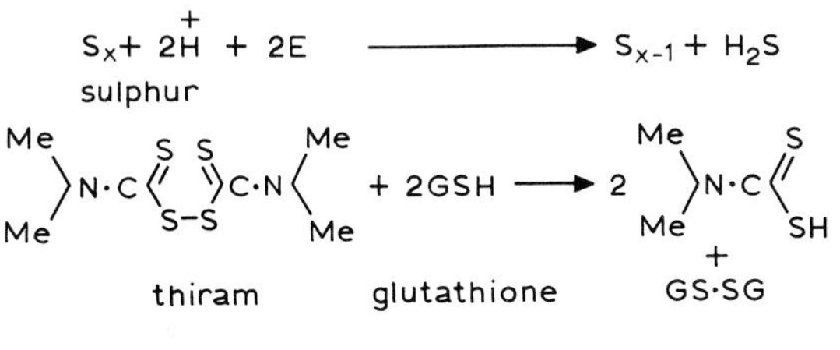

$$S_x + 2\overset{+}{H} + 2E \longrightarrow S_{x-1} + H_2S$$

sulphur

$$\text{thiram} + 2\,\text{GSH} \longrightarrow 2\,Me_2N{\cdot}CS{\cdot}SH + GS{\cdot}SG$$

thiram glutathione

Chitin is also a constituent of the cell wall of many fungi and its biosynthesis is affected by substances such as Kitazin P used as rice fungicide.

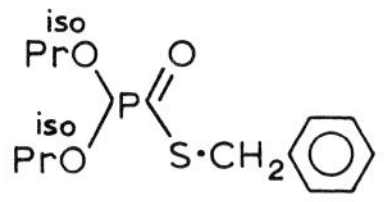

Kitazin P

Ergosterol and related sterols are important components in the cell membranes of certain fungal species and their biosynthesis is a target for many of the recently introduced systemic fungicides.

Plant growth depends on a sensitive balance between various endogenous growth substances such as indole-3-acetic acid (IAA), gibberellins and cytokinins. Herbicides like 2,4-D have similar physiological effects to IAA but are less readily metabolised and therefore affect plant growth. Chemicals which interfere with gibberellic acid biosynthesis are used widely in agriculture and horticulture to control plant height. Plants also differ from other organisms by their dependence on light as a source of energy; a large number of herbicides e.g. ureas, triazine, carbamates, uracils and bipyridylium salts disrupt the flow of reducing power required to drive subsequent dark reactions and protect the chloroplast structure.

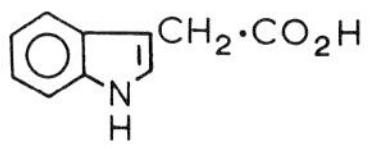

IAA

Greater selectivity in the interest of environmental safety and pesticide efficacy is always being sought. Occasionally selectivity can be attributed to a specific biochemical process but often it is dependent on a subtle balance between uptake, movement, metabolism, excretion of the pesticide. The toxicity of the organophosphorus insecticide malathion is lower to animals than insects due to the ease with which mammalian esterases detoxify the compound:

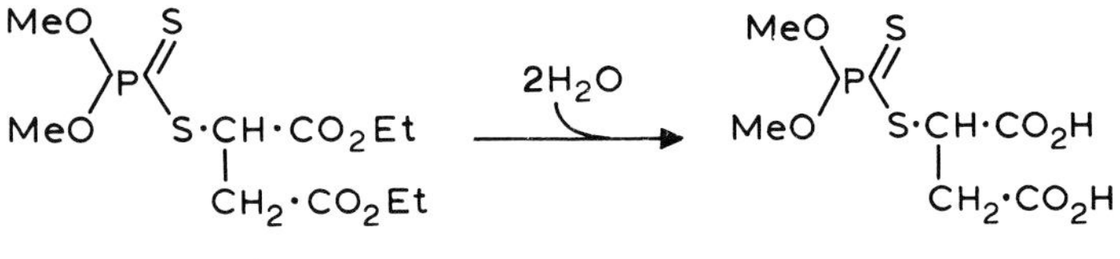

malathion

Dimethoate shows variable toxicity to insects and animals depending on the species; with animals it has been possible to correlate lack of toxicity with the extent to which the insecticide is degraded in the liver.

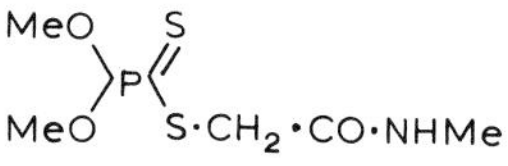

dimethoate

Fish appear to be much more sensitive to rotenone than other vertebrates because of their poor ability to detoxify the insecticide by monooxygenase. Pirimicarb shows remarkable toxicity towards aphids and houseflies and yet is relatively safe to use in the presence of pollinators and predators of glass house pests; nevertheless, the basis of its selective action remains unknown.

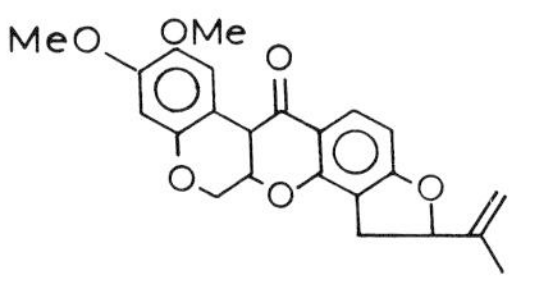

rotenone

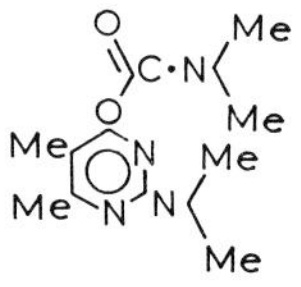

pirimicarb

Fungicides often have characteristic antifungal spectra; however, the older protectant fungicides tend to be multisite and unspecific in action and therefore less discriminating than the more recently developed systemic fungicides such as the acylalanines, benzimidazoles, oxathiins and the diverse range of compounds inhibiting ergosterol biosynthesis. Fungi dependent on chitin as a cell wall constituent are sensitive to inhibitors of chitin synthesis, e.g. *Pyricularia oryzae* and *Aspergillus nidulans* to Kitazin P, and *Neurospora crassa* to the antibiotic polyoxin D.

Pythium and *Phytophora* spp. are not dependent on sterols as a membrane component and are therefore unaffected by such fungicides as triforine and triadimefon which inhibit ergosterol biosynthesis. Compared with *Rhizoctonia solani* and *Pythium ultimum*, the tolerance of *Aspergillus niger* to organo-mercurial fungicides has been attributed to its high cell thiol content.

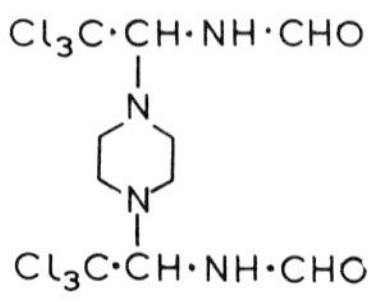

triforine

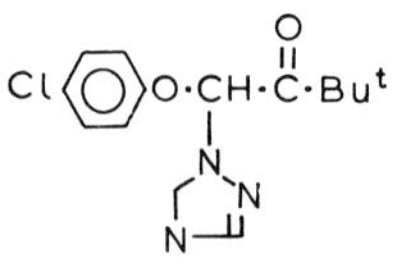

triadimefon

Rhizoctonia solani, which is more sensitive to pentachloronitrobenzene than *Fusarium oxysporum*, has been found to accumulate 10× more fungicide in its mycelium, although detoxification of the fungicide by the latter may also be important.

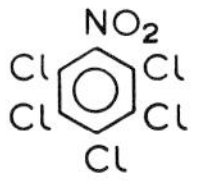

pentachloronitrobenzene

The mechanisms underlying the selective actions of herbicides has probably been more extensively investigated in view of the great diversity of weeds existing in temperate and tropical crops. Differential wetting is important for the selective contact action of ioxynil as indeed it was for the control of broad leaved weeds in cereals by chemicals used in the past, such as sulphuric acid and DNOC.

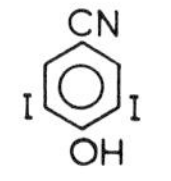

ioxynil

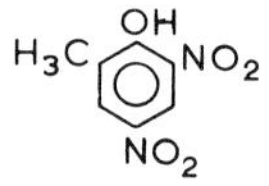

DNOC

Natural constituents occasionally play a part in the detoxification of chemicals. The detoxification of the potentially phytotoxic iodide ion by free thiocyanate ion in plants of the Brassica family parallels the goitrogenic effect of thiocyanates in animals. The presence of 2,4-dihydroxy-7-methoxy-1,4-benzoxazin-3-one in maize is responsible for non-biological detoxification of atrazine to non-phytoxic hydroxyatrazine enabling the herbicide to be used safely in this crop; however, other mechanisms, including detoxification by glutatione transferase, account for the tolerance of other crops such as sorghum.

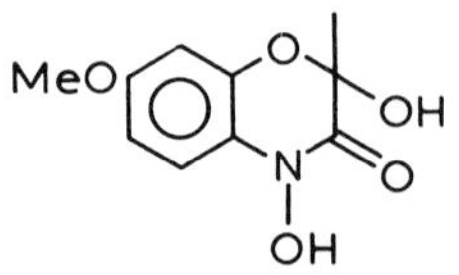

2,4-dihydroxy-7-methoxy-1,4-benzoxazin-3-one

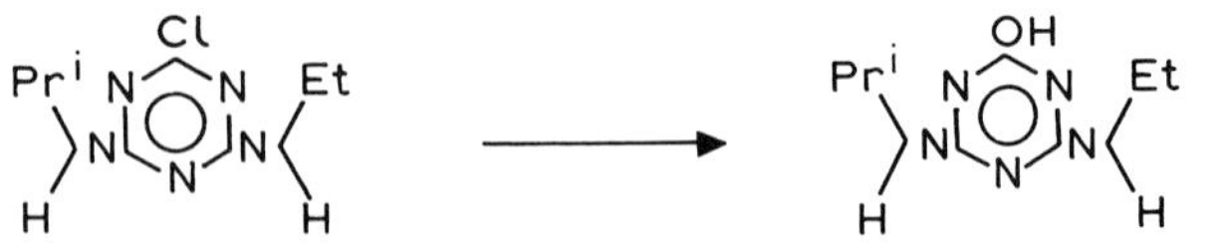

atrazine

hydroxyatrazine

Selective biochemical detoxication of diclofop-methyl by the crop species is important for the control of wild oats in wheat and barley, while both wild and domesticated oats appear to form only the glucose ester which can be readily hydrolysed to reform the phytotoxic diclofop acid.

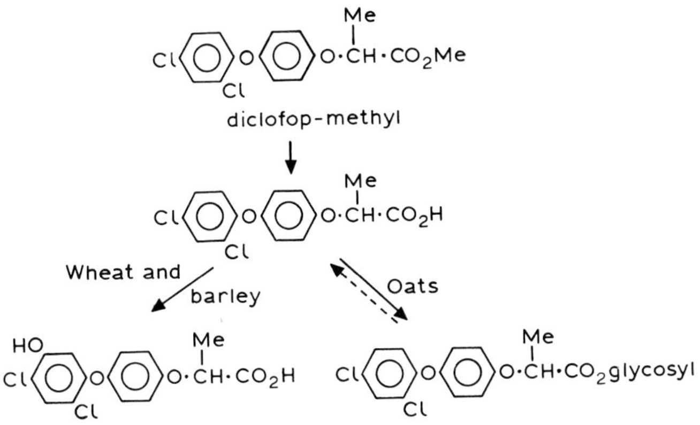

diclofop-methyl

Wheat and barley

Oats

Selective activation of 4-(2,4-dichlorophenoxy)butyric acid (2,4-DB) and 4-(4-chloro-2-methylphenoxy)butyric acid by β-oxidation to 2,4-D and MCPA respectively was probably one of the earliest biochemical mechanisms of herbicide selectivity to be investigated, thus allowing broadleaved weeds to be controlled in peas, clovers and lucerne.

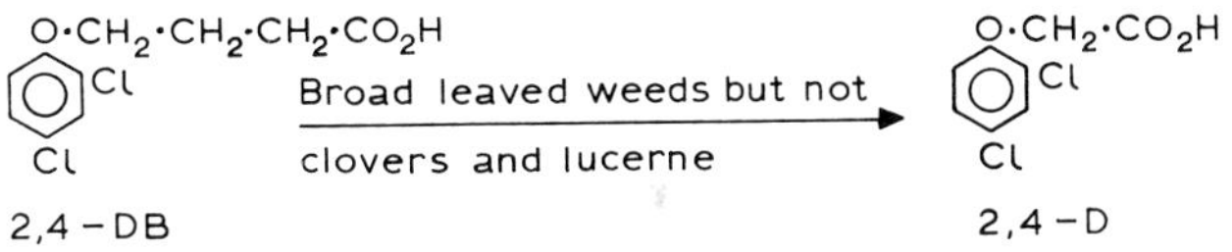

2,4-DB → Broad leaved weeds but not clovers and lucerne → 2,4-D

Animals in the wrong place must also be regarded as pests and none more so than rodents. Rats are probably the most serious vertebrate pest in agriculture, causing structural damage by gnawing as well as fouling of stored crops; they are also carriers of several diseases, the most notable being Weil's disease or Leptospirosis. Early rodenticides included compounds such as strychnine, red squill, white arsenic, barium carbonate, zinc phosphide and thallium sulphate. Most of these compounds have high mammalian toxicity and are no longer used; however, the selective toxicity of red squill is perhaps of greatest interest because it induces most animals, with the exception of the rat, to vomit thus ensuring insufficient is ingested to be toxic. Sodium fluoroacetate and fluoracetamide are extremely toxic to most animals due to the formation of fluorocitrate which blocks the enzyme aconitase of the Krebs cycle; the high toxicity to target animal species of these compounds as well as of corpses containing ingested fluoracetate and fluoracetamide has led to their use being restricted to controlling rats in sewers. Nevertheless, the remarkable tolerance of a number of Australian animals to sodium fluoracetate present in certain indigenous plants is noteworthy and demonstrates successful co-evolution in the presence of such a toxic compound.

Spoiled clover hay has long been known to be toxic to cattle, causing internal haemorrhages due to the presence of dicoumarin. Other related 4-hydroxycoumarins were subsequently synthesised and investigated; warfarin was the most promising. These substances inhibit the process of blood clotting by interfering with the action of vitamin K and the formation of prothrombin — properties which make warfarin useful for the treatment of thrombosis in man. It is widely used as a rodenticide but suffers from the disadvantage of being slow-acting; pockets of resistance, associated with reduced sensitivity of the enzyme vitamin K reductase to warfarin, have also been found among rat populations.

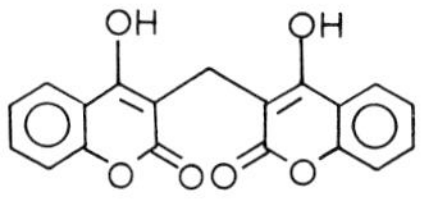

dicoumarin

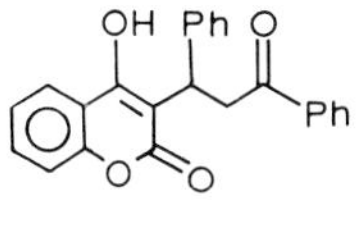

warfarin

More effective coagulants such as difenacoum and brodifacoum are in current use, but the problem of resistance has directed attention towards other chemicals with different modes of action. Norbormide is selectively toxic to rats, causing constriction of the peripheral blood vessels with a concomitant increase in blood pressure; it is of low toxicity to domestic animals but suffers from the disadvantage of rapidly causing bait shyness with rats. α-Chloralose causes death through induced hypothermia but is unreliable as a rodenticide in warm environments. Ergocalciferol (vitamin D_2) is well known in the prevention of rickets in animals; after conversion to 1,25-dihydroxycalciferol it regulates the levels of calcium and phosphorus in blood and bone. Vitamins might appear to be unlikely candidates as rodenticides but excess ergocalciferol leads to mobilisation of bone calcium followed by redeposition in soft tissues and organs leading to their subsequent failure. A similar problem of practical importance has been reported with sheep in Bavaria, West Germany, where high levels of the related cholecalciferol (vitamin D_3) occur naturally in yellow oat grass (*Trisetum flavescens*). The value of ergocalciferol as a rodenticide, particularly in mixtures with anticoagulants such as warfarin and difenacoum, lies with its different mode of action, thus reducing the likelihood of resistant strains of rats occurring.

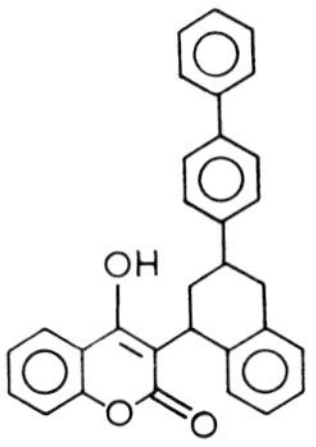

difenacoum 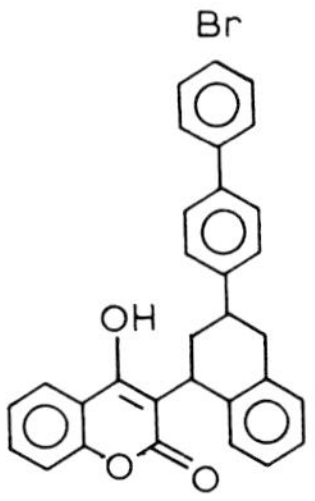 brodifacoum

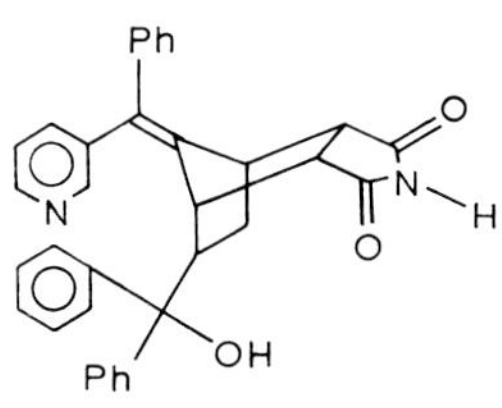

norbormide

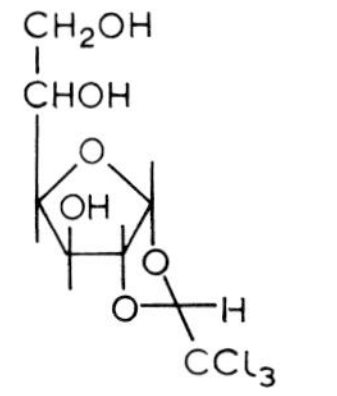

α-chloralose

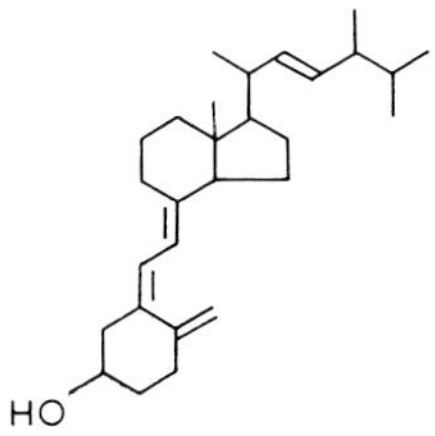

ergocalciferol

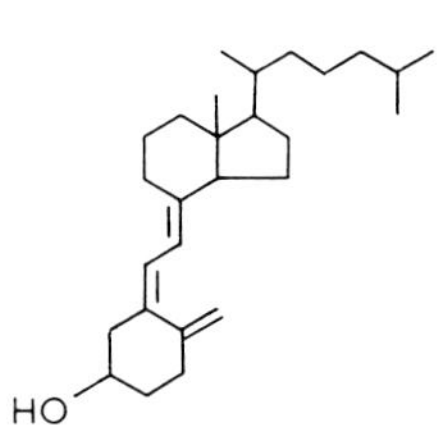

cholecalciferol

CHEMICALS IN CROP PROTECTION PROGRAMMES

The control both of weeds and of crop pests and diseases depends on well-planned strategies based on knowledge of the pest life cycle, threshold levels for economic damage and possible interactions of the proposed control measure with the crop and environment. Chemical pesticides are relatively simple, quick and cheap to apply, and their effectiveness is readily appraised; they lead to improved crop yield and quality with savings of fossil energy, economy with manual labour and lower production costs. However, criticism has been levelled at chemical pesticides because, in contrast to biological methods based on the use of predators and parasites, they lack absolute specificity towards the pest species. In addition, sections of the public remain suspicious about the use of chemicals and the consequences of any pesticide residues remaining in food. It is recognised that serious environmental consequences followed the use of certain persistent organochlorine insecticides and formulations of the herbicide/defoliant based on 2,4,5-trichlorophenoxyacetic acid and containing the contaminant tetrachlorodibenzodioxin. Increasing pressure from the environmental lobby, and changing agricultural practices with a shift towards even more intensive systems of animal and crop production, have tended to focus even more attention on the limitations of chemical pesticides. Intensive cereal production in the United Kingdom has been accompanied by increasing problems from grass weeds such as wild oat (*Avena.* spp.), blackgrass (*Alopecurus myosuroides*), couch (*Agropyron repens*) and meadow grass (*Poa trivalis*), which in turn have had to be met with a new generation of selective herbicides.

Problems associated with resistance to pesticides have become more severe with the increased use of pesticides with specific modes of action; however, the phenomenon is not new in crop protection nor confined to that activity: medicine has also learned to adapt to successions of resistant organisms over many years. Inherited resistance can develop through the selection of tolerant individuals from a diverse natural population through exposure to a chemical pesticide. Such individuals often reproduce rapidly in the absence of competing organisms; they depend either on an ability to degrade the pesticide rapidly, leading to reduced pesticide uptake and penetration, or poor affinity of the pesticide for its normal site of action. Non-inherited resistance in a population can result from exposure to sub-lethal concentrations of pesticide and is often associated with the induction of enzymes concerned with detoxification; such tolerance is rapidly lost on withdrawal of the pesticide. Resistance is found most frequently among insects and fungi; that of insects to DDT is well known and is due to their ability to convert DDT to the non-insecticidal DDE; resistance of insects to malathion is most frequently due to increased esterase activity with subsequent detoxification of the insecticide. Most of the systemic fungicides can be shown to produce resistant strains of fungi in contrast to the older protectant fungicides with their diverse and unspecific modes of action. Resistant weed populations have been reported only relatively recently; typical is the resistance of *Senecio vulgaris* to the herbicide atrazine which results from a decreased affinity of the site of action in the chloroplast for the herbicide.

The potential of pest organisms to develop resistance to chemical pesticides has always to be anticipated by the farmer and grower. It is fairly readily overcome by attention to the spray programme, ensuring that pesticides with the same mode of action or related detoxification mechanisms are not used consecutively. Synergists can sometimes be useful in solving a resistance problem involving insecticides but they must be selected according to the principal route of detoxification in the pest, e.g. piperonyl butoxide inhibits monooxygenase activity while S,S,S-tributyltrithiophosphate is effective where detoxification by esterases is dominant. Mixtures of systemic fungicides with an unspecific protectant fungicide, e.g. metalaxyl with mancozeb, have also proved effective for preventing the emergence of resistant strains of fungi. Methods of pest control based on biological and other non-chemical methods also offer alternative opportunities for averting problems associated with resistance. However, by themselves these methods do not provide the economic levels of pest control sought by farmers and growers and are inevitably used as an essential component of an overall strategy which includes a chemical input.

NON-CHEMICAL METHODS OF PEST CONTROL

Cultural Methods

Rotations have long been the cornerstone of agriculture and have served to preserve soil fertility and interrupt disease, pest and weed establishment. The use of fertilisers and attention to soil drainage ensures vigorous growing crops which are better able to withstand low levels of insect attack, fungal infection and weed competition. Straw and stubble burning, while remaining controversial activities, do serve the useful purpose of removing trash, destroying diseases associated with crop residues and even a proportion of weed seeds. Sowing dates can sometimes be timed so that the young crop escapes attack from such insect pests as migrating aphids and the virus infections they transmit. Removal of alternative host plants can be useful in depriving pests of shelter and food as well as removing reservoirs of disease inocula. It must be borne in mind that certain crop diseases, for example verticillium wilt of hop, can be controlled only by a combination of cultural methods: there is at present no useful chemical fungicide for this disease.

Plant Breeding and Propagation

Plant breeding programmes have been particularly successful in producing new crop varieties with improved yield potential, quality and disease resistance. Recent advances in gene transfer, coupled with cell and tissue culture techniques, have increased greatly the rate with which new lines can be produced to meet the demands of world agriculture for plants with disease resistance, stress tolerance, improved photosynthetic efficiency, economy in fertiliser use and even herbicide resistance. The isolation and fusion of plant protoplasts affords new opportunities in plant breeding which override the usual limitations imposed by techniques such as cross-fertilisation; thus, in principle it is possible to generate new plant hybrids and even new species from sexually incompatible and distantly related species. Alternatively specific gene fragments can be transferred from one plant species to another by means of a suitable intermediatory. For example, the level of trypsin inhibitor in cowpea (*Vigna unguiculata*) has been correlated with field resistance to major pests; in a recent investigation using *Agrobacterium tumefaciens*, the gene encoding the trypsin inhibitor was transferred to tobacco (*Nicotiana tobacum*), producing transformed plants with enhanced trypsin inhibitor activity and resistance to larvae of *Heliothis virescens*. More recently a gene which encodes resistance to bialaphos has been isolated from *Streptomyces hygroscopicus* and transferred to plants such as tobacco, tomato, potato, alfalfa, oilseed rape and sugar beet; the resulting transgenic plants show complete tolerance towards bialaphos and its metabolite glufosinate, thus extending the usefulness of this unselective biological herbicide. Tissue culture is also important for producing virus-free stock although its maintenance is often dependent on the use of chemical insecticides to control vectors of virus diseases.

The value of grafting scions onto wild stocks in viticulture and top fruit production is well known for controlling vigour and improving productivity. The grafting of European vines onto American stocks has also played an important part in controlling the phylloxera mite.

Biological Control

Pest organisms are susceptible to predation and parasitism as well as to diseases caused by fungi, bacteria and viruses; biological control seeks to exploit such situations but relatively few predators, parasites and diseases lend themselves readily to commercial development or are sufficiently reliable in pest control programmes. Potentially useful organisms are often slow to establish, which can be a distinct disadvantage in a rapidly developing pest situation. Native predators can be encouraged by providing suitable shelter or vegetative cover; alternatively, non-indigenous species can be introduced once the pest is established and present in sufficient numbers to sustain a predator population. Whichever approach is adopted, any subsequent use of chemical insecticides and fungicides must be planned with great care in order to conserve the efficacy of the predator.

The first spectacular success with biological control was achieved by the introduction of the vedalia beetle, *Rodolia cardinalis*, into California to control cottony-cushion scale, *Icerya purchasi*, on citrus. In temperate climates it is much more difficult to use insect predators and parasites in the field; nevertheless the value of hardy, free-living predators such as *Typhlodromus pyri* in orchards of the United Kingdom for controlling of the fruit tree red spider mite (*Panonychus ulmi*) is well recognised. However, the glasshouse environment and other protected cropping systems provide a much more favourable environment and organisms such as *Encarsia formosa, Phytoseiulus persimilis* and *Aphidius matricariae* are used extensively to control whitefly, glasshouse red spider and peach-potato aphid, respectively.

Diseases caused by bacteria, fungi and viruses are particularly attractive because that they have high selectivity towards the pest species. *Bacillus thuringiensis* preparations can be used to control the larval stage of a wide range of lepidopteran species in the field or under glass, their effectiveness being due either to a toxin produced by the bacterium or to the production of general septicaemia. Various strains of the fungus *Verticillum lecanii* can be used to control whitefly and the peach potato aphid without harming other useful insect species like *Encarsia formosa* and *Phytoseiulus persimilis*. Viruses are highly specific in action but expensive to produce commercially since they can only be cultured using *in vivo* techniques. While there are reservations about the use of virus-based insecticides to control insect pests on food crops, their value in silviculture and for crops such as cotton and tobacco is well proven. Soil pests are more difficult to control with microbial pesticides due in part to their inaccessibility but the possibilities have been extensively investigated. One of the most promising is the cosmopolitan soil fungus, *Arthrobotrys oligospora*, an organism particularly abundant in soils rich in organic matter and controlling nematodes by an unique trapping action.

The biological control of weeds is not so well developed as that for insect pests. The specificity of biological methods could be a serious limitation to its commercial viability for weeds in field crops as farmers and growers might prefer to use chemicals with broader spectra of activity; however, biological control of weeds would be very suitable for specific problems in undisturbed terrains where the application of conventional herbicides would be uneconomic. While the use of fungi is attractive, insects have been more widely investigated; the most outstanding example of biological weed control is the use of *Cactoblastis cactorum* to control prickly pear *Opuntia stricta* in Australia. *C. cactorum* was brought from Argentina and had the advantages not only of being self-sustaining but of declining as its food source became depleted.

Most work on the biological control of plant diseases has concentrated on pathogens in soil where chemical control methods are less effective and easy to use. Fungal pathogens, such as *Gliocladium* and *Trichoderma* spp., have received much attention and the use of *Trichoderma viride* to control plum silver leaf disease is well known. Commercially, *Trichoderma* spp. have considerable potential and can be used to augment the native soil population or, as seed coatings, to control *Rhizoctonia solani* and *Pythium* spp. responsible for the "damping off" diseases of seedlings. Such organisms occur in soils rich in organic matter and in the root rhizosphere; they are also fairly robust and even show tolerance to some of the older protectant fungicides. It would seem that *Trichoderma* spp. are pathogenic to fungi either through the formation of a fungal toxin or the secretion of glucanases, cellobiases and chitinases which in turn attack the fungal cell wall.

NATURAL PRODUCTS AND THEIR POTENTIAL FOR PEST CONTROL

Substances of biological origin are often more readily accepted by the public as being safer than those from purely synthetic sources. This misconception arises from the idea that only naturally occurring compounds are compatible with living systems while in reality many are very toxic. Mycotoxins produced by fungi of the genera *Fusarium, Aspergillus, Penicillium* and *Alternaria* during the storage of grains under poor conditions pose a considerable hazard to man and animals, hence the need in food production to pay particular attention to the storage of grains and related products. Aflatoxins probably pose the greatest hazard and those produced by *Aspergillus flavus* in maize and peanuts are most frequently encountered. The mycotoxin moniliformin is associated with poorly stored millet infected with *Fusarium fusaroides*. Among Russian peasants during the second world war it was responsible for many deaths from alimentary toxic aleukiae. Yellow rice toxicosis in Japan was found to be due to various mycotoxins produced by *Aspergillus* and *Penicillium* spp. in rice. The toxicity of many plant products is also noteworthy; for example, that of the pyrrolizidine alkaloids in ragwort to cattle and horses is well known and the presence of poisonous weeds such as woody nightshade in crops of green peas and beans can be most dangerous. Thus, the control of fungi, and other organisms, during grain and food storage, and of poisonous plants (usually with chemicals) in pasture and crop production is most important. On the other hand, many microbial and plant products have proved to be invaluable in medicine and there is probably an exciting future for the employment of similar substances in crop protection.

Botanical insecticides based on rotenoids, nicotinoids, and pyrethroids have been used for many years. Besides being unique historically they are of short persistence and low mammalian toxicity. Of the rotenoids, rotenone is the principal insecticidal constituent and is readily isolated from the roots of *Derris elliptica* and *Lonchocarpus utilis*. It is light-sensitive and hence of short persistence; rotenone is well known as a fish poison but is of low mammalian toxicity, except possibly to the pig. The nicotinoids nicotine and anabasine are present in the leaves of *Nicotiana tabacum* and the wood of *Nicothiana glauca*. Nicotine itself is quite toxic to mammals and is used as the safer nicotine sulphate and nicotine soaps; since nicotine is a weak base its toxic action and short persistence is due to the formation of volatile nicotine. Formulations of rotenone (derris) and nicotine are used quite widely but little progress has been made in the search for new compounds based on structural analogues. The natural pyrethroids occur in the flower heads of *Chrysanthemum cinerariifolium* and consist of at least six components of which pyrethrins I and II are the two most important insecticidal constituents. The natural pyrethrins are rapidly inactivated by air and light, imposing a serious limitation on field use; however, their low oral mammalian toxicity with short persistence makes them very suitable for use in public health. Pyrethrin II is characterised by rapid 'knockdown activity' against flying insects, while Pyrethrin I has more effective 'killing' properties. Pyrethrins I and II are rapidly detoxified by monooxygenases; carboxylesterases can also play a part in detoxification but they are less effective in hydrolysing the central ester grouping than that of the side-chain in pyrethrin II.

The natural pyrethrins have contact insecticidal action but monooxygenases in insect tissues lead to rapid detoxification and it is usual to formulate the pyrethrins with a synergist, such as piperonyl butoxide, which functions as an inhibitor of the enzyme.

A large number of synthetic pyrethroids have been screened for use in crop protection and veterinary medicine. Structure-activity studies leading to progressive elimination of groupings sensitive to photodegration and rapid insect detoxification have revealed opportunities for considerable improvements in insecticidal properties. The first synthetic analogue of Pyrethrin I was allethrin, to be followed subsequently by substances like resmethrin but little improvement in light stability was achieved until the isobutenyl grouping was replaced by dichlorovinyl as in permethrin. Further improvement in insecticidal properties was found with esters of 3-phenoxy-benzaldehyde cyanohydrin, e.g. cypermethrin. Few potential targets remain for insect monooxgenase attack and detoxification, as reflected by the reduced effectiveness of synergists; however, the retention of a central ester grouping susceptible to hydrolysis by mammalian esterases, coupled with low polarity and poor adsorption by the gastrointestinal tract, ensures low mammalian toxicity. Even so, insect monoxygenases and esterases are still able to detoxify the synthetic pyrethroids; for example the *gem*-dimethyl grouping on the cyclopropane ring becomes the new point for oxidative attack in permethrin and ester hydrolysis followed by conjugation and excretion is prevalent in certain insect species.

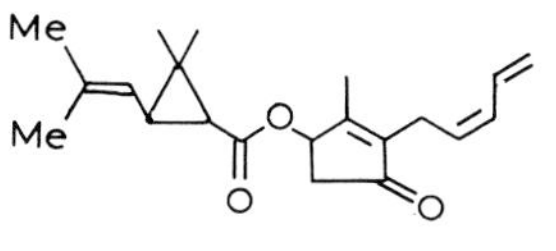

Among other plant products, the unsaturated isobutylamides, quassia and ryania also have useful insecticidal properties. The tropical neem tree, *Azadirachta indica*, is protected from insect attack by a triterpenoid azadirachtin which interferes with insect development. Microorganisms appear to be useful sources of microbial insecticides for the future and the toxin present in *Bacillus thuringiensis* preparations has already been referred to. Recently there has been considerable interest in a group of microbial products termed "avermectins" produced by the soil organism *Streptomyces avermitilis*; these compounds have potent activity against many agricultural insect pests, phytophagous mites and parasitic nematodes.

Observations on the natural reactions of plants to fungal infection may well provide information leading to new antifungal compounds. The process of infection observed in plants exposed to a pathogenic fungus is complex; expressed very simply, the fungal spore alights on a leaf, germinates, penetrates the leaf cuticle and develops in the tissues of its host. The secretion of enzymes which assimilate nutrients and structural elements leads to tissue destruction and lesions characteristic of the pathogen. The fungus encounters certain natural barriers which impede the infection process: the waxy cuticle may contain antifungal compounds, the underlying cutin layer presents a tough physical barrier to penetration,

pyrethrin I

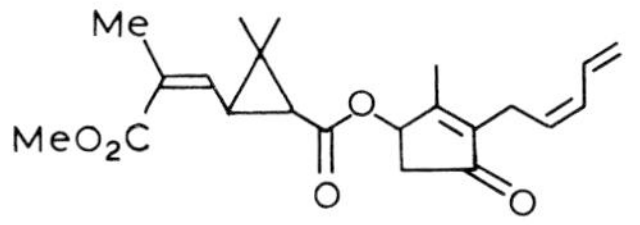

pyrethrin II

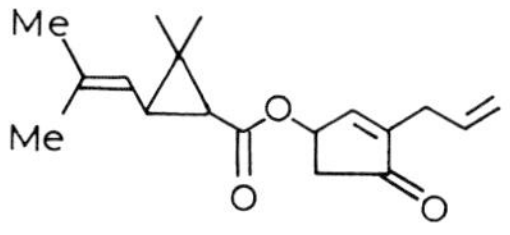

allethrin

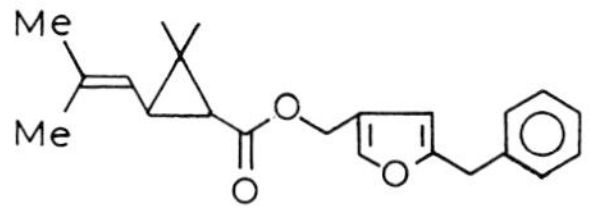

resmethrin

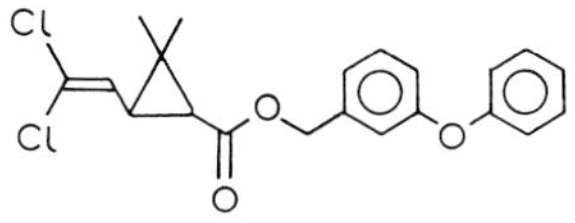

permethrin

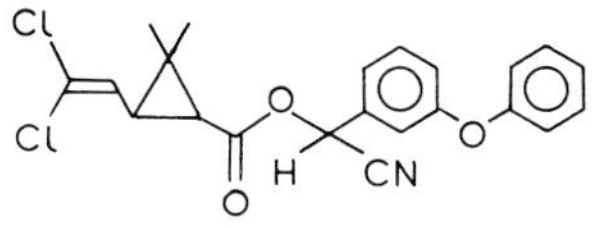

cypermethrin

while antifungal compounds present in the sap or formed in response to the infection process arrest later stages of fungal development. Naturally-occurring antifungal compounds can be divided into three broad groups; preformed compounds which are directly fungitoxic, preformed compounds which require modification or activation to be effective, and post-infectional compounds which are formed in response to fungal infection.

Catechol and protocatechuic acid in onion scales, and juglone in walnut leaves, are well known for the fungitoxicity.

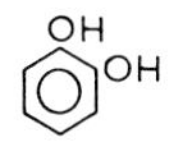

catechol

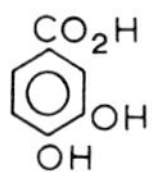

protocatechuic acid

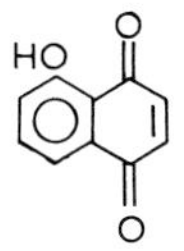

juglone

Phloridzin is a preformed substance occurring in the leaves and bark of apple trees. In cultivars resistant to apple scab (*Venturia inaequalis*), phloridzin is hydrolysed to phloretin which is then converted to 3-hydroxyphloretin; an *o*-quinone formed from the oxidation of 3-hydroxyphloretin is thought to be the fungitoxicant.

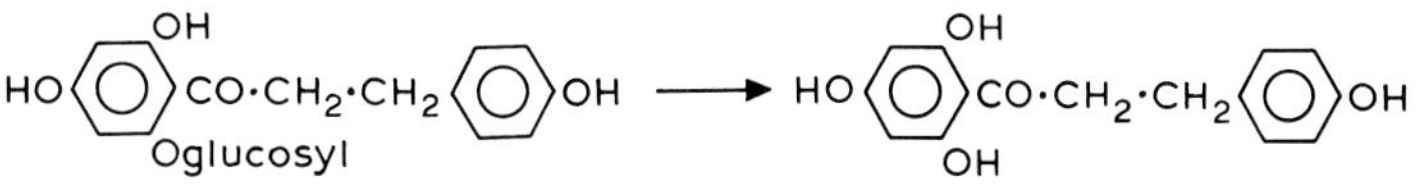

phloridzin → phloretin

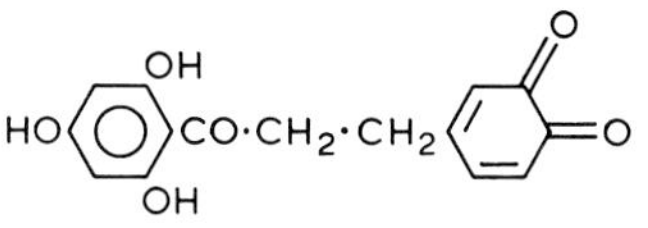

fungitoxic *o*-quinone 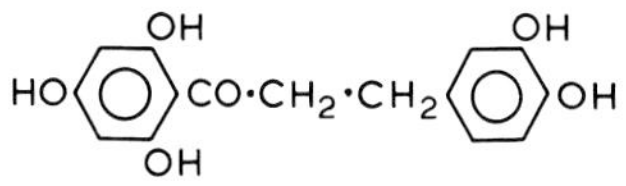   3-hydroxyphloretin

The oxidation and condensation of other phenolic precursors leads to tannins which are well known for their protein-precipitating properties and fungitoxicity.

Phytoalexins are antimicrobial substances synthesised in plant tissues in response to fungal infection or in some cases to physical injury. Pisatin from peas and phaseollin from dwarf bean are examples of two such compounds isolated from diseased tissues; both are fungistatic rather than fungicidal and not surprisingly inhibit mycelial growth more effectively than spore germination. Besides being directly fungitoxic, the accumulation of phytoalexins at the infection site is often associated with tissue death and localisation of the infection. Nevertheless, some pathogenic fungi are unaffected by phytoalexin formation and appear to have specific enzymes which can detoxify these materials. For instance, wyerone and wyerone acid are toxic to many fungi but not to *Botrytis fabae* which has been found to metabolise wyerone *in vitro* to the less fungitoxic wyerol.

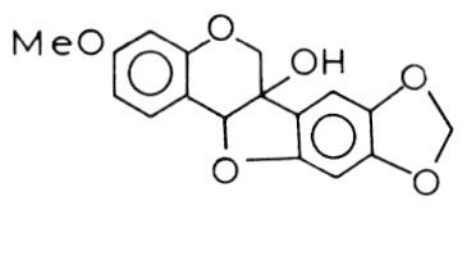

pisatin 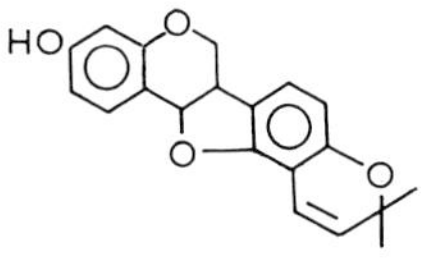   phaseollin

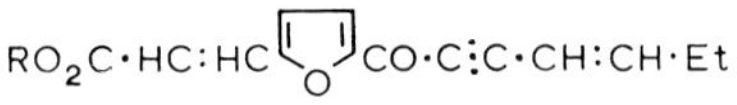

R = Me, wyerone
R = H, wyerone acid

In spite of much research on plant natural products and the mechanism whereby plants resist fungal infection, little of direct practical application has emerged. On the other hand much greater success has been achieved with the use of various microbial products such as blasticidin S, kasugamycin and polyoxins, particularly for the control of rice diseases.

The role of natural phytotoxins in plant competition and succession, i.e. allelopathy, is of ecological interest; the interactions themselves are complex. Many compounds, e.g. plant phenolics and terpenes, isolated from leaf washings and various plant parts have been shown to inhibit seed germination and plant development; they are also associated with decaying leaf litter and other organic matter and are of importance when disposing of crop residues. Whilst it is unlikely that plants will prove to be a good source of novel biological herbicides, allelopathic interactions are of interest in breeding new crop cultivars with the ability to inhibit and compete more effectively with weed growth. Again, microbial products appear to be more promising and one such product, bialaphos, has been isolated from *Streptomyces hygroscopicus*.

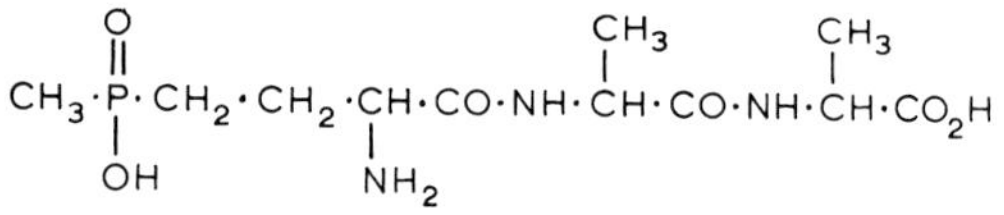

bialaphos

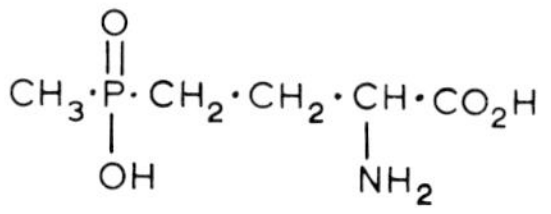

glufosinate

Bialaphos is, in general, an unselective herbicide and is hydrolysed in plants to glufosinate.

CHEMICALS AFFECTING PEST GROWTH AND DEVELOPMENT

Insect development is controlled by two groups of hormones — the juvanoids and ecdysones; the disruption of biosynthesis and degradation of these insect hormones, or the use of analogues which interfere with their action, are potential targets for new insecticides. The juvenile hormone JHIII prevents metamorphosis of the larva to the adult insect, while ecdysones are responsible for triggering the moulting or cuticle shedding process at each stage of insect development. Juvenile hormone JHIII is the most widely occurring natural juvanoid but it is not particularly stable and researchers have sought to improve its stability by eliminating the epoxide group and replacing methyl by isopropyl in the ester moiety, as in methoprene. Such modifications notwithstanding, these substances have but a limited application being of use mostly where control of the adult is required, e.g. malaria-transmitting mosquito, since the juvanoids are only really effective during the late larval stage. Ecdysone and 20-hydroxyecdysone are probably the most widely occurring ecdysones in plants and insects, although various other compounds closely related to ecdysone have been isolated.

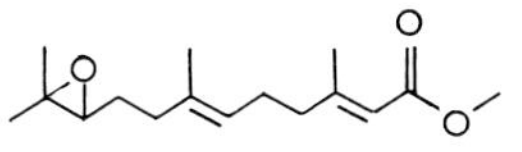

JH III

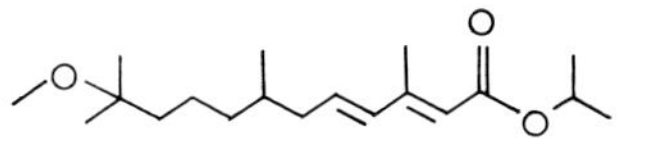

methoprene

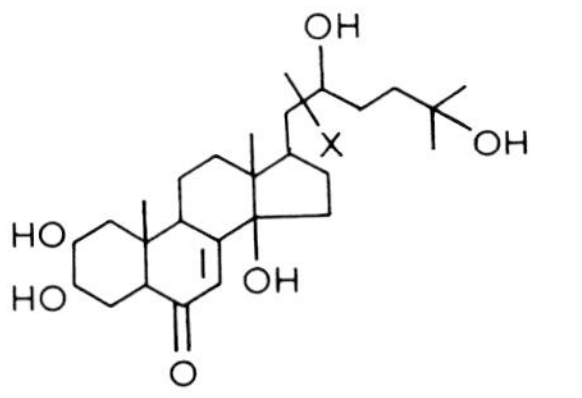

X = H, ecdysone
X = OH, 20-hydroxyecdysone

The occurrence of phytoecdysones in yews and ferns may explain in part the low susceptibility of these plants to insect attack. Many phytoecdysones appear to inhibit the insect moulting process but the complexity of these substances coupled with poor efficacy has made them unattractive for commercial development.

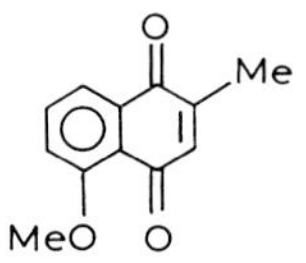

plumbagin

Other substances unrelated to the ecdysones, e.g. plumbagin from the roots of the tropical shrub *Plumbago capensis*, have been isolated and found to impede ecdysis by interfering with the biosynthesis of chitin for the new cuticle. In spite of its simplicity, structure-activity studies on plumbagin have failed to reveal any new compounds with enhanced activity.

Plant growth and development is controlled by at least five different groups of natural substances, i.e. auxins, gibberellins, cytokinins, abscisins and ethene. Cell division and tissue differentiation is initiated and determined by a delicate balance between particular groups such as the auxins, gibberellins and cytokinins. The levels of these substances can readily be manipulated by synthetic chemicals leading to considerable advantage in crop production. 4-[Indolyl-3-]butyric acid (IBA), the more stable analogue of the natural auxin IAA, is used for rooting plant cuttings; gibberellins improve fruit set; substances such as ethepon through decomposition to ethene promote ripening chlormequat chloride inhibits gibberellic acid biosynthesis and is used extensively to reduce cereal straw length with subsequent improved resistance to lodging.

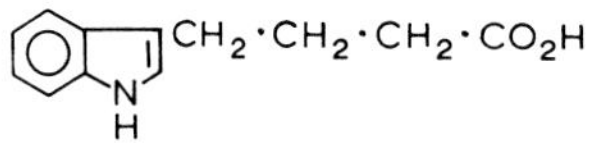

IBA

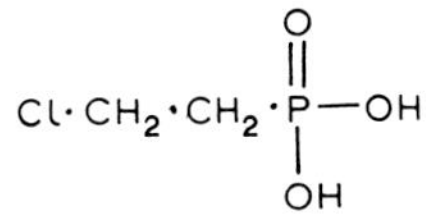

ethepon

chlormequat chloride

The concentration of free IAA in fresh plant tissue is about 100 μg/kg and is regulated by the processes of oxidation and conjugation. Soon after the isolation of IAA a considerable number of synthetic compounds were studied to establish the structural requirements for auxin activity. These can be summarised as being;

1. a ring system, with at least one double bond, as nucleus
2. a side chain attached to the ring system
3. a carboxyl group (or grouping readily converted to carboxyl) on the side chain, at least one carbon atom removed from the ring system.
4. a particular spatial relationship between the ring system and the carboxyl group.

The discovery of the auxin activity of phenoxy acids 2,4-D and MCPA with their selective herbicidal properties revolutionised the control of broad-leaved weeds in cereals; their herbicidal action is due to the disturbance of natural auxin relations within the plant, the phenoxy acids being much more resistant to degradation and conjugation than IAA.

CHEMICALS AFFECTING INSECT BEHAVIOUR

Pheromones are substances which are emitted in small quantities by insects and play an important part in insect communication. They are classified according to the type of activity they stimulate e.g. sex or mating, alarm, trail, social, aggregation and eeding pheromones. Table 3 contains a few examples of sex pheromones emitted by lepidopteran species; they are relatively simple substances and easy to synthesise. Table 3 shows that a number of pheromones are unspecific and it is misleading to associate pheromone activity with a single chemical; it is more likely that attractant properties are due to a subtle mixture of related compounds thus making them more species specific. Pheromones are employed commercially a) to monitor pest insect populations in growing crops, thus enabling pesticide applications to be withheld until a certain pest threshold level has been reached; b) as baits in conjunction with an insecticide, e.g. (*Z*)-9-tricosene

Table 3
Phermones of Various Lepidopteran Species

Phermone	*Insect Species*
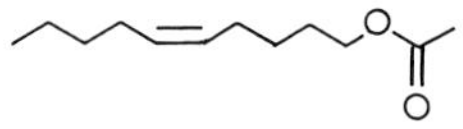 (Z)-5-decen-l-yl acetate	Turnip moth
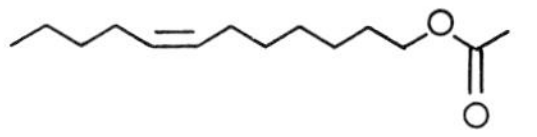 (Z)-7-dodecen-l-yl acetate	Various
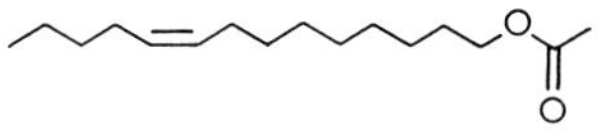 (Z,E)-9,12-tetradecadien-l-yl acetate	Various
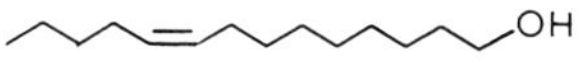 (Z)-9-tetradecen-l-ol	Sunflower moth
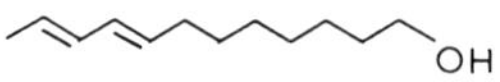 (E,E)-8,10-dodecadien-l-ol	Cooling moth
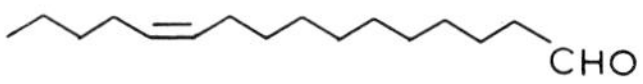 (Z)-11-hexadecenal	Various
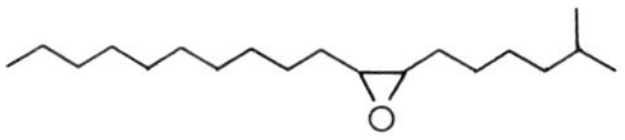 (Z)-7,8-epoxy-2-methyloctadecane (disparlure)	Gypsy moth

(muscalure), a male housefly attractant, is used at 0.025% in a bait containing 1% of the carbamate insecticide methomyl for controlling nuisance insects in animal houses; c) incorporated into a plastic matrix or gelatin capsules and dispersed in a crop to confuse mating activities.

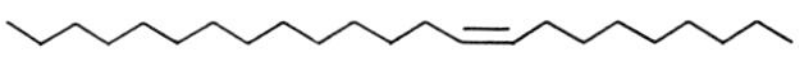

(z)-9-tricosene

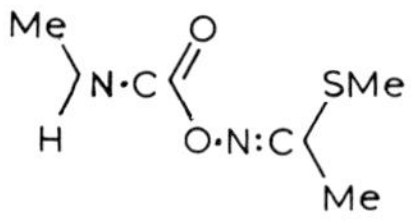

methomyl

The recognition of a suitable host by a potential pest remains one of the more intriguing topics of current biological research. Infection of a plant by a bacterium or a fungus is likely to be a very chancey affair but is nevertheless made possible through discharging large numbers of spores into the environment. Once established, the infection process must be viewed as the result of successful co-evolution of the pathogen with its host. Higher organisms are usually less prolific and need to conserve resources; the recognition process is therefore correspondingly more complex. Man appreciates and is stimulated by a subtlely blended perfume, the aroma of good food and the bouquet and after-flavour of a fine wine. In a similar way, insects are attracted to plants for the purpose of feeding and egg laying through a variety of stimuli. Certain pests of cruciferae, e.g. the cabbage white butterfly (*Pieris brassicae*), the cabbage aphid (*Brevicoryne brassicae*) and flea beetles (*Phyllotreta* spp.), were thought to be attracted to plants of this family by volatiles like allyl isothiocyanate arising from the decomposition of such glucosinolates as sinigrin.

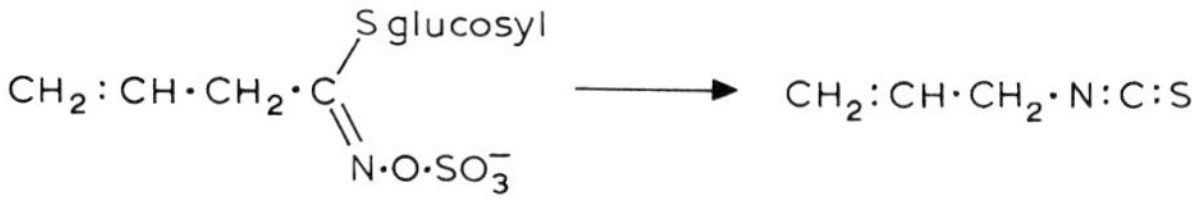

$$CH_2{:}CH{\cdot}CH_2{\cdot}C(S\,glucosyl){=}N{\cdot}O{\cdot}SO_3^- \longrightarrow CH_2{:}CH{\cdot}CH_2{\cdot}N{:}C{:}S$$

sinigrin — allyl isothiocyanate

Some doubt has recently been cast on this hypothesis as allyl isothiocyanate is not a major volatile of crucifers and other substances (perhaps the ester (E)-3-hexenyl acetate) may be involved. Even so, feeding preference has been clearly demonstrated with artificial diets where it has been found that larvae thrive only on diets supplemented with glucosinolate. The hatching of nematode cysts occurs only in the presence of a specific substance, the so-called 'hatching factor', produced by the roots of a potential host, for example *Heterodera rostochiensis* a pest of potato and tomato; the identity of the hatching factor remains elusive. Parasitic weeds such as *Orobanche* spp. and *Striga* spp. cause serious damage to legume and graminaceous crops respectively; in general, the seed of both genera germinate only in the presence of stimulants secreted by a suitable host, followed by attachment of the germinated seed to the roots of the host plant during which further chemicals may be involved. There are plants which secrete germination stimulants but do not permit attachment of the germinated seed to their roots and so serve as useful 'trap' crops by reducing the reservoir of viable seed in the soil. Obviously the chemical nature of such stimulants is of considerable interest and recently a stimulant of this type for the germination for *Striga asiatica* was isolated from a typical host plant, sorghum. However, the stimulant isolated from sorghum bears little relationship to strigol which was isolated much earlier from a non-host plant, cotton; synthetic analogues of strigol have shown some potential for reducing parasitism by stimulating premature germination when used on soil about six weeks before planting a susceptible crop. Alternatively, new approaches can be based on finding hovel crop lines which do not synthesis or secrete the stimulant or are able to present barriers to the attachment of the parasite.

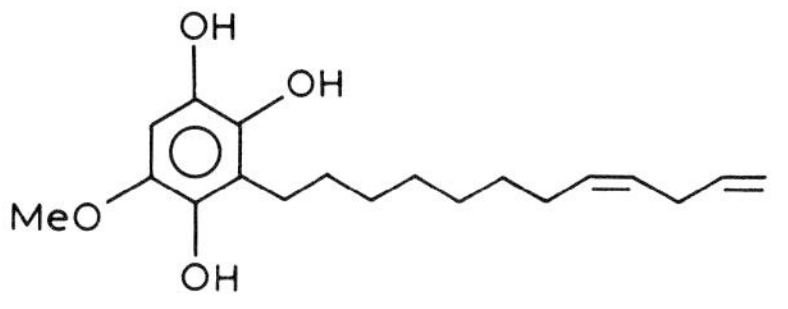

S. asiatica
germination stimulant from sorghum

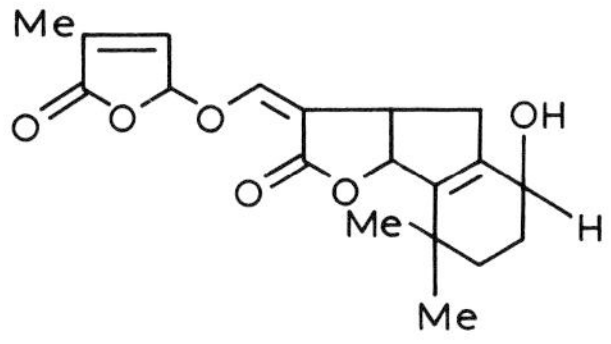

strigol

POTENTIAL APPLICATIONS OF BIOTECHNOLOGY TO PEST CONTROL

The earliest applications of living organisms to the processes of water purification, sewage treatment, microbial leaching of metal ores and fermentation marked the beginning of the biotechnology era. With advances in techniques, the commercial production of enzymes, proteins and antibiotics followed. Recent advances in biochemistry have added a new dimension to biotechnology, namely the ability to select, transfer and incorporate specific fragments of genetic material from one organism to another. But these advances have not suddenly invalidated all the well established traditional techniques; many will continue to provide a basis for culturing organisms whether they be plants, fungi, bacteria, viruses, or insect predators and parasites.

Some of the objectives of plant breeders with respect to disease and pest resistance have been mentioned in this chapter. While acknowledging that classical selection and breeding techniques, as well as even cruder methods based on chemical mutagens and irradiation, have served well, the newer methods are clearly more specific; in conjunction with tissue culture techniques, they offer the potential for realising the breeder's objectives in a shorter time. In crop protection there is considerable interest in plant resistance to pest insects, pathogenic fungi and viruses as well as the ability to survive competition from weeds, thus reducing the dependence on chemical pesticides; resistance to viruses is of particular interest as there is, as yet, no effective chemical viricide. Obviously, engineered plant resistance to pest organisms reduces the need for chemical pesticides which in turn will prove beneficial to the environment. However, the production of new cultivars with improved pest resistance while retaining other desirable characteristics such as yield, quality and ability to tolerate environmental stress, is not without some difficulties; a new cultivar with disease resistance may survive a few seasons, only to succumb to a new virulent strain of pathogen; new cultivars of crops such as oilseed rape may be low in erucic acid, glucosinolates and tannins but more susceptible to insect attack and spoilation during storage. In addition, the plant breeder will need to be supplied with very specific information about the characters to be exploited or deleted; it is here that support from research on the interactions between host, pest, and predator/parasite and the environment is so important for without it the breeder will be groping in the dark. For example, the chemicals that are associated with pest orientation for the purposes of egg laying and feeding are primary targets for deletion while chemicals associated with resistance to pest attack are to be exploited. Nevertheless, the success and efficiency of present day agriculture owe much to the classical methods of plant breeding which stand to be extended further by the new techniques available to plant breeders and geneticists.

The manipulation of bacteria and fungi also afford opportunities for producing microbial products with fungicidal, herbicidal and insecticidal properties. *Escherichia coli* may turn out to be the most popular candidate for this as so much is known about its biochemistry and genetics, using the techniques of recombinant DNA technology; selected fragments of foreign DNA have already been introduced via plasmids thus enabling new *E. coli* constructs to produce insulin, bovine somatotrophin and a range of antibiotics on a commercial scale. The scope for producing new and safer pesticides of biological origin is obvious, there is also a clear need for organisms with improved effectiveness and virulence for the biological control of insect pests, new strains of viruses, for instance, with improved light stability while simultaneously retaining their selectivity and virulence. It is well known that there are different strains of *B. thuringiensis* with different potencies towards lepidopterous, coleopterous and dipterous insects; some of them are of considerable interest with respect to the extended use of this organism in pest control. Microbial pesticides in general are probably one of the most attractive fields for future R & D in pest control Table 4; their high target specificity makes them more acceptable environmentally while simultaneously providing increased operator safety and fewer consumer hazards from residues on food crops. The 1985 world sales of biological pesticides (less than $100 million in the U.S. alone) was no more than 1% of the total for all products used for insect, mite and nematode control; of this, some 0.6% (about $55 million in the U.S.) was accounted for by products based on *B. thuringiensis*. Research and development and registration costs for biopesticides should be much lower than for conventional products; if manufacturing costs, too, can be kept low there will be considerable potential for extending the range and making their use on minor crops more attractive and cost-effective.

Table 4
Advantage and Disadvantages of Microbial vs. Chemical Pesticides

Costs/Benefits	*Microbial*	*Chemical*
R & D	\$0.8–1.6 million	\$20 million
Market size required for profitability	Markets under \$1.6 million may be profitable due to low development costs	\$40 million/year to recoup development costs; therefore limited to major crops
Toxicological testing	\$500,000	\$10 million
Patentability	Still developing	Well established
Discovery		
	Rational selection for specific target pests	Screen 15,000 compounds to identify one product
Efficacy		
Kill	Usually 90–95%	*ca.* 100%
Speed of kill	Can be slow	Rapid
Spectrum of activity	Generally narrow	Generally broad
Resistance	Only one case known	Often develops
Type of action	Generally only curative	Can be both preventative and curative
Safety		
Operator safety	Low operator risk	Chemicals can be hazardous
Environmental impact	Few examples with inundative use of indigenous microorganisms	Many examples
Residues	Crop can usually be harvested immediately after application	Interval before harvest often required

CONCLUSION

The control of pests and diseases is an essential part of crop production strategy. Novel methods of pest control will continue to emerge as the limitations of older methods are revealed and new techniques discovered in response to new demands on cropping systems to produce food in ever more hostile environments. Studies on the development and use of chemical pesticides are truly interdisciplinary and problems can be solved only by close collaboration between agronomists, biologists, chemists and ecologists. Without the availability of chemical pesticides the present achievements in agricultural production would not have been realised; irrespective of problems with particular types of chemical pesticides, much has been learned about the impact of these materials on the environment and greater awareness and sensitivity exist towards their application in crop production. There is no doubt that chemical pesticides will continue to be used; as time progresses, they will probably evolve to include more plant and microbial products or related synthetic compounds. New chemicals will inevitably be more subtle in their actions, many interacting selectively with a specific feature of the pest's biochemical system. Other methods of pest control have shown increasing importance in crop production over the past decade and in the future they will have an expanding role in avoiding some of the particular problems associated with chemical pesticides. The skills of the plant breeder, coupled with present-day technology, will ensure an even greater supply of cultivars with more resistance to diseases and insect attack. Nevertheless, well proven systems of pest control, whether they are chemical, cultural or biological, should not be lightly discarded for the sake of new and novel technology — all must be harnessed to work with the same harmony as that elicited by a conductor of an orchestra, with all the quality of tone, balance and unanimity expected by a listener.

BIBLIOGRAPHY FOR FURTHER READING

Cremlyn, R. (1978). *Pesticides; Preparation and Mode of Action*. Chichester, John Wiley.

Day, P. (editor). (1986). *Biotechnology and Crop Improvement and Protection*. BCPC Monograph No. 34. Thornton Heath, BCPC Publications.

Harbourne, J.B. (1988). *Introduction to Ecological Biochemistry, 3rd edition*. London, Academic Press.

Hoy, M.A. & Herzog, D.C. (editors). (1985). *Biological Control in Agricultural IPIA Systems*. London, Academic Press.

Hussey, N.W. & Scopes, N. (1985). *Biological Control*. Poole, Blandford Press.

LeBaron, H.M., Mumma, R.O., Honeycutt, R.C., Duesting, J.H., Phillips, J.F. and Haas, M.J. (editors). (1987). *Biotechnology in Agricultural Chemistry*; ACS Symposium Series 334, Washington D.C., American Chemical Society.

Martin, H. and Woodcock, D. (1983). *Scientific Principles of Crop Protection, 7th edition*. London, Edward Arnold.

Matsumura, F. & Krishna Murti, C.R. (1985). *Biodegradation of Pesticides*. New York & London, Plenum.

Chapter 25

The Impact of Biotechnology on the Food Industry

Roger Jeffcoat

INTRODUCTION

The developments during the last fifteen to twenty years in biosciences, and in particular in molecular and cell biology, have led to a high expectation for the application and simulation of biological systems in commercial processes. In reality, the slow fulfilment of this potential has a number of economic, technical and political explanations.

The driving force for the exploitation of biotechnology in the food sector has been consumer pressure to move away from processed food and artificial additives and more towards foods with "natural" ingredients and processed in a way that simulates the events which occur in nature. The concept that "we are what we eat" has meant that the food ingredient manufacturer has needed more control over raw materials, an understanding of the natural biochemical processes and the engineering capability to carry them out economically. The emphasis in this chapter will therefore not be to dwell on the difficulties but to highlight those successful ventures and will point to future trends and progress while taking into account a clearer definition of commercial targets and the role that legislation/legislators can have on progressing the new technologies.

WHAT IS BIOTECHNOLOGY?

Although the food business is clearly undergoing a change towards healthier eating — foods with less fat, more fibre, a higher proportion of vegetable oil, less salt and less chemical processing — biotechnology can provide only some of the answers. So what is biotechnology? A number of definitions have been proposed but for the purpose of its application to the food sector it may be defined as the use of living cells, or parts of them, to produce or modify foods and food ingredients. This means that there is nothing magical and it is constrained by the same economic factors which govern all "chemical" processes. Major developments in the understanding of biological systems have however extended the range of possibilities to include biological catalysis rather than the use of chemical catalysts as processing aids and to carry out processes which more closely mimic those occurring in nature. Against this background, the potential opportunities for the impact of biotechnology can be divided into four main areas, as summarised in Figure 1:

- Control of raw materials
- Modification of the raw materials to improve their performance
- Production of novel ingredients

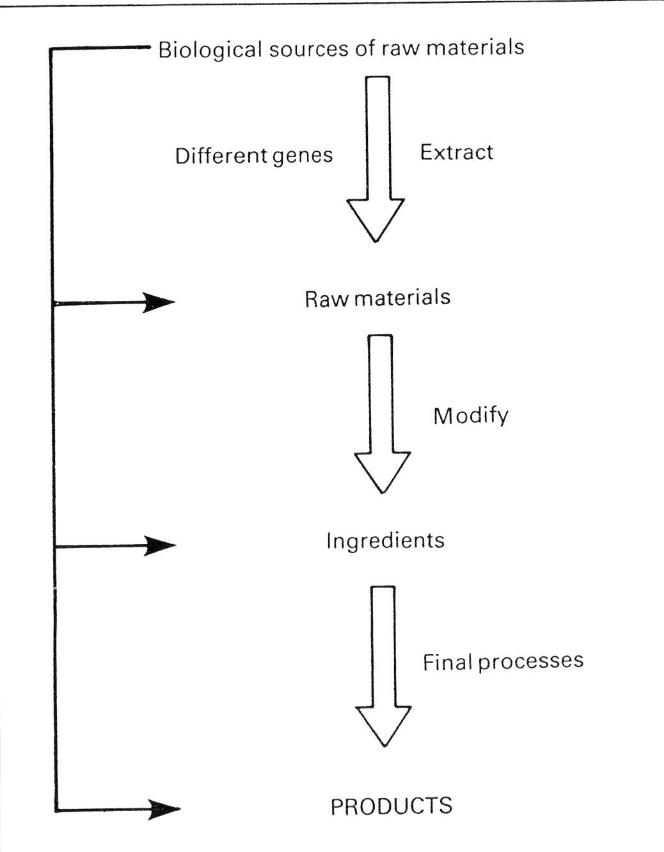

Figure 1. Impact of biotechnology on the raw material food chain.

- Processing systems for the incorporation of ingredients into the finished product.

The first is concerned with the manipulation and selection of raw materials as they occur in the plants or animals which provide the basic ingredients of food systems. The major components are proteins, fats and carbohydrates, produced as storage material for the developing seeds and which have a number of functions as food ingredients, providing foam stability, lubrication, gel structure, aqueous phase thickening. All contribute to mouth feel and to that quality which the consumer recognises as palatability. In addition, minor components, in terms of food content and often referred to as "additives", are also present and include colours, stabilisers, thickeners, flavours, enzymes, preservatives and vitamins. Additives may be derived from the breakdown of ingredients during the natural ripening process. For example, the proteolytic digestion of proteins to yield amino acids, and the digestion of polysaccharides to form sugars, provide the building blocks for the condensation and rearrangement reactions which lead to the formation of the Maillard reaction flavours, schematically represented below:

THE MAILLARD REACTION (non-enzymic browning)

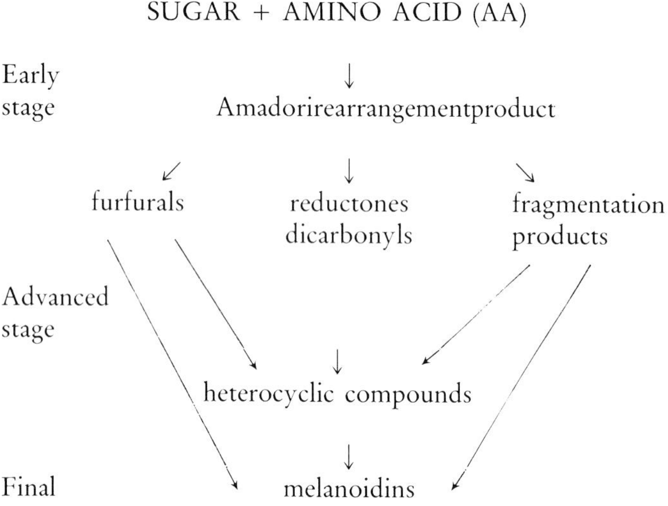

Control of the raw material in terms of protein and carbohydrate will allow better selection of feedstocks which in turn influences the flavour characteristics to be generated. The above reactions are central to the chemistry of producing colour, flavours and anti-oxidant properties (1).

A further advantage of controlling raw materials lies in the ability to standardise a reliable source via the selection and breeding of plants with high levels of individual components and, in so doing, eliminate or reduce the need for downstream processing and purification. In nature, examples of high levels of individual storage compounds already exist in oil bearing seeds and these include 85% ricinoleic acid in castor bean oil, 90% cinammic acid in cassia oil, 80–90% octanoate (C_8), decanoate (C_{10}), or dodecanoic acid (C_{12}) in the triacylglycerols of the Cuphea plant and 90–95% oleic acid in high oleic acid varieties of the sunflower. Applications of molecular biology and plant breeding will extend the range of these examples.

The modification of such raw materials in the past has been achieved to a large extent by chemical processing including the acid hydrolysis of proteins to form savoury flavours or the production of chemically modified starches as the basis for a wide range of functional food ingredients. Biotechnology provides the opportunities to produce similar materials based upon the exploitation of those processes which occur in the animal or plant from which the raw material was isolated.

The practical implications of these opportunities will be dependent on a number of factors; they include economic and political influences as well as the type of exploitation, e.g. traditional versus "modern" biotechnology. The differentiation between these two approaches is summarised below and emphasises the distinction between ingredient/product-based applications and fermentation/molecular biology technologies.

Traditional Biotechnology (Product based)

- Technology — Fermentation
- Targets have mainly been systems with the emphasis on Food — e.g. Raw Material + Micro-organisms/Enzyme → Textural/Flavour Changes + Preservation
- Product — Foods — e.g. Cheese, Wine, Bread, Yoghurt, Meat, Fish, Vegetables

Traditional biotechnology, based on the biochemical observations of E. Buchner working on yeast fermentation in the late 19th century, is now accepted both in terms of the technology (fermentation) and the products (e.g. dairy, bakery products and alcoholic beverages).

Modern Biotechnology (Ingredient based)

- Technology — Molecular Genetics, Applied Enzymology
- Operates at the molecular level to give altered functional properties
- Product — Food Ingredients — e.g. Flavours, Colours, Stabilisers, Thickeners etc., Tailored Fats, Proteins, Carbohydrates.

By contrast, the application of "modern" biotechnology to food systems is directed more at the ingredients tailored to a specific end-use application and makes use of molecular genetics and applied enzymology in conjunction with fermentation technology. However, the application of molecular biology is still often perceived by legislators as an "unknown" entity and, while the technical skills are to a large extent in place, acceptability in the food area is still a problem although much less so than in pharmaceutical applications. The way forward will undoubtedly be a gradual process with the progressive application of molecular biology to the traditional fermentation industry. In the brewing industry strain improvement is commonplace — e.g. Labatt Brewing Co., of London, Ontario, have carried out research which led to the improved stability of yeast with application not only for brewing but also for other ethanolic fermentations and for the expression of cloned eukaryotic genes.

The challenge for the brewing industry, dealt with in more detail in Chapter 16, was to achieve a *Saccharomyces* capable of the complete hydrolysis of starch and this objective had to take into account that these yeasts are responsible for more than 90% of the world ethanol produced by fermentation of starch. In order to reach this objective, it was necessary to produce a yeast capable of synthesising and secreting α-amylase and glucoamylase with debranching activity to produce fermentable sugars.

The key enzymes involved shown in Figure 2 are as follows:

1. α-amylase (α-1,4-glucan 4-glucanohydrolase, EC3.2.1.1.);
2. β-amylase (α-1,4-glucan maltohydrolase, EC3.2.1.2.);
3. Amyloglucosidase (α-1,4-glucan glucohydrolase, EC3.2.1.3.);
4. Amyloglucosidase (α-1,6-glucohydrolase, EC3.2.1.9.);

To acquire these characteristics, workers at Labatt (2) have explored a range of different approaches including hybridisation, rare mating, spheroplast fusion, mutation and selection and transformation. The application of these techniques demands a detailed appreciation of the genetics of the organism in question — for *Saccharomyces* sp. such information is readily available and has been applied to a number of commercial yeasts.

Hybridisation

A knowledge of the life cycle of *Saccharomyces*, shown schematically in Figure 3, allows successful matings to occur between haploid yeasts with different genetic constitutions and opposite mating types in order to produce novel diploid yeasts. The technique has been applied by Stewart *et al.* (3) to a species of *Saccharomyces*, *S. diastaticus*, which can utilise dextrin and starch because of its ability to produce glucoamylase extracellularly. This approach produced a low carbohydrate beer initially having a characteristic phenolic off-flavour due to the formation of 4-vinyl quaicol via the decarboxylation of the ferulic acid which is a constituent of wort (Figure 4).

Rare Mating

Unlike hybridisation, which occurs between cells of opposite mating types, mating between non-maters at a frequency of less than 10^{-6} has been reported (4). When linked to a strain containing a specific Kor 1−1 mutation, it is possible to control the fusion of nuclear genetic information since in these mutants nuclear fusion is diminished or eliminated after

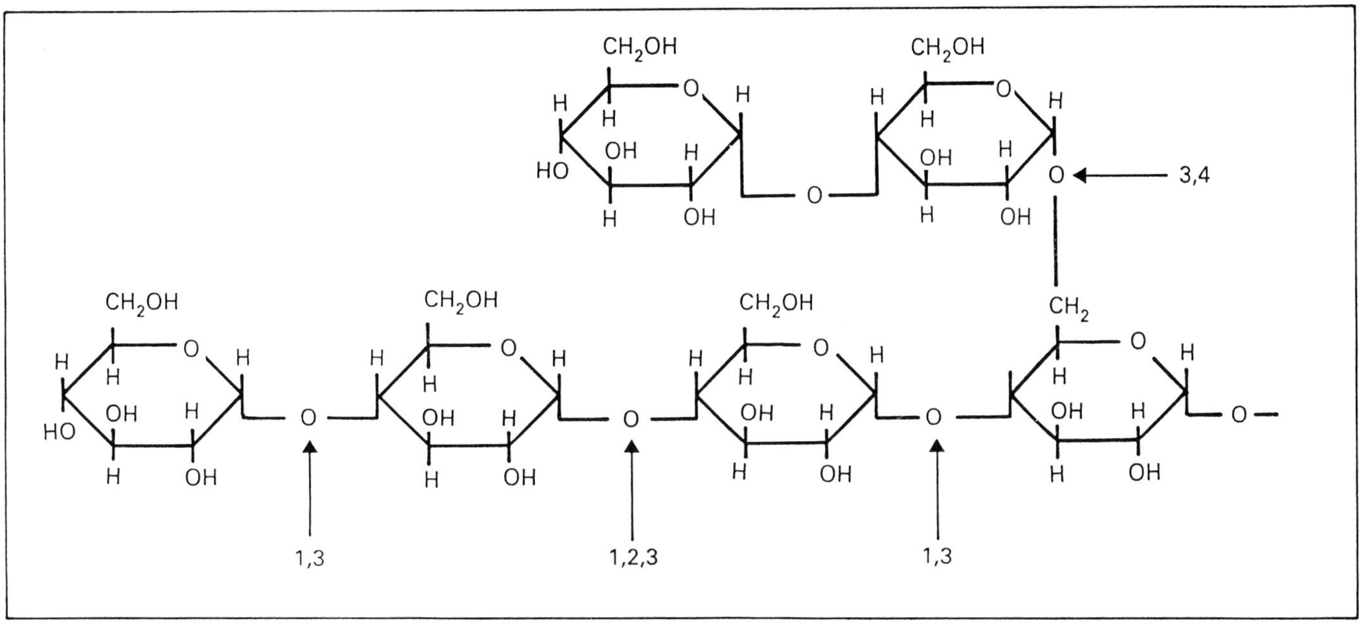

Figure 2. Degradation of starch.

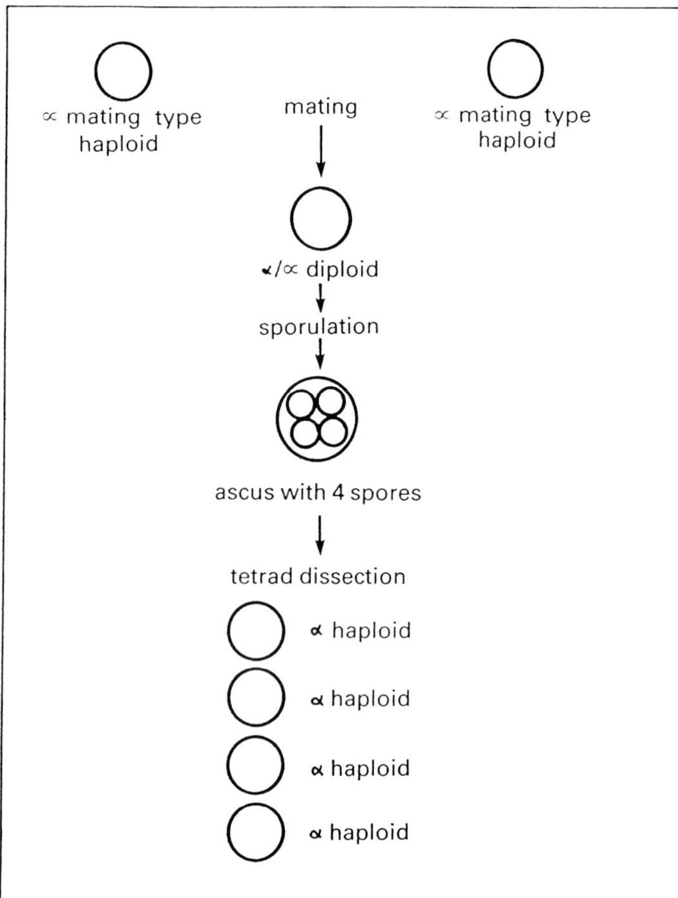

Figure 3. Haploid/diploid life cycle of *Saccharomyces* species. (Taken from Proceedings of the Biotech '84, Online Conference, held in Washington D.C., USA.)

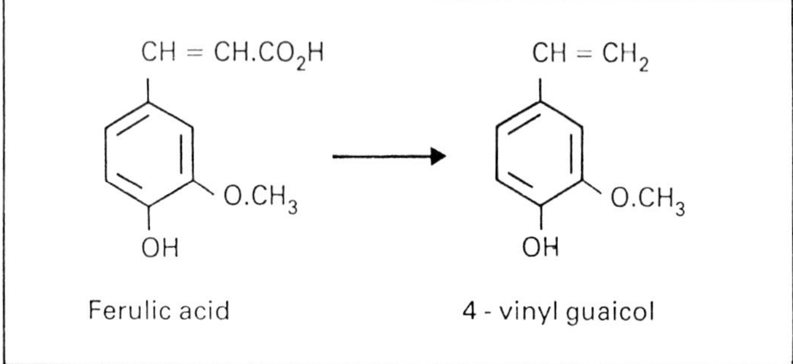

Figure 4. Conversion of ferulic acid to 4-vinyl guaicol.

conjugation. The protocol of rare mating is shown in Figure 5.

Spheroplast Fusion

Removal of the cell wall of yeasts by the use of lytic enzymes yields spheroplasts which can be fused in the presence of polyethylene glycol and Ca^{2+} even if derived from sexually incompatible strains. For example the lager brewing strain *S. uvarum* (*carlsbergensis*) was fused with a genetically constructed *S. diastaticus* which possesses glucoamylase not found in *S. carlsbergensis*. A stable fusion product (Figure 6) was isolated which fermented corn mash at a rapid rate and formed alcohol very rapidly when grown in glucose-peptone-yeast extract media.

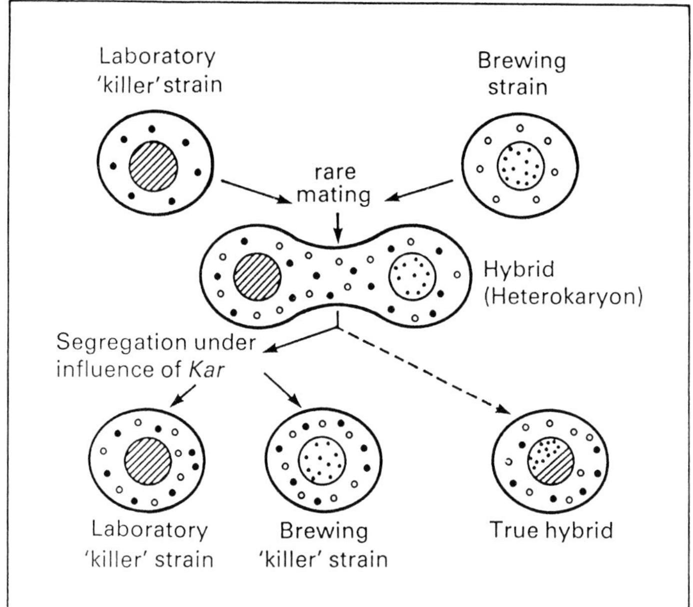

Figure 5. Rare mating protocol to produce brewing strains with zymocidal activity. (Taken from Proceedings of the Biotech '84, Online Conference, held in Washington D.C., USA.)

These techniques, although developed for brewing yeasts, have wide applicability for other food ingredients and fermented foods. For example, in further developments workers at the Cetus Corporation, at Trinity College Dublin (in collaboration with Guinness) and in Japanese companies are applying molecular biology via the cloning of enzymes, e.g. the Guinness group has cloned endo-β-1,3-1,4 glucanase in an attempt to reduce haze formation in beers. The gene for an enzyme which degrades barley β-glucan has also successfully been cloned. The first host was *Escherichia coli* and work is now proceeding towards its expression in a haploid *S. cerevisiae*. The Cetus group has cloned three fungal enzymes for use in different aspects of the food industry: (i) glucoamylase that hydrolyses both α-1,4 and α-1,6 starch linkages for the commercial saccharification of starch; (ii) a cellobiohydralase that cleaves cellobiosyl units from the reducing end of cellulose for ethanol production or for the modification of cellulose to improve its solubility and water binding properties; (iii) pyranose-2-oxidase that converts glucose to 2-oxyglucose, which can be chemically converted to fructose. Thus genes can be inserted for specific enzymes

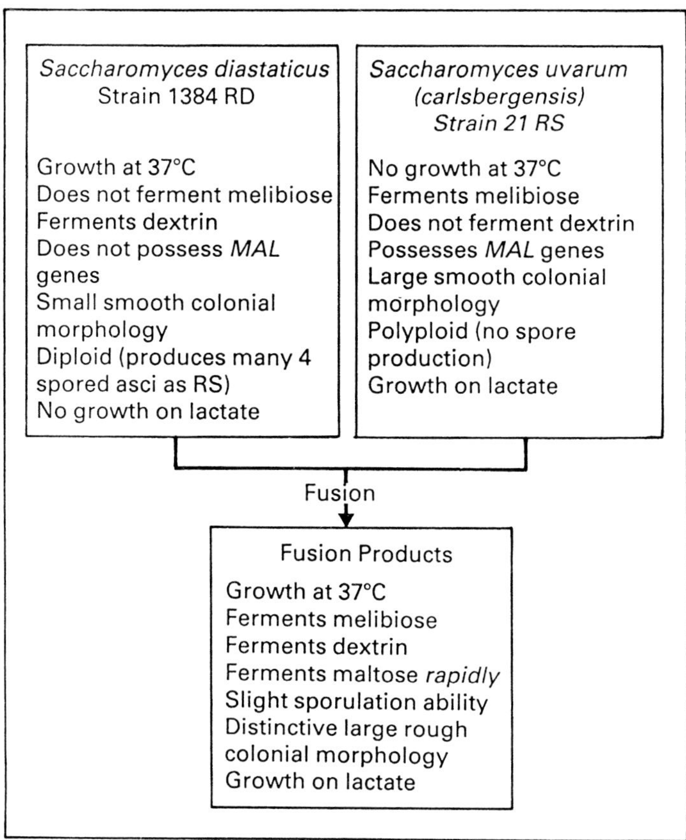

Figure 6. Characteristics of fusion partners and fusion product. (Taken from Proceedings of the Biotech '84, Online Conference, held in Washington D.C., USA.)

which can be isolated and utilised to modify raw materials and produce novel or improved food ingredients.

The primary targets for these new techniques have been improving the metabolism of yeasts to handle a range of carbohydrate-based feedstocks. Success is based upon a knowledge of the biochemistry of polysaccharides degradation and of the molecular genetics of the host organism. Thus, the traditional fermentation industries of brewing and dairy products are very much a part of the modern biotechnology. The molecular techniques which have been developed have found application in other aspects of the food industry (5), e.g. to alter the genetic make up of microorganisms and agricultural crops.

CONTROL OF RAW MATERIALS

We have already noted that for the brewing industry the major raw material is starch which also finds a wider application as a food ingredient. However, starch is just one raw material used either in its natural state or after chemical or enzymic modification. Proteins, oils and fats are, of course, also important raw materials conferring functional properties and/or nutritional benefit. The common factor linking these important biochemicals is that they all represent storage products in seeds where they provide a major source of energy and carbon for germination.

The opportunities which classical plant breeding offers have been manifest in the high yielding cereals and plant molecular biology offers the same opportunity for plants that the microbial geneticist and physiologist has already achieved with microorganisms. Progress with plants has been slower for a number of reasons:

1. Plant biochemistry is more complex;
2. The plant genome is larger and consequently less amenable to analysis and manipulation;
3. Genes have to be targetted to be expressed only in the developing seed — i.e. at the right time and place.

These techniques of molecular genetics are indeed now being applied and successes in the application of cloning, somaclonal variation and genetic engineering integrated into traditional plant breeding programs are being recorded.

Control of raw materials via plant molecular biology can be considered under a number of headings:

1. Cloning;
2. Protoplast fusion;
3. Somaclonal variation;
4. Recombinant DNA technology.

Cloning is the selection of natural variants followed by micro-propagation (Figure 7); it can present a number of unforeseen problems. The technique relies on the selection of desirable expressed characteristics, the phenotype and the faithful regeneration of mature plants or trees from the parent cell-line. By definition all the progeny are identical and display the same desirable properties as well as the same susceptibility to adverse conditions (e.g. drought, disease). Cloning programs, therefore, have to be directed to producing a range of clones; each clone expresses a desirable property and at the same time displays a wide spectrum of secondary traits such that unfavourable environmental changes do not adversely affect the entire population.

Cloning techniques have been used for the production of palm plantlets on a factory scale. The economic implications of producing oil from these clones are increased plantation productivity and reduced extraction and refining costs.

In addition to cloning, which relies on the selective propagation of natural variants, it is possible to alter the genetic information via *protoplast fusion*, analogous to that described for microorganisms. *Somaclonal variation* is another method induced at the callus stage and it is perpetuated through to the new plants which are screened for novel characteristics. Somaclonal variation and genetic engineering provide the tools which can be and are being applied to crop improvement:

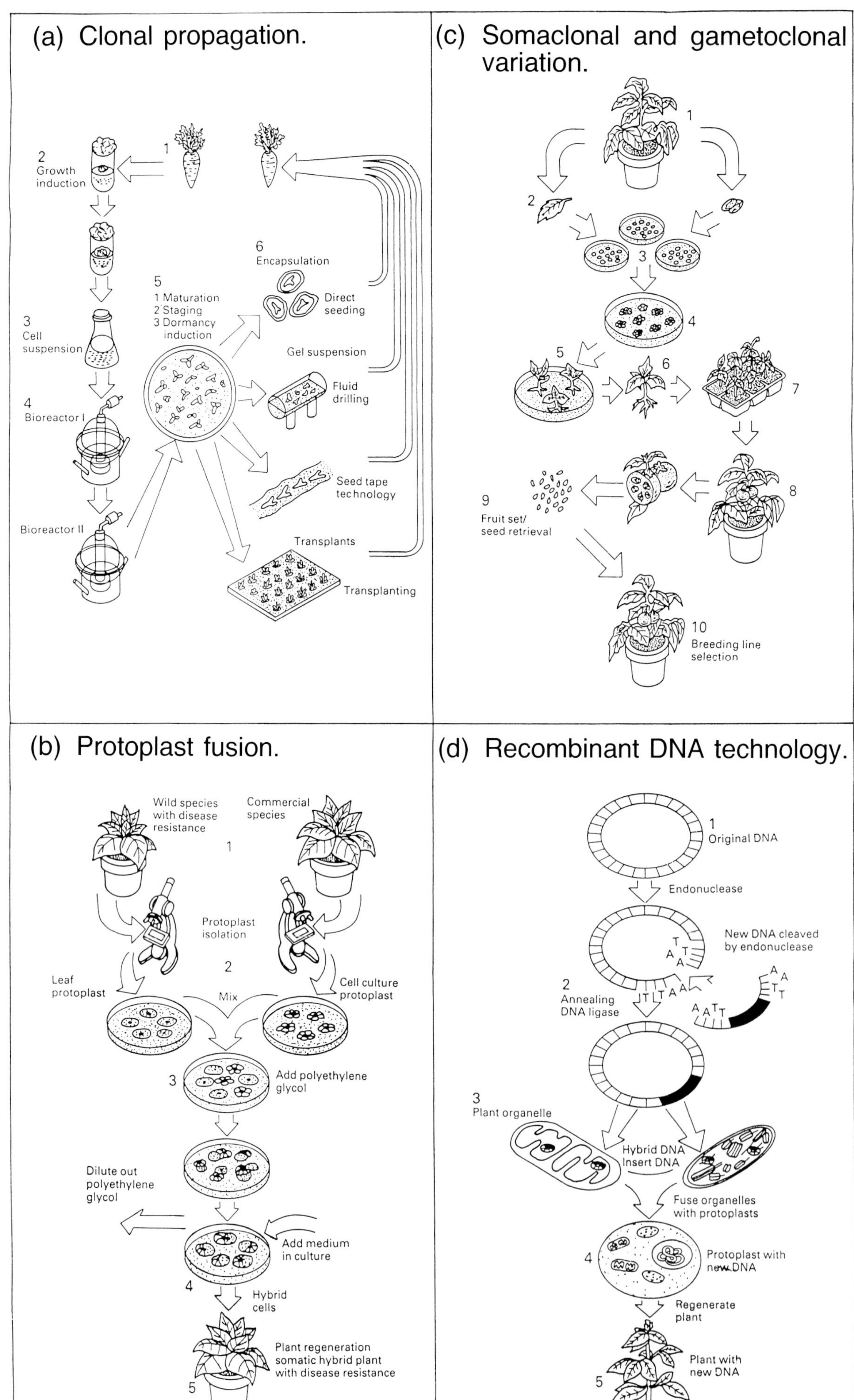

Figure 7. Application of molecular biology to plant breeding.

one example is increasing the solids content of tomatoes by the biotechnology company DNA Plant Technology on behalf of the Campbell's Soups Company. With recombinant DNA technology there are opportunities for the selective and directed insertion or deletion of specific genes in plants. The technique has been admirably demonstrated by the insertion and expression of the gene for a protein from broad beans in the seeds of tobacco. Gene deletion, using antisense-RNA technology, has been applied by Feenstra's group in Groningen to potato starch synthesis, resulting in the production of tubers containing 100% amylopectin. Grierson's group in Nottingham have used it to control the ripening of tomatoes by deletion (~90%) of the polygalacturonase gene. This clearly demonstrates the potential for the genetic manipulation of plant products in a more selective way than has hitherto been possible. This work is directed at whole plants or crop improvement but for a number of years work, notably in Europe, has been focussed on the use of plant cells to produce speciality chemicals (6). More recently immobilised cells and root culture have received increased attention (7).

EXAMPLES OF CURRENT APPLICATION AREAS OF PLANT TISSUE CULTURE

Firmenich/DNAP (Joint venture)	— Flavours
McCormach/NPI (Joint venture)	— Spices
Mitsui Petro Chemicals/Kanebo	— Shikonin, Fragrances
German Natterman & Co.	— Rosemarinic Acid
Calgene	— Mint Oil
FRI Norwich	— Quinine, Saffron
University of Edinburgh/UMIST	— Capsaicin, Ginger, Crocetin

The recognition that the initial commercial products of biotechnology are likely to be the higher added value speciality ingredients is particularly true when considering the potential products from plant tissue culture. It is not surprising that the initial targets for this technology were the flavours and fragrances but nevertheless ironical that the first reported commercial success was a plant pigment, shikonin from *Lithospernum*, which is sold as a colourant for lipsticks and as a pharmaceutical (8). Nonetheless, emphasis is still placed upon flavours and flavour ingredients produced by cells in liquid suspension culture immobilised on supports, e.g. polyurethane foam blocks or, more recently, by the use of plant pathogen *Agrobacterium rhizogenes* to infect the roots of dicotyledonous plants. This results in the production of lateral roots, giving the effect of "hairy roots" which can be propagated *in vitro* in fermenter vessels. These opportunities are being exploited at the Food Research Institute at Norwich, while immobilised cell systems are being developed in Edinburgh and Escagen (formerly the International Plant Research Institute). The latter are attempting to use immobilised cells in hollow-fibre systems to produce the much-valued vanillin. The Institute of Food Science (Ithaca, N.Y.) is also involved in plant tissue culture in the form of suspension cultures of callus from embryonic cocoa beans; they are used to produce cocoa butter and fat with the unusual symmetry of the triacylglycerol forming relatively homogeneous crystals that melt sharply at 32–34°C.

Some authorities on plant tissue culture now believe that this technique will be economic only for a very few products and that it should be used more profitably as a means for generating elite plants which over-produce specific food ingredients. For a review of the potential opportunities and the state of the art the reader is referred to various reports in a symposium on the Biotechnology of Plant Foods (9).

MODIFICATION OF RAW MATERIALS — NOVEL INGREDIENTS VIA ENZYMOLOGY

The raw materials produced from animals and plants can be used either in their own right or further modified by microorganisms or isolated enzymes. The modification of raw materials by enzymic processes is a promising area providing enzymes can be made available with the required activity and specificity at a reasonable cost. A second but equally important consideration if enzymes are to be used effectively is the understanding of the relationship between the structure of a molecule, its functional properties and the expression of those properties when incorporated as part of a more complex system such as a food. It is only with this knowledge that the techniques of molecular biology and applied enzymology can be employed to tailor ingredients for a specific application.

The key raw materials conferring functionality in food systems are proteins, fats and carbohydrates, but even to-day there is still a large gap in our understanding of the fine structural detail of food ingredients in relation to their role in food systems. However, much work has been done on the understanding of the structure/function relationship at the molecular level. A review article by Kinsella (10) describes in some detail the relationship between protein structure and functional properties, recognising that for specific food applications, specific proteins are required. The properties of these proteins cover a wide range of applications, e.g. emulsification, water binding, gelation and foam stability in products such as beverages, meat products and desserts; these can be achieved by careful selection of the raw material and control of processing involving chemical/biochemical modification.

The properties of proteins are influenced by size and amino acid composition which in turn influences the secondary, tertiary and quaternary structure of the protein. The sizes of proteins can be altered by controlled acid or enzyme hydrolysis yielding peptides with functional properties ranging from whipping agents to flavour precursors. The amino acid composition is less easily controlled and, although in theory it is possible to alter amino acids at will using techniques of protein engineering, it is unlikely that this approach will be a commercial option for commodity products. The physicochemical studies aimed at an understanding of the structure/function relationship is beyond the scope of this chapter and will not be discussed further; the reader is directed to the reference cited and to Chapter 12.

Oils and fats are derived from fish, animals and plants and, of the 60 million tonnes produced, approximately 45.4 million tonnes are used for food application (Figures 8 & 9). The fats/oils are produced from a wide range of plant sources and their properties, and hence their applications, are governed by the fatty acid composition of the triacylglycerols which confer either nutritional benefit or textural properties on the food system. By way of an example, a fat containing only saturated fatty acids such as stearic acid has a melting point of 73°C and is therefore a solid at both room and physiological temperature. Introduction of unsaturated fatty acids which, by virtue of the cis-unsaturation, have a much lower melting point than stearic acid, in turn lowers the melting point of the fat (Figure 10). This particular physical characteristic may also be influenced by the chain length of the fatty acid.

More often than not it will be desirable to effect these changes by enzymes immobilised on a support in the form of a stable catalyst (enzyme + support) designed for a specific application (see Chapter 18). The nature of the catalyst will have to take into account the raw material, the processing conditions of temperature, the presence or absence of solvent and the reactor design — stirred tank versus packed bed. Genetic and protein engineering offer routes to improved catalyst to meet the harsh environment imposed on enzyme in many industrial applications. Although significant progress has been made with subtilisin (11), which has potential detergent application, further advances are hampered by a lack of understanding of the structure-function relationship of proteins. Application of enzymes will thus be restricted in the immediate future to those already available.

For example, a process has been developed to produce an improved (natural) emulsifier for food use. Hydrolysis of the phospholipids in egg-yolk using the enzyme phospholipase present in pancreatin yields an emulsifier with a much superior heat stability (Figure 11). This allows the preparation

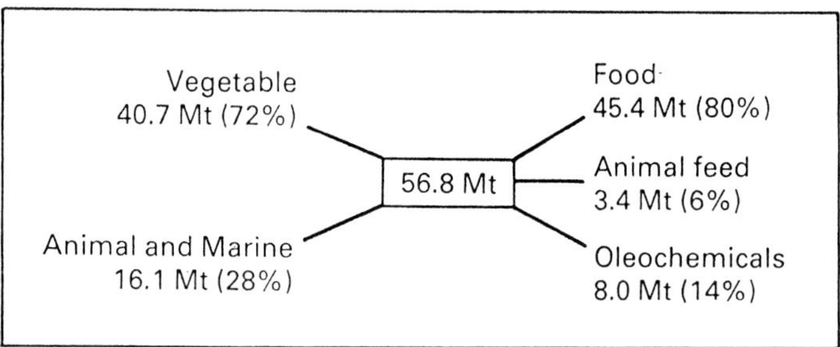

Figure 8. Utilisation of oils and fats.

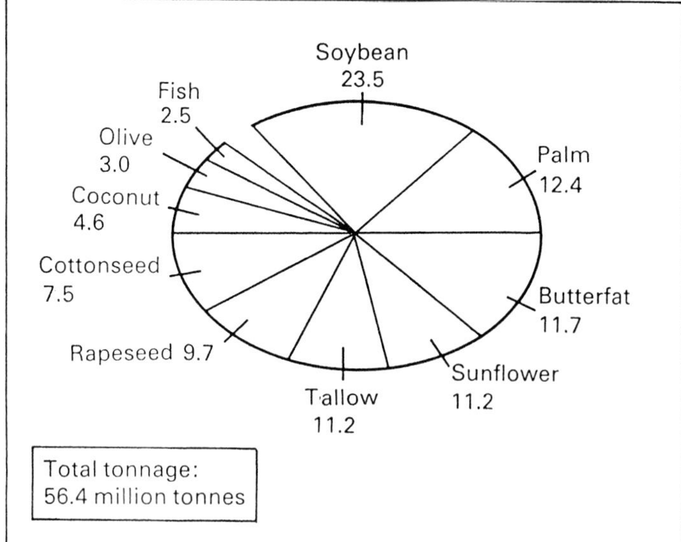

Figure 9. Sources of vegetable oils.

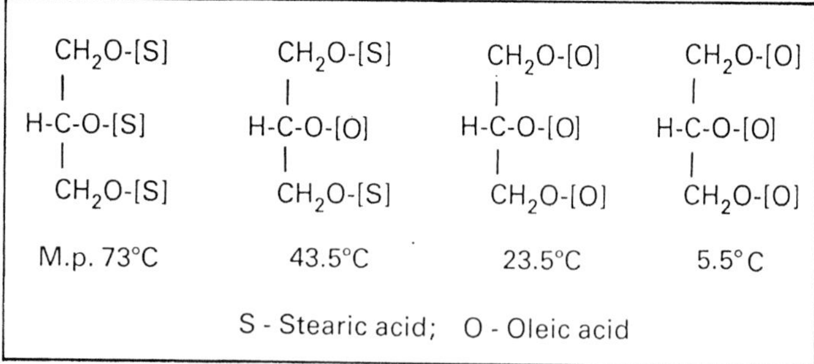

Figure 10. Melting points of triacylglycerols.

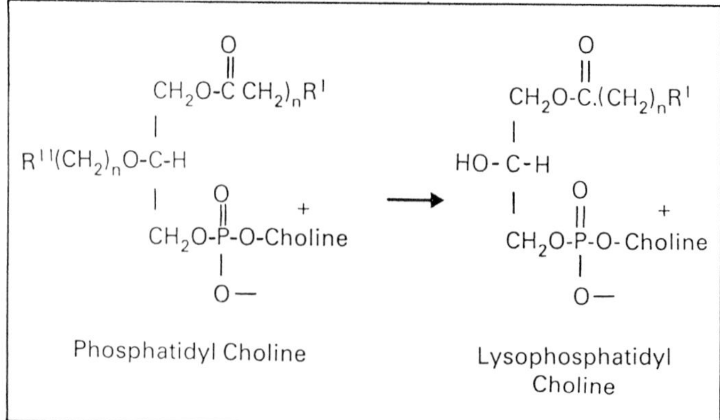

Figure 11. Production of lyso-phosphatidylcholine.

of heat sterilizable oil-in-water emulsions requiring reduced thickening agent in low oil products (12). Enzymic modifications of other raw materials are attractive from a foodstuff viewpoint but await the provision of low cost enzymes and processing systems as well as well defined targets based upon a clear understanding of the role of ingredients, as summarised below:

RAW MATERIALS → INGREDIENTS

1. Tailored Ingredients
   - Triglycerides via interesterification
   - Polysaccharides via "solid state" enzymology
   - Flavour blocks via fermentation
   - Maillard precursors
   - Specific flavours from fatty acids.

2. Tailored Enzymes
   - Novel/improved enzymes via protein engineering
   - Improved enzymes for bioconversions.

3. Skill Base in Molecular Genetics
   - Transfer of gene into suitable microbiological hosts
   - DNA/oligonucleotide synthesis
   - Protein sequencing capabilities.

4. Skill Base in Applied Enzymology
   - Biochemical skills
   - Use of enzymes in "hostile" environments
   - Development of novel catalytic supports.

Perhaps the best documented enzymic modifications are those related to starch (13), for example the action of α-amylase to produce low dextrose — equivalent sugars and the production of high fructose corn syrup (HFCS) by the action of the action of α-amylase on corn starch, glucoamylase for saccharification and glucose isomerase to convert glucose into fructose (see also Chapter 18). This is one of the best examples of applied enzymology in a commercial process but for political and economic reasons is excluded from Europe. The use of glucose isomerase to produce corn sweeteners led to the development of a plant capable of converting 2 million pounds per day of corn starch into high fructose corn syrup. This resulted in 1980 in a sugar import saving of $1.3 billion in the U.S. (Data taken from Commercial Biotechnology. An International Analysis. Washington D.C.: U.S. Congress, Office of Technology Assessment, OTA-BA-218 January 1984). Another important activity is the production of invert sugar from sucrose by the action of invertase to yield a mixture of glucose and fructose (Figure 12); this has markets in sweets, jam and ice-cream. Microbial α-galactosidase is used in the sugar beet industry to convert the trisaccharide raffinose into galactose and sucrose (Figure 13). The importance of this reaction centres on the observation that raffinose, present in sugar beet up to 0.16%, retards the crystallisation of the sucrose. The use of α-galactosidase means that valuable molasses do not have to be discardd but can be more efficiently converted into the desired product.

In the dairy industry, immobilised lactase is used for whey processing (14). Although whey contains a number of nutritional components, lactose is also present to a concentration of 4.5% and this causes a number of problems: it is not very sweet, it is poorly soluble and some people have a β-galactosidase deficiency which makes them unable to metabolise lactose. Hydrolysis of the lactose overcomes many of these problems and it has also been suggested that pre-hydrolysis may shorten yoghurt and cheese production time by as much as 20%.

All these processes are examples of enzymic hydrolyses conducted in aqueous environments; they have been exploited because there are commercial needs, the enzymes are available and the chemistry is simple — i.e. the enzymes require no co-factors. The two cases now to be described are novel processes developed by Unilever; one is carried out in non-aqueous conditions, while the other is a solid-state enzymic modification of a polysaccharide.

MODIFICATION OF OILS AND FATS

Structure-function relationships have been referred to earlier and the link made between fatty acid composition and fat

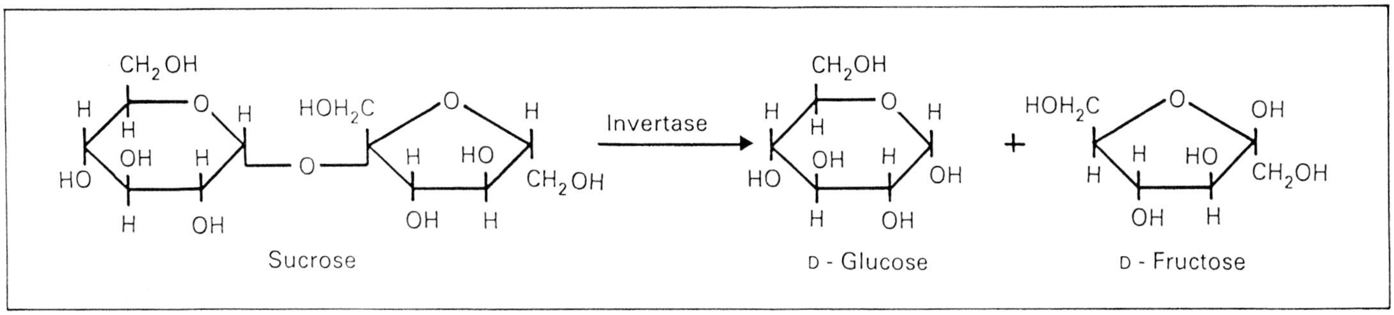

Sucrose —Invertase→ D - Glucose + D - Fructose

Figure 12. Inversion of sucrose to glucose and fructose.

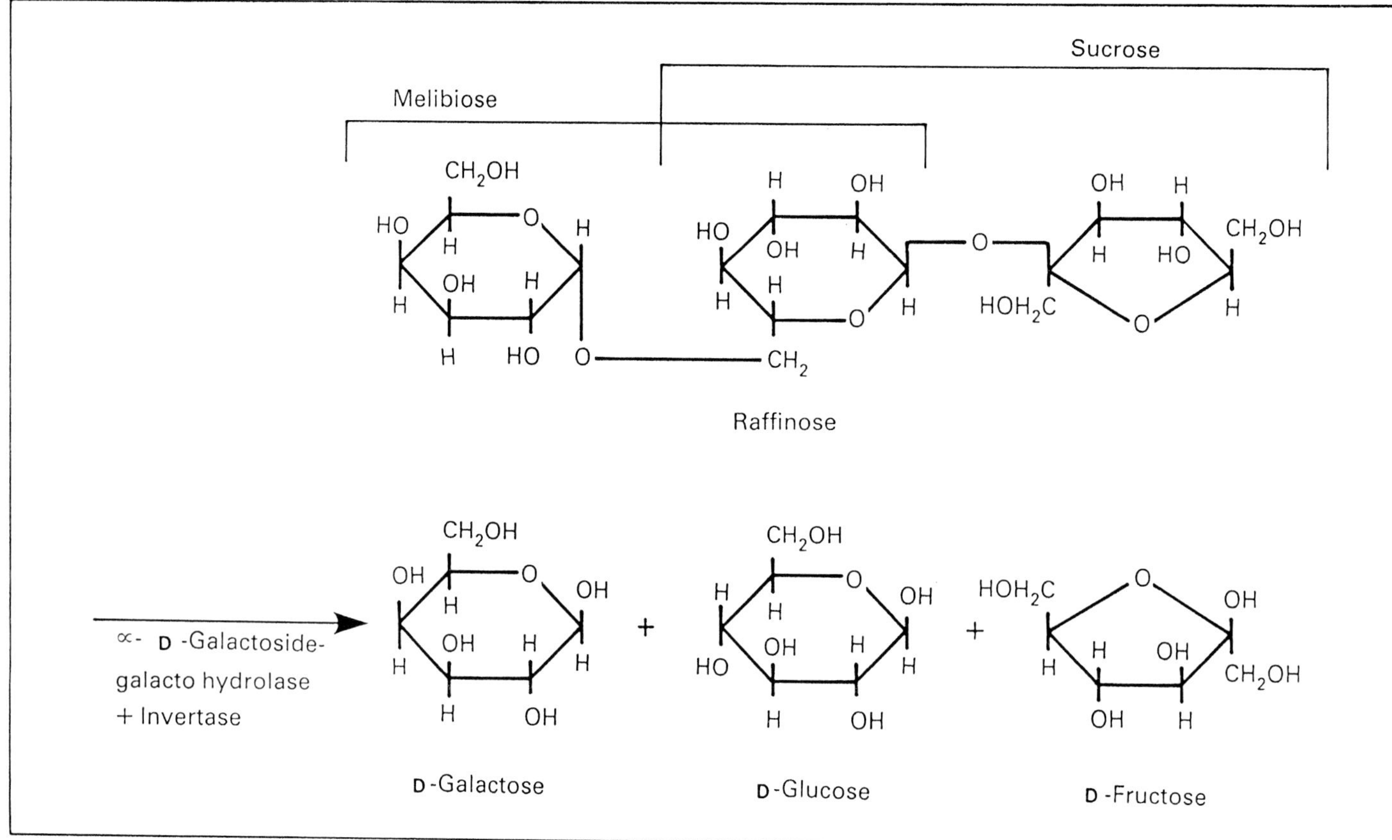

Figure 13. Total hydrolysis of raffinose by invertase and α-galactosidase.

property. These considerations, together with a knowledge of lipase activity in terms of its mode of action and specificity (which can either be fatty acid-specific or regio-selective and show selectivity based upon the position of the fatty acid in the triacylglycerol), have been exploited to up-grade oils and fats to produce cocoa butter-type material (Figure 14).

The process makes use of the reversibility of the splitting of fats by lipases to generate free fatty acids (15, 16). Using this knowledge and the regiospecific nature of lipases under conditions of low water activity, a number of novel and specific triacylglycerols can and have been synthesised (Figure 15). For example 1,3-regiospecific lipase from *Mucor miehei* supported on a bed of diatomaceous earth has been used to up-grade a palm mid-fraction into a valuable confectionery fat. A typical continuous reaction system consists of the feedstocks dissolved into petroleum ether saturated with water (0.06% w/v) and passed over immobilised catalyst at 40°C; the mean residence time in the reactor is about ten minutes (Figure 16).

Manufacturing plants exploiting this technique give very favourable material in terms of chemical composition and physical properties (Figure 17) and are expected to come on stream in the very near future.

CHEMICAL COMPOSITION

TG	Amount in enzyme CBE %	Amount in cocoa butter %
SSS	3	1
POP	16	16
POS	39	41
SOS	28	27
SLnS	8	8
SOO	4	6
Others	2	1

TG = Triacylglycerol; CBE = Cocoa Butter Equivalent; S = Stearate; P = Palmitate; O = Oleate; Ln = Linoleate.

An alternative approach makes use of higher temperatures and a molten feedstock which is made possible by the unexpected thermal stability of lipases.

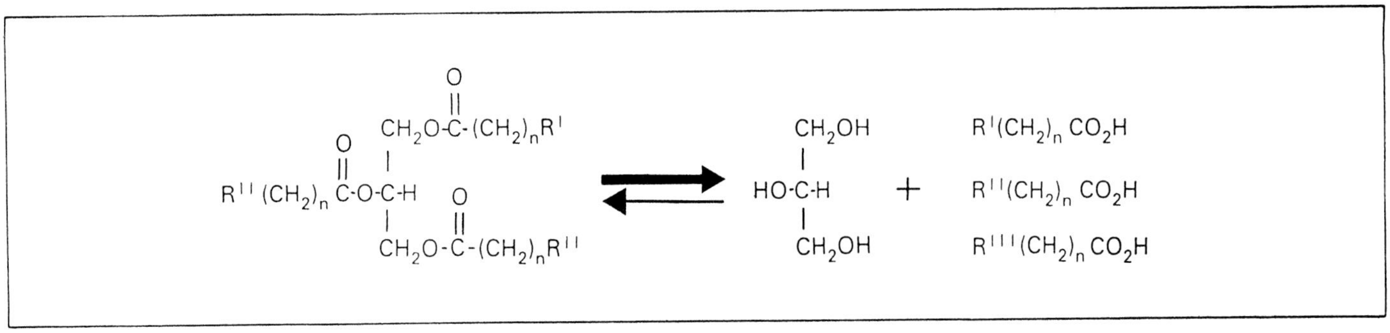

$$\begin{array}{l} CH_2O\text{-}\overset{O}{\overset{\|}{C}}\text{-}(CH_2)_nR^{I} \\ R^{II}(CH_2)_n\overset{O}{\overset{\|}{C}}\text{-}O\text{-}C\text{-}H \\ CH_2O\text{-}\overset{O}{\overset{\|}{C}}\text{-}(CH_2)_nR^{II} \end{array} \rightleftharpoons \begin{array}{c} CH_2OH \\ HO\text{-}C\text{-}H \\ CH_2OH \end{array} + \begin{array}{l} R^{I}(CH_2)_n CO_2H \\ R^{II}(CH_2)_n CO_2H \\ R^{III}(CH_2)_n CO_2H \end{array}$$

Figure 14. Enzymic hydrolysis of triacylglycerols.

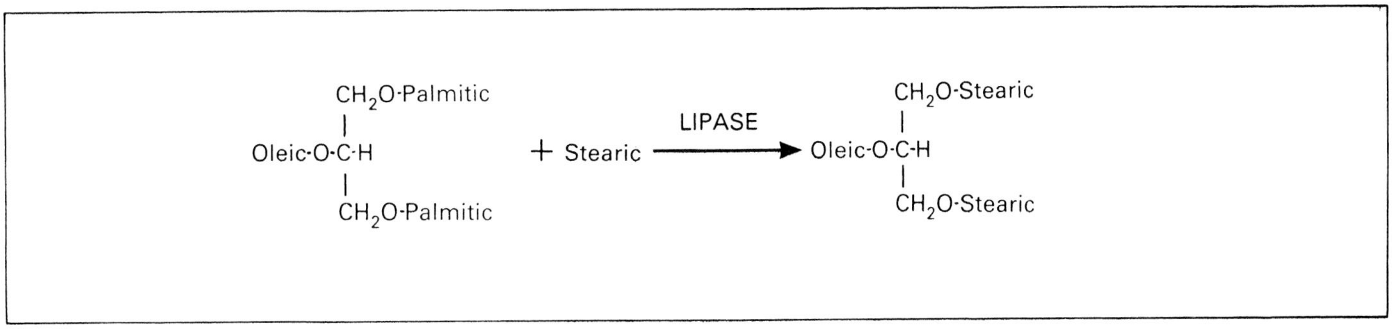

$$\begin{array}{c} CH_2O\text{-Palmitic} \\ \text{Oleic-O-C-H} \\ CH_2O\text{-Palmitic} \end{array} + \text{Stearic} \xrightarrow{\text{LIPASE}} \begin{array}{c} CH_2O\text{-Stearic} \\ \text{Oleic-O-C-H} \\ CH_2O\text{-Stearic} \end{array}$$

Figure 15. Enzymic interesterification.

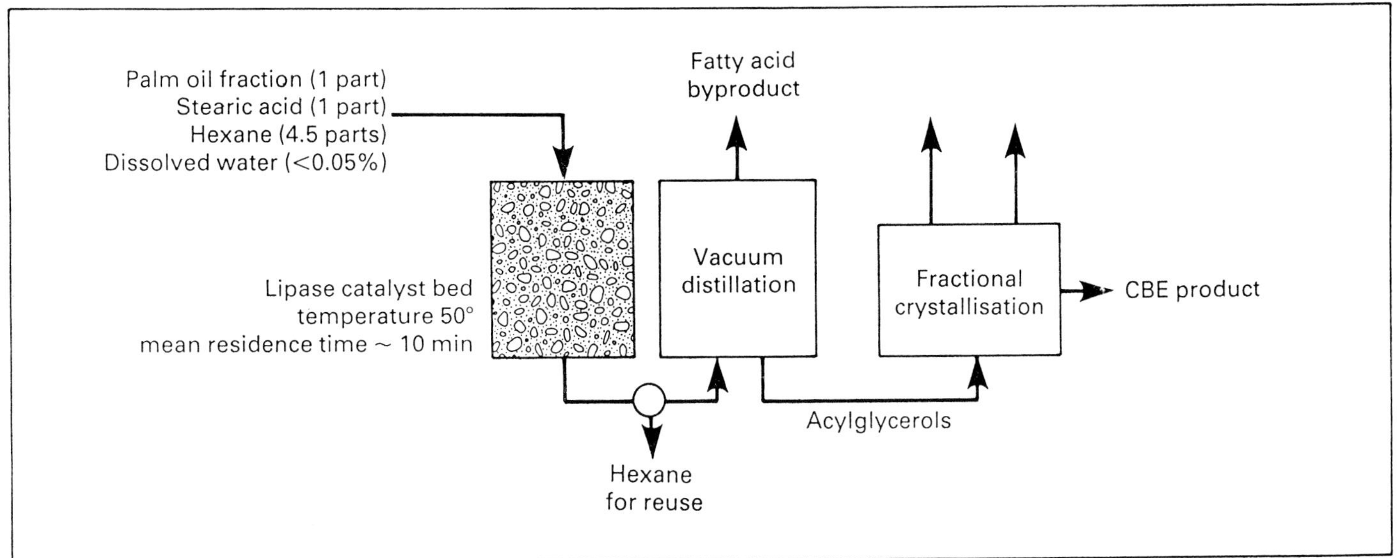

Figure 16. Process flow diagram for interesterification.

MODIFICATION OF POLYSACCHARIDES

Just as there is a wide variety of naturally occurring oils and fats (17), the same is true of polysaccharides which, in conjunction with oligosaccharides and monosaccharides, form an important class of compounds used in the food industry to:

- thicken and gel aqueous phases
- provide distinctive structural and textural attributes
- stabilise emulsions and aerated systems
- provide distinctive sensory attributes.

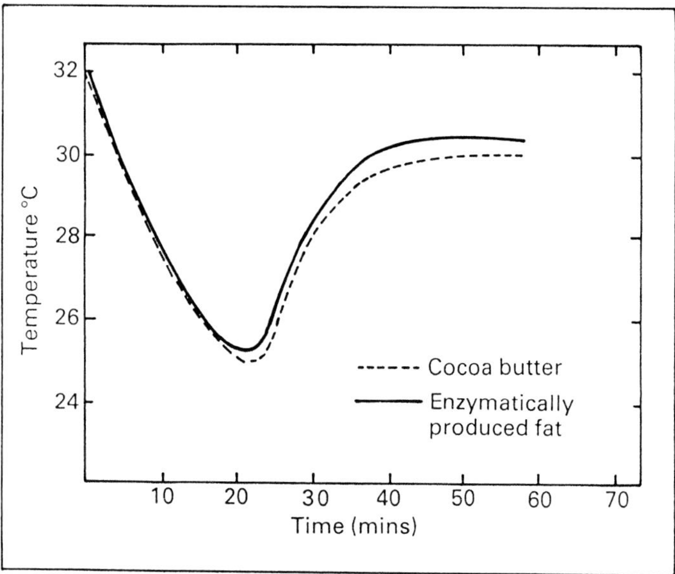

Figure 17. Jensen cooling curves comparing cocoa butter and enzyme modified fat.

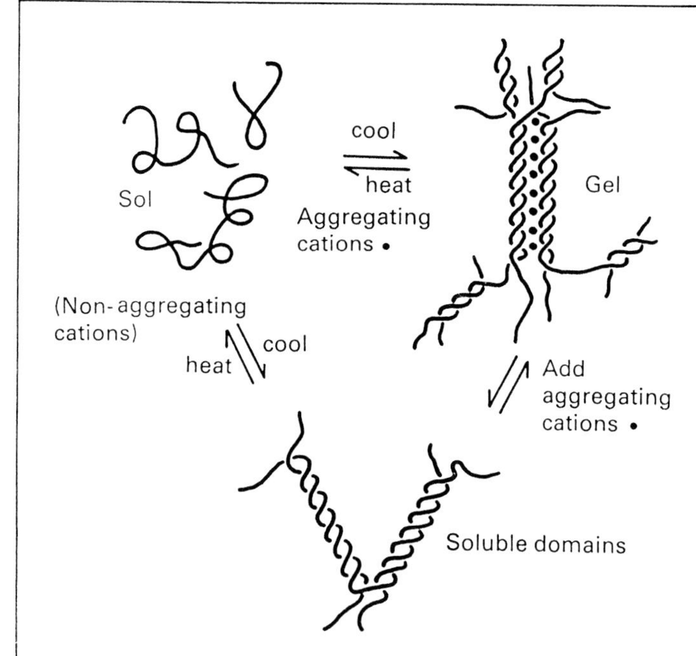

Figure 18. Domain model of carrageenan gelation.

The opportunities for modifying these polymers in a meaningful way will depend on a knowledge of their specific applications and the molecular as well as the intermolecular structure/function relationships within food systems. A detailed study over a number of years has meant that the fine structure of a wide range of polysaccharides is now understood and this, coupled to a knowledge of the function of polysaccharides (such as a protective capsule or viscous extracellular layer around bacteria, a hard exoskeleton in crustaceans, a means of anchoring seaweed to rocks, in lubricating and protecting animal joints and in the hydration of connective tissue) means that polysaccharides, while complex, can be tailored for specific applications. Three examples will be discussed here in detail:

1. **Carrageenan**
   This class of polysaccharides, used in gelled milk desserts, is extracted from the seaweeds (*Chondrus crispus* and related *Rhodophyceae*). They are based upon the alternating repeating sequence of the ι- and ϰ-gel-forming carrageenans ... →3)-β-D-Galp-4-sulphate-(1→4)-3, 6-anhydro-α-D-Galp-(1→ ... In ι-carrageenan the anhydrogalactose residue carries a sulphate group at position 2 which is absent in the ϰ-form. At high temperatures both of these materials exist in solution in a disordered fluctuating chain conformation but on cooling a rigid ordered double helical structure (analogous to that of DNA) is adopted which can be melted out again on reheating. Although interchain association through double helices is the primary event in carrageenan gelation, it does not in itself lead to a cohesive network but only to small clusters of about ten chains called "domains" (shown in Figure 18) which further associate in the presence of K^+ via helix-helix aggregation. The lower charge density of κ-carrageenan in comparison to ι is reflected in greater ease of aggregation and hence in a greater tendency to network contraction and in gel formation at lower temperatures.
2. **Alginate**
   This is the principal polysaccharide of the brown seaweeds (*Phaeophyceae*) and is a (1→4) linked linear copolymer of two different uronic acid salts, β-D-mannuronic acid and α-L-guluronic acid, which are arranged in long homopolymeric blocks of both types as well as in heteropolymeric mixed sequences where both residues occur in approximate alternation. As with pectins, alginate can form gels in the presence of Ca^2 which binds the chains together in what is often described as the "egg-box" dimer structure (Figure 19).

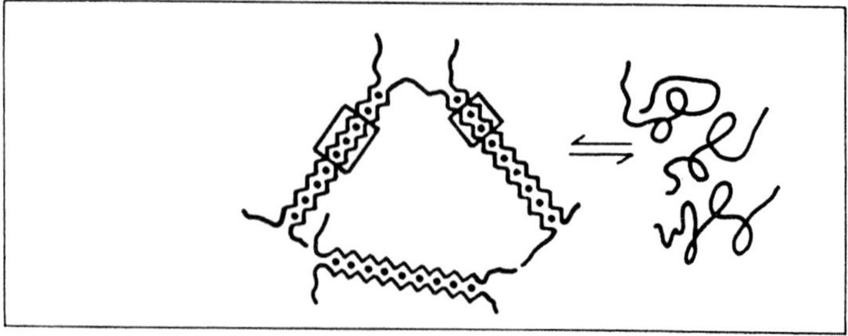

Figure 19. "Egg-box" binding of Ca^{2+} in the gelation of alginate and pectin shown diagrammatically.

3. **Xanthan**
This polysaccharide, which is produced in fermentation vessels as an extracellular material by the bacterium *Xanthomonas campestris*, has become a major industrial gum because it exists in solution as a rigid, rod-like structure rather than a random fluctuating coil; this leads to unusual and technologically valuable solution properties either on its own or in combination with other polysaccharides. The chemical structure of xanthan is based upon a (1→4) linked linear β-D-glucose backbone as in cellulose but is substituted at position 3 of every glucose residue with a charged trisaccharide side chain: it is thus β-D-Manp (1→4) β-D-GpA (1→2)α-Manp-6-OAc(1→, in which a variable portion of the mannose is substituted with pyruvic acid, linked to the sugar as a ketal. In both the solid state and in solution these side chains fold down and pack along the backbone, shown diagramatically in Figure 20. At very high temperatures this ordered structure can be disrupted to produce a disordered random coil. Alternatively, the rod-like structure can interact with galactomannans and glucomannans to produce rigid mixed gels.

The most widely used galactomannans are guar gum and locust bean gum which have many structural properties in common but one major difference. Structurally they are composed of a mannan polymer in which the mannose units are linked via a β-1→4 linkage (Figure 21) and are substituted to a variable extent with single galactose side chains linked via a α-1→6 linkage. Galactomannans all share this basic structure and vary only in terms of the degree of the substitution. Guar gum is composed of 38% galactose and 62% mannose, while locust bean gum has 23% galactose and 77% mannose. This variation in galactose substitution not only affects the gelling properties of the galactomannan itself but also its interaction with other polysaccharides such as xanthan shown in Figure 20, or carrageenan shown in Figure 22. The distribution of the galactose residues in locust bean gum is such that regions of depleted backbone are exposed, thus enabling interaction with the rigid rod structure of xanthan. Both guar gum and locust bean gum are storage polysaccharides which are used as an energy and carbon source in the germinating

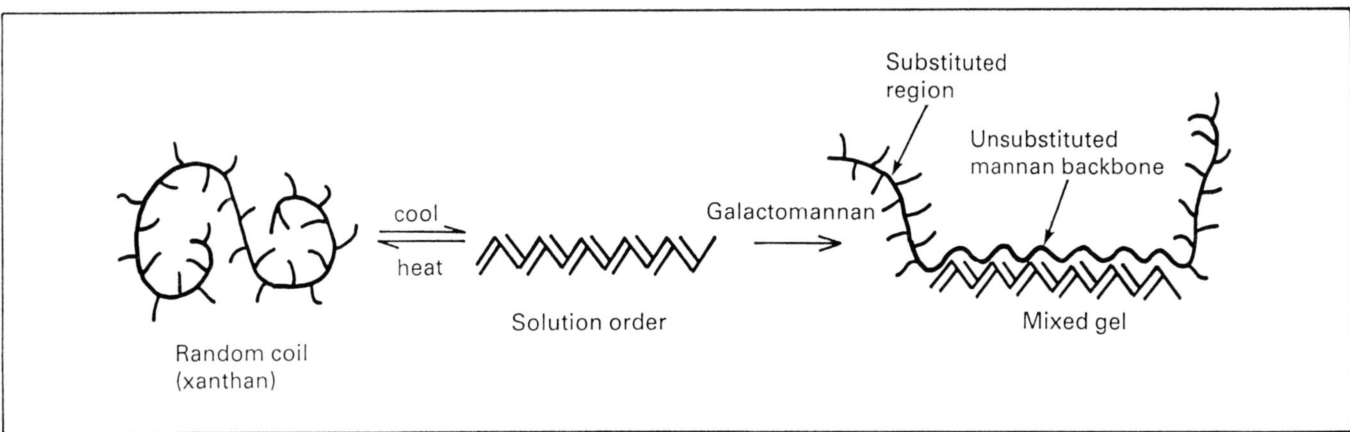

Figure 20. Interaction of xanthan and galactomannans.

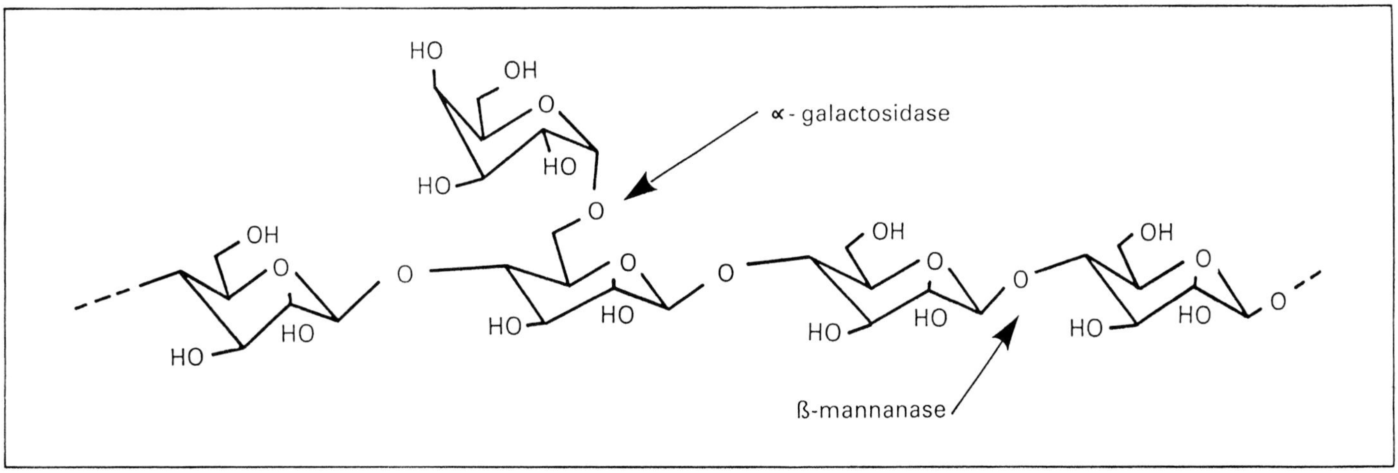

Figure 21. Structure of galactomannans/enzymic modifications.

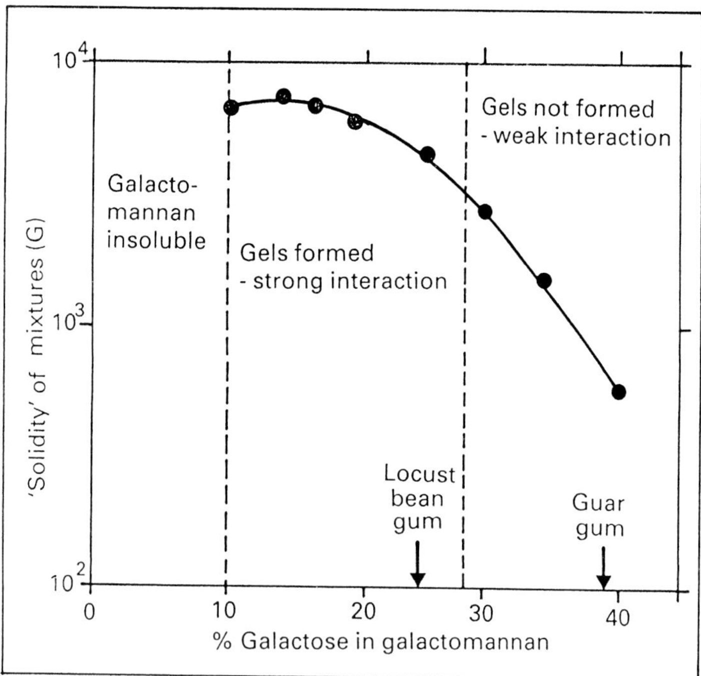

Figure 22. Gel strength of the interactions of galactomannans and carrageenans.

seed. During this process two enzymes, α-galactosidase responsible for debranching and β-mannanase responsible for the depolymerisation of the mannan backbone, degrade the polymer to metabolisable sugars as shown in Figure 21. Since the only difference between the properties of guar gum obtained from the seeds of the annual *Cyamopsis tetragognolobus* and those of locust bean gum, obtained from the seeds of the perennial *Ceratonia siliqua*, lies in the degree of substitution and not in the composition of the backbone, it should be possible to debranch guar gum in a controlled way to produce an enzyme — modified material with properties more akin to those of locust bean gum (18). However, commercial modification of polysaccharide gums presents a difficult problem not only for the biochemist but also for the process engineer. Whilst enzymic modification of polysaccharides in solutions containing 0.1 to 0.5% solids can be demonstrated, the need to remove the water on completion of the bioconversion renders the process uneconomic. The use of a α-galactosidase isolated from certain seeds free from the depolymerising β-mannanase has been shown to operate in semi-solid substrates (19). The mixing of guar flour with an equal weight of water produces a texture analogous to bread crumbs, which is an ideal medium for the enzyme. From a technological point of view the advantage of working at high solids considerably decreases the downstream processing costs. Nevertheless, the process would not be viable if the only source of the enzyme were a purified extract from the germinating seed. Molecular biology provided the tools whereby the gene for α-galactosidase from guar seed was successfully transferred to a number of hosts including *S. cerevisiae* (20). This had the double advantage of not only providing a commercial source of the enzyme but also providing one free from β-mannanase since the host organism does not produce this enzyme. This is particularly important because 0.01% contamination of the depolymerase is detrimental to this novel process as described by Jeffcoat and Overbeeke (21).

In general, much research on enzymic modification has focussed on aqueous solutions whereas in food processing emulsions are commonly encountered. From a process engineering viewpoint the enzymic modification of water-immiscible oils and fats in two-phase systems, or enzymic reactions in solvents or solids with a low water activity, remains a challenge of direct commercial interest.

NOVEL INGREDIENTS VIA FERMENTATION

The production of components by microbial fermentation is a longstanding application of biotechnology of which the manufacture of citric acid, glutamic acid and nucleotides for flavour enhancers remain substantial industries. For example, the world market for amino acids in 1982 was approximately 455,000 tonnes, representing a sales value of $1.15 million which is made up almost exclusively of glutamic acid. The trend to replace natural ingredients has created opportunities for a much broader range of flavours from fermentation products. Twenty years ago a furanone was identified in meat broth which is essential in meat flavour. Until now, this furanone was chemically synthesised starting from xylose. Recently, a natural precursor has been identified (5-keto-gluconic acid) which can be obtained by oxidative fermentation of glucose. Specific heat treatment of the acid results in the desired furanone (22).

The identification of key flavour compounds has also allowed alternative routes for their synthesis to be developed. They are based on the isolation of microorganisms via classical screening and enrichment techniques and their use in batch/continuous fermentation processes or in immobilised cell-reactors. Specific examples are the production of γ-decalactone, a key component of peach flavour, obtained by lactonisation of 4-hydroxydecanoic derived from the β-oxidation of ricinoleic acid — 12-hydroxyoleic acid.

Recombinant DNA technology permits the use of enzymes from microbial sources which would otherwise be scarce. A shortage of the cheese clotting enzyme chymosin, which is usually obtained from calves' stomachs, made it attractive to transfer the gene coding for this enzyme to a microorganism (23). The material has been submitted to the FDA by Gist-Brocades for food use approval.

Although the application of microbiology in fermenters is the traditional use of microorganisms, a number of other reactor designs and uses are emerging. The use of immobilised cells and high cell density systems (100–200 g dry wt/l) as described, for example, by Phillips Petroleum Company for the production of the high nutritive value dried yeast Provesteen, indicate the direction to higher yields, lower costs and hence wider application. The application of the Phillips continuous process is seen in the production of food grade yeasts from ethanol, sucrose and molasses (24).

In addition, the use of high cell density fermentation systems has been applied to the production of fragrances and could be extended to flavour production. A strain of *Torulopsis bombicola* has been grown to a cell density of 40–100 g dry weight per litre of broth and then used to convert palmitic acid to a 2:1 mixture of ω- and ω-1 hydroxypalmitic acid (Figure 23). The acids, isolated as glycolipids of sophorose (a disaccharide of glucose) were released by hydrolysis and lactonised and purified to produce a natural musk (dihydroambrettolide) with highly desirable organoleptic properties (25).

Further application of yeasts as flavour blocks in their own right have been exploited by a number of companies including Gist-Brocades and Quest. The latter has exploited yeast as a source of flavour precursor and developed a natural low salt savoury flavour building block known as "Biosol" (26).

The Biosol approach, schematically shown below, yields a taste enhancer/building block which does not contain salt but does contain the natural taste enhancer quanosine 5′-monophosphate (5′-GMP) and the natural organic acids lactic and succinic.

BIOSOL CONCEPT

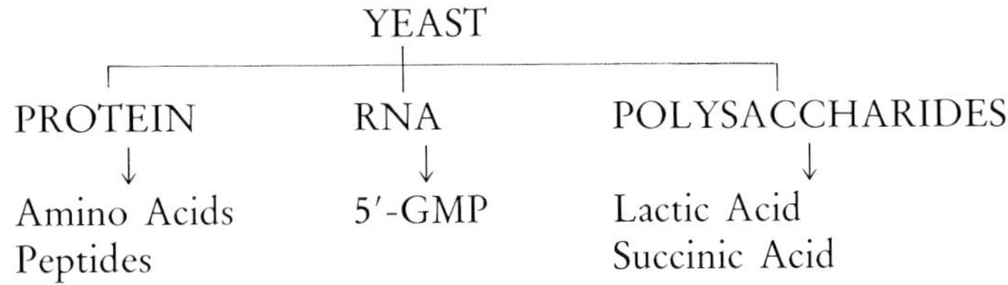

The process requires the use of deactivated yeast in a 2-step process, involving: (i) the addition of an enzyme cocktail with proteolytic, lipolytic and cell wall degrading activity; and (ii) the fermentation with the food grade bacterium *Lactobacillus delbrueckii*. In so doing, protein is converted into amino acids and peptides, RNA into 5′-GMP, and polysaccharides into lactic and succinic acids. The enzymic digestion and fermentation may be carried out simultaneously and the resulting broth, after removal of the insoluble material, is spray dried.

PROCESSING SYSTEMS

Experience from the chemical industry demonstrates that, where possible, continuous production plants achieve greater productivity and lower operating costs than batch operation. Despite this, continuous processing has found relatively little application in biotechnology.

In addition to the use of yeast to produce flavours and other additives, microorganisms have been considered for the production of major food ingredients known as "single cell protein" (SCP) and "single cell oil" (SCO). Neither of these products have enjoyed much commercial success although the initial concept of using a microorganism to convert a

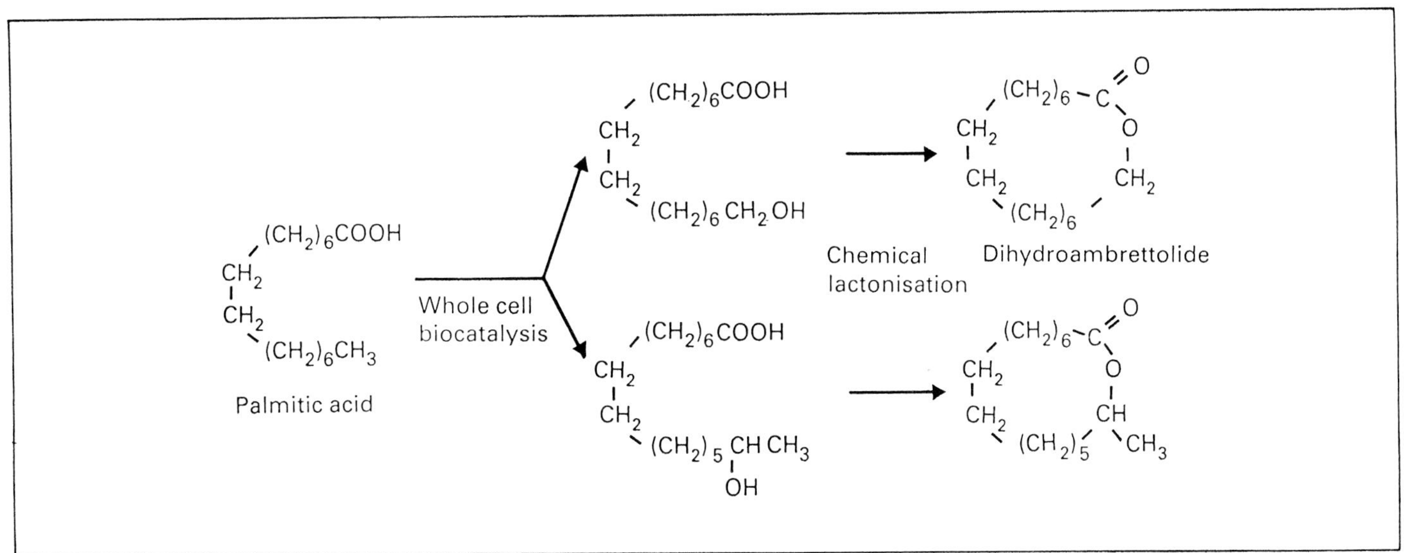

Figure 23. Biotechnology routes to perfumery compounds.

cheap or waste feedstock into a valuable food ingredient appeared attractive. A number of different feedstocks, including carbon dioxide, methane, methanol, sugars and hydrocarbons have been used in conjunction with algae, fungi, yeasts and bacteria. The single cell protein plant to produce Pruteen (27), was based initially on methane as a carbon source and later upon the growth of *Methylophilus methylotrophous* using methanol. The 600 tonne air-lift fermenter was built to produce 50,000–60,000 tonnes of dried product/year and required novel engineering skills to develop a continuous process during which a monoseptic operation was assured. The products of the fermentation, namely the microorganism and the extra-microbial protein, are harvested by flocculation using a combination of heat shock and pH change. By contrast, Phillips Petroleum Company developed a high cell density system based upon the growth of *Torula* yeast on ethanol, sucrose or molassess as the carbon source and ammonia as the nitrogen source. Their modified fermentation processes allowed cell masses of 160 g dry cell mass/l to be achieved which are harvested by spray-drying the total broth. The product, which has been produced at 1500 l. pilot plant scale, has been shown to be a high grade protein product for nutritional supplements in various types of food.

A comparison of the two approaches highlights some interesting differences. The Pruteen process utilises microorganisms to convert a petrochemical feedstock into an animal feed and, although very advanced sophisticated engineering principles have been developed to give a product acceptable in nutritional terms to the farmer, the process is not commercial. Lack of success has largely been due to the high production costs, including an increase in raw material costs, decrease in price of competitive products (i.e. soya), legislative approval, political issues and maybe even the quality of the product due to low levels of such key amino acids as methionine. The high cell density system developed by Phillips not only gives a high yield of high quality biomass but allows cheaper downstream processing by enabling spray-drying of the total fermenter product. Thus, by using microorganisms capable of growth on a range of renewable raw materials, employing cheap processing methods and producing a high nutritional value product with a wide range of applications, a commercial process becomes more realistic. Success in the production of single cell protein has also been achieved by RHM who have developed a process to produce a novel protein which has a microfilamentous structure both in respect of strength and size not too dissimilar from the microfilaments of meat. It is obtained by growth of fungal mycelia from *Fusarium graminearum* and is a protein- and fibre-rich food ingredient — "mycoprotein" as it is known is the only novel food which has been evaluated by the Foods Standards Committee of the U.K. Ministry of Agriculture, Fisheries and Food, and has been accepted for human consumption. A process plant with a capacity of 1,000 tonnes per annum was planned for 1985 with the option subsequently to increase production twentyfold. Similar overall problems to those of Pruteen have also beset the production of SCO which was initially based upon hydrocarbon feedstocks and more recently targetted at the use of cheap carbohydrate feedstocks. Workers in Japan have successfully grown yeasts to produce as much as 80% of their dry weight as storage triacylglycerol but, with the possible exception of the use of dissolved oxygen to influence the level of linoleic acid, very little is known about the control of lipid biosynthesis to enable specific oils and fats to be produced by microorganisms. The future for single cell products is not clear and the indications are that they will be restricted to special situations dictated by politics, local tariff barriers, cheap available feedstocks, applicability of improved reactors such as high cell density systems and a desire to remove the dependence upon raw material import — e.g. the U.S.S.R. practice of exploiting SCP as an alternative to the import of soya bean for animal feed.

An example of a commercial continuous process is a fermentation for the production of microbially soured milk for margarine. During development of this mixed-culture process utilising *Streptococcus cremoris*, various engineering problems were encountered (28). First, unlike the production of a single cell protein, a single fermenter is inadequate for stable operations and two fermenters in series are employed (Figure 24). In practice, the feed of milk between the two stages is controlled so that the balance between growth rate and throughput is obtained automatically by ensuring that the growth rate of the fastest growing organisms are controlled by nutrients produced by the slower ones. Development of the process thus required careful attention to reaction engineering and control. Second, engineering attention was required to ensure the completely aseptic operation which is necessary for product safety assurance. Wide experience gained with the specification of equipment for hygienic food processing plant has assisted the design of an aseptic continuous fermentation plant.

CONCLUSIONS

It is clear that biotechnology can have an impact on the food industry at the level of plant breeding to produce a wider range of raw materials, in higher yield and purer form and therefore having a direct effect on the amount and type of down-stream processing. (For a summary review see reference 29.) In addition, the innovative use of enzymes and microorganisms will allow the development of more economic processes and novel ingredients and these will eventually need legislative clearance. There is no doubt that progress in molecular biology has provided additional dimensions to supplement traditional plant breeding and fermentation technology.

Further application of these skills will be successful only

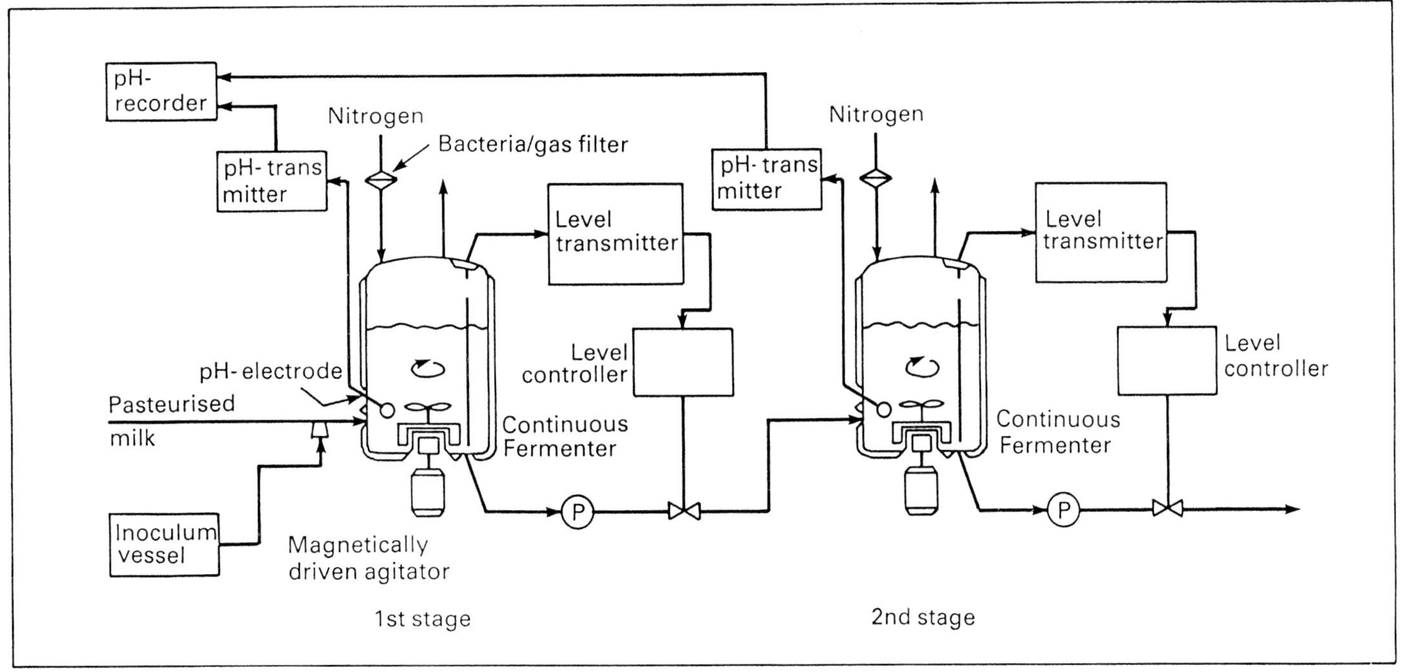

Figure 24. Two stage continuous microbial souring of milk.

with continued efforts by basic science to understand and control the biosynthesis of the raw materials. There must also be a more profound appreciation of the structure/function relationships of biological molecules, leading in turn to more versatile processing aids and novel products.

Commercialisation of the products of this technology as any other demands close collaboration between the scientist, technologist and the process engineer. It must take account of changes in the needs and aspirations of the consumer for healthier eating and for foods processed under conditions which more closely resemble those occurring in nature.

REFERENCES

1. Nursten, H.E. (1986). *Aroma compounds from the Maillard reaction, in Development in Food Flavours.* Chapter 11, pp 173–190 Ed. by G.G. Birch and M.G. Lindley, London and New York, Elsevier Applied Science.
2. Haas, M.J. (1983). *Biotechnology in food production and processing.* Biotechnology, **vol. 2**, pp 575–578.
3. Stewart, G.G., Panchal, C.J., Russell, I. and Sills, A.M. (1983). *Advances in ethanol from sugars and starch — a panoramic paper.* Proc. International Symposium on Ethanol from Biomass. pp 4–57. Eds. Duckworth, H.E. and Thompson E.A. Royal Society of Canada, Ottawa, Canada.
4. Stewart G.G. (1984). *Recent developments in genetically manipulated industrial yeast strains.* Proceedings of the Online Conference, Biotech '84, Washington D.C., USA.
5. *Application of Genetic Engineering to Fermentation* (1986) in Food Technology, **vol. 40**, pp 82–112.
6. Staba, J.E. (1980). *Plant tissue culture as a source of biochemicals.* Boca Raton, Florida: CRC Press Inc.
7. Hamill, J.D., Parr, A.J., Rhodes, M.J.C., Robins, R.J. and Walton, N.J. (1987). *New routes to plant secondary products.* Biotechnology, **vol. 5**, pp 800–804.
8. Laughlin, T.S. and Ferrell, T.M. (1987). *Biotechnology in the cosmetic industry.* Biotechnology, **vol. 5**, pp 1035–1037.
9. *Biotechnology of Plant Foods* in Food Technology, **vol. 39**, pp 112–142 (1985).
10. Kinsella, J.E. (1982). *Protein Structure and Functional Properties: Emulsification and Flavour Binding Effects.* Proc. American Chemical Society Symposium, **vol. 206**, pp 301–326 in Food Protein Deterioration: Mechanical Function.
11. Wells, J.A., Ferrari, E., Heaner, D.S., Estell, D.A. and Chen, E. (1982). Nucleic Acid Research, **vol. 11**, pp 7911–7924.
12. Van Dam, A.F. (1977). *Stabilised edible oil/water emulsions.* U.S. Patent US 4 034 124.
13. Reilly, P.J. (1985). *Enzymic degradation of starch.* Chapter 5, pp 101–142. Starch Conversion Technology. Ed. by G.M.A. van Beynum and J.A. Roels. New York and Basel, Marcel Dekker Inc.
14. Sprossler, B. and Plainer, H. (1983). *Immobilised lactase for processing whey.* Food Technology, **vol. 10**, pp 93–95.
15. Coleman, M.H. and Macrae, A.R. (1981). *Interesterification by enzymes.* U.S. Patent 4 275 081.
16. How, P. and Macrae, A.R. (1987, 1988). *Continuous enzyme interesterification.* European Patent EP-P-O 043 602. U.S. Patent US 4 719 178.
17. Badami, R.C. and Patel, K.B. (1981). *Structure and occurrence of unusual fatty acids in minor seed oils.* Prog. Lipid. Res. **vol. 19**, pp 119–153.
18. McCleary, B.V., Bulpin, P.V. and Critchley, P. (1984). European Patent Application EPO 121 960 A3.
19. Bulpin, P.V., Gidley, M.J., Jeffcoat, R. and Underwood, D.R. (1990). *Development of a biotechnological process for the modification of galactomannan polymers with plant α-*

galactosidase. Carbohydrate Polymers, **12**, 155–168.

20. Overbeeke, N., Fellinger, A.J. and Hughes, S.G. (1987). European Patent Application EPO 255 153; WO 87–07641.
21. Jeffcoat, R., Overbeeke, N. (1989). *A novel process for the enzymic modification of galactomannans*. Enzyme and Microbial Technology (Submitted for Publication).
22. de Rooij, J.F.M. (1984, 1985). *5 ketogluconate precursor*. U.S. Patent 4 464 409; European Patent EP-B-O 058 870.
23. Maat, J. 91983). *Rennin production by transformed micro-organisms*. European patent EP-A-O 077 109.
24. Shay, L.K. and Wegner, G.H. (1985). *Improved fermentation process for producing Torula yeast*. Food Technology, **vol. 10**, pp 61–67.
25. Jeffcoat, R. and Willis, B.J. (1986). *A manufacturing process for hexadecanolide. Flavours and fragrances; a world perspective*. Proceedings of the 10th International Congress of Essential Oils. Edited by B.M. Lawrence, B.D. Mookherjee and B.J. Willis. pp 743–751. Amsterdam and New York, Elsevier.
26. de Rooij, J.F.M. and Hakkaart, M.J.J. (1986). *Food Flavours European Patent Application*. GB 850245, NL 8500956.
27. Smith, S.R.L. (1980). *Single cell protein*. Phil. Trans. R. Soc. London, **B290**, 341–354.
28. Lelieveld, H.L.M. (1982). *Mixed strains continuous milk fermentation*. Process Biochem. **19**, 112–113.
29. Food Technology (1988) **vol. 42**, pp 133–146.

Chapter 26

The Flavour and Fragrance Industry

Peter S.J. Cheetham

In this chapter biotechnological aspects of the flavour and fragrance industry are discussed, concentrating on new developments that are rapidly changing the types of flavours and fragrances used and their applications. Commercial developments, including demographic changes and changes in consumer perceptions and lifestyles such as the trend towards healthy eating, have generated a need for natural food flavours. Such market trends represent challenges to the industry which are being met by technical developments including the impact of biotechnology: among them are enzyme and fermentation technologies and particularly biotransformations and, in the longer term, genetic engineering and plant cell tissue culture.

In order to illustrate fully this new biotechnological approach we have first to put the science and technology into a commercial context by discussing some technical and commercial aspects of the industry itself. Current technical knowledge and new developments are surveyed in order to give an insight into the biochemical basis of flavours and fragrances and to show how biotechnology is providing new opportunities for the industry with the quality and costs of the products as the crucial goals. Hopefully this discussion of some more commercial aspects will show how research and development activities can be synchronised with the market needs of the industry so as to achieve good synchrony between "technology push" and "market pull" forces.

THE FLAVOUR AND FRAGRANCE INDUSTRY

The world market for flavours and fragrances was estimated to have a turnover of ca. $6,000 M in 1986 with about a 5% annual growth rate. Food flavours, for instance, represent about 10–15% by weight, and 25% by value, of the world food additive market. The annual world market for food flavours is about $2 B pa and for cosmetics in Europe about $21–22 B pa.

The industry is very definitely international in nature but is concentrated in three main regions. The most important single market is obviously the USA (ca 26% of world demand in 1986), with Western Europe contributing 35% and Japan 12%. The industry is very fragmented in terms of the geographic distribution and market shares of the companies involved; thus, only about ten corporations have large turnovers and can be considered to have international and diversified businesses compared with the majority of companies that tend to be local and specialised. Flavour- and fragrance-producing companies tend exclusively to engage in mercantile trading to end-use companies such as food and household products manufacturers (Fig. 1). These manufacturing companies sometimes have considerable in-house organoleptic skills particularly when they are backwards diversified into production, which is the case with tea and coffee companies and with brewers. However, in general, perfumers tend not to be employed by the manufacturing companies that use aroma chemicals in their consumer products. Such companies rely on competitive briefs to flavour and fragrance companies who are invited to fragrance the product in trials and tender for the business.

About 50% of the total business is carried out by the 15 largest companies. International Flavours and Fragrances and Quest International, the two biggest companies, each have ca. 10–12% world market shares, followed by a number of companies such as Firmenich, Givaudan, Haarmann and Reimer, Florasynth, Takasago, BBA and Dragoco etc.; certain food and biotechnology companies such as Gist-Brocades, together with a large number of smaller, more specialised and regional companies, make up about the remaining 50% of the industry. Recently a number of mergers and take-overs have taken place with the result that several companies have grown larger, so as to improve their market shares, product ranges and/or the geographical balances of their businesses.

The industry demonstrates a set of clear characteristics. First, there is a wide range in the value of materials used. Fragrances range from very expensive fine fragrances employed only in small amounts to the low-priced bulk materials used for perfuming mass-produced soaps, washing-up liquids, washing powders, etc. Secondly, the structure-function relationships of flavours and fragrance molecules and the mechanisms of their interactions with receptors in the tongue and nose are still uncertain. Third, the number of chemicals used by the industry is very large, of the order of a thousand, although naturally many of them are used occasionally only and/or in small quantities. Some overlap occurs between the

SOME COMMERCIAL AND TECHNICAL FEATURES OF THE FLAVOUR AND FRAGRANCE INDUSTRY

(1) The industry is very fragmented into a large number of companies, most of which are small, privately owned & specialised, with only a few companies being large and diversified, and becoming international in terms of the range of technologies used & the wide range of countries served.

(2) Market growth is modest.

(3) Sales by flavour and fragrance companies are chiefly mercantile sales to companies using flavours and fragrances as ingredients in their own products. Therefore there are only a relatively small number of large corporate customers and buying decisions are complex, involving for instance brand and product managers and technical specialists.

(4) Sales are concentrated in developed countries with consumers with relatively high disposable incomes.

(5) Frequent and large changes in usage patterns of flavours and fragrances occur because of rapid changes in consumer demands, including fashion effects.

(6) A very large number of different chemicals are used by the industry.

(7) Perfumes and flavours are complex mixtures of many chemicals either synthesised chemically or biochemically, or present in essential oils which are compounded together to give the final perfume or flavour. Therefore the most crucial test of quality is organoleptic evaluation rather than chemical analysis.

(8) Very few materials are used in large quantities and some of the most exotic are used only very infrequently for high value products. Therefore economies of scale of production and buying etc. are usually not very significant, & few matericals are of sufficient value to make attractive targets for production by speciality chemicals companies.

(9) Raw materials are derived either from cheap petrochemical sources, or from plant or animal sources that are often subject to variabilities in supply due to climatic or political factors.

(10) Flavour and fragrance materials are usually percieved at, and therefore used at, very low concentrations. Synergy effects are very important and minor components are often crucial in giving the best organoleptic quality.

(11) Scientific structure-function relationships of flavour and fragrance materials are still unclear for most groups of materials.

(12) Functional benefits, other than fragrance and flavour properties, are also important, such as preservative, deodorant, antioxidant, colour etc.

(13) Flavours and fragrances have a wide range of applications with a very wide range of prices from expensive fine fragrances to cheap detergents.

(14) The value of the materials used to make a flavour and fragrance are greatly enhanced upon formulation into complete flavours or perfumes. For instance the creative flavourist or perfumer achieves synergistic effects between the various individual components and gives individuality and character to the product.

(15) Flavour & Fragrance companies are rarely backwards integrated – into the production of specialised raw-materials such as plant derived essential oils, & are also never forwards-integrated into the sale to consumers of finished products. Horizontal diversification into related areas such as food ingredients is however becoming more common.

Figure 1. Some commercial and technical features of the flavour and fragrance industry.

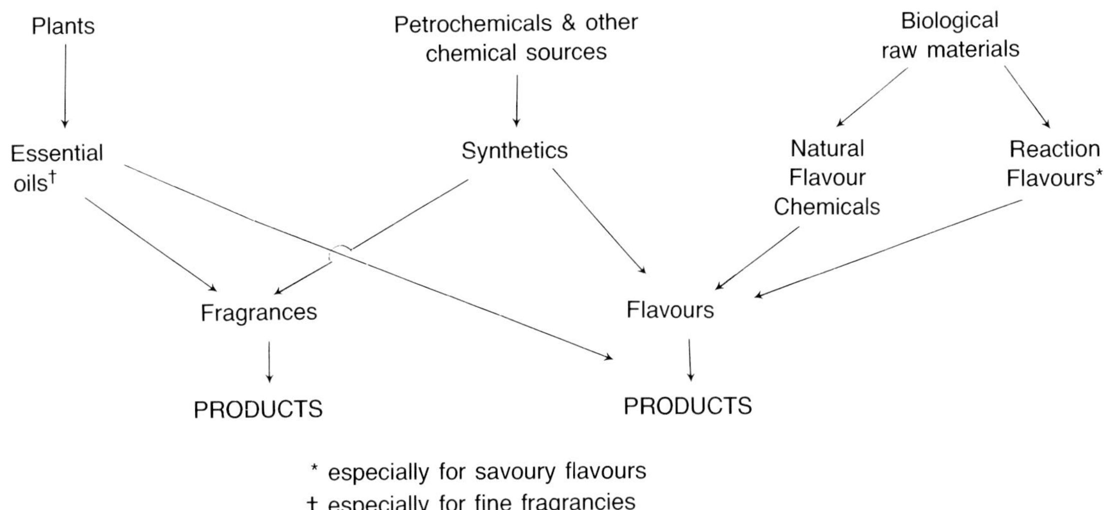

Figure 2. Sources of raw materials for the flavour and fragrance industry.

chemicals and materials used in fragrance and flavour applications as well as between materials used for high and low priced applications (Fig. 2).

The flavour and fragrance industry is thus characterised by the use of a very large number of raw materials to produce a wide range of products. Consequently each product is invariably a very complex mixture of different chemicals which often interact with one another. The optimum composition has been arrived at by exploiting both the synergistic effects between the different components on the basis of the optimal organoleptic quality and the availability and cost of the different materials, some of which will be used only occasionally and in small quantities (Fig. 2).

The same or similar organoleptic effects can often be achieved by using different molecules or different combinations of molecules. Price is directly related to organoleptic quality. For instance, jasmine, at £3,000–5,000 per kg. extracted from the plant flowers, is an order of magnitude more expensive than chemically synthesised nature-identical chemicals such as jasmone or methyl jasmonate, whereas other synthetic molecules such as dihydrojasmonate and methyl dihydrojasmonate cost no more than £10–50 per kg. Obviously the cheaper materials are used much more extensively than the better quality but more expensive products. The industry is therefore characterised by dealing in very few large tonnage flavour chemicals and so, unlike other food and chemicals industries, good economies of scale in production are rarely achieved. This is hardly surprising for an industry whose products are usually very complex mixtures of chemicals, plant extracts, etc., and one furthermore that depends heavily on highly developed skills in the blending of materials to produce products with optimum smell or taste to give individual character and identity to the product (Figs 2 and 3). Thus, in order to understand the flavour and fragrance industry, it is essential to appreciate the key creative roles of the perfumer and flavourist, their deep appreciation of consumer needs, and the high added value perfumers and flavourist achieve by their very skilled formulations (Fig. 3).

Large usage materials include musks, L-menthol and vanillin. High intensity sweetners offer a particularly large, high profit margin market but require very extensive safety testing before approval for manufacture and sale is given by regulatory authorities.

Although there is no clear-cut distinction between materials with flavour and aroma properties in the flavour and fragrance industry five product categories are recognised:

- extracts (for instance, resins and fruit extracts)
- essential oils derived by distillation of plant materials such as flowers and other natural raw materials
- single odour and taste materials (also referred to as "aroma chemicals")
- fragrance compositions
- flavour compositions

Typically, business is divided approximately equally between flavours, fragrance materials and essential oils and aroma chemicals. Of the 3,000 aroma chemicals currently produced, it has been estimated that only about 400 are made in quantities greater than 1 ton per annum. These may be non-chiral molecules, racemates and optically pure chemicals. One of the most extensively used flavours is vanilla. The world market for vanilla derived from vanilla beans is ca 1,350 tons per annum (vanilla beans contain ca 3% vanillin by weight),

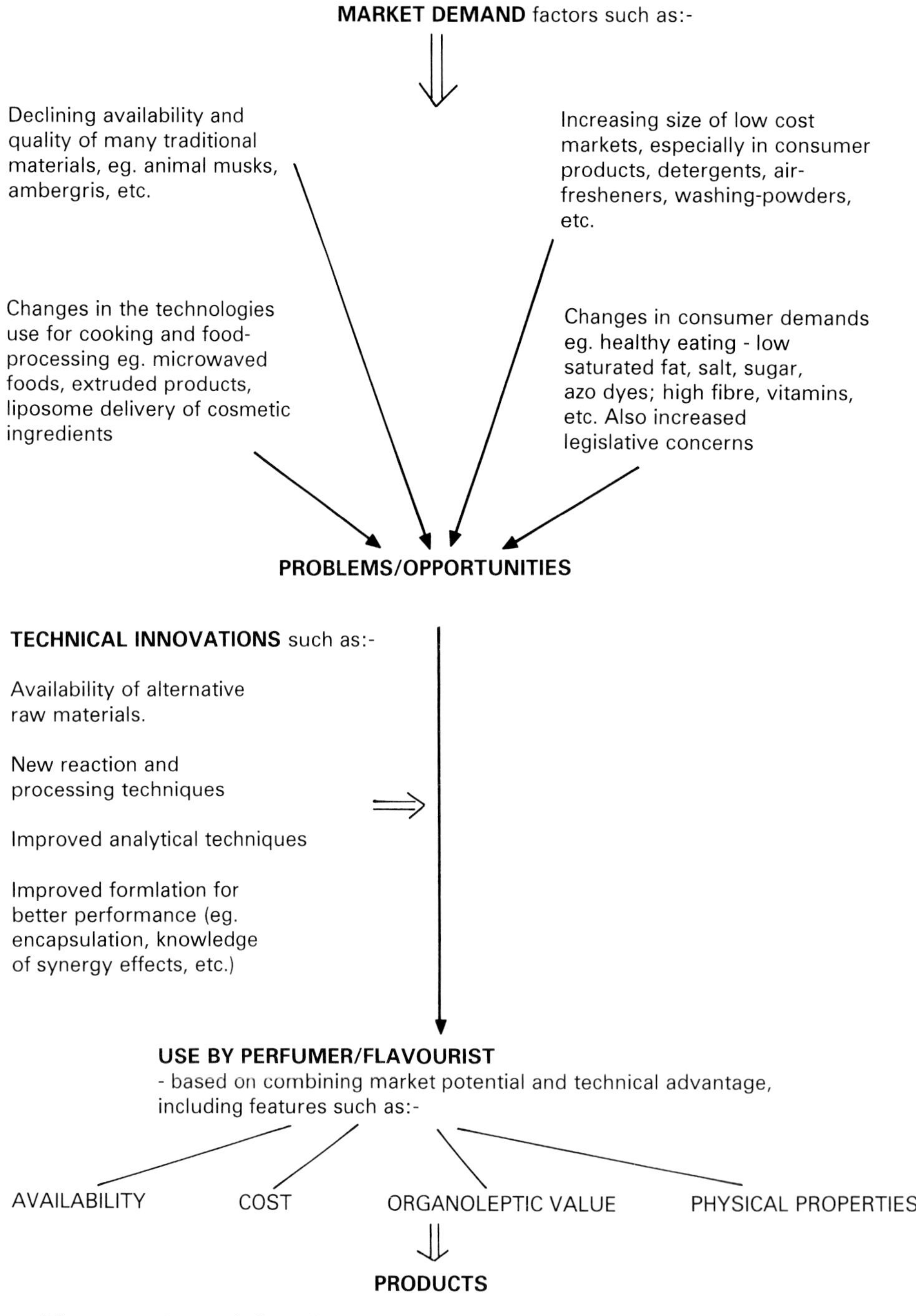

Figure 3. Factors influencing innovation in the flavour and fragrance industry.

equivalent to a business of ca £100M a year, whereas ca 6,500 tons per annum of synthetic vanillin is used representing a market of about £80M.

Up to about 100 years ago all perfumes were made up of naturally occurring plant and animal extracts. About 3,000 essential oils are now known, of which about 150 to 200 are still commercially important (Fig. 4). Typically an essential oil is produced by steam distillation or apolar solvent extraction of the source material to produce a "concrete" and then unwanted lipids are removed in an ethanol extraction step to produce an "absolute". Whereas most citrus oils are by-products of juice production, bergamot is grown principally for its oil. Yields of essential oils from plants are often low making the products expensive. To complicate matters, the yield and composition of the oil often vary with the plant strain used, climate, processing conditions, etc. Thus the price of the essential oil is directly related to its availability and organoleptic quality. Orange oil is the greatest in volume.

NATURAL ISOLATE	SOURCE
1-Carvone	Spearmint
d-Carvone	Caraway, dill
Cedrenol	Cedarwood
Cinnamic aldehyde	Cinnamon, cassia
Cinnamyl cinnamate	Styrax
Citral	*Litsea cubeba,* lemongrass
Citronellal	*Eucalyptus citriadora,* citronella
Citronellol	Citronella
Decanal	Orange
Dimethyl anthranilate	Mandarin, petitgrain
Eugenol	Clove, bay
Geraniol	Citronella
Geranyl acetate	Lemongrass
Hydroxy citronellal	Citronella, *Eucalyptus citriadora*
Linalol	Bois de rose, ho wood
Linalyl acetate	*Mentha citrata,* petitgrain
Menthol	Peppermint
Methyl cinnamate	Sweet basil, *Ocimum canum*
Nerolidol	*Melaleuca viridiflora,* cabreuva

Figure 4. Examples of natural chemicals isolated from essential oils.

In 1984 the world production of orange oil was of the order of 12,000 (metric) tons, followed by others (e.g. lemon, clove and peppermint oils) with a production of about 2,000 tons each per year. The annual production of most essential oils is less than 100 tons per annum. Jasmine, neroli (orange blossom oil), iris root oil and rose oil are some of the most expensive. Others include benzoin, leaf oil, galbanum, labdanum, maté, melilot, mimosa, myrrh, oakmoss, olibanum, opopanax, patchouli, rosemary, sandlewood, vetivert and violet (Fig. 4).

Some 300–400 materials are commonly used in fragrances. Many are cheap commodity chemicals such as α-pinene which is easily isolated from turpentine and costs no more than £10 per kg. The principal component of oil of cloves is eugenol, α-terpineol of lilac, geraniol of rose oil and l-linalol of lavender. (d)-Limonene is invariably the major component of most citrus essential oils (Fig. 8), but it is interesting to note that most of the flavour character of the oil is given by oxygenated terpenes present in very much lower concentrations. The mono- and sesquiterpenes of plants probably have antimicrobial benefits for the plant, or roles in attracting insects to pollinate them or repelling insect pests. Some essential oils are used chiefly as sources of important molecules, others, such as lavender are mostly used as "refined mixtures". The number of naturally occurring compounds known to be important for aromas is at present about 5,000 and may ultimately rise to as many as 10,000. This number is restricted because, in order to be detected by the nose, the vapour pressure of a compound must be above a certain threshold value. In practice, eighteen carbon atoms or a molecular mass of 250 to 300 is about the upper limit of perception.

Organoleptic character and threshold also often depend on whether a material is actually detected by smell or taste. Thus, for instance, acetaldehyde is detected at thresholds of 0.066 ppm in air and 0.00069 ppm in water. This effect is important because most flavours are tasted, i.e. they are detected dissolved in aqueous solution, whereas most fragrances are supplied dissolved in volatile solvents and detected as a vapour. A corrolary of this great number of flavour and aroma chemicals already available is that there are poor prospects for research aimed at the untargeted synthesis of new molecules in the hope that some will have good flavour or fragrance properties.

Flavour compounds are usually present at quite low concenrations in the source; thus, the flavour characteristics compounds in strawberry, banana and tomatoes are present at 2–8, 12–18 and 3–5 ppm, respectively. Roasted meat aroma, and many other aromas produced by heating, are also very complex. Depending on the method employed, a ton of starting material yields 1–10 g of extract; these are found to contain at least 2,000–3,000 components when analysed by gas chromatographic methods which are capable of detecting 10^{-10}–10^{-16} g/g of materials present in the starting mixtures. Likewise, 1 tonne of strawberries contains only 25 g of flavour concentrate which again is a very complex mixture of different chemicals. Yet another complication is that the same flavour chemicals are found in very many different flavour and fragrance sources, organoleptic differences residing in the amounts present and the presence of complex mixtures with other materials.

Flavour and fragrance materials can be classed as natural (i.e. found in natural materials and derived from these sources), nature-identical, (i.e. found in natural materials but manufac-

Natural flavouring substances - obtained by appropriate physical processes (including distillation and solvent extractions) or enzymatic or microbiological processes from material of vegetable or animal origin either in the raw state or after processing for human consumption by traditional food-preparation processes (including drying, torrefaction and fermentation).

Nature-identical flavouring substances - obtained by chemical synthesis or isolated by chemical processes and chemically identical to a substance naturally present in material of vegetable or animal origin.

Artificial flavouring substances - obtained by chemical synthesis but not chemically identical to a substance naturally present in material of vegetable or animal origin.

Flavouring preparations - products, other than natural substances whether concentrated or not, with flavouring properties, obtained by appropriate physical processes (including distillation and solvent extraction) or by enzymatic or microbiological processes from material of vegetable or animal origin, either in the raw state or after processing for human consumption by traditional food-preparation processes (including drying, torrefaction and fermentation).

Process flavourings - products obtained according to good manufacturing practices by heating to a temperature not exceeding 180°C for a period not exceeding 15 minutes a mixture of ingredients, not necessarily themselves having flavouring properties, of which at least one contains nitrogen (amino) and another is a reducing sugar.

Smoke flavourings - smoke extracts used in traditional foodstuffs smoking processes.

taken from Perfumer and Flavourist (1989) **14,** p.3

Figure 5. Definition of flavours.

tured from non-natural raw materials) and synthetic or artificial (i.e. chemically synthesised — see Fig. 5). The market value of "natural" flavours is illustrated by vanilla/vanillin. The world market is estimated to be ca 7,500 tons per annum. This is chiefly satisfied by vanillin extracted from pulped wood. Only about 13% of the market is natural vanilla derived from vanilla beans but, because of its greater organoleptic value and natural status, it commands a much higher price and so represents some 56% of the market by value.

THE ROLE OF FLAVOURS AND FRAGRANCES IN PRODUCTS

Fragrances usually contain several hundred components and tend to contain higher proportions of essential oil ingredients than do flavours. Applications range from very expensive fine fragrances to cheap household products such as detergents and washing-up liquids. Perfumery components are categorised as "top notes" — the light volatile components that make the first impact, "middle-notes" that form the bulk of the perfume and thus give individuality and character, and then "end-notes" that fix the more volatile components and are the longest lasting. An important characteristic of many fragrant products is that the fragrance is the easiest feature to change in order to give the product a new marketing image.

Some flavours and aroma chemicals also have additional valuable functionalites: examples are colour (e.g. saffron and turmeric), mouthfeel, or anti-microbial activities which may extend the shelf-life of foods and enable the amounts of preservatives to be reduced. Anti-oxidants also have significant anti-cancer effects, presumably by mopping-up free radicals before they can have a deleterious effect on the cells nucleic acids. Natural antioxidants have been identified in extracts of rosemary and other botanicals. Other useful properties include the cooling effect of L-menthol (peppermint), the soothing effect of chamomile and the insect-repelling properties of lavender and citronella oils. Other properties, less easy to define, are "substantivity" and "persistence", that is the ability of a fragrance to remain after application, for example on the skin or on a garment after washing.

THE HISTORICAL DEVELOPMENT OF THE FLAVOUR AND FRAGRANCE INDUSTRY (FIG. 6)

Flavours

Four main phases in the historical development of biological food production can be discerned. First there was the discovery, often by accident, of various fermented foods such

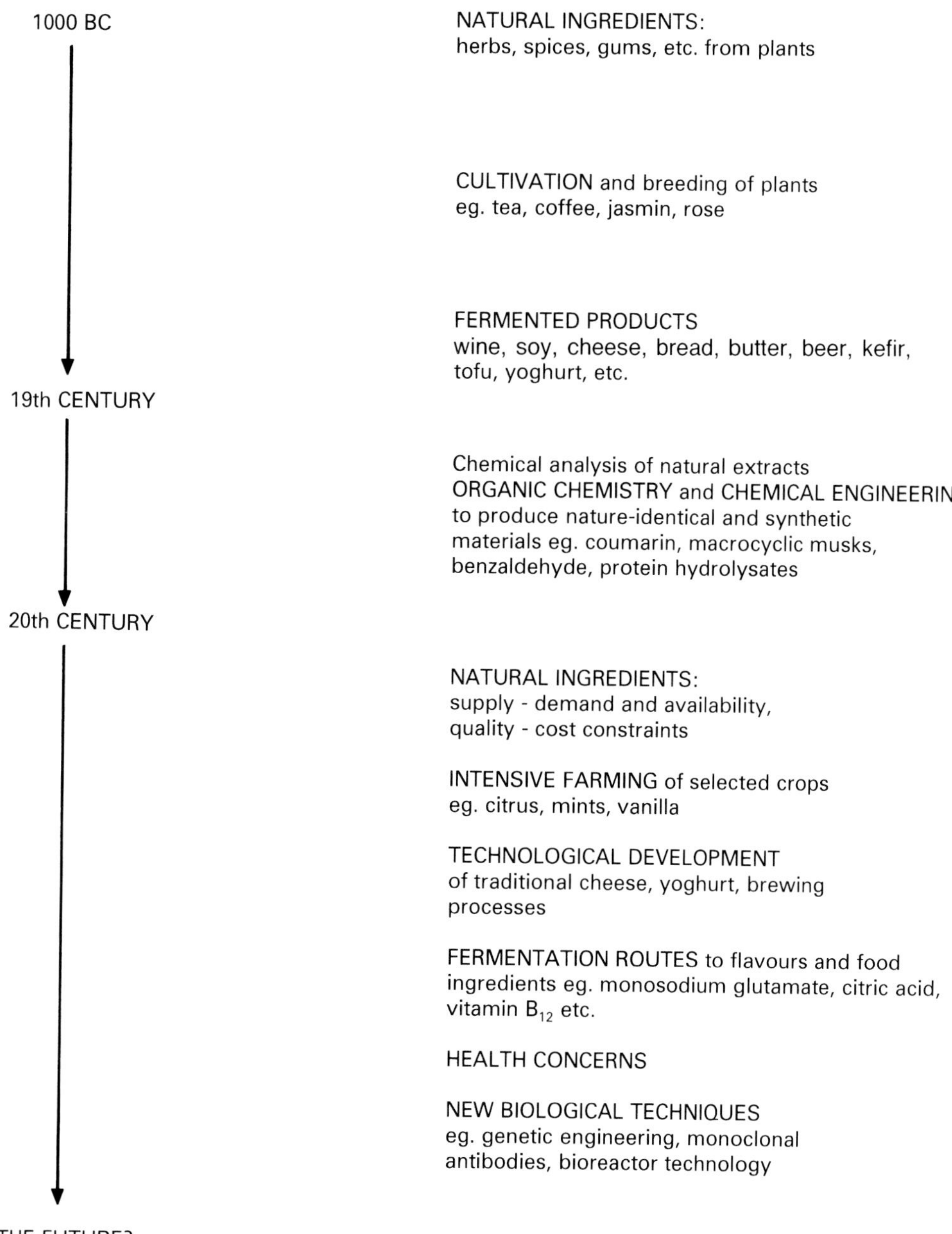

Figure 6. The historical development of the flavour and fragrance industry and the role of biotechnology.

as cheese and yoghurt, etc. (see Chapter 16). Later came the production of primary microbial metabolites such as citric acid and ethanol to be followed by the related microbial production of secondary metabolites and, most recently, by the application of modern technologies such as recombinant DNA and biocatalyst immobilisation techniques.

Historically many food flavours were generated by empirical procedures very often when a primary concern was to enhance the stability of the food towards deterioration and microbial contamination: the generation of an improved flavour was a secondary benefit. This may have been the case for vinegar, cheese, butter, yoghurt, bread, sauerkraut, beer, and wine, and certainly for eastern spiced foods. The antimicrobial and general preservative effects of microbially-generated molecules such as acetic acid, methyl ketones, propionic acid and ethanol were accompanied by desirable flavour development, usually due to the presence of complex mixtures of these acids, alcohols and other products that give individual character and identity to the food or beverage. Subsequently the sensory properties of traditionally flavoured foods were developed and optimised empirically, the determining features being the types of local raw materials and processing technology available and local consumer preferences. Thus, the cumulative result of many centuries of development is that a great variety of different types of fermented foods and beverages are now available, each subtly different in terms of chemical composition and organoleptic impact. This important point illustrates an essential characteristic of most flavours, that they are very often organoleptically and chemically complex mixtures of different chemicals, present very often at quite low concentrations; for instance, methyl ketones, lactones and organic acids are present in dairy products in quantities that are low in weight terms but quite sufficient to impart an overall high-quality taste sensation.

Fragrances

The word "perfume" is a corruption of "par-fume" meaning by smoke. Perfumery was practised in ancient China and India but the earliest records are from ancient Egypt about 1,000 years before Christ. The tomb of Tutankhamun contained jars of aromatic oils which were still fragrant after 3,000 years of storage. In those ancient civilisations perfumes were used lavishly for ceremonial and ritual occasions. Many food ingredients, flavours and fragrance raw materials have for several thousand years usually been derived from plants growing in countries in the botanically more diverse southern latitudes, often in India and Indonesia. Extraction was by physical means, mainly distillation. Trade was via ports such as Venice and Genoa. The products included animal products from civet cat (civetone), whales (ambergris), beaver (castoreum) and musk deer (muskone); herbs, spices and gums such as pepper, vanilla, cloves, gum arabic, ambrette seed oil, etc., which are often still collected from wild indigenous plants; and cultivated plant varieties such as tea, coffee and cocoa which have been improved by selection and breeding procedures. These materials were so highly prized by wealthy people in the consumer countries in Western Europe that the great pioneering voyages of exploration by the Portugese, Spanish and other sailors were frequently motivated by a desire to find better sea routes to the countries from which the flavours and fragrancies came.

With the rapid increase in chemical knowledge after the Renaissance period in Europe came a recognition of the potential of chemistry to produce not only chemicals with applications as medicines, and dye-stuffs but also with perfumery and flavour characteristics. This potential was realised once chemical technology became sufficiently reliable and well-developed during the nineteenth century. Flavour chemical manufacture was first established in the 1870s and so for more than 100 years the industry has been substantially based both on natural products and materials produced by synthetic organic chemistry.

The first perfume to make major use of synthetic ingredients to give new perfume effects (in this case aliphatic aldehydes such as 2-methyl undecanal) and achieve significant commercial success as a perfume, was Chanel No 5, first introduced in 1921. This product marked a landmark in the history of perfumery, demonstrating that synthetics could both simulate and extend natural perfumery materials. This was rapidly followed by the systematic exploitation of increasingly cheap petrochemicals as sources of perfumery materials and the establishment of a large chemically-based flavour and fragrance industry with improved technologies for the isolation of perfumery materials from plant sources. Latterly the identification of new minor components of essential oils by improved analytical methods such as gas-liquid chromatography, mass spectroscopy and NMR has provided a strong fresh impetus. Recent examples of chemically synthesised fragrance materials include top-notes such as geraniol nitrile (a citrus-like material), middle-notes such as monoterpene alcohols and end-notes such as macrocyclic musk lactones. It is of note that the most expensive perfume ever sold contained androstenone, a pig pheremone (sex-attractant)!

Thus, over the centuries, there has been a tendency for the increasing demand for natural flavourings and fragrances from traditional sources to outstrip supply. Coupled with a growing availability of the cheaper, often synthetic, materials the traditional sources have become progressively restricted to high-value, top-of-the-market applications. A good example of this trend is natural vanilla obtained from vanilla beans, 80% of the world's supply being grown in Madagascar; but this is only a small proportion of the total amount of vanillin consumed, most of which is nature-identical vanillin derived from wood pulp.

One particular current issue concerns the provision of raw materials, especially assured cheap supplies of constant quality.

At present many plant sources of flavour and perfumery materials are under threat because of climatic changes, over-exploitation of natural populations, concerns about conservation and political disturbances, but most importantly because the huge modern demand for naturally-derived fragrance and flavour materials can no longer be met from traditional agricultural sources. Other changes include the development of traditional cheese, yoghurt and brewing processes into modern industries and the establishment of large fermentation facilities for the production of materials such as monosodium glutamate. In the future the impact of the new techniques of genetic engineering, monoclonal antibodies and enzyme immobilization will combine to yield biotechnologically-based processed materials replacing or supplementing existing chemical and agricultural sources.

A recent significant development is a shift away from the traditional reliance on standard vanilla, chocolate and strawberry flavours towards new, exotic and chemically more complex tastes such as those of tropical fruits. In many cases this increased complexity demands new flavour chemicals as well as for flavour creation to be initiated at an earlier stage in the product cycle; as a result, the flavour creation team interacts with the food manufacturer sooner than it used to do.

Market Trends

An important current international tendency is towards healthy lifestyles. For many people healthy eating has now become established as part of healthy living: that is, finding the best combination of the amounts and types of food and exercise for each individual depending on their age, work and leisure activities, nutritional status and state of health. Generally speaking, healthy eating involves a reduction in the consumption of artificial additives, sodium and saturated fats while increasing the amounts of natural foods such as salads and fibre in the diet. This approach is best summarised by the British Dietary Guidelines by the British Health Education Council (1983) which recommend reductions in the intake of saturated fatty acids, sugar and salt and increased consumption of polyunsaturated fatty acids and fibre. In pursuit of these objectives, modern trends include the use of exogenous flavours to replace those lost during the processing of foods and an increased demand for savoury flavours, and thus for taste enhancers, such as GMP and IMP. Similarly the increased consumption of microwaved foods that are cooked very rapidly, has generated a requirement for flavours containing pyrazines, compounds that are normally formed only during slow conventional cooking procedures. Flavours also become volatilised more easily during microwaving and browning reactions that generate both flavour and colour take place less readily.

THE ROLE OF BIOTECHNOLOGY IN THE FLAVOUR AND FRAGRANCE INDUSTRY

There are two questions central to the role of biotechnology in the flavour and fragrance industry:

- what makes a high quality flavour or fragrance?
- how can that high quality flavour or fragrance be produced cost-effectively using biotechnology?

The answer to the first question depends largely on an improved knowledge of how we perceive flavour and fragrance coupled with a better understanding of the structure-function relationships between flavour and fragrance chemicals. The response to the second involves our comparatively newly developed capabilities in the biosciences that permit the use of enzymes and microorganisms cost-effectively to produce flavours and fragrances. In the case of food flavours this "technical-push" effect has been complimented by a "commercial-pull" in the form of the recent consumer-led demand for natural food materials. For several reasons, the immediate impact of biotechnology is likely to be much greater in flavours than in fragrances. There is a much greater requirement for "natural" flavours; most flavours are formed biochemically in plant and animal tissues and are thus very amenable to biotechnology research. Many aroma chemicals on the other hand are speciality chemicals synthesised chemically from petrochemical or other sources. Food flavours can be produced either as individual flavour chemicals and then blended together to produce the required complex flavour, or produced in the form of multi-component flavour blocks or even complete flavours.

MICROBIAL FLAVOUR AND FRAGRANCE PRODUCTION

Fermentation offers exciting opportunities to produce flavours and fragrance chemicals, particularly when the microorganisms are supplemented with food-grade enzymes either to extend their activity or to pre-treat the raw materials so as to increase their fermentability into complex flavour blocks. This approach has been sucessfully used to accelerated the koji fermentation to produce soy sauce. The traditional fermentation procedures illustrate well a basic approach: that in wine or beer fermentations variations in the composition of the raw materials and variations in yeast metabolism and processing conditions can be used to generate a range of products with very different tastes (and prices).

Methyl ketones are important flavour components, especially of blue cheeses; *Penicillium roqueforti* for instance produces 2-pentanone, 2-heptanone and 2-nonanone (Fig. 7).

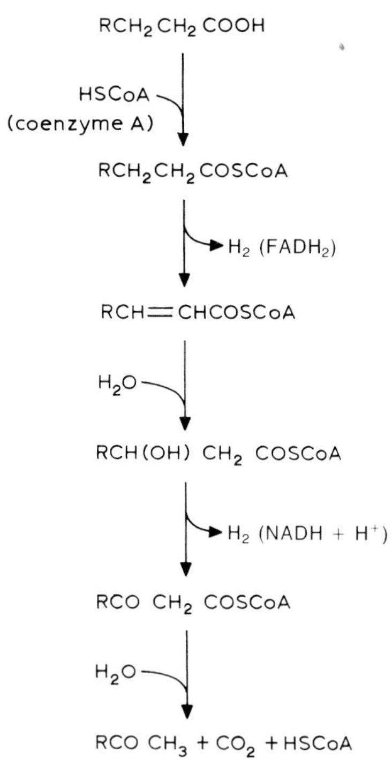

Figure 7. Formation of methyl ketones from fatty acids by microorganisms.

The role of moulds in producing methyl ketones in cheese was first reported in 1924. Diacetyl and acetoin produced by lactic streptococci are flavours characteristic of butter, buttermilk and sour cream. Diacetyl also imparts a yellow colour to dairy products. It is formed from citrate via oxaloacetate and pyruvate which is de-toxified to form diacetyl and acetoin. An essential step is transport of citrate into the cell by an inducible citrate permease. Natural diacetyl can also be obtained from starter distillate, a by-product from the manufacture of dairy starter cultures. The elucidation of the biochemical pathways to such traditional materials, as well as their regulation and the microbial physiology of the producing microorganisms, has helped in the development of large-scale optimised modern processes for their production and provide good opportunities for the application of genetic engineering techniques to further optimise these processes.

Fatty acids such as butyric and propionic are characteristic of Romano, Provolono and Swiss cheeses. In some cases these acids are responsible for the formation of the holes in the cheese and also affect the appearance of the product. Butyric acid has been used to supply butter-like flavour notes. It is produced by obligate anaerobes such as the *Clostridia*, the highest yields being achieved when the pH is maintained at about pH 5.0 with calcium carbonate.

Acids can also be formed by lipases, different lipases having different specificities. Usually enzyme preparations containing a high ratio of esterase to lipase activity are preferred. Lipases producing predominantly short chain acids, e.g. butyric, produce rancid odours while longer chain fatty acids, with a chain length of about C_{12}, have a soapy flavour. More interestingly, medium-size fatty acids in the range C_6-C_{10} are important components of cheddar cheese flavour. Acids such as lactic, produced by lactic acid bacteria, are important components of yoghurt and cheese flavours and acetaldehyde also occurs in yoghurt.

Pyrazines are remarkable flavour materials because they have very low taste thresholds of the order of 0.002 ppb, and because of their widespread occurance. For instance, 2-methoxy-3-isopropyl and isobutyl pyrazines can be tasted at the level of 1 microgramme in 5 hundred litres of water. Obviously this is the level of dilution at which single molecules have a bioactive effect! Other such compounds include 2-methyl-3-isopropyl pyrazine and tetramethyl pyrazine which can be produced from leucine, isoleucine or valine by fermentation using *Corynebacterium glutamicum*. Up to 3 g/l of tetramethyl pyrazine has been formed using a *C. glutamicum* mutant. This pyrazine is believed to be synthesised because the absence of a reducto-isomerase in the leucine-isovaline pathway results in the accumulation of acetoin, followed by the formation of the tetramethylpyrazine from the acetoin and ammonia.

Vegetable flavour chemicals are usually formed by the action of endogenous enzymes on precursors following the mechanical disruption of the vegetable tissues. For instance, 1-octen-3-o1 is the main chemical responsible for mushroom aroma, whereas fruit flavour chemicals and flower fragrances such as β-damascenone (Roses) are usually synthesised by the normal metabolic processes of the fruit during ripening and are therefore present in the intact fruit (Fig. 8). Many fruit flavours also require organic acids like citric and/or malic and tartaric to provide the required sour taste component. Analysis of the spectrum of components also serves to identify the source of raw materials, to substantiate advertising and labelling claims and to prevent counterfeiting of products. The so-called "green" flavours are aldehydes and alcohols produced by endogenous enzymes such as lipoxygenase following the mechanical disruption of plant tissues. They may act as defence mechanisms against infections. These short chain compounds, often C6 aldehydes and alcohols, are derived from fatty acids by the formation of hydroperoxides by lipoxygenase followed by isomerisation and cleavage with hydroperoxide lyases (Fig. 9). The specificity of the enzyme, which varies with its plant source, determines the size of the short chain alcohols produced. Conversion to the corresponding aldehydes can then occur after catalysis by alcohol dehydrogenase. Thus, for example hexanal, cis-3-hexenal and trans-3-hexenal which are characteristic of apple flavours can be produced using a soyabean lyase which generates C6 fragments via a 13-hydroperoxide, while tomato enzymes form 9-hydroperoxides and products such as 3-cis-nonenal (Fig. 9). The olfactory thresholds of hexanal and 2-hexenal are low, being reported to be 0.005 and 0.017 ppm

PLANT	FLAVOUR COMPONENT(s)
Lemon and lime	Geraniol, limonene
Grapefruit	Nootkatone, limonene, thioterpenol
Grape (concord)	Methyl anthranilate, ethyl acetate
Raspberry	1-(p-hydroxyphenyl) butan-3-one
Apple	Ethyl-2-methylbutyrate, hexanal, 2-hexenal
Pear	Ethyl-deca-2, 4-dienoate
Banana	Isoamyl acetate
Peach	gamma-decalactone
Orange	Limonene
Pineapple	4-hydroxy-2, 5-dimethyl furanone
Cucumber	Nona-2, 6-dienal
Melon	Non-6-enal
Mushroom	Oct-1-ene-3-one (and -o1) 1-enthionine
Tomato	Hex-3-enal
Bell pepper	2-isobutyl-3-methoxypyrazine, trans-beta-octimene
Potato (cooked)	3-methylthiopropanal
Red beets	Geosmin
Celery	Sedanolide
Garlic	Diallyl disulphide
Onion (cooked)	Dipropyl disulphide
Cabbage	Allyl isothiocyanates
Radish	4-methylthio-trans-3-butenyl isothiocyanate
Red bean	Oct-1-ene-3-o1, hex-cis-3-enol
Soya bean	Ethyl vinyl ketone
Carrots (cooked)	Non-2-enal
Peas	Non-3-enol
Watercress	2-phenylethyl thiocyanate
Olive oil	Nonanal
Vanilla	Vanillin, p-hydroxybenzaldehyde
Cloves	Eugenol

Figure 8. Significance organoleptic components of some fruits and vegetables.

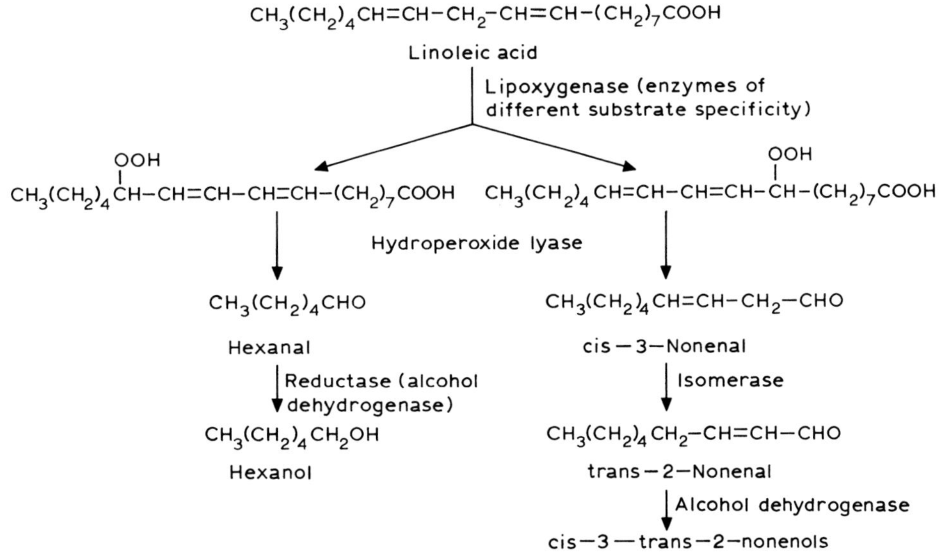

Figure 9. Fatty acid cleavage products.

respectively. A similar mechanism is also responsible for the formation of the unsaturated fatty acid aldehydes that are important components of chicken flavours. In this case arachidonic acid is broken-down to 3-cis-nonenal, 4-cis-decenal, 2-trans-α-5-cis-undecadienal, etc.

Ionone flavours are also formed by the breakdown of plant biomolecules, in this case carotinoids, to form ionones (violets etc.) or damascenones (roses etc.) Microbial conversion of ionones into organoleptically interesting molecules has been reported: for instance β-ionone is changed into 2- and 4-hydroxy-β-ionones by *Aspergillus niger*. An important application of ionones and their derivatures is in tobacco flavourings.

The variety of organoleptic sensations produced by molecules of particular classes is illustrated in Fig. 10 which lists important flavour and fragrance aldehydes. The essential role

(a) Aldehydes

Material		Organoleptic quality
CH_3CHO	Acetaldehyde	fresh
	cis-3-hexenal	'green-leafy'
	vanillin	sweet and creamy vanilla-like
$CH_3-S-(CH_2)_2-CHO$	methional	earth, burnt potatoes
	citronellal	green-citrus-wood
	hydroxycitronellol	lilly of the valley
	benzaldehyde	sweet, almonds-like
	lily aldehyde	lily-like
	heliotropin	sweet, spicy, floral
	anisaldehyde	floral, hay-like
	phenylacetaldehyde	green, floral, sweet 'hyacinth-like'
	cinnamaldehyde	spicy, basalmic, cassia-cinnamon
	hexylcinnamic aldehyde	floral, jasmine
	amylcinnamic aldehyde	herbaceous, floral

Figure 10. The organoleptic properties of related molecules.

of some key flavour chemicals in commercial flavours is illustrated in Fig. 11.

Other character impact chemicals include isopentyl acetate in banana, nootkatone in grapefruit, geraniol and neral in lemon, gingerols and shogoals in ginger, capsaicin and dihydrocapsaicin in peppers and the isothiocyanates found in mustard oils which are formed from glucosylinolates by the action of myrosinase. There are also the flavour enhancers monosodium glutamate and 5′-GMP and 5′-IMP characteristic of meat, sulphides such as dimethyl sulphide, and many others. Combinations of different chemicals generates complexity; for instance mushroom flavour depends on 1-octen-3-o1 plus glutamic acid and 5′-guanylic acid.

Processed foods also have characteristic chemicals; for instance 2-acetyl-1-pyrroline is responsible for wheat bread aroma and 2-methylimino-3-butanone has recently been shown to give corn chips their characteristic smell.

A good example of the biotechnological synthesis of a flavour component is the production of 5-ketogluconic acid (5-KGA) from glucose by *Gluconobacter oxidans* (Fig. 12). 5-KGA is of interest because it can be converted by controlled heating into a particular monomethyl-furanone structure which is an important meat and savoury flavour component. The furanone is normally formed by the thermal degradation of 5′-IMP or 5′-GMP derived originally from the ATP in meat and can react with hydrogen sulphide derived from thiamine or sulphur-containing amino acids to form sulphur containing derivatives with characteristic savoury tastes. This Unilever patented process via 5-KGA is therefore a very convenient route to an important flavour component. It is made possible by the selective and high yielding microbial oxidation of a cheap precursor together with the easy recovery of pure 5-KGA by precipitation from the fermentation broth as its calcium salt following the addition of calcium carbonate.

Acetaldehyde, important in some fruit flavours, has been produced by alcohol dehydrogenase, but this method has the disadvantage of requiring expensive cofactors. A more effective approach is to use whole-cell bioconversion techniques to achieve continued oxidation and cofactor regeneration. For instance, the methylotrophic yeast *Pichia pastoris* containing alcohol oxidase activity has been used successfully to produce acetaldehyde and C6 flavour aldehydes.

The microbial synthesis of γ-decalactone, an important flavour chemical which finds application in peach, apricot and other fruit flavours and also certain fragrances, was first reported in 1962 by the reduction of β-ketocapric acid to hydroxydecanoic acid, the precursor of γ-decalactone, using baker's yeast, *Saccharomyces cerevisiae*. The production of low concentrations of 4-hydroxydecanoic acid from ricinoleic acid by species of the yeast *Candida* (*C. parakrusei, C. guilliermondi, C. stellatoidea, C. pseudotropicalis, C. albicans* and *C. tropicalis*) and by *Escherichia coli* was first reported in 1963. This fermentation, involving β-oxidation of

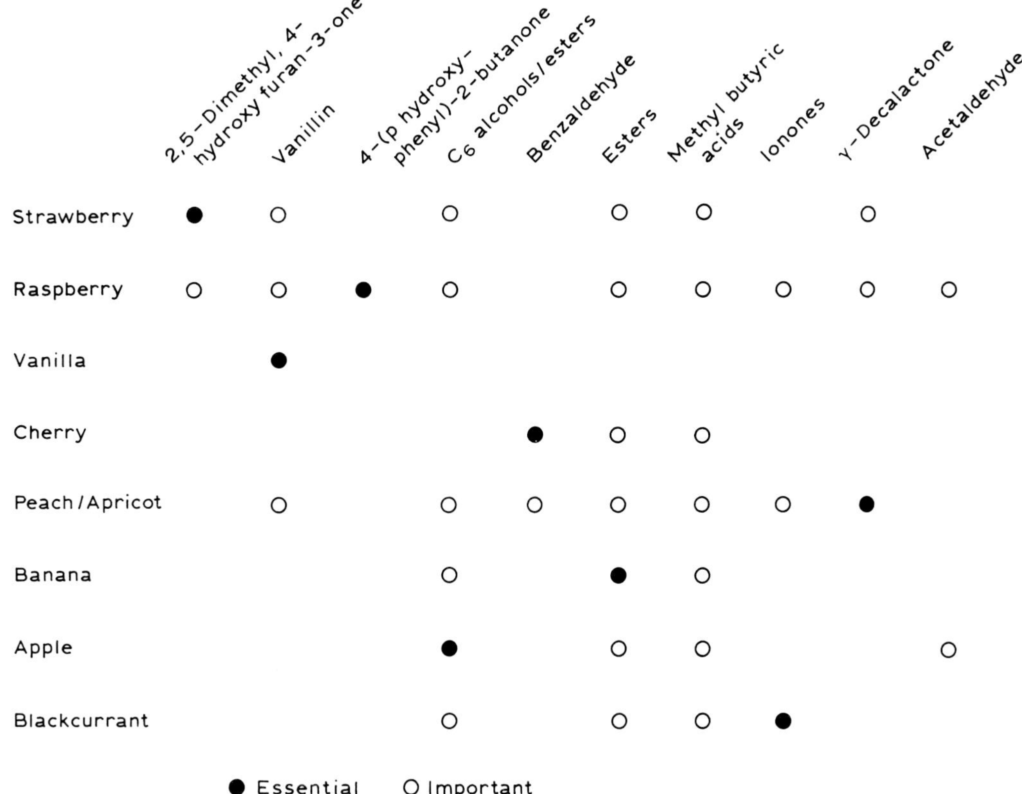

Figure 11. The relevant bases of some key natural flavour chemicals in commercial flavourings.

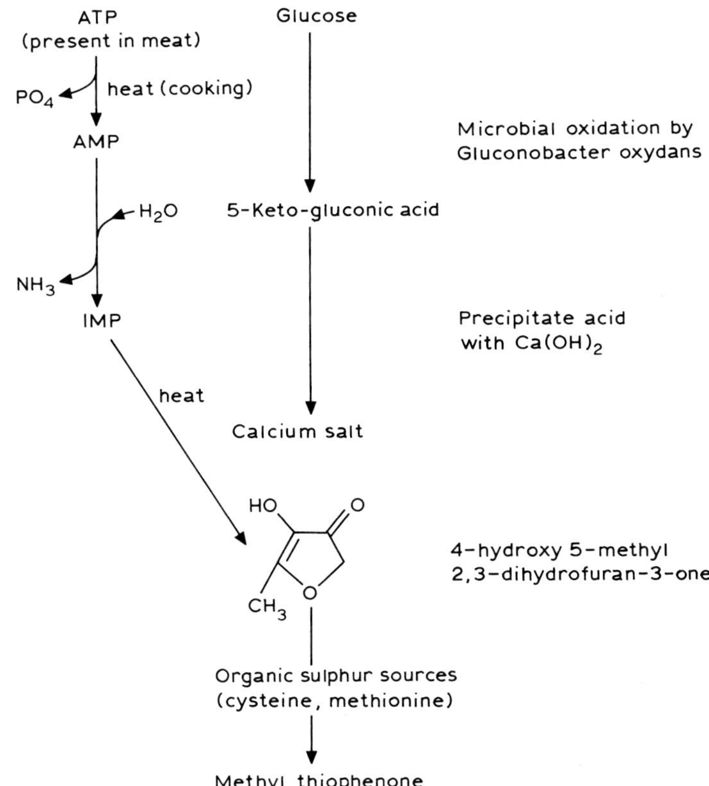

Figure 12. Meat furanone production via the 5-ketogluconic acid fermentation route and during the cooking of meat.

the ricinoleic acid from a C18 to a C10 fatty acid, was later optimised as a patented Quest International process using castor oil as a readily available and cheap source of the ricinoleic acid precursor and lactonising the 4-hydroxydecanoic acid to γ-decalactone by heating at a low pH (Fig. 13). Yields of about 1 g/l were obtained from castor oil after approximately 7 days fermentation.

Methylanthranilate, an important flavour component of Concord grapes and also of some perfumes such as Poison,® has been produced by BASF researchers by the N-demethylation of dimethyl anthranilate by wood-rotting microorganisms such as *Trichoderma versicolour*.

Terpenes

Terpenes are by far the most important class of chemicals as regards fragrance applications. In general, cyclic terpenes have less flexible structures than their non-cyclic counterparts and there are fewer metabolic alternatives available for their breakdown. Microorganisms can be used for the production and modification of fragrance materials and essential oils, often by oxygenation of the ring. However, *de novo* production of terpenes by fermentation is rarely cost-effective by comparison with their extraction from essential oils. Problems include the volatility, toxicity and insolubility in water of terpenes and the need to preserve and create chiral centres. A range of wood-rotting fungai, including *Ceratocystis* and

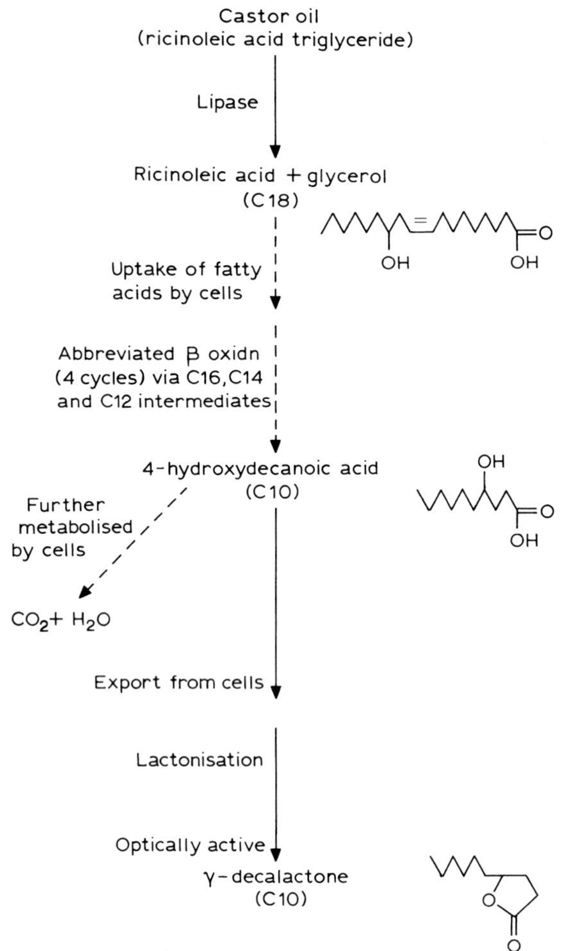

Figure 13. The fermentation of castor oil into γ-decalactone.

Trametes species, have been reported to produce relatively high levels of terpene fragrance chemicals such as esters, often derived from the degradation of lignin. However optimisation, including the selection of high yielding mutants, will be required if such commercially interesting processes as the oxidation of α- or β-pinene to L-carvone (Fig. 14) are to be developed. Although starting from cheap readily available raw materials this conversion has not so far been exploited, and in fact some groups have been unable to repeat the conversion as originally described.

A *Pseudomonas* strain has been shown to convert (+)-α-pinene into (+)-borneol, myrtenol, myrtenic acid and others. By contrast a strain of *S. marcescens*, isolated from sewage, can oxidise α-pinene to produce trans-verbenol as the major product, with verbenone and trans-sobrerol as minor products. A change in nitrogen source caused the bacterium to produce α-terpineol as the major oxidation product; this and other materials were identified by gas-liquid chromatography and mass spectrometry. Pure α-terpineol has also been reported to be produced from racemic limonene in a interesting stereoselective reaction. Yields of α-terpineol were higher

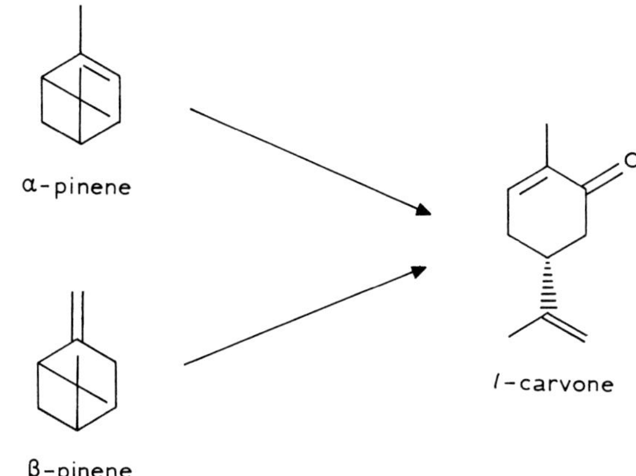

Figure 14. Oxidation of α- and β-pinene to L-carvone.

(46%) when (+)-(R)-limonene was used as the precursor for the reaction.

Some sesquiterpenes can also be selectively transformed. For instance patchoulol, which is a major but odourless component of Patchouli oil, can be microbially hydroxylated at the C10 position as the first step in its conversion to nor-patchoulenol, a minor, but probably important odiferous component of the oil (Fig. 15).

Another example is the conversion of sclareol, which is readily available from clary sage (*Salvia sclanea*) oil, into the important traditional perfumery material Ambroxide, a component of tincture of Ambergris, produced from the sperm whale (Fig. 16). Ambergris is now in short supply because of the decline in whale populations and marine pollution. In particular a selective degradation of the side-chain of schareol was required since only 50% yields of the desired intermediate were obtained by chemical methods in which sclareol was reacted with lead tetraacetate and iodine or iodobenzene diacetate.

A microorganism isolated from soil by researchers at Fritsche, Dodge & Olcott carried out the conversion of sclareol and related compounds to the intermediate diol in

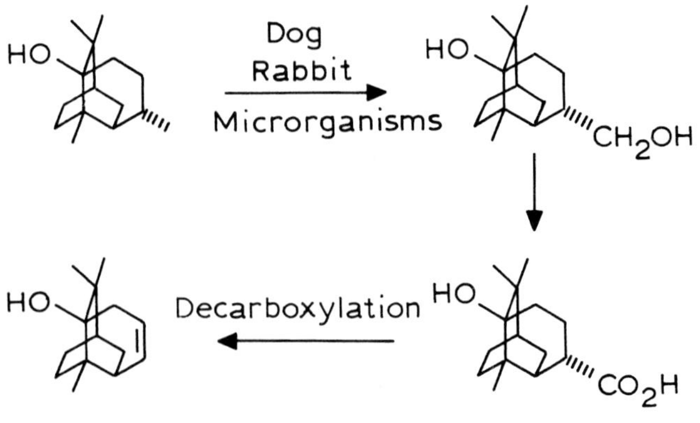

HO
Dog
Rabbit
Microrganisms
HO
CH_2OH
HO
Decarboxylation
HO
CO_2H

Figure 15. Microbial hydroxylation of patchoulol to nor-patchoulenol.

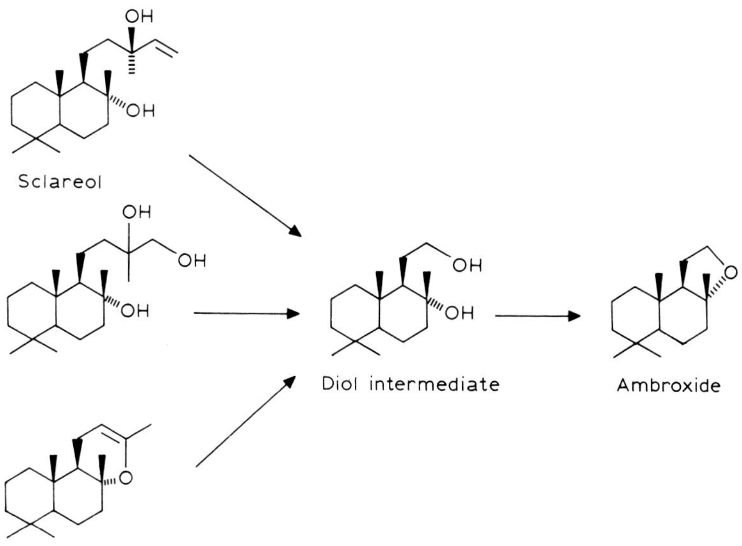

Sclareol

Diol intermediate

Ambroxide

Figure 16. Conversion of sclareol to Ambroxide.

essentially quantitative yields (Fig. 16). Traces of the hydroxy acid and the ketone derivatives isolated from the fermentation broth confirmed the transformation pathway via a diol intermediate. All of the intermediates were synthesised and shown to undergo bioconversion by the microorganisms. The one used proved to be new to science, being a red hyphozyma (*Hyphozyma roseoniger*) which, depending on the culture conditions used, exists either as a yeast or as a filamentous fungus. The process can be carried out as a two-step procedure with fermentation followed by extraction of the diol with ethyl acetate, or by *in situ* cyclisation of the diol in the fermentation broth. Fungi such as *Aspergillus*, *Penicillium*, *Cladosporium* and *Ophiobolus* can be used subsequently to oxidise ambroxide into new materials including 3-keto, 3-β-hydroxy and 3-α-hydroxy ambroxide which are of potential use in tobacco flavours. Tobacco-flavoured compounds can also be produced from β-ionone by *Lasiodiplodia theobromae* or *A. niger*. Using these organisms the main product was β-cyclogeraniol. From the above examples it can clearly be appreciated that a very wide range of enzymes are important in catalysing the formation of flavour and fragrance materials. Some of these are tabulated in Fig. 17.

The potential of this approach is illustrated by the fact that less than 1% of natures' microorganisms have been scientifically examined, and whereas some 20,000 different enzymes have been reported no more than about 50 enzymes are cheaply available in bulk. Thus only a very small proportion of the biocatalysts potentially available from nature can actually be obtained in a form suitable for use in cost efficient processes. Our biocatalytic capability on a commercial scale could be very considerably enhanced if a greater number of industrial biocatalysts were available.

Macrocylic Musks

Molecules with musk-like odours are very useful perfumery materials with applications both in fine fragrances and in perfumed detergents and household products. Macrocylic ketones and lactones such as muskone (Fig. 18), civetone, Ambrettolide and Exaltolide are derived from animal or plant sources. However, such molecules are currently scarce and very expensive and so are at best used in only the most expensure fine fragrances. Therefore the majority of non-macrocylic commercial musks used for higher-volume, lower-cost perfumed products such as soaps and washing powders are produced by chemical synthesis, and are based on cheap benzene, tetraline, indane or isochroman nuclei. Synthesis of natural musks is difficult because of the problems involved in producing bifunctional intermediates and carrying out cyclisation without intermolecular reaction and the consequent formation of linear polymers. Applications depend on the musks' organoleptic quality and physical properties such as stability under extreme conditions, for instance in the presence of bleaches, oxidising agents and at high pHs during the washing of clothes.

The musk hexadecanolide is one attractive target. The chemical synthesis of ω-hydroxy fatty acid precursors is possible and biological routes have also been discovered. Most microorganisms that hydroxylate fatty acids produce an ω-hydroxylated product but several microorganisms including some *Torulopsis* and *Nocardia* strains can convert fatty acids or amines into the ω-hydroxy fatty acid precursors (Fig. 19). In particular, the production of ω- and ω-1-hydroxy hexadecanoic acids from palmitic acid by fermentation using *Torulopsis bombicola* is of interest. These hydroxy acids are

Enzyme	**Product**
Lipoxygenase and hydroperoxide lyase	short chain alcohols, eg cis-3-hexenol
Nitrile lyase	benzaldehyde
Alcohol oxidase/dehydrogenase	aldehydes, eg. acetaldehyde, cis-3-hexenal
Ribonuclease	5′-GMP
Adenyl deaminase	5′-IMP
Lipases and/or esterases	short chain fatty acids, eg. propionic acid - general use in EMC production
	esters, eg. geranyl butyrate
	lactones, eg. macrocyclic musks such as cyclopentadecanolide
Fatty acid hydroxylase	macrocyclic musk precursors
β-oxidation enzymes	hydroxy-fatty acid precursors of lactones, eg. 4-hydroxydecanoic acid
Oxidation and decarboxylation of fatty acids	methyl ketones
Decarboxylase	diacetyl
Oxygenases	dicarboxylic acids (musk precursors)
Metaloprotease (thermolysin)	Aspartame^R

Figure 17. Some enzymes involved in the formation of flavours and fragrances.

obtained in the form of glycolipids in which the hydroxy group has been glycosylated with the disaccharide sophorose. As a result of a metabolic study on the control of the utilisation of radiolabelled palmitic acid and glucose, together with a mutagenesis programme to eliminate β-oxidation, ω-1-hydroxylation and storage of the palmitic acid as a triglyceride, a fermentation yielding several hundred g of sophorolipid/l was obtained by Unilever/Quest. Hydrolysis with aqueous hydrochloric acid yields the free hydroxyacids which are then cyclised to a 93:7 mixture of hexadecanolide and methylcyclopentadecanolide which has excellent properties as a musk fragrance: threshold concentration, chemical stability in hostile base environments, quality olfactory performance and price compatibility with synthetic macrocylic musks are all satisfactory.

In a related approach, ustiliagic acid glucosides have been produced by fermentation using *Ustilago zeae*. The 15D, 16-dihydroxyhexadecanoic acid can be converted into the musk cyclopentadecanone (Exaltone) or via 15-hydroxypentadecanoic acid into 15-pentadecanolactone (Exaltolide). An alternative approach involves the synthesis of the pentadecanolide macroyclic musk from hydroxypentadecanoic acid, and γ-butyrolactone from hydroxybutyric acid, using *Mucor miehei* lipase. Similarly, *Pseudomonas putida* has been used to convert isobutyric acid into (5)-hydroxyisobutyric acid which can then be further converted into R and S muskones.

The Nippon Mining Co. have developed a fermentation process for the production of α, ω-alkanedioic acids (dicarboxylic acids) as precursors of macrocylic musk molecules. They screened microorganisms to find a strain of *C. tropicalis* which produces high yields of the dicarboxylic acids from $C_{10}-C_{18}$ alkanes. This was then mutated to a strain giving 120 g of product/l on a 20 m^3 scale. The organism is optimally active on C_{14} alkenes but also assimilates n-alkenes, saturated and unsaturated fatty acids and their esters, and various fats and oils. As a consequence, tridecanedioic

Macrocyclic lactones

cyclopentadecanolide (Exaltolide) – Angelica

α-methylcyclopentadecanolide – Galbanum

7-cis hexadecan-16-olide (Ambrettolide) – Ambrette seeds

Keto musks

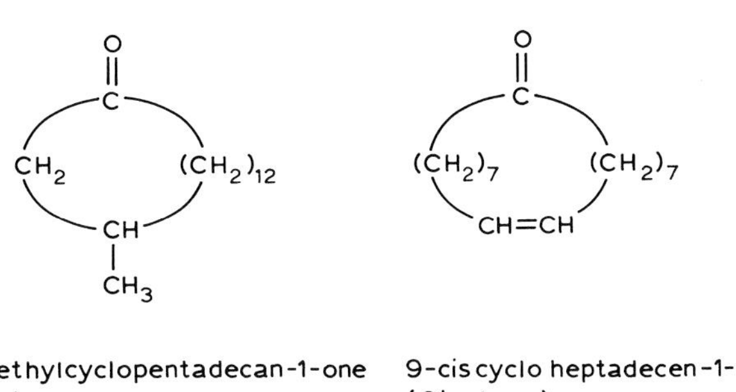

(–)-3-methylcyclopentadecan-1-one (Muskone) – Musk deer and truffles

9-cis cyclo heptadecen-1-one (Civetone) – Civet cats

Figure 18. Naturally occurring musks – structures and sources.

acid can be produced on a scale of 150 tons per annum (Fig. 20) and the macrocyclic musk cyclopentadecanone (deer musk) produced from the dicarboxylic acid intermediate has excellent fragrance properties.

Nucleotide Flavour Enhancers: Ribonucleotide Production by Hydrolysis of RNA

When using soluble phosphodiesterase to produce 5′ ribonucleotides the RNA needs to be DNA-free because the enzyme hydrolyses both polymers thus producing unwanted 5′-deoxyribonucleotides. However, immobilised phosphodiesterase acts solely on RNA because only the lower molecular weight nucleic acid (i.e. the RNA) is accessible to the immobilised enzyme. 5′-Ribonucleotides alone are produced; 3′-isomers, which do not contribute to taste, are not released. Phosphodiesterase from *Penicillium citrinum* and other organisms are used. These hydrolyse the 3′,5′-phosphodiester bonds of single-stranded DNA and RNA in both endo- and exo-fashion but do not attack double-stranded nucleic acids. Another example of an attempt to upgrade a traditional process is the use of immobilised *Leuconostoc oenos* to carry out the malo-lactate secondary fermentation of wine.

Glutamic Acid

L-Glutamate is a well-known taste potentiator. It occurs naturally, particularly high concentrations being present in Parmesan cheese. Commercial production by fermentation is carried out on a large scale by companies such as Ajinomoto.

Large quantities of L-glutamate are currently produced world-wide, mostly by the food industry. Production is by fermentation using *Corynebacterium glutaniciun, C. lilium* and other species, producing glutamate at about 60% of the theoretical yield. This fermentation is of scientific interest as the production of glutamic acid is regulated by the biotin content of the fermentation medium which alters the permeability of the cell membrane and allows leakage of the glutamic acid into the medium. Similarily the flavour enhancer 5′-inosine monophosphate, which acts synergistically with GMP in foods can be produced by fermentation using adenine auxotrophs of *Bacillus ammoniagenes*. The IMP is produced by deaminase activity as a secondary metabolite once the culture is no longer growing at its maximum rate.

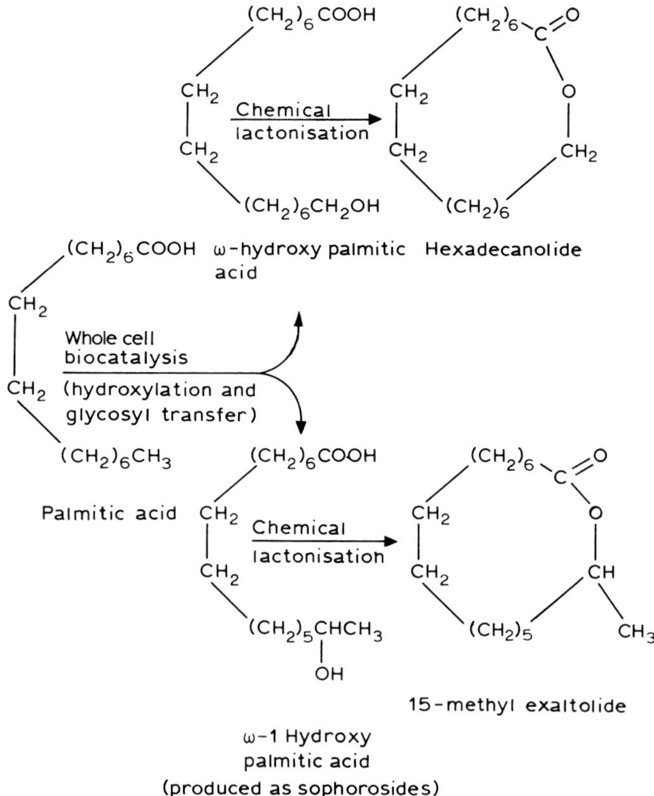

Figure 19. Production of musk lactones from hydroxy fatty acids produced by fermentation of palmitic acid with *Torulopsis bombolica*.

Complex Flavour Blocks

As well as using biocatalysts to produce pure individual odour chemicals, microorganisms and enzymes can also produce mixtures of odour chemicals which can then be used as complex components of flavours and fragrances; these mixtures have the advantages of contributing more individuality and odour-value than single chemicals. For instance, materials such as essential oils can be up-graded by microbial action. In one case basidiomycetes were screened for odouriferous metabolite production and *Ischnoderma benzoinum*, when grown on a fairly simple medium, was found to produce a variety of volatiles including benzaldehyde, 4-methyloxybenzaldehyde, 2-methyl-1-propanol, 2-octen-1-ol and 2-octen-4-olide.

This different approach is also well illustrated by a Unilever patented process to produce flavoured yeast extracts; these are characterised by being low salt sources of flavours, flavour enhancers and colours. In this process yeast is treated with a carefully selected combination of enzymes including proteases, β-glucanases and phosphodiesterases to degrade the yeast biopolymers into their constituent components: proteins into amino acids and peptides, RNA into 5′-nucleotides and polysaccharides into mono and oligosaccharides (Fig. 21). A fermentation step using lactic acid bacteria is then performed so as fully to develop the flavour, for instance by fermenting the sugars into organic acids such as lactic and succinic. Other advantages compared with traditional yeast autolysates include an absence of yeast-like and bitter tastes and the use of exogenous rather than endogenous ribonuclease.

Enzymes

Isolated enzymes are also of considerable commercial value for flavour production. For instance, processes for the

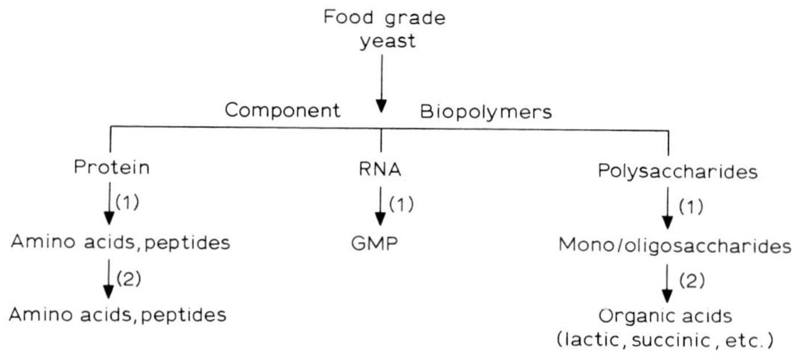

Figure 21. Savoury flavour production from yeast.

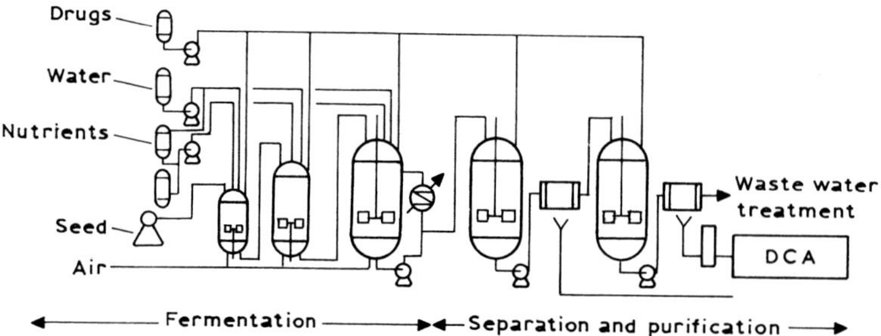

Figure 20. Flow diagram of the Nippon Mining dicarboxylic acid fermentation process. (DCA = dicarboxylic acid.)

enzymic degradation of animal proteins and fats are well established as a method of generating species-specific savoury flavours. Enzymes can also be used for the extraction of essential oils and to treat such fruits as kola nuts, vanilla beans or vegetables so as to enhanced yields of juice, colour and flavour following mechanical disruption and processing. Proteases such as papain are used to accelerate the koji fermentation process by partially hydrolysing the cooked protein raw materials prior to fermentation, thereby decreasing the very long processing time required to make soy sauce by traditional methods. The glutamic acid content and thus flavour quality can be further improved by treating with peptidoglutaminases. Sulphuryl oxidase has been used experimentally to reduce the "cooked" flavour of "Ultra High Temperature" (UHT) milk by re-oxidising disulphide bonds that have been formed during the heating the milk undergoes to sterilise it for long term storage. Many dairy flavours depend on the presence of sulphur-containing components such as methanethiol produced by the further metabolism of amino acids, in this case methionine. Another example of the value of enzymes is the use of specially selected mixtures of lipases and proteases produced (for example by *C. rugosa* or *M. miehei*) for the accelerated ripening of cheeses so as to reduce the cost of lengthy maturation stages. This involves the enzymatic formation of the flavour chemicals specific for the cheese. These are conventionally formed slowly, during the maturation of the cheese, by enzymes derived from traditional cheese microorganisms such as *P. roqueforti*. A particularly suitable strain of *A. ozyzae* was found which produced both a protease and a lipase that formed C_6-C_{10} fatty acids characteristic of cheddar cheese, whereas other lipases produced either shorter acids, such as butyric acid, which have a rancid taste or longer chains which give a soapy taste. Maturation times can thus be reduced from 3–24 months to as little as 12–72 h. This has important economic consequences: the ripening of cheddar cheese, for instance, has been estimated to cost about £1/tonne/day. Blends of proteases and lipases are used to simulate many traditional cheeses. Enzyme-modified cheeses are available at various levels of flavour intensity, in some cases many times the intensity of the traditional product, and are used in various recipes requiring cheese in order either to increase the cheese flavour intensity without increasing the total quantity of cheese solids or to maintain the cheese flavour when the solids content is reduced.

The synthesis of geraniol and citronellol esters has been achieved by workers at Harmaan & Reimer using esterases in reverse. Yields of product were increased from about 40% to 90% by carrying out the reaction in an organic solvent with a water concentration of 2% compared with the 70% water content of a conventional reaction. The best results were obtained using *M. miehei* lipase in n-hexane. Primary and some secondary alcohols can be reacted using this method but all tertiary alcohols appear to be unreactive.

This use of enzymes that has proved successful in the production of enzyme-modified cheese flavours can be extended by adopting a bio-organic approach: higher yielding and lower cost processes are developed by augmenting existing chemical synthetic steps with the stereo- and regioselective properties of enzymes. The use of the mild conditions associated with biocatalysts also results in less degradation of labile flavour components. One example of the chemical-cum-biochemical approach is the synthesis of the important fruit flavour 2,5–dimethyl-4-hydroxy-2,3-dihydrofuran-3-one. Collaborative research between the Massachussetts Institute of Technology and Firmenich devised an ingenious enzymatic synthesis of a precursor, 6-deoxy-D-fructose-1-phosphate, from D-fructose-1,6-bisphosphate (FDP) and D-lactaldehyde. The process comprised the aldolase-catalysed cleavage of FDP to a mixture of dihydroxyacetone phosphate (DHAP) and glyceraldehyde phosphate, the isomerisation of the trioses with triose phosphate isomerase and then the further use of aldolase to catalyse a condensation of the DHAP with D-lactaldehyde to give 6-deoxyfructose-1-phosphate. A final treatment with acid generated the product (Fig. 22). An alternative approach involves the production of rhamnose (6-deoxymannose) as the 6-deoxy sugar intermediate by the selective hydrolysis of a precursor such as naringin.

Unpleasant and therefore undesirable off-flavours are also a concern: the familiar "turned" odour of milk is both unpleasant and unpalatable and 2-methoxy-3-isopropyl pyrazine is responsible for the musty off-flavour sometimes found in eggs and milk. Off-flavours need to be removed or,

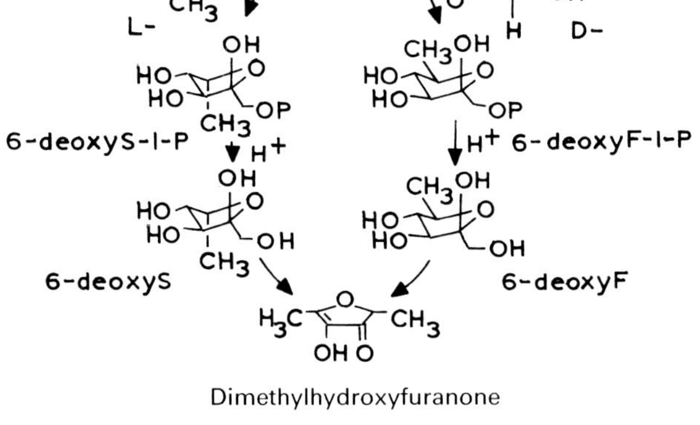

FDP

Aldolase

ATP

6K

$POCl_3$

TP1

DHAP

L-

D-

D-

6-deoxyS-I-P

6-deoxyF-I-P

6-deoxyS

6-deoxyF

Dimethylhydroxyfuranone

Figure 22. Production of 6-deoxyhexoses and dimethyl hydroxyfuranone.

if they are not harmful, at least masked. Biocatalysts have been used to reduce these undesirable flavour characteristics. Well-known examples include the use of sulphydryl oxidase to improve "cooked" UHT milk mentioned earlier, to lower the concentration of diacetyl in beer using the diacetyl reductase of *Aerobacter aerogenes* and to reduce the bitterness of citrus products. Indeed, the bitterness due to limonoids such as limonin and nomilin in certain citrus juices is one of the major global problems of the citrus industry. Workers at the U.S. Food & Drug Administration isolated strains of *Corynebacterium fascians* with nomilin acetyl-lyase activity capable of degrading the limonoids and used cells immobilised in acrylamide gel as the catalyst. Significant reductions in the concentrations of limonin and especially nomilin were achieved (Fig. 23). The other cause of bitterness in citrus products is the presence of naringin and related flavenoid glycosides. Flavinoid-associated bitterness can be reduced by treating the juice with naringinase, a mixture of β-glucosidase and rhamnosidase. This enzyme is a common side-activity present in commercial pectinases. Enzymes have also been used to remove the bitter taste of the sweetener stevioside by glucosylation using dextran-sucrase or α-amylase and to enhance the sweetness of milk by hydrolysis of the lactose using β-galactosidase. This treatment also serves to make the milk suitable for consumers who are lactose-intolerant.

Resolution of DL-menthol

L-menthol has a very valuable mint taste and cooling sensation and finds widespread uses in toothpastes, etc. It can be isolated from peppermint oil or synthesised chemically by a number of routes, for instance by hydrogenation of thymol. This requires the isolation of the l-menthol free from other isomers and racemates present in the source material. Not only does D-menthol, for instance, not have the same taste as L-menthol, it does not have its cooling properties. Isolation of L-menthol can be achieved by the selective hydrolysis of the L-acetate, propionate, caproate or succinate esters of dl-mixtures. Use of organic solvents is advantageous, firstly because both menthol and menthol esters are virtually insoluble in water and secondly to shift the equilibrium of the reaction. Selective hydrolysis of DL-menthyl succinate to pure L-menthol has been achieved in water-saturated hexane at 40°C by the use of cells of *Rhodotorula minuta* var *texensis* entrapped in polyurethane (Fig. 24). The remaining d-menthyl succinate is then hydrolysed and the D-menthol racemised via D-menthone and recycled. Although the enzyme reaction is more selective with short acyl groups, in practice larger ester groups are normally used because the enzymes are considerately less active on the smaller esters. Alternatively DL-menthol can be esterified selectively to produce l-menthol-5-phenylvalerate and D-menthol using *Candida cylindricae* lipase adsorbed onto celite and entrapped in polyurethane; this is followed by separation, recovery and crystallisation of the L-menthol and recycle of the D-menthol. dl-Citronellol and dl-borneol could also be resolved by similar methods, for instance by using the *C. cylindracae* lipase.

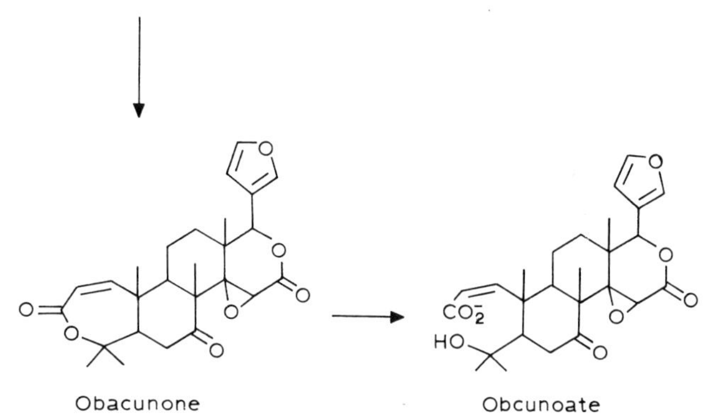

Resolution methods are of general value when only one isomer is bio-active, especially when the wrong isomer has undesirable properties and/or when only one isomer is found in nature. In addition it is of interest that a dehydrogenase from *P. putida* has been found that will convert L-menthone into l-menthol. This may offer an opportunity of obtaining higher yields of l-menthol by harvesting immature plant tissue and enzymically converting the l-menthone into L-menthol. Very recently the Mitsui Co. have reported a similar process using the L-menthone reducing activity of *Cellumonas turbata* in a two-phase bioreactor with a NADH recycling capability.

Nomilin Limonin Obacunone Obcunoate

Figure 23. Removal of nomilin with the acetyl-lysase.

High Intensity Sweeteners

Sweetness is one of the most basic and attractive tastes. The production and uses of conventional sweeteners such as sucrose, invert sugar and glucose and high fructose syrups, that are all of relatively low sweetness intensity, is well described elsewhere. Over the last 20 years a search has been conducted for molecules with high intensity, sweetness comparable with that of other flavour molecules. Much of this work has been carried out chemically but enzyme technology has also had an important role to play.

Undoubtedly the most successful high intensity sweetener

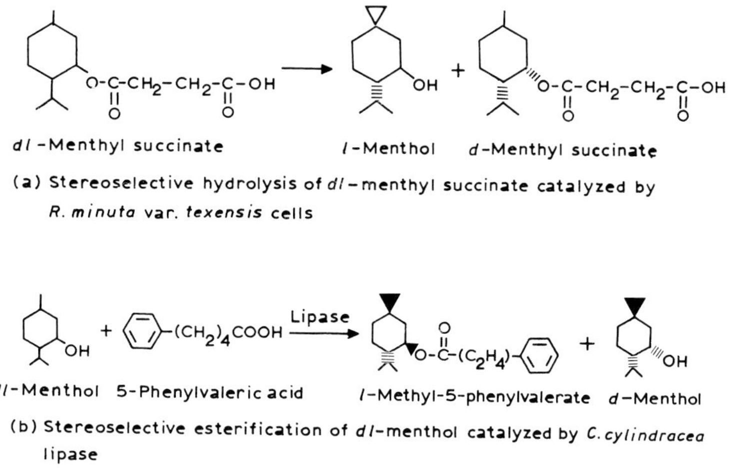

Figure 24. Stereoselective hydrolysis of DL-menthyl succinate and esterification of DL-menthol.

produced so far is Aspartame[R] which is 200 times sweeter than sucrose. It is formed by the coupling of blocked aspartic acid and phenylalanine methyl ester to form the dipeptide ester (Fig. 25). Aspartic acid produced by fermentation is readily available but considerable biotechnological effort had to be put into the development of large-scale cost-effective fermentation and bioconversion methods for the production of the phenylalanine which was not originally available cheaply and in large quantities. The first Aspartame produced

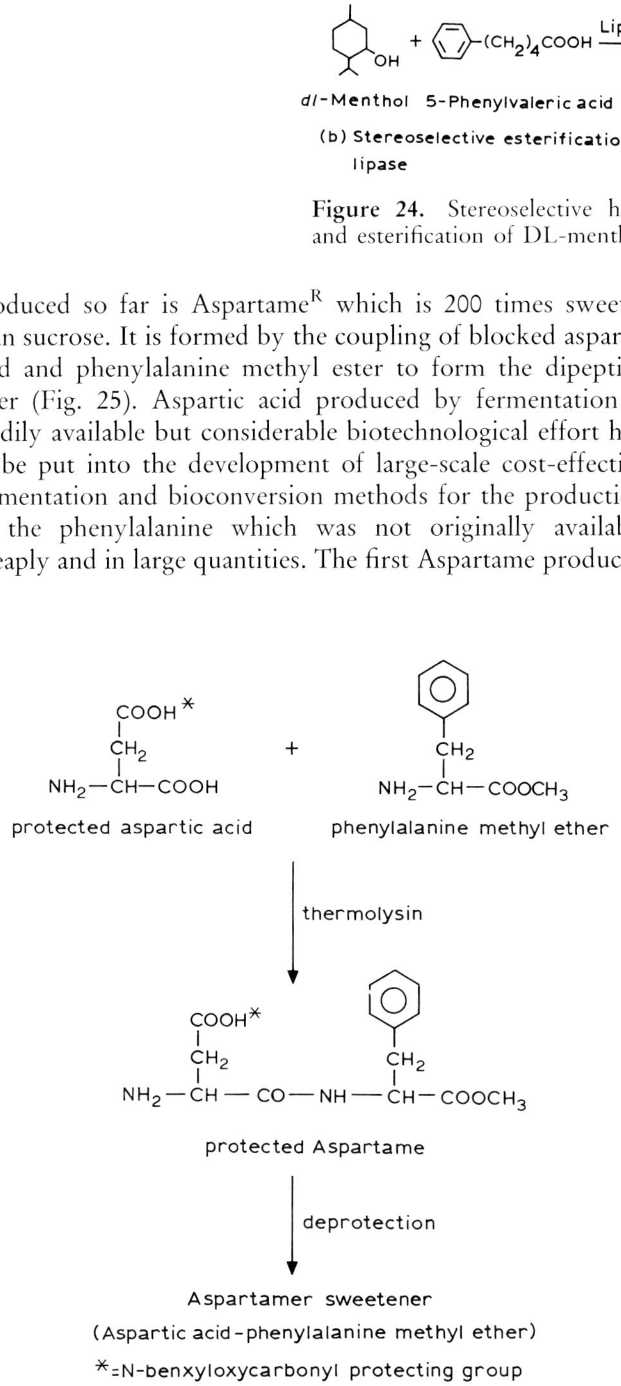

Figure 25. The enzymic synthesis of Aspartame[R].

was synthesised from its constituent amino acids chemically, but more recently an enzymic synthesis has been discovered and scaled-up to a production scale. It uses the metalo-proteinase thermolysin working "in reverse" to synthesise the peptide bond between the amino acids. Thermolysin was selected since unlike most proteases it lacks esterase activity, a very undesirable property in this application since it results in the hydrolysis of the methyl ester, a part of the molecule absolutely necessary for the high sweetness of Aspartame (Fig. 25).

A second example of the application of biotechnology to high intensity sweeteners is in the synthesis of sucralose[R] (4,1′,6′-trichlorotrideoxy*galacto*sucrose), which is some 600 times as sweet as sucrose. This molecule can be synthesised chemically from sucrose. However, a crucial technical problem is the protection of the C6 primary hydroxyl of the glucose moiety of sucrose. Although this is the most reactive hydroxyl group in sucrose, the presence of substituents at this position results in over-substituted molecules of lower sweetness. This problem was overcome by Tate & Lyle by the use of C6-blocked intermediates. For instance, glucose-6-acetate can be produced from glucose by fermentation, and the intermediate sucrose-6-acetate then formed by the action of a specific fructosyl-transferase enzyme. The sucrose-6-actate can then be selectively chlorinated and sucralose produced satisfactorily (Fig. 26).

This approach has also been used to produce a number of related tri-halo disaccharide sweeteners based on the sucrose analogues xylsucrose and 6-deoxysucrose produced from their constituent monosaccharides using the fructosyl-transferase described above. An alternative approach is to utilise raffinose as the C6-blocked intermediate, chlorinate to form a tetra-chloro-raffinose and then hydrolyse the α-1,6 bond between the galactose and glucose to liberate sucralose. A specially selected α-galactosidase from *Mortierella vinacae* was used (Fig. 26).

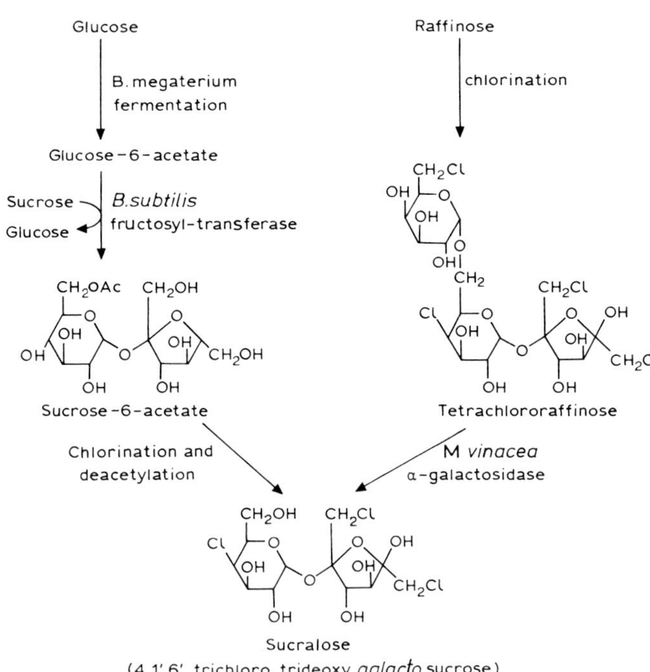

Figure 26. The bio-organic synthesis of sucralose from glucose or raffinose via sucrose 6-acetate or tetrachlororaffinose intermediates.

Delivery Systems

Delivery systems for flavours and fragrances are of growing importance. Usually they rely on encapsulation of the flavour or fragrance which has the advantages of protecting the encapsulated materials and achieving selective delivery to the required site; selective effects of this sort permit economies to be made in the amounts of flavour or fragrance used. Controlled release effects have a number of possible uses. A recently commercialised example is the "Capture®" liposome technology developed by Christian Dior in collaboration with the Institute Pasteur. In this treatment liposomes have been used to deliver skin care materials such as thymus extracts, hyaluronic acid and collagen and elastine peptide with the objective of increasing the fluidity of the cell membranes of the skin cells, thereby hopefully improving the tone and elasticity of the skin.

Encapsulation has also been deployed for food applications: cheese-ripening enzymes contained within liposomes have been used to accelerate the maturation of cheese while cyclodextrins have been proposed as controlled release encapsulating agents for flavours.

Technological Developments

A number of developments in biotechnology are taking place which may in the next ten years or so become sufficiently far advanced to be adopted as regular production techniques by the flavour and fragrance industry. They include:

- plant culture techniques;
- synthetic biocatalysts (perhaps involving cofactor recycling);
- gas-phase reactions;
- integration of product formation and recovery (e.g. membrane reactors);
- multi-phase reactors;
- bio-organic syntheses;
- novel or modified biocatalysts;
- stereo/regioselective catalysis.

Fermentation and enzyme technologies, well established in other industries, have been the first to be applied successfully, with newer methodologies such as genetic engineering and plant science technologies having longer term potential.

Some features are well worth commenting on: an obvious first requirement is for products either of sufficient added-value, or for ones that are required in sufficiently large amounts to achieve the required economics of scale to make a process economic. Secondly, successful biotechnology processes very frequently depend on the exceptional biological properties of the product: the antimicrobial action of antibiotics or the very desirable organoleptic properties of fermented beverages, cheese and yoghurt are cases in point. Or there may be some exceptional biological properties of the biocatalyst such as a strain of microorganism that will over-produce amino acids, or the very high thermo-stability of the α-amylase used in corn starch processing. Thirdly, despite the large amount of basic research information that is now available, invariably far too little is known about anyone particular topic to allow the easy development of a new process or product.

Several major basic problems remain to be solved before the range of commercial applications of biotransformations can be extended. They include co-factor recycling and biocatalyst stability, fouling of immobilised biocatalysts by particulate and colloidal materials, product inhibition and easy modification and control of metabolic regulation, particularly as regards cost-effective large-scale use.

Plant Biotechnology

Agricultural sources of essential oils are normally produced by conventional cultivation procedures followed by standard operations such as grinding drying, steam distillation and solvent extraction. There is nevertheless considerable scope for new biotechnological methods for:

* the development of improved varieties of plants, e.g. higher yielding strains or ones that will grow in different conditions
* an improved understanding of post-harvest biochemistry and physiology which will help to maximise the yield and stability of the important aroma chemicals.

In the longer term plant cell culture techniques may have considerable commercial potential especially as current plant sources of aroma chemicals are often low yielding. They also represent the most "natural" biotechnological approach to making flavours, utilising the pathways and organisms that have been the traditional sources of these materials. Only two commercially successful plant culture products have so far been developed and these are discussed below.

Several distinct approaches are subsumed under the term "plant tissue culture". Firstly they include the cultivation of parts of plants in liquid suspension culture, as with the commercial production of Shikonin (see below). Secondly, they refer to plant cell cultures in which isolated plant cells are grown, usually in air-lift fermenters, so as to maximise yields of secreted products. This term is also used for immobilised cell cultures which allow some organised growth of the cells, but such cultures are restricted to the generation of products easily excreted from the cells.

Essential to all these approaches is a good understanding of plant primary and secondary metabolism and its regulation, so as to maximise the rates and yields of processes and facilitate the ready selection of types and sources of plant material most likely to be useful and productive. For instance, while some interesting studies have tried feeding flavour precursors to substantially intact fruit and vegetables, devising cost-effective production processes is a very challenging technical problem because complex and labile enzyme are involved, including lyases and oxido-reductases. It is also most important to realise that, with the very few exceptions such as onion, jasmine and mint (Fig. 27), we have a comparatively poor understanding of plant metabolic pathways leading to flavour components. Hence only two commercial processes have so far been developed:

- berberine, produced by cultures *Coptis japonica* cells at levels as high as 7 g./l.;
- shikonin, a purple pigment used in Japan for cosmetics (lipsticks) and also in traditional medicine because of its anti-microbial and wound-healing properties. A successful process for shikonin was used for a short period by the Mitsui Co. Segments of the plant *Lithosperma erythrorhizon* served as the biocatalyst in a two-stage process with different media for the cell growth and subsequent product formation stages. The main stimulus for this work was the virtual extinction of the native plant in the wild state.

Other plant secondary products used as flavours or fragrances (vanilla, saffron, capsaicin, jasmine, etc.) offer attractive commercial goals: jasmine, for instance, retails at about $5,000/kg (Fig. 28).

Currently there are several examples of plant cell cultures producing levels of metabolites in excess of the concentrations found in the original plant. It may therefore eventually be

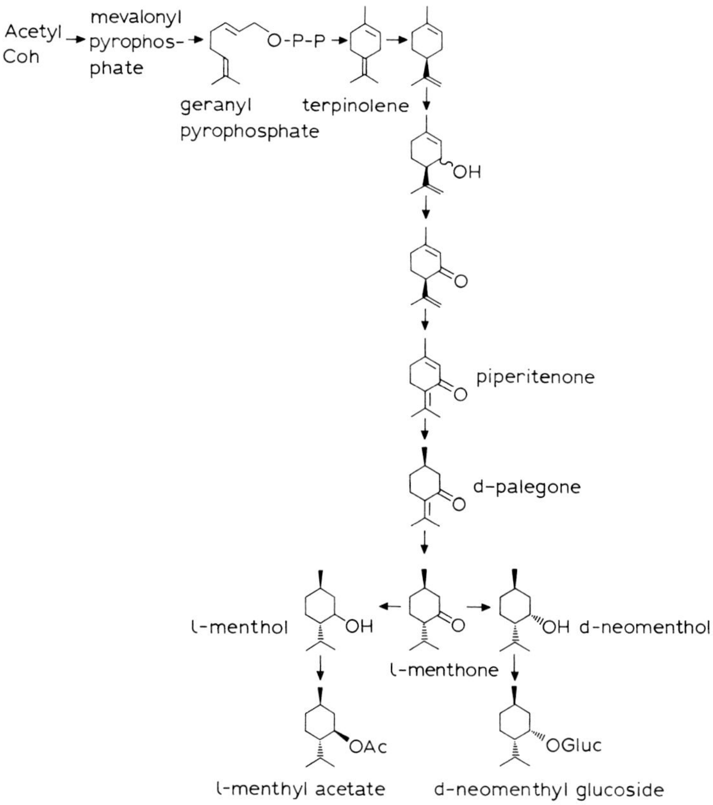

Figure 27. The metabolic pathway producing L-menthol in *Mentha* spp.

possible to achieve commercially successful processes using these procedures. An important incentive to the development of new production methods is that such materials are invariably produced in remote countries subject to the vagaries of climate, pests and political factors: there is a clear analogy here with the problems of crude oil recovery in distant places (see Chapter 29). Furthermore, the concentrations of the desired materials in plant tissues are very often low and extraction may be difficult.

Sensory Perception

Another frontier in bioscience research is in sensory perception. Whereas taste is comparatively easy to describe in terms of sweet, sour, bitter, unami, etc., smell is much more difficult and complicated. Thus perfumers use a much more complex vocabulary — woody, green, citrus, musk, etc. An overriding objective is to obtain a more precise and systematic structure-function understanding of how flavours interact with physiological systems at the molecule-taste receptor level. The information content of a molecule is roughly proportional to its size and to the number of chiral centers present. In addition the three-dimensional structure of flavour and fragrance molecules provides some information about receptor structure. Receptors may include not only sweet, acid, sour and bitter

SUBSTANCE	SPECIES
Cinnamic acid/carvoxone	*Nicotiana tabacum*
4-Hydroxy-3-methoxybenzoic acid	*Linum usitatissimum*
Caryophyllene	*Lindera strychnifolia*
2-Undecanone, 2-undecanyl acetate	*Ruta graveolens*
Stevioside	*Stevia rebaudiana*
Limonene, linalool	*Perilla fructescens*
Anethol	*Foeniculum vulgare*
Carvone	*Mentha spicata*
Diallyl disulfide	*Allium cepa*
Farnesol	*Andrographis paniculata*
2-Phenylethylglycoside	*Tropeaolum majus*
Glycyrrhizin	*Glycyrrhiza glabra*
'Apple aroma'	*Malus silvestris*
1-Glutamine	*Symphytum officanale*
Nootkatone	*Citrus sps*
Digoxin	*Digitalis lanata*
Sesquiterpenes	*Solanum tuberosum*
5-formyl-ellipticine	*Cholsya ternata*
Anthroquinones	*Galium moolugo*
Vanillin	*Vanilla planifolia*
Saffron	*Crocus sativas*
Capsaicin	*Capsicum frutescens*
Glucosinolates	*Callus cultures*

Figure 28. Biosynthetic products of plant cell cultures of potential interest as flavours and fragrances.

tastes but also the perception of astringency and unami (savoury) flavours as well as hotness (peppers) and coldness (1-menthol).

Improved understanding of such interactions is of course fundamental to the scientific basis of the flavour and fragrance industry and should enable a more rational and direct approach to be made to the synthesis and formulation of fragrances and flavours and the understanding of odour and malodour counteraction. Thus, approximate rules for the design of musks, and sweeteners (the AHB theory) exist and indicate that molecular size and shape are more important than chemical structure in determining organoleptic properties. Nevertheless, and despite the extensive use of quantitative structure-activity relationships, a detailed understanding and ability to rationally design flavour and fragrance molecules still eludes us. In particular we need to explain anosmia (complete absence of smell and taste) which is a rare conditions found in certain individuals.

A significant recent advance is the isolation of an odorant-binding protein from rat nasal epithelium by scientists at Johns Hopkin's University. This protein is structurally related to α-2-microglobulin and may serve to bind, and thereby concentrate, odour molecules and transport them to olfactory receptors located deeper within the nasal epithelium.

CONCLUSIONS

This chapter has tried to give some representative examples of biotechnological work in the flavour and fragrance industry, to illustrate general trends and principles, to place the research in a commercial context and also to show some of the ways in which technical innovations have taken place and how new products are made available at sufficiently low prices and high quality to allow cost-effective use by customers. Emphasis has been placed on new and emerging applications, the crucial technicals problems that have to be overcome and new factors such as the demand for natural food materials.

In conclusion it is important to emphasize that the flavour, fragrance and food ingredients industry is highly science-based and that biotechnology has an important future role in it. A vital feature of biotech, research is that it is very multidisciplinary, with biochemists, geneticists and microbiologists interacting with chemists, engineers, food scientists, computer scientists, etc. (Fig. 29). Indeed, highly qualified scientists are frequently employed in "non-scientific" buying, marketing and sales jobs.

Important changes are taking place in the flavour industry in terms of the amounts and types of flavours required by the

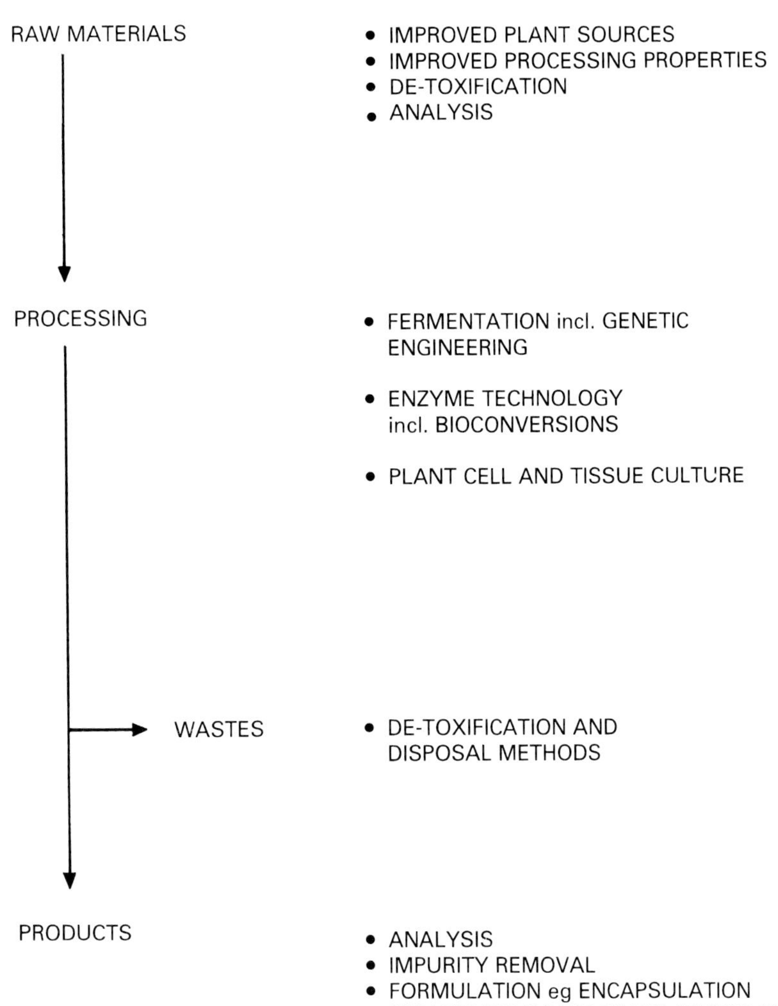

Figure 29. The impact of biotechnology on the flavour and fragrance industry.

food and other industries which result from changes in consumer preferences (influenced, of course, by the industry itself through its own innovations and publicity) and the impact of new technologies. This dynamic situation creates new opportunities, particularly since successful novel products rely heavily on high quality flavouring or fragrancing for their success in the market place. An essential feature is to identify good targets for research that combine technical advantage with good market opportunities.

FURTHER READING

Arctander, S. (1969). *Perfume & Flavor Chemicals*, Montclair (N.J., U.S.A.).

Armstrong, D.W. and Yamazaki, H. (1986). *Natural flavours production, a biotechnological approach*, TIBTECH Oct, 165–268.

Buttery, R.G. (1981). *Vegetable and Fruit Flavours*, Flavour Research Recent Advances (ed. Teronishi, R. *et al.*). Marcel Dekker, 7, 175–216.

Cheetham, P.S.J. and Lecchini, S.M.A. (1988). "Flavours of the Future" in Food Technol. Int. (ed. Turner, A.). Sterling Publications, Ltd. 257–264.

Dourtloglou V., (1986). *Production of natural flavourings, perfumes and other fine chemicals by infected plants*, Symbiosis, **2**, 1898–200.

Gatfield, I.L. (1988). *Enzymatic generation of flavour and aroma components* in Advances in Food Biotechnol. (ed. King, R.D. and Cheetham, P.S.J.), Elsevier Science Publishers, 2, 59–82.

Heath, H.B. (1981). *Source Book of Flavors*, AVI Publishing Co.

Kempler, G.M. (1983). *Production of flavour compounds by micro-*

organisms, Advs. Appl. Microbiol, **29**, 29–44.
Laughlin, T.J. and Ferrell, T.M. (1987). *Biotechnology in the cosmetics industry*, Biotechnology, **5**, 1035–1037.
Ruttloff, H. (1982). *Biotechnology & Aroma production* Die Nahrung **26**, 575–589.
Salunkhe, D.K. and Do, J.Y. (1976). *Biogenesis of aroma constituents of fruits and vegetables*, Critical Revs. in Food Sci. and Nutrition, Nov. 161–190.
Schwimmer, S. (1981). *Source Book of Food Enzymology*, AVI Publishing Co.
Sharpell, F.H. (1988). *Microbial Flavours and 'Fragrances' in Comprehensive Biotechnol.*, **3**, 965–981.
Theimer, E.T. (ed.) (1982). *Fragrance Chemistry, the Science of the sense of smell*, Academic Press.
Trivedi, N. (1986). *Use of microorganisms in the production of unique ingredients*, Biotech. Food Process (ed. Harleuder, S.K.), 115–132.
Unger, L. (1989). *Strategic Factors for Business Success in the Flavour and Fragrance Industry*. Perfumer & Flavourist, **14**, 57–81.
Van Brunt, J. (1985). *Nibbling at the flavour market*, Biotechnology, **3**, 525–538.

Chapter 27

Waste Treatment and Pollution Clean-up

Richard J.F. Bewley, Robert Sleat and John F. Rees

INTRODUCTION

Growing public awareness over environmental problems in recent years has stimulated interest in finding alternative means of waste disposal and novel methods for decontaminating toxic residues. The conventional means of dealing with land contaminated with such materials has been to excavate the polluted soil and remove it to landfill. However, there is a growing scarcity of suitable disposal sites and a recognition that such a solution has merely relocated the problem rather than actually removed it.

The importance of microorganisms in decomposing natural organic residues in soils, sediments and aquatic systems has long been recognized. The potential for harnessing such natural processes to deal effectively with waste treatment and pollution clean-up in an ecologically acceptable manner is attracting much attention.

There is a vast number of pollutants and waste materials disposed into the environment annually. Any attempt to give a brief overview of the use of microorganisms for treating such a disparate group of compounds could never encompass all such possibilities.

There is also already a wide body of literature concerning use of microorganisms for industrial waste stream treatment by such processes as activated sludge with and without anaerobic digestion. This chapter will consequently consider two specific areas of the application of microorganisms to waste treatment and pollution clean-up: the disposal of municipal waste into methanogenic landfills, with the possibility of using such systems for the microbial degradation of a range of industrial wastes, and the treatment of land which has already been polluted with undesirable and noxious compounds.

MICROBIAL TREATMENT OF HAZARDOUS WASTE

Precedents

Rather than a completely novel concept, the use of microorganisms for the decontamination of natural environments polluted by industrial waste is an extension of their application to existing environmental problems, particularly sewage treatment, composting and sludge farming. The activated sludge process has long been used to treat industrial effluents such as coke oven liquor: it utilizes microorganisms in a sludge mass rather than in a dispersed state to produce a clear effluent. Essentially, the process is similar to that used in sewage treatment but with conditions modified to take account of any toxic compounds present: these include rapid mixing of tank contents to achieve continuous movement of the sludge contents through the aqueous phase. Other aerobic treatments include aerated lagoons, digesters, trickling filters and fixed film reactors. Enzyme systems in a free or immobilized state for treating effluent have also been extensively described.

These are all essentially closed systems in which conditions can be carefully controlled. Sludge farming on the other hand is the addition of oily refinery waste into natural soil in order to effect degradation of hydrocarbons by the natural microflora. Stimulation of the natural soil microflora is achieved by the addition of appropriate nutrients and tilling to provide adequate aeration. Sludges suitable for treatment in this manner should be homogeneous types free from toxic compounds, especially heavy metals, acids, alkalis and persistent compounds.

Applications and Rationale for Treatment

Recently, interest has been focussed on the extension of these techniques to treat soils and other subsurface areas such as aquifers which have become contaminated through a variety of industrial activities. They include gasworks sites, pitch fibre works, wood preservative sites, chemical factories and spills of specific xenobiotic compounds.

There is a complete spectrum of biodegradability of the most widely reported xenobiotics, ranging from some of the simple aromatic compounds associated with particular oil spills such as benzene, through to the highly complex polychlorinated aromatic compounds.

These include some of the higher poly-chlorinated biphenyl (PCB) isomers together with dibenzofurans and dioxins for which there is little to no evidence of biodegradation.

Such chemicals persist because their structures are not recognized by the transport, enzyme or induction systems of the natural microflora or possibly because they are present in low concentrations below the thresholds at which biodegradation may take place.

If however the compound is known to be biodegradable in concentrations at which it occurs in the soil, then its persistence at a contaminated site may be attributable to one or more physical, chemical or biological factors pertaining to the prevailing soil environment. Such physicochemical factors include the presence of nutrients, oxygen or other suitable electron acceptor, moisture, soil texture and structure, pH, temperature, pollutant solubility and presence of toxic compounds. All such factors are closely interrelated: the occurrence of anaerobic conditions in a waterlogged soil, for instance, will be influenced by both the texture and structure of the soil.

The occurrence of toxic compounds may be of particular importance as groups of organic pollutants might be associated with heavy metals which can inhibit microbial activity. The toxicity of heavy metals, however, is also influenced by acidity and the presence of clay minerals which mitigate their influence through adsorption to the cation exchange complex.

These physical and chemical factors can, to a greater or lesser degree, be adjusted to optimize conditions for microbial activity. In some cases, especially with the more labile compounds, this alone is sufficient for biodegradation to take place as evidenced by the success of land-farming treatments. Other compounds however may take far longer to undergo degradation even after environmental optimization and such persistence may be a reflection of microbiological factors. In addition to the pollutants present, the contaminated soil will contain a large number of organic compounds associated with the naturally-occurring humic materials present. These will provide additional carbon sources for a wide range of fungi, bacteria and actinomycetes. Optimization of aerobic microbial activity through manipulation of soil physical and chemical conditions will also stimulate these other organisms which will then compete directly with the pollutant degraders for available resources such as oxygen and macro- and micronutrients. Suppression of pollutant-degrading organisms may also occur through antagonistic interactions which include production of antibiotics, volatiles such as hydrogen cyanide, ammonia and hydrogen sulphide and the secretion of extracellular enzymes which can digest the cell walls of other organisms.

Selection of Microorganisms

It is therefore important that not only are the physical and chemical conditions optimized for biodegradation but that the pollutant-degrading organisms have a competitive advantage over the other organisms present. This can be achieved by the reintroduction into the soil of appropriate inocula of specific "vanguard" microorganisms responsible for key transformations in the biodegradation of the xenobiotic compounds.

For the more complex compounds such as oils and tars it is highly unlikely that any single organism can degrade even a majority of the myriad of component compounds.

Co-metabolism, by which mechanism an organism may transfer an organic pollutant without actually utilizing it as a nutrient or energy source, may be an important ecological mechanism in the degradation of many environmental pollutants. The purpose of reintroducing vanguard organisms is therefore to catalyse initial key stages in the degradation pathway, followed by the other naturally — occurring microorganisms to complete the mineralization process, rather than to attempt to supersede the activity of the existing microbial community.

Vanguard organisms should possess a number of characteristics similar to those suggested by Atlas[1] for a "hydrocarbonoclastic superbug". These are: genetic stability, a capability to be stored for long periods of time (and for rapid reproduction following storage), enzymatic activity and growth in the environment into which they are introduced, competitive ability within that environment, non-pathogenicity and absence of toxic metabolites.

While the contaminated site itself should be the first place to look for suitable organisms, since the indigenous microflora there will already have adapted to the local ecological conditions, it may be possible to use microorganisms isolated from other contaminated environments, activated sludge, or even culture collections as vanguard organisms provided they can adapt to the prevailing physical, chemical and biological conditions at the site where they are to be used. Equally important will be their interaction with the soil microbial community, especially those organisms which are capable of metabolizing the degradation products.

There are a number of possibilities for enrichment of such vanguard organisms. Batch culture is probably the simplest way, inoculating a suspension of the contaminated soil into a growth medium with the pollutant as sole carbon or nitrogen source. Far more complex systems can be developed using chemostat enrichment cultures such as plasmid-assisted molecular breeding. Here, several microorganisms recovered from sites contaminated with the pollutant of concern, and containing plasmid-encoded enzymes for degradation of structures chemically similar to the actual pollutant itself, are inoculated into a chemostat. Concentrations of the pollutant within the growth substrate are then gradually increased.

Eventually, growth on the pollutant as sole carbon source may be achieved. Repeated subculturing is then carried out to attempt to isolate pure strains of the vanguard microorganisms capable of growth on the pollutant.

The advent of recombinant DNA technology has led to a number of discussions about its possible contribution to the microbial degradation of xenobiotics. For example, it has been proposed that specific biochemical pathways may be combined in a single organism to allow for complete mineralization of a compound. Such a system has been suggested as a possibility for PCB degradation, where enzymes of the ortho-fission pathway (which are active both on chlorinated and non-chlorinated compounds) could be combined with enzymes required for the initial meta-fission pathway (which are active only on non-chlorinated aromatics) to produce a bacterium capable of growth directly on PCBs. However, no clear evidence has yet emerged to show that genetically engineered organisms introduced into the environment will break down known biodegradable pollutants better than the indigenous community; furthermore, there is the obvious public concern over the fate and possible side effects of such microbes (see Chapter ?).

It is not proposed to review these here except to state that there are "few convincing reasons to propose that some new genotype will, or will not, cause a detrimental effect in addition to bringing about the desired changes."[2].

Even supposing that unforeseen consequences from release do not occur, the enthusiasm for the application of recombinant DNA technology has to be tempered by our understanding, or lack of it, of the physicochemical complexity of the soil environment, especially at a molecular level.

There are, however, persistent xenobiotics for which there exist no known degradation pathways: such compounds may be present in concentrations so low that microbial growth cannot be sustained, or microorganisms may have developed reduced permeabilities to avoid their toxic effects: i.e. the organisms can survive in the presence of the pollutant without actually metabolising it. In a closed system such as a bioreactor there may therefore be a role for organisms engineered with particular degradative capacity for such compounds.

Treatment Scheme Options

The type of treatment scheme will depend on a number of factors, of which the distribution of the contaminant, geology and geotechnical properties of the soil are paramount.

Soil treatment processes can be divided into truly *in situ* schemes or techniques involving excavation of the soil. Truly *in situ* techniques consist either of simple landfarming for soils (where the contaminant is confined to a shallow depth and the soil can be tilled with conventional agricultural equipment) or recirculation schemes applicable to pervious subsurface material (in which the selected nutrients, together with additional microorganisms if required, are injected and pumped through the contaminated material). Several such schemes have been used to treat contaminated aquifers in Europe where injection wells or trenches are established upgradient of the contaminated zone with recovery wells downgradient to induce a subsurface flow of flushwater through the aquifer. The injection water is supplemented with nutrients as necessary. Treatments such as stripping and filtration of the contaminated groundwater recovered from the extraction well may take place prior to recirculation.

Biological wastewater treatment techniques, including activated sludge, aerated lagoons, trickling filters, aerobic digestion, composting and waste stabilization, may be employed here to acclimatise bacteria for the restoration of contaminated aquifers. These acclimatised bacteria may also be added directly to the aquifer for degradation of the contaminant *in situ*.

A number of examples of this process have been described; they have had varying degrees of success. The introduction of hydrogen peroxide has been suggested as a means of enhancing oxygen supply but there are problems of toxicity to the indigenous bacteria. Pretreatment of groundwater with ozone prior to reinfiltration back into the system not only provides further oxygen but may also increase the susceptibility of the contaminants to biodegradation. The disadvantages of biological treatment of aquifers include the plugging of soil by bacteria with subsequent reduction of circulation, adverse effects on adjacent surface water by introduction of nutrients, taste and odour problems from residues, cost of treatment and dependance on good permeability of the subsurface material. On the other hand, it is a fast, safe process, ecologically sound and generally good for short-term treatment.

There are several possible treatment schemes which involve excavation of the soil. These may or may not be carried out on site. The term "landfarming" has been used not only to refer to *in situ* schemes but also to treatments in which the contaminated soil is excavated and spread out on the top of a drained sand bed. Plastic foil or some other barrier is used to isolate the contaminated soil from the subsoil. In open composting systems, the soil is excavated and placed in suitably engineered treatment beds such as pyramid-shaped windrows or in mounds into which air is periodically pumped through perforated pipes (the "Beltsville" system). An organic bulking agent (e.g. refuse or wood chips) may be used to condition the material and facilitate air penetration. Heat released through oxidation of the material enhances the temperature of the mound and increases biodegradation. In closed systems, the soil may be treated in a container such as the horizontal rotating Dano drum,. or passed through a vertical column as used in the Kneer, Schnorr or Triga systems.

THE GREENBANK GASWORKS SITE: A CASE STUDY

Introduction

A number of approaches may be adopted in the development of a microbiological treatment strategy. A typical programme involves isolation of specific pollutant-degrading organisms from the polluted site, optimization of their activity in laboratory microcosms and field trials, and finally, the reintroduction of the organisms into the site under proper conditions in an appropriate engineered system.

This procedure was adopted at the Greenbank Gasworks site at Blackburn in Lancashire. The site supported a gasworks and tar distillery from the early 1900s until 1970. Following demolition, it lay derelict, unable to be developed because of the toxic compounds present. A scheme was devised to treat the contamination on-site using a combination of both conventional and microbiological techniques; this obviated the need to remove large quantities of toxic soil to landfill with all the inherent associated nuisance and environmental problems.

Contaminants Common to Gasworks Sites: Biodegradation Potential

Coal tar is one of the most common pollutants at gasworks sites. Its chemical composition is highly variable due to differences in both the origin of coal and the carbonization conditions used at different sites. Most of the low molecular weight hydrocarbons such as benzene and xylene are degraded relatively easily by microorganisms and will have disappeared in weathered material a result of biotic and abiotic processes, leaving residual deposits composed of heavier distillates which solidified on cooling. These include polyaromatic hydrocarbons (PAH) which are either known or suspected carcinogens. Biochemical degradation of some of the lower molecular weight, two and three ring PAH such as naphthalene, anthracene and phenanthrene is well known and involves hydroxylation of the benzene ring to produce intermediates which are further degraded to catechol. The ring structure is then cleaved to produce organic acids which are eventually metabolized to carbon dioxide and water.

Less is known however about the degradation pathways of the four or five ringed PAH.

Phenolic compounds, including phenol, cresols, xylenols and naphthols, are also associated with tarry materials but, due to increased solubility, tended to be more widespread within the Greenbank site than PAH. Degradation of such compounds is widely reported.

Although the free cyanide present was also potentially biodegradable, at the Greenbank site it tended to be associated with the non-degradable ferro and ferri-cyanides. This complex cyanide, together with metals present in spent oxide which could not be treated microbially, was placed in a purpose-designed clay-lined landfill on site beneath a proposed road embankment. This illustrates the importance of integrating novel microbial treatment into an overall strategy for dealing with the total contamination present.

At the Greenbank site, different contaminants were produced as a result of distinct processes and deposited in separate areas, so it was possible to delineate those areas of the site to be treated conventionally from the phenolic and tarry areas to be treated microbiologically. The relative extent of conventional versus microbiological treatment will of course vary from one site to the next.

Microbial Isolation and Testing

For degradation of PAH and phenols, vanguard microorganisms were isolated from soil samples recovered from the site in batch cultures using preparations of the individual pollutant compounds (e.g. phenanthrene, naphthalene, phenol, etc.) as the sole carbon source in a conventional mineral salts medium.

Ground coal tar itself supported an increase in microbial biomass in batch culture but one of the major problems involved in degradation concerned the insolubility of the PAH.

To overcome this, a variety of surfactants were screened for their efficacy in enhancing the availability of the pollutant to the inoculum. Such tests may take several forms, either as a leaching exercise or a visual assessment as used in the present study, in which the reduction in turbidity of a tarry suspension inoculated with a mixed microbial culture was quantified with and without the surfactant.

The vanguard organisms were then introduced into small quantities of polluted soil together with combinations of macro- and micronutrients and surfactants.

These systems were maintained at a constant temperature of 15°C with optimal soil moisture conditions and pollutant degradation rates were monitored. A series of these microcosm studies was carried out to develop the optimal combination of vanguard microorganisms, nutrients and surfactant.

Following development of the appropriate chemical and biological treatment in the laboratory, field trials were established to optimize physical parameters required for successful degradation (e.g. moisture content and particle size), in a suitably engineered treatment bed such as a trapezoidal soil mound. The most important factor however was the provision of sufficient oxygen: at the Greenbank site it was found that subsoiling of the material was more effective than forced aeration from the base of the mound.

The prototype soil treatment mound was laid down in four 0.19 m layers divided into a number of sections, each of which was sampled prior to spraying with specific microbe-nutrient-surfactant treatments. The trial took place in a polytunnel heated to 20°C to simulate the range of temperatures expected over the full-scale summer treatment period.

The client required a reduction of coal tar concentrations (measured as the sum of the 16 PAH compounds defined as priority pollutants by the U.S. EPA) to below 10,000 ppm. In the optimal treatment employing a specific microbe, ERB002, nutrients and surfactant, the total PAH content was reduced from 12,500 ppm to 7,600 ppm, i.e. a 40% reduction, in an 8 week treatment period. Average percentage reductions in those PAH compounds reduced by a statistically significant level were 37% for benz(a)anthracene from 558 to 353 ppm, 44% for indeno(1,2,3,-cd)pyrene from 316 to 177 ppm, 72% for fluoranthene from 3,664 to 1,019 ppm, and 56% for each of benz(a)pyrene (159 to 70 ppm), benz(b) fluoranthene (552 to 244 ppm) and pyrene (833 to 356 ppm).

The same combination of microbial and chemical reagents also reduced PAH concentrations in a further treatment from 8,000 to 5,100 ppm. Statistically significant reductions in fluoranthene (from 2,271 to 647 ppm), pyrene (524 to 209 ppm) and benz(a)pyrene (from 100 to 45 ppm) were again obtained. However, when the microorganisms were omitted from the treatment, no significant reductions in any of the individual PAH compounds occurred and, in fact, mean coal tar levels actually increased from 3,500 to 5,300 ppm. This was probably due to the action of the subsoiler which continued to break up remaining lumps of coal tar and increased the distribution of the pollutant.

Such a finding underlines the importance here of actually adding a specific microorganism rather than relying on the stimulation of the natural microflora through addition of nutrients and surfactant. A similar result occurred when all three of the ingredients (microorganisms, nutrients and surfactant) were omitted, and mean coal tar levels were 4,300 ppm after 8 weeks compared with 2,900.

Full Scale Operations

Following demonstration of reduction of coal tar contamination to below the target concentration, the process was scaled-up to treat the entire site after performing similar trials to monitor degradation of phenolic compounds.

In order to optimize particle size and the need to use agricultural equipment, the contaminated material was passed through a screen. Larger lumps of rubble were rejected on a primary grid, the material passing continuously through a shredder box consisting of two sets of rotating teeth, meshed to the required size and discharged by means of a conveyor belt over a second grid. This resulted in a homogeneous material of suitable particle size which was dozed into treatment beds.

Rejected material was also incorporated into these beds following crushing. The nutrients, surfactant and microorganisms, delivered to the site in 100 litre batches, were mixed in a pneumatically driven tank and evenly dispensed onto each layer of the treatment bed using a conventional agricultural boom sprayer. Rotorvation of the material was carried out to ensure a thorough mixing of the material.

Periodic subsoiling of the treatment beds together with applications of water to restore moisture levels to optimal conditions took place over the treatment period. Booster inocula were later applied to treatment beds with high levels of contamination the following spring when ambient temperatures were beginning to rise. An example of the degradation of total phenols in one such treatment bed is presented in Fig. 1. The objective was to reduce the total phenol concentration to below 5 ppm. This total represented the summated concentrations of phenol, *o*- and *m*-cresols, 2,3- and 2,4-

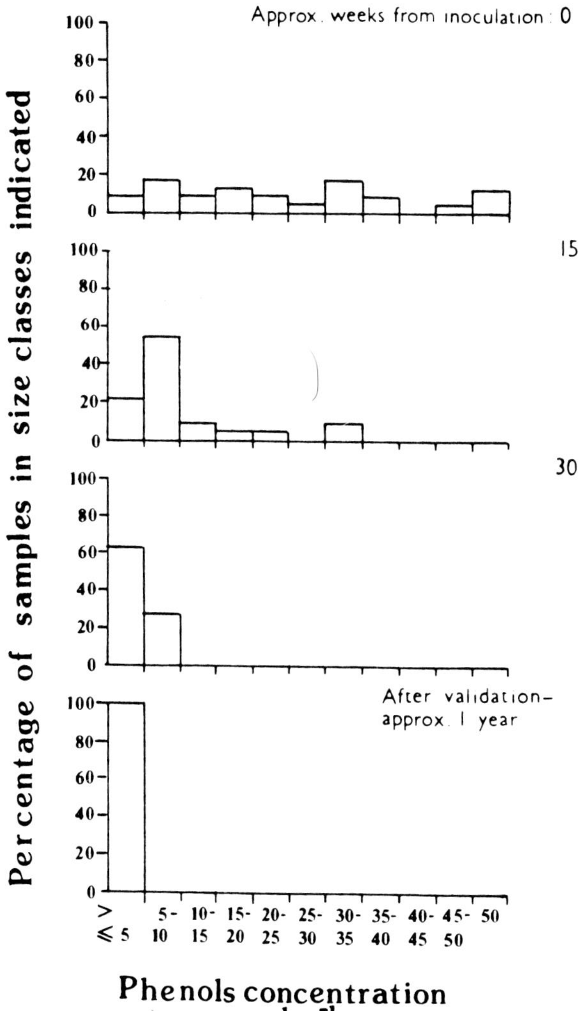

Figure 1. Percentage of samples containing total phenolic compounds in size levels of 5 ppm recovered from a microbial soil treatment bed.

xylenols, 2- and 1-naphthols and 2,4,6-trimethylphenol. The data are presented in terms of a frequency histogram to illustrate the initial variability and the gradual elimination of the higher size classes of phenols as the degradation proceeded. After 30 weeks, the mean phenol concentration in this bed was 4.5 ± 0.4 ppm (S.E.M.).

Final independent validation of the treatment beds indicated that 80% of the samples analysed contained no more than 1 ppm total phenols and that 95% were below the target concentration of 5 ppm. All samples analysed for coal tar were below the target concentration of 10,000 ppm and over 90% of these did not contain more than 1,500 ppm PAH, most being below 500 ppm.

The costs of microbiological treatment will necessarily vary from one site to the next. The economic benefits will be related not only to site-specific factors such as geological and hydrological characteristics, the relative proportions of biodegradable and non-biodegradable pollutants, nature and distributions of the contamination, initial starting concentration and target concentrations required but also to the costs of alternative treatments. The latter will include, for example, the costs of excavation, removal and transport to the nearest landfill available which could accept the contaminated material. In the case of the Greenbank site, the contract value was worth £760,000, with bioremediation representing a saving of at least £70,000 over conventional remediation techniques.

Future Prospects

Microbiological treatment of contaminated soil has a number of advantages over conventional techniques. On-site treatment is economically cost-effective in comparison with conventional methods of removing the soil and transport to landfill. As it represents an intensification of a natural process, it is ecologically sound and the destruction, rather than relocation, of the pollutant is obviously environmentally advantageous. On the other hand, biological treatment must be integrated with conventional engineering methods of site treatment especially in areas where there is a mix of biodegradable and non-degradable pollutants, as at gasworks sites.

Finally, the treatment should be site-specific: just as the geology and distribution of the pollutant peculiar to the site in question need to be taken into account in designing the engineering processes, so must the microbiological treatment take cognizance of the ecological interactions between the microorganisms responsible for pollutant degradation and the physical, chemical and biological components of the particular soil environment.

LANDFILLING AND ITS POTENTIAL FOR THE MICROBIAL TREATMENT OF WASTES

Introduction

The effective and environmentally safe disposal of waste material is one of the major problems facing society today. Waste materials are derived from many sources including the mining, agricultural, industrial, commercial and domestic sectors of the economy and their composition varies accordingly. Disposal strategies do not reflect the varied nature of wastes: the majority of commercial and municipal solid wastes (MSW) are disposed to landfills. The number of sites available for the disposal of wastes is limited. A thorough understanding of the fate of waste materials under controlled landfilling is therefore a pre-requisite for the effective use of this disposal route.

The actual amounts of MSW arising every year are extremely difficult to quantify. It has been estimated that in the U.K. in 1983 25 million tonnes of MSW were generated. This was equivalent to 1.22 kg per person per day. During the same period in the U.S., approximately 165 million tonnes of MSW were generated which equates to 1.96 kg per person per day.

Internationally, The composition of MSW varies significantly. Wastes arising from developed countries are characterized by a much higher paper content compared to underdeveloped countries, where vegetable matter predominates. The balance is comprised of metals, glass, textiles and plastics. A recent analysis (1986) of domestic refuse from one area of the U.K. is presented in Table 1. By weight, the vegetable, putrescible, paper and card fractions comprise greater than 63% of the refuse. It is these fractions that contain the biodegradable material present in refuse. The major components of the biodegradable material are the polymers, cellulose, lignin, hemicellulose and proteins, which account for between 35–37%, 7–9%, 1.5–4.5% and 5–6%, respectively of the dry weight of refuse. Other biodegradable components in refuse are starches, sugars and lipids, which account for no more than 1.5% of refuse dry weight.

Refuse Biodegradation

It is not within the scope of this chapter to describe the landfilling process in great detail. Generally, the refuse is deposited in 1.5–2.5 m layers which are covered with 0.2–0.3 m of earth.

The refuse is compacted to give densities of between 0.6–0.8 tonnes per m^3. This deposition method and initial aerobic microbial activity quickly results in the depletion of oxygen within the refuse. The majority of refuse biodegradation therefore occurs under anaerobic conditions.

Table 1

	Domestic refuse by weight	*Composition[a,b] by volume*
Vegetable and putrescible	36.2	11.0
Paper and card	27.7	34.0
(packaging)	(14.6)	(23.0)
(newsprint)	(13.1)	(11.0)
Plastic	8.3	27.0
(film)	(6.1)	(18.0)
(containers)	(2.2)	(9.0)
Glass	7.3	6.0
Textiles	7.0	7.0
Metal	6.0	10.0
(ferrous)	(5.5)	(8.0)
(non-ferrous)	(0.5)	(2.0)
Screenings	5.4	2.0
Unclassified	2.1	3.0
(flammable)	(1.7)	(2.0)
(non-flammable)	(0.4)	(1.0)

[a] Percent compositions given
[b] Data provided by Merseyside Waste Disposal Authority

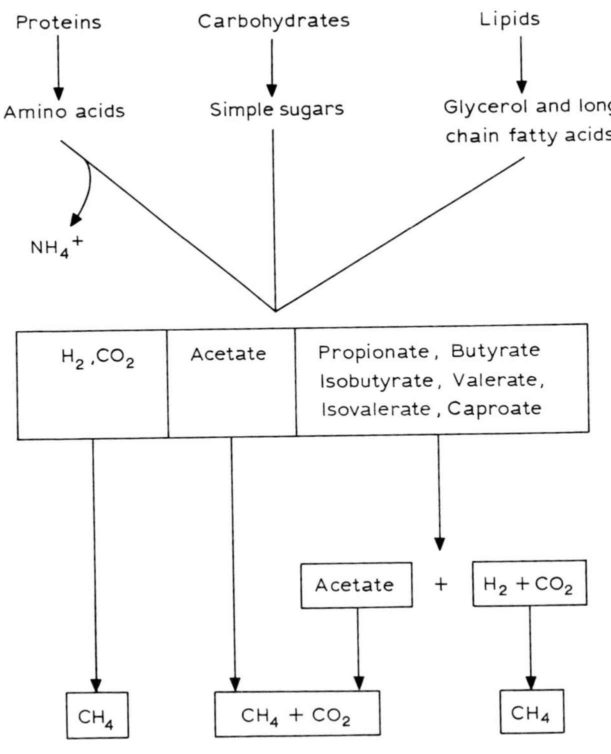

Figure 2. Degradation scheme for the major landfill polymers.

The anaerobic degradation of refuse polymers is summarized in Fig. 2. This scheme or one similar has been proposed by many workers and is now generally accepted.

Under ideal conditions, the major polymeric components of refuse are hydrolysed to their component monomers which are then fermented to a range of volatile fatty acids, hydrogen and carbon dioxide. The volatile fatty acids (>C2) are converted to acetate, hydrogen and carbon dioxide. The final stage in refuse biodegradation is the production of methane from the methanogenic precursors — acetate, hydrogen and carbon dioxide.

A range of microbial groups, varying widely in their metabolic capacities, are involved in the complete degradation of the refuse polymers to methane and carbon dioxide.

The scheme illustrated in Fig. 2 suggests that the only products of refuse biodegradation in landfills are methane, carbon dioxide and ammonia. However, most landfills are characterized by the presence of high BOD, low pH leachates and poor methane production. Extremely high concentrations of volatile fatty acids are associated with the high BOD of such leachates. Increasing volatile fatty acids concentrations cause the pH of the leachate to fall, resulting in the solubilization of a wide range of metal ions (Fig. 3). In landfill sites with elevated production of methane, the volatile fatty acids and soluble metal ion concentrations are decreased. Unless contained within the site, landfill leachates pose a serious environmental threat.

A rapid initial fermentation of carbohydrates, simple sugars and proteins to volatile fatty acids, hydrogen and carbon dioxide is accompanied by a rapid decrease in the pH of the system. This results in a marked decrease in the activities of methanogenic microorganisms which are present initially in low numbers.

The acetogenic conversion of volatile fatty acids to acetate is dependent on the maintenance of low partial pressures of hydrogen within the system.

A decrease in methanogenic activity means that the rate of hydrogen removal is not sufficient to allow the acetogenic conversion of volatile fatty acids. The degradation of refuse polymers to methane and carbon dioxide is uncoupled at the level of the acetogenic conversion of volatile fatty acids to acetate. However, the microorganisms responsible for the production of volatile fatty acids, hydrogen and carbon dioxide from refuse polymers are not affected by the decrease in pH to the same extent, resulting in further production of these metabolites with concomitant pH fall. Eventually, a situation is reached whereby all microbial activities are inhibited by the high volatile fatty acid, low pH conditions and the

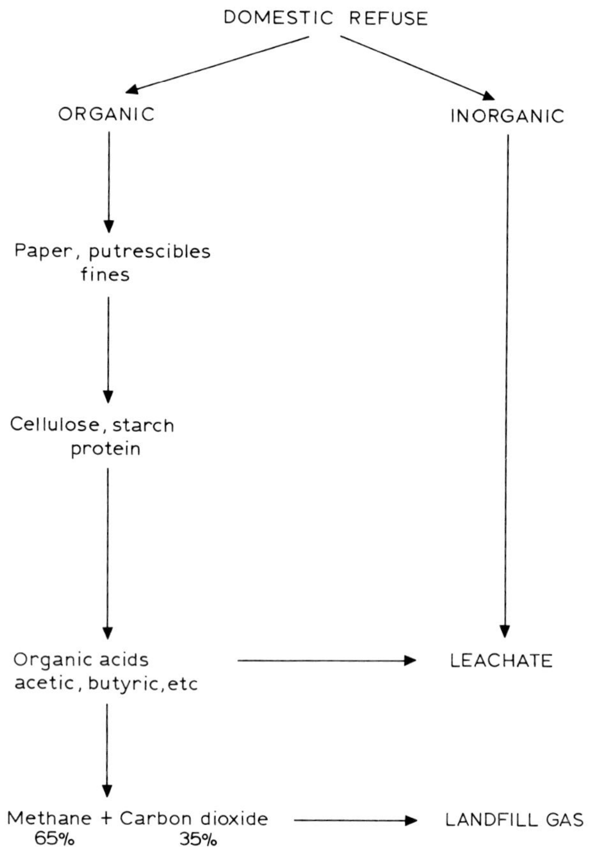

Figure 3. Flow paths for landfill organic and inorganic fractions.

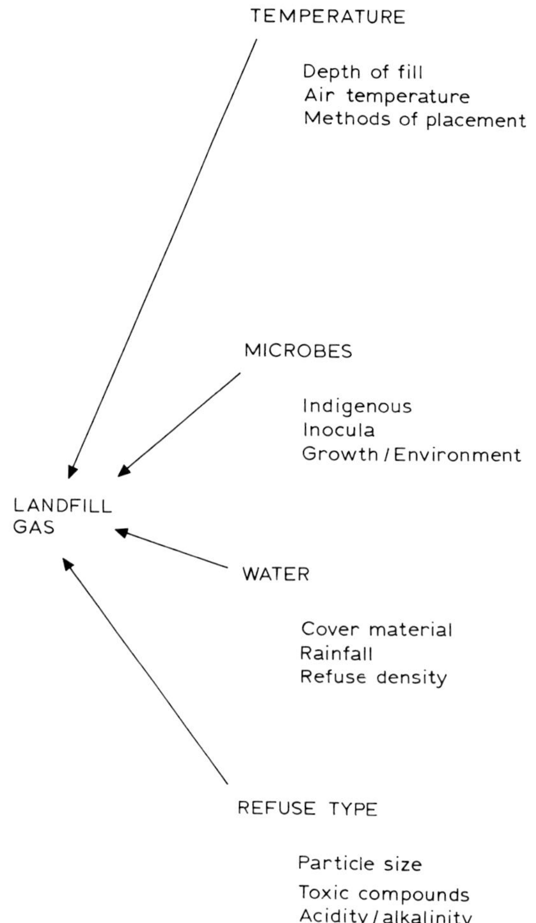

Figure 4. Factors affecting the production of landfill gas.

landfill is said to be "soured". Recovery from the "soured" state is extremely difficult to achieve, and the leachate present in soured sites has tremendous potential for environmental damage. Refuse in such landfill sites is only partially stabilized, limiting the scope for site development.

Factors Controlling Refuse Biodegradation

The coupling of refuse degradation to methane production allows a more rapid stabilization of the landfill site. The leachate poses less of an environmental threat, although the high concentrations of ammonia present must be removed before disposal can be considered.

The promotion of methane production from landfill sites would appear to be of benefit, but uncontrolled gas migration in itself can have severe (and, indeed, explosive!) environmental consequences. Any scheme proposed to establish effective methane production from landfill sites must incorporate gas migration control.

Factors affecting refuse biodegradation and landfill gas production are summarized in Fig. 4. The influence of water activity and temperature on microbial activities is well documented. In the U.K., refuse just prior to landfilling has a water content of 25–35% wet weight. Laboratory and field data have shown that the methane production rate from methanogenic refuse is directly related to the water content. Water addition to freshly deposited or soured refuse does not promote gas production. A high BOD — low pH leachate is generated through stimulation of the acid-forming phase of the refuse degradation with a consequent uncoupling of methane production. Increasing the water content of landfills to promote methane production is not consistent with current landfill operational practices, which aim to minimize water ingression to control leachate production. The type of cover material, refuse density and local rainfall will all influence the water content of landfills.

The temperature within landfills is dependent on the depth of fill, air temperature, methods of placement and microbial activities. Freshly deposited refuse will undergo a brief period of aerobic degradation which can raise the temperature significantly. Under anaerobic conditions, less heat is produced and the insulating effect of further layers of refuse causes temperatures within landfills generally to be in the mesophilic range.

The refuse type will greatly influence microbial activities. The presence of elevated concentrations of toxic materials will have a detrimental effect on all microbial activities, whilst the influence of pH has been discussed previously.

The least understood factor controlling refuse degradation and gas production in landfills is microbial activities. Surprisingly little information is available on the relationship between microbial activities and refuse degradative processes.

It has been argued that of all the physiological groups required for the methanogenic degradation of fresh refuse, the methanogens are probably limiting.

The maintenance of high numbers and activity of this pivotal group of microorganisms is of paramount importance in preventing the souring of landfill refuse. The seeding of freshly deposited refuse with anaerobically digested sewage sludge has been used in an attempt to introduce high numbers of methanogens. The effectiveness of this approach in initiating methanogenesis in refuse is still unproven.

Normal landfill operation practices, which aim to maximize refuse placement and minimize leachate production, do not appear to be consistent with the conditions required for good methanogenesis. The establishment of methane production through the application of alternative inoculation procedures and control of the nutrient status in discrete areas can be achieved without compromising the overall requirements to maximize refuse placement.

The controlled addition and physical movement of water through the refuse would promote methane production in the surrounding refuse masses. The overall effect of this strategy would be to increase the rate of refuse decomposition and improve leachate quality through coupling refuse degradation to methane production.

The operation of landfills as efficient methanogenic bioreactors has many benefits which are consistent with the general aims of landfill management (Table 2). The enormous metabolic potential of such complex methanogenic systems may also be used as a means of treating a wide range of environmental pollutants. This possibility will be discussed in greater detail in the next section.

Table 2

General landfill management aims	*Benefits accruing from landfill operating as methanogenic bioreactor*
Maximize placement density	Operation consistent with maximizing placement density.
	Increased rate of refuse degradation results in increased settlement rate, allowing placement of further refuse.
Control of gas migration	Abstraction of increased yields of methane will form part of gas migration control scheme.
Minimize odour production	Controlled abstraction of gas results in reduced odour problems.
Control of leachate	Improvement of leachate quality through coupling refuse degradation to methane production.
Promote conditions suitable for end use	More rapid stabilization of refuse for end use allows earlier redevelopment of site.
	Use of abstracted gas for energy generation.

Co-disposal of Hazardous Wastes

Approximately 3.7 million tonnes of hazardous wastes were generated in England and Wales in 1985. The disposal routes for these wastes are detailed in Table 3. A simple guide to defining special or hazardous wastes has been prepared by the Land Wastes Division of the U.K. Department of the Environment[3]:

> "If a waste contains prescription only medicines or substances which have flash points of 21°C or less, or contains known or probable human carcinogens at a concentration of 1% (w/w) or more or is likely to

Table 3
Disposal Routes for Hazardous Wastes in England and Wales in 1985

Disposal route	*Percentage of total arising*[1]
Landfill	78.7
Solidification	3.6
Mineshafts	1.6
Sea (including sea incineration)	7.0
Chemical treatment	7.5
Incineration	1.6

[1] 3.5 million tonnes

cause serious tissue damage on exposure for a period up to 15 minutes or if ingestion of up to 5 cm^3 is likely to cause death or serious tissue damage to a 20 kg child, then it is classified as a special waste."

The range of compounds covered by these definitions is enormous but can be divided into the general categories listed in Table 4. This list is by no means definitive but provides a guide to the types of wastes that can be considered hazardous.

Biodegradability of Selected Hazardous Wastes Under Anaerobic Conditions

The general categories in Table 4 can be divided into predominantly inorganic or organic wastes. The former include metal-containing compounds and the inorganic cyanides, inorganic halogen- and sulphur-containing compounds as well as some phosphorus-containing materials. However, this simple division is further complicated by the presence of organometallic wastes. The organic wastes comprise the hydrocarbons, heterocyclics, organic halides, pharmaceutical and veterinary compounds, some biocides and tarry materials.

The controlled disposal of hazardous organic wastes into actively methanogenic landfills may allow the effective detoxification of these materials through microbial action. The biological degradability under methanogenic conditions of selected organic wastes will be discussed further.

Table 4
General Categories of Special Wastes[1]

Metal and metal-containing compounds	
Antimony	Mercury
Arsenic	Nickel
Barium	Selenium
Beryllium	Silver
Boron	Tellurium
Cadmium	Thallium
Chromium	Vanadium
Copper	Zinc
Lead	
Asbestos	
Biocides, phytopharmaceutical, pharmaceutical and veterinary compounds	
Phosphorous and its compounds	
Heterocyclic organics	
Hydrocarbons and their derivatives	
Inorganic halogen-containing and sulphur-containing compounds and cyanides	
Organic halogen compounds	
Tarry materials and tar residues	

[1] Waste Management Paper No. 23: Special wastes: a technical memorandum providing guidance on their definition. Her Majesty's Stationery Office (London), 1981

Organic Acids and their Derivatives

The range of organic acids used in industry is vast. Amongst the most important are:

1. Low molecular weight saturated and unsaturated monocarboxylic acids and their derivatives, e.g. acetic, propionic, glycolic, lactic, acrylic, crotonic, lauric, oleic, palmitic.
2. Saturated and dicarboxylic acids and their derivatives, e.g oxalic, malonic, malic, citric, maleic.
3. Aromatic and substituted aromatic carboxylic acids, e.g. benzoic, phthalic, anthranilic, salicylic.
4. Substituted and unsubstituted sulphonic acids, e.g. methanosulphonic, chlorosulphonic, sulphonic.
5. Others, e.g. phenols.

There is a wide body of evidence in the scientific literature that the compounds in groups 1–3 and 5 are degraded under methanogenic conditions. In some instances, the degradation occurs after a prolonged adaptation period.

This may be accompanied by an initial inhibition of methane production. Little information is available on the fate of sulphonic acids under methanogenic conditions.

Biocides

Biocides are compounds which can "kill or inhibit the growth of organisms"[3]. They can be inorganic, organometallic, phosphorus-containing, nitrogen-containing, halogen-containing, sulphur-containing, organic or of biological origin.

The microbial degradation of the halogen-containing biocides will be discussed later. The carbamate, amide-, urea, amine-, aniline- and nitro-based biocides will in all probability be degraded or significantly transformed under anaerobic conditions.

Azo, triazine- and quaternary ammonium-based biocides are highly resistant to aerobic degradation and it is doubtful if significant degradative effects will occur anaerobically. Degradation of some phosphorus-containing organic biocides is initiated by the hydrolytic removal of the phosphorus-containing group. This hydrolytic step does not require oxygen.

Further degradation of the biocide is dependent upon the

structure of the dephosphorylated compound remaining. Biocides of botanical or microbiological origin by definition are not xenobiotic compounds. Such biocides are generally amenable to biological degradation.

Heterocyclic Organics

Heterocyclic organics are ring compounds where one or more of the atoms in the ring are elements other than carbon. The most commonly encountered types are summarized in Table 5. Furans, pyrroles, thiophens and pyridines have all been shown to be degraded aerobically.

There is no conclusive evidence as to the fate of the remaining heterocyclic compounds aerobically. There is good evidence for the anaerobic degradation of both the pyridine and pyrrole groups of heterocyclics. A variety of micro-organisms can use pyridine as the sole carbon source under anaerobic conditions. The heterocyclic base adenine can be degraded to xanthine which can be further metabolized to the methanogenic precursors, acetate, formate and carbon dioxide.

Other compounds known to be degraded under methanogenic conditions are tryptophan and indole. Little information is available on the biodegradation of the remaining heterocyclic groups under anaerobic conditions.

Table 5
Types of Heterocyclic Compounds

Name	*Atoms in ring*	*Atoms other than carbon*
Furan	5	1 oxygen
Pyrrole	5	1 nitrogen
Thiophen	5	1 sulphur
Azole	5	2 nitrogens
Oxazole	5	1 nitrogen and 1 oxygen
Triazoles	5	3 nitrogens
Pyridine	6	1 nitrogen
Pyran	6	1 oxygen
Diazine	6	2 nitrogens
Dioxin	6	2 oxygens
Oxazine	6	1 nitrogen and 1 oxygen
Thiazine	6	1 sulphur and 1 nitrogen
Triazine	6	3 nitrogens

Hydrocarbons and their Derivates

This group contains the majority of chemical types likely to be found in wastes. The hydrocarbons (both aliphatic and aromatic) can be further subdivided into a range of organic types.

1. Hydrocarbons
2. Alcohols and glycols
3. Aldehydes and ketones
4. Esters
5. Ethers
6. Phenols
7. Amines
8. Amides

In general, those aromatics substituted with an oxygen-containing moiety have been shown to be amenable to methanogenic degradation.

However, recent evidence has shown that both toluene and benzene are mineralized to methane and carbon dioxide under anaerobic conditions. The initial oxidation stage is achieved through the incorporation of oxygen from water. The methanogenic fermentation of aniline has also been demonstrated.

It has been reported that methane is metabolized by pure cultures of methanogenic bacteria although the significance of the observation for the methanogenic degradation of longer chain aliphatic hydrocarbons is unclear. There is conclusive evidence for the degradation of a wide range of hydrocarbons under methanogenic conditions but such evidence for the degradation of other derivatives under methanogenic conditions is lacking.

Organic Halogen Compounds

The organic halogen compounds differ from the hydrocarbons discussed in the previous section by the replacement of one or more protons by a halogen moiety, usually chlorine.

The synthetic halogenated organics have a wide range of inherent applications including the manufacture of pharmaceuticals, chemicals, biocides, etc. The degradation of halogenated organics under a variety of environmental conditions has recently attracted much attention. This has arisen because of increasing concern over the discovery of halogenated organics in drinking water, waste water and ground water.

Chlorinated benzoates and phenols are readily degraded under methanogenic conditions by acclimatized anaerobic systems. Degradation is initiated by the reductive dehalogenation of the aromatic moiety. The specificity of this activity is generally dependent on prior acclimatisation of the anaerobic environment to a particular halogenated aromatic. The dechlorinated aromatic can then be readily metabolized to methane and carbon dioxide. However, partially dehalogenated aromatics may be persistent in anaerobic environments.

Several 1- and 2-carbon halogenated aliphatics are degraded under methanogenic conditions. Chloroform, carbon tetrachloride, and 1, 2-dichloroethane are oxidized to carbon dioxide under methanogenic conditions.

Reductive dehalogenation of tetrachloroethylene and 1,1,2,-2-tetrachloroethane to trichloroethylene and 1,1,2-trichloroethane, respectively, prior to the production of non-chlorinated end products has also been observed.

The transformations under anaerobic conditions of selected halogenated biocides into less halogenated products has been known since the late 1960s. The first well documented example was the conversion of DDT into DDD. Other chlorinated biocides now known to be transformed under anaerobic conditions include:

Lindane	Trifluralin	Methoxychlor	Aldrin
Toxaphene	Thiobencarb	Pentachlorophenol	Endrin
Diuron	α-HCH	Propanil	HCE
2,4,5-T	Heptachlor	Dieldrin	Mirex

These transformations generally involve only the simple replacement of a chlorine atom by a proton as with DDT or dieldrin. These reactions may be considered as detoxification mechanisms rather than mineralization because the dehalogenated product accumulates.

Tarry Materials and Tar Residues

Tars are organic residues generated during the carbonisation of organic materials. Crude tar may be distilled to yield oils, refined tars and pitch. Further processing of the oil fractions can yield naphthalene, anthracene, phenols, creosols and xylenols.

As discussed previously the phenolic components of tars are amenable to methanogenic degradation. Naphthalene and anthracene belong to the PAH group of compounds. The PAHs of prime environmental concern are non-substituted, which may have implications for their biodegradation under anaerobic conditions. However the non-substituted hydrocarbon, benzene, is amenable to methanogenic degradation.

Metal Wastes

While not previously mentioned, the potential of methanogenic landfills for the disposal of heavy metal wastes may also exist. Partitioning of the metals with the solid phase of anaerobically digested sludges is chemically determined and pH dependent.

The pH effect suggests that weakly acidic ligands are involved and that competition exists between metals and hydrogen ions for these sites. Similar absorption of metal ions could occur in landfill systems, providing the pH was maintained above 6.5. The simplest way of achieving this would be through the establishment of an actively methanogenic system. Under methanogenic conditions, heavy metals can also be sequested through complexing with sulphide ions. This reaction, too, is pH dependent, and occurs readily at the pHs found in actively methanogenic systems providing sulphide is not limiting.

Properties of Compounds Determining Anaerobic Biodegradability

The previous sections have attempted to summarise the potential for biodegrading a range of hazardous wastes under the conditions found in actively methanogenic landfills. Water solubility, volatility, molecular size, number and type of functional groups, stability and presence of substituent groups have all been identified as the properties of compounds that determine their anaerobic biodegradability.

Microbial activity is of equal importance in determining biodegradability. By ensuring that landfills are operated to promote the rapid methane-dependent degradation of MSW then conditions conducive for the transformation and detoxification of selected hazardous wastes are generated.

CONCLUSIONS

Clearly there is a great potential for the use of microbial systems for waste treatment and pollution clean-up.

There are already examples of applying the technology to the remediation of both contaminated land and aquifers. It is important to recognize however that these are site-specific and not general treatment strategies, the feasibility of such treatment being dependent upon the nature of the contamination and the prevailing environmental conditions.

The co-disposal of industrial effluents with municipal solid wastes offers tremendous scope for a treatment regime which is both cost-effective and ecologically acceptable. The degradation and detoxification of such effluents will be dependent on the establishment and maintenance of a diverse metabolically active microbial population within the landfill. This is best achieved through the stimulation and promotion of the methane-dependent decomposition of municipal solid wastes.

Whereas attention has previously been focussed on the application of biotechnology primarily to the pharmaceutical and agricultural industries, microorganisms can be used to address society's needs in other ways, particularly in the environmental sphere. This is reflected in the growing number of industries able to offer a biotechnological solution to waste treatment and pollution clean-up.

REFERENCES

1. Atlas, R.M. (1977). *Stimulated petroleum degradation*. Critical Reviews in Microbiology, **vol. 5**, pp. 371–386.
2. Alexander, M. (1984). *Ecological Constraints on genetic engineering*, in Genetic Control of Environmental Pollutants, pp. 151–168. Ed. by G.S. Omenn and A Hollaender. New York: Plenum Press.
3. Waste Management paper No. 23 (1981). *Special Wastes: A technical memorandum providing guidance on their definition*. London: Her Majesty's Stationery Office.

FURTHER READING

Bartha, R. (1986). *Biotechnology of petroleum pollutant biodegradation*. Microbial Ecology, **vol. 12**, pp 155–172.

Berry, L.D.F., Francis, A.J. and Bollag, J-M (1987). *Microbial metabolism of homocyclic and heterocyclic aromatic compounds under anaerobic conditions*. Microbiological Reviews, **vol. 51**, pp 43–59.

Bull, A.T. (1980). *Biodegradation: some attitudes and strategies of microorganisms and microbiologists*, in: Contemporary Microbial Ecology, pp 107–136. Ed. by D.C. Ellwood, J.N. Hedger, M.J. Latham, J.M. Lynch and J.H. Slater. London: Academic Press.

Gibson, D.T. (1984). *Microbial Degradation of Organic Chemicals*. New York: Marcel Dekker Inc.

Rees, J.F. (1985). *Landfills for treatment of solid wastes*, in: Comprehensive Biotechnology, **vol. 4**, pp 1071–1087. Ed. by C.W. Robinson and J.A. Howell, Oxford: Pergamon Press.

Sleat, R. and Robinson, J.P. (1984). *The bacteriology of anaerobic degradation of aromatic compounds*. Journal of Applied Bacteriology, **vol. 57**, pp 381–394.

Chapter 28

Biomass

Carl A. Batt

INTRODUCTION

Biomass is a term loosely used to define the total amount of carbon and nitrogen incorporated into all polymeric organic material by biological processes. It has been estimated that the total worldwide biomass is in excess of 10^{12} tons. Plants are the main source of biomass and their annual production of approximately 10^{11} tons is a result of photosynthesis. It is therefore by nature a renewable resource since in a balanced system the biomass removed for substrate usage can be replaced by replanting and reforestation. There is, however, a great danger when forestland is removed at an excessive rate because it also serves to remove carbon dioxide from the atmosphere and to generate oxygen. The ecological impact of deforestation with its contribution to the "greenhouse" effect and global warming is beyond the focus of this chapter but the reader should be cognizant of the implications. Within the currently available agricultural waste materials there is sufficient biomass to fuel a great deal of biotechnological processes, obviating the need for massive deforestation. Selected crops can be planted for biomass production, for example, sugar-cane and sugar beets yield 7.5 and 4.1 dry tons of biomass per acre respectively.

In the United States estimates on the fuel consumption from biomass are approximately 1.5×10^{15} BTU per year. This compares to the total plant biomass produced in the United States which is approximately 54×10^{15} BTU per year. In 1980, the total energy consumption in the United States was estimated at 78×10^{15} BTU; therefore biomass currently accounts for approximately 2% of the total energy used. Obviously, even if an absolutely efficient system were developed to convert biomass into a fuel, the total available biomass would not satiate current energy needs. Furthermore, a significant amount of this plant biomass is used for both human and animal feed in addition to forest product needs. One hundred years ago when wood was combusted for heating and cooking, greater than 90% of the energy needs were supplied by biomass. Now petroleum and natural gas are the principal fuel sources.

The most abundant examples of biomass are cellulose (approximately 40% of all plant biomass), hemicellulose, lignin and starch. The term "cellulosic biomass" encompasses cellulose, hemicellulose and lignin although at times the reader might find reference to hemicellulosic biomass referring specifically to the pentose sugar fraction.

Interest in biomass encompasses a variety of interactive issues, including environmental, political and of course biotechnological concerns. In the past twenty years the interest in biomass has been directly proportional to the price of petroleum. In the mid-1970s as the petroleum supplies became tenuous, an extensive program was initiated in the United States to develop alternative fuel sources. Included within this effort were programs to establish processes for conversion of agricultural commodities to fuel grade ethanol. The great abundance and continuous renewal of biomass is exemplified by the estimated production of approximately 70 kg of biomass per person per day. When calculated on a energy equivalent, the total amount of biomass being produced converts into 10,000 barrels of petroleum per second. In the United States the principal agricultural commodity was corn and commercial scale plants to produce ethanol were built. 'Gasohol,' a mixture of gasoline with up to 10% ethanol, was introduced as a fuel for automobiles with the incentive of extending available petroleum supplies. As the political and economic climate changed and the price of petroleum decreased, the programs on alternative fuels similarly decreased. Gasohol has since disappeared from the market and almost all of the facilities for producing fuel grade ethanol were closed.

BIOMASS AS A SUBSTRATE FOR BIOTECHNOLOGICAL PROCESSES

The manufacture of any product via a biotechnology-derived process must be economically feasible. The harsh reality is that the market demands with respect to the cost-benefit of a product hold true for any biotechnology process. Tissue plasminogen activator can, in theory, command a very high price in the marketplace due to its benefit in mediating coronary thrombosis. The same price structure cannot be applied to the majority of other potential biotechnology products, such as ethanol, proteases, amino acids, etc.

A significant cost factor in the manufacture (beyond the initial research and development costs of the process) of any biotechnology product is the substrate used to proliferate the biological production system (see Chapter 14). If we limit the discussion to microbial systems including bacteria, yeast and fungi then the basic substrate most frequently used as a cost-measure is glucose. There are notable exceptions such as the methanol catabolizing yeast, *Pichia*. A simple rule for determining the cost effectiveness of a given process is that its product's market value must exceed the cost of glucose as a substrate. Clearly, then the cost of glucose is a significant consideration in developing any biotechnology process. Molasses is a frequently used source of glucose and its current market price is approximately $0.05–0.10 per kilogram.

Are there alternative substrate sources? The answer is an unqualified yes, and hence the interest in biomass. The challenge is to design an efficient process for conversion of biomass into a form that can be readily catabolized by the microbial system being used to produce the biotechnological product of interest.

As mentioned previously, the principal examples of biomass are cellulose, hemicellulose, lignin and starch. With the exception of lignin, all of the other forms are polymers of sugars; cellulose and starch are polymeric glucose, while hemicellulose is composed mainly of the pentose sugar xylose. The exact composition of each varies depending upon its source, a factor which complicates any process to convert it to a readily usable substrate. Moreover, the minor constituents of a biomass source can present problems, especially when they are toxic to the microorganism which will be grown on this substrate. A notable example is sulfite in paper mill wastes, which can inhibit the growth of a variety of microorganisms.

COMPOSITION OF BIOMASS

Cellulose, hemicellulose and lignin are the major components in plant biomass (Figure 1). Wood and agricultural wastes can be fractionated by chemical, physical and enzymatic methods into these components. Each one has a different chemical structure and routes for hydrolysis must be addressed individually with respect to any process to convert it into a usable substrate. Considered separately among these forms of biomass, starch is perhaps the easiest to transform into a usable form.

The composition of any given biomass varies with respect to its cellulose, hemicellulose and lignin content. For example, barley straw contains approximately 40% hexose sugars, of which 93% is glucose. Hemicellulose accounts for 19%, lignin is approximately 14% of the total and ash comprises 10%. Rice straw in contrast has only 10% lignin, 15% hemicellulose, 39% cellulose and 12% ash. The variation in the composition of a given biomass material precludes any general method for conversion which is applicable to all types of biomass.

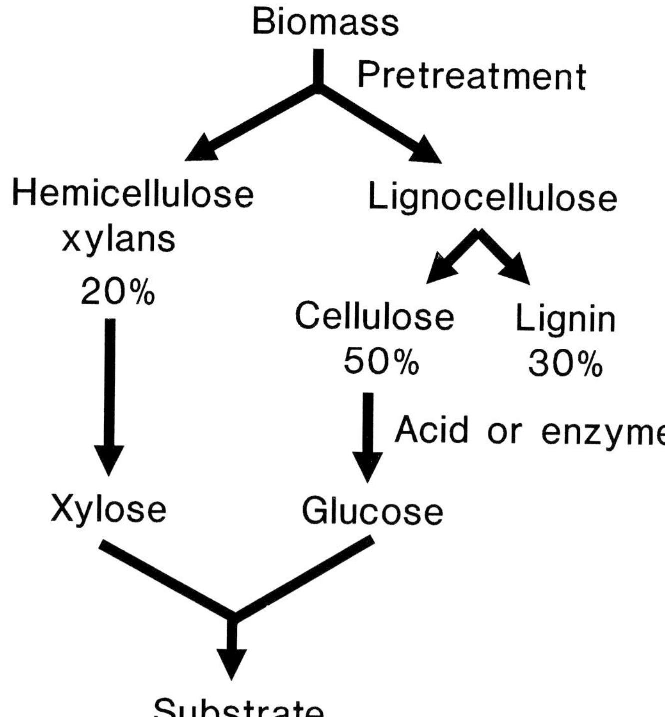

Figure 1. Components of lignocellulosic biomass

Cellulose

Cellulose occurs as fibers in plant cell walls as well as in bacteria, fungi and algae. It is a linear $\beta(1\rightarrow4)$-anhydroglucospyranose polymer. The number of glucose residues can exceed 15,000 per polymer molecule corresponding to molecular weights of 200–2,000 kDa. Although there are few, if any, covalent crosslinks between chains, hydrogen bonding between hydroxyl groups is extensive both within individual chains and between adjacent chains, resulting in a highly recalcitrant and water-insoluble crystalline material. The chains are so strongly bound by these forces that, as a consequence, cellulose is insoluble in all solvents except those which cause hydrolysis of the glycosidic linkages between glucose residues or which disrupt the hydrogen bonding between chains. Within a chain each D-glucosyl residue is rotated approximately 180° with respect to its nearest neighbors and thus cellobiose (a disaccharide) becomes the true repeating-unit within the chain.

Lignin

Lignin is unique among the biomass substrates to be described. It has a rather complex structure composed of phenolic residues instead of the simple repeating units observed in cellulose, xylan or starch. Lignin is an amorphous polymer composed of phenyl propane subunits primarily syringyl, guaiacyl and *p*-hydroxyphenol.

Lignin is highly resistant to chemical, enzymatic or microbiological hydrolysis due to the extensive crosslinking. It is also chemically and physically bound to the cellulose and hemicellulose. Therefore lignin is frequently removed simply to gain access to the cellulose.

Hemicellulose

Hemicellulose is intimately associated with cellulose in the cells walls of almost all higher plants especially hardwoods and grasses. Monocots are the primary source of xylans which constitute only a minor component of dicots: Birch wood, for example, can contain up to 35% xylan. It is a β,1–4 linked polymer of xylose with acetyl, arabinosyl or glucuronsyl substituents. Xylan appears to serve as the major interface between lignin and other carbohydrates in the cell wall of plants. It may form both covalent and noncovalent linkages with a number of cell wall constituents, including pectin, glucan and various proteins. Xylan may function to protect the cellulose from degradative enzymes. Removal of the xylan by selective extraction appears to make the cellulose more accessible to cellulase hydrolysis. Whether it forms a protective coating or simply acts to crosslink the matrix is difficult to delineate.

Starch

Starch is a polymer that is stored in a number of plants, most notably potatoes and corn. It does not have the same true structural role as is attributed to lignocellulose. It is composed of both amylose and amylopectin in varying ratios. Amylose in an α(1→4)-D-glucopyranose polymer. Amylopectin has a structure similar to amylose but with additional side branches of 20–30 glucose residues with α(1→6) linkages. The macrostructures are granules from 15–100 microns in diameter containing both amylose and amylopectin.

HYDROLYSIS OF BIOMASS

Physical

Physical pretreatment of lignocellulose biomass is an important prelude to further conversion steps, whether they be chemical or enzymatic. Simply reducing the particle size functions to increase the surface area accessible to enzyme attachment and hydrolysis. Furthermore, physical disruption can increase the pore size of the matrix, facilitating the entry of enzyme complexes into the interior of the substrate. Physical disruption can include milling, shredding or mulching. Steam treatment at temperatures of 180–240°C has also been used to pretreat lignocellulosic biomass.

Steam explosion is a variation on standard steam treatment and has been incorporated into a number of commercial processes. It is critical that the temperature in the process is above the transition temperature for the individual components of the lignocellulosic complex: 125°C for lignin, 165°C for xylan and 234°C for cellulose. Another important aspect of the process is that this temperature is reached in a very short time, on the order of 45–60 seconds, to avoid any significant decomposition of the substrate.

The Techtrol/Iotech steam explosion process was developed and is similar to the process used for the production of masonite. The lignocellulosic material is loaded into the chamber and steam is injected in order to read a temperature of 245–250°C. The sample is cooked for 5 seconds and then the pressure is released rapidly, hence the term "steam explosion". The resulting material can then be enzymatically hydrolyzed and after lignin removal and recovery used as a substrate for subsequent fermentation (see further).

Chemical

There are a number of routes toward the chemical hydrolysis of biomass, including the use of alkali, ammonia, sulfite, organic solvents and acid. Of these, acid hydrolysis appears to be the most feasible and has therefore received the greatest attention.

Acid catalyzes the breakdown of cellulose by the following mechanism. First, the glycosidic oxygen group is protonated by the acid in a step that appears to occur very rapidly. Next the glucose molecule must undergo a conformational change from the more favored chair structure into a semiplanar configuration. This step appears to be slow, perhaps due to the rotational energy required and the rigidity of the structure imposed by the cellulose backbone. It is this step that may be the rate limiting point in the process. Then, at a very rapid rate, a molecule of water is eliminated and finally a proton is released to complete the process.

Acid hydrolysis was one of first treatments to hydrolyze cellulose and initial reports using sulfuric acid date back to the early 1800s; the first plant to use sulfuric acid to hydrolyze cellulose was built in the United States in 1910. There are a number of different ways to employ sulfuric acid hydrolysis, including the "Scholler" process, which involves the addition of 0.6% acid at 184°C. The result of this treatment is a 50% conversion with a final glucose concentration of 3%.

In addition to sulfuric acid, other processes involve the use of hydrochloric acid and hydrofluoric acid. The latter is very efficient at hydrolyzing cellulose but is approximately five times the cost of the other acids and is very toxic. Therefore the use of hydrofluoric acid is far more expensive when the capital costs of the equipment necessary for its containment are factored into the total operating costs. The estimated costs of acid hydrolysis range from $0.09/kg for sulfuric acid, $0.26/kg for hydrochloric to $1.35/kg for hydrofluoric acid.

There are several advantages of acid hydrolysis over enzymatic hydrolysis, including its simplicity and rapid rate of hydrolysis. When concentrated acid is used high yields are obtained, up to 100% total hydrolysis. Dilute acid solutions are easier to handle than concentrated solutions but the yields are lower and there are more decomposition products formed which can inhibit subsequent bacterial growth, an important consideration when the hydrolysate is to be used in a fermentation.

Temperature is another important parameter in acid hydrolysis and can be used to accelerate the reaction rate in dilute acid processes. For example, a 1% acid concentration is unable to hydrolyze crystalline cellulose until the temperature is raised above 180°C. Lower temperatures can be used, but a more concentrated acid solution is required. In general, the higher the temperature and the greater the acid concentration, the more rapid the hydrolysis and the less degradation products that are formed. Hemicellulose is far more sensitive to acid hydrolysis as compared to cellulose but furan degradation products are also formed more rapidly. To limit the amount of degradation, systems have been designed to remove the free sugars from the reaction mixture. Percolation is one method to achieve this but the resulting eluate sugar stocks are dilute.

The acid used in any hydrolysis process must be recovered both for environmental and economic reasons. In a recycle system the acid solution after recovery must be concentrated before reuse. For example, a process that uses hydrochloric acid for hydrolysis at initial concentration of 41% for 1 hour at 35°C results in 100% hydrolysis into biodegradable carbohydrate. The concentration of the hydrochloric acid after recovery is only 30%, necessitating its reconcentration back to 41% before recycling. This is an expensive process, requiring elaborate containment materials consisting of either special alloys, glass-lined steel or graphite.

A process developed by the Tennessee Valley Authority for the acid hydrolysis of lignocellulose is presented in Figure 2. It employs two hydrolysis steps and uses grinding for the initial pretreatment. The first hydrolysis is accomplished using the acidified products from the end of the process and is followed by the removal of both the hexoses and the pentoses. In the final step the lignin is recovered and can be used for other purposes.

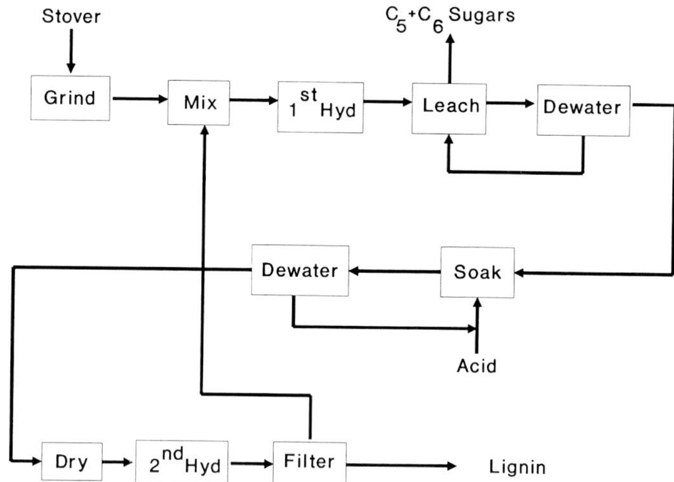

Figure 2. Simplified scheme of hydrolysis of lignocellulosics with concentrated sulfuric acid (Tennesee Valley Authority). Adapted from Fiechter, A. *Advances in biochemical engineering/biotechnology.* 1989. NY: Springer-Verlag, p. 59.

Enzymatic

Enzymatic hydrolysis of biomass substrate is appealing because of its specificity and absence of any harsh chemicals or expensive capital equipment. Furthermore, there is no significant substrate loss due to chemical modification which occurs when acid hydrolysis is used. There are, however, considerable economic hurdles which limit the use of enzymes for the hydrolysis. It is estimated that the cost of the enzymes represents 40% or more of the total cost of producing ethanol from biomass. A number of factors contribute to the high cost of enzymes, including their relatively low specific activity, especially when a crystalline substrate is encountered, and the inhibition of their activity by the reaction products.

The large complement of enzymes required to hydrolyze lignocellulosic biomass include cellulases, endo-1–4 β-xylanases, β-xylosidases, α-1,3 arabinosidases, α-1,2 glucuronosidases, mannanases and acetylesterases. Organisms have evolved this group of enzymes specifically to enhance their ability to infect plants. Plants in response have evolved resistances to these pathogens based in part on alterations in their cell wall.

Cellulases

The most extensively studied enzymatic hydrolysis process is the breakdown of cellulose by a group of enzymes collectively termed cellulases. This term is deceiving as there is not one single enzyme capable of breaking down cellulose to glucose. Cellulose breakdown is accomplished by the concerted action of a number of enzymes with endocellulolytic and exocellulolytic activities (Figure 3). There are three distinct enzymatic activities required for the hydrolysis of cellulose to glucose. These include a β 1,4 glucan glucoanohydrolyase which has endocellulase activity, a β 1,4 glucan cellobiohydrolyase which has exocellulase activity and a β-glucosidase which cleaves

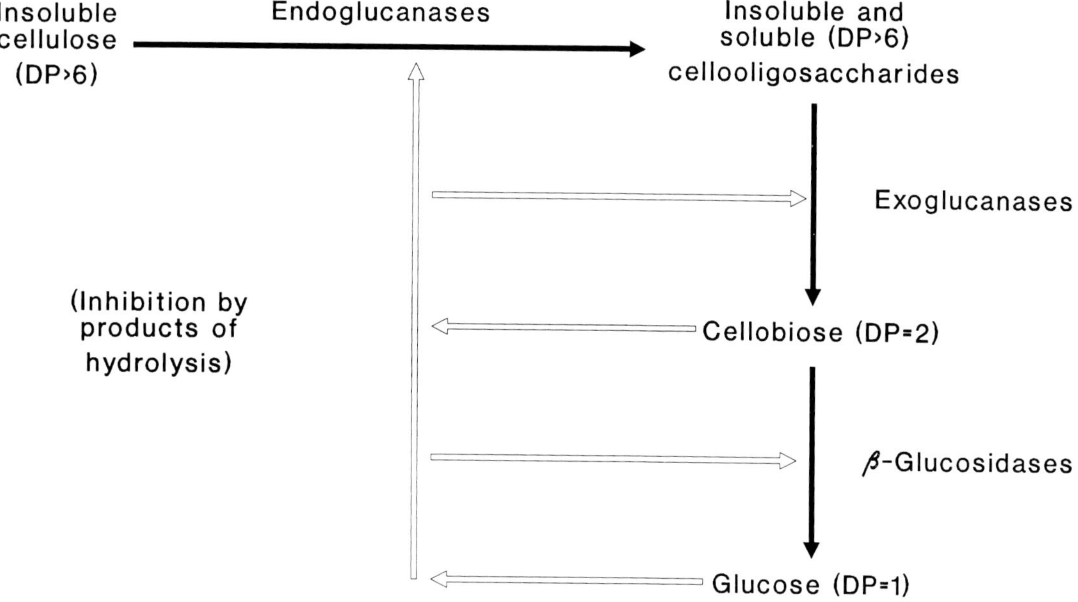

Figure 3. Mode of action of cellulase. Adapted from Fiechter, A. *Advances in biochemical engineering/biotechnology*. 1989. NY: Springer-Verlag, p. 8.

cellobiose to glucose. The specificities of these enzymes have been investigated on a variety of substrates, including cotton, Avicel, CM-cellulose, filter paper and cellobiose. Each substrate differs with respect to its degree of polymerization and hence its sensitivity to hydrolysis. As cellulosic biomass in nature is mainly crystalline, the rate of hydrolysis observed for the enzyme preparations on these other substrates is much higher than for crystalline cellulose.

The hydrolysis of cellulose begins with a random internal attack by the endoglucanase to disrupt the crosslinking and to create new polymer ends accessible to the exocellulase. This also solubilizes the substrate by reducing intrachain hydrogen bonding. The cellobiohydrolase attacks the nonreducing end of cellulose and generates cellobiose with some higher molecular weight oligosaccharides. Finally, the β-glucosidase completes the breakdown process by generating glucose monomers.

In most cases the production and/or activity of cellulases are inhibited by their respective hydrolysis products. This feedback inhibition limits either the amount of enzyme produced or its activity in an attempt on the part of the organism to conserve energy when sufficient glucose is present. This regulatory system, unfortunately, is not amenable to the biotechnologist's desire to produce copious amounts of enzyme. The solution is either to isolate mutations which eliminate this regulatory control or to remove the genes coding for these cellulases and to express them in the absence of these regulatory checks (see further).

It is common to find a large number of cellulases with distinct biochemical and catalytic properties within a single bacterium or fungus. The multiple activities observed are indicative of the synergism in the cellulase systems. The efficient hydrolysis of crystalline cellulose requires an orchestrated attack by a number of enzymes, each balanced to avoid an accumulation of intermediates which might inhibit activity. A number of biochemical, immunological and electron microscopic studies have supported the concept that these cellulases are present in a complex, termed the "cellulosome". These cellulosomes may consist of more than 14–18 proteins and reach a total molecular weight of 2,000–4,000 kDa. The cellulosome appears to have a high affinity for cellulose and therefore facilitates the localization of the various cellulase activities. Microscopic studies on bacterial cellulosomes reveal a protuberance extending from the exterior of the cell surface.

A number of bacteria and fungi produce cellulases with a wide range of activities. Perhaps the most thoroughly characterized system is *Trichoderma reesei*, a fungus which was first isolated in the 1950s. It contains a fairly active cellulase system but, as mentioned previously, this organism regulates its own cellulolytic activity. Before the age of recombinant DNA technology, a sequence of mutagenesis and selection routines was carried out to enhance the cellulase activity in *T. reesei*. The genealogy of these events is presented in Figure 4. The wild-type *T. reesei* strain was first isolated at the United States Army Natick Laboratory. After either irradiation or chemical mutagenesis of this strain a number of mutants were isolated which possess enhanced cellulase and xylanase activities. The final isolate was not only a hyperproducing strain but was also not subject to catabolite repression. Similar strategies can and have been applied to a number of other cellulolytic organisms with varying success.

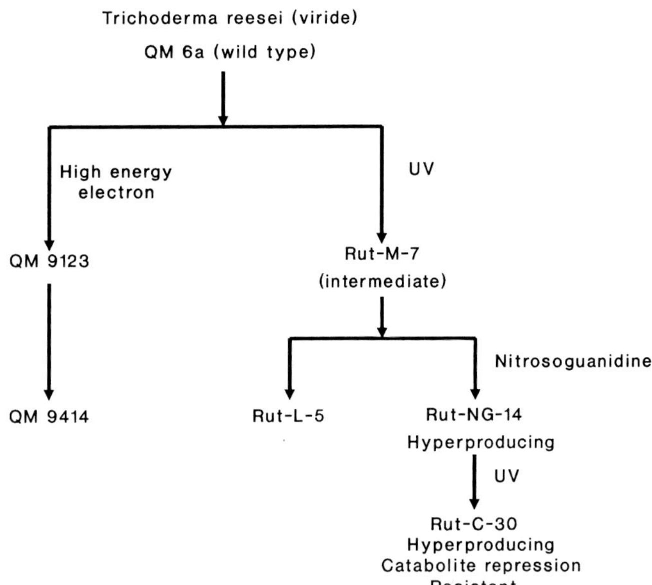

Figure 4. Geneology of high yielding cellulase *T. reesei* mutants. Adapted from Fiechter, A. *Advances in biochemical engineering/ biotechnology*. 1989. NY: Springer-Verlag, p. 4.

The limitations are the number and complexity of the regulatory circuits controlling cellulase synthesis and activity. The stability of the resulting mutants must also be considered. Since these regulatory systems have evolved to maximize energy efficiency, unregulated mutants tend to be less competitive in culture in the absence of selection. Hence, any reversion events which reinstate these regulatory circuits result in a more energetically efficient organism that will quickly dominate the population.

The genes coding for a large number of cellulases have been cloned from both bacteria and fungi. The identification of genes from fungal sources by making gene libraries in a prokaryote (i.e. *Escherichia coli*) is complicated by the presence of introns which are not spliced out in the bacterial host. It is therefore not possible to screen by direct activity assays in *E. coli* an *E. coli* gene bank constructed from genomic fungal DNA for a cellulase gene. In most cases, however, genes from a diverse array of bacteria are expressed directly in *E. coli* and surprisingly secreted via their own signal sequences.

The genes coding for most of the cellulase activities present in *T. reesei* have been cloned and characterized. These include the 1,4-β-D-glucan cellobiohydrolase (CBHI) and the endo-1,4-β-D-glucanase (EGI). Both were cloned into *E. coli* from cDNA libraries constructed from mRNA isolated from *T. reesei*. The mRNA was hybrid selected, taking advantage of the selective induction of cellulase transcription in *T. reesei*. By subtractive hybridization with mRNA isolated from an uninduced culture (glucose grown) of *T. reesei*, the population of mRNA could be enriched for transcription products induced by growth on cellulose. The enriched mRNA fraction was then further enriched by translation and immunoprecipitation with antibodies raised against the selected cellulase. The cDNA synthesized from this enriched, selected population was in turn used to probe genomic libraries for the cellulase gene. Since genomic cellulase genes from a eukaryote are not correctly translated into active proteins in *E. coli*, additional proof of their identity is achieved by determining the nucleotide sequence of the genes. Final confirmation is usually gathered by determining the amino acid sequences for the purified cellulase proteins and comparing them to the amino acid sequences deduced from the nucleotide sequences of the cloned DNA. The nucleotide sequences also provide the information necessary to make genetic constructs for expression in a heterologous host that might not recognize the native transcriptional or translational signals (see further).

The cellulases from thermophilic bacteria have also been extensively examined. Among them, *Clostridium thermocellum* is perhaps the most extensively characterized thermophilic, anaerobic, cellulose-degrading organism. Interest in thermophilic bacteria lies in the belief that enzymes isolated from them will have superior thermostability and hence will have longer half-lives at high temperatures. Although this is not always the case, the cellulases isolated from *C. thermocellum* have very high specific activities, especially against crystalline forms of cellulose that have proven resistant to other cellulase preparations.

The genes coding for a number of prokaryotic cellulases genes have been cloned and characterized. These include genes from *C. thermocellum*, *Cellulomonas fimi*, *Bacillus* sp. and *Thermomonospora fusca*. In almost all cases the cellulase genes were identified by direct screening for activity of gene banks constructed in *E. coli*. Cellulase activity can be detected on an agar plate by incorporating cellulose and allowing the bacterial colonies to grow on the surface. The agar plate is then flooded with a Congo Red dye which, when washed with a saline solution, gives a red color in the presence of cellulose. Colonies that possess an enzyme activity which degrades cellulose surrounding the colony have a clear zone whose diameter is proportional to the activity. Gene banks can be constructed in *E. coli* using either a plasmid, cosmid or a bacteriophage vector for carrying the fragments of foreign DNA. In a similar manner, β-glucosidase genes can be screened using agar plates containing esculin. Upon hydrolysis of the indicator, a black color is deposited around the colony, suggesting the presence of β-glucosidase activity.

The genes coding for nine different cellulase genes have been cloned from *C. thermocellum*. These genes are scattered throughout the chromosome and do not appear to cluster in classical operons. Differences in the level of expression of these cellulases suggest some sort of global regulation which would be advantageous given the need to have each individual activity in the correct proportion for maximum hydrolysis.

As the nucleotide sequences (and hence the translated amino acid sequence of the resulting protein) for an assortment of cellulases are collected, interesting questions can be asked concerning their homology on an amino acid level. Although one would expect that the nucleotide sequence would drift depending upon the preferred codon usage of a particular host organism, some similarity would be predicted on an amino acid level. Curiously, there is only a limited degree of sequence homology when a number of organisms are compared. One observation that has been made is that a given cellulase from one organism might be more homologous to a cellulase from a completely different organism than to a different cellulase isolated from the same organisms. A similarity in amino acid sequence can be observed between cellulases isolated from bacteria and those found in plants, i.e. the avocado. These observations have suggested that either subtle yet important differences in the spectrum of activity of cellulases are evolutionarily conserved in the amino sequences or that genetic scavenging has used by bacteria to collect a number of different cellulases.

One engaging sidelight of the current studies of cellulases is the use of these cellulose-binding domains for immobilization of chimeric enzymes. The extensive structure/function studies on the *Cellulomonas fimi* cellulases revealed specific regions of the protein whose function appears to be binding of the enzyme to cellulose substrate. This cellulose-binding domain could be removed via *in vitro* genetic techniques and still retain its ability to bind to cellulose. When the cellulose-binding domain of the *C. fimi* exoglucanase protein is genetically fused to the β-glucosidase from *Agrobacterium*, the resulting protein chimera can be immobilized via its affinity to cellulose. There are a number of potential applications for this technology, specifically with regard to the site-specific immobilization of enzymes using cellulose as a relative inexpensive support.

One of the common features observed for all enzymes which hydrolyze biomass substrates is that they are secreted from the producing organism. The requirement that these enzymes be secreted is obvious; the biomass substrates in their native form are too large to pass directly through the cell wall and membrane, necessitating their extracellular hydrolysis before being catabolized. All of the enzymes studied to date contain the requisite signal sequences which directs their secretion. As described later, these signal sequences are remarkably universal and promote secretion in a number of heterologous systems. All cellulase genes reported hitherto possess a signal sequence at the beginning of the coding region which functions to direct the translated peptide out of the cell. Since the signals are cleaved off during the secretion process, their presence could not be easily confirmed before the genes coding for these proteins were cloned and sequenced. Translation of the nucleotide sequences from the amino terminals of the coding regions revealed the signal peptides and allowed their sequences to be compared. All are approximately 10–25 amino acids in length and are predominantly hydrophobic. Although the secretion mechanism is not completely understood, it appears that the signal assists in orienting the protein toward the membrane. There is an array of associated proteins within the membrane that functions to secrete the proteins and concurrently remove the signal sequences.

Secretion of heterologous cellulases has been observed even when fungal cellulases are introduced into bacteria. It appears that the basic features of a signal sequence are universal and can function in a diverse array of hosts. Attempts to capitalize on this observation by fusing the signal sequence from a secreted protein to a cytoplasmic protein to effect its secretion have not been always successful. It now appears that there are certain features inherent in the body of the protein beyond the signal that are important for secretion.

Xylanases

Hemicellulose, consisting primarily of xylan, can be hydrolyzed by an enzyme xylanase which is found in both bacteria and fungi. The enzymes from various microbial sources have not been studied as extensively as the cellulases and information to date suggests that they are very similar to the enzymes which degrade cellulose. This is not unexpected as the two substrates are intimately associated and the coevolution of these enzymes would be obligatory for synergistic reasons. Xylanases are either endo-, β1–4-D-xylan xylanohydrolase or exo-, β-xylosidase. In certain cases enzymes are incorrectly classified as xylanases since their activity toward xylan is not their predominant function. It is of course possible that minor contaminants in enzyme preparations might be responsible for low level xylanase activities. There are, however, certain enzymes that truly hydrolyze two very different substrates; for example, the enzyme from *Trichoderma viride* has activity against both carboxymethylcellulose and xylan.

Xylanases are found in cellulolytic organisms but not all organisms capable of degrading cellulose can degrade xylan. Fungi, including a number of *Trichoderma* sp. and *Aspergillus*, contain xylanases while the bacterial sources include *Streptomyces*, *Bacillus* and *Clostridium*. As observed for the cellulases, most organisms possess several xylanase activities. These might be a reflection of the heterogeneity of the xylan linkages requiring enzymes with subtle differences in activity for complete degradation. Only some xylanases can release the arabinosyl substituents of xylan. Similarly, all xylanases are secreted, implying the presence of signal sequence in the proenzyme.

The number of xylanase genes which have been cloned and characterized is not as extensive as reported for the cellulases. They include the genes from *B. subtilis*, *B. pumilis*, *Aeromonas*, *Cryptococcus*, *Streptomyces lividans*, *Clostridium* and *Ruminococcus*. The multiplicity observed in the xylanase activities for a single microorganism can be verified as a function of multiple genes. Although there appears to be extensive posttranslational modification of xylanase, the diversity is principally a result of multiple genes.

In practice, enzymatic hydrolysis of xylan is not the method of choice since it can, as mentioned previously, be broken down by mild alkali treatment. There is, however, some benefit in the use of xylanase for biopulping of paper.

Ligninases

With the exception of the fungi, lignin is not easily degraded by most microorganisms. More specifically, the white-rot fungi are the only organisms which can efficiently degrade it due to their complement of ligninases, cellulases and hemicellulases. White-rot fungi belong to the class *Basidomycetes* and can be observed growing in most forests on fallen logs or tree stumps. Unfortunately, most white-rot fungi do not grow rapidly and hence do not compete well in scaled-up biological hydrolysis processes. Most of them grow well only in solid-state fermentation which is not amenable to a continuous process.

The term "ligninase" is used to refer to all enzymes which degrade lignin. The biodegradation of lignin is carried out by lignin peroxidases, aryl methoxyl demethylase, phenol oxidases and others. An extracellular hydrogen peroxide-dependent lignin degrading enzyme from *Phanerochaete chrysosporium* has been purified and characterized. The ligninase is a heme-containing protein that is also glycosylated. It is one of perhaps 15 extracellular enzymes produced by this organism. Since the enzyme's activity is dependent upon hydrogen peroxide, the production of that compound is also an important consideration. It would seem unlikely that a cell free system to degrade lignin is feasible given the complexity of the enzymatic hydrolysis and the cofactor requirements that would necessitate continual regeneration.

Amylases

Starch can be hydrolyzed into glucose by a single enzymes, amylase. As noted for cellulases, amylases are produced by a variety of bacteria, yeast, fungi and plants. The bacteria include a number of bacilli, *Bacillus amyloliquefaciens*, *B. stearothermophilus* and *B. licheniformis*. The fungi include *Aspergillus oryzae*, *As. awamori* and *Trichoderma viride*. There is at least one strain of yeast, *Schwanniomyces alluvius* that can directly catabolize starch and produce ethanol.

Genes coding for amylases have been identified in *Aspergillus*, *Bacillus*, and *Clostridium*. Those directly expressible in *E. coli* can be identified by plating into agar medium containing starch and then flooding the plates with iodine. Thus recombinant colonies that produce amylase display a clear zone indicating the hydrolysis of the starch.

The degradation of starch requires amylases with both endo- and exolytic activities. Bacterial α-amylases are usually able to hydrolyze starch molecules internally but cannot attack the α-1,6 bonds of amylopectin. The glucoamylases found in fungi are capable of degrading starch from the nonreducing end and are also able to hydrolyze α-1,6 linkages. Typically, a process to hydrolyze starch to glucose includes the sequential addition of α-amylases and glucoamylases (Figure 5). Between each addition the reaction conditions, especially pH, are altered to the optimal for the given enzyme. Heat stable enzymes are favored since the hydrolysis can be made to proceed more rapidly by running the reactions at higher temperatures (60°C). The progress of hydrolysis is followed by the release of glucose in 'dextrose equivalent' of DE units.

In any enzymatic process the basic issue is to hydrolyze the substrate to its component monomers without appreciable loss to the microbial system used for hydrolysis. The most obvious solution is to employ enzyme preparations free from any viable microbial cells which might consume the hydrolysis products. This approach is, however, far more expensive than using cell cultures directly since the cost of purification must be factored in. Furthermore, during purification some activity may be lost and the hydrolysis rate reduced commensurately. This is frequently observed with cellulase preparations where, as noted earlier, a proper balance of both exo and endo activities are required in a synergistic fashion. Finally, purified enzyme preparations are invariably less stable than intact cell cultures. The instability of the enzymes is probably a reflection of the evolution of these enzyme systems. There is little benefit for the producing organism to synthesize an very stable enzyme that will outlive the producing organism and provide utilizable substrate to the nonproducing flora that occupy the same ecological niche.

INTEGRATED PROCESSES FOR BIOMASS HYDROLYSIS

The individual processes for either physical, chemical or enzymatic hydrolysis of biomass have been discussed. There are clear advantages to combining different methods to enhance the rate and extent of hydrolysis. Usually a physical or chemical treatment of the biomass is carried out to expose the cellulose and hemicellulose. Although intact cellulose can be directly hydrolyzed using enzymes alone, the cost-benefit ratio is not economically favorable.

One of the most extensively studied processes is the Techtrol/Iotech process for biomass hydrolysis (Figure 6). Initially, the biomass is steam exploded to release the cellulose/hemicellulose from the lignin. The lignin is not extensively degraded and can be recovered as a byproduct. The hemicellulose is solubilized and is removed from the mixture by water washing. Cellulases for hydrolysis of the cellulose are produced in a separate bioreactor and added to the steam exploded material. Hydrolysis of the cellulose to glucose renders it soluble leaving the lignin as the only insoluble

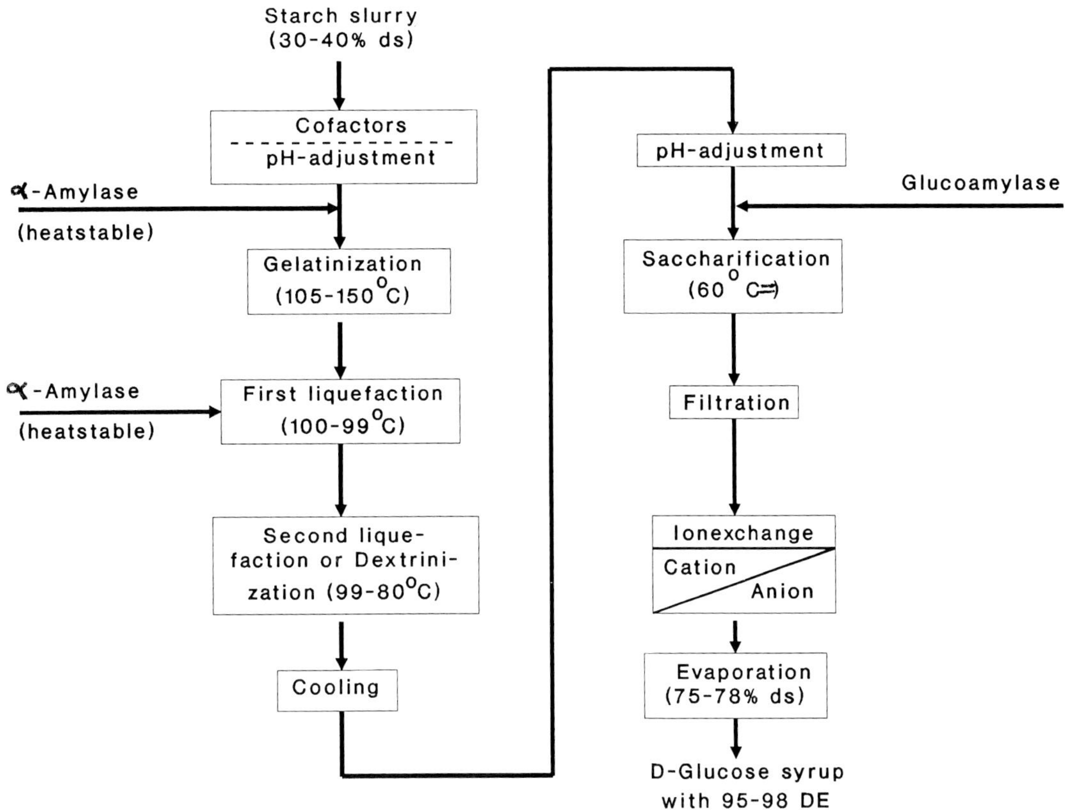

Figure 5. Glucose production by enzymatic starch conversion.

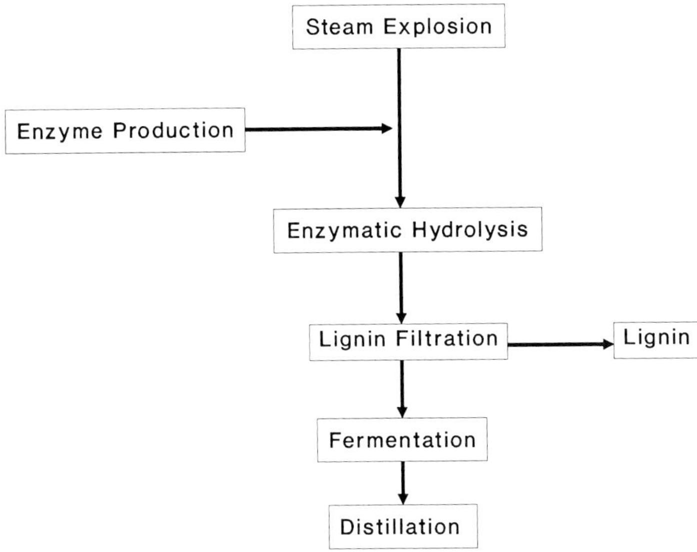

Figure 6. Techtrol/Iotech process flow diagram.

component which can then be removed by filtration. The liberated glucose can then be used as a substrate for any one of a number of fermentation products, as described later.

Another process which relies more intensively on enzymatic hydrolysis is the Natick process (Figure 7). Cellulases are used to hydrolyze the cellulose after milling, which functions to increase the surface area accessible to enzyme attack. The cellulase preparation used is obtained from *T. reesei* and is produced in a separate reactor. The glucose solution is recovered at a 10% concentration and then fed into a fermentation to produce ethanol. The system as configured can handle approximately 50 million kg of substrate per year and yields approximately 2.5 million gallons of ethanol.

The production of enzymes for lignocellulose hydrolysis requires a substrate for the growth of the cellulolytic organisms and most of these enzymes are produced only when the microbes are grown on cellulosic materials. Therefore a fraction of the incoming biomass after physical pretreatment must be diverted for enzyme production (Figure 8). In path A the enzymes produced in a separate reaction vessel are separated and partially purified before their addition to the balance of the lignocellulose. This is exemplified by the Natick process. However, there is a cost incurred in the enzyme recovery step. Furthermore, since the enzyme complex tends to associate with the cellulosic material, some of it is lost during the recovery process. The addition of the broth from the enzyme production step without any purification circumvents this problem (path B). The disadvantage is that the cellulolytic organism is now present in the fermentation vessel and competes for the hydrolyzed substrate. The conditions during the

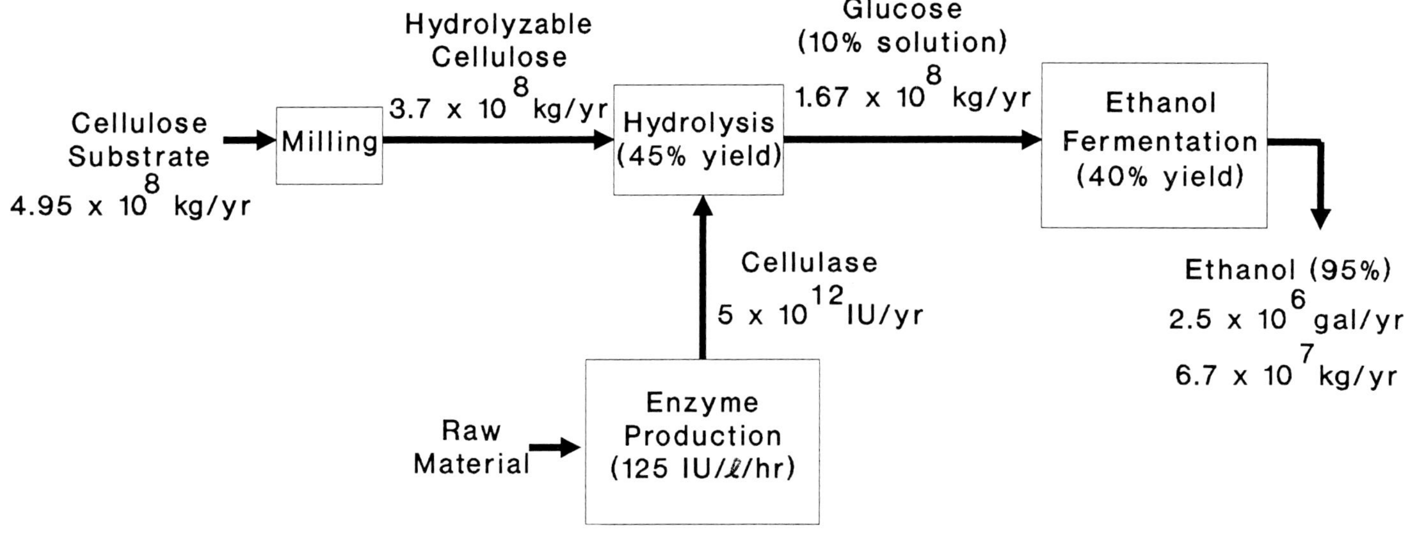

Figure 7. Natick Process. Adapted from Wilke, C.R. *et al. Enzymatic hydrolysis of cellulose.* 1983. Park Ridge, NJ: Noyes Data Corporation, p. 65.

Cellulase fermentation
Enzyme recovery
or
A
Delignification
Enzymatic hydrolysis
Ethanol fermentation
Pentose fermentation
Ethanol recovery
Ethanol
Lignin
Heat
Combustion
Cellulase fermentation
Cellulosic biomass
Size reduction and pretreatment
B
Hydrolysis reactor
Ethanol recovery
Ethanol
Heat
Combustion
Lignin
C
Direct fermentation of cellulosic biomass
Ethanol recovery
Ethanol
Heat
Combustion
Lignin

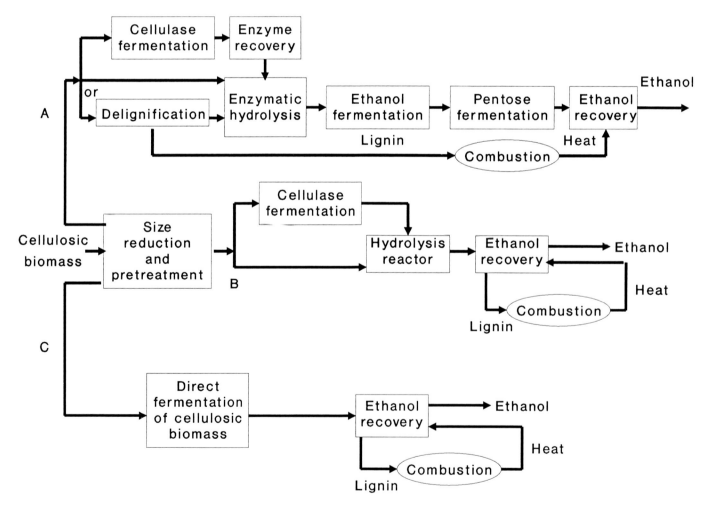

Figure 8. Alternative schemes for enzymatic hydrolysis of cellulosic biomass for ethanol production. Courtesy of A.J. Sinskey, MIT.

fermentation step to produce ethanol would be designed to enhance the performance of the ethanol producer. In the final approach (path C) the hydrolysis and fermentation are simultaneous, and this is described below. In all cases described the lignin is recovered and combusted to generate heat for the recovery of ethanol by distillation.

DEVELOPMENT OF SINGLE STEP CONVERSION PROCESSES

The economics of biomass utilization for the manufacture of biotechnological products might benefit from the development of single step conversion processes. The goal is to engineer the microbial system used for production of the desired product to hydrolyze directly the biomass substrate with as minimal a pretreatment as possible. Because the individual steps in the process are usually optimal under distinctively different conditions, some compromise is necessitated. The basic problem has long been that most of the microorganisms favored for the production of the desired product are usually unable to metabolize these substrates or at best do so inefficiently. A frequently cited example is the yeast *Saccharomyces cerevisiae* which is very adept at producing ethanol but feeble at hydrolyzing most polymeric carbon source substrates. The advent of recombinant DNA technology has provided the tools for potentially altering the metabolic pathways of these organisms. In practice, however, what appears facile as a "paper biochemistry" exercise is usually far more complicated or even impossible.

The now classic approach to engineer an organism to hydrolyze a substrate that it does not normally degrade is to introduce the genetic information from an organism that does possess the desired activities. We have already observed that, the genes coding for a wide variety of cellulases, xylanase and amylases have been isolated and characterized from bacteria, yeast and fungi. When the host is similar to the organism from which the gene(s) have been isolated, there is a high probability that the native promoter and regulatory sequences will function appropriately. For example, the cellulase genes from *Cellulomonas fimi* are expressed and secreted in *E. coli*. In contrast, the amylase gene from *Clostridium thermocellum* would not be expressed properly in a eukaryote (e.g. *S. cerevisiae*).

High level expression of a given gene product is dependent upon two potentially rate-limiting steps, transcription and translation. In prokaryotes, the process of transcription is mediated by a RNA polymerase and the rate of transcription depends in part on the affinity of the RNA polymerase for the promoter sequence and the type of RNA polymerase that is bound. The key components of the promoter are the −35 and −10 sequences which appear to be the points of contact with the RNA polymerasse. The binding of the RNA polymerase to the promoter is a function not only of the nucleotide sequence but also of the spatial positioning within the promoter. Promoter sequences capable of high level expression in *E. coli* including the *tac* and the *omp*F promoters are extremely well defined. High level transcription of a target gene is usually straightforward and involves positioning the promoter at an appropriate distance from the start of the coding sequence. This however does not always lead to a high level of product formation. In several cases, although abundant mRNA transcripts are found, the amount of protein produced is limited by translational difficulties.

The second step, translation is not as well understood and the important sequences required upstream of the coding region are not always predictable. It is apparent that the interaction between the ribosome and the ribosome binding site (RBS) on the mRNA is mediated by the homology between the 16S rRNA and the RBS. Efficient translation is therefore in part a function of the placing of the appropriate RBS sequence within the optimum distance from the start of the coding region. The intervening sequences between the RBS and the start codon as well as the sequence after the start codon all influence the level of translation. In certain cases, the structures formed by the hydrogen bonding between the ribonucleotides at the end of the mRNA transcript inhibit its ability to be translated.

One must also take editing into consideration when the genes from a eukaryote, e.g. from *T. reesei*, are introduced into a prokaryote. Since the *T. reesei* genes contain introns which cannot be properly excised by a prokaryotic host, there is absolutely no chance that a functional enzyme can be produced.

Finally, since cellulose hydrolysis requires the synergistic action of a number of enzymes in the appropriate stoichometry, the simple expression of a single cellulase in a selected recombinant organism will not yield an organism capable of cellulose digestion.

The *T. reesei* EGI and EGIII enzymes have been expressed in *S. cerevisiae* using promoters derived from the yeast phosphoglycerate kinase gene to drive the cDNA genes. Endo-β-1,4 glucosidase activity was detected using carboxymethylcellulose as a substrate and the enzyme activity is secreted. Both the enzyme produced in *T. reesei* and that produced by recombinant *S. cerevisiae* carrying the EGI or EGIII gene were glycosylated although some qualitative differences in the pattern were observed. These differences in glycosylation do not affect activity of the enzyme and may impart a greater level of thermostability to the *S. cerevisiae*-produced enzyme. Similarly, the *C. fimi* endo-1,4-β-glucanase has been successfully expressed in *S. cerevisiae* with a yeast alcohol dehydrogenase promoter and the K1 toxin secretion signal. Again activity could be detected in the culture medium using carboxymethylcellulose as a substrate. Finally, the *C. thermocellum* endoglucanase A has been expressed in *S. cerevisiae* using the yeast promoter and signal sequence for the mating factor, MFα1 gene. Although they have β-glucosidase activity, these yeast strains are not capable of cellulose degradation due to the absence of the complementary enzyme activities. Addition of these other cellulase activities will undoubtedly complicate the genetic manipulation especially in respect of efforts to achieve balanced synthesis of each enzyme.

The fermentation of pentose sugars obtained by the hydrolysis of hemicellulosic biomass has also received considerable attention. Even when the monomeric substrate is available, *S. cerevisiae*, the yeast used most often for ethanol production, cannot ferment pentose sugars. The defect limiting the ability of *S. cerevisiae* to catabolize the principal pentose sugar, xylose, appears to be a failure to properly balance cofactors required for the initial metabolic steps. In eukaryotes, xylose is transported into the cell via a permease. The first step is a reduction reaction involving the enzyme xylose reductase and the cofactor NADPH to yield $NADP^+$ and xylitol (Figure 9). Xylitol is then metabolized to xylulose by xylitol dehydrogenase and NAD^+. Since the first reaction consumes NADPH and the second reaction generates NADH, the cofactors are not balanced and the latter accumulates. Most organisms regenerate NAD^+ from NADH via electron transport oxidation, a reaction sequence that is not very efficient in *S. cerevisiae* during microaerobic fermentation conditions. It is for this reason that *S. cerevisiae* produces copious amounts of ethanol. Clearly, the metabolism of xylose is diametrically opposed to the production of ethanol as an end product. There are several yeasts which can ferment pentose to ethanol, including *Pachysolen tannophilus*, *Pichia stipitis* and *Candida shehtae*. The major drawback of these strains is that they do not produce copious amounts of ethanol and there is no historical precedence for their use in the fermentation industry.

In prokaryotes, the initial step in the conversion of xylose to xylulose is carried out by a single enzyme, xylose isomerase. No cofactors are required for this enzyme, and it has been isolated and characterized from a number of bacteria, including *Lactobacillus brevis*, *Streptomyces rubiginosus*, *Bacillus coagulans*, *E. coli* and *Actinoplanes missouriensis*. Furthermore,

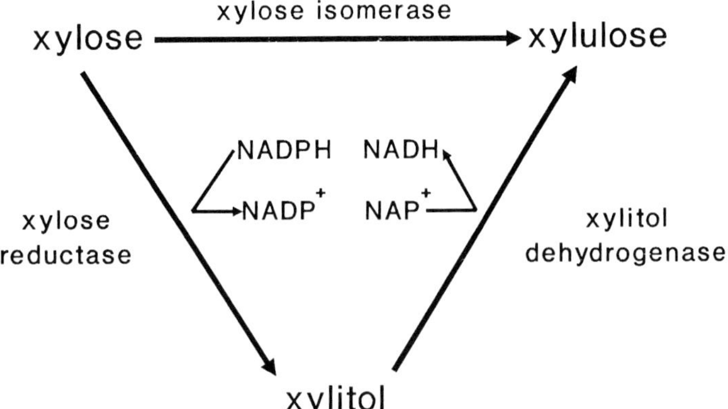

Figure 9. Two pathways for the conversion of xylose.

the genes coding for a number of these xylose isomerases have been cloned and sequenced.

It would seem that the most obvious route to a strain of *S. cerevisiae* able to ferment xylose to ethanol would be to introduce a gene coding for the prokaryotic xylose isomerase. Although the strategy is in theory sound, despite several independent attempts an active xylose isomerase is in practice not produced. There is ample evidence for the expression of the enzyme in *S. cerevisiae* cells carrying the xylose isomerase gene, but no activity has been observed. The problem probably lies in the folding of the polypeptide into the appropriate conformation to yield an active enzyme. It represents one of the pitfalls of molecular biology; we have become very adept at the genetic engineering routes to solve a given problem but cannot predict *a priori* the unknown complications that may arise.

The development of yeast strains to degrade and ferment starch has met with more direct success than efforts with cellulose and hemicellulose. This is partly because soluble starch can be degraded by glucoamylase alone. Therefore, the introduction and expression of a single gene can transform a strain of *S. cerevisiae* into an organism capable of degrading starch. The *Aspergillus awamori* cDNA coding for glycoamylase has been expressed in *S. cerevisiae* using the yeast enolase promoter but the native glucoamylase signal sequence. This single strain could under the conditions tested (25% soluble cornstarch) degrade approximately 95% of the soluble starch and produce 118 g/l ethanol after a 12 day fermentation.

As an alternative to engineering a single organism which can hydrolyze and ferment the biomass without extensive pretreatment, co-cultivation with either two (or more) organisms or an organism and an enzyme preparation is feasible. The ecological communities found in nature to degrade biomass rarely consist of a single organism but more likely a mixed, heterogenous population. Mixed populations are more efficient at hydrolyzing biomass since they usually do not accumulate any intermediates which might feedback repress the initial hydrolytic reactions. The major problem is that these populations are adapted to degrading biomass for their own purposes and do not usually amass a high concentration of a substrate useful for any subsequent biotechnological fermentation.

It is often difficult to identify every member of a given ecological niche and then reconstruct the population from isolated cultivated members. The traditional microbiological methods of agar plate cultivation requires that every member of the population is capable of growth on the selected medium under the selected conditions. In the past the members of a given community were identified on the basis of their growth on microbiological medium. Now, with advent of DNA probes for detection of microorganisms without the need for cultivation, the true extent of these populations are being reinvestigated. The factors to be considered in reconstituting a population include not only the types of organisms but also their relative numbers. Furthermore, even if the initial balance of all community members can be established, the continued dynamic equilibrium is difficult to maintain. Natural communities do not usually degrade biomass at a rate that is satisfactory for most biotechnological processes. Attempts by biotechnologists to increase their rates of hydrolysis are frequently disastrous.

It is also feasible to achieve biomass conversion by culturing a given microorganism with either a purified or partially purified enzyme preparation. This is advantageous in that the step carried out by the enzyme preparation can be more easily controlled. In addition, the other metabolic reactions usually carried out by the organism which is the source of the enzyme preparation are eliminated. The enzyme preparation need not be purified and, in selected cases, dead cells can be employed. The key to the success of this approach is the balance between the activity of the enzyme preparation and the population of organisms. Examples of this approach include the addition of cellulases to yeast fermentations to facilitate the conversion of cellulose. Another is the addition of exogenous xylose (glucose) isomerase to cultures of *S. cerevisiae* to effect the catabolism of pentose sugars. In the latter the xylose is isomerized to xylulose, which is then taken up by the yeast and further metabolized to xylulose. The xylulose, which is an inhibitor of the isomerase, is quickly removed from the medium by the yeast. A number of environmental conditions must be compromised including temperature, pH and ionic strength. Most cellulases operate at higher temperatures relative to the yeast *S. cerevisiae*. Therefore, consideration has been paid toward the more thermophilic yeast, *Schizosaccharomyces pombe*, which can grow and produce ethanol at 40°C.

If the system is to be operated on a continuous basis, the enzyme preparation needs to be immobilized to retard its loss from the system. In contrast to the organism, the enzyme does not proliferate to maintain itself in the bioreactor. Immobilization of either whole cells or enzymes favors their retention and/or recovery from the fermentation broth. A complete treatise on immobilization is beyond the scope of this chapter and will be addressed elsewhere (see Chapters 17 and 18). Obviously, the major consideration in selecting the immobilization system is that the enzyme retains maximal activity. This problem arises from the conformational defects imposed in the enzyme structure by the immobilization process. Furthermore, especially for biomass conversion where the substrates are large molecular weight molecules, steric hindrances caused by the immobilization matrix are potentially encountered.

Beyond the advantages of immobilization with respect to the retention/recovery of the enzyme, immobilization localizes the enzyme activity. In principle the cellulosome function is to direct the various cellulase activities at a single point on the substrate in a manner similar to immobilization. The reaction rate is therefore a function of the interactions of the entire enzyme complex rather than limited by the sum of the substrate enzyme interactions for each individual component. Given the current technology is it not possible to arrange the various cellulase activities in the appropriate matrix to attain maximum activity. Presumably the cellulosome has evolved to organize the different enzymes in the appropriate arrangement that is optimal to degrade intact cellulose.

Systems to co-immobilize a hydrolytic enzyme with a whole cell have been developed. They have the advantage of retaining the enzyme in the system as noted for simple immobilization of enzymes alone (Figure 10). Furthermore, by maintaining a close proximity between the enzyme and the cell destined to consume the product of the enzyme, diffusion of the product into the bulk medium is reduced. This serves to eliminate any limitation in the overall fermentation rate that might be encountered due to the diffusion of the hydrolytic product. In addition, the product is quickly consumed from the system by the fermenting cell and does not accumulate to inhibit the hydrolytic enzyme.

Co-immobilization can be accomplished by either co-entrapment of the enzyme and the cell in the same matrix or by directly attaching the enzyme to the cell surface. Co-entrapment using polymeric materials is difficult due to the distinct size difference between the enzyme and the cell. If a matrix with too large a pore size is selected, the enzyme can leach out and become lost in the bulk medium. In contrast, a very tight polymer matrix introduces diffusion limits with respect to the subtrate's ability to enter and contact the enzyme. It must be remembered that, especially for biomass material, the initial size of the substrate is very large and does not easily diffuse into most polymer matrices.

The enzyme can also be directly attached to the cell surface using a number of reagents, most notably glutaraldehyde. This reagent is rather nonspecific and has been extensively used to crosslink proteins. Crosslinking with glutaraldehyde invariably leads to cell death which compromises the ability of the cell to carry out its fermentation duties.

ECONOMICS OF BIOMASS AS A SUBSTRATE

There is little doubt that processes can be developed and in fact have been developed to utilize biomass as a subtrate. Beyond an academic exercise, the future of biomass depends upon the economics of the conversion process, whether it be chemical, enzymatic or a combination of both. A number of estimates have been computed based upon existing or potential technologies.

One obvious factor is that, regardless of the process, transportation of the biomass material from its source to the conversion site must be kept to an absolute minimum. For example, an analysis of a process using forage biomass shows

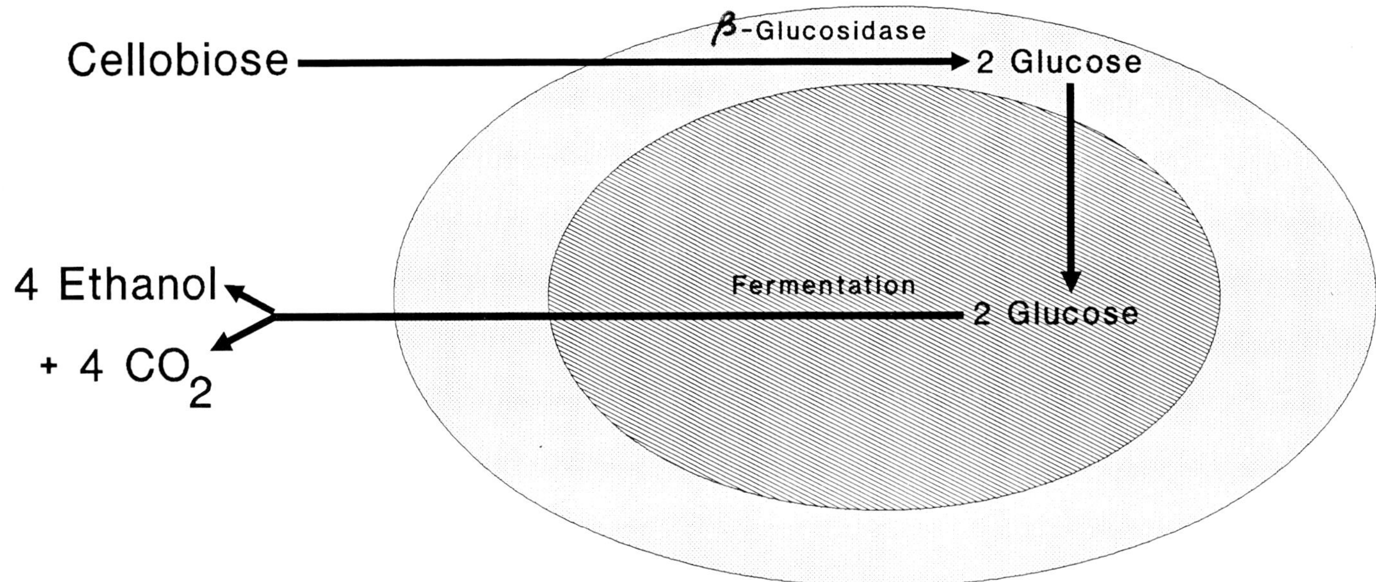

Figure 10. Configuration and reactions of the yeast/β-galactosidase co-immobilizate.

that approximately 35% of the expected energy would be consumed in transporting the substrate a distance of 15 miles. This considerable expenditure of energy simply to transport the starting biomass dictates that any conversion plants be of moderate size and in close proximity to production source.

The current technology clearly favors the use of acid hydrolysis for the conversion of biomass where, for example, the end product is ethanol. There is probably little future improvement that can be realized with acid hydrolysis methods and their cost estimates have therefore reached a minimum. The future of enzymatic hydrolysis is, however, more optimistic given the potential for the existence of new cellulolytic organisms and the prospects for improving existing strains via either classical or recombinant genetics.

Another major consideration is the present usage of the biomass targeted for conversion. Is this biomass a waste byproduct of an existing industrial or agricultural process? In most cases there is an inherent cost associated with the disposal of waste materials. Depending upon the waste material, it may be incinerated, landfilled or recycled, all of which contribute to the cost of the process which generates it. Incineration of biomass generated as a waste byproduct may not be a debit if there is a net energy return. Waste materials from the lumber and paper industry can be used directly as a fuel for firing furnaces obviating the need for petroleum or coal.

The cost of disposing process waste byproducts through a municipal sewage system is a factor of the biological oxygen demand (BOD). The greater the BOD, the more expensive it is to discard. Conversion of this type of biomass, for example starch from a potato processing operation, reduces the BOD significantly and hence the cost of its disposal. Therefore, the economic return from utilizing this waste biomass as a substrate for another process may be economically advantageous when the cost of disposal is factored into the process.

WHAT CAN WE MAKE FROM BIOMASS SUBSTRATES?

The most simplistic answer to the question of what can we make from biomass substrates is that virtually any product can be made from biomass once it is converted into its basic monomeric sugars (as for cellulose and hemicellulose). Commodity chemicals, where a significant cost is attributable to the substrate, are a frequently cited example (Figure 11).

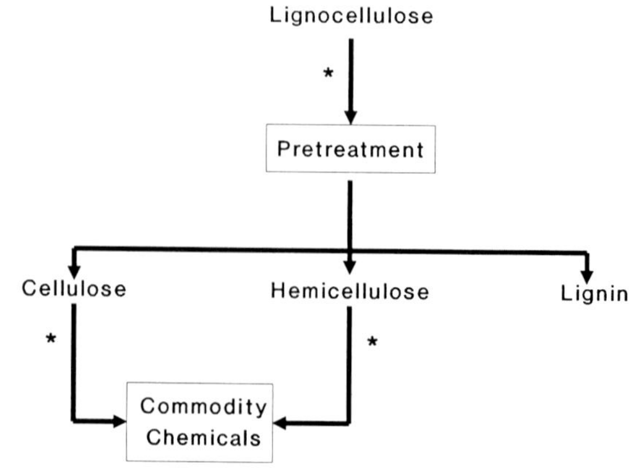

Figure 11. Conversion of biomass to commodity chemicals. Courtesy of A.J. Sinskey, MIT.

Here a significant advantage will be realized if the substrate costs can be reduced by using biomass-derived substrates. It is doubtful that such substrates will be used for producing pharmaceuticals where a high degree of purity is mandated. The purity of a fermentation product is initially dependent upon the contaminants in the starting fermentation broth: with crude biomass substrates the load of contaminants introduced in the system will need to be removed during the subsequent purification of the product. Therefore, for pharmaceuticals any cost benefit achieved by using a biomass-derived substrate will be lost in terms of the additional purification steps.

Lignin is the most difficult component of biomass to degrade, due to its heterogenicity. In fact, lignin may be more valuable in its intact form, as compared to its worth as a substrate after hydrolysis. The utility of lignin is a function of its molecular weight and potential reactivity which are in turn dependent upon the method used to release it from the biomass. The simplest use of lignin is as a solid fuel and a considerable amount of it is combusted to generate steam or other energy. It can also be used as an adhesive, principally for plywood or particle board manufacturing. Here it replaces phenol in phenol formaldehyde thermosetting resins although it has not been extensively employed. Other potential applications include the use of lignin as a surfactant, rubber reinforcer or an asphalt extender. In the latter usage a potential market of 4×10^9 lbs has been estimated.

In the United States, corn is a principal source for starch, which can then be used either directly or as a substrate for fermentation commodity chemicals (Figure 12). Depending upon the weather conditions and other factors, corn yields range from 80–120 bushels per acre. The corn after pretreatment to release the starch can then be hydrolyzed as described earlier, either completely to yield glucose or partially to yield syrups. If the glucose in the starch is completely hydrolyzed and converted exclusively to ethanol, 200–300 gallons of ethanol per acre can be expected. The other components that remain after the starch has been removed are useful as feed additives for both human and animal consumption.

A number of industrial chemicals obtained from fermentation processes can be produced from biomass. They include ethanol, acetic acid, acetone, isopropanol, n-butanol, methanol, vitamins, antibiotics and 2,3 butanediol. Each has a direct usage and can serve as a feedstock chemical for other processes. For example, ethanol can be dehydrated to ethylene and similarly, propanol can be dehydrated to propylene. Furfurals obtained from the acid hydrolysis of pentosans have a market as solvents in the oil industry and elsewhere. Integration of chemical feedstocks derived from biomass would depend not only on the existence of an efficient process

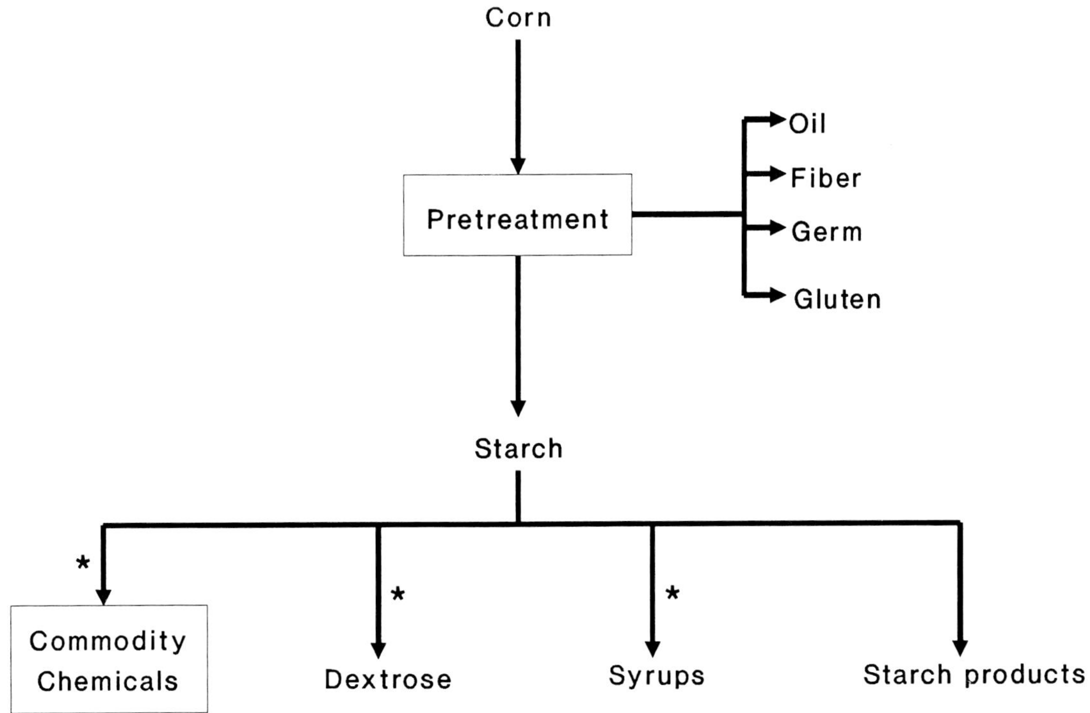

Figure 12. Conversion of biomass to commodity chemicals. Courtesy of A.J. Sinskey, MIT.

for conversion but, as always, the current market value of petroleum-based substrates.

A discussion of the potential products obtained using biomass-derived substrates would not be complete without a mention of single-cell protein for human or animal consumption, an ephemeral target of biotechnologists for the past fifty years. When the need, the market and the technology stabilize for single-cell protein, biomass-derived substrates should certainly be considered for their production.

THE REAL WORLD

The most frequently cited example of a fermentation product which could be (and is) made from a biomass-derived substrate is ethanol. Its primary use is likely to be as an alternative transportation fuel to petroleum. A number of ethanol processes have been developed and subjected to extensive economic scrutiny. Perhaps the most frequently cited and largest volume example is the process to produce ethanol from sugar being used in Brazil. Although this chapter has not intensively reviewed sugar as a biomass substrate, it is still educational to review the history of this process (see also Chapter 16).

The Brazilian ethanol industry was initiated in the mid-1970s during the most severe petroleum shortage, for which the slogan 'the oil crisis' was coined. The decision to invest in ethanol production represented an aggressive attempt to develop an alternative fuel source which, in principle, would be make the country self-sufficient. But the economics of biomass conversion to ethanol are at the mercy of petroleum prices, which fluctuate on a daily basis. Unfortunately, the use of alternative fuels such as ethanol requires a commitment to convert all engines to run on these fuels. In Brazil more than 80% of the cars have been designed or retrofitted to run on ethanol despite some initial performance deficiencies. To foster the use of ethanol, its price was fixed at 65% of the equivalent petroleum product which was feasible before the price of petroleum began to decline in the mid-1980s. Ethanol is made exclusively from the domestic sugar-cane, which has in turn placed a burden on the government to subsidize the sugar-cane farmers. As these subsidies have been reduced the motivation to grow sugar-cane has declined and therefore the feedstock for ethanol has become more costly. Also, as with any agricultural commodity, the climatic variation can effect the yield of sugar-cane in addition to the world price for sugar. Increases in the world price of sugar encourage Brazilian sugar-cane growers to export their crop while poor weather conditions limit the production. Since the owners of ethanol-powered automobiles are committed to using ethanol as a fuel, they are forced to endure any shortages in ethanol.

Editorial Note

The Real World is a hard place as the Brazilians have discovered. In March 1990 "The Economist" reported that all was not well with the ethanol program in Brazil. While more than a third of all cars in that country, and more than three-quarters of all new ones, run on alcohol from sugar-cane, ethanol is now in shorter supply than gasoline. The use of ethanol for cars has not obviated the need for crude oil which has anyway to be imported and refined in order to provide the diesel fuel the country requires for trucks as well as the liquified petroleum gas most households use for cooking. Refining crude oil to make diesel produces gasoline as a by-product; because so many cars are committed to ethanol, Brazil has such a surplus of gasoline it has to find foreign markets in which to sell it. Worse follows: for financial reasons, the government cut subsidies to sugar-cane farmers, who accordingly switched to other products, while rising world sugar prices have encouraged exports. As a consequence ethanol production is expected to fall at least 10% below target. The Brazilian government plans to cover the shortfall by using a fuel blended from 60% ethanol, 7% gasoline and 33% methanol — and will have to import millions of liters of methanol to meet their needs!

FURTHER READING

Bungay, H.R. (1982). *Biomass refining*. Science **218**, 643–646.

Wilke, C.R., Yang, R.D., Sciaamanna, A.F. and Freitas, R.P. (1981). *Raw materials evaluation and process development studies for conversion of biomass to sugars and ethanol*. Biotech. Bioeng. **23**, 163–183.

Parisi, F. (1989). *Advance in lignocellulosics hydrolysis and in the utilization of the hydrolyzates*. Adv. Biochem. Eng. **38**, 53–87.

Chapter 29

Oil Production and Processing

Vivian Moses

INTRODUCTION

Concern with biotechnology among oil producers is mostly confined at the present time to the control of production problems: the damage resulting from the hydrogen sulfide generated under certain conditions by sulfate-reducing bacteria is probably the most important. In recent years, however, a number of proposals have been made for using microorganisms actually to improve the efficiency of oil production from the reservoir; collectively they have often been called *microbial enhanced oil recovery (MEOR)*. Their attractiveness lies in the promise of low cost and simplicity of operation but all are in the development stage and few have been extensively tested in the field. In order to appreciate their significance it is important first to consider what an oil reservoir is like, how oil is recovered from it, what factors limit production and how they might be at least partly overcome. In the account that follows we will outline the technical bases of these microbiological techniques, summarize the information available from field pilots, attempt some analysis of their economic benefits and comment on the attitude of various sectors of the oil industry and others towards them. Note, incidentally, that the biotechnological methods discussed in this chapter are designed to be carried out in environments which are largely uncontrollable and must be accepted in the state in which they currently exist.

Although not without its difficulties, the industry has been hugely successful in prospecting for and producing oil. In spite of its vast experience, the amount of oil economically producible on a worldwide basis from a typical reservoir by present technology nevertheless falls far short of complete recovery. The reasons are many and complex. Some technical limitations to recovery may be overcome by the injection into the reservoir of various chemicals. But those chemicals, produced from petrochemical feedstocks or by microbial fermentation in conventional plants, are themselves so costly, and required in such large quantities, that in most cases setting the expense of using them against the value of the incremental oil to be expected fails to show any clear cost-benefit. It is in this context that interest has arisen in the possibility of employing bacteria injected directly into the rock to produce the chemicals from inexpensive feedstocks, so reducing input costs; the reservoir itself would serve as the fermenter. The problems of doing so are considerable but not insuperable; as will hopefully become clear in the following discussion, a good deal of development work will be required to tailor biological systems optimally to the tasks in hand but revolutionary developments in the biological sciences are not prerequisites. The exercise, indeed, is mainly one of *biological engineering*, adapting biotechnological potential to practical ends under field conditions which often cannot be defined as precisely as the average laboratory scientist would wish.

THE NATURE OF OIL RESERVOIRS

Crude oil is an extremely complex and variable mixture of compounds; some samples are said to contain thousands or tens of thousands of different chemical species. Many are hydrocarbons varying from simple aliphatics and aromatics to complex, multi-ring structures of high molecular weight. Within this range of substances are those which contain sulfur, nitrogen, oxygen and other elements. The proportion of these many components varies widely in different deposits: generally, the higher the content of shorter chain compounds the *lighter* and more mobile the crude. Viscous *heavy* oils, and even more so bitumens, are deficient in the light fractions, possibly reflecting the extent of *in situ* maturation or the result of their loss over geological time by evaporation or microbial action. Some components of crude oil are known to be susceptible to microbiological attack: they tend to be the lower molecular weight materials and an attack on a pure hydrocarbon always seems to require the involvement of molecular oxygen. A few bacterial species may be capable of anaerobic metabolism on compounds containing elements additional to carbon and hydrogen but not, it seems, on pure hydrocarbons. Viscosity is, of course, highly dependent on temperature so that the effective mobility of the crude oil in the reservoir is the result both of its composition and of the local temperature. The physical properties of the oil in any particular location thus reflect its history as well as its environment.

Accumulations of crude oil are found throughout the world in the interstices of porous sandstone and within fine fractures and pores of limestone and chalk (Figure 1). Reservoirs occur at all depths, from the surface to the limit of contemporary drilling technology at several kilometers and presumably beyond: the environmental conditions within each reservoir will naturally reflect its location. Temperatures are fairly directly related to depth although the thermal gradient does vary in different regions. Before the extraction of oil begins reservoirs are commonly under considerable pressure, largely from dissolved gas but often with a contribution from an underlying aquifer which communicates ultimately with surface water and is thus subject to a hydrostatic head of pressure corresponding to depth.

It is generally believed that underground accumulations of hydrocarbons originated from the organic remains of living organisms which, over geological time and under conditions of high temperature and pressure, have become degraded and modified to give the contemporary deposits of liquid crude oil, natural gas, shale oil and bitumen. At reservoir temperatures shale oil and bitumen are too viscous to flow and must be recovered by mining. Conventional crude oil, however, is liquid and can be produced by drilling into the reservoir and allowing the oil to be driven into the wells by the existing reservoir pressure. That pressure is often sufficient to raise the oil to the surface but, if not, a lift-pump is inserted into the well bottom.

Because oil is commonly less dense than water it migrates upwards through the pores of the rock, usually floating on an aquifer, until it reaches a layer of impervious rock which prevents further upward movement. If the impervious *cap rock* is folded into a dome the migrating oil may remain trapped beneath it to form a reservoir. Occasionally the oil reaches the surface where in time it loses its volatile components, the residue remaining as a tar pit. Prospecting for underground oil requires an understanding of the geological conditions in which it is likely to be found and is often combined with seismic prospecting, the explosion of small charges on the surface coupled with an analysis of the reflected sound waves to identify likely rock domes. But positive identification of the presence of an actual reservoir requires drilling wells and finding oil. It has been suggested that hydrocarbon-utilizing microorganisms might be used to locate oil reservoirs by observing their growth on volatile alkanes seeping upwards through the overlying rock and such methods are probably used on a small scale for prospecting. The hydrocarbons escaping through the ground above the reservoir are likely to be diverted locally by cracks, fractures and discontinuities in the rock strata, making the precise location of their origin uncertain. Drilling holes remains the only sure way of determining the presence and extent of an exploitable reservoir of crude oil.

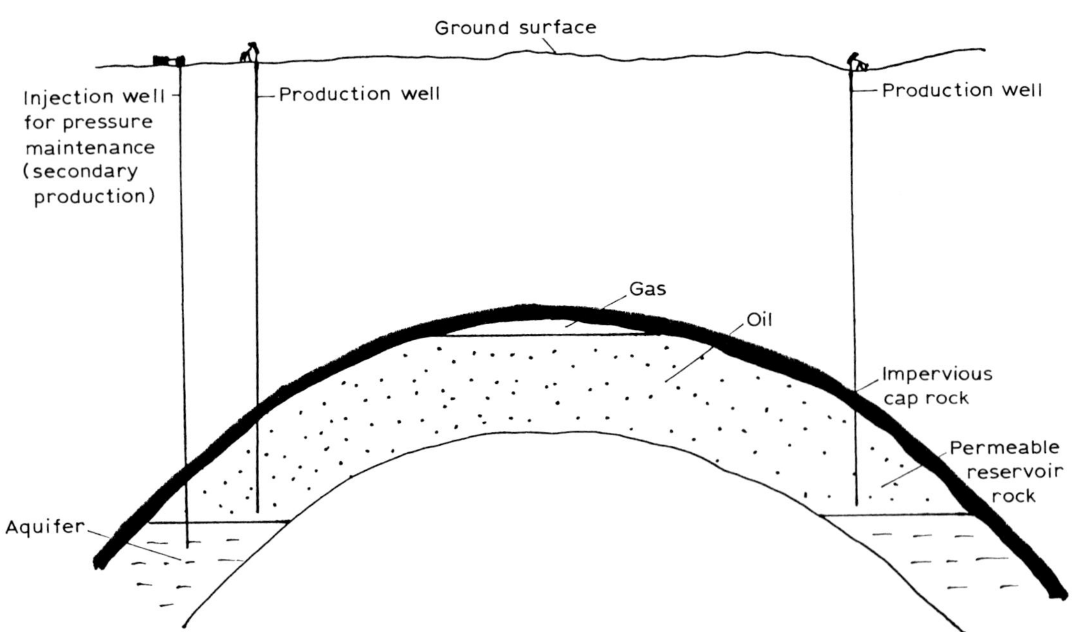

Figure 1. Structure of a Typical Oil Reservoir
The porous oil-bearing rock is often sited above an aquifer and oil is preventing from migrating any further upward by an impermeable cap rock. The oil usually contains dissolved gas, some of which may be present as a bubble (gas cap). Reservoir pressure results from the presence of dissolved gas, the upward force of the aquifer (which, via ultimate contact with the surface, will be under a head of water pressure corresponding to its depth), and the weight of the overburden.

RECOVERING THE OIL

The modern era of oil production began in 1859 in Titusville (Pennsylvania) and since then a highly successful global industry has developed with an impressive record of exploration and production from an enormous variety of reservoirs in all manner of hospitable and inhospitable geographical locations. But in spite of their accumulated skill and experience, operators at the present time are unable to recover at a competitive market price more than about a third of the oil originally present in a reservoir. Improving this rate of recovery cost-effectively is clearly desirable from many points of view. The technical hurdles are considerable and biotechnology may be able to offer ways of surmounting some of them. To understand how this might be achieved it is necessary first to explore the most important methods of oil production which the industry presently employs.

Primary Production

When a well is drilled into a hitherto untapped reservoir, local pressure drives the oil from the surrounding rock into the well-bore; if the pressure is high enough, the oil will be raised to the surface where, if not controlled, it may spurt from the wellhead as a *gusher*. Since it is always desirable to achieve an early return on invested capital, securing a maximum rate of recovery from a particular field demands bringing on stream as many wells as possible consistent with drilling and operating costs. Drilling is expensive, usually less so onshore than offshore, but costs are likely to be higher in remote and inhospitable areas. So the spacing between wells is determined by economic and operational factors as well as by geological and technical considerations. Onshore, in sparsely populated areas with shallow reservoirs, the linear distance between wells may be as low as a few tens of meters. Offshore, in deep waters and difficult climatic conditions, many wells are drilled outwards in a deviating configuration so as to tap a large area of the field from a single platform. The distance between the well bottoms deep under-ground in the oil-bearing zone may be as much as a kilometer.

As oil is progressively withdrawn from the reservoir the downhole pressure tends to fall, largely because of expansion of the gas cap: inevitably the rate of oil recovery declines. An initial *gas drive* may be replaced by a less effective *water drive* originating from the aquifer. In time the rate of oil production becomes unacceptably low and it will then be necessary to assist recovery with a lift-pump inserted into the well bottom and operated mechanically or electrically from the surface (Figure 2). The pump becomes a point of low

Figure 2. A Typical Wellhead Pump
The oscillating boom, operated by an electric motor, actuates the pump via a string of rods extending to the bottom of the well. (Photographed in Romania)

pressure in the reservoir to which the oil will drain assisted by gravity, although its expulsion from the rock pores by reservoir pressure progressively declines in importance and the rate of oil production is likely to fall. Another problem often arises: if vertical communication between the underlying aquifer and the oil-bearing zone is good, the suction exerted by the pump may cause a cone of water to rise from the aquifer to the well bottom. The produced oil then becomes more and more diluted with water and the economic returns of the operation diminish. It may indeed become necessary to stop the pump for a period (a practise called "stopcocking") in order to allow the cone to subside but when pumping is restarted the cone will probably be reinstated (Figure 3). *Coning* is a major production difficulty not readily overcome; dealing with this problem is one of the ways in which biotechnological methods might prove useful to the industry in the immediate future. Eventually a combination of all these effects reduces the flow of oil to uneconomic levels and the stage of *primary production* is at an end. Although the proportion of the original oil-in-place to be recovered by primary production will vary greatly between different reservoirs, the average worldwide is probably 15–20%.

Secondary Production

Further recovery of oil requires the maintenance of the down-hole reservoir pressure which is achieved by the injection of fluids; the obvious candidates are gas and water. In some cases the very gas which was originally dissolved under pressure in the oil, and which separates in the riser pipe or at the surface, may be reinjected for pressure maintenance. However, gas is itself a saleable commodity and may be too valuable to be used for reinjection. That decision will depend on the location of the reservoir in relation to potential markets and on the availability of a pipeline or other means of transportation to carry the gas to the consumer. At offshore locations with no pipeline, but for which future plans may exist to construct one, reinjection of the gas can be a good way of storing it for later use while simultaneously improving the current production of oil.

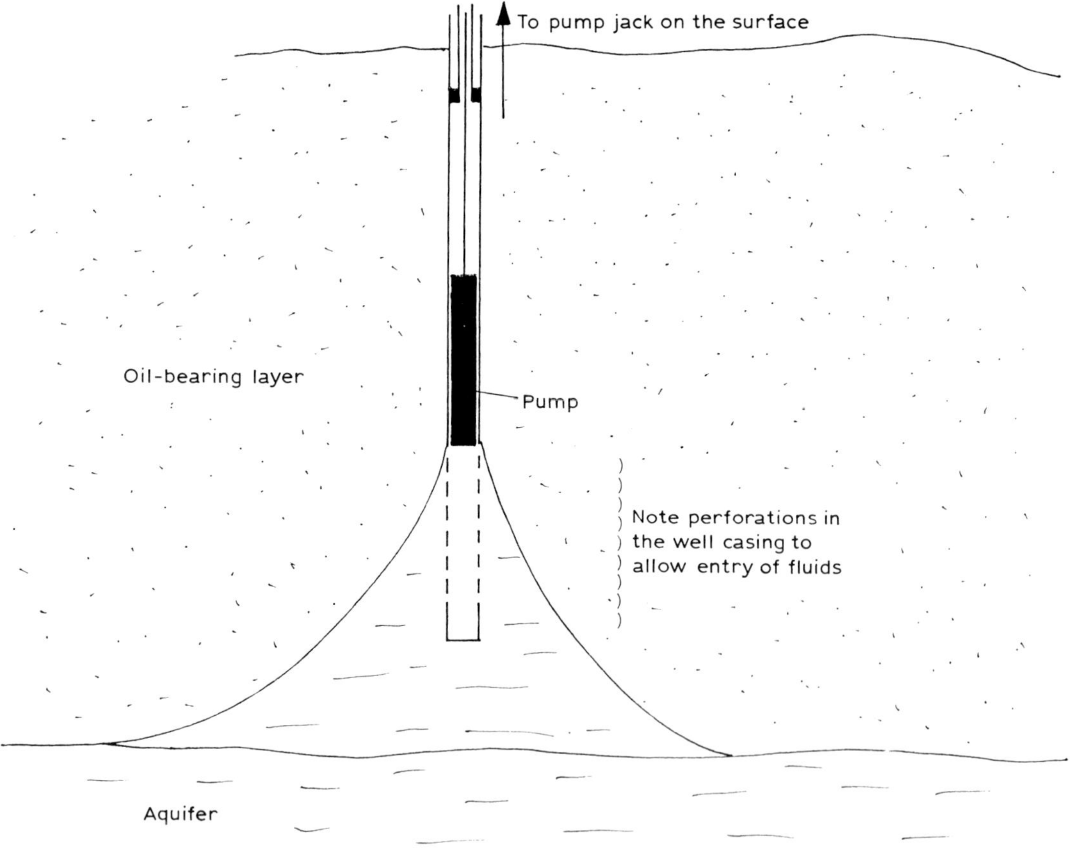

Figure 3. The problem of Coning
Coning occurs because of the suction exerted by the pump, the relatively high viscosity of the oil and the lower viscosity of the water; if vertical communication is good, the point of comparatively low pressure at the well bottom may cause a cone of water to be drawn up from the aquifer. The well bottom and pump are sited low in the oil-bearing zone to achieve maximum drainage but this increases the likelihood of establishing a water cone.

Commonly the fluid injected is water, either water produced from the oilfield itself or surface water available locally. Most oilfield waters are brines with a variable, and often high, content of calcium, magnesium and barium. Surface waters, particularly those from the sea, may contain sufficient quantities of various anions to risk the formation of insoluble metal precipitates when injected into certain oilfields, thereby plugging the reservoir pores (particularly those close to the injection wells) and impeding fluid flow. (Seawater often contains relatively high concentrations of sulfate and its injection may encourage the downhole growth of sulfate-reducers unless biocides are used: the latter add significantly to the cost of the additional oil recovered.) Figures 4 and 5 show a treatment plant in which water for injection is filtered, polished, deoxygenated and, if necessary, treated with biocide. The water may be injected below the oil-bearing zone, directly into the aquifer, although this is likely to exacerbate any coning which had already occurred during primary production. Alternatively, water is pumped into the oil-bearing zone itself with the objective of sweeping oil from injection wells to producers; such a procedure is termed a *waterflood*. A field may be drilled with a pattern of injector and producer wells, each producer being surrounded by, say, four injectors and each injector serving a similar number of producers; this is called a *five-spot pattern of wells*. The wellhead equipment at an injection well is illustrated in Figure 6 while a tank battery is shown in Figure 7.

Two main problems follow. No porous rock is homogeneous on a microscale: inevitably some pores are larger than others, some channels more permeable. In most reservoirs the oil viscosity is greater than that of water; as a result the injected water fails to sweep the oil evenly and uniformly before it but tends to flow preferentially through the most accessible pathways, *fingering* past the oil, and leaving much of it behind (Figure 8). (Note that this effect is in principle similar to coning although the local configuration is different.) In some cases the rock formation is extensively fissured or fractured on a macro-scale, or highly permeable sedimentary layers are present. Most of the water then tends to flow through these high permeability *thief zones* (Figure 9) without contacting the oil and they can present major operating difficulties.

A second problem is that oil droplets become impacted in narrow pore throats. Because of the high interfacial tension between oil and water (familiar as a repulsion between the two fluid phases), expelling such a droplet from its entrapment into the stream of flowing water requires more pressure than is available within the pore (Figure 10). There is a limit to the pressure with which the water can be injected because of the risk of fracturing the rock, thereby providing high permeability channels for water flow and simply magnifying the problem. These difficulties result, as they do with primary production, in the water content of the produced fluid increasing until economic production is no longer possible and the phase of *secondary production*, too, comes to an end. As with primary recovery, the total yield of original oil in place at the end of secondary production is variable over quite wide limits but a global average is about 35%. In recent years pressure maintenance procedures have often been instituted from the very beginning of oil recovery so that the primary and secondary stages are combined.

It is important to realize that the distance between wells in an oilfield is an important factor in determining the effectiveness with which oil can be recovered. Inevitably there are areas between wells which are not swept by any injected fluid during secondary recovery procedures and the closer the wells are to one another the smaller will be the unswept areas. However, in-fill drilling is expensive and in offshore locations, particularly those (as in the North Sea, which lie in deep waters and inhospitable climates) based on deviant wells and in which the well bottoms, thousands of meters below the seabed, can be up to a kilometer apart, fluid injected into one well may take several years to reach a neighboring producer!

The potential value of residual oil unrecovered by primary and secondary production is, of course, enormous and is of major economic and political importance; very approximate estimates for various regions of the world are given in Table 1. However, recovering some of the remaining two-thirds of the oil still left in the reservoir after secondary production requires elaborate and expensive methods, most of them still at an experimental stage of development. It is nevertheless this phase of *enhanced* (or *tertiary*) *oil recovery* that offers some of the most important opportunities for biotechnological intervention.

Enhanced Oil Recovery (EOR)

While it is true that a number of general techniques for enhanced oil recovery, including microbial methods, are under development, oilfields differ markedly from one another and a solution designed for one might be quite inappropriate for others. Ideally the problem needs precise definition in each case but unfortunately that may not be possible because the exact information on which it must be based can be obtained only from rock cores resulting from drilling. So managing an oilfield has many problems. Drilling is costly and in difficult locations it can be prohibitively so. Both during operations to explore the extent and nature of the field, and later for production, it is essential to drill as few wells as possible. Thus, at the beginning of a field's working life, at the very point when important operating decisions need to be made, least is known about it. As production proceeds through the various stages the field becomes more extensively understood; paradoxically most is known when its useful life is at an end! Inevitably the decisions which need to be made with respect to enhanced recovery techniques

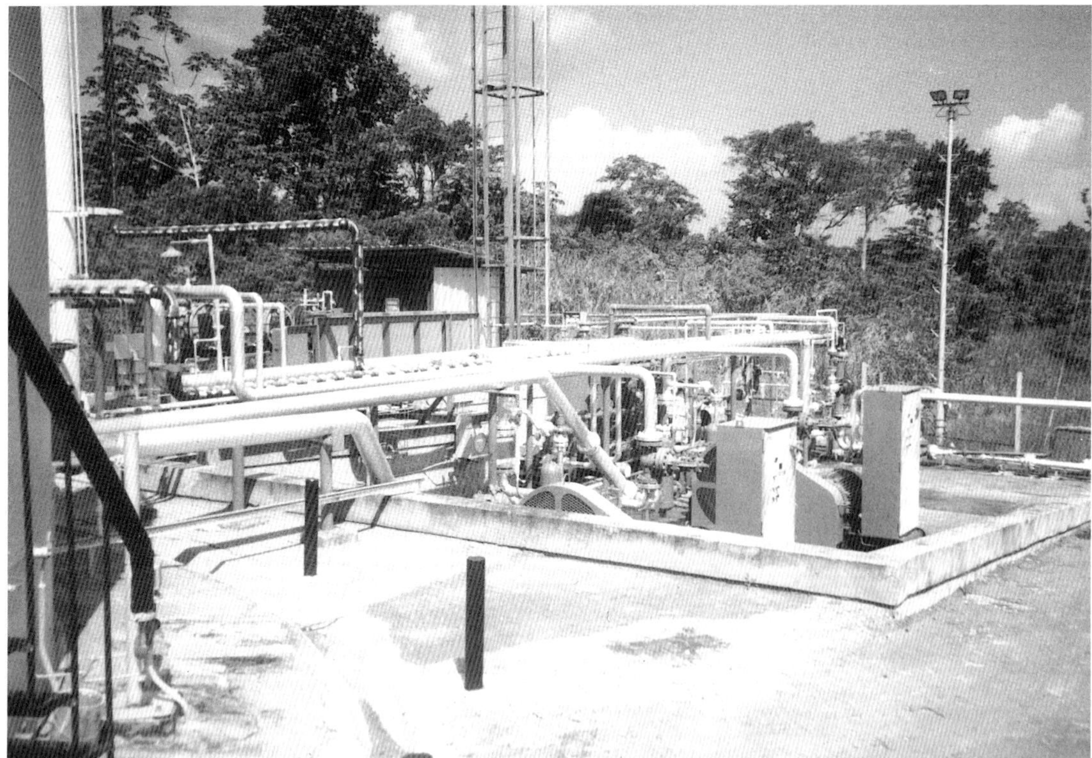

Figures 4 and 5. Water Treatment Plant
These two views show the water storage tank as well as the extensive pipework and equipment required even for a modest water injection operation. (Photographed in Trinidad)

Figure 6. Injection Equipment at the Wellhead
There is not much to be seen: just the valving of the wellhead itself together with the water line, gate valves and gauges. This injection facility is actually being used for a microbial flood. (Photographed in Oklahoma)

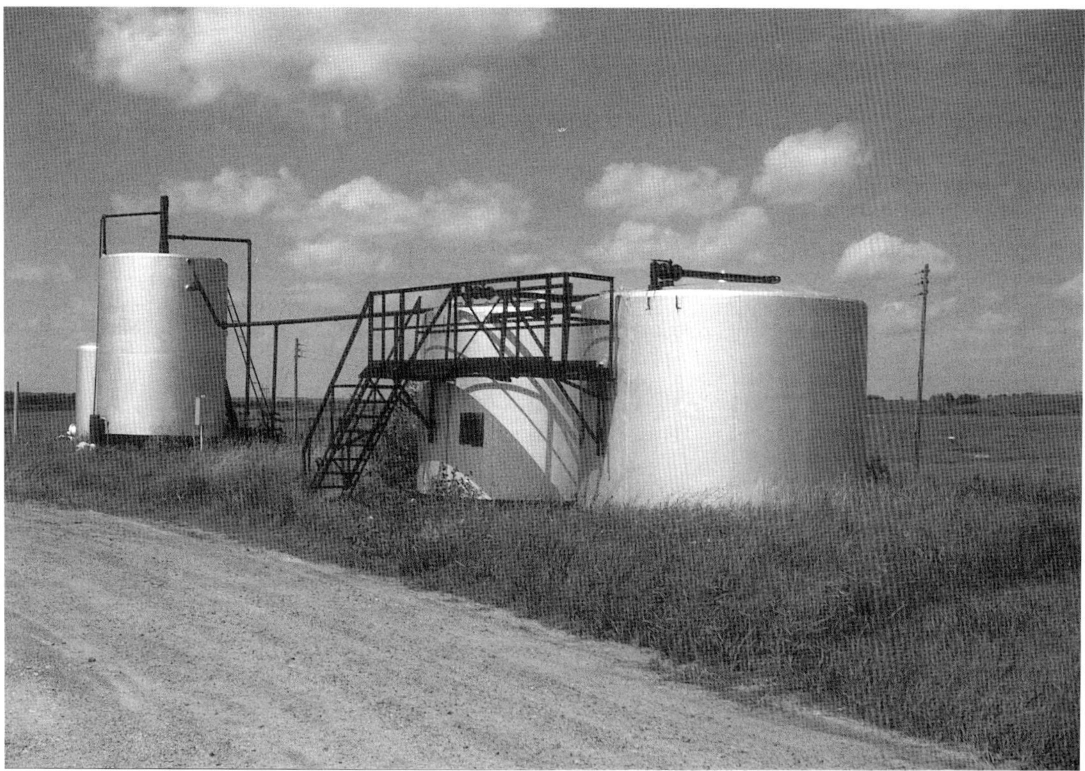

Figure 7. Tank Battery
This view of a microbial flood shows the water/oil separator tank at the left with the oil and water storage tanks at the right-hand end of the assembly. (Photographed in Oklahoma)

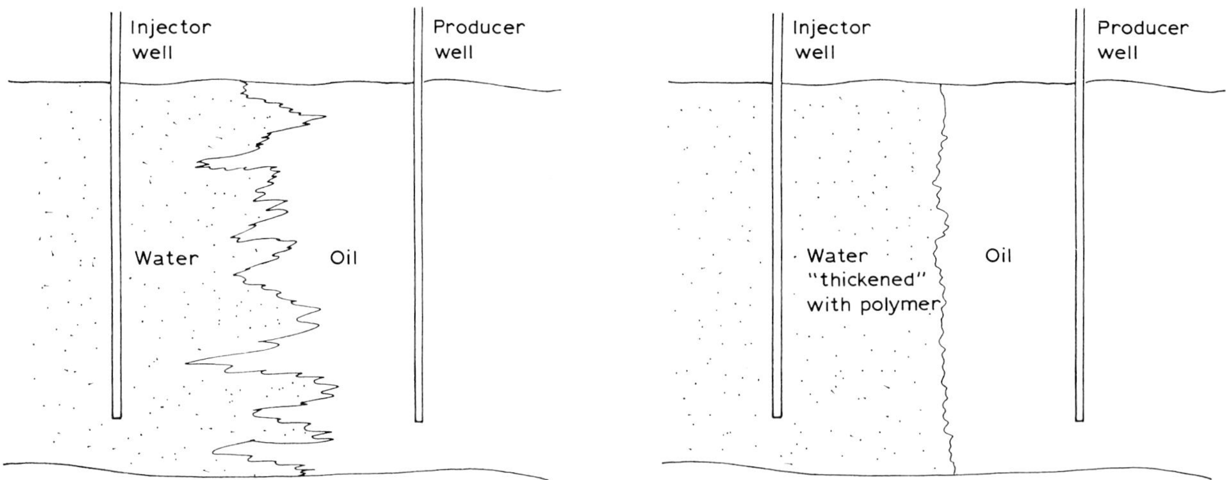

Figure 8. The Phenomenon of "Fingering" and its suppression
An irregular boundary may be produced at the water/oil interface. This results from inhomogeneities in the pore structure of the rock and the mismatching of the water and oil viscosities (viscosity of the oil higher than that of the water). Fingering can often be suppressed by increasing the viscosity of the water with polymer so that it exceeds that of the oil.

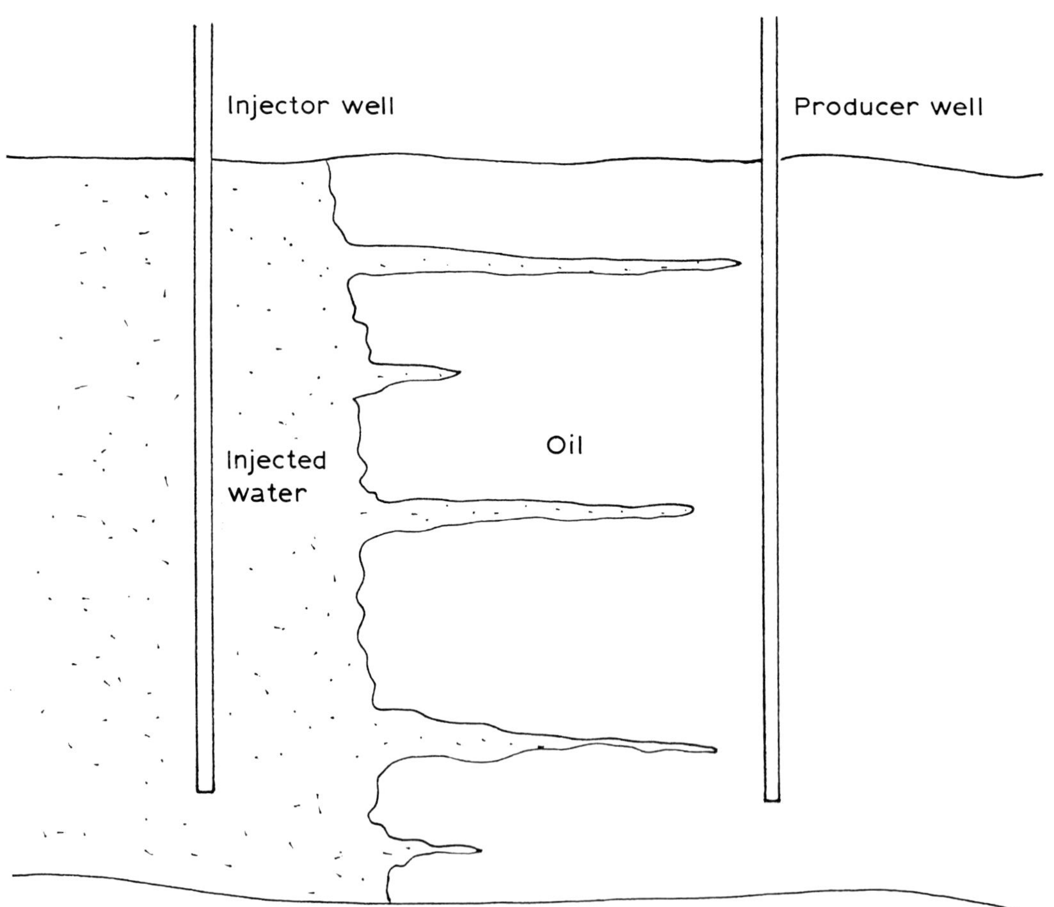

Figure 9. Problems of "Thief Zones"
Fractures or other high permeability structures in the reservoir may allow rapid migration of injected water to the producer well, thereby uselessly by-passing oil in the reservoir stratum. Excessive quantities of injected water are produced compared with the yield of oil.

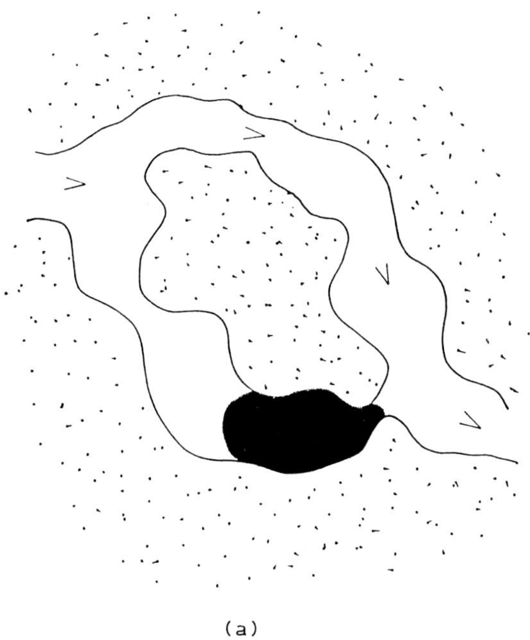

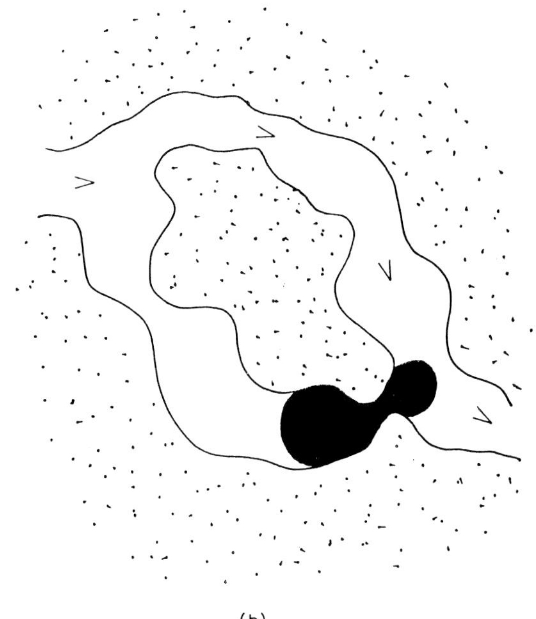

Figure 10. Entrapment of Oil Droplets
(a) Oil droplet trapped in a pore throat and by-passed by the water flow.

(b) Expulsion of the droplet entails increasing the area of oil/water contact against a high interfacial tension.

Table 1
World Target Sizes for Enhanced Oil Recovery

Approximate value of oil not economically recoverable by present technology. Note that only a proportion of this oil is likely to be recoverable by any technique.

Assumptions: (a) a crude oil price of \$18.00 per barrel
(b) that proven reserves (i.e. reserves regarded as presently recoverable) represent 35% of the original oil-in-place

Source Region	Estimated Value of Oil Unrecoverable by Present Technology ($\$ \times 10^{12}$)
Asia-Pacific	0.6
Western Europe	0.8
Middle East	12.4
Africa	1.9
Western Hemisphere	4.1
Communist States	2.9
Total for the Whole World	22.7

For comparison, in 1987 the Gross National Products of the United States and the United Kingdom were $\$4.4 \times 10^{12}$ and $£4.1 \times 10^{11}$ [$\$6.6 \times 10^{11}$ @ £1.00 = \$1.60], respectively.

are based on an imperfect appreciation of field characteristics. Since an oil reservoir is a large and valuable asset, one which will already have merited major investment in exploration and production facilities to bring it to the end of the secondary recovery stage, operators may well decide that it makes sense to invest in additional development for EOR to be applied to their fields if they see the possibility of profitably recovering a further significant quantity of oil, thereby improving the financial return on their original investment.

In general, enhanced recovery requires the injection of something into the reservoir. In the case of viscous heavy oil the prime need is to reduce viscosity, an effect most readily achieved by heat. Thus one technique is significantly to raise the temperature of a portion of the heavy oil by the injection of superheated steam (*steam soak*), the hot and more mobile oil being subsequently recovered through the same well as the one used for the injection; this procedure is often described as *huff-and-puff*. Variants include the use of steam to drive oil through the reservoir (*steam drive*) and even the injection of air accompanied by the ignition of the oil underground to create a *fire-flood* which drives a bank of heated mobile crude towards the production wells. Methods like these are very expensive in terms of fuel for heating; as much as a third of the oil recovered may be used to generate steam or is lost in underground combustion.

With lighter oils enhanced recovery is based on the injection with the waterflood of specific chemicals intended to overcome the problems of the particular reservoir. Suppression of fingering requires *thickening* the waterflood with a polymer in order match more closely the viscosities of the drive water and the oil. Polymers presently available include various polyacrylamides made from petrochemical feedstocks, and xanthan gum produced microbiologically. Control of water flow by the blocking or plugging of thief zones is also likely to be based on the emplacement of polymer; some non-biological products intended for this purpose are currently on the market but many operators are not persuaded of their effectiveness. Mobilization of trapped oil droplets, on the other hand, needs a major reduction of the interfacial tension between the waterflood and the residual oil to a value at least as low as 10^{-3} mNm^{-1}; this is achieved by the inclusion of a surfactant (detergent). Surfactants presently being tested to a limited extent by the industry are derived from petrochemicals; they have been shown to be effective in a number of field trials but they are very expensive and the cost of oil recovered in this way is far higher than the international market price. Although there is a clear need for further development, there are chemicals already on the market for enhanced recovery but at the present time, and perhaps for the foreseeable future, the additional crude they yield will cost much more to produce than cheap oil from primary and secondary production elsewhere in the world.

The high cost of chemicals for injection dictates the way they are used. Typically, only a portion of a waterflood will contain the chemicals because the first contact between different fluid phases is the most effective. For instance, as a surfactant solution contacts impacted oil droplets the reduction of interfacial tension will hopefully mobilize the oil; the surfactant solution which comes behind the initial front will have no further effect since the droplets will already have been moved on. The total quantity of surfactant to be injected will therefore take account of estimates of the amount of oil to be contacted. As the surfactant front moves through the reservoir the oil droplets it mobilizes coalesce into a moving band of oil and it is that *bank* which sweeps up further oil droplets as it advances. Thus, a surfactant flood might comprise first the injection of a limited quantity (called a *slug*) of surfactant solution to contact and mobilize oil droplets, followed by a slug of polymer solution to control fingering, both slugs being driven just by water. In this way the expense of the operation is minimized without sacrificing effectiveness.

OPPORTUNITIES FOR BIOTECHNOLOGY IN CRUDE OIL PRODUCTION

First we need to distinguish between two uses of the term "MEOR": it has been applied both to the use of microbial products (polymers and surfactants) in conventional EOR procedures (sometimes called *ex situ* MEOR) and to the emplacement of microorganisms downhole to make these products within the reservoir rock itself (*in situ* deployment). The factory production of microbial products for oil recovery is, of course, no different in principle from their production for any other purpose: it involves the choice of suitable organisms, fermentation protocols and downstream processing techniques. Ultimately these products, as any other, must be packaged, marketed and delivered to the users although in some locations they might conceivably be made at the wellhead and injected directly. The manufacture in conventional production facilities of some microbial products for oil recovery is discussed briefly under industrial chemicals in Chapter 17; in this chapter we are concerned with the use of living microbial systems underground, the so-called "*in situ* systems". Note also that MEOR is used by many people to encompass all downhole uses of microorganisms, whether or not they would actually be recognized by the oil industry as "enhanced (or tertiary) oil recovery".

At the present time interest centers primarily on four main targets for *in situ* MEOR: (i) well stimulation; (ii) matrix acidizing; (iii) profile improvement and the control of water flow within the reservoir; and (iv) downhole polymer and surfactant floods. Each is an area of active development with the emphasis varying among different R & D organizations as a result of their individual relationships with sections of the oil industry.

Well Stimulation

The productivity of wells often declines with time, not only because of a falling reservoir pressure but also as the result of reduced local permeability of the reservoir matrix in the immediate neighborhood of the well-bore. Part of the fall in permeability results from particulates. The rock often contains fine particles of sand or clay which are carried along with the flowing oil and water. As the fluids approach the well-bore along an inward radial, the rate of flow increases and particles which would perhaps readily pass through pore throats if they were moving slowly and well separated from others, become impacted when they are traveling faster and the flux is greater. The pressure differential exerted by a downhole pump may not be sufficient to move them. A second difficulty arises from the deposition of wax and asphalt ("tar balls") in the rock near the well. This may happen because the drop in pressure associated with each stroke of the pump causes a local temperature drop which, in certain conditions and with certain types of oil, leads to a separation of higher molecular weight components in a solid or semi-solid form. Thirdly, metallic scale may be deposited, especially if there is water incompatibility; it was noted earlier that this may lead to matrix plugging. These factors may collectively impede the entry into the well bottom of oil (and water) by the formation of a *skin* in the rock matrix probably no more than a few centimeters from the well casing. Conventional treatment of the skin depends on its chemical nature and may include flushing with hot oil, or with hydrofluoric or hydrochloric acids. With acid flushing the downhole pump and well tubing may have to be removed and cleaned with all the attendant expense of bringing both labor and workover equipment to the site.

Effective though acid flushing often is, its cost may be too high. For example, in some parts of the U.S. (especially in states such as Kansas, Louisiana, Texas and Oklahoma) many wells are operated by individuals or by small independent companies with limited resources. The wells are often old, have usually repaid their original capital investment and are nearing the end of their useful lives with a daily production of no more than a few barrels of oil. (Note that a barrel contains about 159 l, equal to 42 U.S. or 35 Imperial gallons.) Those yielding less than 10 barrels a day are called *stripper wells*. In 1984 there were believed to be more than 400,000 of them in the continental U.S., collectively accounting for about 20% of domestic production, although the fall in the international price of crude oil in 1986 resulted in many of them being shut in and plugged. Not only is this a significant national resource but it is an important element in U.S. policy making and a major economic factor in the local state economies. The further survival of many of these small operations might depend on the availability of an inexpensive and effective alternative method for stimulating stripper wells.

More effort has been devoted to this problem, and more field trials conducted, than on any other aspect of MEOR. Its importance is not confined to the southwest of the U.S. Other mature and declining oil industries face similar difficulties, not least in the countries of Eastern Europe and the Third World which have insufficient resources of convertible currencies to purchase oil on the world markets (however cheap it might be in dollar terms) and are accordingly anxious to maximize yields even from marginal domestic resources.

Most of the techniques are based on a set of ideas originally propounded in the mid-1940s by Claude ZoBell[1] in La Jolla, California. He recognized that bacteria are able to produce surfactants and polymers as well as organic acids, solvents and gases, all of which might usefully contribute to improving oil production. Furthermore, many producing strains can subsist on inexpensive agricultural products of which molasses has proved the most popular. The usual approach is thus to inject the well with some tens of liters of a cocktail containing a range of microbial species chosen most frequently for their ability to produce copious quantities of gas (probably mostly carbon dioxide) and solvents (usually aliphatic alcohols). Sometimes surfactant producers are included. Nutrient support consists of the injection of one or two tonnes of molasses diluted with perhaps 50 tonnes of water, originally from the reservoir itself or obtained from a surface source. Mineral salts and a source of nitrogen are supplied as judged necessary.

The well is shut in for a period, oil production is temporarily suspended and the progress of the underground fermentation followed by measurements of the downhole pressure which is expected to rise as a result of gas production. When the fermentation is considered to be complete (or perhaps when the operator insists on switching the pump on!), the well is reopened and production resumed. Although hundreds of wells are believed to have been treated by such methods in areas as far apart as the U.S., Czechoslovakia, Hungary, Poland and Romania, hard evidence of the consequences is difficult to obtain. There are many anecdotal reports of sand and tarry masses being expelled from the wells, of production having benefited to an unrecorded extent, and for an undefined period, but the details are usually missing. There are, however, a few publications (particularly papers by Karaskiewicz[2] in Poland) giving more specific and encouraging detail and all those early results appearing by 1982 were collected and republished in English by Hitzman[3]. In the most encouraging cases the rate of oil production from a single treatment was increased up to threefold, in some instances for periods up to eight years. For a typical oil-bearing zone with a thickness of, say, 10 meters and a porosity of about 25% the volume of bacterial culture injected is not likely to travel more than about 2.5 meters from the point of injection. Additional rates of oil production sustained for long periods following a single treatment can hardly originate from the small volume of the reservoir contacted by the injected fluid; the treatment most probably facilitates the flow from a wider area of the reservoir by improving fluid access to the well. It seems nevertheless likely that a new skin will develop in time and production again falter, but if the treatment is sufficiently inexpensive it might be repeated at suitable intervals. Microbial field tests are discussed again in a later section of this chapter.

Little has been done to investigate mechanisms in detail or to design techniques specially to deal with problems identified in particular wells and reservoirs. These are, of course, likely to differ widely as a result both of differences in geology and of operating practice and history. Some workers are now trying to attack directly the reasons for the fall-off in production rates and to devise microbial systems to deal specifically with scale deposition, wax accumulation and other skin factors.

If microbial methods for well stimulation are to find a use in the market place the attitude of operators to them is obviously of critical importance. With few exceptions, all microbial field tests have been carried out on stripper wells. Production engineers in major companies note the impressive *percentage* increase in the rate of oil recovery but are likely to comment that an *absolute* increase from, say, one to three barrels a day holds little interest for them since they are concerned with wells yielding possibly thousands of barrels a day. Indeed, major companies with high overheads rarely operate such poor producers as stripper wells: if their own wells decline to those levels they are usually sold to independents. Therefore few if any majors are presently interested in microbial methods for well stimulation; their operations justify the expense of well-tried chemical procedures. Independents have a quite different view. For them the marginal cost of operation is crucial because a well producing no more than a few barrels of oil a day provides little revenue margin for maintenance operations. The prospect of a microbial procedure costing perhaps $500–1,000 per well, as against a much higher charge for a conventional (non-biological) treatment, may well represent the difference between keeping a well flowing and permanently closing it down. The problem for independents is often lack of awareness of the possibilities, coupled with limited resources to undertake development work; in some countries, notably the United States in which most independent operators are located, government agencies such as the Department of Energy undertake sponsorship. The situation is different again in countries with hard currency difficulties. In some of them (e.g. Poland and Czechoslovakia in the past and Romania at the present time) the national oil company or its affiliates fund development of microbial methods while in others (e.g. Brazil) MEOR is promoted by private biotechnology companies. We will return to these matters in a later section.

Wax and scale removal

Another production problem is the deposition of paraffin wax or metallic scale in the well-bore tubing and pump, in some cases eventually jamming any further movement. Conventional treatment is to circulate hot oil to dissolve the wax or use acid to remove scale. Barium sulfate scale poses a particularly difficult problem of removal by chemical means and may have to be dealt with mechanically by pulling out the pump and reaming the tubing with a cutting tool. In the last few years bacterial preparations have been marketed to correct these problems. For wax removal, a small volume of an aerobic hydrocarbon-oxidizing bacterial preparation, with or without a specific proprietary nutrient, is introduced into the well via the air-filled annular space surrounding the production tubing. After a brief period for the bacteria to act, pumping is resumed and large quantities of wax are said often to be expelled. Some companies also sell bacteria to remove metallic scale (including calcium carbonate and barium sulfate) which may be deposited in injection wells as a consequence of ionic incompatibility between the injection and connate waters. Anecdotal reports from field operators tell of these bacterial methods being effective at removing wax and scale deposits, and inhibiting their further formation, but precise information supported by experimental evidence is not easy to obtain. An example of one report, on a "To Whom It May Concern" basis, reads in part: *Our firm has been using [X-Brand] microorganisms for several months with unqualified success in solving a variety of problems ..... We pulled a well and found the tubing anchor plugged with barium sulfate. We installed a new tubing anchor and treated the well with microorganisms. After a few weeks, we pulled the well to examine for scale and found the tubing, pump and rods to be scale-free ..... Recently we began treating for paraffin with microorganisms in wells located in [a particular place]. The treated wells have gone beyond the time that would normally require hot oiling and are pumping smoothly without evidence of paraffin build-up .....*

Matrix Acidizing

When a well is first drilled various procedures are put in train to maximize its productivity. One of them ensures the presence of adequate flow channels draining oil from the surrounding matrix into the well-bore. This is often achieved by fracturing the rock in the immediate neighborhood of the well. Water is pumped into the surrounding reservoir at such a pressure that the rock is actually cracked. The cracks are kept open after the excess pressure is relieved by including "proppant" particles suspended in a viscous fracturing fluid: grains of sand or other hard material which will prevent the crack from sealing itself as the rock settles back into place. Fracturing is expensive, requiring the use of high-pressure equipment brought to the well-head. Having fractured, it is of additional advantage to open up further flow channels into the fractures by dissolving part of the adjacent reservoir rock, a procedure called *fracture acidizing*. Silica, of course, is highly refractory to dissolution but many oil reservoirs are to be found in limestone, or in sandstone reservoirs in which the sand particles are cemented together with carbonate. It is this carbonate which can be dissolved by injections of acid, usually hydrochloric. However, hydrochloric is so powerful that its acidity is rapidly expended close to the well-bore and it becomes difficult to dissolve carbonate further into the reservoir without using massive quantities or the more expensive inhibited acid. Furthermore, hydrochloric acid is, of course, very corrosive to the metallic well casing: corrosion inhibitors have to be employed to minimize damage, and equipment maintenance is expensive, all of which adds to the expense of its use. Formation and fracture acidizing is also used with older wells in order to improve productivity by enhancing the flow channels in the neighborhood of the well.

Placing bacteria downhole to generate organic acid in place of hydrochloric has certain advantages. Firstly, they are likely to be cheaper because the cost per unit of acid generated from an inexpensive bacterial nutrient (such as molasses) is less than the equivalent quantity of mineral acid. Secondly, since organic acids such as formic, acetic and lactic are end products of bacterial fermentation, they accumulate progressively as the culture develops. Thus, injecting into the reservoir rock, and particularly into the cracks, a culture of acid-generating bacteria together with their nutrient feedstock will ensure that most of the acid is produced after the inoculum has penetrated deeply into the depths of the fractures, well away from the well-bore. This will have a markedly beneficial effect on opening up additional and more distant drainage channels through which crude oil can flow into the well.

It might indeed be possible to use a bacterial system to dissolve carbonate around the well (*matrix acidizing*) as a comparatively inexpensive substitute for fracturing. By injecting a considerable volume of nutrient medium containing an inoculum of acid-generating bacteria at a pressure too low to cause fracturing of the rock, a *pad* of liquid extending many meters from the well may gradually be infiltrated into the pay zone over a number of hours. As the bacteria grow and ferment the feedstock, the acid they produce will erode the carbonate around the well-bore and so promote fluid drainage. The cost of bacterial acidizing is likely to be much lower than the that of fracturing and probably well worth some loss of production while waiting for the fermentation to complete.

Profile Improvement (Selective Plugging/ Channel Plugging)

Techniques for the selective plugging of high permeability thief zones are technically difficult. The only access to them is from the surface via the well-bores. There must be uncertainty at the time of injection as to the exact path which will be traveled underground by injected water and every procedure is in a sense an experiment; only later, as a consequence of observing the subsequent behavior of the reservoir, might it be possible to reconstruct the event and by then not only will time (and perhaps production) have been forfeit but, if the plugging agent went to the wrong place, the damage will long since have been done. Inevitably microbial methods for selective plugging suffer potentially from the same uncertainties. Their value to the industry will accordingly depend on the perception of their cost and efficacy compared with other methods; nevertheless, among the whole range of possible MEOR methods the industry tends to look most favorably on their use for selective plugging. The reasons are not difficult to discern: alternative methods are not widely regarded as satisfactory and plugging is seen as an operation fairly rapidly completed. Operators and others making technical decisions may for the moment find it most acceptable to consider microorganisms for such short-term deployment in the reservoir, probably close to the injector well. There may be another potential advantage: once in place it is difficult to do anything with a chemical plug but biopolymer plug in the wrong location might be removable enzymatically.

Plugging thief zones

Protocols for using bacteria selectively to plug parts of the reservoir are usually based on anaerobic polymer-producers although it has been proposed that the deposition of an inorganic precipitate might be less expensive and more long-lasting at high temperatures and where there is a danger of biodegradation. The general concept is therefore to inject a dilute inoculum of the desired bacteria suspended in an appropriate aqueous nutrient medium with the expectation that an inoculum with a viscosity close to that of water itself will flow through those same rock channels as injected water. As the bacterial culture grows, and eventually produces a viscous or insoluble polymer to gel the medium, the water channels will be blocked. Water subsequently injected will thus be diverted into other, less permeable pathways, hopefully those containing residual oil which will thereby be expelled and produced.

Several anaerobic polymer-producing strains are able to grow on such inexpensive feedstocks as sucrose or molasses; some are able to do so at temperatures above 50°C. *Leuconostoc mesenteroides* is a familiar example although few if any strains of this organism produce polymer much above 35°C. With some species the polymers are soluble but so viscous, and produced in such quantity, that they can effectively block long fissures and fractures in the rock. Other organisms generate insoluble products. Polymer-producing bacteria normally attach themselves to a surface by means of their polymer so that the plug will ultimately consist of bacterial cells and extracellular polymer stuck to sand grains and spanning the channels between them.

Designing a bacterial plug must take account of the temperature at which the bacteria are to grow and generate polymer, their rate of growth and polymer production at that temperature and the stability, both chemical and biological, of the polymer in the reservoir environment. The microbiological temperature limitation is obvious but the temperature in the relevant parts of the reservoir, obtained from a computer simulation of the downhole system (inserting thermometers is difficult!), may not be known with certainty. The temperature of the produced oil, corrected for heat lost in the riser pipe, will give a good indication of the general downhole temperature, but if the reservoir has already been flooded with surface water for a protracted period, the channels through which the injected water has flowed will be at a lower temperature than the reservoir as a whole. It is, of course, just those channels which will receive the bacterial inoculum so that microbial polymer production will take place in an environment cooler than the bulk of the reservoir.

The rate of growth and polymer production will limit the total time available for filling the thief zone. Polymer production is likely to take place roughly in step with growth; most of it will probably occur during the exponential phase or shortly after, with the viscosity of the medium rising rapidly as polymer accumulation reaches a maximum. The flow of the culture through the rock channels will therefore terminate fairly abruptly; any part of the high permeability zone not already filled with bacterial culture will become inaccessible once the culture has become very viscous or has gelled. Even with a very dilute bacterial inoculum, growth and polymer production at reservoir temperatures will probably be complete within a few days unless very slowly growing bacteria can be employed. Note that both the time needed to fill thief zones with injected fluid and the need for very deep plugging are highly variable. If there is poor communication between a thief zone and the surrounding matrix, a shallow plug near the injector might be sufficient. In reservoirs with short interwell distances filling may be complete in one or a few days. But in some offshore fields, with interwell distances approaching a kilometer, it may take weeks or months of water injection to fill a sufficient proportion of the high permeability volume and it would be necessary somehow to delay bacterial growth and polymer synthesis until the individual organisms had penetrated deeply into the reservoir. Another consideration is the ability of bacterial cells to penetrate far into a reservoir without becoming impacted in pore throats. Recent work by Costerton[4] in Alberta has suggested that these difficulties might be overcome by the use of microforms (ultra-microbacteria, or UMBs) of polymer producers, much smaller in size than normal vegetative cells. He regards these small cells as better suited to deep penetration and proposes that the inoculum should consist of UMBs injected without nutrient support and allowed in the first instance to attach themselves to rock surfaces in the reservoir. Nutrient would subsequently be injected and converted to polymer at those sites carrying bacteria. The problem, however, remains of generating viscosity very deep in the reservoir. Unless means can be devised of ensuring that no bacteria attached themselves close to the injector well, polymer production will begin shortly after injected nutrient contacts emplaced cells. Those channels reached first will rapidly become plugged with polymer and this will prevent the flow of more fluid through them long before the nutrient reaches the most distant bacteria.

Finally there is the matter of polymer survival. Even though a thief zone might be cooled by an earlier waterflood, once it has been plugged no further cooling will be possible and the plug itself will gradually warm up to the ambient reservoir temperature. It is therefore important to use bacteria which produce a sufficiently thermostable polymer. There are other risks: a polymer produced by one microorganism will inevitably serve as a nutritional substrate for others. Major operators in the oil industry often take elaborate precautions to prevent microbial contamination downhole so that in their fields microbial attack on the polymer plug is improbable. But many reservoirs not so carefully treated are already contaminated and it might be impossible to protect the polymer from microbial degradation without the concomitant use of a biocide. This would mean using a biocide-resistant polymer-producing strain (made, perhaps, by genetic engineering), together with the presence of biocide in the inoculum, to prevent a subsequent attack on the polymer by indigenous organisms, always assuming that the latter are biocide-sensitive. Sometimes, though, not everything is against you: if the indigenous organisms were physiologically able to survive only in the cooled waterflooded zone, that very rise in temperature of the polymer plug mentioned earlier would itself protect the polymer against bacterial attack.

It is these factors, together with cost, which have suggested the value of an inorganic precipitate (such as a metal sulfide) as a plug. The industry, it is true, has a well-founded and traditional distaste for sulfate-reducing bacteria (the hydrogen sulfide they generate may corrode pumps and pipework, precipitate metallic sulfides in the reservoir and *sour* the oil, thereby increasing its refining costs, reducing its value and constituting a health hazard for the operatives) and, indeed, the main reason for the exclusion of *all* microorganisms from injection waters is to prevent access by sulfate-reducers. Nevertheless, many reservoirs are already contaminated; in those cases misfortune might be turned to advantage with a plugging system based on the deliberate precipitation of metal sulfide in high permeability zones.

Controlling coning

In principle, the use of microbial plugs for the control of coning is little different from the selective plugging of any other part of the reservoir matrix. The distinction is mainly operational: the plugging of thief zones as described above is concerned with the behavior of injected waters while coning control seeks to regulate the pattern of outflow of the indigenous reservoir brine. For coning control, injection of the microbial inoculum will need to take place through each production well affected. When the pump is turned off, the pressure at the well bottom equilibrates with that in the surrounding matrix and, without the pressure differential, the cone will collapse at some rate. Depending on reservoir characteristics, the microbial inoculum may be designed either (a) to be introduced into the top of the cone and drawn down to the oil/water interface as the cone subsides, or (b) to be injected under appropriate pressure into the cone in the expectation that it will enter those rock channels through which the water of the cone had flowed. In either case the composition of the inoculum is configured to promote gelling within the proper time frame and, as this type of plugging takes place very close to the point of injection, it will be complete fairly quickly. The resultant plug will be located either as a pancake at the oil/water interface or within the flow channels of the cone; the choice of which technique to use will depend on the rate at which the cone subsides as well as on other operational considerations. The plug may retard water movement rather than prevent flow entirely but significant retardation could be very important.

Suppression of a cone may not prevent its later reappearance outside the volume or area of the implanted plug or pancake; if that were to happen, one or more further injections of the polymer-producing system would be required as part of regular field maintenance.

Polymer and Surfactant Floods

The operation of downhole bacterial polymer and/or surfactant floods requires the continuous synthesis of those materials for long periods of time, almost certainly from an inexpensive feedstock supplied from the surface. Many bacterial polymers and surfactants are already known and some have been extensively characterized. While the variety synthesized by anaerobes is more limited than the corresponding aerobic products, a number of potentially useful compounds are being explored and several laboratories are actively seeking to extend their range. Examples are noted in Chapters 17 and 25.

The configuration of bacterial systems for (soluble) polymer and surfactant flooding is very different from those for selective plugging (Figure 11). Plugging is a limited procedure necessarily, and for reasons advanced earlier, of short microbiological duration; provided sufficient inoculum and nutrient can be injected as a single operation, there are few micro-

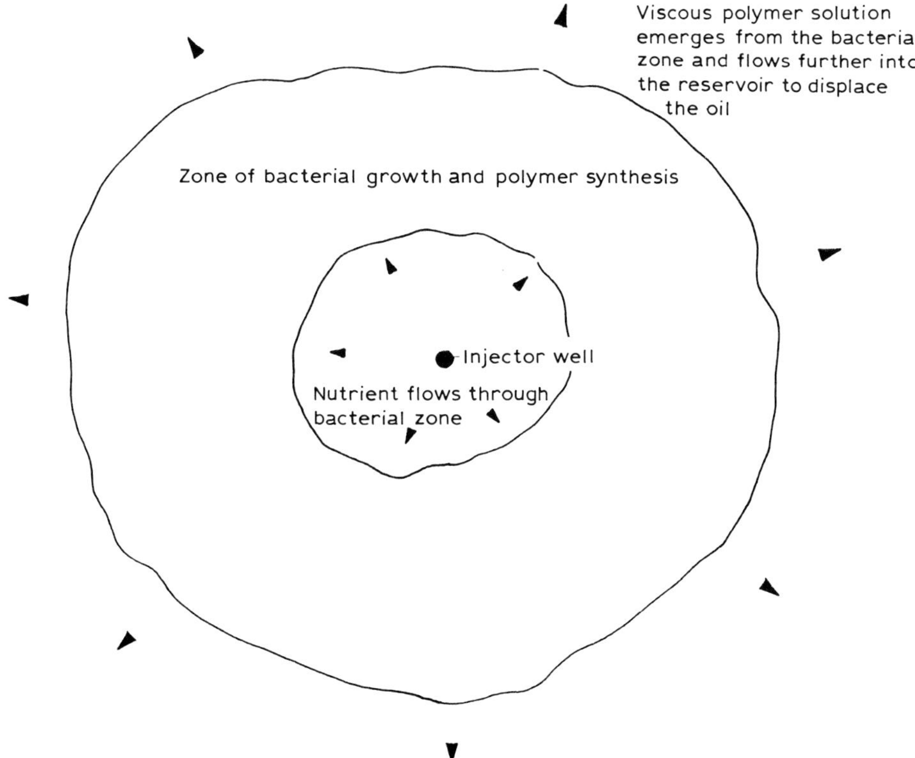

Figure 11. Bacterial Polymer Flood
Design of a possible model system for the continuous downhole synthesis of bacterial polymer.

biological problems in conducive reservoir environments other than the desirability in some cases of achieving bacterial migration over long distances. Polymer and/or surfactant flooding, however, may be required to operate continously for months or even years, particularly in very large and widely spaced offshore fields, with the obvious problems both of providing adequate nutritional support and of ensuring an active and stable bacterial population throughout such long periods. It was once thought that selected bacterial populations could subsist anaerobically on crude oil itself if an appropriate electron acceptor (perhaps nitrate) were supplied from the surface; this would have provided an elegant and very inexpensive solution to the problem of nutrition. Subsequent experiments cast serious doubts on its practical value. In the presence of nitrate some natural mixed bacterial populations do indeed appear to grow anaerobically on crude oil (although not on pure hydrocarbons), but their rates of growth and metabolism are so low, and have proved so resistant to improvement, that they cannot reasonably be regarded as a basis for an operating system. Although there has recently been new evidence suggesting that under methanogenic conditions some bacteria might be able to use aromatic and polycyclic hydrocarbons, the rates remain low and the provision of a suitable growth substrate from the surface is probably the only realistic nutritional option.

Continuous feeding from the surface is likely to be based on a cheap agricultural feedstock although in some locations waste products from other activities might be obtained at no cost or no more than the expense of transportation. An obvious widely available feedstock is a raw or partly refined sugar (sucrose) preparation; indeed, most field trials of MEOR have used molasses. In recent years there has at times been a world surplus of sugar and sugar products, leading to very low prices. That situation might change if large quantities were used for MEOR but, on the other hand, new suppliers might choose to enter an expanding sugar market or existing growers may increase their output.

An important aspect of feeding bacteria from the surface is ensuring that in the porous rock the bulk of the feedstock is converted into product and not into an accumulation of bacterial mass which would not only be wasteful but also probably cause matrix plugging. Some polymer- and surfactant-producing bacteria are known in batch culture to synthesize much of their product late in the growth cycle, after the end of the exponential phase. They do so at that time because changes in the medium resulting from the earlier growth process produce a physiological condition able to support product formation but no further accumulation of biomass. The design of any continuously-fed downhole system will probably require the definition of an environmental regime allowing the separation of product formation from growth.

An inoculum of a selected strain is thus introduced into the reservoir in the expectation that many cells will attach themselves to the rock surface in the neighborhood of the injection well; the inclusion of some nutrient in the primary injectate will assist that attachment. This is followed by the injection of enough complete growth medium to permit the establishment of a downhole bacterial population. The organisms distribute themselves more-or-less radically around the injection well, following the flow pattern of the injected fluid. After a period for the cells to grow and the population to become established, the composition of the injected fluid is changed from one able to support growth to one designed primarily for the synthesis of product, although a low concentration of growth-promoting components may be necessary to allow the maintenance of a synthetically active population. From that point on the system is effectively an immobilized microbial culture continuously converting injected feedstock into the product which is swept forward by the waterflood into the reservoir, there to mobilize oil.

The active cells will inevitably be located close to the injector well because it is there that the feedstock will first become available to them. The bacterial colony will approach the injection well itself as closely as the scouring effect of the incoming waterflood allows and will extend away from the well to the point where the nutrient becomes exhausted. Thus, the culture may reasonably be expected to adopt an annular configuration around the injection well, bathed by a uni-directional flow of nutrient oriented at any point away from the injector and towards the reservoir. Lateral mixing of the culture will be restricted by the flow pattern of the waterflood and the labyrinthine nature of the matrix (Figure 11). One interesting consequence is that the effect of a chance contaminant or mutation is likely to be expressed predominantly in a narrow radial sector extending from the locus of the contaminant or mutant outwards to the boundary of the populated zone (Figure 12). Those consequences will accordingly be much less serious for the continued proper functioning of the system than they would be in a conventional stirred fermenter. Another problem arises, of course, from the possibility of microbial contaminants degrading the product after it has been washed away from the producing zone. Evaluation of this risk might lead to the need for protective measures. If contaminants can effectively be kept out of the waterflood by pre-sterilization of the injectate at the surface the products may run no risk of degradation; some operators already do this by continuously irradiating the injected water with banks of powerful ultra-violet lamps. An alternative, providing the producing strain can be made biocide-resistant, is to include a biocide in the waterflood. As in the case of selective plugging, temperature can also be a help: the polymer or surfactant will be swept away from the region of bacterial synthesis in the coolest part of the reservoirs, close to the injector, towards an environment which becomes progressively hotter. In deep reservoirs, where the interwell temperature is high, few contaminating microorganisms are likely to survive the increase in temperature and the products will be relatively safe from biodegradation.

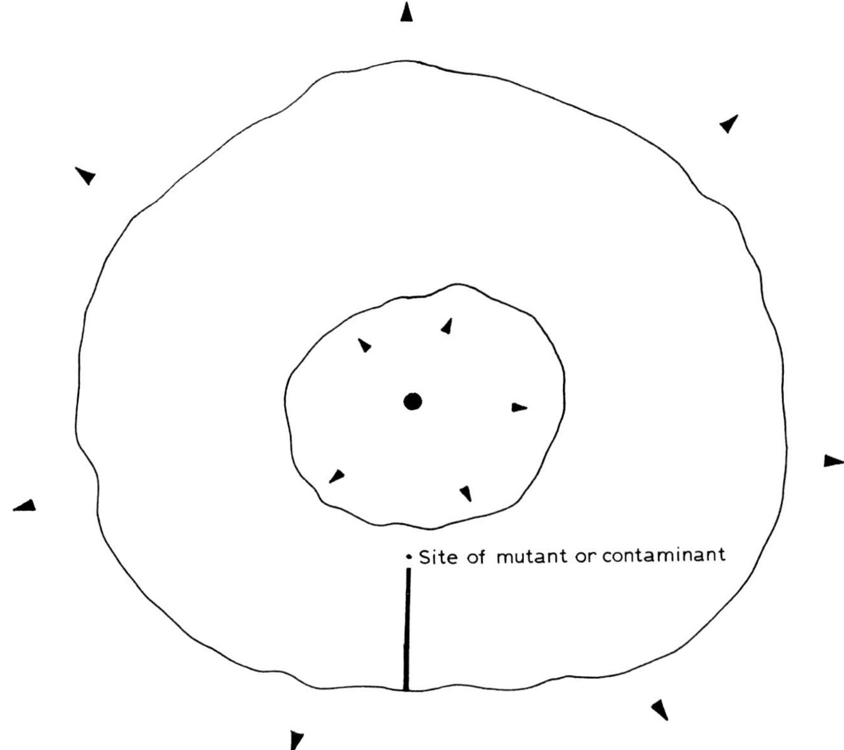

Figure 12. Effects of Limited Lateral Mixing
In the system shown in Figure 6 note that there is little or no lateral mixing in the zone of bacterial activity: the fluid flows essentially outwards in a radial direction from the injection well. The effect of a mutant (or contaminant) sited at position "X" will be minimal and confined to a narrow radial sector.

Systems of this sort are at the stage of laboratory development but none has yet been tested in the field. Cost-effectiveness compared with the direct injection of polymer from the surface is at present difficult to evaluate although preliminary calculations suggest that the downwhole synthesis of polymer would be the cheaper by a wide margin (Table 2); a more extensive cost-benefit analysis of possible MEOR procedures is presented later in this chapter. Another unresolved point is how to configure a combined surfactant and polymer flood. In conventional EOR technology the surfactant is injected first and is driven by a following polymer flood but it is not certain that this effect can be reproduced with microorganisms. One conceivable way is first to emplace a surfactant-producing system and, after a suitable period of weeks or months for the production of a sizable surfactant slug, to inoculate a polymer producer with such different nutritional requirements that a shift to the new medium will bring surfactant production to a halt to be replaced by the synthesis of polymer. Another is to inject both organisms together and generate a mixture of polymer and surfactant on a continuous basis. Yet a third way, at least in theory, is to find (or produce) an organism which can make both and to switch from one to the other by changing an appropriate effector in the injected medium. These are all practical matters to be dealt with before large-scale production operations can commence, but none has yet been resolved.

Heavy Oil Production

In addition to all the other production problems which might arise (poor water flow, coning, etc.), heavy oil is highly viscous. Techniques for facilitating production are mostly concerned with reducing viscosity and improving mobility. This usually requires the application of heat either in the form of injecting superheated steam or of underground combustion. Clearly biotechnology cannot accomplish an improvement of mobility by the production of sufficient heat.

There may be other ways of reducing viscosity in the reservoir. One might be based on the introduction into the oil-bearing zone of bacteria which would attack the high molecular weight components of the oil (those predominantly contributing to its viscosity) but not further metabolize the fragments: the average chain length of oil compounds would thereby presumably be reduced. While not inconceivable, this hardly seems a promising approach. Bacteria are not only less likely to attack high, rather than low, molecular weight substances but, even were they to do so, they would

Table 2
Feedstock Costs: Estimates for a North Sea Pilot

EOR using Xanthan
- requirement: 500–1,500 tonnes per year
- concentration: 500–2,000 ppm
- price per tonne for xanthan: £3,100–4,700 ($5,000–7,500)
- volume of water to be injected per year: 1.57–18.8 million bbl.

cost per bbl of injected water: at 500 ppm = 25–37p (39–60¢)
2,000 ppm = 99–149p (158–230¢)

Range of possible annual costs:
1.57 million bbl at 25p per bbl = £0.39 m ($0.62 m)
18.8 million bbl at 149p per bbl = £28.0 m ($44.8 m)

MEOR using Molasses
- price per tonne: £62.50 ($100.00)
- concentration required: 2–5%

cost per bbl of injected water: at 2% = 20p (32¢)
5% = 50p (80¢)

Range of possible annual costs:
1.57 million bbl at 20p per bbl = £0.31 m ($0.50 m)
18.8 million bbl at 50p per bbl = £9.4 m ($15.0 m)

Range of comparative feedstock costs: molasses/xanthan = 0.34–0.79.

Note that the costs for the biological procedures are for processes at an early stage development: technical improvements are expected to lead to a fall in input costs.

hardly trim them down to a size more amenable to the operator and then leave them alone.

Another idea is to use surfactant-producing bacteria, injected together with water and nutrients, to encourage the formation of an oil/water emulsion (with a viscosity markedly lower than that of the original oil) which would be recovered more readily than the crude oil itself. The oil could be separated from the water on the surface, perhaps by breaking the emulsion enzymatically. Some laboratory work has already been done on emulsification and there are grounds for optimism. How such a system might operate underground, however, is less clear. Since the problem is largely one of the sluggish oil flow, it would be difficult, if not impossible, to use the microbial system as a surfactant flood to push the oil to the producing well. Most probably, injection and production would have to take place through the same well on a *huff-and-puff* basis but a major difficulty is how to introduce the bacteria together with their nutrient medium. In fields with a residual gas cap it might be possible to inject the microbial inoculum and medium under pressure some distance into the reservoir but an inoculum confined to the immediate surroundings of the injection well, from which the oil had already been recovered, would have little value. Somehow the bacteria would have to be encouraged to infiltrate into the oil itself and that is more difficult to arrange. One factor helping matters is that most oil reservoirs are *water wet*: i.e. individual rock particles are covered by a film of water separating the rock from the oil. So bacteria might migrate through the water film but in order to have any major effect they would need to penetrate the oil zone to a distance of at least several meters and it is not immediately clear why they should do so or how they might be persuaded; perhaps a repellent would be effective. In the short term, at least, the use of biotechnology in the production of heavy oil seems more likely to be confined to improving the flow of such oil through pipelines, as we discuss below.

MICROBIAL SURVIVAL AND BEHAVIOR IN RESERVOIR ENVIRONMENTS

The most important factors influencing bacterial growth and metabolism in the reservoir matrix are nutrition, aeration, temperature, pressure and the possible toxic effects of the indigenous oil and water. Oil reservoirs are highly anaerobic places and are likely to remain so. The injection of molecular oxygen, or oxygenated water, to allow aerobic metabolism would be severely frowned upon by most operators. Oxygen is highly corrosive to steel pipework and pumps: operators often go to considerable lengths to remove oxygen from their injection waters specifically to reduce the corrosion risk. In practical terms this means that downhole microbial systems must be based upon anaerobic metabolism: because, as we have already noted, crude oil is such a poor substrate in those conditions, there is little option but to inject nutrients capable of being readily fermented anaerobically.

Temperature is clearly a major limitation: mesophilic organisms grow to about 45°C but many reservoirs are hotter than that. Although some thermophiles survive up to about 100°C their variety is more restricted than that of the mesophiles. Extreme temperatures, however, may not prove to be a serious drawback: note how many of the MEOR procedures described above are designed to operate in near-well environments, in regions which will have been extensively waterflooded and correspondingly cooled (Figure 13). For example, in some North Sea fields which have a reservoir temperature of about 90°C, waterflooding is estimated to have reduced the downhole near-well temperature to 30–40°C. But where this does not hold (e.g. in some cases of well stimulation and coning control) it will be necessary to use strains able to proliferate in whatever is the local downhole temperature; clearly there will be some instances beyond the reach of biological methods.

High pressure, too, is unlikely to be an insuperable problem since fortunately most bacteria are rather barotolerant. Many readily survive pressures up to about 300 atmosphere above the ambient in their natural habitats and some will tolerate a pressure of 1,000 atmospheres or more. Reservoir pressures vary from essentially 1 atmosphere for the shallowest fields to hundreds of atmospheres at great depths. It is clear that microbes must be chosen for injection in the light of their degree of barotolerance as well as their ability to generate the desired products.

Finally, toxicity of reservoir fluids appears never to have been reported as a problem in field tests; both the presence of an indigenous microflora in contaminated reservoirs and the ability to culture microorganisms in the laboratory in media containing oil-saturated reservoir brines suggests either an absence of toxicity, or at least the existence of widespread resistance. Furthermore, in almost all the MEOR techniques described above the injected bacteria would find themselves in the presence of injected rather than indigenous water and out of close contact with residual oil.

RESERVOIR MICROBIOLOGY

There is growing evidence for the presence of bacteria underground to quite remarkable depths and many reservoirs carry a mixed population of bacteria: how did they get there, how

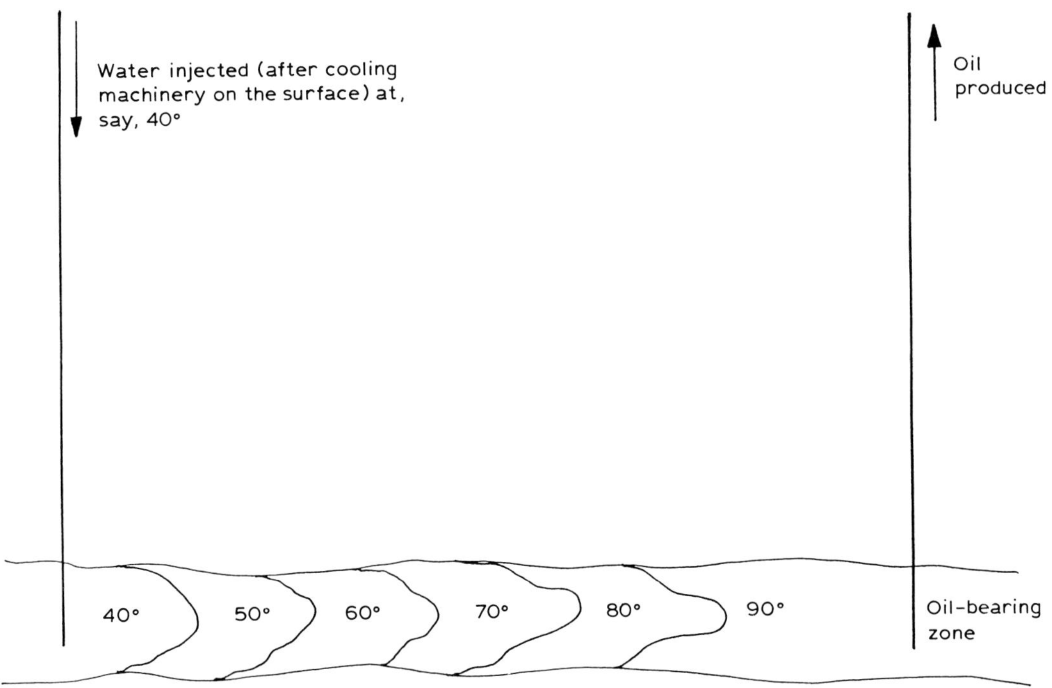

Figure 13. Reservoir Isotherms
Prolonged waterflooding will cool the region of the oil-bearing zone near the injection well to a temperature lower than that of the bulk of the reservoir (assumed in this model to be 90°C) and a series of isotherms will be established through the water-swept portion.

do they survive and what effect might they have on some of the MEOR systems described in this chapter which depend on the deliberate introduction of a specific microbial population?

It is widely held that bacteria have in many cases entered reservoir rock via channels ultimately connected to surface or aquifer waters. A very slow flow of water might be enough to carry bacteria down to the oil-bearing zone together with sufficient mineral salts for growth, albeit at very low rates. The nature of the carbon source, however, is clearly a problem. There is little convincing evidence for the ability of bacteria to attack hydrocarbons under anaerobic conditions (but see comments made earlier in this chapter): molecular oxygen seems almost always to be a requirement. However, those very water channels allowing bacteria to access the crude oil might also be the route for oxygen entry: not much oxygen, it is true, but sufficient over long periods to allow for a slow utilization of downhole hydrocarbon and the maintenance of a resident microbial population.

The very act of drilling is itself likely to contaminate the reservoir unless stringent precautions are taken to avoid it. Drilling does not take place under sterile conditions; inevitably bacteria and other microorganisms will be carried into the well on the drills and in the circulating drilling mud. Some of them will remain downhole. What happens to them depends on their nutritional opportunities.

Waterflooding is an obvious way for nutrient substrates to enter the oilfield. In many such floods no efforts are made to remove oxygen from injection waters originating from lakes, ponds and rivers; aerobic organisms close to the well-bore will use oxygen thus introduced into the reservoir as an oxidizing agent for the metabolism of hydrocarbon. Aerobic metabolism will continue as long as oxygen is available, with the release into the water stream of various organic metabolites: these will serve to sustain the growth of anaerobes once all the oxygen has been removed by the aerobic species upstream. An ecological sequence may accordingly become established, extending from a relatively aerobic zone near the well to a progressively more and more anaerobic environment the further the water moves into the reservoir.

Many of the resident bacteria are likely to be present in biofilms adhering to the sand particles and rock faces rather than as free planktonic cells. It is not difficult to appreciate that close to the well-bore the surface of a biofilm might contain mostly aerobic bacteria shielding underlying colonies of anaerobes from oxygen present in the flowing water. Deeper into the reservoir and under the biofilms the oxygen tension will be low and the bacterial population predominantly anaerobic. Thus, near the well one might expect to find strains of *Bacillus, Pseudomonas, Micrococcus, Acinetobacter* and other aerobes followed, as the oxygen tension falls, by *Clostridia* and ultimately by *Desulfovibrio* and *Methanobacterium*.

Because of its corrosive effects on metalwork (including pipe casing, liners and pumps), major operators (and many minor ones as well) go to great lengths to reduce the oxygen content of injection waters virtually to zero. Under these conditions an initial aerobic attack on indigenous crude is essentially impossible, no metabolites are released for anaerobes to utilize and the downhole microbial population probably remains very low unless the injection waters already contain soluble organic subtances. The amounts in fresh water will be variable and depend on its source. Seawater also contains soluble biodegradable organic compounds although their concentrations are, not surprisingly, very low: glucose, amino acids, acetate, tricarboxylic acid cycle intermediates and other metabolites have all been detected. Glucose, for instance, has been reported at levels of less than 10μm glucose carbon/1 with a few recordings near the surface at values up to 50 μg/1. But the volumes of water actually pumped into the reservoirs are sometimes very large: on one typical North Sea platform the rate of injection through individual wells is about 3 tonnes/minute. Even at those low glucose concentrations, 150 mg glucose carbon will be injected each minute, or more than 200 g each day, and the injection of water might go on for months or years! There will obviously be plenty of substrate for a hefty bacterial population to develop downhole if the environmental conditions are otherwise acceptable.

Some workers (see next section) have conceived of MEOR procedures based on stimulating an indigenous population by the injection solely of organic nutrients (and mineral supplements where necessary) but it is difficult to define the objectives and operation of such procedures or predict their outcome in either chemical or engineering terms. Of course, the introduction of bacteria and substrate specifically intended for the production of polymer and/or surfactant in a controlled operation is likely also to stimulate a reaction by the indigenous flora. Matrix acidizing as well as thief zone plugging and coning control by polymer generation are probably not very vulnerable to interference by the pre-existing population because they are in effect batch operations soon completed; but protocols for biologically-based downhole polymer or surfactant floods must include the introduction of a sufficiently large inoculum effectively to overwhelm the existing population or otherwise to ensure the desired result in a predictable fashion. Clearly there are risks associated with MEOR and any system design must take them into account.

MEOR IN THE FIELD

Since the late 1940s hundreds of fields tests have been carried out using microbial systems in actual reservoirs. The earliest ones were in the U.S. but until the mid-1970s the price of oil in the west was too low, and oil was too readily available on the world market, to excite much interest in such new technologies. The situation was very different in countries like Czechoslovakia, Hungary, Poland, Romania and the Soviet Union because their convertible currency problems made oil purchases on the open market difficult and encouraged maximization of domestic oil productions; they were therefore keen to maintain a high rate of recovery from their own national resources. Most of the field tests between about 1955 and 1975 were thus conducted in Eastern Europe and a summary (in English) of activity worldwide up to 1982 was assembled by Hitzman[3]; this has subsequently been updated[5]. Serious interest reawakened in the west after the oil price rises of 1973 and 1978.

Much of the earlier testing centred on single well stimulation although more recently interest has extended to multiple well designs. Many of the single well MEOR field pilots reported either in the literature[3] or anecdotally at conferences and elsewhere are probably of this type. Both the objectives and the results of these pilots are almost always reported only in the most general terms of seeking to improve oil recovery. The reasons for the diminution of the flow rate in the first place are usually not recorded and the bacterial inoculum and nutrient support appear rarely if ever to have been designed to meet the specific problems of a particular reservoir or well.

There does nevertheless seem to be little doubt that, under some conditions at least, bacterial systems injected into reservoirs do stimulate an increase in the rate of oil recovery. The Polish work[2] during the 1970s, for all the obscurities and uncertainties associated with the condition of the wells and the state of the reservoir, coupled with a lack of clear understanding as to *why* the production rate increased after treatment, undoubtedly demonstrates that something beneficial happened; the problem is to decide what took place and the reasons for it.

No microbial tests specifically directed to matrix acidizing have been reported but a small number of selective plugging trials have been conducted, mostly by Jack and his colleagues in Canada[6]. Details of these trials available in the literature suggest that, while in some cases at least the behavior of the test was satisfactory from a microbiological point of view, the trials did not have the desired effect because of limitations in the reservoir engineering (i.e. the bacteria produced their expected products but did so in the wrong place). Correct placement might turn out to be the major limitation of attempts to control water movement in the reservoir.

No field tests of a polymer flood appear to have taken place. However, an *in situ* MEOR pilot currently under way in Oklahoma[7] is probably at least partly a surfactant flood: aside from an earlier trial which may have had a surfactant component, it is the only one to have been fairly extensively documented in the public literature. After more than two years into the test, the results were encouraging and suggested that the field test would ultimately have been judged technically successful; there was not yet sufficient information to determine whether it would also have proven to be cost-effective. Severe operational difficulties then arose because of other field activities which began close to the test pattern and the trial is being rescheduled to start again in another part of the field remote form the interference. This difficulty illustrates the type of problem not infrequently encountered by those who attempt MEOR field pilots: operators cannot always be relied upon to manage the field in such a way as to isolate the test pattern from outside influences. Indeed, in some cases ownership or management of the field has changed hands during the test with the new owners/managers being less dedicated than those previously in charge.

Another approach to MEOR seeks to make maximal use of reservoir ecology by injecting nutrient to stimulate the indigenous downhole microflora rather than introducing an extraneous microbial system designed to synthesize a specific product or set of products. There are various ways of doing this. In the Soviet Union injection waters are not normally deoxygenated: workers in that country are thus able to stimulate indigenous population simply by introducing aerated water containing mineral sources of nitrogen and phosphorus as necessary. This allows an aerobic attack on crude oil hydrocarbons which sets in train a whole host of subsequent microbial reactions and interactions; the actual metabolic products will obviously depend both on the existing flora and the reservoir conditions. How predictable and effective this procedure may be is a matter for debate. The effect is probably not very different from standard industry practise in the past: the use of clean, deoxygenated water for injection purposes is comparatively recent. Before that began, injection waters drawn from surface accumulations or stored in open pits until required were not only in contact with air but were often heavily contaminated with all manner of organic and inorganic substances originating from discarded automobiles, rotting vegetation, dead cows and other debris. In those days the technique for producing oil was sometimes not so much a waterflood as a "bug flood"!

A number of workers in effect use a combined system of specific bacteria injected into the reservoir interacting with an indigenous biological population. In Romania, where the experimental reservoirs are heavily contaminated, the emphasis is on injecting bacteria chosen for maximizing gas production from molasses, an agricultural product hitherto extremely cheap in that country although it may not remain so in the future. A group in Australia base their protocols on the ecological approach of inducing metabolic activity in a biological system rather than attempting to inject microorganisms in order to produce defined metabolites. Generalized nutrients like molasses are avoided because many indigenous strains fail to respond to it. Instead the microflora of each reservoir is individually evaluated and an appropriate medium designed. But additional bacteria are introduced, for example to provide surfactant effects: this is done not with *surfactant-producing strains* but by using bacteria cells in the UMB form which themselves act as surfactant by virtue of their own surface properties. The basis of the Australian trials is that microbial activity is likely to achieve increased production via the simultaneous application of profile improvement of aquifer sweeping (i.e. selectively plugging high flow water channels), increased pressurization and surfactant. Results to date do indeed show an increase in oil production as well as a reduction in water cut (all, moreover, at a cost consistent with the economic potential of the reservoir) but whether the mechanisms of increased oil production are the ones intended cannot readily be determined from the available data. Even with prior laboratory exploration to characterize them reliance on a pre-existing reservoir population to generate an appropriate collection of metabolites just right for stimulating oil production in any particular reservoir may be rather a complex and risky strategy. It seems unlikely to commend itself to major operators who insist quite properly on having a detailed understanding as well as a computer model of any proposed activity in their fields.

A collection of papers detailing the most recent information on field tests can be found in the proceedings of the 1990 conference on MEOR[8].

SHALE OIL AND TAR SANDS

Enormous quantities of hydrocarbon are to be found worldwide in deposits of shale oil and tar sands; the total reserves of these sources of hydrocarbons is believed to be many times greater than those in conventional crude oil reservoirs. In oil shale, the hydrocarbon is found as a solid material (kerogen) dispersed in the rock. In tar sands, highly viscous bitumen is associated with loosely consolidated, or totally unconsolidated, sand particles. Because the hydrocarbon is in neither case liquid the source material must be mined and processed on the surface. The cost of removing large amounts of rock by mining is, of course, high compared with drilling a comparatively small number of wells and allowing, or forcing, liquid crude to rise the surface. The deep mining of oil shales and tar sands is probably nowhere economically feasible and their recovery is restricted to surface strip mining. The cost of producing shale oil always tends to be higher than that of crude; this has been a powerful factor depressing the development of shale oil production except when the world price of crude has been very high or as a consequence of very special economic or political factors.

The production of shale oil starts with mining the rock. Next, the process of *beneficiation* achieves as much preliminary separation as possible of the mineral rock from the kerogen in order to save heating costs in the following stage of retorting, a high temperature cracking process yielding a liquid product. The resulting crude shale oil is upgraded by high pressure hydrogenation to increase the hydrogen content and is then ready for refining. Like other oils it may contain undesirably high concentrations of sulfur-, nitrogen- and oxygen-containing compounds which are expensive to remove during the refining process. Biotechnological methods for the desulfurization of oil are relevant here and will be discussed later.

While it is perhaps impossible to perceive a rôle for biotechnology in the mining of shale, there have been suggestions for the deployment of microbial systems in beneficiation. One proposition is to assist the mechanical separation of rock and kerogen by violent agitation of the crushed shale in the presence of a fermentation broth containing biosurfactant but there are no reports of this having been tested. Another is for a microbial attack on the mineral element of the mined shale; studies by Yen and his colleagues have shown this to be very slow and probably not cost-effective. The substitution of biotechnological procedures for existing methods of retorting and hydrogenation appear most unlikely.

In bitumen production, too, the most likely involvement of biotechnology is in the separation of sand from bitumen using microbial surfactants. Laboratory studies have shown that separation is indeed assisted but whether or not this could form the basis of an industrial process is not clear. One of the main commercial sources of tar sands is the Athabasca deposit in Alberta where the operations are conducted on a huge local scale (Figures 14 and 15) and, in winter, under very severe climatic conditions. It is doubtful whether rather slowly acting microbiological operations could successfully be introduced in that climate on the scale required and in competition with existing methods.

PIPELINING

Oil must sometimes be transported by pipeline over large distances from remote fields to refineries and consumers. The viscosity of heavy oils introduces serious flow problems and obviously increases the energy requirement of pumping. It is possible significantly to reduce viscosity, and hence facilitate transportation, by producing a stable oil/water emulsion. The cost of such a process will include that of the emulsification process itself, the burden of transporting useless water, the increased risk of corroding the inside of the pipes and ultimately the separation of oil and water before refining. Nevertheless, the expense of building a pipeline is itself very high and while the inclusion of water in the emulsion would obviously increase the total volume of liquid to be transported, a sufficient reduction in viscosity might actually improve fluid flow to such an extent that more oil could be moved through a given pipe. Here, too, microbial surfactants and emulsifiers are being experimentally screened for their suitability for pipelining and some may prove useful.

TANKER CLEANING

Microbial surfactants and emulsifiers have also found a rôle in oil tanker cleanout. One example, *emulsan*[9], is already being marketed and is in use for cleaning the tanks of oil barges on the Mississippi River. It was at one time suggested

Figure 14. Mining Tar Sand
The equipment is huge as the size of this machine illustrates. (Photographed in Alberta)

Figure 15. A Tar Sand Mine
The scale of the operation needs no comment. (Photographed in Alberta).

by Gutnick and Rosenberg[10] that the tanks of ocean-going oil tankers, traveling in ballast back to the oilfields, might be filled with a nutrient medium inoculated with emulsan-producing bacteria to facilitate the cleaning of their tanks during the voyage. The oil detached from the tank walls would float to the surface of the aqueous medium and could be recovered by skimming. The method would eliminate manual cleaning of tanks with its attendant risk of explosion. It appears, nevertheless, that this method had not been adopted by shippers, perhaps because they are too unfamiliar with microbiology and feel uncomfortable at the prospect of filling their ships' tanks with, as they see it, a new and unquantifiable hazard.

DOWNSTREAM PROCESSING

Most work on the microbial downstream processing of crude oils has been directed to desulfurization. High-sulfur crudes are undesirable because, unless their combustion effluents are extensively (and expensively) scrubbed, they pollute the environment with acidic oxides of sulfur and have unpleasant effects on living organisms and corrosive consequences for equipment; a high sulfur content also adds to the cost of refining. Nevertheless, as oil supplies gradually become constrained the world will become increasingly dependent on high-sulfur crudes. Yet desulfurization by conventional technology is energy-intensive and therefore expensive. Possible microbial alternatives are based on the observation that some bacteria are able partially to oxidize various sulfur-containing compounds often found in crude oil to water-soluble materials which can be washed out in a water stream. Studies published in the early 1970s[11] suggested the following pathway:

Detailed studies by Finnerty and Hartdegen[12] showed that strains of *Pseudomonas* carry plasmid-encoded enzymes specific for sulfur-containing heterocyclics. The enzymes have no appreciable effect on the composition or properties of the crude oil other than the elimination of some or all of the organic sulfur. The organisms were tested on a number of high-sulfur crudes, mostly from Texas and Venezuela, and were able in laboratory experiments essentially to eliminate all the dibenzothiophene within a few hours.

Inevitably such a procedure requires the mixing or emulsifying of the oil with water, partly because the bacteria are, of course, water-based and partly to allow the removal of the water-soluble oxidation products. The dispersion of oil in water is itself energy-intensive although under certain circumstances, as we have noted in the discussion on heavy oil, it might conceivably already have taken place in the reservoir as part of a microbially-assisted production process. Not only must the oil and water phases be intimately mixed but almost certainly an emulsion of some stability will be necessary because of the prolonged contact time required for the microbial oxidation to take place; good aeration is also likely to be a prerequisite.

Finnerty and Robinson[13] refer to a preliminary cost-benefit analysis based apparently on 1982 prices. Compared with a then market price for low-sulfur oil of $24.95 per barrel, the improvement by (non-biological) hydrodesulfurization of high-sulfur oil (costing $21.18 a barrel) would actually have cost a total of $31.90. Oil which had undergone microbial desulfurization with the technology then current would have cost $48.40 a barrel although a target price for the microbial product of $30.00 might not have been unreasonable as a result of technical improvements. Nevertheless, even that price would have been some $5.05 per barrel more expensive than the prevailing market price for the low-sulfur crude. The outstanding questions are clearly whether further technical improvements could make the method more competitive and how the differential between high- and low-sulfur oils might move in the future. It does appear at present that microbial desulfurization of crude oil is a marginal commercial prospect.

MICROBIAL CORROSION

The most immediate interaction between the oil industry and microbiology results from a concern with corrosion, and especially with the generation of hydrogen sulfide by sulfate-reducing bacteria. Hydrogen sulfide poses four main problems: (a) it is very toxic to people and thus poses a severe health hazard; (b) it dissolves in crude oil, thereby increasing its sulfur content and refining costs, and reducing its market value; (c) it may result in the precipitation of insoluble inorganic sulfides in the reservoir matrix and thereby impede fluid flow; (d) it is acidic and hence corrosive to pipes, pumps, valves and other metallic fittings.

Major operators go to considerable lengths to eliminate sulfate-reducing bacteria from their fields. Injection waters are carefully filtered and polished to remove particulates. If the danger is considered to be sufficiently grave a biocide may be dissolved in the injection water although this adds significantly to the expense of oil recovery. Recently, ultraviolet irradiation has been introduced as a means of sterilizing injection wates. In spite of these efforts fields sometimes do "go sour", presumably as the result of invasion by sulfate-reducers. The problem may be more severe in offshore fields because seawater contains more dissolved sulfate than do fresh waters. Since offshore fields are always operated by major or national oil companies it is they, rather than independents dealing with fresh water, who may be more worried by and sensitive to the presence of sulfate-reducers.

ATTITUDES OF OIL COMPANIES

Notwithstanding the potential value of microbial procedures for enhancing the recovery of oil and for facilitating a number dibenzothiophene

1, 2-dihydro-1, 2-dihydrodibenzothiophene

1, 2-dihydroxydibenzothiophene

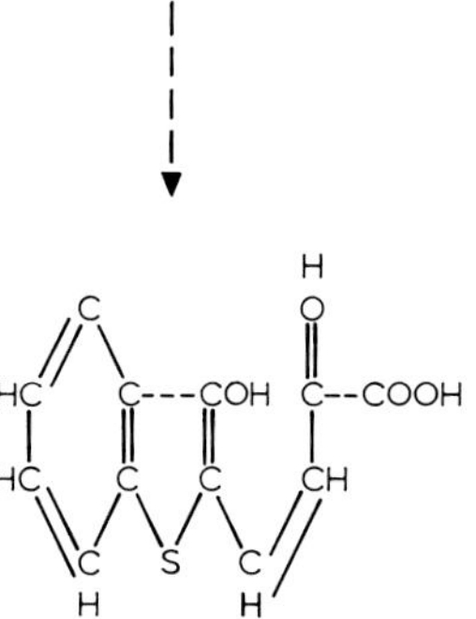

cis-4-(3-hyroxybenzo [*b*] thiophen-2-yl)-2-oxobut-3-enoic acid

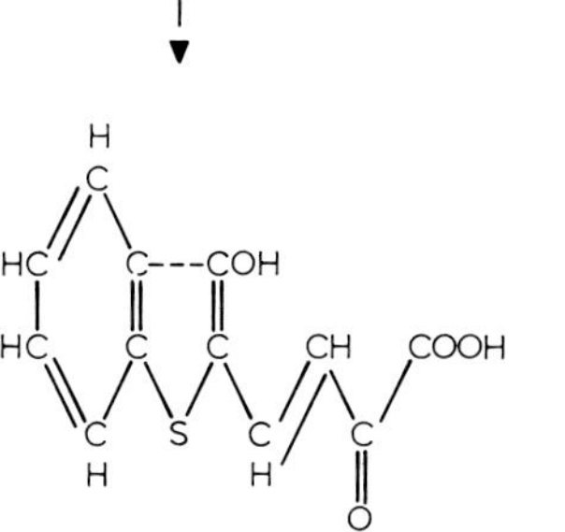

trans-4-(3-hyroxybenzo [*b*] thiophen-2-yl)-2-oxobut-3-enoic acid

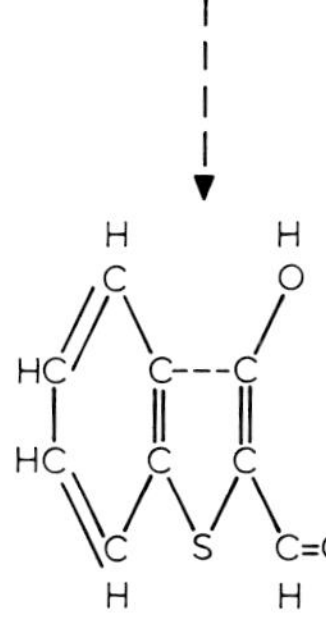

3-hydroxy-2-formylbenzo [*b*] thiophene

of other production procedures, it is relevant to ask why for the most part the industry itself has not been in the forefront of their development. The answer has several strands, some to do with economics and priorities and some to do with people.

One important consideration is that the industry is in some respects rather conservative; people who work in oil often prefer to apply their existing skills rather than become involved with new, and to them perhaps strange, approaches the scientific bases of which do not form part of their own technical experience. Major oil companies have a long history of very successfully producing, refining and marketing oil and they have their own traditions for doing so, traditions which do not usually include a positive rôle for biological methods. This reluctance to become involved with unproven technologies is compounded by another attitude not uncommon in the industry: wait for the new ideas to be developed elsewhere (in the universities, for example, or in the specialist biotechnology companies), comfortably and realistically confident that when they become ready for use the industry will be able to buy in.

Another reason is that many oil companies have no R&D facilities of their own while others which do operate research divisions have no direct experience of microbiology: neither category is likely to be a leader in MEOR development. However, of corporations with their own laboratories, and particularly those with an existing presence in biotechnology, there are some which do indeed work in this area. A complicating factor nevertheless follows from a style of internal organization and budgeting common in large corporations. Seen from without, they appear overwhelmingly powerful and endowed with vast resources. Seen from within, those very resources are divided into myriad subsidiary budgets, each one necessarily constrained and subject to many demands. Inevitable pressure on research budgets, even large ones, results in a hierarchy of priorities and as a result new technologies need people to champion them within a company if they are to compete successfully for resources. Some companies have such MEOR champions right now: others do not, although they may have had them in the past and they may well appear again in the future. But it is not easy for someone without a sound understanding of microorganisms to assess the potential for MEOR and promote support for it in competition with other desirable developments. The problems some reservoir and production engineers experience with sulfate-reducing bacteria color their attitude to all aspects of microbiology. They become unreceptive to proposals for developing MEOR methods, frequently being unwilling to judge them on their merits and preferring instead to regard all consideration of deliberately introducing microorganisms into reservoirs with the same horror they would have for proposing the injection of sulfate-reducers. Under these circumstances the priority given at local level to MEOR may well be low. Convincing head office, or the scientists in the research laboratories, will obviously help but in the final analysis it is not usually they who make operating decisions in the field.

For MEOR technologies to play a significant part in oil production their value and effectiveness need first to be demonstrated to people whose responsibility it is to maintain production levels in the oilfields. Only evidence of the successful deployment of MEOR under field conditions is likely to convince the skeptics: at that stage the technology will become of direct interest to the operations management and no longer remain the concern predominantly of the research departments. At the time of writing (November 1989) a number of well-designed field trials are being planned or are already taking place: their results will clearly be of crucial importance.

Independent operators are in a very different position. Sharing many of their traditions with the majors (people in independent companies have often built their careers in the employ of large oil corporations), they nevertheless frequently show a greater degree of interest in new methods. Their operations are more often at the margins of cost-effectiveness and they are likely to benefit immediately from cheaper technologies. But, unlike the majors, they have fewer financial resources and usually no laboratory facilities at their disposal. Sponsorship by a government agency may be the most effective route to the testing and development of the new microbial methods for the resolution of their particular problems and this, too, is happening in a number of countries.

One oil company main board director, well versed in microbiology, recently wrote to the author: *With this widespread interest it would be very surprising if MEOR was not employed in local fields within the next five years.* That may be as good an indication as any of the way things are going.

COST-BENEFIT ANALYSIS OF MEOR

Few attempts have been made to analyze in detail the probable input costs of materials and labor and to compare them with output benefits measured as incremental oil produced. Nevertheless, in one recent study a number of reasonable and conservative assumptions are made and their consequences explored[14]; the reader should bear in mind that the parameters employed are indeed assumptions and, for the most part, are not the result of direct field experience.

The first of two models considers single well stimulation. It assumes a trial involving four stripper wells, each producing 1 barrel a day of crude oil. The wells are treated identically: they are injected with an appropriate microbial population and then shut in for one week. Thereafter each receives 15 gallons (57 l) of nutrient every month for six months; 2 tonnes of feedstock are required in total, costing $200. A plausible response is assumed to be: no change in the rate of oil production for the first 2 months, followed by a rise in daily production of each well to 3 barrels per day for the next 6 months, with a return to 1 barrel a day for the final 4 months of the year. Thus, compared with the pre-injection baseline, an additional 1,410 barrels of oil will have been produced over the one-year pilot project.

The costs involved are assumed to include $2,000 for minimal laboratory design and testing activities in advance of the injections, $600 for modifications to surface facilities, and $200 for nutrient as noted above. Furthermore, $300 is lost because of suspended production during the one-week shut-in period. Operating expenses are estimated at $5.50 per barrel of crude oil produced.

At a market price for crude oil of $16.50 per barrel, this scenario breaks even during the fourth month and yields an increase in net income over the year of $12,700, some 1.8 times the yield without the microbial treatment; the project shows a return on investment greater than 355%. The sensitivities in the system are most marked with respect to oil price and the number of wells treated. Thus, for the 4-well system, an oil price of $10.50 per barrel gives an increases in net income of $4,260 (52% return on investment), while at $20.50 per barrel the corresponding values are $18,400 and 556%. Reducing the number of wells treated greatly minimizes the return because the incremental cost of treating more wells is essentially that of the nutrient, together with minor surface modifications: if the above parameters are applied to 1-, 3- and 5-well systems the values for increased net income are $1,200, $8,900 and $16,600, giving net returns on investment of −53%, 224% and 481%, respectively. But changing the price of the nutrient has little effect as it constitutes only a small proportion of the total cost. For the 4-well system, nutrient costs of $100, $200 and $400 give increases in net income of $12,700 (as in the original calculation), $12,500 and $12,100 (return rates of 355%, 318% and 257%), respectively.

The second example contrasts a polymer flood using

chemical injection with the downhole generation of polymer by microorganisms (compare these calculations with the data in Table 2). The reservoir model used was typical for mid-continental U.S. fields: a 20-acre (8 ha) pattern, with 490,000 barrels of oil assumed originally to have been in place. The hypothetical project supposes that at the time of the trial, 53% of the original oil (260,000 barrels) remained, giving a residual oil saturation of 37%. The calculations include assumptions of a federal income tax at 34% and severance tax and royalty rates of 7% and 12.5%, respectively.

As detailed reservoir simulation has not yet been developed for MEOR systems, a polymer flood predictive model generated by the U.S. Department of Energy was employed to simulate responses to the microbial activity. The input parameters, again conservative, assumed a reduction of residual oil saturation from 30%, produced by waterflooding, to 25% following the MEOR treatment. Again, the oil price was taken as $16.50 per barrel, the cost of polymer as $1.39/lb and the nutrient cost was estimated at $100/tonne, with 250 tonnes being injected into the 20-acre test pattern each year for two years. More extensive preliminary laboratory work is necessary for a microbial polymer-generating system that for single-well stimulation, costing 3–5 times more, and this is included in the calculations. More reservoir engineering is required, involving, for instance, a tracer study of reservoir water flows: similar costs would be incurred for any EOR programme. Operating expenses and taxes were assumed to be the same for chemical-based and microbial polymer floods.

While the individual calculations are too extensive to be reproduced here (the interested reader might wish to refer to the original paper), the conclusions are instructive. The economic life of a polymer flood using chemical injection is 14 years with a payout, based on after-tax, discounted cash flow, of 12 years. The net profit per barrel of oil is $0.79 and the rate of return on capital invested is 11.8%. For the microbial polymer system the comparable values are 8 years, 7 years, $1.57 and 14.9%, respectively. At an oil price of $20 per barrel the net profit is $3.22 per barrel for the microbial system versus $2.62 for chemical injection. Although in the very long term (20 years) the ultimate cumulative production of oil is about the same in each system, the use of microorganisms recovers oil faster. If the two processes are compared at 8 years (the economic life of the microbial flood), the MEOR procedure, which has a positive cash flow, has produced 11,180 barrels more than the polymer system, which at that time shows a negative cash flow. Rapid return on capital, an important factor in any investment decision, clearly favors the microbiological flood.

ECONOMIC AND POLITICAL FACTORS

Because the economic benefits of successfully enhancing the recovery of oil can be so huge, many fields are large enough to warrant the development of site-specific EOR or MEOR methods tailored exactly to their requirements. Of course, the cost of adapting an existing core of experimental knowledge for application to a particular field must be justified in terms of the value of the additional oil to be recovered, but the magnitude of each operation is expected to keep low the *development costs per barrel of incremental oil.* Nevertheless, there may be a number of alternatives to using injected chemicals or microbes to increase the recovery from a group of wells or from a particular reservoir: they include drilling more wells or opening up new fields. An operator will obviously weigh up the comparative costs and benefits of each course of action. He will be influenced by many factors, including, for example, the tax regime under which he operates. Several countries have at various times introduced tax benefits based upon incremental oil produced by EOR techniques. Such tax rules will influence operators to follow one course of action rather than another. Further considerations include planning and environmental regulations pertaining to drilling new wells which, if they make it difficult and expensive to secure permission and avoid despoilation, will encourage maximizing the yields from existing investment. The interaction of all these influences is of great complexity in each individual case and we can here do little more than point to their existence.

A recent paper[15] has discussed in some detail the interaction of tax incentives, price supports and other factors influencing the economics of enhanced oil recovery. In an analysis based on New Mexico, Oklahoma and the United States as a whole the authors conclude that, at oil prices below $28 per barrel, incentives *stimulate* significant EOR production while at lower oil prices incentives in some form are *necessary* to make new EOR projects viable. Done the right way, incentives can yield a net profit to the public sector and often even to the agency granting them. Indeed, such incentives granted by one level of government can benefit other levels at no net cost. By combining tax incentives with anticipated improvements in technology, the authors conclude that the threshold oil price at which future EOR projects become viable can be reduced by as much as $8 a barrel: that would add significantly to recoverable U.S. oil reserves.

Corporations and governments are acutely sensitive to a great variety of geopolitical factors. Multinationals need to take account of the present and future political climate of the areas in which they operate. The prospect of political instability or hostility must predispose them to extract more from their stable holdings rather than risk investment with an uncertain outcome. Governments are concerned with the interactive effects of the stability of oil supplies, tax revenues and balance of payments problems. For both political and foreign exchange reasons, they may use tax incentives to encourage the development of domestic reserves and thereby reduce dependence on external supplies. They may directly subsidize research and development of new methods in pursuit of those objectives. Command economies may decide to allocate resources in such a way as to maximize their perceived national advantage almost irrespective of the cost in their own currencies. All of these fiscal and political techniques have been used in a number of countries through the years and they seem likely to continue to be employed if and when they appear to be appropriate to those in charge. It makes the future part to be played in the industry by MEOR technologies difficult to predict precisely although extrapolation from present and earlier trends suggests a continuous and steady increase of their use in the field.

COMMERCIALIZING MEOR

MEOR makes sense only in a commercial context. As this book has made clear from the outset, biotechnology is by its very nature a business activity. Thus, as the mechanisms underlying MEOR procedures become more clearly defined, and successive field tests demonstrate their effectiveness for improving oil production, the question of marketing becomes increasingly important.

From both technical and commercial standpoints, two versions of MEOR may be emerging. The more precisely focused procedures aim to use specific microbial system designs essentially imposed upon the reservoirs environments. They seek to provide *in situ* microbial counterparts for existing EOR concepts such as chemical flooding or the control of water movement and they will ultimately be marketed on their ability to do so more cost-effectively than conventional methods.

Developing in parallel are more empirical, less focused systems. They have grown from experiments in which, instead, of aiming to achieve specific target mechanisms, various more-or-less *ad hoc* microbial protocols, rather imprecisely assembled to generate a variety of characterized and uncharacterized products, were observed to have beneficial effects on the release of incremental oil. Sometimes, but by no means always, attempts were made to understand their mechanisms, presumably with the objective of improving the technology. Because they were not intended to be specific, once some sort of oil-releasing procedure had been developed these empirical methods could be operated inexpensively in the field with little or no site-specific modifications. Simple reservoir assessments were sufficient to show whether or not a particular reservoir would provide an acceptable environment for microbial activity. Microbial inoculants comprised mixtures of strains which, in laboratory experiments, produced a collection of products expected in a general way to have desirable effects: sometimes the emphasis was on gas production, at other times solvents or acids were judged equally or more important. Some evidence of surfactant activity was regarded as an additional benefit.

Thus, without being able to define just how oil was to be released, it was felt that cocktails of chemicals with various activities ought to be effective: and, indeed, often they were, stimulating production to a useful extent for a small-scale operation. In time some people went further and began to argue that there was neither need nor advantage in introducing extraneous microbial strains; why not simply inject nutrients to stimulate the indigenous population in the hope and expectation that it, too, would produce useful chemicals?

These two ways of using MEOR may be giving rise simultaneously to parallel commercial trends. Highly focused systems, aiming at the control of water flows and the establishment of well understood surfactant or polymer floods, depend on a high degree of reservoir characterization as well as precise system design and operation. These in turn require a level of resource investment which implies that such designs will primarily be targeted to high-producing, relatively large-scale operations in which they will make major contributions to revenue streams.

On the other hand, the demand for very inexpensive procedures to use in marginal, small-scale (stripper) operations will offer opportunities for some of the generalized empirical methods. As long as failure to increase oil production does not actually cause damage, it might make good economic sense with a stripper operation to take a gamble with cheap technology. Provided that the rewards of success are believed to outweigh the costs of failure, some small independents will take that gamble; indeed, a number are already doing so. Preparations are sold for dewaxing and descaling with which some operators express satisfaction. More worrying is the presence now on the market of commercial products whose modes of action seem to rely on something close to magic. Reservoir engineers and petroleum microbiologists know that all sorts of materials introduced into reservoirs, including quantities of water, will temporarily raise production rates a little. Whether or not the rise is maintained and the procedure has any lasting effect is another matter. A number of bizarre products and procedures fall into this category and no doubt oil men will in time come to their own conclusions about their value.

A more detailed discussion of the problems of commercializing these technologies will be found in the proceedings of the 1990 MEOR conference[8].

REFERENCES

1. ZoBell, C.E. (1946). *Bacteriological Process for Treatment of Oil-Bearing Earth Formations.* U.S. Patent 2,413,278.
2. Karaskiewicz, J. (1974). *Zastosowanie Metod Mikrobiologicznych w Intensyfikacji Eksploatacji Karpackich Złóz Ropy Naftowego*, Prace Instytutu Naftowego (Krakow), pp. 1–66. Katowice: Wydawnictwo "Śląsk".
3. Hitzman, D.O. (1983). *Petroleum Microbiology and the History of Its Rôle in Enhanced Oil Recovery.* Proceedings of 1982 International Conference on Microbial Enhancement of Oil Recovery, pp. 162–218. ed. by E.C. Donaldson and J.B. Clark. Bartlesville, Oklahoma: Technology Transfer Branch,

Bartlesville Energy Technology Center. U.S. Department of Energy CONF-8205140.
4. Costerton, J.W. (personal communication).
5. Hitzman, D.O. (1988). *Review of Microbial Enhanced Oil recovery Field Tests*. Proceedings of the Symposium on Applications of Microorganisms to Petroleum Technology (1988). ed. by T.E. Burchfield and Rebecca S. Bryant. Bartlesville, Oklahoma: Bartlesville Project Office. U.S. Department of Energy NIPER-351/CONF-870858 (DE 88001232), VI/1-VI/41.
6. Jack, T.R. & Stehmeier, L.G. (1988). *Selective Plugging in Watered Out Oil Reservoirs*. Proceedings of the Symposium on Applications of Microorganisms to Petroleum Technology (1988). ed. by T.E. Burchfield and Rebecca S. Bryant. Bartlesville, Oklahoma: Bartlesville Project Office. U.S. Department of Energy NIPER-351/CONF-870858 (DE 88001232), pp. VII/1-VII/14.
7. Bryant, R.S., Burchfield, T.E., Dennis, D.M., Hitzman, D.O., & Porter, R.E. (1989). *Microbial-Enhanced Waterflood Field Experiment*. Topical Report prepared for the U.S. Department of Energy, Assistant Secretary for Fossil Energy by IIT Research Institute, National Institute for Petroleum and Energy Research, Bartlesville, Oklahoma; NIPER-356 (DE89000718).
8. Proceedings of the 1990 International Conference on Microbial Enhancement of oil Recovery, Norman, OK, May 27–Jun. 1, 1990. To be published by Elsevier Science Publishers B.V., Amsterdam.
9. Rosenberg, E., Zuckerberg, A., Rubinovitz, C. and Gutnick, D.L. (1979). *Emulsifier of Arthrobacter RAG-1: isolation and emulsifying properties*. Applied and Environmental Microbiology, **vol. 37**, pp. 402–408.
10. Gutnik, D.L. and Rosenberg, E. (1977). *Oil Tankers and Pollution: a Microbiological Approach*. Annual Reviews of Microbiology, **vol. 31**, pp. 379–396.
11. Kodama, K., Umehara, K., Shimizu, K., Nakatani, S., Minoda Y. and Yamada, K. (1973). *Identification of Microbial Products from Dibenzothiophene and its Proposed Oxidation Pathway*. Agricultural and Biological Chemistry, **vol. 37**, pp. 45–50.
12. Finnerty, W.R. & Hartdegen, F.J. (1984). *Microbial Desulfurization of Fossil Fuels*. Proceedings of Biotech '84 Europe, **vol. 1**, pp. 611–622. Pinner, Middlesex: Online Publications Ltd.
13. Finnerty, W.R. & Robinson, M. (1982). *Microbial Desulfurization of Fossil Fuels: A Review*. Workshop on Biotechnology for the Mining, Metal-Refining and Fossil Fuel Processing Industries, Biotechnology and Bioengineering Symposium No. 16, p. 205. ed. by H.L. Ehrlich and D.S. Holmes.
14. Burchfield, T.E. and Carroll, H.B., jun. (1988). *Economics of MEOR Processes*. Proceedings of the Symposium on Applications of Microorganisms to Petroleum Technology (1988). ed. by T.E. Burchfield and Rebecca S. Bryant. Bartlesville, Oklahoma: Bartlesville Project Office. U.S. Department of Energy NIPER-351/CONF-870858 (DE 88001232).pp. XIX/1-XIX/20.
15. Brashear, J.P., Becker, A., Biglarbigi, K. & Ray, R.M. (1989). *Incentives, Technology and EOR: Potential for Increased Oil Recovery at Lower Oil Prices*. Journal of Petroleum Technology, **vol. 41**, 164–170.

FURTHER READING

1. Yen, T.F. (ed.) (1976). *Science and Technology of Oil Shale* Ann Arbor, Michigan: Ann Arbor Science.
2. *Our Industry Petroleum* (5th ed.) (1977). London: The British Petroleum Co. Ltd.
3. Van Poollen, H.K. (1980). *Fundamentals of Enhanced Oil Recovery*. Tulsa, Oklahoma: PennWell Books.
4. Moses, V. & Springham, D.G. (1982). *Bacteria and the Enhancement of Oil Recovery*. London and New Jersey: Applied Science Publishers.
5. Brown, Melanie J., Moses, V., Robinson, J.P. & Springham, D.G. (1986). *Microbial Enhanced Oil Recovery*. CRC Critical Reviews in Biotechnology, **vol. 3**, pp. 159–197.
6. Rosenberg, E. (1986). *Microbial Surfactants*. CRC Critical Reviews in Biotechnology, **vol. 3**, pp. 109–132.
7. Various papers in *Proceedings of the Symposium on Applications of Microorganisms to Petroleum Technology* (1988). ed. by T.E. Burchfield and Rebecca S. Bryant. Bartlesville, Oklahoma: Bartlesville Project Office. U.S. Department of Energy NIPER-351/CONF-870858 (DE 88001232).
8. Donaldson, E.C., Chilingarian, G.V. & Yen, T.F. (1989). *Microbial Enhanced Oil recovery*. Amsterdam, Oxford, New York, Tokyo: Elsevier.
9. Yen, T.F. (ed.) (1990). *Microbial Enhanced Oil Recovery: Principle and Practicê*. Boca Raton, Florida: CRC Press Inc.

Chapter 30

Metal Recovery and Processing

Melanie J. Brown

INTRODUCTION

Biological leaching processes for recovering metals, such as copper, from low grade ores are a traditional component of the metal extraction industry. Although the uptake of metals from solution by biological materials is a well known and documented phenomenon, commercial processes for metal removal have only recently begun to emerge. Current trends in public awareness of environmental pollution accompanied by legislation have created opportunities for novel biological technologies which offer low cost, environmentally-friendly solutions to metal pollution or extraction problems. These biological processes may replace certain conventional technologies which are becoming environmentally unacceptable, or may find application alongside conventional technologies as polishing treatments designed to meet the demands of new and tighter legislation.

This chapter addresses the opportunities for novel biological processes to find applications for removing heavy metals from industrial effluents. It also describes the traditional biological processes for extracting metals from ores and identifies future trends and opportunities for biological leaching in this industry.

METAL REMOVAL AND RECOVERY FROM WASTEWATERS

Accumulation of Metals by Biological Systems

It has long been known that organisms living in aqueous environments have the capacity to accumulate metal ions from the surrounding waters in their tissues. Between 1953 and 1960 the accumulation of mercury by fish in Minimata Bay, Japan, resulted in an outbreak of mercury poisoning (known as Minimata disease) among the local population. Mercury was released into the bay in effluent from a plastics factory in the form of mercuric sulfate. Microorganisms in sediments transformed it into dimethyl mercury, a much more toxic compound, which then entered the foodchain. The consumption of contaminated fish by the local population had tragic consequences and many people died over the course of a few years. The delay in identifying the source of the mercury resulted from ignorance concerning the ability of microorganisms to methylate the inorganic mercury.

The capacity of plants for accumulating metals from the soil has been observed at sites contaminated with metals as a result of mining activities or the application of fertilizers, such as sewage sludge. For example lettuce accumulates cadmium and zinc more effectively than most other crop plants. Thus government recommendations have set upper limits to metal concentrations permissible in soil used for growing vegetables.

The ability of organisms to accumulate metals, in many cases up to a million-fold, from their environment was first observed as a result of their toxic effects. More recently it has stimulated interest in the use of biomass as an adsorbent material to remove toxic or precious metals from waste solutions. Biomass from a variety of different organisms, including fungi, algae and bacteria, has been evaluated for this purpose. Table 1 lists some organisms that have been reported to accumulate various metals and metalloids.

Market Opportunities

Public concern over the discharge of heavy and potentially-toxic metals into the environment continues to mount rapidly. Government agencies at local, national and international levels increasingly legislate to control industrial emissions and discharges. In the developed countries at least, the populace is becoming more aware through media influences of the effects of heavy metals on health.

Many industrial effluents contain potentially-toxic heavy metals, for example:

- mining activities,
- metallurgical recovery, smelting and refining,
- metal plating and finishing operations,
- nuclear fuel reprocessing,
- chemicals manufacture,
- landfill leachates.

Table 1
Bioaccumulation of Metals

Element	*Example of organisms capable of accumulation*
Aluminium	*Aspergillus niger*
Antimony	*Staphyloccus aureus*
Arsenic	*Duniella* sp.
Cadmium	*Zoogloea ramigera*
Cesium	*Saccharomyces cerevisiae*
Chromium	*Pseudomonas aeruginosa*
Cobalt	*Chlorella regularis*
Copper	*Cladosporium resinae*
Gold	*Chlorella vulgaris*
Hafnium	*Klebsiella aerogenes*
Indium	*Escherishia coli*
Iron	*Leptothrix* sp.
Lanthanum	*Candida albicans*
Lead	*Spirogyra* sp.
Manganese	*Gallionella* sp.
Mercury	*E. coli*
Molybdenum	*Spirogyra* sp.
Nickle	*Chlamydomonas* sp.
Palladium	*Thiobacillus ferrooxidans*
Platinum	*Chlorella* sp.
Radium	*Penicillium chrysogenum*
Selenium	*Pseudomonas* sp.
Silver	*Anaerobic sludge*
Strontium	*Citrobacter* sp.
Thorium	*Rhizopus arrhizus*
Tin	*Pseudomonas* sp.
Uranium	*R. arrhizus*
Vanadium	*P. aeruginosa*
Yttrium	*Algae*
Zirconium	*K. aerogenes*

The introduction of new legislation to restrict emissions of metals into the environment in the USA and the EEC has lead to demand for new and improved methods of treatment. The continuing pressure for higher performance means that many of the conventional technologies for metal removal are reaching the limits of their performance capabilities and this is creating opportunities for novel biological treatment processes.

Biological systems for industrial metal recovery applications need to present advantages over existing processes, for example:

- the ability to adsorb and concentrate metals present at very low concentrations (<1 mg/l) from solution;
- the ability to adsorb one metal selectively, while leaving others in solution;
- the ability to remove metals in the presence of organic contaminants or higher concentrations of calcium, magnesium, potassium or sodium,
- the potential to recycle metals eliminating the need for disposal.

Organisms currently used for the industrial production of biochemicals such as enzymes and antibiotics, provide a potential source of cheap, available biomass for metal recovery. Table 2 lists of some of the ones currently used in industrial processes: large quantities of biomass from these sources are generated as by-products and hence are available at little or no cost. The yeast resulting from the brewing process is marketed at low cost as a food additive by some breweries; the opportunity to market waste yeast depends on the size and location of the brewery. Transportation of such low value products dictates the economics of their use by other industries.

Table 2
Examples of Biomass By-products from Industrial Processes

Process	*Organism*
Brewing	*Saccharomyces cerevisiae*
Citric acid production	*Aspergillus niger*
Enzyme production	*Bacillus subtilis*
Penicillin production	*Penicillium chrysogenum*
Wastewater treatment	Activated sludge, digested anaerobic sludge

Uptake of Soluble Metals

The biological uptake of soluble metals is described as adsorption, complexation or binding. Adsorption may be defined as the concentration of a substance at a surface and does not necessarily imply physical binding.

The vast majority of metal ions, including nickel, zinc, copper, chromium, tin and selenium, are essential trace elements for the growth of living systems. Many function as activators in enzyme reactions, for example Ca^{2+} binds to trypsin (a digestive enzyme) protecting it against denaturing agents. Some are structural components in biological molecules, for example iron in hemoglobin. Trace elements are micronutrients which become toxic above a certain threshold concentration (Figure 1). Most living organisms possess mechanisms for detoxifying metals; these usually involve exclusion from the cell or the segregation of the metal from the cytoplasm by incorporation into granules, precipitation within the cell wall, complexation by extracellular polymers, or transformation of the metal by oxidation or reduction, so rendering it harmless to the host.

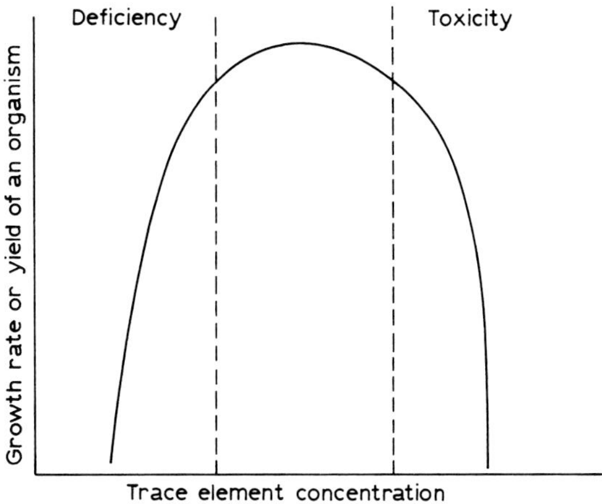

Figure 1. Typical growth response of an organism to trace element concentration.

Ferromanganese-depositing bacteria and fungi accumulate iron and manganese oxides extracellularly. The sulfate-reducing group of bacteria use sulfate as the terminal electron acceptor, reducing it to sulfide at neutral pH in anoxic environments. This reaction results in the precipitation of metals from solution as sulfides and has been proposed as a method of removing heavy metals from effluents but the fastidious nutritional requirements of the sulfate-reducing bacteria have presented problems in developing such a process.

Mercury, lead, arsenic, gold, tin, platinum and selenium can be methylated by microorganisms as a detoxification mechanism. Selenium, tellurium, arsenic, vanadium, molybdenum and mercury can all be reduced by *Micrococcus sp.* among others, resulting in a decrease in the valence of the metal, in some cases to the free metallic state. The bacterium *Escherichia coli* reduces mercuric ion (Hg^{2+}) to metallic mercury (Hg^0), which readily diffuses out of the cells and is lost to the atmosphere by volatilisation. *Micrococcus luteus* immobilizes lead in its cell wall; less than 1% of the lead taken up is accumulated in the cytoplasm. The production of extracellular polymer in the form of a capsule plays a protective role for some microorganisms. Capsulated strains of the bacterium *Klebsiella aerogenes* are more resistant to copper toxicity than uncapsulated strains. The toxicity of the metal dose to the organism is reduced as a result of complexation with its extracellular polymers.

Metal Binding Sites

Microbial biomass possesses a large number of chemical sites at which metals may be bound. Metal binding sites include carboxyl, carbonyl, hydroxyl, phosphate and sulfydryl groups present in cell walls and capsular polymers. It is difficult to resolve the relative contributions of these sites to the binding of a particular metal.

A simple ionic bonding has been demonstrated in many cases: ionic bridges form between negatively charged cells and cations. This type of ionic bond has been proposed as playing an important role in the flocculation of microorganisms, for example in the activated sludge process of wastewater treatment (see Chapter 27). Adsorption isotherms have indicated that a simple ion exchange process operates for biomass of *Aspergillus niger* in which uranyl cations reversibly replace cations on the amino acid groups of proteins in the cell wall. A simple exchange between H^+ and ${UO^{2+}}_2$ occurs at a singly charged anion on the biomass surface. Peptidoglycan is the primary agent for metal deposition in *Bacillus subtilis* cell walls, acting via the carboxyl groups of glutamic acid.

Certain proteins, known as metallothioneines, strongly bind specific metal ions. The metal components of enzymes and pigments are examples of this type of compound. Magnesium is found covalently bonded inside the porphyrin ring of plant chlorophyll. The four iron (II) ions in hemoglobin are each held inside a four coordinate porphyrin ring and are also attached to two of the four chains that intertwine to make up the hemoglobin molecule. This attachment is covalent to one of three imidazole nitrogens belonging to a histidine amino acid residue. The ferrous iron sits deep inside a pocket of the protein molecule. Gold is strongly complexed by thiol ligands such as L-cysteine and methionine. These complexes are very stable and are believed to be covalently bonded.

Metallothioneines can be very specific to individual metals. It may be possible genetically to manipulate microorganisms to produce such compounds on a large scale as metal complexing agents. Although this is likely to prove an expensive method of recovering metals from waste solutions, it may find application in separations of precious metals during metal processing operations. A patent has recently been filed describing the cloning of human metallothioneine genes and their expression in a bacterium with a view to producing the metallothioneines for metal recovery from aqueous effluents.

Factors Affecting Metal Adsorption by Biomass

The timecourse of metal uptake by biomass has been measured for a large number of different organisms; the characteristic response is shown in Figure 2. In general when the biomass contacts the metal solution, more than 90% of the metal taken up is adsorbed in less than 10 minutes; subsequently the metal is adsorbed at a much slower rate over a period of several hours until the system reaches equilibrium. Dependence of the second phase of metal uptake on metabolic activity has been demonstrated for some organisms to be the result of progressive chemical reactions to detoxify metals, causing further uptake into the cell.

Comparisons have been made between the ability of live and dead biomass to adsorb metals. In some instances dead biomass has been shown to adsorb a considerably greater

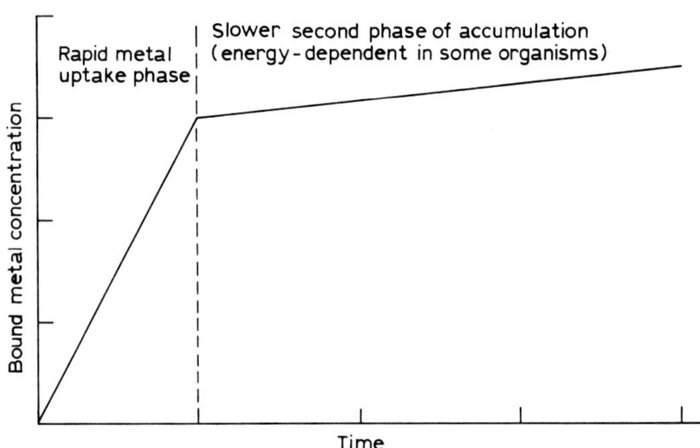

Figure 2. Typical pattern of metal accumulation by organisms.

quantity of metal than viable material. For example, inactivated cells of *Thiobacillus ferrooxidans* adsorbed 10–40% more uranium than living cells. However the method employed to inactivate the biomass, such as heat or solvent treatment, is also likely to modify the surface properties of the biomass and hence affect its metal binding properties.

pH is an important factor affecting metal uptake. Heat-killed pellets of *A. niger* showed the greatest amount of uranium adsorption at pH 5.8. Adsorption of uranium by *A. niger* and *Rhizopus sp* decreased below pH 3. Some metals readily precipitate at alkaline pH; these precipitates may become physically trapped in the biomass matrix and hence be removed from suspension by sedimentation with the biomass during a settling process. Medium composition affects the structure of cell wall polymers and can also influence metal binding capacity.

The complexation of metals with extracellular polymers and cell wall polymers allows microorganisms to survive in aqueous environments containing concentrations of metals that would be lethal if present in the cytoplasm of the cell. Provided that the biomass is not saturated with metal, in many cases more than 98% of a metal present in solution may be adsorbed by the biomass and subsequently removed from solution by sedimentation with the biomass. This has led to a commercial interest in developing industrial scale processes to remove and recover metals from wastewaters.

Metal Separations by Microorganisms

In most cases in which microorganisms have been exposed to solutions of mixed metals, they have accumulated different metals to different extents, some organisms showing a much greater affinity for one metal than for another. A patent application has recently been filed for a process using spent mycelial wastes from antibiotic production to separate rare earth elements by sorption at pH 2–6. The rare earths are notoriously difficult to separate by physical/chemical means.

In the development of a process to recover gold from dilute solution, the alga *Chlorella vulgaris* was found to have a greater affinity for gold than three other strains of gold-accumulating algae. This alga accumulated gold from solution in preference to other metals that it is known to accumulate in the absence of gold.

Metal Removal by Growing Biomass

In processes requiring the continuous growth of organisms for metal removal, toxicity of the metal to the organisms will set an upper limit on the tolerance of the system to increasing metal concentration. It is also essential that nutrients required for growth of the organisms are present in the waste metal solution.

Metal removal by activated sludge

The activated sludge process of wastewater treatment is an example of a process employing a continuously growing culture of microbes to oxidize the organic compounds present in wastewater, which simultaneously removes metals from solution (Fig. 3). Many studies on metal transport through wastewater treatment plants have demonstrated that metals are removed in the biological, secondary, activated sludge treatment process[1]. This process consists of two stages. First is an aerated biological reactor in which populations of microorganisms oxidize suspended or dissolved organic compounds in wastewater and convert them into carbon dioxide, water and cell material. The resulting ‘mixed liquor’ then passes into the phase separator or settling tank. The microbial aggregates or flocs settle out from the aqueous phase by gravity sedimentation and are returned to the reactor. The supernatant (final effluent) is discharged to a water course. Any substance which is absorbed or adsorbed by the microbial flocs is removed from the water passing through a sewage treatment plant. Therefore a combination of flocculation and settling is the mechanism by which metal removal is achieved in the activated sludge process. Any factor affecting flocculation or settling properties of a sludge will also affect its capacity to remove metals. Table 3 shows some typical metal removal values for activated sludge; on occasion metal removal efficiencies of 100% are observed although efficiency depends on influent concentration, physical and chemical characteristics of the wastewater, sludge flocculation and settling characteristics and the operating conditions of the plant. Activated sludge plants are rarely if ever operated in a regimen designed to optimize metal removal.

Factors affecting metal removal in activated sludge

Precipitation of metal hydroxides occurs at high pH while at low pH metals are frequently associated with organics. Some metals, such as lead and iron, precipitate readily in wastewater

Figure 3. View of modified activated sludge simulation units.

and are therefore efficiently removed. Other metals, for example nickel and manganese, remain soluble or associated with very fine particles (<8 μm) in suspension and are not removed efficiently from the final effluent. The presence of soluble chelating agents, such as EDTA (ethylenediaminetetra-acetic acid) or the detergent builder NTA (nitrilotriacetic acid) in wastewater also tends to solubilize metals and reduce removal efficiencies. These powerful chelating agents have a stronger affinity for metals than does sludge biomass.

Many activated sludge bacteria produce extracellular polymers which are believed to play a significant role in both flocculation and metal removal in activated sludge. A polymer-producing strain of *Zoogloea ramigera* accumulated twice as much metal as a non-capsulated strain. Polymers extracted from activated sludge were capable of complexing between 90 and 100% of cadmium and nickel from solutions containing 0.1 mg/l.

The better the settling characteristics of a sludge the greater the efficiency of metal removal. A short retention time in the reactor (3 days) results in sludges with a greater capacity to adsorb metals than longer retention times (9–18 days).

Metal toxicity and acclimation of activated sludge organisms

Shock doses of metal in wastewater entering an activated sludge plant may be toxic to the microorganisms and may

Table 3
Metal Removal in the Activated Sludge Process

Metal	*Influent metal concentration (mg/l)*	*Average removal efficiency (%)* (range)
Cadmium	0.001–0.12	50 (11–100)
Chromium	0.01–38	69 (33–99)
Copper	0.01–0.66	71 (55–98)
Iron	0.46–2.95	86 (72–98)
Lead	0.01–1.1	67 (42–100)
Manganese	0.02–0.1	17 (6–31)
Mercury	0.0002–0.009	62 (17–100)
Nickel	0.02–1.6	41 (0–100)
Zinc	0.18–8.94	65 (44–99)

severely inhibit the process, resulting in poor quality effluents. Metal toxicity in activated sludge causes a decrease in the diversity of species and hence in the stability of the community. However, these sludges can acclimate to high metal doses and bacterial growth is resumed after a lag period. Acclimation may be the expression of the synthesis of metal detoxifying enzymes or, on a longer timescale, it may represent the period required to select metal-tolerant strains.

Metal removal from tailings lagoons by algae

The removal of metals from tailings lagoons is another process that requires the growth of organisms, in this case algae. It encourages the multiplication of those species able to tolerate the metal concentrations present in the waste.

Lead milling effluents are passed into sedimentation lagoons before being discharged to receiving streams. High levels of lead, copper and zinc in these effluents can produce algal blooms of nuisance proportion in receiving streams. One mine-mill complex has introduced a meander system and a secondary settling lagoon[2]. Algae were encouraged to grow in the meander stream and were prevented from escaping from the secondary lagoon. The system removed 99% of the dissolved and particulate heavy metals, ensuring that the effluent quality was maintained within the required limits. This type of system for metal recovery is very simple and cheap to install and operate. The lack of development work carried out to date suggests that there is considerable scope for improving performance.

Removal of Metals by Non-growing Biomass

A metal removal process employing biomass that is viable, but grown prior to contacting the metal solution is not limited by metal toxicity as in the case of a growing system; nor does it require nutrients to be supplied with the metal-contaminated effluent. In some instances inactivated biomass has been shown to be more effective at adsorbing metals than living material. It has the additional advantages of being more compactable and it can be recycled many times without being degraded.

Metal removal by anaerobic sludges

A process has been developed to the pilot plant stage which employs viable, anaerobic sludge (the waste sludge arising from anaerobic digestion) in an upflow sludge bed reactor to remove heavy metals from aqueous solutions[3]. Removal efficiency was greater than 99% for copper, nickel, zinc and mercury at initial concentrations of 40 mg/l over an 8 month period of operation. The sludge bed was also effective at recovering precious metals: more than 90% of silver at 41–120 mg/l was removed over a 3 month period and 99% of gold at 26–54 mg/l was removed over a 2 month test period. The sludge accumulated metal to a higher concentration than ores that are currently mined for gold. Incineration more than doubled the metal content, yielding powders containing 12% silver and 7% gold.

The sludge in this process is viable, although growth does not occur. The biomass is pre-grown and functions as an adsorbent. If metal concentrations reach levels toxic to the sludge microorganisms, this will not significantly affect the adsorption process.

Anaerobic sludge is a waste product that requires disposal. It is currently dumped at sea or disposed of in landfill or applied to land as a fertilizer, although its heavy metal content makes it unsuitable for many types of crop. It is thus available in very large quantities at the cost of transportation.

Removal of radionuclides from effluents

Liquid radioactive wastes arise from cooling ponds at reactors (where irradiated fuel is stored prior to reprocessing), the reprocessing operation, fuel fabrication plants and nuclear research establishments. The main types of waste generated are actinides (heavy atoms resulting from the adsorption by uranium of neutrons produced during fission) and activation products (reactor components made radioactive by the neutrons emitted when uranium nuclei split) such as radiocesium and radiostrontium. These low level waste streams are currently treated by ion exchange and discharged to sea. They are not amenable to further treatment by conventional methods due to their large volume, low specific activity and high concentration of inactive salts. New technologies for polishing these effluents, such as selective ion exchange and the use of microbial biomass, are being considered by the nuclear industry in response to pressure to reduce further emissions of radioactive waste to the sea.

Uranium can be adsorbed semi-continuously by heat-killed pellets of the fungus *A. niger* fluidized in a compartmentalised column[4]. Uranium-loaded pellets were withdrawn from the bottom compartment with a pump: the mechanical flexibility of the pellets allowed them to squeeze between compartments. The uranium concentration in an aqueous effluent was reduced from 10 g/l to 0.2 g/l; the loaded biomass contained 42.5 mg U/g.

Strontium removal from aqueous solution was achieved by the bacterium *Citrobacter* immobilized in polyacrylamide gel[5], shredded and packed into glass columns. The sequential flow of a strontium nitrate solution (200 mg/l) through five linked columns at a rate of 30 ml/h resulted in the removal of 95% of the strontium by the immobilized biomass at a pH of 9.25.

Immobilized biomass for metal recovery

A number of processes employing biosorbent materials immobilized into beads or granules to recover metals from wastewaters are currently under development. The biosorbents can be packed into conventional hydrometallurgical processing equipment and used in a similar way to ion exchange resins. Stirred tanks, fixed bed and fluidized bed reactors have all been used for contacting biosorbents with effluents.

A granulated product has been derived from biomass of *Bacillus subtilis* (a by-product of fermentation) by treating cells with a caustic solution[6]. The granulated biosorbent showed a substantially enhanced uptake of metal cations from solution compared with the living cells. The granules were packed into either a fixed bed canister to accomodate flows of up to 5.7 l/min or a fluid bed unit capable of processing up to 500 l of waste water per minute. Pilot fluidized bed units 4.6 m high and 0.5 m in diameter containing 79 kg of granules with a 50% bed expansion have been field tested. During operation of the fluidized bed, the granules loaded with metals became heavier and settled to the bottom. These metal-loaded granules were removed from the reactor at intervals and replaced with fresh material. The bacterial granules accumulated a significant proportion of their own weight as metal. They have been shown to remove metal with a high efficiency at metal concentrations below 10 mg/l, the range in which other metal removal technologies become ineffective. The granules removed soluble and precipitated metals and were reported to be capable of accumulating 0.8 mmol Ag/g, 1.9 mmol Cd/g, 2.1 mmol Zn/g, 2.4 mmol Cu/g and 2.9 mmol Pb/g with greater than 99% removal efficiency.

Algae immobilized into a polymeric matrix bound up to 10% of the cell dry weight as metal, concentrating heavy metal ions by many thousand fold from waste waters containing metals at μ/l concentrations[7]. The immobilized algae were immersed in aqueous solution for up to two years with no decrease in metal binding efficiency.

A variety of biomass materials have been immobilized in porous polysulfone beads[8]. The biomass beads have been packed into fixed beds and shown to be durable and very effective at polishing metal contaminated effluents.

These systems may be effective as a complete waste treatment or a polishing treatment coupled with another process, such as activated carbon. They allow metals which are intrinsically valuable or expensive to discharge to be removed and recovered from effluents.

Recovery of Metals from Biomass

Recovery of metals from biosorbents is important for two reasons:

(i) it allows waste materials to be recycled back to the industry and hence avoids the need for disposal of metals;
(ii) it allows the biosorbent to be reused which will be important if a significant cost is incurred in generating the biosorbent.

Metals have been eluted from biosorbent using dilute mineral acids although under some conditions alkali solutions (such as sodium carbonate) and EDTA have also been effective. Most of the metal elution from polysulfone beads containing biomass occurred within the first 30 min of contact; the process was complete within one hour. Fifty bed volumes of a waste water containing 10.7 mg/l zinc and 0.062 mg/l cadmium were passed through a packed bed of beads. The metals were concentrated after four elution cycles with sulfuric acid yielding solutions containing 1.05 g/l Zn and 6.42 mg/l Cd, a concentration factor of 100-fold.

Metals can be stripped from immobilized algae with sulfuric acid yielding solutions containing up to 10 g/l metal. The metals can either be recovered through electrowinning or further concentrated by evaporation. Polysulfone beads containing duckweed showed no decrease in metal sorption efficiency nor any sign of physical deterioration after 75 extraction/elution cycles.

No marked difference was found between the abilities of hydrochloric, nitric and sulfuric acids to recover copper from filamentous fungi. Uranium was readily stripped from *A. niger* biomass with 0.1 M nitric acid to give a solution containing 1,200 g U/m^3. This was concentrated by a factor of 12 over the initial uranium solution. Cyanide has been used to complex gold accumulated by algae. Gold was selectively removed from the algae even when copper and zinc were also bound to the biomass.

Incineration of biomass has also been employed as a method of recovering and concentrating metals such as uranium, gold and silver. The process using anaerobic sludge to remove metals from solution generated powders containing, for example, 12% silver. Incineration obviously destroys the biosorbent and therefore is only suitable for recovering metals from very low-cost biomass such as sludges. Where biomass is produced specifically to act as a metal sorbent, it is desirable and cost-effective to reuse it.

Comparison of Biosorbent with Conventional Treatments

Caustic and sulfide precipitation currently account for 90% of wastewater treatment systems in operation for heavy metal removal. Both these processes generate metal sludges which present a problem of safe disposal. Ion exchange resins and reverse osmosis are also employed to remove metals from solution. Biosorbent materials are in general more effective than conventional technologies at effluent polishing. Compared with five commercially-available ion exchange resins, polysulfone beads containing a blue-green alga were four times more effective at adsorbing zinc and manganese at an initial concentration of 5 mg/l and their effectiveness was even more pronounced at 1 mg/l. At concentrations above 18 mg/l the ion exchange resins became more effective than the algal beads. In another example algal beads extracted 90% of cadmium from waste water containing 45 μ/l Cd, whereas ion exchange resins adsorbed between 15 and 45%.

IRA-400 (Rohm and Haas) is currently used to treat uranium mining effluents. Comparisons of the performance of this resin with biosorbents have shown that *A. niger* pellets adsorb uranium 14 times more efficiently at pH 4 and *Rhizopus arrhizus* biomass adsorbed 4 times more uranium than the maximum loading exhibited by the ion exchange resin. *A. niger* pellets reduced a 10 g/l solution of uranium to 0.2 g/l, whereas IRA-400 yielded a 5.5 g/l uranium effluent. Adsorption of radium by *Penicillium chrysogenum* exceeded the capacity of conventional ion exchange systems by a factor of 14.

The biomass metal adsorption systems generally have a higher wet volume to dry mass ratio than the ion exchange systems, making them less compatible with intensive plant. The IRA-400 resin occupied one twentieth of the volume of hydrated *A. niger* pellets, sustained five times the flow rate and had better selectivity as an ion exchanger. However the biomass achieved a lower concentration of metal in the final efluent and therefore may be effective as a "polishing" process following an ion exchange treatment. Biomass requires compacting if it is to compete with full-scale conventional treatments for heavy metal removal.

Biosorbent materials have been shown effectively to remove metal in the presence of both organic compounds and high background concentrations of dissolved salts. Immobilized algae were particularly effective at heavy metal removal from waters containing organic residues which often foul ion exchange resins and limit their use for certain applications. In addition they were capable of preferentially removing heavy metals from waters containing high concentrations of dissolved sodium, potassium, calcium, magnesium, chloride or sulfate. Polysulfone biomass beads also exhibited selectivity for heavy metals compared with calcium and magnesium: more than 99% of Zn, Cd and Mn were removed from waste water, whereas only 9% Ca and 4% Mg were extracted.

METAL RECOVERY FROM ORES

Metals can be dissolved from insoluble metal sulfide minerals as a result of the oxidation of sulfur or iron compounds in the minerals by microorganisms. An industrial process passing water through ore dumps to recover copper was operated by the Romans in 1000 BC. A leaching process was also used in Angelsey in Wales in the 16th century and at Rio Tinto in Spain in the 18th century. However it was not until 1947 that the first paper appeared describing microbial participation in ore leaching.

The world consumption of metals has shown a general upward trend during the last half century. Accessible high grade deposits, especially in the developed world, have been thoroughly exploited and the mining industry is moving progressively to lower grade ores. The average ore grade for copper in the US has declined from 2% in 1914 to 0.6% in 1988. Copper ore deposits currently mined in Arizona in the USA, ranging from 0.15–0.35% Cu and valued at $4 per tonne, are in many cases lower grade than the tailings piles from the 2–4% Cu Chilean ore deposits valued at $35 per tonne. Similar reductions in ore grade have occurred for other base and precious metals. Lower grade ores lead to higher production costs. This decline in ore grade will make an increasing number of deposits uneconomical to mine by conventional means. As the ore grades have fallen, the tonnage of waste has increased. Economic recovery of copper from this waste ore can be achieved only by the low capital cost, low labor cost, low energy-requiring bacterial leaching process. In addition to the cost benefits, the technology is simple to operate; hence it is very appealing to many of the developing countries with vast mineral resources, including Zambia, Peru, India, Chile and Brazil. Chile has become the world's leading producer of copper, with an annual production exceeding 1×10^6 tonnes in the last few years. As the Chilean copper industry has grown, thousands of tonnes of waste ore have accumulated and stimulated interest in bacterial leaching.

Bacterial leaching also eliminates the environmental hazards and liabilities inherent in smelting sulfide ores. The limitation of sulfur dioxide emissions from smelters costs the copper industry over $2 billion in capital expenditure for air pollution control and 10–15 cents per lb of copper produced. As further legislation restricting the emissions of metals is enforced, environmentally-superior technologies will swiftly also become economically-superior processes. Microbial metal recovery is currently a $450 million business in the US, growing at a rate of 12–15% annually.

Mechanism of Bacterial Leaching

The dominant organisms in this process are those capable of oxidising reduced iron and sulfur compounds, although other heterotrophic bacteria, fungi, yeasts, algae and protozoa are also involved to a lesser extent.

The most widely reported leaching bacterium is *Thiobacillus ferrooxidans*, which can oxidize both reduced sulfur and iron compounds at an optimum pH of between 1 and 2.5. It was first isolated from acid mine waters and has since been found ubiquitously. Other microbes frequently play a role in gradually reducing pH via a microbial succession to produce conditions favorable for the growth of *T. ferrooxidans*. *T. thiooxidans*, *T. acidophilus* and *T. organoparus* are also important leaching bacteria which obtain energy from elemental sulfur and other reduced sulfur compounds at pH values as low as 0.65. *Leptospirillum ferrooxidans* oxidizes only the iron moiety of pyrite. These organisms are strictly aerobic chemoautotrophs deriving energy from reduced iron or sulfur and fixing carbon dioxide from the atmosphere; they do not require an organic carbon source. The carbon dioxide fixation reactions in *T. ferrooxidans* are coupled to the production of energy from ferrous iron oxidation. Laboratory studies have shown that *T. ferrooxidans* can use organic carbon sources but it is not known whether this happens in nature.

Metal leaching bacteria display two different modes of attacking ores or metal sulfides: direct and indirect. In nature both mechanisms usually operate simultaneously and are difficult to separate.

Direct leaching is by enzymatic attack on the mineral causing electrons to be transferred from the iron or sulfur to oxygen:

$$2FeS_2 + 7O_2 + 2H_2O \xrightarrow{bacteria} 2FeSO_4 + 2H_2SO_4 \quad (1)$$

$$4FeSO_4 + O_2 + 2H_2SO_4 \xrightarrow{bacteria} 2Fe_2(SO_4)_3 + 2H_2O \quad (2)$$

$$FeS_2 + Fe_2(SO_4)_3 \longrightarrow 3FeSO_4 + 2S \quad (3)$$

$$2S + 3O_2 + 2H_2O \xrightarrow{bacteria} 2H_2SO_4 \quad (4)$$

The overall reaction is:

$$4FeS_2 + 15O_2 + 2H_2O \xrightarrow{bacteria} 2Fe_2(SO_4)_3 + 2H_2SO_4 \quad (5)$$

The organisms attach themselves to the sulfide moieties on minerals. Attachment and sulfide oxidation result in pitting of the mineral surface.

The indirect leaching process uses ferric iron generated by the bacterial oxidation of soluble ferrous iron (equation 2). Ferric iron is itself a powerful oxidizing agent that transforms other metals into a soluble oxidized form in a sulfuric acid solution (equation 3). Ferrous iron is again produced during this reaction and is rapidly reoxidized by the bacteria and recycled in the leaching process. There is a very slow rate of abiotic ferrous iron oxidation at low pH but bacteria greatly accelerate the process (by a factor as great as 10^6).

Some reactions between ferric iron and metal sulfide minerals result in the formation of secondary minerals and elemental sulfur (equation 3). *T. ferrooxidans* plays a role in oxidizing the sulfur to sulfuric acid (equation 4), thus exposing the metal for further leaching.

A variety of copper and uranium minerals have been subjected to bacterial leaching on a commercial scale. Chalcopyrite ($CuFeS_2$), chalcocite (Cu_2S) and covellite (CuS) are all leached by *T. ferrooxidans* by both direct and indirect mechanisms. Chalcopyrite, for example, is leached (a) directly and (b) indirectly according to the following reactions:

$$\text{(a)} \quad 4CuFeS_2 + 17O_2 + 2H_2SO_4 \rightarrow 4CuSO_4 + 2Fe(SO_4)_3 + 2H_2O$$

$$\text{(b)} \quad CuFeS_2 + 2Fe_2(SO_4)_3 \rightarrow CuSO_4 + 5FeSO_4 + 2S$$

Although *T. ferrooxidans* can directly oxidize reduced compounds of uranium, this process has no major significance in current practices of leaching due to the abundance of iron sulfides in uranium minerals that generate ferric iron. The ferric iron is responsible for the indirect leaching of uranium:

$$UO_2 + Fe_2(SO_4)_3 \rightarrow UO_2SO_4 + 2FeSO_4$$

Bacterial Leaching Processes

Dump and heap leaching

Recovery of copper from ore dumps and heaps is the most important and widespread application of bacterial leaching although uranium has also been recovered in this way. Chalcopyrite is the principle sulfide mineral in most dumps, while chalcocite predominates in some ores. In 1989, over 25% of all copper produced in the U.S. came from bacterial leaching. Both dump and heap leaching processes involve the deposition on impermeable ground of low-grade ores (<0.4% Cu) resulting from mining operations, preferably on a slope enabling the leach solutions to be readily collected. Heap leaching accompanies existing mining operations and is designed to optimize the leaching rate by using finer particles of more concentrated ore on prepared drainage pads. Dump leaching uses ores from past mining operations, deposited on existing topography, where little opportunity for process optimization exists. It is normally carried out on a much larger scale than heap leaching, with some dumps containing as much as 3.6×10^{12} kg of ore. Diagrams of the heap or dump leaching process are shown in Figures 4 and 5 with a photograph in Figure 6. The top of the dump or heap is leveled off and irrigated by spraying, flooding or injecting a leach solution on the surface. Sulfuric acid is normally added to the leach solution, reducing the pH to between 1.5 and 3 to increase the leaching rate and to prevent the deposition of ferric salts which reduce the permeability of the dump. The acid concentration is usually higher in heap leaching than dump leaching processes.

The bacteria proliferate in the top meter of the dump when conditions are favorable for their growth; they are not normally inoculated into the dumps themselves. Cell numbers of *T. ferrooxidans* can reach 10^6/g of rock material. They

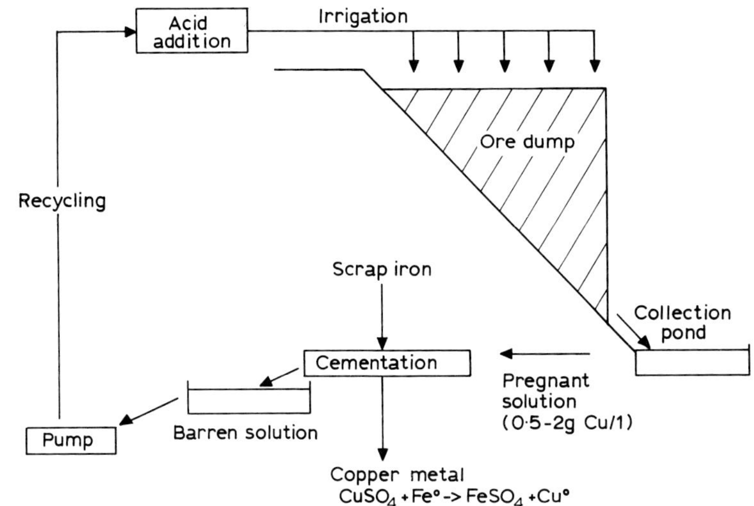

Figure 4. Diagram of dump or heap leaching process.

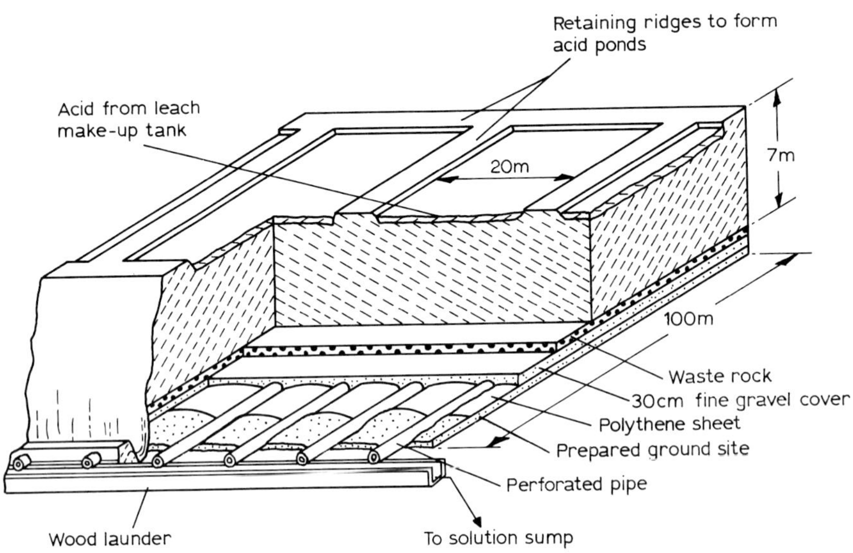

Figure 5. Schematic representation of a more sophisticated leaching operation. (*Reproduced by permission of Prof. A.E. Torma.*)

dissolve the copper as the leach solution percolates through the dump by oxidizing sulfur or iron compounds present in the minerals. The "pregnant" leach solution is collected at the base of the dump and passed over scrap iron where copper powder is precipitated by cementation. The finely divided "cement copper" is periodically recovered and refined for sale. The "barren" solution resulting from the cementation is then recycled to irrigate the dump. Solvent extraction is also used to recover a pure, concentrated copper sulfate solution for high grade electrolytic applications. The most significant costs involved in the dump leaching process are those of acid and scrap iron. The cost of labor, electricity, pumps, freight, maintenance and overheads combined are less than half of the cost of supplying acid and iron.

In situ leaching

In situ leaching has been applied intermittently in Canada since the 1960s for the recovery of uranium from the stopes and tunnels of underground mines. Water or dilute sulfuric acid is pumped into the mine and the "pregnant" solutions drain to the lower points of the mine and accumulate in sumps. The solution is then pumped to the surface for uranium recovery by ion exchange or solvent extraction. *In situ* leaching is also used for the extraction of uranium from sandstone formations. The leach solution contains a chemical oxidant which solubilizes the uranium. The "pregnant" solution is pumped to the surface via recovery wells. Bacteria are probably not involved in this process.

Figure 6. Kennecott dump leaching operation in New Mexico. (*Reproduced by permission of Prof. A. E. Torma.*)

Fracturing low-grade copper ore bodies with powerful explosives has been employed in some cases to make the deposits more permeable for *in situ* bacterial leaching. Leach solution and oxygen or air are injected under pressure and copper-enriched solutions are recovered from wells drilled below the ore body. This process has not been implemented on a large scale due to problems with loss of leach solution and uncertainty of microbial performance at high temperatures and pressures. There is evidence that leaching bacteria can withstand pressures of up to 410 atmospheres and dissolved oxygen levels of 24–49 mg/l, which would permit leaching at depths greater than 2000 m.

Vat leaching

Vat leaching is used to a limited extent by the mining industry for the recovery of uranium, gold, silver and copper. The ore is ground up to a small particle size and added to open tanks with stirrers and air injection. The reaction time is short (usually a few hours). Vat leaching requires higher grade ores than dump or heap leaching to justify the additional capital cost. The process has been most successfully developed for gold, one of the few metals maintaining a high price. Gold production is increasing in Canada, the U.S., Brazil and China.

Gold, silver and platinum frequently occur finely disseminated in sulfide minerals such as pyrite and arsenopyrite. These refractory ores respond poorly to direct cyanidation; an oxidation pre-treatment is therefore necessary to liberate the metals from the sulfide matrix prior to cyanidation. Gold can be solubilized by microbial leaching but this is a very slow process and is unlikely to be economic. However the oxidation and solubilization of the sulfide present in the minerals by *T. ferrooxidans* can increase the gold recovered from $<50\%$ to $>90\%$. The gold is left as a solid residue and is separated on a belt filter. The alternative roasting treatment is expensive and generates air pollutants such as sulfur dioxide and volatile arsenic compounds.

A number of pilot plants for vat leaching of gold are being tested in Canada and Papua New Guinea; one full-scale plant is reported to be in operation in South Africa. A demonstration plant in Canada's Northwestern Territories processed 400 tonnes of ore in a two month test, recovering 95.6% of the available gold. Cyanide treatment alone yielded only 65–70% of the gold. Cost estimates for a 1000 tonne per day full-scale plant for a gold bioleaching process indicated that bioleaching would be more economical than roasting or pressure oxidation, two alternative methods of treating the ore before cyanidation (Table 4). Capital costs of biological leaching are less than those for pressure oxidation or roasting. Operating costs are also less due to less severe operating conditions requiring fewer and less skilled operators.

One of the problems with the bacterial pretreatment of gold ores is the generation of water-soluble toxic arsenic compounds which inhibit the process. This has led to research into the genetic control of arsenic resistance in *T. ferrooxidans*

Table 4
Comparison of cost effectiveness of bioleaching of gold with roasting and pressure oxidation for a 1000 tonne per day plant

	Bioleach	*Roasting*	*Pressure oxidation*
Capital costs	\$23.1 m	\$26.2 m	\$33.9 m
Operating costs	\$18.67 m	\$19.42 m	\$20.31 m

to enhance gold recovery.

Vat leaching offers the possibility of much greater process control in terms of particle size, pH, oxygen concentration, temperature, nutrient levels and microorganisms present. The more efficient process performance must be balanced with the increased capital and operating costs compared to dump leaching.

Factors Controlling Leaching Rate

There is great variation in reported leaching rates due to differences in size, shape and watering procedures of dumps, particle size, mineral type, pH of leach solution, temperature, oxygen availability and metal tolerance of the organisms.

If the flow of air to the interior of the dump is impeded due to compaction or precipitation of ferric hydroxides or channeling, the leaching rate can be dramatically reduced. The smaller the particle size, the more efficient is the leaching rate.

Temperature has a pronounced effect on iron oxidation; leaching by *T. ferrooxidans* occurs optimally at temperatures in the range 25–45°C. Recently organisms from the genus *Sulfolobus* capable of oxidising sulfur, ferrous iron and metal sulfides have been isolated at temperatures up to 85°C. It is not clear whether these organisms play a significant role in the natural leaching process or whether they could be employed in a high temperature leaching process. Heat generation by the microbial oxidation is significant and internal temperatures of dumps as high as 80°C have been recorded. The interior of the dump is maintained at a constant temperature all year round and in colder climates the higher temperature differential in winter causes increased air flow through the dump and therefore increased copper recovery.

The pH of the leach solution depends on the amount of acid added and the amount of pyrite present in the ore, which increases sulfuric acid production.

A number of laboratories are investigating the use of genetic manipulation and mutation studies to produce improved strains of *T. ferrooxidans* capable of faster leaching rates and showing increased metal resistance. However at present little is known about the molecular genetics of this bacterium and the lack of a transformation system for *T. ferrooxidans* has held back developments in this field. Genetic probes employing DNA hybridization have been developed to detect and monitor organisms present in biomining operations. These techniques will be particularly important if genetically-manipulated strains of *T. ferrooxidans* are to be released into the environment. Significant regulatory hurdles must be overcome if genetically-manipulated leaching organisms are to be released into the environment.

Potential for Bacterial Leaching of Other Metals

In addition to copper, uranium and gold, many other metals and metalloids can be solubilized as a result of bacterial leaching: antimony, arsenic, bismuth, cadmium, cobalt, gallium, indium, iron, lead, manganese, molybdenum, nickel, selenium, tellurim, thallium, tin and zinc. The indirect leaching of molybdenum, cobalt, lead, zinc and nickel is likely to be of greatest interest in the near future because of their value and strategic importance. Nickel and cobalt recoveries of >80% were reported for a semi-continuous laboratory leach of sulfide ores with a residence time of 14 days. Plans exist to build a pilot plant to evaluate this process in South Africa. Reduced forms of antimony, arsenic, copper, manganese and selenium, in addition to reduced iron and sulfur compounds, can serve as bacterial energy sources. For example, copper selenide can be the sole energy source for *T. ferrooxidans*:

$$CuSe + O_2 + 2H^+ \rightarrow Cu^{2+} + Se^0 + H_2O$$

Some of these reactions may find applications in the industrial processing and separations of metals.

METAL RESISTANCE

All microbial metal recovery and leaching processes requiring growth of the organisms may be limited by the toxicity of metals accumulating either in solution or in the living protoplasm. Uranium, arsenic and tellurium inhibit iron oxidation at concentrations in the range 0.8–3 mM; molybdate ions are inhibitory above 0.5 μM.

Plasmid-mediated resistance has been reported for mercury, tellurium, arsenic, silver, nickel, cobalt, zinc, cadmium, copper and lead in heterotrophic bacteria. Metal ion resistance would be a particularly useful selective marker for genetic manipulation studies on *T. ferrooxidans*. The culture conditions of *T. ferrooxidans* limit the choice of potential genetic markers; many antibiotics are unstable at low pH and high metal ion concentration. Genetic studies on *T. ferrooxidans* have been held up for many years by the difficulty of cultivating this organism on solid medium and of developing an effective transformation system: the use of agarose instead of agar has now overcome the cultivation problem. Plasmids from a number of *T. ferrooxidans* strains have been isolated and characterized; the organisms contained between one and six plasmids ranging from 4.5 to 27.5 kilobases in size. All of these plasmids are cryptic.

In order to introduce novel characteristics into *T. ferrooxidans*, it is essential to develop a plasmid transfer system whereby the cells can take up exogenous genetic material. This may be achieved either by transformation of the cells with isolated plasmid DNA or by direct conjugation transferring broad host range plasmids between host and recipient cells.

T. ferrooxidans plasmids from metal ion-tolerant strains have been cloned in *E. coli* where they are all cryptic. An *E. coli* plasmid was inserted into a plasmid isolated from an arsenic-resistant strain of *T. ferrooxidans* to construct a recombinant plasmid. This was shown to replicate in *E. coli* using an origin of replication located on the *T. ferrooxidans* plasmid. This plasmid may be a suitable shuttle vector allowing the transfer of genetic material between the two organisms. A number of *T. ferrooxidans* proteins were produced in an *E. coli* DNA-directed cell-free system containing four *T. ferrooxidans* plasmids. This evidence suggests that some regulatory signals on autotrophic plasmid DNA molecules are recognised by heterotrophic transcription and translation machinery. Genetic transformation of auxotrophs to prototrophy of another species of *Thiobacillus*, *T. thioparus*, has been achieved. However a transformation system still remains to be achieved for *T. ferrooxidans*.

The incompatibility of growth conditions between acidophilic autotrophs, such as *T. ferrooxidans*, and heterotrophs has posed problems in developing a system for the direct transfer of genetic material by conjugation. Conjugal transfer of some broad host range plasmids from *E. coli* into non-iron oxidizing strains of *Thiobacillus*, such as *T. novellus*, has been demonstrated. These plasmids were subsequently transferred from *T. novellus* to other thiobacilli. This is a mechanism which may also prove effective for transferring genetic material into *T. ferrooxidans*.

Broad host range plasmids coding for mercury or tellurium resistance have been inserted into *T. ferrooxidans* and some expression has been observed. One strain of *T. ferrooxidans* has been shown to have mercury reductase activity similar to heterotrophic bacteria but the gene coding for this enzyme was present on the main chromosome, and not on a plasmid. Recent patents report the construction of arsenic-resistant plasmids for the enhanced recovery of gold by bacterial leaching.

Organisms showing increased tolerance to certain metals can be obtained by mutation selection during repeated subculturing. Some metal removal processes, such as the algal meander stream, naturally select metal-resistant organisms capable of growth at the prevailing metal concentrations.

FUTURE PROSPECTS

The use of biomass to recover highly toxic or valuable metals from dilute effluents offers great potential for the future. As public pressure and legislation progressively reduce emissions of toxic metals into the environment, biological methods of metal adsorption, which are much more effective at low metal concentrations than the conventional ion exchange treatments, will increasingly find commercial application.

Most of the processes that are currently being developed to remove metals from effluents employ biomass that has been generated as a by-product or a waste product from another industrial process. The use of such biomass as a raw material would have little or no direct cost (excluding those of transportation and storage) and, if biomass were to be produced specifically for metal recovery, it would need to be many times more effective than existing sources of available biomass in order to justify the additional cost of production. Separations of highly valuable metals may not be so sensitive to the cost of biomass and may allow the use of new and perhaps genetically-improved organisms with increased affinities for particular metals. If the organisms are inactivated prior to use, they will not be subject to the regulatory requirements for the release of genetically-manipulated organisms.

The introduction of bacterial leaching for metals other than copper, uranium and gold will depend on economic and strategic factors. Molybdenum, cobalt, lead, zinc and nickel are likely to be of the greatest interest in the near future because of their value and strategic importance. The most energy-intensive and environmentally malign metal extraction processes are the most likely to be replaced by biological leaching. As metal reserves become progressively depleted, bacterial leaching processes for a number of different metals are likely to appear. The use of genetic manipulation to improve the performance of strains of *T. ferrooxidans* may also improve the economics of bacterial leaching, allowing other metals to be recovered using this method. The development of the technology for *in situ* leaching of ore bodies by the injection of leach solutions and microbes into wells drilled into the rock offers the potential of reaching metal reserves too low grade to be mined by conventional methods. The methodology for such processes will have much in common with the use of microbes to recover oil from underground reservoirs, a technology which is undergoing field testing at the present time.

Debus[9] has recently produced an interesting market appreciation of the opportunities for microbial leaching particularly in the US. A survey of American mining executives revealed energy consumption, liability for environmental damage and labor costs as the most difficult problems they will need to resolve if they are to remain competitive in the future. The least cost-effective of their production processes were judged to be smelting and refining, followed closely by ore extraction. The key attributes critical to the success of microbiological methods were perceived to be:

- *in situ* capabilities,
- lower energy costs,
- lower capital costs,
- lower labor costs,
- ability to convert a waste product into a resource,
- "passive" system approach,
- new capabilities not available with other technology,
- favorable environmental impact,
- mild operating conditions (temperature and pressure).

Twenty per cent of the executives identified *in situ* mining and optimization and control as being the technology areas with the greatest potential, for improving competitiveness. Advanced rock breaking and intelligent mining were believed by 15% of executives to have the greatest potential, while 12% placed microbiological methods first with 50% of the precious metal executives in this category. *In situ* mining combined with microbial leaching and new rock fragmentation methods could develop into an economical and powerful new technology.

Thus, biological metal recovery and leaching processes offer a number of specific advantages which will become increasingly important as the search for new technologies intensifies. They are likely to find application in the metal extraction and processing industries to recover metals that are at present lost in effluents and waste ore material and to separate metals that are not amenable to conventional chemical separations.

REFERENCES

1. Brown, M.J. and Lester, J.N. (1979). *Metal removal in activated sludge: the role of bacterial extracellular polymers.* Water Research, **vol. 13**, pp 817–837.
2. Gale, N.L. (1986). *The role of algae and other micro-organisms in metal detoxification and environmental clean-up*, in Workshop on Biotechnology for the Mining, Metal-refining and Fossil Fuel Processing Industries p 171. Ed. by H.L. Ehrlich and D.S. Holmes, Biotechnology and Bioengineering Symposium No 16: John Wiley & Sons, New York.
3. Morper, M. (1986). *Anaerobic sludge — a powerful and low cost sorbent for heavy metals*, in Immobilization of Ions by Bio-Sorption p 91. Ed. by H. Eccles and S. Hunt: Ellis Horwood Ltd, Chichester.
4. Yakubu, N.A. and Dudeney, A.W.L. (1986). *Biosorption of uranium with Aspergillus niger*, in Immobilisation of Ions by Bio-sorption p 183. Ed. by H. Eccles and S. Hunt: Ellis Horwood Ltd, Chichister.
5. Macaskie, L.E. and Dean, A.C.R. (1985). *Strontium accumulation by immobilised cells of a Citrobacter sp.* Biotechnol. Lett., **vol. 7**, pp 627–630.
6. Brierley, J.A., Goyak, G.M. and Brierley, C.L. (1986). *Considerations for commercial use of natural products for metals recovery*, in Immobilization of Ions by Bio-sorption p 105. Ed. by H. Eccles and S. Hunt: Ellis Horwood Ltd, Chichister.
7. Darnall, D.W. (1989). *Removal and recovery of heavy metal ions from wastewaters using a new biosorbent; algasorb.* in Innovative Hazardous Waste Treatment Technology, Ed. H. Freeman, Technomic Publishing Company.
8. Jeffers, T.H., Ferguson, C.R. and Seidel, D.C. (1989). *Biosorption of metal contaminants using biomass.* presented at Biohydrometallurgy '89, Jackson Hole, WY, (August 13–18).
9. Debus, K.H. (1989). *Identifying the biohydrometallurgical processes with the greatest probability of commercial adoption*, a paper presented at Biohydrometallurgy '89, Jackson Hole WY (August 13–18).

FURTHER READING

Brierley, C.L., Kelly, D.P., Seal, K.J. and Best, D.J. (1985). *Materials and Biotechnology*, in Biotechnology Principles and Applications, Ch. 5, p 163. Ed. by I.J. Higgins, D.J. Best and J. Jones: Blackwell Scientific Publications.

Hutchins, S.R., Davidson, M.S., Brierley, J.A. and Brierley, C.L. (1986). *Microorganisms in reclamation of metals.* Ann. Rev. Microbiol., **vol. 40**, pp 311–336.

Lundgren, D.G. and Silver, M. (1980). *Ore leaching by bacteria.* Ann. Rev. Microbiol., **vol. 34**, pp 263–283.

Nicolaidis, A.A. (1987). *Microbial mineral processing: the opportunities for genetic manipulation.* J. Chem Tech. Biotechnol **vol. 38**, pp 167–185.

Woods, D. and Rawlings, D. (1984). *Molecular genetic studies on the thiobacilli and the development of improved biomining bacteria.* BioEssays, **vol. 2**, pp 8–10.

Chapter 31

Microbiological Desulphurisation of Coal

Shane Maloney and Vivian Moses

INTRODUCTION: THE NATURE OF THE PROBLEM

The reason for removing sulphur from coal arises from the need to decrease sulphur dioxide emissions into the atmosphere. Concern about acid rain now has a high public profile and the relationship between consumption of high-sulphur fuels (mostly by power stations) and acidic precipitation is no longer questioned. As a result, more stringent controls are being introduced in most industrial countries aimed at controlling the release of sulphurous gases.

It has been known for many years that certain bacteria are able to solubilise the inorganic pyrite fraction of coal. Recent work has indicated the possibility of using different organisms to remove also some of the organic sulphur. Whether or not biotechnological systems based on these properties will have a part to play in reducing sulphur dioxide emissions does not depend only on technical considerations. Even if a system were to be developed and shown in field trials under realistic conditions indeed to remove significant amounts of sulphur, there would be other factors to influence its adoption in practice: capital and operating costs, reliability, suitability for year-round operation and how those individuals who must make the relevant decisions feel about using a biologically-based rather than some other technique with which they might be more familiar and have more confidence. After all, a good deal of money will be involved. Similar themes recur in most discussions of industrial biotechnology. In order, therefore, to offer an understanding of the issues involved and the choices which might be available for the control of sulphur emission in coal burning, this chapter opens with an in-depth analysis of the problems themselves and looks at the range of alternative ways of dealing with them.

One way of meeting the legislative controls on sulphur emission is to burn low-sulphur coal (less than 1% total sulphur). In many countries domestically-mined coal contains a higher content of sulphur so that, unless some way could be found of removing sulphur before combustion, low-sulphur coal would have to be imported from elsewhere. The country's coal industry would be gravely damaged with the possibility of serious social and economic implications.

Throughout the world, as the demand for low-sulphur coal increases, its price can be expected to rise rapidly. The incentives to reduce sulphur dioxide emissions are intensifying partly by the enactment of legislation with its threat of financial penalties, and partly as the result of social pressure. In general, two main options are open: to remove the offending substances from flue gases by some form of scrubbing or to extract some or all of the sulphur from the coal before combustion. This chapter discusses the possibility of using microbial systems to achieve significant desulphurisation of high-sulphur coals. Implementation of microbial desulphurisation depends directly on its cost-effectiveness compared with competing technologies. Only of the overall cost-benefit aspects of a microbial system are better than those of competing systems is it likely to be deployed.

Structure of Coal and Forms of Sulphur Present

Coal is a heterogeneous substance of fossil origin. It consists mostly of fixed carbon and hydrogen together with varying amounts of fixed oxygen, sulphur, nitrogen and several trace elements as integral parts of the coal matrix. Quantities of minerals are also present, predominantly metal silicates and pyrites: these are trapped within the coal matrix, of which they are not an integral part, and are largely responsible for the ash content of coal.

Sulphur is present in three forms:

1. Sulphide minerals, in particular iron pyrite (FeS_2), which is dispersed throughout the coal matrix;
2. Organically bound sulphur, present as an integral part of the coal matrix;
3. Minor amounts of sulphate, usually derived from the oxidation of small quantities of pyrite during the mining, washing and transport of coal.

Cubic iron pyrite crystals are a part of the chemical structure of coal (Figure 1) and can be removed without destroying the chemistry of the matrix. Pyrite is distributed throughout the

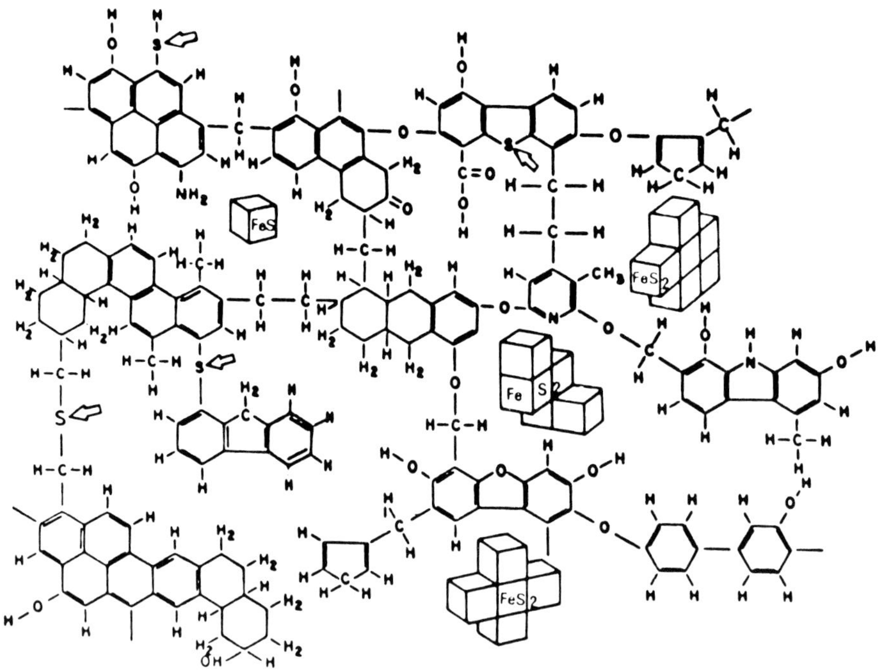

Figure 1. Representative chemical structure for bituminous coal. *(Reproduced by permission of John Wiley & Sons, Inc.)*

coal with particle diameters generally around 20 µm. Organic sulphur, on the other hand, is chemically bonded to carbon and cannot be removed without altering some of the matrix integrity. In common bituminous (hard or black) coal the organic component comprises predominantly dibenzothiophene and benzothiophene. Both organic and pyritic sulphur are in a chemically reduced form. Coal quality is by no means uniformly distributed in coal seams: the sulphur content of coal mined on different days from the seam will differ. Nor is there a firm relationship between pyritic and organic sulphur in any coal; the fact that one is high does not necessarily mean that the other will be low.

Combustion of Coal

The reduced forms of sulphur in coal can be oxidised in air with the concomitant release of energy and the formation of oxidised sulphur, mostly gaseous sulphur dioxide (SO_2). In the atmosphere, in the presence of oxygen, moisture and light, sulphur dioxide is further oxidised to sulphur trioxide (SO_3). These gases dissolve in water to yield sulphurous and sulphuric acids, respectively, which return to earth during precipitation.

While coal mined in the U.K. averages about 1.4% sulphur, supplies to power stations contain about 1.6%. Nationally, about 75% of the mined coal is burned in power stations. In the U.S. the average total sulphur content is near to 3.0% and one-third of the total coal reserves could not be consumed without some form of emission control because of their high-sulphur content. There, too, utilisation of low-sulphur reserves is having serious economic consequences for the producers of high-sulphur coals. A large proportion of U.S. coal comes from the Appalachian fields where there is a high total sulphur content in the range 3.0–5.5%.

Regulations for Sulphur Dioxide Emissions

As well as seeking to control atmospheric pollution, regulations act as strong incentives for coal desulphurisation. At the present time the regulations in the U.K., administered by H.M. Inspectorate of Pollution (under the Department of Energy), are unclear. From the point of view of desulphurisation it is important to note that no level of sulphur content in coal has been set. Despite this, a total sulphur content of 1% or less is a generally accepted standard for emissions released to the atmosphere from combustion plants. By the year 2003 sulphur dioxide emissions from existing plants must be 60% better than they were in 1980. The restrictions for new plants take a different form: for example, plants rated at 400 MW or greater have a limit of 800 mg/m^3 for sulphur dioxide. If, however, because of the high sulphur content of its feedstock and the excessive cost of the technology, a new plant cannot realistically meet the permitted sulphur dioxide emission levels, it may alternatively meet certain desulphurisation rates. For a 400 MW plant the desulphurisation rate would be approximately 75%, i.e. three quarters of the sulphur would have to be removed from the fuel before combustion by a process especially designed for this purpose. If precombustive forms of sulphur removal were used as a way of minimizing sulphur dioxide emissions, microbial desulphurisation might have a niche in Britain. Similar directives have already been en forced in the U.S. giving parallel possibilities for implementation of a microbial technology there.

COMPETING PROCESSES FOR REDUCING SULPHUR-RELATED POLLUTION

The objective of desulphurisation is clearly to decrease as much as possible the environmental damage due to sulphur oxides. Since the vast majority of coal mined is burned in power stations it is that coal which will primarily be considered in this discussion. Conventional technology, widely in use at the present time, is generally not capable of lowering sulphur-related pollution to the levels required, so that a number of specific strategies are presently under review and in some cases are already in use. The following section briefly assesses current coal cleaning processes, an improved combustion system, flue gas desulphurisation and the potential coal cleaning technologies.

Current Conventional Coal Cleaning

In the U.K., coal for power generation is usually prepared by removing the finer fractions (less than 6 mm diam.) as uncleaned fines, cleaning the plus 6 mm coal and automatically blending together the washed and uncleaned components to produce the final feedstock (Figure 2).

The minus 6 mm fines are not cleaned because the cost of doing so is nearly twice as high as for the minus 3 mm fines: minus 6 mm is chosen as the minimum target size for particle washing because size differentiation on such a large scale is

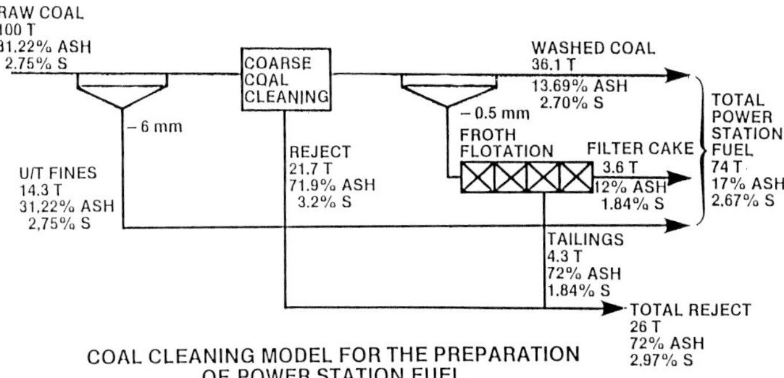

Figure 2. Flowchart for current preparation of coals for power stations. (*Reproduced by permission of P. Cammack and British Coal*)

difficult. Partial washing has the effect of reducing the sulphur content on a thermal basis (grams of sulphur per gigajoule of power generated) by 20–30%. Paradoxically, the absolute sulphur level in the coal does not decrease as a result of cleaning (indeed it sometimes increases), but the calorific value of the fuel rises so that less of it has to be burned in order to generate a specified heat output and correspondingly less sulphur dioxide on that basis is released into the atmosphere. Conventional coal cleaning, though reducing the release of sulphur dioxide, does not bring high-sulphur coals within the 1% total sulphur content value.

Fluidised Bed Combustion

A fluidised bed combustor consists of a cylindrical vessel which contains a mass of fine coal particles kept in a state of suspension ("fluidised") by means of an upward current of air: the air also supplies oxygen for combustion. A most important advantage of fluidised bed combustion is that, because of the temperature and other conditions in the combustor, sulphur in the coal may be retained in the bed and removed as sulphate with the ash.

TRW Incorporated, an Ohio-based engineering contractor, has developed one such system. The distinguishing features are the high temperature at which pulverised coal is burned and the short combustion time. This so-called "slagging" burner can take coal straight from the coal face, without washing or grading, and/or utilise refuse coal. Powdered limestone added to the pulverised coal combines with any sulphur present, trapping it in the molten slag which is discharged from the burner base into a cooling water spray where it solidifies. Low levels only of sulphur oxides are released. The new combustion process has the further advantage of keeping the formation of nitrous oxides to a minimum, attributable to a low oxygen concentration in the primary combustion stage. The overall effects of this new technology will unfold over the coming years. If it proves successful, pre-combustive coal treatment would, for the most part, be unnecessary.

Flue Gas Desulphurisation (FGD)

An FGD plant installed at a 2000 MW power plant in the U.K. costs £160 million. At 90% efficiency, the system can remove 160,000 tonnes of sulphur dioxide per year. This is significantly more than can be achieved by conventionally cleaning all the coal supplied to power stations. Furthermore, the removal of 1 tonne of sulphur by current conventional cleaning costs five times more than its removal by FGD. Obviously, FGD is more efficient and less expensive than current conventional cleaning.

Although FGD has been the chosen route for reducing sulphur dioxide emissions, it does have several disadvantages.

Firstly, it is very expensive: Britain's current program of retrofitting desulphurisation systems to 12,000 megawatts of existing power station capacity is to cost £2 billion, plus another £180 million to replace lost capacity. Coupled with this, the cost of treating the gases per tonne of coal combusted is relatively expensive, one reason why microbial desulphurisation might prove to be more cost-effective. Furthermore, FGD is prone to serious equipment wear and corrosion problems. Not all power plants will be retrofitted and, indeed, it would not be economically viable to do so at smaller plants because of the high capital investment required. Power stations without FGD might be prime candidates for the utilisation of desulphurised coals.

Potential Coal Treatment Technologies

New methods are under consideration for the treatment of minus 0.5 mm fines produced from washing coarser coal (Figure 2). For application to cleaning all coal produced for combustion, pulverisation of larger coal sizes would be necessary for the treatment to be effective.

Dense medium processes

These are based on the fact that pyrite has a relative density of about 5.0, compared with typical values of 1.4–1.5 for coal; the process can be used with relative densities for coal in the range 1.3–2.0. Coal and pyrite should thus in principle be separable on density differences if the pyrite is liberated from coal by pulverisation. However, the design of a plant to separate out pyrite in this way has yet to be resolved and the technology is still under development.

Magnetic separation

The production of high magnetic gradients facilitates the capture of even the smallest weakly magnetic particles, including pyrite particles liberated from coal by pulverisation. A capture matrix is revolved through a magnetic field and, as they move out of the magnetic head, the captured magnetics are flushed from the matrix. Although there was some early interest in this process for application at power station grinding mills, it has now been abandoned in Britain.

Chemical treatment

Chemical methods have the potential to remove a major part of the organic as well as the pyritic sulphur. However, the process is energy intensive, operating at high temperatures and pressures, and requires the coal be held under these conditions for a period of hours. A further disadvantage is that there may be a decrease in the final calorific value of the coal due to the partial oxidation of the contained hydrogen and carbon. The high cost of this treatment renders it noncompetitive.

Flotation separations

Separation of clean coal is achieved by passing air upwards through a suspension of coal to which a frothing agent (commonly methylisobutyl carbinol) has been added. The lighter clean coal particles attach themselves to air bubbles and rise with them to the top where they are skimmed off with the froth. Methylisobutyl carbinol reagents, at a very low dosage rate of about 20 ml per tonne, have been shown to produce flotation concentrates of low sulphur content. Unfortunately, if the dosage rate is increased in order to produce coal of low ash content, the sulphur content also increases: when the latter is decreased by these agents, the yield of coal also decreases so that flotation methods result in an energy loss.

Microbial desulphurisation

Pyrite removal from pulverised coal by microbial action has been shown to be efficient, with 90% reduction of this inorganic phase in two weeks. The removal of organic sulphur is a process still in its infancy, with a capacity at the present time for eliminating about 50% of the sulphur in this phase. Coal pulverisation has a compressive effect on the resultant particles which may slow down the microbial attack on organic sulphur components. New devices are pulverising by explosive rather than compressive methods.

For coal in which the removal of pyrite alone is enough to reduce the sulphur content to below 1%, microbial desulphurisation is already competitive with other technologies. Detz and Barvinchak (see Further Reading) estimated the cost of treating coal in this way to be \$10–14 per tonne, compared with \$16.50 per tonne for flue gas desulphurisation and \$20 per tonne for chemical treatment. Couple this with the possible emergence of effective organic sulphur removal and a microbial system would appear to be an attractive choice to reduce sulphur oxide emissions.

MICROBIAL DESULPHURISATION OF COAL

The two major forms of sulphur in coal provide two approaches to microbial desulphurisation: removal of organic sulphur and removal of pyritic sulphur. The technology for liberating organic sulphur is relatively recent and is still in an early stage of development. Liberation of pyritic sulphur is well documented and in many coals the removal of this fraction would be sufficient to bring the sulphur content to below 1%.

Removal of Organic Sulphur From Coal

Organic sulphur is the most difficult of the forms of sulphur to remove as it is chemically bonded within the coal. While coal contains many such species, the heteroaromatic sulphur compounds are those most commonly found; they are considered to be refractory compounds. Bacterial removal of organic sulphur-containing compounds is also of interest in connection with the desulphurisation of crude oil: this is discussed in Chapter 29.

Mesophilic, acidophilic iron- and sulphur-oxidising bacteria (the organisms utilised for pyrite removal) are not effective in releasing organic sulphur from coal. There have been several reports of organic sulphur removal by thermophilic strains of *Thiobacillus ferrooxidans* and *Sulfolobus acidocaldarius*. These organisms are capable of solubilising inorganic sulphur, but their ability to deal with organic sulphur is dubious.

A microorganism denoted CB1, developed by Atlantic Research Corporation (ARC) in the U.S., can oxidise thiophenic sulphur in coal to form soluble sulphate. A continuous pilot plant utilising CB1, capable of treating 1,100 kg coal per day, was constructed according to the system indicated in Figure 3. This plant has had limited testing: the fermenter and ultrafiltration systems apparently worked well but slurry formation and flow were problematic. (This is a serious shortcoming: problems of handling form one of the main disadvantages of coal treatments which incorporate slurries.) Development with CB1 is apparently continuing and ARC (with the backing of the U.S. Department of Energy) are confident that a use will be found for this process.

Organism CB1 has at best removed only 57% of the organic sulphur from coal and that would not be sufficient to bring the majority of high-sulphur coals within regulations for combustion. Microbiologically, the process would need to be combined with technology which removes pyritic sulphur, possibly in concert with further microorganisms able to liberate some of the other organic fractions of coal. In this regard, note that suitably adapted strains of *S. brierleyi* have been reported to remove 90% of the pyritic and 30% of the organic sulphur from untreated coal.

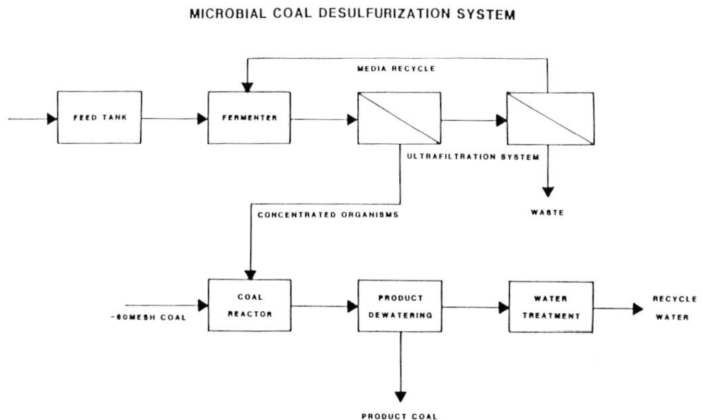

Figure 3. Flow diagram for continuous removal of organic sulphur from coal. (*Reproduced by permission of J.D. Isbister and ARCHTEC Inc.*)

Removal of Pyritic Sulphur From Coal

Of all the significant sulphur forms in coal, pyrite is easiest to solubilise. Microbial removal of pyritic sulphur can be achieved by the use of two genera of bacteria: *T. ferrooxidans* and closely related species function at ambient temperatures (10–37°C) while the thermophilic archæbacterium *S. acidocaldarius* and its relatives are able to operate in hotter environments (55–80°C). Both *T. ferrooxidans* and *S. acidocaldarius* are aerobic and acidophilic, thriving in the pH range 1.0–4.0. Furthermore, both obtain energy for cellular activity and carbon dioxide fixation by oxidising inorganic forms of iron and sulphur; the pyrite fraction of coal is, of course, formed of these elements. *S. acidocaldarius* is faster than *T. ferrooxidans* at solubilising pyritic sulphur probably because the rate of pyrite solubilisation is temperature-dependent and *S. acidocaldarius* is more thermotolerant. The chemistry of these processes is described in Chapter 30 in relation to the leaching of metals from sulphide ores.

The applications of high temperature sulphur- and iron-oxidising organisms have received limited attention only with respect to coal desulphurisation. Studies indicate that *S. acidocaldarius* does indeed remove sulphur from coal, but process variables will need to be more closely defined before an operating system becomes possible. However, *T. ferrooxidans* has been the subject of more intense study and this chapter will refer on the whole to the action of that species.

Attachment of Bacteria

Bacterial contact with pyrite particles is a pre-requisite for surface attack since no extracellular enzymes appear to be secreted in the microbial oxidation of pyrite. The bacterium attaches itself to the mineral by means of adhesion (the exact mechanism is unknown), not by pili as previously thought. Once attached, pitting occurs in the immediate vicinity as the pyrite is solubilised. Chemotaxis is not involved in attachment; instead, the cells attach randomly to all phases of the matrix and in places without oxidisable substrate the bacteria die. The surface area of the pyrite is thus very important: increased surface area improves the opportunities for bacterial attachment and this in turn enhances solubilisation of pyrite.

Major factors affecting rate of bacterial pyrite removal from coal pH

The most rapid rates of pyrite solubilisation occur in the pH range 2.0–3.5 but problems may occur with the precipitation of Jarosites (complex hydrated iron sulphates) even at pH levels below 2.0.

Temperature

Desulphurisation is fastest with *T. ferrooxidans* at 28°C, the rate rapidly falling off at temperatures in excess of 30°C.

Concentration of bacteria

The rate of pyrite removal from coal is dependent on the initial cell concentration. At low cell concentrations the rate is limited by the number of cells adsorbed onto the coal particles, the rate increasing with increasing cell concentration. When the concentration is high, the rate reaches its maximum value and is limited only by the total accessible surface area of pyrite particles. Any further increases in cell concentrations therefore do not increase the rate of pyrite decomposition.

Coal particle size

With large coal particles the rate is limited by the total accessible surface area of the pyrite: some pyritic sulphur will be completely inaccessible within the coal. As the coal particle size is decreased, the accessible surface area of pyrite particles increases, resulting in more bacterial attachment and thus more rapid solubilisation.

Heterotrophic bacteria

T. ferrooxidans is inhibited by low molecular weight organic compounds, both autotoxic by-products of its own metabolism and those which leach from coal in a slurry. α-Keto acids are particularly toxic, ultimately causing the bacterial cell wall to disrupt. The simultaneous presence of acidophilic heterotrophs such as *T. perometabolis, T. acidophilus, T. thiooxidans, T. novellus* and *T. neopolitanus* results in the utilisation of these organic compounds thereby alleviating the inhibition.

INDUSTRIAL MICROBIAL DESULPHURISATION

In practical terms, the bacterial removal from coal of pyritic sulphur alone might well form the basis of a potential industrial process if it were to bring the sulphur content to below 1%.

While several proposals have been made for engineering *T. ferrooxidans* activity for coal beneficiation, the overriding design factor is a continuous mode of operation in order to avoid the repetitive confrontation with lag phases which would be encountered with any batch process. Typical protocols envisage feeding the reactor with a slurry of raw coal (pulverised to less than 100–200 mesh [0.074–0.149 mm diam.] to liberate pyrite) together with the bacterial inoculum (consisting of *T. ferrooxidans* mixed with acidophilic heterotrophs to remove low molecular weight organic compounds) and trace elements as necessary for microbial growth: the aim is to recover cleaned product while the microbial population is recycled (Figure 4). The pH is initially adjusted to 2.0: the system will become self-sustaining as long as the pH is maintained by appropriate treatment of the recycled liquid with limestone.

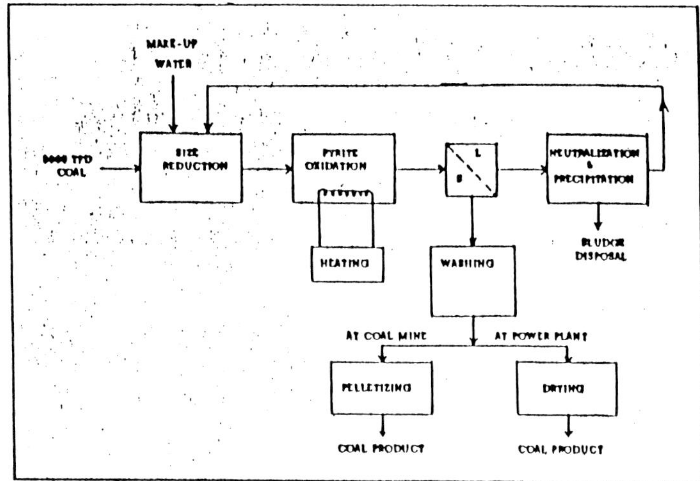

Figure 4. Flow diagram for microbial desulphurisation process.

A significant fraction of the capital investment and operating costs of a microbial desulphurisation plant is related to the volume of slurry which is processed. It is therefore important to use a slurry as concentrated as possible while ensuring that enough carbon dioxide can reach the microorganisms. Another important consideration is that at slurry concentrations as high as 30–40% some bacteria, such as *Sulfolobus*, are fragile over the long term, the cells presumably being damaged by abrasion. It has generally been found that a slurry containing 20% by weight of coal in water minimises both handling problems and the volume to be processed but does not inhibit microbial activity as long as the slurry is aerated. Pulverisation of coal already occurs at power stations so that existing equipment can be used to produce the fine coal needed.

One approach has been likened to the technology used for aerobic domestic or industrial waste treatment processes (Figure 5). A 40% slurry of coal in water (very concentrated in comparison with the method described earlier) could be held in suspension with aeration and agitation. When the agitation is terminated the coal settles out quickly, allowing for separation of the treated material. Return of 5–10% of

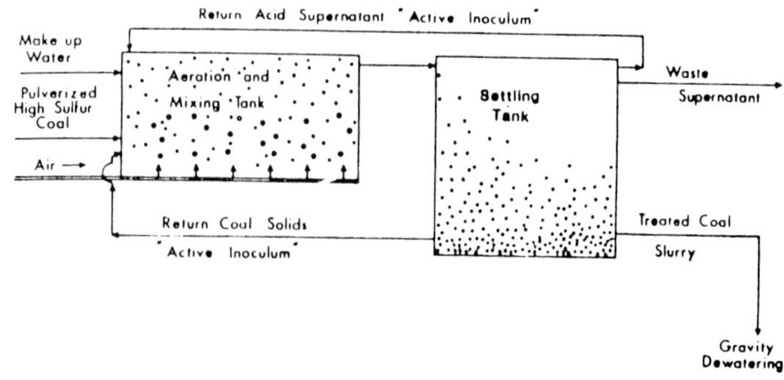

Figure 5. Schematic diagram for desulphurisation of pulverised coal.

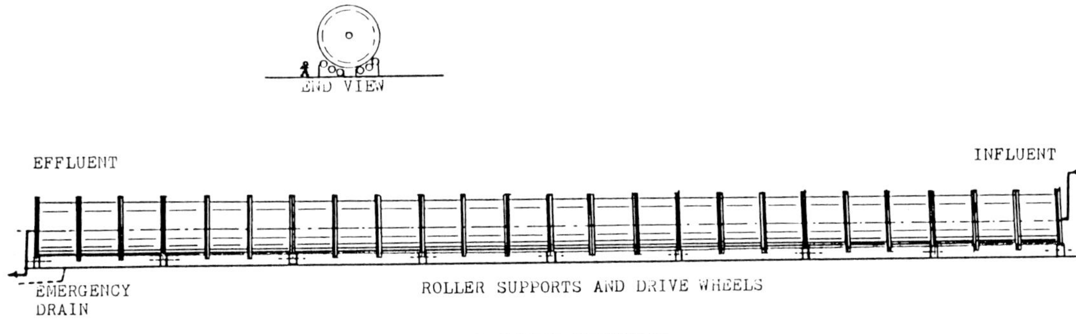

Figure 6. Horizontal rotating drum continuous bioreactor.

the coal solids in the recycle would provide an inoculum for the continuous process together with return of some of the supernatant to provide acidification. Once a steady state had been achieved it is probable that in this sytem, too, 90% pyrite removal could be achieved with retention times of about two weeks.

Another configuration has been suggested (Figure 6) in which the bioreactor is a long, horizontal narrow tube or drum supported on external rollers which produce a slow rotation of the drum around its long axis. Bacteria and coal slurry are fed in at one end and mixed along the drum via rifling ridges, gradually moving to the other end where the treated coal is collected. Some of the treated slurry is recycled as inoculum at the influent end and the drum is well aerated for maximum bacterial growth. Coal is kept in suspension both by aeration and by the mixing action of the slowly rotating drum. In a commercial process there would probably be more than one bioreactor: some designs envisage a primary bioreactor 146.3 m long by 7.32 m in diameter, to be followed by three parallel operating secondary bioreactors with similar dimensions. Such an arrangement is projected to process 100,000 tonnes of coal per year.

As yet, however, no industrial scale microbial desulphurisation plant has been considered a suitable choice for lowering the sulphur content of coal and no production plants have been installed although, as discussed below, a pilot operation is being planned in Italy.

ADVANTAGES AND DISADVANTAGES OF MICROBIAL DESULPHURISATION

A major technical difficulty with microbial desulphurisation (which also has cost implications) is that coal has not only to be extensively pulverised for bacteria-pyrite contact but has also to be slurried in water. In itself pulverisation is not a problem as modern power stations already burn only powdered coal but coal-water slurries can be difficult to handle. This was the major problem with the pilot plant for organic sulphur removal mentioned earlier. Secondly, and most importantly, after microbial treatment and rinsing the coal has to be dewatered. It need not be completely dried because modern boilers can handle up to 25% water in the coal. British Coal estimates a U.K. cost of approximately £25 for the thermal evaporation of 1 tonne of water. In their view this would add an unacceptable expense to the microbial processing of coal and would make their product even less desirable for British power stations. However, the responsibility for reducing atmospheric pollution lies not with British Coal but with the Central Electricity Generating Board (CEGB). Thus, the view of British Coal that microbial desulphurisation is too expensive (which from their point of view it is) must be set against the requirements of the CEGB (or its private sector successors) to meet emission requirements. They may well be impressed by the demonstration, albeit in the laboratory, that microbial desulphurisation can be the least expensive route to precombustive sulphur removal, and less expensive than flue gas desulphurisation. In terms of overall costs of desulphurisation, the expense of dewatering the coal may not be too high to exclude the technology on the grounds of cost. Nevertheless, in Britain at least, it is likely for a variety of reasons that flue gas desulphurisation will be the method chosen. In spite of its high capital cost, factors favouring its adoption will include availability and existing familiarity of the decision-makers with chemical engineering methods compared with both the novelty, in their view, and their lack of operating experience of a biotechnological solution. However, as this book was going to press, the U.K. government announced a reduced programme of FGD retrofitting, from 12,000 megawatts of generating capacity at a cost of £2 billion down to 8,000 megawatts costing £1.2 billion on the ground that "the full programme is unnecessary". The target reduction in atmospheric sulphur emissions is to be achieved by switching to low-sulphur fuels. Such a change in policy might open some doors to opportunities for microbial coal desulphurisation in the U.K.

Although there is a reluctance in the mining industry to desulphurise the coal on site because of the extra costs entailed, this approach does have certain advantages. Pyrite is removed together with some ash (by acid leaching). The reduced weight of coal which has to be moved to the consumer thus decreases transport costs. Conventional transport by road or rail requires the treated coal to be pelleted because fines are easily lost but pelleting could be avoided if coal slurry pipelines were employed; pipelines to transport coal from mine to power plant are already in operation at some sites in the U.S. Microbial desulphurisation is complementary to such a technology.

One disadvantage of the microbial process is that it is relatively slow, typically requiring a coal retention period of 10–20 days. While not in itself a major problem since power stations normally maintain a 90-day stock to guard against interruptions in supply, the long retention time implies very large reactor volumes in order to keep up with the demands of a power station; this, in turn, almost certainly means a need for large land areas creating severe problems in densely populated areas. A high temperature process, by shortening the retention time, would lower the land area requirement but space is nevertheless likely to be a major economic factor in areas of intensive land use and where land is expensive. Compared with a *T. ferrooxidans*-based desulphurisation plant, a high temperature system for the removal of pyrite using *S. acidocaldarius* might prove more cost-effective and require less land area per tonne of coal desulphurised although temperature maintenance would probably impose an additional fuel cost. It has been estimated that for the treatment of 8,000 tonnes of coal per day, 25 acres (10 ha) of land would be required for *T. ferrooxidans* compared with 8 acres (3.2 ha) for *S. acidocaldarius*. The thermophile achieves more than 90% pyrite removal in 6 days compared with 18 days for the mesophile. There is, however, another problem associated with long retention times: at the low pH of the process corrosion might become troublesome. Corrosion is not a problem unique to microbial desulphurisation but common to all types of pollution control involving the removal of sulphurous compounds.

In comparison with competing precombustion sulphur removal technologies, microbial desulphurisation is more energy efficient. A continuous process in a steady state produces its own heat (which might favour a thermophilic system) and continuous operation would require only aeration and the addition of trace minerals whereas high pressure, temperature and chemical processes all demand substantial inputs of energy. Unlike competing technologies, microbial desulphurisation does not result in a loss in the energy value of coal. Present (non-biological) procedures for cleaning fines, for example, can result in excess of 50% loss of the calorific value of the product. Other advantages of a microbial desulphurisation process include the possibility of useful by-products (e.g. an acid solution of iron and aluminium could be used as a flocculation aid for domestic waste water treatment), the reclamation and upgrading of dumped coal refuse and the complementation of other types of coal cleaning which are already in place (the so-called "polishing" of coal).

With so much apparently in its favour, microbial desulphurisation seems bound to acquire major industrial significance but so far there are few signs of it actually being used for coal beneficiation. The main drawbacks are perceived to be its inflexibility. At present, microorganisms can effectively remove only the pyritic sulphur fraction from coal; this limits the process to coals which have high pyrite and low organic sulphur contents. Such coals are common but they are not ubiquitous so that a power plant committed solely to a microbial process might become dependent on a restricted range of fuels. Flue gas desulphurisation, on the other hand, recovers some 90% of the sulphur dioxide emitted regardless of the coal combusted and is flexible in the sense that the power plant is not limited to a fuel of a particular sulphur content. The managers of large power stations, with an obligation to reduce sulphurous emissions, are thus likely to view FGD as the primary form of pollution control. Similarly, the emerging "clean" combustion systems, such as the TRW slagging burner, also have flexibility in comparison with microbial desulphurisation. The slagging burner can combust low grade coal directly, without pre-treatment, essentially achieving the same ends in one step which would take two stages in a system involving microbial desulphurisation.

Nevertheless, microbial desulphurisation may not be entirely without a future. In Britain, for instance, the electricity generating industry is to be privatised. The resulting independent companies will have to find cost-effective ways to meet the regulations on sulphur dioxide emissions. Coal naturally low in sulphur will become more expensive, and the potential for upgrading less expensive coal sources will certainly be explored. It is not inconceivable that a *coal refining industry*, distinct from coal producers and power generators, could develop using this technology. Their incentive would be to start with relatively low grade coals, even coal refuse, and produce a saleable low-sulphur product.

ECONOMIC ASPECTS OF MICROBIAL DESULPHURISATION

The value of the treated product has to be great enough to warrant desulphurisation of high-sulphur coals. The technical process of microbial desulphurisation has been shown on a laboratory scale to compete favourably with other ways of reducing the sulphur content of coal-fired power station emissions but, of course, it has also to compete successfully on cost when scaled up to industrial operation. If it proves to be more expensive than comparable technologies to install and run, microbial desulphurisation will certainly not be used. One study calculated that microbial desulphurisation is the least expensive route to the precombustion removal of pyrite as well as being less expensive than flue gas desulphurisation. It was therefore concluded that, where removal of pyritic sulphur alone is sufficient to meet emission requirements, microbial desulphurisation should be the preferred choice.

Of course, not all of the world's coal deposits are high in sulphur. Coal with less than 1% sulphur is available from many sources and can be combusted without causing any significant pollution but as the demand for low-sulphur coal grows its price will inevitably increase and provide a stimulus to the development of cheap methods for desulphurisation either of feedstock coal or of the effluent gases. An important issue is thus the value of the coal desulphurised by microbial methods compared with naturally occurring low-sulphur coal. To provide the basis for a comparison, a study of low-sulphur coal used by Ohio power generators has been made: 56% of the coal delivered to the power plants there originates within the state and very little of it contains less than 1% sulphur. Increasing amounts of low-sulphur coal have consequently been imported, mostly from Kentucky and West Virginia. Figure 7 summarises for a six-month period during 1985 the average cost of coal from Kentucky and West Virginia to Ohio power plants versus percent sulphur content. There is clearly a direct relationship between the cost of coal and its sulphur content: power plants have to pay more for low-sulphur coal.

In one desulphurisation experiment run with *T. ferrooxidans* together with heterotrophs at 22°C, the pyritic sulphur was reduced from 4.2 to 0.5% (88% removal) and the total sulphur content was reduced from 5.4 to 1.7% (67% removal). The apparent increase in organic sulphur was due to the loss in coal weight from pyrite removal. In 1978 the cost premium for a lower-sulphur coal was approximately $3.40 per tonne per 1% sulphur. A greater premium was paid for a sulphur content lower than 1.5% at a rate of approximately $11.00 per tonne per 1% sulphur below 1.5%. This implies that the desulphurisation experiment increased the coal value by $14.00 per tonne ($3.40 × 3.7%). Removal of a further 1% sulphur would have increased the coal value by an additional $9.48 per tonne at the 1978 prices. At 1984 prices this represented a $22.75 per tonne increase in coal value, with a $29.50 per tonne increase for an extra 0.6% sulphur removal. An estimate of the cost of microbial treatment in 1984 was $18.00. This example shows that microbiological desulphurisation treatment is potentially able to increase the net value of the coal by $4.75 net per tonne, or $11.50 per tonne if a further 0.6% sulphur is removed. Thus, microbial desulphurisation might well pay for itself and make the utilisation of high-sulphur coals realistic.

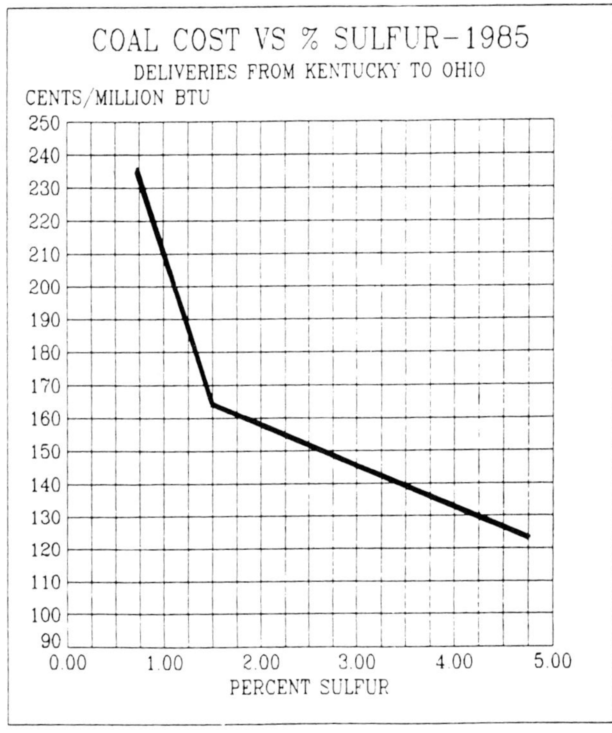

Figure 7. Summary curve representing the average cost of coal versus percent sulphur content for Kentucky and West Virginia coal delivered to Ohio utilities during 1985.

Coal desulphurisation cannot be considered solely in monetary terms because the sulphur problem has important social consequences. In the U.S., most (62%) of the low-sulphur coal is found west of the Mississippi, whereas 90% of the coal used for power generation originates east of the river. Utilisation of low-sulphur coal is detrimental to eastern coal-producing communities resulting in closure of eastern mines and the prospective unemployment of miners. Methods permitting the continued use of high-sulphur coals into the future would thus provide both the incentive and the mechanism for eastern producers to avoid the decline of their industry. Coal is likely to remain globally an important fuel for power generation for decades or even centuries to come. Increasing moves for pollution abatement, together with political and social pressures to retain employment in areas producing high-sulphur coals, will all serve to stimulate the development of low-cost desulphurisation procedures.

In Britain there is no real comparable *regional* conflict but imported coal with half the sulphur content is less expensive than the domestic deep-mined product. The approaching privatisation of electric power generation will probably increase the tendency to import cheap low-sulphur coal. If, however, there is a political commitment to continue Britain's local industry, then the high-sulphur reserves would obviously benefit from a process which increases their value and permits their use in a non-polluting manner. Clearly, if there is only a limited future for British coal in the light of cheaper low-sulphur imports, there is not realistically much opportunity for microbial desulphurisation.

The situation is different again in Italy. In that country, native deposits of fossil fuels are in very short supply: there is little or no petroleum and only one deposit of coal. The

Italian authorities are concerned at their dependence on foreign sources and, to protect electricity supplies in the event of future oil crises, oil-burning power stations have been equipped to replace oil with a slurry of domestic coal should the need arise. But as the one national deposit is of a high-sulphur coal, there is considerable interest in techniques of desulphurisation, including the use of microbial systems.

A European Community project, involving teams from Italy itself as well as from The Netherlands, the U.K. and West Germany, is directed towards developing a working microbial desulphurisation system; hopefully by 1991 or 1992 a pilot treatment plant will be built and operating in Northern Sardinia, the location of the mines. The system offers some prospects of removing organic as well as pyritic sulphur. Preliminary estimates of costs suggest that they will not be low although they may well come down as the techniques are further improved. Compared with flue gas desulphurisation at \$30–40 per tonne of coal burned, microbiological desulphurisation is presently calculated to cost \$60–65 per tonne of coal, including capital-related costs, labour, overheads, electricity, calcium hydroxide for neutralising the acid effluent, sludge disposal, auxiliary materials and other utilities.

While realistic prospects for microbial treatment remain unclear, there is sufficient interest by national and supranational agencies, as well as by commercial operators, to encourage the further development and refinement of the prospective technology. Coal desulphurisation is just one activity among several (such as enhanced oil recovery and heavy metal removal from industrial effluents) in which a prospective biotechnological method is in direct competition with non-biological techniques. Worldwide, the largest coal reserves are in to be found in the USSR, with other major deposits in China, Australia, Germany and South Africa. These countries may offer the most promising opportunities for microbial desulphurisation but it will probably be some years before the relative viability of the biological approach can be determined in the field.

FURTHER READING

1. P.R. Dugan. *Desulfurization of Coal.* In Workshop on Biotechnology for the Mining, Metal-Refining and Fossil Fuel Processing Industries, Biotechnology and Bioengineering Symposium Number 16. (1986). Ed. by H.L. Ehrlich and D.S. Holmes, p 185.
2. C.M. Detz and G. Barvinchak. *Microbial Desulfurization of Coal.* Mining Congress Journal (1979), **vol 65**(7), p. 75.
3. V.A. Vaseen. *Commercial Desulfurization of Coal.* Proceedings of First International Conference on Processing and Utilisation of High Sulphur Coals (October 13–17, 1985), Columbus, Ohio. Ed. by Y.A. Attia, p. 699.
4. P.R. Dugan. *Increased Value of Refined High Sulfur Coal.* Mining Engineering (1987), **vol 39**(8), p. 804.
5. Various papers in Proceedings of Bioprocessing of Fossil Fuels Workshop (August 8–10, 1989), Tysons Corner, Virginia. Ed. by P.E. Bayer. Sponsored by U.S. Department of Energy Office of Fossil Energy and Idaho Operations Office in co-operation with Idaho National Engineering Laboratory Bioprocessing Center. CONF-890884.

INDEX

Index